PRAGATI

CHEMISTRY

MCQs

(MULTIPLE CHOICE QUESTIONS)

FOR

NEET/JEE (MAINS & ADVANCED)
AIPMT/AIIMS/AFMC & OTHER COMPETITIVE EXAMS

Dr. Meena Dhami

LEARNING SIMPLIFIED

- ★ **Author of Great Repute**
- ★ **Latest Inputs as per CBSE Syllabus**
- ★ **Complete Chapterwise MCQs**
- ★ **More than 5000 MCQs**
- ★ **Questions from Competitive Exams**
- ★ **Practice Papers with Answers**
- ★ **Latest Papers with Answers included**

I0592942

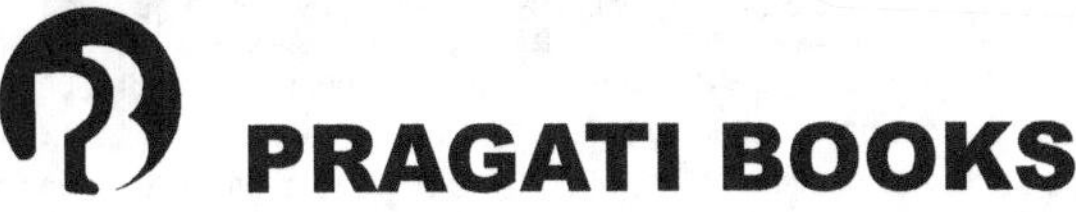

PP032

Pragati - Chemistry (MCQs)

First Edition : **January 2017**

© : **Author**

Published By :   **Polyplate**
NIRALI PRAKASHAN
Abhyudaya Pragati, 1312, Shivaji Nagar,
Off J.M. Road, PUNE – 411005
Tel - (020) 25512336/37/39, Fax - (020) 25511379
Email : niralipune@pragationline.com

☞ **DISTRIBUTION CENTRES**

PUNE
Nirali Prakashan : 119, Budhwar Peth, Jogeshwari Mandir Lane, Pune 411002, Maharashtra
Tel : (020) 2445 2044, 66022708, Fax : (020) 2445 1538
Email : bookorder@pragationline.com, niralilocal@pragationline.com

Nirali Prakashan : S. No. 28/27, Dhyari, Near Pari Company, Pune 411041
Tel : (020) 24690204 Fax : (020) 24690316
Email : dhyari@pragationline.com, bookorder@pragationline.com

MUMBAI
Nirali Prakashan : 385, S.V.P. Road, Rasdhara Co-op. Hsg. Society Ltd.,
Girgaum, Mumbai 400004, Maharashtra
Tel : (022) 2385 6339 / 2386 9976, Fax : (022) 2386 9976
Email : niralimumbai@pragationline.com

☞ **DISTRIBUTION BRANCHES**

JALGAON
Nirali Prakashan : 34, V. V. Golani Market, Navi Peth, Jalgaon 425001,
Maharashtra, Tel : (0257) 222 0395, Mob : 94234 91860

KOLHAPUR
Nirali Prakashan : New Mahadvar Road, Kedar Plaza, 1st Floor Opp. IDBI Bank
Kolhapur 416 012, Maharashtra. Mob : 9850046155

NAGPUR
Pratibha Book Distributors : Above Maratha Mandir, Shop No. 3, First Floor,
Rani Jhanshi Square, Sitabuldi, Nagpur 440012, Maharashtra
Tel : (0712) 254 7129

DELHI
Nirali Prakashan : 4593/21, Basement, Aggarwal Lane 15, Ansari Road, Daryaganj
Near Times of India Building, New Delhi 110002, Mob : 08505972553

BENGALURU
Pragati Book House : House No. 1, Sanjeevappa Lane, Avenue Road Cross,
Opp. Rice Church, Bengaluru – 560002.
Tel : (080) 64513344, 64513355,Mob : 9880582331, 9845021552
Email:bharatsavla@yahoo.com

CHENNAI
Pragati Books : 9/1, Montieth Road, Behind Taas Mahal, Egmore,
Chennai 600008 Tamil Nadu, Tel : (044) 6518 3535,
Mob : 94440 01782 / 98450 21552 / 98805 82331,
Email : bharatsavla@yahoo.com

niralipune@pragationline.com | www.pragationline.com
Also find us on f www.facebook.com/niralibooks

PREFACE

The entrance examination scenario has witnessed many changes in the pattern of question papers varying from subjective to multiple choice questions, since the time prestigious institutions such as IITs and AIIMS have come into existence.

This book is an attempt to provide an updated and in-depth coverage of the latest syllabus and pattern of question papers for all the Entrance Examinations i.e. IIT-JEE, JEE (MAINS), MHT-CET AIIMS and other medical and engineering colleges. The book has been shaped entirely according to the student perspective and a sincere effort has been made to present the material in a very functional and practical manner so that students enjoy the learning process as they proceed through the lesson rather than experiencing it as an ordeal. This book will not only strengthen the conceptual foundation of the students but also equip them with the necessary speed, accuracy and confidence for the entrance examinations.

Each unit has been designed with the objective of testing an aspirant's grasp and understanding of concepts. Furthermore, each unit begins with comprehensive information about the topic, solved examples, MCQs and MCQs from different competitive examinations with their complete solutions.

The author shall be grateful to the readers for any constructive suggestions or inputs for the improvement of the text. The author wishes to record her thanks to the publisher whose efforts went a long way in bringing out this work.

Suggestions for the improvement and further enhancement of the scope of the book will be welcome.

Dr. MEENA DHAMI

CONTENTS

❑❑❑

UNIT 1

SOME BASIC CONCEPTS OF CHEMISTRY

1. The triple point in matter is defined as ......
   (a) The combination of pressure and temperature at which solid, liquid, gas phase coexist at equilibrium
   (b) The combination of standard temperature, pressure and volume
   (c) The combination of pressure and temperature at which liquid, gas and plasma phase all exist in equilibrium
   (d) The combination of temperature and pressure at which liquid and gas cannot be separated.

2. During change of state in a matter, the temperature remains the same due to ......
   (a) Loss of heat
   (b) Less supply of heat
   (c) Latent heat
   (d) Lattice energy

3. In which of the following does a chemical change occur?
   (a) $2Ag_{(s)} + O_{2(g)} \rightarrow 1Ag_2O_{(s)}$
   (b) $NaCl_{(s)} \rightarrow NaCl_{(aq)}$
   (c) $I_{2(s)} \rightarrow I_{2(g)}$
   (d) $Mg_{(s)} \rightarrow Mg_{(l)}$

4. A mixture that can be separated by sublimation method is ......
   (a) $HgCl_2 + NH_4Cl$
   (b) $HgCl_2 + NaCl$
   (c) $MgCl_2 + NaCl$
   (d) $PbCl_2 + NaCl$

5. Sodium sulphate and barium sulphate mixture can be separated by ......
   (a) Crystallization
   (b) Chromatography
   (c) Fractional crystallization
   (d) Filtration and crystallization

6. SI unit of mass is ......
   (a) Gram
   (b) Kilogram
   (c) Milligram
   (d) Microgram

7. When we convert 25365 mg into basic unit, the answer is ......
   (a) 2.5365×10^{-2} kg
   (b) 2.5365×10^{-2} g
   (c) 2536.5×10^2 kg
   (d) 2536.5×10^2 g

8. The density of a metal is 9.5 g cm^{-3} and its corresponding value in SI units is ......
   (a) 95×10^3 kg m^{-3}
   (b) 9.50×10^3 kg m^{-3}
   (c) 9.50×10^{-3} kg m^{-3}
   (d) 950×10^3 kg m^{-3}

9. Which of the following is correct ?
   (a) $1 L = 10$ dm^3
   (b) $1 L = 1$ m^3
   (c) 1 dm$^3 = 10^3$ cm^3
   (d) 1 dm$^3 = 10$ L

10. Convert 23.4°C into °F.
    (a) 74.1 °F
    (b) 741 °F
    (c) 55.5 °F
    (d) 23.4 °F

11. The weight of a metal is 57.4 grams and its volume is 6.2 cm^3. Calculate the density in g/cm^3 using significant figures.
    (a) 9.3
    (b) 9.26
    (c) 9.258
    (d) 9

1.1

12. When the external pressure is 101.3 kPa torr, at what temperature will the water boil?
(a) 12.8 °C (b) 100 °C (c) 14.5 °C (d) 8 °C

13. How many joules are equivalent to 36 kilojoules ?
(a) 36000 joules (b) 0.036 joules (c) 3600 joules (d) 0.36 joules

14. A student determined the heat of fusion of water to be 366.9 J g^{-1} but the actual value is 333.6 J g^{-1}. What is the percent error ?
(a) 200% (b) 10.0% (c) 5.0% (d) 15.0%

15. Increasing order of prefix : micro, nano, pico and femto
(a) micro < nano < pico < femto (b) nano < micro < pico < femto
(c) pico < nano < micro < femto (d) femto < pico < nano < micro

16. 1 amu is equal to how many electron volt, if mass of one atom is 1.6605×10^{-27} kg and velocity of light is 2.9979×10^8 ms^{-1}.
(a) 931.44 (b) 931.46×10^7 (c) 932 (d) 931.4×10^5

17. How many significant figures are present in the number 10450?
(a) Three (b) Four (c) Five (d) Six

18. How many significant figures are there in 5.010×10^3 measured quantity?
(a) 6 (b) 4 (c) 3 (d) 5

19. Express the following number in exponential notation rounded to three significant figures : 87660.
(a) 8.77×10^{-4} (b) 8.76×10^4 (c) 0.877×10^5 (d) 8.77×10^4

20. Do the following addition and give an answer with the proper number of significant figures : 48.2 m + 3.87 m + 48.4394 m
(a) 100.5 m (b) 101 m (c) 100.5094 m (d) 100.4 m

21. Do the following subtraction and give an answer with the proper number of significant figures : 451 g – 15.46 g
(a) 435.54 g (b) 4.4×10^2 g (c) 466 g (d) 435.5 g

22. Solve the following problem and give an answer with the proper number of significant figures : 5.61 × 7.891/9.1
(a) 4.86 (b) 4.9 (c) 4.86×10^3 (d) 486

23. State the following number with four significant figures : 1.78986×10^3
(a) 17.90×10^3 (b) 1.790×10^3 (c) 17897×10^3 (d) 179×10^3

24. Express 6.607892 upto four significant figures.
(a) 66.08 (b) 660.8 (c) 6.608 (d) 6608

25. Write 654.6 in scientific notation.
(a) 6.546×10^2 (b) 65.46×10^2 (c) 6.546×10^{-2} (d) 65.46×10^3

26. Express 0.00862 in scientific notation in three significant figures.
(a) 86.2×10^3 (b) 8.62×10^{-3} (c) 862×10^{-3} (d) 86.2×10^{-3}

27. In which of the following numbers, all zeroes are significant?
(a) 0.0008 (b) 0.0050 (c) 90.000 (d) 0.600

28. Round up the number 0.04597 upto three significant figures.
(a) 0.0460 (b) 0.045 (c) 0.04 (d) 0.451

29. The percentage of carbon in two compounds is 42.9% and 27.3%. These figures show ...
(a) Law of multiple proportion
(b) Law of reciprocal proportion
(c) Law of conservation of mass
(d) Law of combining volume

30. A balanced chemical equation is according to ......
(a) Law of conservation of mass
(b) Law of reciprocal proportion
(c) Law of multiple proportion
(d) Law of combining volume

31. 2 litres of N_2 combine with 6 litres of H_2 to form 4 litres of ammonia under the same conditions of pressure and temperature. This is in accordance to the ......
(a) Law of multiple proportion
(b) Law of reciprocal proportion
(c) Law of definite proportion
(d) Law of combining volume of gas

32. 100 ml of hydrogen combines with 50 ml of oxygen to give 100 ml of water vapour. This illustrates ......
(a) Law of definite proportion
(b) Law of multiple proportion
(c) Law of reciprocal proportion
(d) Gay Lussac's law of gaseous volume

33. 12 gm of carbon combines with 64 gm of sulphur to form CS_2. 12 gm of carbon also combines with 32 gm of oxygen to form CO_2. It illustrates the ......
(a) Law of definite proportion
(b) Law of multiple proportion
(c) Law of reciprocal proportion
(d) Law of gaseous volume

34. Nitrogen reacts with oxygen and forms compounds.

Mass of N_2	**Mass of O_2**
1. 14 gm	16 gm
2. 14 gm	32 gm
3. 28 gm	48 gm
4. 28 gm	80 gm
5. 28 gm	16 gm

This is in accordance with ......
(a) Law of multiple proportion
(b) Law of definite composition
(c) Law of reciprocal proportion
(d) Law of conservation of mass

35. Two gaseous samples on analysis give the following information :
(i) One sample had 1.2 gm of carbon and 3.2 gm of oxygen.
(ii) Second sample had 27.3% of carbon and 72.7% of oxygen.
These observations are in accordance with ......
(a) Law of reciprocal proportion
(b) Law of definite proportion
(c) Law of multiple proportion
(d) Law of conservation of mass

36. The law of definite proportion was proposed by ......
(a) Lavoisier
(b) Dalton
(c) Proust
(d) Gay-Lussac

37. The law of multiple proportion was proposed by ......
(a) Dalton
(b) Proust
(c) Lavoisier
(d) Gay-Lussac

38. Which of the following laws suggests that different elements combine with each other by their equivalent weights?
    (a) Law of multiple proportion
    (b) Law of gaseous volume
    (c) Law of reciprocal proportion
    (d) Law of definite proportion

39. Which of the following combinations illustrate the law of reciprocal proportion?
    (a) PH_3, P_4O_6, P_4O_{10}
    (b) CH_4, CO_2, H_2O
    (c) NaCl, NaBr, NaI
    (d) N_2O, N_2O_3, NO_2

40. Indivisibility of an atom was proposed by ......
    (a) Bohr
    (b) Rutherford
    (c) Dalton
    (d) Thomson

41. The smallest particle of a substance that is capable of independent existence is ......
    (a) Molecule
    (b) Atom
    (c) Electron
    (d) Proton

42. An atom is 15 times heavier than $1/12^{th}$ of the mass of carbon 12. The mass in a.m.u is
    (a) 12
    (b) 14
    (c) 15
    (d) 1.25

43. The number of atoms in a molecule of the elementary substance is called ......
    (a) Atomic number
    (b) Avogadro's number
    (c) Atomicity
    (d) Atomic mass

44. Avogadro's number represents the number of atoms in ......
    (a) 32.0 gm of sulphur
    (b) 12 g of C–12
    (c) 1 g of C–12
    (d) 32 g of O

45. One molecule of a diatomic gas weighs 1.8×10^{-21} g, its atomic mass is ......
    (a) 27
    (b) 54
    (c) 160
    (d) 108

46. 19.7 kg solid gold was recovered from a dacoit. How many atoms of gold were recovered?
    (a) 6023×10^{25}
    (b) 6.023×10^{23}
    (c) 3.012×10^{23}
    (d) 3.012×10^{25}

47. If atomic mass unit of carbon is assumed to be 10 amu, what will be the value of Avogadro's number?
    (a) 6.023×10^{22}
    (b) 5.0×10^{22}
    (c) 6.023×10^{23}
    (d) 5.05×10^{23}

48. The mass of one molecule of water is approximately ......
    (a) 18 gm
    (b) 3×10^{-23} g
    (c) 1.5×10^{-23} g
    (d) 4.5×10^{-23} g

49. 1.7 gm of ammonia contains the same number of nitrogen as present in given ......
    (a) 22.4 litre of ammonia at STP
    (b) 1 litre of ammonia at STP
    (c) 6.3 g of nitric acid
    (d) 3.2 g of hydrazine

50. The total number of protons in 10 g of $CaCO_3$ is ......
    (a) 1.5×10^{24}
    (b) 2.05×10^{24}
    (c) 3.011×10^{24}
    (d) 4.09×10^{24}

51. The largest number of atoms are in ......
    (a) 71 g of chlorine
    (b) 48 g of magnesium
    (c) 127 g of iodine
    (d) 4 g of hydrogen

52. Which of the following weighs least?
    (a) 22.4 l of hydrogen
    (b) 6.023×10^{23} molecules of oxygen
    (c) 10 g of nitrogen
    (d) 10 ml of H_2O

53. If specific heat of one element is 0.64 then its approximate atomic mass is ......
    (a) 10
    (b) 100
    (c) 200
    (d) 20

54. The equivalent weight of magnesium is ......
    $2Mg + O_2 \rightarrow 2MgO$
    (a) 12
    (b) 24
    (c) 48
    (d) 32

55. The mass of one amu is approximately ......
(a) 1 gm
(b) 3.2×10^{-23} gm
(c) 0.5 gm
(d) 1.66×10^{-24} gm

56. 1.2 litres of a gas at STP is found to have a mass of 22 gm. The molecular mass of the gas is ......
(a) 22
(b) 44
(c) 88
(d) 32

57. Volume at STP of 0.22 gm of CO_2 is the same as that of ......
(a) 0.01 gm of hydrogen
(b) 0.085 g of NH_3
(c) 320 mg of gaseous SO_2
(d) All of these

58. The number of atoms of oxygen present in 0.2 equivalent of Na_2CO_3 will be ......
(a) 6.02×10^{22}
(b) 12.04×10^{22}
(c) 1.806×10^{23}
(d) 31.8

59. The number of molecules present in a drop of water of volume 0.06 cc is approximately ......
(a) 10^{21}
(b) 2×10^{21}
(c) 3×10^{21}
(d) 4×10^{21}

60. An element of equivalent mass E forms a general oxide X_yO_z, its atomic mass is ......
(a) $\dfrac{ME}{2z}$
(b) $\dfrac{2}{E_z}$
(c) $\dfrac{E}{z}$
(d) $2ME_z$

61. Haemoglobin contains 0.33% of iron by weight. The number of iron atoms in each molecule of haemoglobin is ......
[Molecular mass of haemoglobin – 67200; Ar : Fe–56]
(a) 5
(b) 2
(c) 4
(d) 3

62. If 10^{21} molecules are removed from 200 mg of CO_2, then number of moles of carbon dioxide left are ......
(a) 28.8×10^{-3}
(b) 0.288×10^{-3}
(c) 2.73×10^{-3}
(d) 1.66×10^{-2}

63. How many moles of electrons weigh one kilogram?
(a) $\dfrac{1}{9.109} \times 10^{31}$
(b) 6.023×10^{23}
(c) $\dfrac{1}{9.109} \times \dfrac{10^8}{6.023}$
(d) $\dfrac{6.023}{9.109} \times 10^{54}$

64. If the density of water is 1 gm cm^{-3} then the volume occupied by one mole of water is ......
(a) 22400 cm^3
(b) 6.02×10^{-23} cm^3
(c) 3×10^{-23} cm^3
(d) 18 cm^3

65. How many atoms of carbon are present in 18 gm of glucose $C_6H_{12}O_6$?
(a) 3.6×10^{23}
(b) 6.0×10^{22}
(c) 3.6×10^{24}
(d) 6.0×10^{23}

66. Which statement about the mole of metal is always correct?
(a) It contains the same number of atoms as 1 mole of hydrogen atoms
(b) It contains the same number of atoms as 1/2 mole of C–12
(c) It has the same mass as 1 mole of hydrogen atoms
(d) It is liberated by 1 mole of electrons

67. What is the number of molecules in 500 cm^3 of oxygen under room conditions ?
[Volume of the gas at stp –24 dm^3]
(a) 1.25×10^{22}
(b) 3.0×10^{22}
(c) 1.34×10^{22}
(d) 3×10^{26}

68. Which of the following gas contains the same number of atoms as 1 g of hydrogen?
(a) 22 g of CO_2
(b) 8 g of CH_4
(c) 20 gm of neon
(d) 8 gm of ozone

69. Avogadro's law states that ......
(a) The volume of a gas is directly proportional to its temperature in Kelvin
(b) The volume of a gas is directly proportional to the number of moles present
(c) The volume of a gas is directly proportional to the ideal gas constant
(d) The volume of a gas is directly proportional to the pressure

70. How many moles of nitrogen are present in a 200 L container, at a pressure of 1.0 atm and at 25°C?
(a) 8.92   (b) 8.18   (c) 19.3   (d) 8.5

71. The common isotopes of carbon are C–12 and C–13. The average mass of carbon is 12.01115 amu. What is the abundance of the C–13 isotope?
(a) 1.115%   (b) 98.85%   (c) 0.480%   (d) 99.52%

72. If the abundance of ^6Li (6.015121 amu) is 7.500% and the abundance of ^7Li (7.016003 amu) is 92.500%, what is the average atomic mass?
(a) 6.0750 amu   (b) 6.0902 amu   (c) 6.9250 amu   (d) 6.9409 amu

73. Which one of the following is present in one mole of Na_2CO_3?
(a) Only one mole of cations   (b) Only one mole of anions
(c) Only one mole of oxygen atoms   (d) Total six moles of ions

74. How many moles of oxygen atoms are contained in 0.020 mol of $Na_2SO_4.10H_2O$? (Molar mass = 306.0 g mol^{-1})
(a) 0.020 mol   (b) 0.200 mol   (c) 0.28 mol   (d) 2.00 mol

75. What is the percentage by weight of nitrogen in aluminium nitride (AlN?)
(Molar mass = 41.0 g mol^{-1})
[Atomic weight mass of Al = 27, N = 14]
(a) 14%   (b) 34.1%   (c) 42.0%   (d) 65.9%

76. What is the mass of one molecule of nitrogen gas N_2?
(a) $\dfrac{14.0}{(2 \times 6.023 \times 10^{23})}$ g   (b) $\dfrac{14.0}{(6.023 \times 10^{23})}$ g
(c) $\dfrac{2 \times 14.0}{(6.023 \times 10^{23})}$ g   (d) $2 \times 14.0 \times 6.023 \times 10^{23}$ g

77. How many moles of ions are there in 11.1 g of $CaCl_2$? (Molar mass = 111.0 g mol^{-1})
(a) 0.100 mole   (b) 0.200 mole   (c) 0.300 mole   (d) 11.1 mole

78. A cylinder A contains 0.5 mole of CO_2 and another identical cylinder B contains 0.5 mole of CO gas. Which of the following statements is correct?
(a) The number of molecules of the gas in A is greater than that in B
(b) The number of molecules of the gas in A is lower than that in B
(c) The number of molecules of the gas in A is the same as that in B
(d) The information given in the question is not sufficient

79. 5.6 litres of a gas at STP are found to have a mass of 22 g. The molecular mass of the gas is ......
(a) 32   (b) 22   (c) 44   (d) 88

80. What is the number of molecules of water in 1 g of water?

(a) 3.34×10^{22}　　　(b) 3.34×10^{23}　　　(c) 33.4×10^{22}　　　(d) 6.64×10^{23}

81. How many aluminium and oxide ions are present in 51 g of Al_2O_3 ?

[molecule of Al_2O_3 – 102]

(a) 12×10^{23} Al^{3+} and 2.7×10^{23} O^{2-} ions 　　(b) 6×10^{23} Al^{3+} and 9×10^{23} O^{2-} ions

(c) 6×10^{23} Al^{3+} and 6×10^{23} O^{2-} ions 　　(d) 1.2×10^{23} Al^{3+} and 1.7×10^{23} O^{2-} ions

82. What is the volume of 3.5 g of hydrogen at room temperature?

(a) $42\ dm^3$　　　(b) $4.2\ dm^3$　　　(c) $3.92\ dm^3$　　　(d) $39.2\ dm^3$

83. How many moles of calcium ions and chloride ions are present in 2.5 moles of calcium chloride?

(a) 1 mole of calcium ion and 2 moles of chloride ions

(b) 2.5 moles of calcium ions and 5 moles of chloride ions

(c) 2 moles of calcium ions and 1 mole of chloride ion

(d) 2.5 moles of calcium ions and 2.5 moles of chloride ions

84. What is the mass percent of each element in CH_2Cl_2?

(a) 10.06% C, 60.24% H, 29.70% Cl 　　(b) 12.00% C, 20.04% H, 60.00% Cl

(c) 33.87% C, 0.22% H, 65.91% Cl 　　(d) 14.11% C, 2.35% H, 83·54% Cl

85. A molecule is found to contain 47.35% C, 10.60% H and 42.05% Cl. What is the empirical formula?

(a) C_2H_6O　　　(b) $C_3H_8O_2$　　　(c) $C_4H_8O_3$　　　(d) $C_4H_8O_3$

86. A 2.00 g sample of $COCl_2.xH_2O$ is heated in an oven. The mass of the anhydrous salt is 1.565 g. What is the value of water of crystallization?

(a) 1　　　(b) 2　　　(c) 3　　　(d) 4

87. 1.056 g of a metal carbonate of unknown metal is heated to give metal oxide and 0.376 g of CO_2 gas. Identify the metal.

$$MCO_{3(s)} \xrightarrow{\ \Delta\ } MO_{(s)} + CO_{2(g)}$$

(a) Ni　　　(b) Ba　　　(c) Cu　　　(d) Ca or Zn

88. A sample of 2.00 g of $Fe_2(SO_4)_3$ is dissolved in water to give 100 cm^3 of aqueous solution. What is the concentration of SO_4^{2-} ions? [$Fe_2(SO_4)_3$ is 400 gm mol^{-1}]

(a) 1.5×10^{-3} mol dm^{-3} 　　　　(b) 5×10^3 mole dm^{-3}

(c) 1.5×10^{-2} mole dm^{-3} 　　　　(d) 1.5×10^{-1} mole dm^{-3}

89. A sample of 0.025 mole of chloride of an element M was dissolved in water and the solution made upto 500 cm^3. 12.5 cm^3 of this situation completely reacted with 25 cm^3 of 0.1 mol dm^{-3} $AgNO_3$ solution. What is the formula of the chloride?

(a) MCl　　　(b) MCl_4　　　(c) MCl_2　　　(d) M_2Cl

90. 10.0 cm^3 of 0.10 mole dm^{-3} of iron (II) sulphate was titrated against $KMnO_4$ solution of concentration 0.025 mol dm^{-4} in the presence of an excess of fluoride ions. 10.0 cm^3 of the $KMnO_4$ solution is required to reach the end point. What is the oxidation number of manganese at the end point ?

(a) +2　　　(b) +3　　　(c) +4　　　(d) +5

91. 0.20 g sample of a monobasic acid requires 8.0 cm^3 of 0.40 mol dm^{-3} NaOH solution for complete neutralization. What is the relative molecular mass of the acid?

(a) 250   (b) 625   (c) 62.5   (d) 630

92. Oxalate, $C_2O_4^{2-}$ ions are oxidized by acidified aqueous KMnO$_4$ solution according to the equation

$$2MnO_{4\ (aq)}^- + 5C_2CO_{4\ (aq)}^{2-} + 16H_{(aq)}^+ \rightarrow 2Mn_{(aq)}^{2+} + 10CO_{2(g)} + 8H_2O_{(l)}$$

What volume of 0.20 mol dm^{-3} KMnO$_4$ solution is required to oxidize completely 1.0×10^{-3} mol of potassium oxalate salt?

(a) 20 cm^3 (b) 40 cm^3 (c) 50 cm^3 (d) 125 cm^3

93. How many grams of oxygen are required for reaction with 162 gram of ammonia during the following reaction?

[Molar mass of O$_2$ = 32; Molar mass of NH$_3$ = 17.0] $4NH_3 + 5O_2 \rightarrow 4NO + 6H_2O$

(a) 381 g   (b) 108 g   (c) 212 g   (d) 182 g

94. 25.0 ml of Na$_2$SO$_4$ was treated with 0.15 mole dm^{-3} barium nitrate solution of which 30.00 ml was needed for complete reaction. Find out molarity of the sodium sulphate solution.

$$Ba(NO_3)_2 + Na_2SO_4 \rightarrow BaSO_4 + 2NaNO_3$$

(a) 0.09 M   (b) 0.18 M   (c) 0.36 M   (d) 0.45 M

95. 31.15 ml of 3M NaOH solution completely reacted with sulphuric acid of unknown concentration to get pink phenolphthalein end point. Calculate the number of moles of sulphuric acid in the solution.

$$2NaOH + H_2SO_4 \rightarrow Na_2SO_4 + 2H_2O$$

(a) 0.0625   (b) 0.10   (c) 0.46   (d) 0.192

96. 54.2 ml of aqueous hydrochloric acid solution has 23.0 g of hydrochloric acid and 40.0 g of water. Find out the density of the solution.

(a) 0.43   (b) 0.86   (c) 23.0   (d) 1.16

97. How many moles of PCl$_3$ will be produced by the complete reaction of 2.0 moles of chlorine with excess of P$_4$?

[Molar mass of Cl$_2$ = 71; P$_4$ = 124; PCl$_3$ = 136.5]

$$P_4 + 6Cl_2 \rightarrow 4PCl_3$$

(a) 1.5   (b) 3.0   (c) 1.34   (d) 4.0

98. How many millilitres of 6.0 mol dm^{-4} aqueous sodium chloride should be taken and diluted with sufficient water to make 2 litres of a 0.30 M sodium chloride solution?

(a) 10.0   (b) 30.0   (c) 60.0   (d) 100

99. How many moles of Fe^{2+} ions are formed when excess of iron is treated with 50 ml of 4.0 M HCl under inert atmosphere assuming no change in volume?

(a) 0.1   (b) 0.2   (c) 0.4   (d) 0.8

100. A X molal solution of a compound in benzene has mole fraction of solute 0.2. The value of X is ......

(a) 14   (b) 3.2   (c) 1.4   (d) 2

101. 5 ml of N HCl, 20 ml of N/2 H_2SO_4 and 30 ml of N/3 HNO_3 are mixed together and the volume made to 1 litre. The normality of the resulting solution is ......

(a) $\dfrac{N}{40}$ (b) $\dfrac{N}{20}$ (c) $\dfrac{N}{10}$ (d) $\dfrac{N}{5}$

102. The molarity of a solution which contains 49 g H_3PO_4 in 2.0 L of a solution is ......

(a) 0.25 M   (b) 0.50 M   (c) 0.75 M   (d) 1.0 M

103. The relationship between molarity, molality and density of a solution is given by : (M_R molar mass of solute)

(a) $m = \dfrac{(d - MM_r)}{M_r}$ (b) $m = \dfrac{(d + MM_r)}{M_r}$

(c) $m = \dfrac{M}{(d - MM_r)}$ (d) $m = \dfrac{M}{(d + MM_r)}$

104. The molar concentration of Cl^- ion in a solution obtained by mixing 300 ml of 0.3 M NaCl and 200 ml of 0.4 $BaCl_2$ is ......

(a) 0.25 M   (b) 0.5 M   (c) 0.9 M   (d) 1.5 M

105. The mass of 60% HCl required for the neutralization of 10 l of 0.1 M KOH is ......

(a) 22.8 g   (b) 21.9 g   (c) 100 g   (d) 219 g

106. Sodium carbonate reacts with hydrochloric acid according to the following equation. What mass of CO_2 is produced if 2.94 g of Na_2CO_3 reacts with excess HCl ?

$$Na_2CO_{3(s)} + 2HCl_{(aq)} \rightarrow 2NaCl_{(aq)} + H_2O_{(l)} + CO_{2(g)}$$

(a) 1.22 g   (b) 2.44 g   (c) 2.94 g   (d) 5.88 g

107. 500.0 ml of 2.500 M HCl is mixed with 250.0 ml of 3.750 M HCl. The concentration of HCl is ......

(a) 2.917 M   (b) 3.250 M   (c) 1.500 M   (d) 2.750 M

108. How many grams of cast iron can be produced by the reduction of Fe_2O_3 in the blast furnace?

$$Fe_2O_{3(s)} + 3CO_{(g)} \rightarrow 2Fe_{(s)} + 3CO\uparrow$$

[Atomic mass of Fe = 55.8; O = 16]

(a) 6.98 g Fe   (b) 69.8 g Fe   (c) 6.98 kg Fe   (d) 698 g Fe

109. Calculate the amount of H_2 gas produced when 0.30 moles of zinc is added to 0.52 mol of HCl.

(a) 0.30 mol H_2 (b) 0.25 mol H_2 (c) 0.52 mol H_2 (d) 0.13 mol H_2

110. Potassium superoxide is used to make oxygen generating masks. If 0.25 mol of KO_2 and 0.15 mol H_2O are mixed in a reaction, the limiting reactant and moles of oxygen produced are ......

$$4KO_{2(s)} + 2H_2O_{(s)} \rightarrow 4KOH_{(s)} + 3O_{2(g)}$$

(a) 0.225 mol O_2, KO_2 (b) 0.187 mol O_2, KO_2

(c) 0.187 mol O_2, H_2O (d) 0.225 mol O_2, H_2O

111. 12.8 g of calcium fluoride and 13.2 g of sulphuric acid is heated to give hydrogen fluoride ......

$$CaF_{2(s)} + H_2SO_{4(l)} \rightarrow 2HF_{(g)} + CaSO_{4(s)}$$

What is the amount of HF produced in grams ?

[Atomic mass of Ca = 40, F = 19, S = 32, H = 1]

(a) 5.3 g　　　　(b) 6.5 g　　　　(c) 53 g　　　　(d) 65 g

112. Aspirin ($C_9H_8O_4$) is obtained by acetylation of salicylic acid ($C_7H_6O_3$) with acetic anhydride ($C_4H_6O_3$). What is the percent yield if 2.00 g of salicylic acid is heated with 4.00 g of acetic anhydride. Actual yield of aspirin is 1.86 g.

$$C_7H_6O_3 + C_4H_6O_3 \rightarrow C_9H_8O_4 + CH_3COOH$$

(a) 23.07%　　　　(b) 71.5%　　　　(c) 75%　　　　(d) 25%

113. Mass of one atom of the element is 3.9854×10^{-23} g. The number of atoms in one gram of this element are ......

(a) 2.6×10^{-23} atom　　　　　　　　(b) 2.5092×10^{22} atom

(c) 2.51×10^{-23} atom　　　　　　　　(d) 2.61×10^{22} atom

114. 40 g of $CaCO_3$ was heated to a high temperature. What volume of CO_2 gas is evolved at STP ? (Atomic mass of Ca = 40, C = 12, O = 16]

(a) 22.4 lit　　　　(b) 0.4 lit　　　　(c) 89.6 lit　　　　(d) 8.96 lit

115. Glauber salt on strong heating losses 55.9% by mass and becomes anhydrous. The number of water of crystallization is ......

(a) 5　　　　(b) 10　　　　(c) 6　　　　(d) 7

116. How many millilitres of 0.250 M NaOH must be added to react completely with 35 ml of 0.175 M H_2SO_4 ?

(a) 47.0 ml　　　　(b) 48 ml　　　　(c) 49 ml　　　　(d) 50 ml

117. Equivalent weight of potassium permanganate (VII) in alkaline medium is ......

[Molar mass of $KMnO_4$ = 158]

$$MnO_4^- \rightarrow MnO_2$$

(a) 31.6　　　　(b) 53.0　　　　(c) 52.66　　　　(d) 39.5

118. How many millilitres of 0.375 M nickel sulphate will react with 45.7 ml of 0.265 M sodium phosphate?

(a) 24.2 lit　　　　(b) 48.4 lit　　　　(c) 484 lit　　　　(d) 242 lit

119. What is the mass percentage of ethanoic acid in vinegar when 5.0 g of sample of vinegar is titrated with 39.1 mol of 0.108 M NaOH for complete neutralization ?

(a) 2.58%　　　　(b) 25.8%　　　　(c) 51.6%　　　　(d) 5.16%

120. When 6.3 g of $NaHCO_3$ are added to 15.0 g of CH_3COOH solution, the residue is found to weigh 18.0 g. The mass of CO_2 released in the reaction is ......

(a) 9.4 g　　　　(b) 3.3 g　　　　(c) 2.9 g　　　　(d) 0.08 g

121. What volume of 3 M H_2SO_4 is required when 12 M H_2SO_4 and 3 M H_2SO_4 are mixed to prepare 1 litre of 8 M H_2SO_4 ?

(a) 444 ml　　　　(b) 556 ml　　　　(c) 55.6 ml　　　　(d) 44.4 ml

122. 2 g of oxygen contains a number of atoms equal to that in ......

(a) 0.5 g of hydrogen   (b) 4 g of sulphur

(c) 7 g of nitrogen   (d) 2.3 g of sodium

123. The number of valence electrons in 4.2 g of nitride ion is ......

(a) $2.4\ N_A$ (b) $4.2\ N_A$ (c) $1.6\ N_A$ (d) $3.2\ N_A$

124. The number of moles of helium that occupies 2.24 litres at 0°C and 1 atmosphere pressure is ......

(a) 1.0 mole   (b) 0.1 mole   (c) 10 mole   (d) 1×10^{-2} mole

125. The number of moles of oxygen in one litre of air (21% oxygen by volume) at STP would be ......

(a) 0.186 mole   (b) 0.21 mole   (c) 2.10 mole   (d) 0.0093 mole

126. The number of hydrogen atoms in 4.25 g of NH_3 is approximately ......

(a) 1×10^{23} (b) 4.5×10^{23} (c) 2×10^{23} (d) 6×10^{23}

127. 4.4 g of unknown gas has a volume of 2.24 litres at STP. The gas may be ......

(a) CO_2 (b) CO (c) O_2 (d) SO_2

128. Aluminium reacts with oxygen to produce aluminium oxide.

$$4Al + 3O_2 \rightarrow 2Al_2O_3$$

If 5.0 moles of Al react with excess oxygen, how many moles of Al_2O_3 can be formed?

(a) 1.0   (b) 2.0 mole   (c) 2.5 mole   (d) 5 mole

129. 50 g of $CaCO_3$ was completely burn in air. What is the weight of CaO? [Ca = 40, C = 12, O = 16]

(a) 2.8 g   (b) 28 g   (c) 4.4 g   (d) 44 g

PREVIOUS YEAR'S QUESTIONS

1. A bivalent metal has an equivalent mass of 3.2. The molecular mass of the metal nitrate is ...... **[KCET 2009]**

(a) 168   (b) 192   (c) 188   (d) 182

2. 1.5 g of $CdCl_2$ was found to contain 0.9 g of Cd. Calculate the atomic weight of Cd. **[EAMCET 2009]**

(a) 118   (b) 112   (c) 106.5   (d) 53.25

3. The volume of 2N H_2SO_4 solution is 0.1 dm^3. The volume of its decinormal solution (in dm^3) will be ...... **[MHT CET 2009]**

(a) 0.1   (b) 0.2   (c) 2   (d) 1.7

4. 10 g of hydrogen and 64 g of oxygen were filled in a steel vessel and exploded. Amount of water produced in this reaction will be ...... **[CBSE AIPMT 2009]**

(a) 3 mol   (b) 4 mol   (c) 1 mol   (d) 2 mol

5. What volume of CO_2 will be liberated at NTP, if 12 g of carbon is burn in excess of oxygen? **[AFMC 2009]**

(a) 11.2 litre   (b) 22.4 litre   (c) 2.24 litre   (d) 1.12 litre

6. The equivalent weight of $MnSO_4$ is half of its molecular weight, it is converted to **[AFMC 2009]**

(a) Mn_2O_3 (b) MnO_2 (c) MnO_4 (d) MnO_4^{2-}

7. x moles of potassium dichromate oxidize 1 mole of ferrous oxalate in acidic medium. Here x is ...... **[AIIMS 2009]**

(a) 3   (b) 1.5   (c) 0.5   (d) 1.0

8. Excess of carbon dioxide is passed through 50 ml of 0.5 M calcium hydroxide solution. After the completion of the reaction, the solution was evaporated to dryness. The solid calcium carbonate was completely neutralized with 0.1 N hydrochloric acid. The volume of hydrochloric acid required is ...... (Atomic mass of calcium = 40)   **[KCET 2009]**

(a) $200 \, cm^3$ (b) $500 \, cm^3$ (c) $400 \, cm^3$ (d) $300 \, cm^3$

9. The equivalent mass of potassium permanganate in alkaline medium is its ......

[J & K CET 2009]

(a) $\dfrac{molar \ mass}{5}$ (b) $\dfrac{molar \ mass}{3}$ (c) $\dfrac{molar \ mass}{2}$ (d) molar mass itself

10. One atom of an element weighs 1.8×10^{-22} g. Its atomic mass is ......   **[Manipal 2009]**

(a) 29.9   (b) 154   (c) 108.36   (d) 18

11. The number of atoms of He in 100 μ of He (atomic weight of He is 4) are ...   **[BCECE 2008]**

(a) 25   (b) 100   (c) 50   (d) $100 \times 6 \times 10^{-23}$

12. If two oxides of iron, the first contained 22% and the second contained 30% of oxygen by weight. The ratio of weights of iron in the two oxides that combine with the same weight of oxygen is ......   **[J & K CET 2008]**

(a) 3:2   (b) 2:1   (c) 1:2   (d) 1:1

13. In an oxidation-reduction reaction, MnO_4^- is converted to Mn^2. What is the number of equivalents of $KMnO_4$ (molecular weight = 158) present in 250 mL of 0.04 M $KMnO_4$ solution?   **[MP PMT 2008]**

(a) 0.02   (b) 0.05   (c) 0.04   (d) 0.07

14. The number of gram molecules of chlorine in 6.02×10^{25} hydrogen chloride molecules is ......   **[KCET 2007]**

(a) 10   (b) 100   (c) 50   (d) 5

15. Gram molecular volume of oxygen at STP is ......   **[KCET 2007]**

(a) $32000 \, cm^3$ (b) $5600 \, cm^3$ (c) $22400 \, cm^3$ (d) $11200 \, cm^3$

16. The crystalline salt $Na_2SO_4 \cdot xH_2O$ on heating losses 55.9% of its weight. The formula of the crystalline salt is ......   **[Kerala CEE 2007]**

(a) $Na_2SO_4 \cdot 5H_2O$ (b) $Na_2SO_4 \cdot 7H_2O$ (c) $Na_2SO_4 \cdot 2H_2O$ (d) $Na_2SO_4 \cdot 10H_2O$

17. If 25 g of MCl_4 contains 0.5 mole chlorine then its molecular weight is ......   **[PMT 07]**

(a) $100 \, g \, mol^{-1}$ (b) $200 \, g \, mol^{-1}$ (c) $150 \, g \, mol^{-1}$ (d) $400 \, g \, mol^{-1}$

18. The decomposition of a certain mass of $CaCO_3$ gave $11.2 \, dm^3$ of CO_2 gas at STP. The mass of KOH required to completely neutralize the gas is ......   **[KCET 2006]**

(a) 56 g   (b) 28 g   (c) 42 g   (d) 20 g

19. A gas is found to have a formula $(CO)_x$. If its vapour density is 70, the value of x is ......

[AMU 2006]

(a) 2.5   (b) 3.0   (c) 5.0   (d) 6.0

20. The equivalent weight of phosphoric acid (H_3PO_4) in the reaction,

   $NaOH + H_3PO_4 \rightarrow NaH_2PO_4 + H_2O$ is ......   **[AIIM 1999; BHU 2005]**

   (a) 25   (b) 49   (c) 59   (d) 98

21. On reduction with hydrogen, 3.6 g of an oxide of metal left 3.2 g of metal. If the vapour density of metal is 32, the simplest formula of the oxide would be ......   **[DUMET 2004]**

   (a) MO   (b) M_2O_3 (c) M_2O (d) M_2O_5

22. One Fermi is ......   **[Haryana CEET 1994; DPMT 2004]**

   (a) 10^{-13} cm   (b) 10^{-15} cm   (c) 10^{-10} cm   (d) 10^{-12} cm

23. The prefix zepto stands for ......   **[DPMT 2004]**

   (a) 10^{9} (b) 10^{-12} (c) 10^{-15} (d) 10^{-21}

24. The significant figures in 3400 are ......   **[BHU 2004]**

   (a) 2   (b) 5   (c) 6   (d) 4

25. If the density of water is 1 g cm^{-3} then the volume occupied by one molecule of water is approximately ......   **[PB PMT 2004]**

   (a) 18 cm^3 (b) 22400 cm^3 (c) 6.02×10^{-23} cm^3 (d) 3.0×10^{-23} cm

26. The number of moles of oxygen in 1 litre of air containing 21% oxygen by volume, in standard conditions, is   **[CBSE PMT 1995; Pb PMT 2004]**

   (a) 0.186 mol   (b) 0.21 mol   (c) 2.10 mol   (d) 0.0093 mol

27. The mass of $BaCO_3$ produced when excess CO_2 is bubbled through a solution of 0.205 mol $Ba(OH)_2$ is ......   **[UPSEAT 2004]**

   (a) 81 g   (b) 40.5 g   (c) 20.25 g   (d) 162 g

28. Avogadro's number is the number of molecules present in ......   **[AFMC 2003]**

   (a) 1 litre of molecule   (b) 1 g of molecule

   (c) gram of molecule mass   (d) 1 g – atom of molecule

29. The significant figures in 1.0024, 1,240 and 0.0020 are respectively ......

   [Punjab PMET 2003]

   (a) 5, 4, 2   (b) 3, 3, 1   (c) 5,3, 4   (d) 5, 3, 2

30. 1.0 gm of magnesium is burnt with 0.56 g of oxygen in closed vessel. Which reactant is left in excess and how much?   **[AIPMT 2014]**

   (a) Mg, 0.44 g   (b) Mg, 0.16 g   (c) O_2, 0.28 g   (d) O_2, 0.16 g

31. When 22.4 litres of hydrogen is mixed with 11.2 litres of chlorine each at STP then the moles of HCl formed is equal to ......   **[AIPMT 2014]**

   (a) 0.5 mol of HCl   (b) 1.5 mole   (c) 1 mol   (d) 2 mol

32. How many grams of concentrated nitric acid solution should be used to prepare 250 ml of 2.0 M HNO_3 ? The concentration of HNO_3 is 70%.   **[NEET 2013]**

   (a) 54 g   (b) 45 g   (c) 90 g   (d) 70 g

33. An excess of $AgNO_3$ is added to 100 ml of a 0.01 M solution of dichlorotetraaqua chromium (111) chloride. The number of moles of AgCl precipitated would be ......   **[NEET 2013]**

   (a) 0.01   (b) 0.001   (c) 0.002   (d) 0.003

34. 1 amu is equal to ......   **[MHT CET 2010]**

   (a) 1.492×10^{-10} J   (b) 1.492×10^{-7} J   (c) 1.492×10^{-13} J   (d) 6.023×10^{23} J

35. The number of atoms in 0.1 mol of triatomic gas is ......   **[CBSE PMT 2010]**

   (a) 6.026×10^{22} (b) 1.806×10^{23} (c) 1.800×10^{22} (d) 3.600×10^{23} J

36. The number of atoms present in 4.25 g of NH_3 is ...... **[AFMC 2010]**

(a) 6.026×10^{23}

(b) $4 \times 6.026 \times 10^{23}$

(c) 1.7×10^{24}

(d) $4.25 \times 6.026 \times 10^{23}$

37. The hydrogen phosphate of a certain metal has the formula $MHPO_4$. The formula of metal chloride is ...... **[BHU 2002]**

(a) MCl (b) MCl_2 (c) M_2Cl_3 (d) MCl_3

38. The reaction of 10.0 g $H_{2(g)}$ with 10 g of $O_{2(g)}$ yields 8.43 g $H_2O_{(g)}$. What is the percent yield of this reaction? **[CBSE 2001]**

$$2H_2 + O_2 \rightarrow 2H_2O$$

(a) 9.43%   (b) 27.3%   (c) 42.2%   (d) 66.8%

39. 40 g of a sample of carbon on combustion left 10% of it unreacted. The volume of oxygen required at STP for this combustion reaction is ...... **[CBSE 2002]**

(a) 62.2 litre   (b) 44.8 litre   (c) 22.4 litre   (d) 11.2 litre

40. In a redox reaction, dichromate ion ($Cr_2O_7^{2-}$) is reduced to Cr^{3+} ion. The equivalent weight of $K_2Cr_2O_7$ is ...... **[CBSE 2003]**

(a) Molecular weight/3

(b) Molecular weight/6

(c) Molecular weight/1

(d) Molecular weight

41. X g of calcium carbonate was completely burn in air. The weight of the solid residue formed is 28 g. What is the value of X in grams? **[CBSE 2003]**

(a) 44   (b) 200   (c) 150   (d) 50

42. What are the oxidation numbers of nitrogen in NH_4NO_3? **[CPMT 2000]**

(a) +2; +2   (b) +3; −6   (c) −3; +5   (d) +3; −5

43. Two gm of sulphur is completely burn in the presence of oxygen to give 50 g SO_2. Calculate the volume of oxygen in litres of STP.

[Molecular mass of S = 32; O = 16] **[Pb. PMT 2000]**

(a) 22.414/30   (b) 22.4/16   (c) 32/22.414   (d) 16/22.414

44. How many litres of oxygen at STP are required for complete combustion of benzene? **[Pb. PMT 2001]**

(Molecular mass of C = 12, H = 1, O = 16)

(a) 84   (b) 42   (c) 22.4   (d) 11.2

45. Four grams of hydrocarbon on complete combustion gave 12 g of CO_2. What is the empirical formula of hydrocarbon? (Molecular mass of C = 12; H = 1) **[Pb. PMT 2002]**

(a) CH   (b) CH_3 (c) C_3H_8 (d) C_4H_9

46. Which two compounds have least weight of oxygen?

Sr. No.	Compound taken	(Mol. wt.)	Weight of the compound
I	CO_2	44	4.4 g
II	NO_2	46	2.3 g
III	H_2O_2	34	6.8 g
IV	SO_2	64	1.6 g

[Pb. PMT 2003]

(a) II and IV   (b) I and III   (c) I and II   (d) III and IV

47. 25 ml of a solution of $Ba(OH)_2$ on titration with 0.1 M solution of hydrochloric acid gave a litre value of 35 ml. The molarity of barium hydroxide solution is ...   **[Pb. PMT 2003]**

    (a) 0.35 M   (b) 0.07 M   (c) 0.14 M   (d) 0.25 M

48. What volume of hydrogen gas at 273 K and 1 atm pressure will be consumed in obtaining 21.6 g of elemental boron (Atomic mass = 108 g) from the reduction of boron trichloride by hydrogen? [Atomic mass of B = 10.8 g]   **[DPMT 2003]**

    (a) 22.4 L   (b) 89.6 L   (c) 67.2 L   (d) 44.8 L

49. 6.02×10^{20} molecules of urea are present in 100 ml of its solution. The concentration of urea solution is ......   **[DPMT 2003]**

    (a) 0.001 M   (b) 0.01 M   (c) 0.02 M   (d) 0.1 M

50. To neutralize 20 ml of 0.1 M aqueous solution of phosphorous acid (H_3PO_3), the volume of 0.1 M aqueous KOH solution required is ......   **[AMU 2006]**

    (a) 10 ml   (b) 20 m   (c) 40 ml   (d) 60 ml

51. Two solutions of a non-electrolyte are mixed. 380 ml of 1.5 M solution is mixed with 520 ml of 1.2 M solution. What is the molarity of the final solution?   **[AMU 2007]**

    (a) 1.344 M   (b) 2.70 M   (c) 1.20 M   (d) 1.50 M

52. How many moles of magnesium phosphate $Mg_3(PO_4)_2$ will contain 0.2 moles of oxygen atoms?   **[AMU 2008]**

    (a) 2.5×10^{-2} (b) 3.125×10^{-2} (c) 0.02   (d) 1.25×10^{-2}

53. In a chemical reaction
$$K_2Cr_2O_7 + xH_2SO_4 + ySO_2 \longrightarrow K_2SO_4 + Cr_2(SO_4)_3 + zH_2O$$
the values of x, y, z are ......   **[B.H.U. 1994, 2000]**

    (a) 1, 3, 1   (b) 4, 1, 4   (c) 3, 2, 3   (d) 2, 1, 2

54. Assuming full decomposition, the volume of CO_2 released at STP on heating 9.85 g of $BaCO_3$ (Atomic mass of Ba = 137) will be ......   **[C.B.S.E. 2000]**

    (a) 0.84 litre   (b) 0.24 litre   (c) 4.06 litre   (d) 1.12 litre

55. The number of equivalent of $Na_2S_2O_3$ required for the volumetric estimation of one equivalent of Cu^{2+} is ......   **[Kerala E.E.E. 2000]**

    (a) 1   (b) 2   (c) 3/2   (d) 3

    (e) beteen 2% to 5% of 22.4 litres

56. In a mole of water vapour at STP, the volume actually occupied or taken by the molecules (i.e. Avogadro's No. × volume of one molecule) is ......   **[Kerala E.E.E. 2000]**

    (a) Zero   (b) Less than 1% of 22.4 litres

    (c) About 10% of the volume of container   (d) 1% to 2% of 22.4 litres

    (e) between 2% to 50% of 22.4 litres

57. Complete combustion of 0.858 g of compound X gives 2.63 g of CO_2 and 1.28 g of H_2O. The lowest molecular mass of X can have ......   **[Kerala M.E.E. 2000]**

    (a) 43 g   (b) 85 g   (c) 129 g   (d) 172 g

    (e) 22 g

58. An organic compound contains 49.3% carbon, 6.84% hydrogen and its vapour density is 73. Molecular formula of the compound is ......   **[M.P.C.E.T. 2000]**

    (a) $C_3H_5O_2$ (b) $C_6H_{10}O_4$ (c) $C_3H_{10}O_2$ (d) $C_4H_{10}O_2$

59. In the following reaction, which choice has value twice that of the equivalent mass of the oxidizing agent ?   **[Delhi P.M.T. 2000]**

$$SO_2 + H_2O \longrightarrow 3S + 2H_2O$$

   (a) 64   (b) 32   (c) 16   (d) 48

60. Vapour density of a gas is 22. What is its molecular mass?   **[A.F.M.C. 2000]**

   (a) 33   (b) 22   (c) 44   (d) 11

61. How many atoms are contained in one mole of sucrose ($C_{12}H_{22}O_{11}$) ?   **[Pb. P.M.T. 2002]**

   (a) $45 \times 6.02 \times 10^{23}$ atoms/mole   (b) $5 \times 6.62 \times 10^{23}$ atoms/mole

   (c) $5 \times 6.02 \times 10^{23}$ atoms/mole   (d) none of these

62. 1.5 mol of O_2 combine with Mg to form oxide MgO. The mass of Mg (atomic mass 24) that has combined is ......   **[Karnataka C.E.T. 2001]**

   (a) 72 g   (b) 36 g   (c) 48 g   (d) 24 g

63. The mass of 112 cm^3 of CH_4 gas at STP is ......   **[Karnataka C.E.T. 2001]**

   (a) 0.16 g   (b) 0.8 g   (c) 0.08 g   (d) 1.6 g

64. The volume of water to be added to 100 cm^3 of 0.5 N H_2SO_4 to get decinormal concentration is ......   **[Karnataka C.E.T. 2001]**

   (a) 400 cm^3 (b) 500 cm^3 (c) 450 cm^3 (d) 100 cm^3

65. The reaction of calcium with water is represented by the equation   **[Kerala P.M.T. 2001]**

   $$Ca + 2H_2O \longrightarrow Ca(OH)_2 + H_2$$

   What volume of H_2, at STP would be liberated when 8 g of calcium completely react with water ?

   (a) 4480 cm^3 (b) 2240 cm^3 (c) 1120 cm^3 (d) 0.4 cm^3

   (e) 0.2 cm^3

66. Among the following pairs, the one which illustrates the law of multiple proportion is

   [Kerala P.M.T. 2001]

   (a) NH_3, HCl   (b) H_2S, SO_2 (c) CuO, Cu_2O (d) CS_2, $FeSO_4$

   (e) $FeCl_2$, $FeSO_4$

67. The mixture of sand and sulphur may best be separated by ......   **[Kerala C.E.T. 2001]**

   (a) Fractional crystallization from aqueous solution

   (b) Magnetic method   (c) Fractional distillation

   (d) Dissolving in CS_2 and filtering   (e) Sublimation

68. The set of numerical coefficients that balances the chemical equation

   $$K_2Cr_2O_4 + HCl \longrightarrow K_2Cr_2O_7 + KCl + H_2O \text{ is ......}$$ **[Kerala C.E.T. 2001]**

   (a) 1, 1, 2, 2, 1   (b) 2, 2, 1, 1, 1   (c) 2, 1, 1, 2, 1   (d) 2, 2, 1, 2, 1

   (e) 2, 2, 2, 1, 1

69. 0.126 g of acid required 20 ml of 0.1 N NaOH for complete neutralization. The equivalent mass of an acid is ......   **[M.P.P.E.T. 2001]**

   (a) 45   (b) 53   (c) 40   (d) 63

70. Which law directly explain the law of conservation of mass ?   **[A.F.M.C. 2001, 2003]**

   (a) Dalton's law   (b) Avogadro's law   (c) Berzelius law   (d) Hund's rule

71. Molarity of liquid HCl with density equal to 1.17 g/cc is ......   **[C.B.S.E. 2001]**

   (a) 36.5   (b) 18.25   (c) 32.05   (d) 4.65

72. The modern atomic weight scale is based on ......   **[M.P.P.M.T. 2002]**

   (a) C^{12} (b) O^{16} (c) H^1 (d) C^{13}

73. The prefix 10^{18} is ......   **[Kerala P.M.T. 2002]**
   (a) giga   (b) exa   (c) kilo   (d) nano
   (e) mega

74. X litres of carbon monoxide are present at S.T.P. It is completely oxidized to CO_2. The volume of CO_2 formed is 11.207 L at STP. What is the value of X in litres ? **[E.M.C.E.T. 2002]**
   (a) 22.414 L   (b) 11.207 L   (c) 5.6035 L   (d) 44.828 L

75. 25 ml of a solution of barium hydroxide on titration with 0.1 molar solution of hydrochloric acid gave a titre value of 35 ml. The molarity of barium hydroxide solution is ......
                    [A.I.E.E.E. 2003]
   (a) 0.07   (b) 0.14   (c) 0.28   (d) 0.35

76. A metal M of equivalent mass E forms an oxide of molecular formula M_xO_y. The atomic mass of the metal is given by the correct equation   **[Kerala P.M.T. 2008]**
   (a) 2E (y/x)   (b) xy/E   (c) E/y   (d) E/s (x/y)
   (e) y/E

77. 2 g of aluminium is treated separately with excess of dilute H_2SO_4, and excess of NaOH, the ratio of volumes of hydrogen evolved is ......   **[Kerala Engg. 2004]**
   (a) 1 : 1   (b) 2 : 3   (c) 1 : 2   (d) 2 : 1
   (e) 3 : 1

78. Which of the following contain maximum number of molecules ?   **[Kerala Engg. 2004]**
   (a) 100 cc of CO_2 at STP   (b) 150 cc of N_2 at STP
   (c) 50 cc of SO_2 at STP   (d) 200 cc of NH_3 at S.T.P.
   (e) 150 cc of O_2 at STP

79. The numerical value of N/n (where N is the number of molecules in a given sample of gas and n is the number of moles of the gas) is   ......   **[Kerala Engg. 2004]**
   (a) 8.314   (b) 6.02×10^{23} (c) 0.0821   (d) 1.62×10^{-24}

80. When 32.25 g of ethyl chloride is subjected to dehydrohalogenation reaction, the yield of alkene formed is 50%. The mass of the product formed is (atomic mass of chlorine = 35.5)
                    [Kerala Engg. 2005]
   (a) 14 g   (b) 28 g   (c) 64.5 g   (d) 7 g
   (e) 56 g

81. 100 g of $CaCO_3$ is treated with 1 litre of 1 N HCl. What would be the weight of CO_2 liberated after the completion of the reaction ?   **[Kerala Engg. 2005]**
   (a) 5.5 g   (b) 11 g   (c) 22 g   (d) 33 g
   (e) 44 g

82. The mass of carbon anode consumed (giving only carbon dioxide) in the production of 270 kg of aluminium metal from bauxite by Hall process is (Atomic mass of Al = 27) ...
                    [C.B.S.E. P.M.T. 2005]
   (a) 180 kg   (b) 270 kg   (c) 540 kg   (d) 90 kg

83. For the formation of 3.65 g of hydrogen chloride gas, what volumes of hydrogen and chlorine gas are required at N.T.P. conditions ?   **[Kerala Med. 2005]**
   (a) 1.12 litre, 1.12 litre   (b) 1.12 litre, 2.24 litre
   (c) 3.65 litre, 1.83 litre   (d) 1 litre, 1 litre
   (e) 3.55 litre, 1.83 litre

84. The decomposition of certain mass of $CaCO_3$ gave 11.2 dm^3 of a CO_2 at STP. The mass of KOH required to completely neutralize the gas is ...... **[Karnataka C.E.T. 2006]**

(a) 56 g　　　　　　(b) 28 g　　　　　　(c) 42 g　　　　　　(d) 20 g

85. 4 moles of each of SO_2 and O_2 gases are allowed to react to form SO_3 in a closed vessel. At equilibrium, 25% of O_2 is used up. The total number of moles of all the gases at equilibrium is ...... **[Karnataka C.E.T. 2006]**

(a) 6.5　　　　　　(b) 7.0　　　　　　(c) 8.0　　　　　　(d) 2.0

ANSWER KEY

1. (a)	2. (c)	3. (a)	4. (b)	5. (d)	6. (b)	7. (a)	8. (c)
9. (c)	10. (a)	11. (a)	12. (b)	13. (a)	14. (b)	15. (d)	16. (b)
17. (c)	18. (b)	19. (d)	20. (a)	21. (a)	22. (b)	23. (b)	24. (c)
25. (a)	26. (b)	27. (c)	28. (a)	29. (a)	30. (a)	31. (d)	32. (d)
33. (c)	34. (a)	35. (b)	36. (c)	37. (a)	38. (c)	39. (b)	40. (c)
41. (a)	42. (c)	43. (c)	44. (b)	45. (b)	46. (a)	47. (c)	48. (b)
49. (c)	50. (c)	51. (d)	52. (a)	53. (a)	54. (a)	55. (d)	56. (b)
57. (d)	58. (c)	59. (b)	60. (c)	61. (c)	62. (c)	63. (c)	64. (d)
65. (a)	66. (a)	67. (a)	68. (c)	69. (b)	70. (a)	71. (b)	72. (c)
73. (b)	74. (a)	75. (b)	76. (c)	77. (c)	78. (c)	79. (d)	80. (a)
81. (b)	82. (a)	83. (b)	84. (d)	85. (b)	86. (b)	87. (a)	88. (d)
89. (b)	90. (b)	91. (c)	92. (b)	93. (a)	94. (b)	95. (c)	96. (d)
97. (c)	98. (d)	99. (a)	100. (b)	101. (b)	102. (a)	103. (c)	104. (b)
105. (a)	106. (a)	107. (a)	108. (d)	109. (b)	110. (b)	111. (a)	112. (b)
113. (b)	114. (d)	115. (b)	116. (c)	117. (c)	118. (b)	119. (d)	120. (b)
121. (a)	122. (b)	123. (a)	124. (b)	125. (d)	126. (b)	127. (a)	128. (c)

Previous Years Questions

1. (c)	2. (c)	3. (c)	4. (b)	5. (b)	6. (b)	7. (c)	8. (b)
9. (d)	10. (c)	11. (a)	12. (a)	13. (b)	14. (b)	15. (c)	16. (d)
17. (b)	18. (b)	19. (c)	20. (d)	21. (c)	22. (a)	23. (d)	24. (a)
25. (d)	26. (d)	27. (b)	28. (c)	29. (a)	30. (c)	31. (c)	32. (b)
33. (b)	34. (a)	35. (b)	36. (a)	37. (b)	38. (a)	39. (a)	40. (b)
41. (d)	42. (c)	43. (b)	44. (a)	45. (c)	46. (a)	47. (b)	48. (c)
49. (b)	50. (c)	51. (a)	52. (b)	53. (a)	54. (d)	55. (b)	56. (b)
57. (a)	58. (b)	59. (b)	60. (c)	61. (a)	62. (a)	63. (c)	64. (a)
65. (a)	66. (c)	67. (d)	68. (d)	69. (d)	70. (a)	71. (c)	72. (a)
73. (b)	74. (b)	75. (a)	76. (a)	77. (a)	78. (d)		

❑❑❑

ATOMIC STRUCTURE

1. Almost the entire mass of an atom is concentrated in the
   - (a) Protons
   - (b) Electrons
   - (c) Nucleus
   - (d) Neutrons

2. Which of the air pressures is appropriate for the production of cathode rays in the discharge tube?
   - (a) 1 cm Hg
   - (b) 1 mm Hg
   - (c) 0.001 cm Hg
   - (d) 0.01 mm Hg

3. Electrons were discovered by
   - (a) Chadwick
   - (b) Thomson
   - (c) Goldstein
   - (d) Bohr

4. Cathode rays are deflected or attracted towards
   - (a) Positive electrode
   - (b) Negative electrode
   - (c) Both electrodes
   - (d) None of the electrodes

5. Which is not true with respect to cathode rays?
   - (a) A stream of electrons
   - (b) Charged particles
   - (c) Move with same speed as that of light
   - (d) Can be deflected by electric field

6. Which of the following does not characterise X-rays?
   - (a) The radiation can ionise the gas
   - (b) It causes fluorescence effect on ZnS
   - (c) Deflected by electric and magnetic fields
   - (d) Have wavelength shorter than UV-rays

7. Cathode rays are
   - (a) Electromagnetic waves
   - (b) Stream of α-particles
   - (c) Stream of electrons
   - (d) Stream of positrons

8. Atomic number is equal to the
   - (a) Number of neutrons in the nucleus
   - (b) Number of protons in the nucleus
   - (c) Sum of protons and neutrons
   - (d) Atomic mass of the element

9. Compared to the charge and mass of a proton, an electron has
   - (a) the same charge and a smaller mass
   - (b) the same charge and the same mass
   - (c) opposite charge and a smaller mass
   - (d) opposite charge and the same mass

10. When alpha particles are used to bombard gold foil, most of the alpha particles pass through undeflected. This result indicates that most of the volume of a gold atom consists of
    - (a) Deuterons
    - (b) Neutrons
    - (c) Protons
    - (d) Unoccupied space

11. A proton has approximately the same mass as
    - (a) a neutron
    - (b) an alpha particle
    - (c) a beta particle
    - (d) an electron

12. The absolute charge of an electron is
    - (a) -1.6×10^{-19} C
    - (b) $+1.6 \times 10^{-19}$ C
    - (c) 1.6×10^{-19} C
    - (d) 16×10^{-19} C

13. The mass of an atom is determined by number of

(a) Neutrons

(b) Neutrons and protons

(c) Electrons

(d) Electrons and neutrons

14. Rutherford's alpha particle scattering experiment eventually led to the conclusion that

(a) Mass and energy are related

(b) Electrons occupy space around the nucleus

(c) Neutrons are buried deep in the nucleus

(d) The point of impact with matter can be precisely determined

15. Cathode rays have same charge to mass ratio as

(a) anode rays	(b) γ rays	(c) β rays	(d) protons

16. Particles that affect material properties are

(a) Neutrons	(b) Protons	(c) Electrons	(d) Valence electrons

17. In Rutherford's alpha-scattering experiment, a foil of element that was used is

(a) Gold	(b) Silver	(c) Aluminium	(d) Magnesium

18. The proton is heavier than an electron by

(a) 1850 times	(b) 1840 times	(c) 1000 times	(d) 100 times

19. Chadwick got the Nobel Prize for the discovery of

(a) Protons	(b) Neutrons	(c) Electrons	(d) Mesons

20. The volume of nucleus of an atom when compared to the extranuclear part is

(a) Bigger	(b) Smaller	(c) Same size	(d) Unpredictable

21. A neutron has approximately the same mass as a

(a) An alpha particle	(b) A beta particle	(c) An electron	(d) A proton

22. Rutherford's scattering experiment is related to the size of the

(a) Nucleus	(b) Atom	(c) Electron	(d) Neutron

23. Which atom contains exactly 15 protons?

(a) P-32	(b) S-32	(c) O-15	(d) N-15

24. Which of the following describes the atomic structure of an isotope?

	No. of protons	No. of electrons	No. of neutrons
(a)	16	15	15
(b)	15	16	16
(c)	16	16	15
(d)	15	15	16

25. An atom of element G contains 19 protons and 20 neutrons. The representation of this atom is

(a) $_{19}^{29}G$	(b) $_{39}^{20}G$	(c) $_{19}^{39}G$	(d) $_{20}^{19}G$

26. Which of the following atoms has the largest number of neutrons?

(a) $^{239}_{94}W$ (b) $^{239}_{93}X$ (c) $^{235}_{92}Y$ (d) $^{234}_{91}Z$

27. Which of the following statements about isotopes are correct?

(1) They have the same number of electrons

(2) They have the same number of protons

(3) They have the same number of neutrons

(a) (1) and (2) only   (b) (1) and (3) only

(c) (2) and (3) only   (d) (1), (2) and (3) only

28. The triad of nuclei that is isotonic is

(a) $^{14}_{6}C,\ ^{15}_{7}N,\ ^{17}_{9}F$ (b) $^{12}_{6}C,\ ^{14}_{7}N,\ ^{19}_{9}F$ (c) $^{14}_{6}C,\ ^{14}_{7}N,\ ^{17}_{9}F$ (d) $^{14}_{6}C,\ ^{14}_{7}N,\ ^{19}_{9}F$

29. The other name of $^{1}_{1}H$ is

(a) Protium   (b) Tritium   (c) Deuterium   (d) Proton

30. The fixed circular paths around the nucleus are called

(a) Orbits   (b) Orbitals   (c) Nucleons   (d) Mesons

31. Carbon-12 atom has

(a) 6 electrons, 6 protons, 6 neutrons   (b) 6 electrons, 12 protons, 6 neutrons

(c) 12 electrons, 6 protons, 6 neutrons   (d) 18 electrons, 6 protons and 6 neutrons

32. Mass number is equal to the

(a) Number of protons + Number of electrons

(b) Number of protons + Number of neutrons

(c) Number of neutrons + Number of electrons

(d) Number of electrons

33. During a chemical reaction, atomic number

(a) Changes   (b) Remains same

(c) Changes and then is restored   (d) Changes alternately

34. What is the energy of one mole of light that has a wavelength of 400 nm?

(a) 4.97×10^{-28} J   (b) 4.97×10^{-19} J   (c) 2.99×10^{-4} J   (d) 2.99×10^{5} J

35. If the ionisation potential of hydrogen atom is 13.6 volt, the energy required to remove an electron from the second orbit of hydrogen atom is

(a) 0.54 eV   (b) 0.85 eV   (c) 1.51 eV   (d) 3.4 eV

36. In Bohr series of lines of hydrogen spectrum, the third line from the red end corresponds to which one of the following inter–orbit jumps of the electron for Bohr orbits in an atom of hydrogen?

(a) $3 \rightarrow 2$ (b) $5 \rightarrow 2$ (c) $4 \rightarrow 1$ (d) $2 \rightarrow 5$

37. Which element has a hydrogen like spectrum whose lines have wavelength one fourth of atomic hydrogen?

(a) He^{+} (b) Li^{2+} (c) Be^{3+} (d) B^{4+}

38. The wave number of first line of Balmer series of hydrogen is 15200 cm^{-1}. The wave number of first Balmer line of Li^{2+} ion is:

(a) 15200 cm^{-1} (b) 60800 cm^{-1} (c) 76000 cm^{-1} (d) 136800 cm^{-1}

39. The electron in a hydrogen atom in the ground state absorbs energy equal to 12.1 eV and gets elevated to the highest possible excited state. What will be change in the angular momentum of the electron? (h = Planck's constant)

(a) h/π (b) 2h/π (c) 3h/π (d) h/2π

40. In the hydrogen spectrum the frequency of a line resulting from the transition of the electron from the orbit of quantum number n_x to quantum number n_1 is f. In a hydrogen-like atom the same transition gives rise to a spectral line of frequency $9f$. The hydrogen-like atom has atomic number ......

(a) 1   (b) 2   (c) 3   (d) 6

41. The limiting line in Balmer series will have a frequency of

(a) 3.65×10^{14} sec^{-1} (b) 3.29×10^{15} sec^{-1}

(c) 8.22×10^{14} sec^{-1} (d) -8.22×10^{14} sec^{-1}

42. Unit of Rydberg constant is ......

(a) cm sec^{-1} (b) cm^{-1} (c) cm^{3} (d) cm^{-2}

43. Uncertainty in position of a particle of 500 kg is 3.8×10^{-34} m Hence uncertainty in velocity (ms^{-1}) is (Planck's constant h = 6.6×10^{-34} Js)

(a) 2.8×10^{-4} (b) 2.1×10^{-3} (c) 5.6×10^{-4} (d) 2.8×10^{-2}

44. Uncertainty in position of an electron (mass = 9.1×10^{-31} kg) moving with a velocity 300 ms^{-1}, accurately upto 0.001% will be (h = 6.63×10^{-34} Js)

(a) 19.2×10^{-2} m   (b) 5.76×10^{-2} m   (c) 1.92×10^{-2} m   (d) 3.84×10^{-2} m

45. The wavelength associated with a golf ball weighing 200 g and moving at a speed of 5 m/h is of the order ......

(a) 10^{-10} m   (b) 10^{-20} m   (c) 10^{-30} m   (d) 10^{-40} m

46. The uncertainty in the momentum of an electron will be ...... if the uncertainty in its position is zero.

(a) h/2π (b) zero   (c) infinity   (d) h/π

47. The ratio of de-Broglie wavelength of an electron (λ_1) and that of neutron (λ_2) both moving with the same velocity is

(a) 3.8×10^{2} (b) 1.9×10^{3} (c) 1.76×10^{3} (d) 3.4×10^{2}

48. What possibly can the ratio be the de-Broglie wavelength for two electrons having the same initial energy and accelerated through 50 volts and 200 volts? $\left(\textbf{Hint}: \lambda = \dfrac{h}{\sqrt{2mqv}} \right)$

(a) 1 : 3   (b) 3 ; 1   (c) 1 : 2   (d) 2 : 1

49. The wavelength of an electron accelerated by 1000 V (potential difference) will be

(a) 3.87×10^{-11} m   (b) 387 nm

(c) 3.87×10^{-11} cm   (d) 3.87 Å

50. If the debroglie wavelength of electron is same as proton then velocity of an electron will be

    (a) $1836\,V_P$ (b) $1/1836\,V_P$ (c) $> 1836\,V_P$ (d) $< 1836\,V_P$

51. Splitting of spectral lines under the influence of a magnetic field is called

    (a) Stark effect   (b) Zeeman effect

    (c) Photoelectric effect   (d) None of these

52. Atomic spectra is an example of

    (a) line spectra   (b) continuous spectra

    (c) band spectra   (d) both (a) and (b)

53. Shortest wavelength in Lyman series is equal to

    (a) Rh   (b) Rh/2   (c) 1/Rh   (d) 2/3Rh

54. Balmer series in the region of electromagnetic spectrum is in

    (a) infrared region   (b) ultraviolet region   (c) visible region   (d) x-ray region

55. Series that lies in infrared region of electromagnetic spectrum is

    (a) Lyman series   (b) Balmer series

    (c) Bracket series   (d) both Lyman and Balmer

56. Which one of the following series of lines is found in the U.V. region of atomic spectrum of hydrogen?

    (a) Balmer   (b) Paschen   (c) Bracket   (d) Lyman

57. Series which is further divided into smaller lines is

    (a) Balmer   (b) Pfund   (c) Brackett   (d) Lyman

58. Wave numbers decrease from

    (a) Lyman to Pfund series   (b) Pfund to Lyman series

    (c) Balmer series to Brackett series   (d) none

59. When electron jumps to n − 1 orbit, series of spectral lines obtained is called

    (a) Balmer series   (b) Pfund series   (c) Brackett series (d) Lyman series

60. Helium can be singly ionized by losing one electron to become the He^+ cation. Which of the following statements is true concerning this helium cation?

    (a) Spectrum of this helium cation will resemble the line spectrum of a hydrogen atom.

    (b) Spectrum of this helium cation will resemble the line spectrum of a lithium

    (c) Spectrum of this helium cation will remain the same as that for unionized helium.

    (d) Spectrum of this helium cation will resemble the line spectrum of a lithium

61. In which of the following figure, shape of 3d orbital is best represented by means of probability area ?

(a) 's'   (b) p_x (c) d_{xy} (d) d_{z^2}

62. Which of the following electron configurations represent the electron configuration for a magnesium cation Mg^{2+}?

(a) $1s^2 2s^2 2p^6 3s^2$ (b) $1s^2 2s^2 2p^6 3s^2 3p^2$ (c) $1s^2 2s^2 2p^6$ (d) $1s^2 2s^2 2p^4$

63. Which of the following orbital diagrams represent silicon, which has 14 electrons?

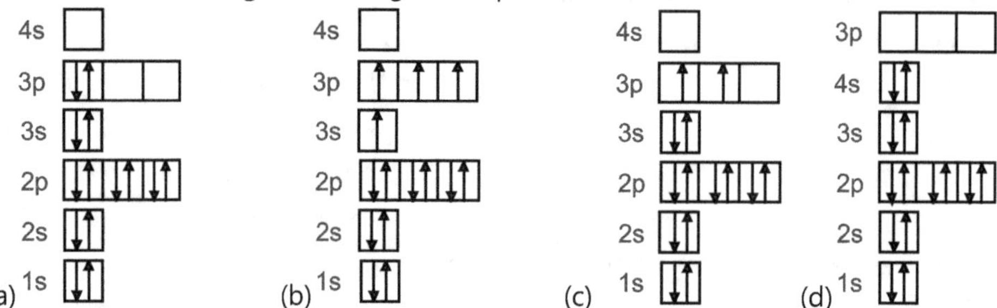

64. Any p-orbital can accommodate upto

(a) Four electrons   (b) Two electrons in parallel groups

(c) Six electrons   (d) Two electrons with opposite spins

65. The principal quantum number of an atom is related to the

(a) Size of the orbital   (b) Spin angular momentum

(c) Orbital angular momentum   (d) Orientation of the orbital in space

66. Correct set of four quantum numbers for the valence (outermost) electron of rubidium (Z = 37) is :

(a) 5, 0, 0, +1/2   (b) 5, 1, 0, +1/2   (c) 5, 1, 1, +1/2   (d) 6, 0, 0, +1/2

67. Bohr's model can explain

(a) The spectrum of hydrogen atom only

(b) Spectrum of an atom or ion containing one electron only

(c) The spectrum of hydrogen molecule

(d) The solar spectrum

68. Select the incorrect graph for velocity of electron in an orbit versus $Z, \dfrac{1}{n}$ and n :

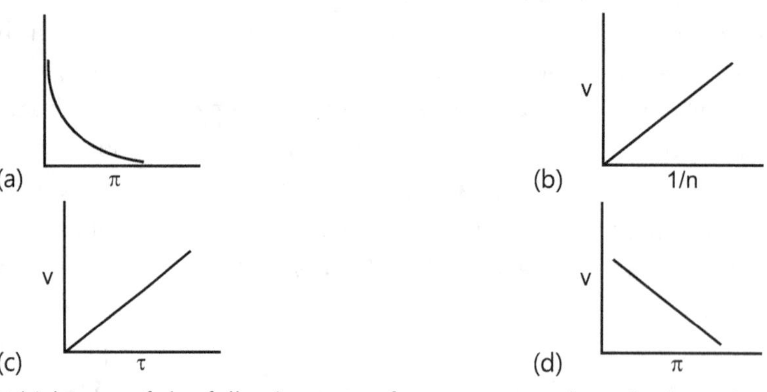

69. Which one of the following sets of quantum numbers (n, l, m, s) represent an impossible arrangement?

(a) 3, 2, −2, 1/2   (b) 4, 0, 0, 1/2   (c) 3, 2, −3, 1/2   (d) 5, 3, 0, −1/2

70. The mean distance between atoms is in the range of
(a) 25 nm　　(b) 2.5 nm　　(c) 0.25 nm　　(d) 0.025 nm

71. When electrons in an atom in an excited state falls to lower energy level, energy is
(a) Absorbed only
(b) Released only
(c) Neither released nor absorbed
(d) Both released and absorbed

72. Which element's ionic radius is smaller than its atomic radius?
(a) Neon　　(b) Nitrogen　　(c) Sodium　　(d) Sulfur

73. The total number of electrons in a principal energy shell is designated by expression
(a) n^2　　(b) $n + 1$　　(c) $2n^2$　　(d) $2n + 1$

74. The value of Bohr's radius of hydrogen atom is
(a) 0.0529×10^{-6} cm
(b) 0.0529×10^{-12} cm
(c) 0.0529×10^{-8} cm
(d) 0.0529×10^{-10} cm

75. Difference in lines in Balmer series of hydrogen atom lie in
(a) I.R. region　　(b) Visible region　　(c) U.V. region　　(d) Far infra red region

76. Which of the following ions has the electronic structure 2, 8 ?
(1) Ne　　(2) F^{2-}　　(3) S^{2-}　　(4) Al^{3-}
(a) (1) only
(b) (1) and (3) only
(c) (2) and (4) only
(d) (1), (2) and (4) only

77. The increasing order (lowest first) for the values of e/m (charge/mass) for electron (e), proton (p), neutron (n) and alpha particle (a) is
(a) e, p, n, a　　(b) n, p, e, a　　(c) n, p, a, e　　(d) n, a, p, e

78. Which electronic level would allow the hydrogen atom to absorb a photon but not to emit a photon?
(a) 3s　　(b) 2p　　(c) 2s　　(d) 1s

79. The maximum number of electrons in s, p and d subshells are
(a) 2, 6 and 10　　(b) 4 in each　　(c) 2 in each　　(d) 2, 6 and 12

80. The radius of an atomic nucleus is of the order of
(a) 10^{-10} cm　　(b) 10^{-13} cm　　(c) 10^{-15} cm　　(d) 10^{-8} cm

81. Electromagnetic radiation with maximum wavelength is
(a) Ultraviolet　　(b) Radio wave　　(c) X-ray　　(d) Infrared

82. The ratio of the energy of a photon of 2000 Å wavelength radiation to that of 4000 Å radiation is
(a) 1/4　　(b) 4　　(c) 1/2　　(d) 2

83. The wavelength of a spectral line for an electronic transition is inversely related to
(a) The number of electrons undergoing the transition
(b) The nuclear charge of the atom
(c) The difference in the energy of the energy levels involved in the transition
(d) The velocity of the electron undergoing the transition

84. The outermost electronic configuration of the most electronegative element is
(a) ns^2np^3　　(b) ns^2np^4　　(c) ns^2np^5　　(d) ns^2np^6

85. The correct ground state electronic configuration of chromium atom is

(a) $[Ar]\, 3d^5 4s^1$ (b) $[Ar]\, 3d^4 s^2$ (b) $[Ar]\, 3d^6 4s^0$ (d) $[Ar]\, 4d^5 5s^1$

86. The correct set of quantum numbers for the unpaired electron of chlorine atom is

	n	l	m
(a)	2	1	0
(b)	2	1	1
(c)	3	1	1
(d)	3	0	0

87. Which of the following sets of quantum numbers is correct for an electron in 4f orbital?

(a) $n = 4,\ l = 3,\ m = +4,\ s = +\dfrac{1}{2}$ (b) $n = 3,\ l = 2,\ m = -2,\ s = +\dfrac{1}{2}$

(c) $n = 4,\ l = 3,\ m = +1,\ s = +\dfrac{1}{2}$ (d) $n = 4,\ l = 4,\ m = -4,\ s = -\dfrac{1}{2}$

88. The number of photons emitted by 100 W bulb in 10 hours if λ of photon is 5800 A°

(a) 1.45×10^{24} (b) 1.45×10^{19} (c) 2.42×10^{19} (d) 2.42×10^{24}

89. There are how many values of m_l are there for $l = 2$?

(a) 1   (b) 2   (c) 5   (d) 7

90. The electrons identified by quantum numbers n and l, (i) n = 4, l = 1, (ii) n = 4, l = 0, (iii) n = 3, l = 2, and (iv) n = 3, l = 1 can be placed in order of increasing energy, from lowest to highest, as

(a) iv < ii < iii < i   (b) ii < iv < i < iii   (c) i < iii < ii < iv   (d) iii < i < iv < ii

91. A 3p-orbital has

(a) Two non-spherical nodes

(b) Two spherical nodes

(c) One spherical and one non-spherical node

(d) One spherical and two non-spherical nodes

92. The orbital angular momentum of an electron in 2s-orbital is

(a) $\dfrac{1}{2} \cdot \dfrac{h}{2\pi}$ (b) Zero   (c) $\dfrac{h}{2\pi}$ (d) $2 \cdot \dfrac{h}{2\pi}$

93. The first use of quantum theory to explain the structure of atom was made by

(a) Heisenberg   (b) Bohr   (c) Planck   (d) Einstein

94. For a d-electron, the orbital angular momentum is

(a) $\dfrac{1\,h}{2\,2\pi}$ (b) $\dfrac{2h}{2\pi}$ (c) $(h/2\pi)$ (d) $2(h/2\pi)$

95. The number of nodal planes in a p_x orbital is

(a) One   (b) Two   (c) Three   (d) Zero

96. The electronic configuration of an element is $1s^2,\ 2s^2,\ 2p^6,\ 3n^2,\ 3p^6,\ 3d^5,\ 4s^1$. This represents its

(a) Excited state   (b) Ground state   (c) Cationic form   (d) Anionic form

97. The shortest wavelength in hydrogen spectrum of Lyman series (R_H = 109678 cm^{-1}) is
(a) 911.7 A° (b) 1002.7 A° (c) 1215 A° (d) 1127 A°

98. The quantum numbers +1/2 and −1/2 for the electron spin represent
(a) Rotation of the electron in clockwise and anticlockwise direction respectively
(b) Rotation of the electron in anticlockwise and clockwise direction respectively
(c) Magnetic moment and characters of quantum numbers represent an impossible arrangement of p-orbtial of the electron pointing up and down respectively
(d) Two quantum mechanical spin states which have no classical analogue

99. How many electrons in a given atom can have following quantum numbers n = 2, l = 1, m = − 1.
(a) 2 (b) 4 (c) 6 (d) 1

100. The radius of which of the following orbits is same as that of the first Bohr's orbit of hydrogen atom?
(a) He^+ (n = 2) (b) Li^{2+} (n = 2) (c) Li^{2+} (n = 3) (d) Be^{3+} (n = 2)

101. The number of radial nodes of 3s and 2p-orbitals are respectively
(a) 2, 0 (b) 0, 2 (c) 1, 2 (d) 2, 1

102. The number of radial nodes for 3p orbital is ________.
(a) 3 (b) 4 (c) 2 (d) 1

103. The number of angular nodes for 4d orbital is ________
(a) 4 (b) 3 (c) 2 (d) 1

104. Which of the following is responsible to rule out the existence of definite paths or trajectories of electrons?
(a) Pauli's exclusion principle (b) Heisenberg's uncertainty principle
(c) Hund's rule of maximum multiplicity (d) Aufbau principle

105. Total number of orbitals associated with third shell will be ________.
(a) 2 (b) 4 (c) 9 (d) 3

106. Orbital angular momentum depends on ________.
(a) l (b) n and l (c) n and m (d) m and s

107. Chlorine exists in two isotopic forms, Cl-37 and Cl-35 but its atomic mass is 35.5. This indicates the ratio of Cl-37 and Cl-35 is approximately
(a) 1:2 (b) 1:1 (c) 1:3 (d) 3:1

108. The pair of ions having same electronic configuration is ________.
(a) Cr^{3+}, Fe^{3+} (b) Fe^{3+}, Mn^{2+} (c) Fe^{3+}, Co^{3+} (d) Sc^{3+}, Cr^{3+}

109. For the electrons of oxygen atom, which of the following statements is correct?
(a) Z_{eff} for an electron in a 2s orbital is the same as Z_{eff} for an electron in a 2p orbital.
(b) An electron in the 2s orbital has the same energy as an electron in the 2p orbital.
(c) Z_{eff} for an electron in 1s orbital is the same as Z_{eff} for an electron in a 2s orbital.
(d) The two electrons present in the 2s orbital have spin quantum numbers m_s but of opposite sign.

110. Which is an example of violation of Pauli's exclusion principle ?
(a)
(b)
(c)
(d)

111. Hund's rule is helpful

(a) To write stable electronic configuration　　(b) To find number of unpaired electrons

(c) To find multiplicity　　(d) All of these

112. Hund's rule is applied mainly for

(a) Any orbital　　(b) Degenerate orbitals only

(c) Sub-orbitals only　　(d) Orbits only

113. Violation of both Pauli and Hund's rule is observed in

(a) $\boxed{\uparrow\downarrow}\ \boxed{\uparrow\downarrow\ |\ \uparrow\ |\ \uparrow}$　　(b) $\boxed{\uparrow\downarrow}\ \boxed{\uparrow\uparrow\ |\ \uparrow\ |\ }$

(c) $\boxed{\uparrow\downarrow}\ \boxed{\uparrow\ |\ \uparrow\ |\ \uparrow}$　　(d) $\boxed{\uparrow\uparrow}\ \boxed{\uparrow\uparrow\ |\ \uparrow\uparrow\ |\ \uparrow}$

114. Which of the following electron transitions in a hydrogen atom will have largest amount of energy ?

(a) From n = 1 to n = 2　　(b) From n = 2 to n = 3

(c) From n = α to n = 1　　(d) From n = 3 to n = 5

115. The angular part of the wave function depends on

(a) l　　　　(b) n　　　　(c) s　　　　(d) Both n and l

116. The energy of the electron in n^{th} Bohr's orbit in the hydrogen atom is given by expression

(a) $\dfrac{-2\pi^2 m^4 e^2 Z^2}{n^2 h^2}$　　(b) $\dfrac{-n^2 h^2}{2\pi^2 Z^2 m e^4}$　　(c) $\dfrac{-2\pi^2 Z^2 e^4 m}{n^2 h^2}$　　(d) $\dfrac{-2\pi m^2 e^2 Z^4}{n^2 h^2}$

117. For an f electron, mvr will be

(a) $\sqrt{2}h$　　(b) $\sqrt{12}h$　　(c) $\sqrt{6}h$　　(d) Zero

118. The wave number of first line of Balmer series of hydrogen atom is 15200 cm^{-1}. What is the wave number of first line of Balmer series of Li^{2+} ion?

(a) 15200 cm^{-1}　　(b) 6080 cm^{-1}　　(c) 76000 cm^{-1}　　(d) 136800 cm^{-1}

119. A photon of radiation of wavelength 6000A° has an energy E. The wavelength of photon of radiation that corresponds to an energy equal to 2E is

(a) 6000 A°　　(b) 3000 A°　　(c) 12000 A°　　(d) 2400 A°

120. "No two electrons in an atom will have all four quantum numbers same." This statement is known as

(a) Pauli's exclusion principle　　(b) Uncertainty principle

(c) Hund's rule　　(d) Aufbau principle

121. The two electrons occupying an orbital are distinguished by

(a) Principal quantum number　　(b) Azimuthal quantum number

(c) Magnetic quantum number　　(d) Spin quantum number

122. The quantum numbers for outer electrons of an atom are given by

$$n = 2;\ l = 0;\ m = 0;\ s = +\,1/2$$

(a) Lithium　　(b) Beryllium　　(c) Hydrogen　　(d) Boron

123. For a given principal level n = 4, the energy of its sub-shells is of the order
   (a) s < d < f < p　　　(b) s < p < d < f　　　(c) d < f < p < s　　(d) s < p < f < d

124. I.E of Helium is 13.6 eV. The ionization energy of Li^{2+} in it will be
   (a) 54.4 eV　　　(b) 122.4 eV　　　(c) 27.2 eV　　　(d) 13.6 eV

125. Sodium chloride imparts a yellow colour to the Bunsen flame. This can be interpreted due to the
   (a) Low ionization energy of sodium
   (b) Sublimation of metallic sodium to give yellow vapour
   (c) Emission of excess energy absorbed as a radiation in the visible region
   (d) Photosensitivity of sodium

126. Which of the following sets of quantum numbers is not possible ?
   (a) n = 3, l = 0, m = −1　　　　　　　(b) n = 3, l = 2, m = + 1
   (c) n = 3, l = 2, m = −1　　　　　　　(d) n = 3, l = 2, m = 0

127. The number of neutrons in heavy hydrogen atom is
   (a) 0　　　　　(b) 1　　　　　(c) 2　　　　　(d) 3

128. The value of Planck's constant is
   (a) 6.6×10^{-32} g m^2 sec　　　　　(b) 6.6×10^{-34} kg m^2 sec^{-1}
   (c) 6.6×10^{-33} kgm sec　　　　　(d) 6.6×10^{-34} gm^2 sec

129. In a set of degenerate orbitals the electrons distribute themselves to retain similar spins as far as possible. This statement is attributed to
   (a) Pauli's exclusion principle　　　　　(b) Aufbau principle
   (c) Hund's rule　　　　　　　　　　　　(d) Slater rules

130. The electron in an atom
   (a) Moves randomly around the nucleus
   (b) Has fixed space around the nucleus
   (c) Is stationary in various energy levels
   (d) Moves around its nucleus in definite energy levels

131. Which statement is correct for photoelectric effect ?
   (a) Number of ejected electrons depend upon frequency of light radiation
   (b) Number of ejected electrons depend upon intensity of light radiation
   (c) Number of ejected electrons depend upon wave length of light radiation
   (d) Number of ejected electrons depend upon both intensity and frequency of light radiation

132. The set of quantum numbers not applicable to an electron is
   (a) $1, 1, 1 + \dfrac{1}{2}$　　　(b) $1, 0, 0 + \dfrac{1}{2}$　　　(c) $1, 0, 0 - \dfrac{1}{2}$　　　(d) 2, 0, 0

133. The radius of hydrogen atom in the ground state is 0.53 A°, the radius of Li_3^{2+} in the similar state is
   (a) 1.06 A°　　　(b) 0.265 A°　　　(c) 0.17 A°　　　(d) 0.53 A°

134. Which statement is correct for photoelectric effect
  (a) Kinetic energy of ejected electron is directly proportional to the intensity of light.
  (b) Kinetic energy of ejected electron is inversely proportional to the frequency of light
  (c) Kinetic energy of ejected electron is directly proportional to the intensity of light.
  (d) Kinetic energy of ejected electron is inversely proportional to the frequency of light

135. Electrons with a kinetic energy of 6.023×10^4 J/mol are evolved from the surface of a metal, when exposed to a radiation of wavelength of 600 nm (photoelectric effect). The minimum amount of energy required to remove an electron from the metal atom is :
  (a) 2.3125×10^{-19} J　　(b) 3×10^{-19} J　　(c) 6.02×10^{-19} J　(d) 6.62×10^{-34} J

136. Heisenberg's uncertainly principle is of great significance for :
  (a) Only microscopic particles　　　　　(b) Only macroscopic particles.
  (c) All the particles　　　　　　　　　(d) None of these

137. Two particles C and D are in motion. If the wavelength of particle C is 5×10^{-8} m, calculate the wavelength of particle D if its momentum is half of C.
  (a) 10^{-7} m　　　　(b) 10^{-5} m　　　　(c) 10^{-9} m　　　　(d) 10^{-6} m

138. Calculate the frequency of the particle wave, if the kinetic energy of sub-atomic particle is 5.85×10^{25} J. ($h = 6.66 \times 10^{-34}$ kg m^2 s^{-1})
  (a) 1.76×10^{8} s^{-1}　　(b) 1.76×10^{9} s^{-1}　　(c) 2.34×10^{8} s^{-1}　(d) 2.34×10^{9} s^{-1}

139. The mass of an electron is taken as 10^{-30} kg. The kinetic energy of an electron is 5×10^{-5} eV. Calculate the wavelength of the wave associated with the electron.
  (a) 1.73×10^{-7} m　　(b) 2.06×10^{-7} m　　(c) 1.65×10^{-7} m　(d) 3.0×10^{-9} m

140. The mass and wavelength of a moving body is 0.1 mg and 3.31×10^{-29} m respectively. Calculate its kinetic energy. ($h = 6.625 \times 10^{-34}$ J sec)
  (a) 2×10^{-5} J　　　(b) 2×10^{-3} J　　　(c) 3×10^{-3} J　　　(d) 3×10^{-5} J

141. If the uncertainty in the position of an electron is zero, the uncertainty of its momentum would be
  (a) Zero　　　　　(b) > h/4　　　　(c) < h/4π　　　　(d) Infinite

142. Calculate the uncertainty in the position of an electron if the uncertainty in its velocity is 5.7×10^5 m/sec. ($h = 6.6 \times 10^{-34}$ kg m^2 s^{-1}, mass of electron $= 9.1 \times 10^{-31}$ kg)
  (a) $+ 10^{-10}$ m　　　(b) $- 10^{-10}$ m　　　(c) $\pm 10^{-10}$ m　　　(d) None of these

143. Calculate the uncertainty in the velocity of a moving bullet of mass 10 g, if the uncertainty in the position is 10^{-5} m.
  (a) 6.13×10^{-28} ms^{-1}　　　　　　(b) 5.75×10^{-26} ms^{-1}
  (c) 8.03×10^{-26} ms^{-1}　　　　　　(d) 5.25×10^{-28} ms^{-1}

144. In the following radial distribution function graph versus radius represent for 3d orbital

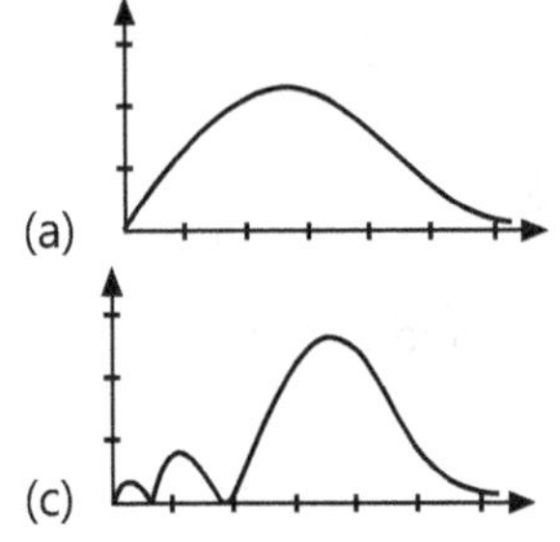
(a)　　　　　　　　　　(c)

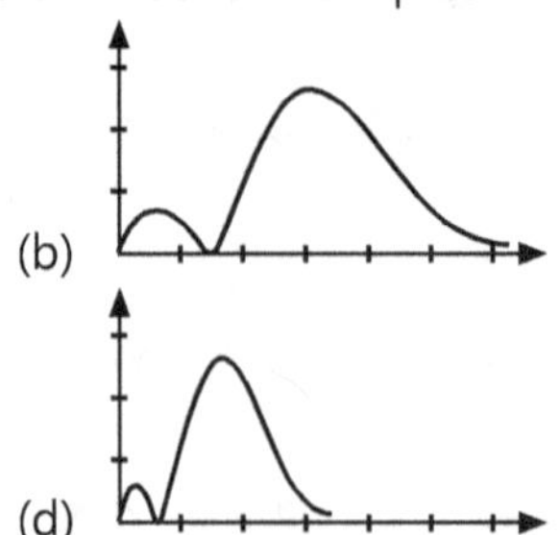
(b)　　　　　　　　　　(d)

145. The uncertainty in the momentum of an electron is 1.0×10^{-5} kg m s^{-1}. The uncertainty in its position will be ($h = 6.62 \times 10^{-34}$ kg m^2 s^{-1})

(a) 1.05×10^{-28} m   (b) 1.05×10^{-26} m   (c) 5.27×10^{-30} m   (d) 5.25×10^{-28} m

146. The ground state electronic configuration of chromium is

(a) [Ar] $3d^5, 4s^1$,   (b) [Ar] $3d^4, 4s^2$ (c) [Ar] $3d^6, 4s^0$ (d) [Ar] $4d^5, 4s^1$

147. An electron has principal quantum number 3. The number of its (i) subshells and (ii) orbitals would be respectively

(a) 3 and 5   (b) 3 and 7   (c) 3 and 9   (d) 2 and 5

148. The four quantum numbers of the valency electron of potassium are

(a) 4, 1, 1, 1/2   (b) 4, 0, 0, 1/2   (c) 4, 1, 0, 1/2   (d) 4, 4, 0, 1/2

149. Which of the following configurations is correct for iron?

(a) $1s^2, 2s^2, 2p^6, 3s^2, 3p^6, 3d^5$ (b) $1s^2, 2s^2, 2p^6, 3s^2, 3p^6, 4s^2, 3d^5$

(c) $1s^2, 2s^2, 2p^6, 3s^2, 3p^6, 4s^2, 3d^7$ (d) $1s^2, 2s^2, 2p^6, 3s^2, 3p^6, 4s^2, 3d^6$

150. Who modified Bohr's theory by introducing elliptical orbits for electron path ?

(a) Hund   (b) Thomson   (c) Rutherford   (d) Sommerfeld

151. Which graph shows the shapes of the radial wave functions, $R_{nl}(r)$, for 2p orbital

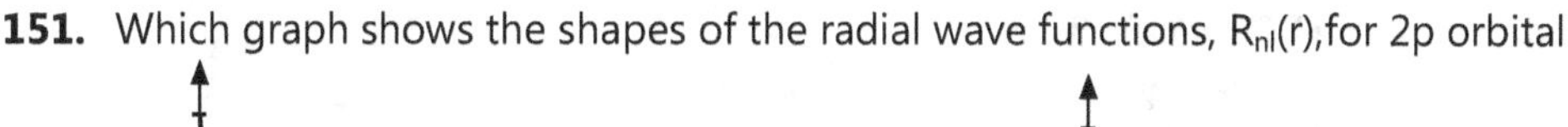

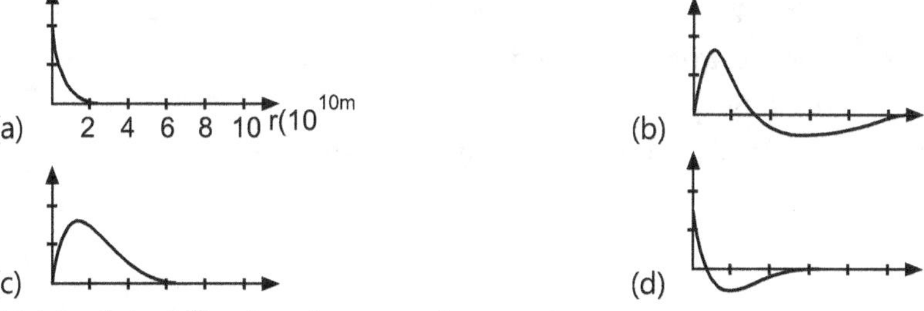

152. Which of the following does not characterise X – rays?

(a)   The radiation can ionise the gas

(b)   It causes fluorescence effect on ZnS

(c)   Deflected by electric and magnetic fields

(d)   Have wavelength shorter than ultraviolet rays

153. The increasing order for the values of e/m (charge/mass) is :

(a) e, p, n   (b) n, p, e   (c) n, p, e   (d) n, p, e

154. The number of spectral lines if an electron jumps from n = 4 to n = 1 is

(a) 10   (b) 5   (c) 6   (d) 3

155. The volume of nucleus is about

(a) 10^{-4} times to that of an atom   (b) 10^{-15} times to that of an atom

(c) 10^{-5} times to that of an atom   (d) 10^{-10} times to that of an atom

156. An electron in an atom jumps in such a way that its kinetic energy changes from x to $\dfrac{x}{y}$ .The change in potential energy will be ......

(a) $+\dfrac{3}{2}x$ (b) $-\dfrac{3}{8}x$ (c) $+\dfrac{3}{4}x$ (d) $-\dfrac{3}{4}x$

157. The potential energy of an electron in the hydrogen atom is -6.8 eV. Indicate in which excited state, the electron is present?

(a) first　　　　(b) second　　　　(c) third　　　　(d) fourth

158. What is the potential energy of an electron present in N- shell of the Be^{3+} ion?

$$\left(\textbf{Hint}: \text{T.E} = \frac{-Z^2}{n^2} \times 13.6, \text{P.E} = 2 \times \text{T.E}\right)$$

(a) −3.4 eV　　　　(b) −6.8 eV　　　　(c) 13.6 eV　　　　(d) −27.2 Ev

159. The kinetic and potential energy (in eV) of electron present in third Bohr's orbit of hydrogen atom are respectively : [**Hint :** R.E = − (−TE)]

(a) −1.51, −3.02　　(b) 1.51, −3.02　　(c) −3.02, 1.51　　(d) 1.51, −1.51

160. The distance between 4th and 3rd Bohr orbits of He^+ is : $\left[D = \dfrac{0.529}{z}(n_2^2 - n_1^2) \text{A°}\right]$

(a) 2.645×10^{-10} m　　(b) 1.322×10^{-0} m　　(c) 1.851×10^{-10} m (d) none

161. What atomic number of an element "X" would have to become so that the 4th orbit around would fit inside the 1st Bohr orbit?

(a) 3　　　　(b) 4　　　　(c) 16　　　　(d) 25

162. The ratio of velocity of the electron in the third and fifth orbit of Li^{2+} would be :

(a) 3 : 5　　　　(b) 5 : 3　　　　(c) 25 : 9　　　　(d) 9 : 25

163. If radius of second stationary orbit (in Bohr's atom) is R, then radius of the third orbit will be : $\left[\dfrac{r_1}{r_2} = \dfrac{n_1^2}{n_2^2}\right]$

(a) R/3　　　　(b) 9R　　　　(c) R/9　　　　(d) 2.25 R

164. What is the frequency of revolution of electron present in 2nd Bohr's orbit of hydrogen atom?

(a) 1.016×10^{16} s^{-1}　(b) 1.626×10^{15} s^{-1}　(c) 1.626×10^{15} s^{-1}　(d) 8.13×10^{16} s^{-1}

165. What should be the percentage of deuterium in heavy water?

(a) 80%　　　　(b) 60%　　　　(c) 40%　　　　(d) 20%

166. The molecular weight of an oxide of nitrogen is 30. What is the number of electrons?

(a) 45　　　　(b) 30　　　　(c) 60　　　　(d) 15

167. If the velocity of first second , third and fourth orbit of hydrogen atom are v_1, v_2, v_3 and v_4 respectively , what is the increasing order of velocity $\left[\textbf{Hint}: \left(v \times \dfrac{1}{n}\right)\right]$

(a) $v_1 > v_2 > v_3 > v_4$　　　　　　　(b) $v_4 < v_3 < v_2 < v_1$

(c) $v_1 > v_2 > v_3 > v_4$　　　　　　　(d) $v_1 = v_2 = v_3 = v_4$

168. What should be the velocity of the electron present in the forth orbit of hydrogen, if the velocity of electron in 3rd orbit is 7.29×10^7 cms^{-1} ? $\left[\textbf{Hint}: \dfrac{v_3}{v_4} = \dfrac{n_4}{n_3}\right]$

(a) 5.46×10^7 cm s^{-1}　　　　　　(b) 4.56×10^7 cm s^{-1}

(c) 6.54×10^7 cm s^{-1}　　　　　　(d) 5.46 cm s^{-1} $\left(\dfrac{v_3}{v_4} = \dfrac{v_4}{v_3}\right)$

169. If the radius of 1st, 2nd, 3rd and 4th orbital hydrogen atom are r_1, r_2, r_3, r_4 respectively, increasing order is (**Hint :** $r \propto n^2$)

(a) $r_1 < r_2 < r_3 < r_4$

(b) $r_1 > r_2 > r_3 > r_4$

(c) $r_1 = r_2 = r_3 = r_4$

(d) $r_2 > r_1 > r_3 > r_4$ $(r \times n^2)$

170. The ratio of radius of the fifth orbit of He^+ and Li^+ will be $\left[\textbf{Hint :} \left(\dfrac{r_1}{r_2} = \dfrac{Z_2}{Z_1} \right) \right]$

(a) $2 : 3$　　　　(b) $3 : 2$　　　　(c) $3 : 5$　　　　(d) $5 : 3$

171. An electron travels with a velocity of x ms^{-1}. For a proton to have the same de-Broglie wavelength, the velocity will be approximately ......

(a) $\dfrac{1840}{x}$　　　　(b) $\dfrac{x}{1840}$　　　　(c) $1840x$　　　　(d) x

172. According to Bohr's atomic theory, which of the following is correct ?

Consider the following statements regarding Bohr-Sommerfield's model. Select the correct statement/s.

(a) Around the nucleus, some of the paths are elliptical and others are circular

(b) When an electron revolves around the nucleus in a circular path, the angle of rotation is changed.

(c) Both, angle of rotation and distance from the nucleus, are changed when an electron revolves in an elliptical path.

(d) All are correct

173. The number of waves made by a Bohr electron in 4th orbit are ......

(a) 8　　　　(b) 4　　　　(c) 2　　　　(d) 16

PREVIOUS YEAR'S QUESTIONS

1. Magnetic moment 2.83 is given by which of the following ions ?　　　**[AIPMT 2014]**

(a) Cr^{3+}　　　　(b) Mn^{2+}　　　　(c) Ti^{3+}　　　　(d) Ni^{2+}

2. Be^{2+} is isoelectronic with which of the following ions ?　　　**[AIPMT 2014]**

(a) Na^+　　　　(b) Mg^{2+}　　　　(c) H^+　　　　(d) Li^{2+}

3. Calculate energy in joule corresponding to light of wavelength 45 nm.　　　**[AIPMT 2014]**

(a) 4.42×10^{-15}　　(b) 4.42×10^{-18}　　(c) 6.67×10^{11}　　(d) 6.67×10^{15}

4. What is the maximum number of orbitals that can be identified with the following quantum numbers : $n = 3$, $l = 1$ and $m = 0$?　　　**[AIPMT 2014]**

(a) 3　　　　(b) 4　　　　(c) 1　　　　(d) 2

5. The value of Planck's constant is 6.63×10^{-34} Js. The speed of light is 3×10^{17} nms^{-1}. Which value is closest to the wavelength in nanometer of a quantum of light with frequency of 6×10^5 s^{-1} ?　　　**[NEET UG 2013]**

(a) 75　　　　(b) 10　　　　(c) 25　　　　(d) 50

6. Based on equation $E = -2.178 \times 10^{-19}$ J $\left(\dfrac{z^2}{n^2}\right)$, certain conclusions are written. Which of them is not correct ? **[NEET UG 2013]**

  (a) For n = 1, the electron has a more negative energy than it does for n = 6 which means that the electron is more loosely bound in the smallest allowed orbit.

  (b) The negative sign in equation simply means that the energy of electron bound to the nucleus is lower than it would be if the electrons were at the infinite distance from the nucleus.

  (c) Larger the value of n, larger is the orbit radius.

  (d) Equation can be used to calculate the change in energy when the electron changes its orbit.

7. What is the maximum number of electrons that can be associated with the following set of quantum numbers ?　n = 3, l = 1 and m = –1 **[NEET UG 2013]**

  (a) 2　　　　　　　(b) 10　　　　　　　(c) 6　　　　　　　(d) 4

8. The orbital angular momentum of a p-electron is given as **[AIPMT 2012]**

  (a) $\sqrt{3}\,\dfrac{H}{2\pi}$　　　　(b) $\sqrt{\dfrac{3}{2}}\dfrac{H}{\pi}$　　　　(c) $\sqrt{6}\sqrt{\dfrac{H}{2\pi}}$　　　(d) $\dfrac{H}{\sqrt{2\pi}}$

9. The energies, E_1 and E_2 of two radiations are 25 eV and 50 eV respectively. The relation between their wavelengths i.e. λ_1 and λ_2 will be...... **[CBSE AIPMT 2011]**

  (a) $\lambda_1 = \dfrac{1}{2}\lambda_2$　　　(b) $\lambda_1 = \lambda_2$　　　(c) $\lambda_1 = 2\lambda_2$　　　(d) $\lambda_1 = 4\lambda_2$

10. For Balmer series in the spectrum of atomic hydrogen, the wave number of each line is given by $\bar{\upsilon} = R_H\left(\dfrac{1}{n_1^2} - \dfrac{1}{n_1^2}\right)$, where R_H is a constant and n_1 and n_2 are integers. Which of the following statement(s) is (are) correct ? **[Kerala CEE 2011]**

  As wavelength decreases, the lines in the series converge.

  The integer n_1 is equal to 2.

  The ionization energy of hydrogen can be calculated from the wave number of these lines.

  The line of longest wavelength corresponds to n_2 = 3.

  (a) 1, 3 and 3　　　(b) 2, 3 and 4　　　(c) 1, 2 and 4　　　(d) 2 and 4 only

  (e) 2 only

11. The total number of atomic orbitals in fourth energy level of an atom is **[CBSE AIMPT 2011]**

  (a) 4　　　　　　　(b) 8　　　　　　　(c) 16　　　　　　　(d) 32

12. If n = 6, the correct sequence of filling of electrons will be **[CBSE AIPMT 2011]**

  (a) ns $\rightarrow$ np $\rightarrow$ (n – 1) d $\rightarrow$ (n – 2) f　　　　(b) ns $\rightarrow$ (n – 2) f $\rightarrow$ (n – 1) d $\rightarrow$ np

  (c) ns $\rightarrow$ (n – 1) d $\rightarrow$ (n – 2) f $\rightarrow$ np　　　　(d) ns $\rightarrow$ (n – 2) f $\rightarrow$ np $\rightarrow$ (n – 1) d

13. When the electron of a hydrogen atom jumps from n = 4 to n = 1 state, the number of spectral lines emitted is ...... **[AMU 2010]**

(a) 15   (b) 9   (c) 6   (d) 3

14. Which of the following sets of quantum numbers represents the 19th electron in chromium ? (Z = 24 for Cr) **[AMU 2010]**

(a) $4, 0, 0, \dfrac{1}{2}$ (b) $4, 1, -1, \dfrac{1}{2}$ (c) $3, 2, 2, \dfrac{1}{2}$ (d) $3, 2, -2, \dfrac{1}{2}$

15. **Assertion :** In Lyman series of H-spectra, the maximum wavelength of lines is 12-65 nm.

Reason : Wavelength is maximum if there is transition from the very next level.

[AIIMS 2009]

(a) Both Assertion and Reason are true and Reason is the correct explanation of the Assertion.

(b) Both Assertion and Reason are true but Reason is not the correct explanation of Assertion.

(c) Assertion is true but Reason is false.

(d) Both Assertion and Reason are false.

16. Probability of finding an electron at the nodal surface is **[AMU 2009]**

(a) unity   (b) low   (c) high   (d) zero

17. The wavelengths of electron waves in two orbits are 3 : 5. The ratio of kinetic energy of electrons will be ...... **[EAMCET 2009]**

(a) 25 : 9   (b) 5 : 3   (c) 9 : 25   (d) 3 : 5

18. The uncertainty in the position of an electron (mass = 9.1×10^{-28} g) moving with a velocity of 3.0×10^{4} cm^{-1} accurately upto 0.011% will be **[Manipal 2009]**

(a) 1.92 cm   (b) 7.66 cm   (c) 0.175 cm   (d) 3.84 cm

19. If uncertainty in position and velocity are equal then uncertainty in momentum will be

[Manipal 2009]

(a) $\dfrac{1}{2}\sqrt{\dfrac{mh}{\pi}}$ (b) $\dfrac{1}{2}\sqrt{\dfrac{h}{\pi m}}$ (c) $\dfrac{h}{4\pi m}$ (d) $\dfrac{mh}{4\pi}$

20. Maximum number of electrons in a subshell of an atom is determined by the following

[CBSE AIPMT 2009]

(a) $4l + 2$ (b) $2n^2$ (c) $4l - 2$ (d) $2l + 1$

21. n and l for some electrons are given. Which of the following is expected to have least energy? **[AIIMS 2009]**

(a) n = 3, l = 2   (b) n = 3, l = 0   (c) n = 2, l = 1   (d) n = 4, l = 0

22. The wavelength (in A) of an emission line obtained for Li^{2+} during an electronic transition from $n_2 = 2$, $n_1 = 1$ is ...... (R = Rydberg constant) **[EAMCET 2008]**

(a) $\dfrac{3R}{4}$ (b) $\dfrac{27R}{4}$ (c) $\dfrac{4}{3R}$ (d) $\dfrac{4}{27R}$

23. The uncertainties in velocities of two particles, A and B are 0.05 and 0.02 ms^{-1} respectively. The mass of B is five times to that of the mass of A. What is the ratio of uncertainties in their positions $\left(\dfrac{\Delta X_A}{\Delta X_B}\right)$?

(a) 2   (b) 0.25   (c) 4   (d) 1

24. Consider the following sets of quantum numbers   **[CBSE AIPMT 2007]**

	n	l	m	s
(i)	3	0	0	$+\dfrac{1}{2}$
(ii)	2	2	1	$+\dfrac{1}{2}$
(iii)	4	3	-2	$-\dfrac{1}{2}$
(iv)	1	0	-1	$-\dfrac{1}{2}$
(v)	3	2	3	$+\dfrac{1}{2}$

Which of the following sets of quantum number is not possible ?

(a) (ii), (iii) and (iv)   (b) (i), (ii), (iii) and (iv)   (c) (ii), (iv) and (v)   (d) (i) and (iii)

25. An element X has the following isotopic compositions :   **[CBSE AIPMT 2007]**
$^{200}X : 90\%;\ ^{199}X : 8.0\%;\ ^{200}X : 2.0\%$. The weighted average atomic mass of the naturally occurring element X is closed to ......

(a) 200 u   (b) 201 u   (c) 202 u   (d) 199 u

26. If the wavelength of photon is 2.2×10^{-11} m, h = 6.6×10^{-24} then the momentum of photon is ......   **[AFMC 2007]**

(a) 3×10^{-23} kgm s^{-1} (b) 3.33×10^{22} kgm s^{-1}

(c) 1.452×10^{-44} kgm s^{-1} (d) 6.89×10^{43} kgm s^{-1}

27. Which pair is of isoelectronic species?   **[BHU 2006]**

(a) K^+, Cl^-, Na^+ (b) K^+, Cl^-, Ca^{2+} (c) F^-, Al^{3+}, K^+ (d) Fe^{2+}, Cu^{2+}, V^{3+}

28. The first emission line on hydrogen atomic spectrum in the Balmer series appears at (R = Rydberg constant)   **[EAMCET 2006]**

(a) $\dfrac{5R}{36}$ cm^{-1} (b) $\dfrac{3R}{4}$ cm^{-1} (c) $\dfrac{7R}{144}$ cm^{-1} (d) $\dfrac{9R}{400}$ cm^{-1}

29. Given, the mass of electron is 9.11×10^{-31} kg, Planck constant is 6.626×10^{-34} Js, the uncertainity involved in the measurement of velocity within a distance of 0.1 A° is   **[CBSE AIPMT 2006]**

(a) 5.79×10^6 ms^{-1} (b) 5.79×10^7 ms^{-1} (c) 5.79×10^9 ms^{-1} (d) 5.79×10^5 ms^{-1}

30. The energy of second Bohr orbit of the hydrogen atom is -328 kJmol^{-1}, hence the energy of third Bohr orbit would be   **[CBSE AIPMT 2005]**

(a) -41 kJ mol^{-1} (b) -1312 kJ mol^{-1} (c) -164 kJ mol^{-1} (d) -148 kJ mol^{-1}

31. Consider the ground state of Cr atom (Z = 24). The number of electrons with the Azimuthal quantum number, l = 1 and 2 are respectively ......   **[AIEEE 2004]**

(a) 16 and 5   (b) 12 and 5   (c) 16 and 4   (d) 12 and 4

32. The value of Planck's constant is 6.63×10^{-34} Js. The velocity of light is 3.0×10^8 ms^{-1}. Which value is closest to the wavelength (in nanometer) of a quantum of light with frequency 8×10^{15} s^{-1} ?   **[CBSE AIPMT 2003]**

(a) 4×10^1 (b) 3×10^7 (c) 2×10^{-25} (d) 5×10^{-18}

33. The number of orbitals in L energy level are　　　　　**[BHU 2003]**

    (a) 1　　　　　(b) 2　　　　　(c) 3　　　　　(d) 4

34. The de Broglie wavelength of a tennis ball of mass 60 g moving with a velocity of 10 meters per second is approximately　　　　　**[AIEEE 2003]**

    (a) 10^{-25} meters　　(b) 10^{-33} meters　　(c) 10^{-31} meters　　(d) 10^{-16} meters

35. In Bohr series of lines of hydrogen spectrum, the third line from the red end corresponds to which one of the following inter-orbit jumps of the electron for Bohr orbits in an atom of hydrogen?　　　　　**[AIEEE 2003]**

    (a) $2 \rightarrow 5$　　　　(b) $3 \rightarrow 2$　　　　(c) $5 \rightarrow 2$　　　　(d) $4 \rightarrow 1$

36. In Bohr's orbit, what is the ratio of total kinetic energy and total energy of electron ?　　　　　**[RPMT 2002]**

    (a) -1　　　　(b) -2　　　　(c) 1　　　　(d) $+2$

37. Quantum numbers $n = 3$, $l = 2$, $m = +2$ show how many orbitals　　　**[CPMT 2001]**

    (a) 1　　　　　(b) 2　　　　　(c) 3　　　　　(d) 4

38. Which of the following represents noble gas configuration?　　　**[B.H.U. 2000]**

    (a) $1s^2, 2s^2, 2p^6, 3s^2, 3p^6, 3e^{10}, 4s^2, 4p^6, 4d^{10}, 5s^2, 5p^6$

    (b) $1s^2, 2s^2, 2p^6, 3s^2, 3p^6, 3d^{10}, 4s^2, 4f^{14}, 5s^2, 5p^6, 5d^1$

    (c) $1s^2, 2s^2, 2p^6, 3s^2, 3p^6, 3d^{10}, 4s^2, 4p^6, 4d^{10}, 5s^2, 5p^6, 5d^1, 5s^2$

    (d) $s^2, 2s^2, 2p^6, 3s^2, 3p^6, 3d^{10}, 4s^2, 4p^6, 4d^{10}, 5s^2, 5p^6, 5d^6, 6s^2$

39. The element with electronic configuration of its atom $1s^2, 2s^2, 2p^6, 3s^2, 3p^6, 3d^{10}, 4s^1$ is

    [Kerala M.E.E. 200]

    (a) Fe　　　　　(b) Cu　　　　　(c) Ni　　　　　(d) Zn

40. The equation $\Delta x \cdot \Delta p \geq \dfrac{h}{4\pi}$ shows　　　　　**[M.P.C.E.T. 2000]**

    (a) de-Broglie relation　　　　　　　(b) Heisenberg's uncertainty principle

    (c) Aufbau principle　　　　　　　　　(d) Hund's rule

41. What will be de-Broglie wavelength of an electron moving with a velocity of 1.20×10^5 m^{-1} ?　　　　　**[M.P.C.E.T. 2000]**

    (a) 6.068×10^{-9}　　(b) 3.133×10^{-37}　　(c) 6.626×10^{-9}　　(d) 6.018×10^{-7}

42. Which of the following has same number of electrons in the last shell ?　　**[A.F.M.C. 2000]**

    (a) As and B　　　(b) Sn and Pb　　　(c) N and O　　　(d) Fe and Cr

43. The de-Broglie wavelength associated with ball of mass 200 g and moving at a speed of 5 m hour is of the order of (h = 6.625×10^{-34} Js) ......　　**[Kerala P.M.T. 2001]**

    (a) 10^{-15} m　　　(b) 10^{-20} m　　　(c) 10^{-30} m　　　(d) 10^{-25} m

    (e) 10^{-35} m

44. Rutherford's atomic model suggests the existence of ......　　　**[A.F.M.C. 2001]**

    (a) Atom　　　　(b) Nucleus　　　　(c) α-particle　　　(d) Mesons

45. For how many orbitals, the quantum numbers $n = 3$, $l = 2$, $m = +2$ are possible ?

    (a) 1　　　　　(b) 2　　　　　(c) 3　　　　　(d) 4　**[C.B.S.E. 2001]**

46. In the ground state, an element has 13 electrons in its M shell. The element is

[E.A.M.C.E.T. 2001]

(a) Copper　　　　(b) Chromium　　　　(c) Nickel　　　　(d) Iron

47. One of the following pairs of ions have the same electronic configuration ?

[E.A.M.C.E.T. 2001]

(a) Cr^{3+}, Fe^{3+}　　　(b) Fe^{3+}, Mn^{2+}　　　(c) Fe^{3+}, Co^{3+}　　　(d) Sr^{3+}, Cr^{3+}

48. Which of the following ions has the maximum magnetic moment ?　　　**[A.I.E.E.E. 2002]**

(a) Mn^{2+}　　　(b) Fe^{2+}　　　(c) Ti^{2+}　　　(d) Cr^{2+}

49. Chloride ions and potassium ions are isoelectronic. Then　　　**[Kerala C.E.T. 2002]**

(a) their sizes are same

(b) chloride ion is bigger than potassium ion

(c) potassium is relatively bigger

(d) depends on the other cation or anion

50. Which of the following is not isoelectronic ?　　　**[M.P.C.E.T. 2002]**

(a) Na^+　　　(b) Mg^{2+}　　　(c) O^{2-}　　　(d) Cl^-

51. The energy of the first electron in helium will be　　　**[Bihar C.E.E. 2002]**

(a) -13.6 eV　　　(b) -54.4 eV　　　(c) -5.44 eV　　　(d) zero

52. The configuration $1s^2$, $2s^2$, $2p^5$, $3s^1$, shows　　　**[Pb. P.M.T. 2002]**

(a) Excited state of O_2^-

(b) Excited state of neon

(c) Excited state of fluorine

(d) Ground state of fluorine atom

53. The value of Planck's constant is 6.63×10^{-34} Js. The velocity of light is 3.0×10^8 ms^{-1}. Which value is closest to the wavelength in nanometers of a quantum of light with frequency of 8×10^{15} s^{-1} ?　　　**[C.B.S.E. 2003]**

(a) 3×10^7　　　(b) 2×10^{25}　　　(c) 5×10^{-18}　　　(d) 4×10^1

54. The de-Broglie wavelength of a tennis ball of mass 60 g moving with a velocity of 10 metres per second is approximately　　　**[A.I.E.E.E. 2003]**

(a) 10^{-33} metres　　　(b) 10^{-31} metres　　　(c) 10^{-16} metres　　　(d) 10^{-25} metres

Planck's constant, h = 6.63×10^{-34} Js.

55. The number of d-electrons retained in Fe^{2+} (Atomic number of Fe = 26) ion is ......

[A.I.E.E.E. 2003]

(a) 3　　　(b) 4　　　(c) 5　　　(d) 6

56. The number of orbitals present in 3rd shell is　　　**[A.F.M.C. 2003]**

(a) 1　　　(b) 3　　　(c) 9　　　(d) 18

57. Rutherford's model suggests the existence of　　　**[A.F.M.C. 2003]**

(a) atoms　　　(b) nucleus　　　(c) α-particles　　　(d) mesons

58. Unpaired electrons in Ni^{++} (Z = 28) are　　　**[Kerala Engg. 2003]**

(a) 0　　　(b) 2　　　(c) 4　　　(d) 8

(e) 10

59. The emission spectrum of hydrogen is found to satisfy the expression for the energy change ΔE (in joules) such that

$$\Delta E = 2.18 \times 10^{-18} \left(\frac{1}{n_1^2} - \frac{1}{n_2^2} \right) J$$ **[Kerala Engg. 2003]**

where $n_1 = 1, 2, 3, \ldots$ and $n_2 = 2, 3, 4, \ldots$ The spectral lines correspond to Paschen series if

(a) $n_1 = 1$ and $n_2 = 2, 3, 4$ (b) $n_1 = 3$ and $n_2 = 4, 5, 6$

(c) $n_1 = 1$ and $n_2 = 3, 4, 5$ (d) $n_1 = 2$ and $n_2 = 3, 4, 5$

(e) $n_1 = 1$ and $n_2 = $ infinity

60. Nuclear theory of an atom was put forward by   **[Karnataka C.E.T. 2004]**

(a) Rutherford   (b) Aston   (c) Neils Bohr   (d) J. J. Thomson

61. Among the following series of transition metal ions, the one where all metal ions have same 3d electronic configuration is ......   **[C.B.S.E. P.M.T. 2004]**

(a) $Ti^{2+}, +V^{3+}, Cr^{4+}, Mn^{5+}$ (b) $Ti^{3+}, +V^{2+}, Cr^{3+}, Mn^{4+}$

(c) $Ti^{+}, +V^{4+}, Cr^{6+}, Mn^{7+}$ (d) $Ti^{4+}, +V^{3+}, Cr^{2+}, Mn^{3+}$

62. Which of the following electronic configurations is not possible according to Hund's rule ?

(a) $1s^2, 2s^2$ (b) $1s^2, 2s^1$ **[Kerala P.M.T. 2004]**

(c) $1s^2, 2s^2, 2p_x^1, 2p_y^1, 2p_z^1$ (d) $1s^2, 2s^2, 2p_x^2$

(e) $1s^2, 2s^2, 2p_x^2, 2p_y^1, 2p_z^1$

63. The atomic number of an element is derived from   **[Kerala P.M.T. 2004]**

(a) Number of electrons   (b) Number of protons

(c) Number of neutrons   (d) Number of isotopes

(e) Number of nucleons

64. Which of the following sets of quantum numbers is correct for an electron in 4f-orbital ?

[A.I.E.E.E. 2004]

(a) $n = 4, l = 3, m = +4, s = + 1/2$ (b) $n = 3, l = 2, m = -2, s = + 1/2$

(c) $n = 4, l = 3, m = +1, s = + 1/2$ (d) $n = 4, l = 4, m = -4, s = 1/2$

65. The wavelength of radiation emitted when in a hydrogen atom electron falls from infinity to stationary state 1, would be (Rydberg constant $= 1.09 \times 10^7 \, m^{-1}$)   **[A.I.E.E.E. 2004]**

(a) 91 nm   (b) 9.1×10^{-8} nm   (c) 406 nm   (d) 192 nm

66. Effective magnetic moment of Sc^{3+} ion is   **[Kerala Engg. 2005]**

(a) 1.73   (b) 0   (c) 5.92   (d) 2.83

(e) 3.87

67. The energy of second Bohr orbit of the hydrogen atom is $-328 \, kJ \, mol^{-1}$, hence the energy of fourth Bohr orbit would be   **[C.B.S.E. P.M.T. 2005]**

(a) $- 41 \, kJ \, mol^{-1}$ (b) $- 1312 \, kJ \, mol^{-1}$ (c) $-164 \, kJ \, mol^{-1}$ (d) $- 82 \, kJ \, mol^{-1}$

68. The atomic numbers of elements X, Y and Z are 19, 21 and 25 respectively. The number of electrons present in 'M' shells of these elements follow the order   **[E.A.M.C.E.T. 2005]**

(a) $Z > X > Y$ (b) $X > Y > Z$ (c) $Z > Y > X$ (d) $Y > Z > X$

69. The most probable radius (in pm) for finding the electron in H^+ is   **[A.I.I.M.S. 2005]**

   (a) 00   (b) 52.9   (c) 26.5   (d) 105.8

70. A metal surface is exposed to solar radiations.   **[D.P.M.T. 2005, 2006]**

   (a) The emitted electrons have energy less than a maximum value of energy depending upon the frequency of the incident radiation.

   (b) The emitted electrons have energy less than the maximum value of energy depending upon the intensity of the incident radiation.

   (c) The emitted electrons have zero energy.

   (d) The emitted electrons have energy equal to energy of photons of the incident light.

71. Which of the following transitions will have minimum wavelength ?   **(D.P.M.T. 2005)**

   (a) $n_4 \longrightarrow n_1$ (b) $n_2 \longrightarrow n_1$ (c) $n_4 \longrightarrow n_2$ (d) $n_3 \longrightarrow n_1$

72. The angular momentum of an electron revolving in a p-orbital is   **(Kerala P.E.T. 2006)**

   (a) zero   (b) $\dfrac{h}{\sqrt{2\pi}}$ (c) $\dfrac{h}{2\pi}$ (d) $\dfrac{1}{2}\cdot\dfrac{h}{2\pi}$ (e) $\dfrac{h}{2\sqrt{2\pi}}$

73. For a Bohr atom, angular momentum of an electron is (n = 0, 1, 2, ...)

   [U.P. Engg. Entrance Exam. 2006]

   (a) $\dfrac{n^2h^2}{4\pi}$ (b) $\dfrac{nh^2}{4\pi}$ (c) $\dfrac{\sqrt{n}h}{2\pi}$ (d) $\dfrac{nh}{2\pi}$

74. Which of the following statements is incorrect ? An atomic orbital   **[H.P.U. 2006]**

   (a) is a single electron wave function

   (b) describes trajectory of an electron in an atom

   (c) defines distribution of an electron density in space

   (d) can be represented by boundary surface

75. What is the wave number of 4th line in Balmer series of hydrogen spectrum ? $R = 1,09,677 \text{ cm}^{-1}$ **[E.A.M.C.E.T. Medical 2007]**

   (a) 26630 cm^{-1} (b) 24360 cm^{-1} (c) 24730 cm^{-1} (d) 24372 cm^{-1}

76. The radius of the first Bohr orbit of hydrogen atom is 0.59 A°. The radius of the third orbit of He^+ will be   **[Kerala P.E.T. 2007]**

   (a) 8.46 A°   (b) 0.705 A°   (c) 1.59 A°   (d) 2.38 A°   (e) 1.41 A°

77. When the Azimuthal quantum number has the value of 2, the number of orbitals possible are   **[Karnataka C.E.T. 2008]**

   (a) 3   (b) 0   (c) 7   (d) 5

78. $[Ar]^{18} \, 3d^{10}, 4s^1$ electronic configuration belongs to   **[M.P.C.E.T. 2008]**

   (a) Ti   (b) Tl   (c) Cu   (d) V

79. What are the values of n_1 and n_2 respectively for H_B line in the Lyman series of hydrogen atom spectrum ?   **[U.P.C.P.M.T. 2008]**

   (a) 3 and 5   (b) 2 and 3   (c) 1 and 3   (d) 2 and 4

80. Which of the following is not possible for 4p or 3d electrons ? **[B.H.U. (Med.) Prelim 2008]**

(a) $n = 3, l = 2, m = +1, s = +\dfrac{1}{2}$

(b) $n = 4, l = 1, m = 0, s = +\dfrac{1}{2}$

(c) $n = 3, l = 3, m = +3, s = +\dfrac{1}{2}$

(d) $n = 4, l = 1, m = -1, s = +\dfrac{1}{2}$

81. Which of the following represents the molarity of pure water ? **[B.H.U. (Med.) Prelim 2008]**

(a) 55.5   (b) 56.5   (c) 50.5   (d) 57.55

82. What is the atomic number of the element with M^{2+} ion having electronic configuration $[Ar]\ 3d^8$? **[Gujarat C.E.T. 2009]**

(a) $4, 1, 0, \dfrac{1}{2}$ (b) $3, 1, 0, \dfrac{1}{2}$ (c) $4, 0, 0, \dfrac{1}{2}$ (d) $3, 0, 0, \dfrac{1}{2}$

83. A body of mass x kg is moving with a velocity of $100\ ms^{-1}$. Its de-Broglie wavelength is 6.62×10^{-35} m. Hence x is $(h = 6.02 \times 10^{-34}\ Js)$ **[Karnataka C.E.T. 2009]**

(a) 0.1 kg   (b) 0.25 kg   (c) 0.15 kg   (d) 0.2 kg

84. The number of unpaired electrons in Fe^{3+} $(Z = 26)$ is

[Manipur M.B.B.S./B.D.S. Entrance Exam. 2009]

(a) 0   (b) 2   (c) 3   (d) 5

85. Common salt obtained from sea water contains 95% NaCl by mass. The approximate number of molecules present in 10.0 g of the salt is **[D.P.M.T. 2009]**

(a) 10^{21} (b) 10^{22} (c) 10^{23} (d) 10^{24}

86. The wavelength of electron waves in two orbits is 3 : 5. The ratio of kinetic energy of electrons will be **[E.A.M.C.E.T. (Engg.) 2007]**

(a) $25 : 9$ (b) $5 : 3$ (c) $9 : 25$ (d) $3 : 5$

87. If the de Broglie wavelength of the fourth Bohr's orbit of hydrogen atom is 4 A°, the circumference of the orbit is ...... **[Chhattisgarh P.E.M.T. 2010]**

(a) 4 A°   (b) 4 nm   (c) 16 A°   (d) 16 nm

ANSWER KEY

1. (c)	2. (d)	3. (b)	4. (a)	5. (c)	6. (b)	7. (c)	8. (b)
9. (c)	10. (d)	11. (a)	12. (a)	13. (b)	14. (b)	15. (c)	16. (c)
17. (a)	18. (b)	19. (b)	20. (b)	21. (d)	22. (a)	23. (a)	24. (d)
25. (c)	26. (b)	27. (a)	28. (a)	29. (a)	30. (a)	31. (a)	32. (b)
33. (b)	34. (d)	35. (d)	36. (b)	37. (a)	38. (d)	39. (d)	40. (c)
41. (c)	42. (b)	43. (a)	44. (a)	45. (c)	46. (b)	47. (b)	48. (d)
49. (a)	50. (a)	51. (b)	52. (a)	53. (c)	54. (c)	55. (c)	56. (d)
57. (d)	58. (a)	59. (d)	60. (a)	61. (d)	62. (c)	63. (b)	64. (c)
65. (a)	66. (a)	67. (b)	68. (d)	69. (c)	70. (c)	71. (b)	72. (c)

73. (c)	74. (c)	75. (b)	76. (d)	77. (d)	78. (d)	79. (a)	80. (c)
81. (b)	82. (d)	83. (c)	84. (c)	85. (a)	86. (c)	87. (c)	88. (a)
89. (c)	90. (a)	91. (c)	92. (c)	93. (c)	94. (d)	95. (a)	96. (a)
97. (a)	98. (a)	99. (a)	100. (a)	101. (a)	102. (d)	103. (c)	104. (b)
105. (c)	106. (a)	107. (c)	108. (b)	109. (d)	110. (d)	111. (c)	112. (b)
113. (b)	114. (c)	115. (a)	116. (c)	117. (b)	118. (d)	119. (b)	120. (a)
121. (d)	122. (a)	123. (d)	124. (b)	125. (c)	126. (a)	127. (b)	128. (b)
129. (c)	130. (d)	131. (b)	132. (a)	133. (c)	134. (c)	135. (d)	136. (a)
137. (a)	138. (a)	139. (c)	140. (a)	141. (a)	142. (c)	143. (d)	144. (a)
145. (c)	146. (a)	147. (c)	148. (b)	149. (d)	150. (d)	151. (c)	152. (b)
153. (b)	154. (a)	155. (b)	156. (a)	157. (b)	158. (d)	159. (b)	160. (c)
161. (c)	162. (b)	163. (d)	164. (d)	165. (d)	166. (d)	167. (b)	168. (a)
169. (a)	170. (b)	171. (b)	172. (d)	173. (b)			

Previous Years Questions

1. (d)	2. (d)	3. (b)	4. (c)	5. (d)	6. (a)	7. (a)	8. (d)
9. (c)	10. (c)	11. (c)	12. (b)	13. (c)	14. (a)	15. (b)	16. (d)
17. (d)	18. (c)	19. (a)	20. (a)	21. (c)	22. (d)	23. (a)	24. (c)
25. (a)	26. (a)	27. (b)	28. (a)	29. (a)	30. (d)	31. (b)	32. (a)
33. (d)	34. (b)	35. (c)	36. (a)	37. (a)	38. (a)	39. (b)	40. (b)
41. (a)	42. (b)	43. (c)	44. (b)	45. (a)	46. (b)	47. (b)	48. (a)
49. (b)	50. (d)	51. (b)	52. (b)	53. (d)	54. (a)	55. (d)	56. (c)
57. (b)	58. (b)	59. (b)	60. (c)	61. (a)	62. (d)	63. (b)	64. (c)
65. (a)	66. (b)	67. (d)	68. (c)	69. (c)	70. (a)	71. (a)	72. (b)
73. (d)	74. (b)	75. (d)	76. (d)	77. (d)	78. (c)	79. (c)	80. (c)
81. (a)	82. (a)	83. (a)	84. (d)	85. (c)	86. (a)	87. (c)	

❏❏❏

CLASSIFICATION OF ELEMENTS AND PERIODICITY IN PROPERTIES

1. The first list of 23 elements was made by ......

   (a) Dmitri Mendeleev   (b) Lothar Meyer

   (c) Antoine Lavoisier   (d) John Newlands

2. This English scientist noticed that properties of elements repeat with every eighth element. He attempted to arrange the elements using the octave rule as a basis in 1864. Who was he?

   (a) Dmitri Mendeleev   (b) Lothar Meyer

   (c) Antoine Lavoisier   (d) John Newlands

3. This German chemist was a contemporary of Dmitri Mendeleev in that he also discovered the relationship between atomic mass and elemental properties. However, he did not publish his results in time. What was his name?

   (a) Henry Moseley   (b) Lothar Meyer

   (c) John Newlands   (d) Antoine Lavoisier

4. Inspite of Mendeleev's version of the periodic table being accepted, it contained a fundamental flaw. Arranging the elements by atomic mass led to some elements being out of place. In 1913, an English chemist decided to arrange the elements by their atomic numbers. Who was this man?

   (a) Henry Moseley   (b) Lothar Meyer

   (c) Antoine Lavoisier   (d) John Newlands

5. The statement that there is a periodic repetition of physical and chemical properties of the elements when arranged by increasing atomic number is known as ......

   (a) The Mendeleevian rule   (b) The Lavoisier principle

   (c) Periodic law   (d) Periodic table

6. Modern periodic table is based on the atomic number of elements. The experiment which proved the significance of the atomic number was ......

   (a) Millikan's oil drop experiment   (b) Moseley's work on X-ray spectra

   (c) Bragg's work on X-ray diffraction   (d) Discovery of X-rays by Roentgen

7. Mendeleev arranged the elements according to ......

   (a) Atomic number and atomic weight   (b) Atomic weight and chemical reactivity

   (c) Electron configuration and atomic weight (d) Physical state and relative abundance

8. Dobereiner's work led to the law of triads which states that ......

   (a) Atomic weight of any one element was found to be approximately the mean of the other two elements of a triad
   (b) Atomic weight of the middle element was found to be approximately the mean of the other two elements of a triad
   (c) Atomic number of any one element was found to be approximately the mean of the other two elements of a triad
   (d) Atomic number of the middle element was found to be approximately the mean of the other two elements of a triad.

9. Scientist who classified the known elements into metals, non metals and their derivatives was ......

   (a) Dobereiner　　(b) Lothar Meyer　(c) Newlands　　(d) Mendeleev

10. Law of octave states that ......

   (a) The properties of every 6th element from the given one were similar to the first
   (b) The properties of every 9th element from the given one were similar to the first
   (c) The properties of every 8th element from the   given one were similar to the first
   (d) The properties of every 7th element from the given one were similar to the second

11. The vertical columns in the periodic table are commonly referred to as ......

   (a) Groups　　　　(b) Families　　　(c) Periods　　　(d) Verticals

12. The law of octaves was given by ......

   (a) Dobereiner　　(b) Lothar Meyer　(c) Newlands　　(d) None of these

13. Mendeleev's Periodic Table was based on ......

   (a) Atomic number　　　　　　(b) Atomic mass
   (c) Atomic volume　　　　　　(d) Electronic configuration

14. The modern periodic table is given by ......

   (a) Mendeleev　　(b) Einstein　　(c) Moseley　　(d) Lavoisier

15. Eka aluminium and Eka silicon are ......

   (a) Gallium and germanium　　　(b) Aluminium and silicon
   (c) Gallium and gadolinium　　　(d) Germanium and titanium

16. In which group of the periodic table does an element with the outer ground state electronic configuration ns^2np^3 belong?

   (a) Group 15　　　(b) Group 13　　(c) Group 5　　　(d) Group 3

17. The number of electrons in the valence shell is equal to its ......

   (a) Atomic mass　(b) Group number　(c) Period number　(d) Atomic volume

18. The atomic number of the element which preceeds the element with atomic number Z = 83 in the same group is ......

   (a) 51　　　　　(b) 55　　　　(c) 65　　　　(d) 73

19. An element has configuration 2, 8, 1. It belongs to ......

   (a) IA group and 3rd period　　　(b) 3rd group and 1st period
   (c) 1st group and 8th period　　　(d) 17th group and 3rd period

20. The properties of an element in the periodic table depend on its ......

(a) Atomic size   (b) Atomic mass

(c) Electronic configuration   (d) Number of protons

21. Which of the following groups of elements contain metals and non-metals?

(a) Group 18   (b) Group 3   (c) Group 2   (d) Group 14

22. Neon is an example of ......

(a) Alkali metal   (b) Noble gas   (c) Halogen   (d) Rare earth metal

23. The second row transition-metal period involves filling up of which sub-shell?

(a) 4d   (b) 3f   (c) 3d   (d) 2d

24. Elements belonging to groups 1 to 17 are called ......

(a) Representative elements   (b) Normal elements

(c) Transition elements   (d) Inner transition elements

25. An element that has two valence or outer level electrons would be considered as ......

(a) Non-metal   (b) Noble gas   (c) Halogen   (d) Metal

26. Sodium is in the same group or family as ......

(a) Lithium   (b) Helium   (c) Calcium   (d) Thorium

27. Iodine is an example of a ......

(a) Noble gas   (b) Halogen   (c) Alkali metal   (d) Rare earth metal

28. If an element is a gas at room temperature, then it must be ......

(a) Alkali metal   (b) Non-metal   (c) Halogen   (d) Alkaline earth metal

29. If an element has one to three valence or outer level electrons, then it is a ......

(a) Non-metal   (b) Halogen   (c) Noble gas   (d) Metal

30. Which of the following elements belongs to the group that includes the most active metals?

(a) Aluminium   (b) Sodium   (c) Iron   (d) Mercury

31. The non-metallic element present in the third period other than sulphur and chlorine is ...

(a) Oxygen   (b) Fluorine   (c) Nitrogen   (d) Phosphorus

32. For a p-block element, its 3d, 3s, 3p and 4s orbitals are completely filled and the differentiating electron goes to the 4p orbital. The element should have its atomic number in the range ......

(a) 13 - 18   (b) 21 - 26   (c) 31 - 36   (d) 49 - 54

33. The most common lanthanide is ......

(a) Lanthanum   (b) Cerium   (c) Samarium   (d) Plutonium

34. "s" and "p" block elements are also called ......

(a) Transition elements   (b) Inert elements

(c) Typical elements   (d) Rare earth elements

35. Which of the following is a d-block element ?

(a) Po   (b) Rn   (c) Ir   (d) Gd

36. Which of the following elements are analogous to lanthanides?

(a) Actinides   (b) Borides   (c) Carbides   (d) Hydrides

37. Coinage metals are present in ......
    (a) s-block　　　(b) d-block　　　(c) p-block　　　(d) f-block

38. Elements present in same group have the same ......
    (a) Atomic number　　　　　　　　(b) Molecular weight
    (c) Chemical properties　　　　　　(d) Electronic configuration

39. Consider the isoelectronic species Na^+, Mg^{2+}, F^- and O^{2-}. The correct order of increasing length of their radii is ......
    (a) $F^{-2} < Mg^{2+} < Na^+$　　　　　　(b) $Mg^{2+} < Na^+ < F < O_2$
    (c) $O_2 < F^- < Na^+ < Mg^{2+}$　　　　(d) $O_2 < F^- < Mg^{2+} < Na^+$

40. Which one of the following statements is incorrect?
    (a) The radius of Na is larger than Na^+
    (b) The radius of Mg is larger than Na
    (c) The ionization energy of Na is smaller than Na^+
    (d) The electron affinity of Cl is more negative than C

41. Which of the following property decreases along a period ?
    (a) Electronegativity　　　　　　　(b) Electron affinity
    (c) Atomic radii　　　　　　　　　(d) Ionization enthalpy

42. The elements in which of the following have most nearly the same atomic radius?
    (a) Be, B, C, N　　　(b) Ne, Ar, Kr, Xe　　　(c) Mg, Ca, Sr, Ba　　(d) Cr, Mn, Fe, Co

43. Which of the following properties generally decrease across the periodic table, from sodium to chlorine?
    (a) First ionization energy　　　　　(b) Atomic radius
    (c) Electronegativity　　　　　　　(d) Maximum value of oxidation number

44. Which of the following neutral atoms would be the smallest?
    (a) Cs　　　(b) Li　　　(c) Rb　　　(d) K

45. Which of the following has the smallest size?
    (a) Na^+　　　(b) Mg^{2+}　　　(c) Al^{3+}　　　(d) Cl

46. When going across a period in the periodic table, the ......
    (a) Metallic character increases and the atomic radius increases
    (b) Metallic character increases and the atomic radius decreases
    (c) Metallic character decreases and the atomic radius increases
    (d) Metallic character decreases and the atomic radius decreases

47. The atomic size of noble gases is expressed as ......
    (a) Covalent radius　　　　　　　(b) Metallic radius
    (c) Ionic radius　　　　　　　　　(d) Van der Waal's radii

48. The properties of an element in the periodic table depend on its ......
    (a) Atomic size　　　　　　　　　(b) Atomic mass
    (c) Electronic configuration　　　　(d) Number of protons

49. Which statement about metallic radii is incorrect?

(a) Values of metallic radii increase down the group 2.

(b) Values of metallic radii increase across the first row of the f-block.

(c) Values of metallic radii increase down the group 13 from Al onwards

(d) Values of metallic radii increase down the group 1.

50. Which of the following statements are incorrect?

(a) Atoms tend to get larger as one goes across the periodic table from left to right in a given period.

(b) Atoms get larger as one proceeds down a given group.

(c) For a given pair of isoelectronic ions, cations are smaller than anions.

(d) The first ionization energy for a given element tends to be smaller than the second ionization energy.

51. Which of the following statements is incorrect?

(a) Atoms get larger as one moves down a group in the periodic table.

(b) Atoms get larger as one moves to the right across a period in the periodic table.

(c) Atoms get smaller when electrons are removed.

(d) Ne atoms are smaller than Na atoms

52. Which of the following will have the largest size?

(a) Br　　　　　(b) I^{-1}　　　　　(c) I　　　　　(d) F

53. Which of the following increases as you proceed down a group in the periodic table?

(a) Atomic radius　　　　　(b) Ionization energy

(c) Electron affinity　　　　　(d) Electronegativity

54. Which of the following species has the largest size?

(a) S　　　　　(b) Se　　　　　(c) Se^{2-}　　　　　(d) O_2

55. Ionic radii are ......

(a) Directly proportional to square of effective nuclear charges

(b) Inversely proportional to effective nuclear charge

(c) Inversely proportional to square of effective nuclear charge

(d) Directly proportional to effective nuclear charge.

56. The order of screening effect of electrons of s, p, d and f orbitals of a given shell of an atom on its outer shell electrons is ......

(a) s > p > d > f　　　　(b) f > d > p > s　　　　(c) p < d < s > f　　　(d) f > p > s > d

57. Mark the correct statement ......

(a) Na^+ is smaller than Na atom　　　　　(b) Na^+ is larger than Na atom

(c) Cl^- is smaller than Cl atom　　　　　(d) Cl^- and Cl are equal in size

58. Which of the following has the largest size?

(a) O　　　　　(b) Rb　　　　　(c) Al^{3+}　　　　　(d) K^+

59. Which of the following ions has the largest radius ?

(a) Al^{+3}　　　　　(b) Cl^{-1}　　　　　(c) F^{-1}　　　　　(d) O^{-2}

60. Which of the following is arranged in the decreasing order of size ?

(a) $Cl^+ > Cl^- > Cl$　　(b) $Cl^+ > Cl > Cl^-$　　(c) $Cl > Cl^+ > Cl^-$　　(d) $Cl^- > Cl > Cl^+$

61. Which of the following has the largest radius?

(a) Na^+　　(b) Li^+　　(c) Cl^-　　(d) Cl

62. Which of the following has the largest radius?

(a) K　　(b) K^+　　(c) Cl^-　　(d) Cl

63. Which of the following is smallest in size?

(a) K^{+1}　　(b) O^{-2}　　(c) F^{-1}　　(d) Na^+

64. Which of these elements has the smallest ionic radius for its most commonly found ion?

(a) O　　(b) La　　(c) Rb　　(d) Mg

65. In the periodic table, as the atomic number increases from 11 to 17, what happens to the atomic radius?

(a) It remains constant　　　　　　　(b) It increases only

(c) It increases, then decreases　　　(d) It decreases only

66. Arrange the ions N, O, Mg, Na and F in the order of increasing ionic radius, starting with the smallest first.

(a) Mg, Na, F, O, N　　(b) N, Mg, O, Na, F　　(c) N, O, Mg, F, Na　　(d) N, O, F, Na, Mg

67. Which of the following most likely represent the atomic radius of a Cr atom, the ionic radius of a Cr ion, and the ionic radius of a Cr ion?

(a) 128 pm for Cr, 167 pm for Cr, and 193 pm for Cr

(b) 128 pm for Cr, 147 pm for Cr, and 193 pm for Cr

(c) 128 pm for Cr, 109 pm for Cr, and 63 pm for Cr

(d) 128 pm for Cr, 89 pm for Cr, and 63 pm for Cr

68. Which of the following isoelectric ions possesses largest size ?

(a) O^{2-}　　(b) F^-　　(c) N^{3-}　　(d) Mg^{2+}

69. Which of the following statements about ionic radii is incorrect?

(a) The ionic radius of Br is less than the covalent radius of Br.

(b) The ionic radius of Fe^{3+} is less than that of Fe^{2+} for a constant coordination number

(c) Values of ionic radii of M^{2+} increase down the group 2.

(d) The ionic radius of F is less than that of Cl.

70. The lowest ionization energies are found in the ......

(a) Inert gases　　　　　　(b) Alkali metals

(c) Transition elements　　(d) Halogens

71. The unit of ionization energy is ......

(a) Joule　　(b) Calorie　　(c) Electron volt　　(d) None of these

72. The energy required to convert a ground state atom in the gas phase to a gaseous positive ion is ......

(a) Activation energy　　(b) Free energy　　(c) Ionization energy　　(d) Kinetic energy

73. Which list below correctly gives the relative values of ionization energy level 1 or IE_1 for the elements stated?

(a) $Ne < F < O < N < C < B$

(b) $Ne > F > O > N > C > B$

(c) $Ne > F > O < N > C > B$

(d) $Ne < F < O > N < C < B$

74. Values of IE_1, IE_2 and IE_3 for Al are 579, 1814 and 2740 kJ mol. Which statement below is correct?

(a) For $Al_{(g)} \rightarrow Al^{3+}_{(g)}$, the energy required is 5133 kJmol

(b) For $Al_{(s)} \rightarrow Al^{3+}_{(g)}$, the energy required is 2740 kJ mol

(c) For $Al_{(s)} \rightarrow Al^{3+}_{(g)}$, the energy required is 5133 kJ mol

(d) For $Al_{(g)} \rightarrow Al^{3+}_{(g)}$, the energy required is 2740 kJ mol

75. Identify the element in the second period (row) whose first six successive ionization energies in units of electron volts are listed below ......

(a) Boron (b) Carbon (c) Nitrogen (d) Oxygen

76. Which of the following atoms will have the highest second ionization energy?

(a) Na (b) Mg (c) Al (d) Ca

77. Which of the following decreases in going down the halogen group?

(a) Ionic radius (b) Atomic radius (c) Ionisation potential (d) Boiling point

78. The ionization energy of nitrogen is more than oxygen because of ......

(a) More attraction of electrons by the nucleus

(b) More penetration effect

(c) The extra stability of half filled p orbital

(d) The size of nitrogen atom is smaller

79. Which of the following statements is correct?

(a) Ionization energies get smaller as more electrons are removed from an atom

(b) The ionization energy increases as one moves down a group

(c) The ionization energy increases as one moves to the right across a period

(d) Electron affinities are always larger than ionization energies

80. Gradual addition of electrons in the shells of the noble gases causes a decrease in their ......

(a) Ionization energy (b) Atomic radius (c) Boiling point (d) Density

81. The successive ionization energies of a certain element in units of kJ/mol are: $I_1 = 578$; $I_2 = 1820$; $I_3 = 2750$; $I_4 = 11,600$. [I_1 is the first ionization energy; I_2 the second, etc.] This element most likely is ......

(a) Na (b) Mg (c) Al (d) Si

82. The correct order of second ionization potential of carbon, nitrogen, oxygen and fluorine is ......

(a) $C > N > O > F$ (b) $O > N > F > C$ (c) $O > F > N > C$ (d) $F > O > N > C$

83. The decreasing order of ionic size is ......

(a) $N^{-3} > Na^+ > O^{-2} > F^-$

(b) $N^{-3} > O^{-2} > F^- > Na^+$

(c) $Na^+ > O^{-2} > N^{-3} > F^-$

(d) $O^{-2} > F^- > Na^+ > N^{-3}$

84. Which element has the highest first ionization energy?
    (a) Aluminium   (b) Magnesium   (c) Silicon   (d) Sodium

85. Which of the order for ionization energy is correct ?
    (a) $Be > B > C > N > O$
    (b) $B < Be < C < O < N$
    (c) $B < Be < C < N < O$
    (d) $B < Be < N < C < N < O$

86. Which element has the highest first ionization energy?
    (a) Beryllium   (b) Boron   (c) Hydrogen   (d) Lithium

87. Which of the elements below has the smallest first ionization energy?
    (a) F   (b) Mg   (c) Kr   (d) K

88. Identify the element having the first three ionization energies as follows: $I_1 = 900$ kJ/mol; $I_2 = 1760$ kJ/mol; $I_3 = 14,900$ kJ/mol
    (a) H   (b) He   (c) Li   (d) Be

89. Which of the following species has the highest ionization potential ?
    (a) Li^+ (b) Mg^+ (c) Al^+ (d) Ne

90. Which one of the following species will have the highest ionization energy?
    (a) Na   (b) Ne   (c) F   (d) O

91. In the long form of the periodic table, the transition metals are placed in ......
    (a) s-block   (b) f-block   (c) d-block   (d) s and p-block

92. The first ionization enthalpy of Na, Al and Si are in the order ......
    (a) $Na < Mg > Al < Si$
    (b) $Na < Al < Mg < Si$
    (c) $Na < Mg < Al > Si$
    (d) $Na > Mg > Al < Si$

93. Six elements A, B, C, D, E and F have the following atomic numbers (A = 12, B = 17, C = 18, D = 7, E = 9 and F = 11). Among these elements, the element which belongs to the 3rd period and has the highest ionization potential, is ......
    (a) A = 12   (b) B = 17   (c) C = 18   (d) D = 7

94. A factor that affects the ionization potential of an element is ......
    (a) Atomic size
    (b) Electron affinity
    (c) Electronegativity
    (d) Neutrons

95. Which one of the following statements is incorrect in relation to ionization enthalpy?
    (a) Ionization enthalpy increases for each successive electron
    (b) The greatest increase in ionization enthalpy is experienced on removal of electron from core noble gas configuration
    (c) End of valence electrons is marked by a big jump in ionization enthalpy
    (d) Removal of electron from orbitals bearing lower n value is easier than from orbital having higher n value

96. The number of electrons in the valence shell is equal to its ......
    (a) Atomic mass   (b) Group number   (c) Period number   (d) Atomic volume

97. Which of the following does not reflect the periodicity of elements?
    (a) Bonding behaviour
    (b) Electronegativity
    (c) Ionisation potential
    (d) Neutron/proton ratio

98. In a period, elements are arranged in strict sequence of ......

(a) Decreasing charges in the nucleus

(b) Increasing charges in the nucleus

(c) Constant charges in the nucleus

(d) Equal charges in the nucleus

99. Which of the following pairs has elements containing same number of electrons in the outermost orbit ?

(a) N-O　　　　　(b) Na-Cl　　　　　(c) Ca-Cl　　　　　(d) Cl-Br

100. At the end of each period, the valence shell is ......

(a) Incomplete　　　　(b) Half filled　　　　(c) Singly occupied　(d) Completely filled

101. Which of the following sets is isoelectronic with Xe?

(a) I^-, Cs^+, Ba^{2+}, La^{3+}

(b) Br^-, I^-, Cs, Cs^+

(c) He, Ne, Ar, Kr

(d) Sn^{2+}, Sb^{3+}, Te^{2-}, I^-

102. An element X has an outer ground state electronic configuration of $4s^2\,3d^4$. Element X ......

(a) Has four valence electrons

(b) Will readily form an anion

(c) Is a non-metal

(d) Is a metal

103. Choose the incorrect statement regarding the elements with electronic configurations

(A) $[Xe]6s^1$　　　　(B) $[Xe]4f^{14}5d^16s^2$　　　　(C) $[Ar]3d^{10}4s^24p^5$　(D) $[Ar]3d^74s^2$

(a) A is a strong reducing agent

(b) The compound between A and C is electrovalent.

(c) C is a halogen

(d) B is a d-block element

(e) D exhibits variable oxidation states.

104. Which of the following sets are not all isoelectronic?

(a) Se^{2-}, Sr^{2+}, Br^-, Rb^+　(b) S^{2-}, Cl^-, Li^+, Be^{2+}　(c) N^{3-}, O^{2-}, F^-, Ne　(d) Ar, K^+, Ca^{2+}, Sc^{3+}

105. An element X has the outer ground state electronic configuration ns^2np^5. Which statement about X is incorrect?

(a) X forms diatomic molecules

(b) X forms an X ion

(c) Compared to other elements in its period, X has a relatively low first ionization energy

(d) X is in group 17

106. Given that the electronic structure of the nitrogen atom is $1s^22s^22p^3$, how many unpaired electrons are present in atomic oxygen?

(a) 2　　　　　(b) 4　　　　　(c) 3　　　　　(d) 8

107. An element Z has an outer ground state electronic configuration of $3s^23p^3$. Element Z ......

(a) Is a gas at 298 K

(b) Has three valence electrons

(c) Is a non-metal

(d) Will readily form a cation

108. Which of the following pairs is isoelectronic?

(a) F, Cl　　　　　(b) K, Cl　　　　　(c) Li^+, H　　　　　(d) H^-, He

109. Given that the electronic structure of oxygen is $[He]2s^22p^4$, how many unpaired electrons are there in O^{2-}?

(a) 8　　　　　(b) 2　　　　　(c) 4　　　　　(d) 0

110. For a p-block element, its 3d, 3s, 3p and 4s orbitals are completely filled and the differentiating electron goes to the 4p orbital. The element should have its atomic number in the range ......
(a) 13 - 18   (b) 21 - 26   (c) 31 - 36   (d) 49 - 54

111. The ion correctly matched with its ground state electron configuration is ......
(a) Ni^{2+} : $[Ar]3d^8$ (b) Cr^{+3} : $[Ar]4s^2 3d^1$ (c) Fe^{3+} : $[Ar]3d^6$ (d) Zn^{+2} : $[Ar]4s^2 3d^8$

112. The electron configuration of a certain element is $[X]4s^2 3d^{10} 4p^2$, where X stands for a noble gas. The element in question and the noble gas X are, respectively ......
(a) Ga and Ar   (b) Ge and Ar   (c) Sn and Kr   (d) Ge and Kr

113. Which of the species below has the electronic configuration $1s^2 2s^2 2p^6$?
(a) Na^+ (b) O^{2-} (c) N^{3-} (d) All of these

114. From its position in the periodic table, the most stable ion of the Z = 88 element radium is likely to be ......
(a) Ra^+ (b) Ra^{2+} (c) Ra^{3+} (d) Ra^{2-}

115. In the modern periodic table, the period indicates the value of ......
(a) Atomic number   (b) Atomic mass
(c) Principal quantum number   (d) Azimuthal quantum number

116. Which of the following pairs is isoelectronic?
(a) Li, Be^{2+} (b) F^-, Na^+ (c) O, F^- (d) Li^+, Na^+

117. How many unpaired electrons are there in Arsenic (As)?
(a) 0   (b) 1   (c) 2   (d) 3

118. An element has an electron configuration of $1s^2$, $2s^2$, $2p^6$, $3s^2$. Which electrons experience the greatest effective nuclear charge, and which experience the most shielding, respectively?
(a) $1s^2\ 2s^2$ (b) $2s^2\ 3s^2$ (c) $3s^2\ 2s^2$ (d) $3s^2\ 2p^2$

119. Choose the electron configuration that results when the outermost electron is ionized from the Se atom.
(a) $[Ar]4s^2 3d^{10} 4p^4$ (b) $[Ar]4s^2 3d^{10} 4p^3$ (c) $[Ar]4s^2 3d^{10} 4p^5$ (d) $[Ar]4s^1 3d^{10} 4p^3$

120. The size of isoelectronic species F^-, Ne and Na^+ is affected by ......
(a) Nuclear charge (Z)
(b) Valence principal quantum number (n)
(c) Electron-electron interaction in the outer orbitals
(d) None of the factors because their size is the same

121. Four elements along a period have atomic numbers (11, 13, 16 and 17). The most metallic among these has an atomic number of ......
(a) 11   (b) 12   (c) 17   (d) 17

122. Which orbital is being filled in the lanthanide series?
(a) 4f   (b) 4d   (c) 5f   (d) 5d

123. Which two of the following are isoelectronic with one another?
(a) Na^+ and O   (b) Na^+ and K^+ (c) Na^+ and Ne   (d) Ne and O

124. Ionization energy is lowest for ......

(a) Inert gases   (b) Halogens   (c) Alkali metal   (d) Alkaline earth metals

125. Which of the following has highest first ionization potential?

(a) Carbon   (b) Oxygen   (c) Nitrogen   (d) Boron

126. The ability of an element to act as an oxidizing agent tends to ......

(a) Increase as the ionization energy decreases

(b) Increase as the electronegativity increases

(c) Increase as the atom becomes larger.

(d) Increase as the element becomes more metallic

127. The electronegativity of C and S, H, O and N are 2.5, 2.1, 3.5, 3.0 respectively. Which of the following bond is most polar?

(a) O-H   (b) S-H   (c) S-H   (d) C-H

128. Arrange the following atoms in the order of increasing electron affinity ......

(a) Br < Rb < Cl < I   (b) I < Rb < Cl < Br

(c) Rb < I < Br < Cl   (d) Cl < Br < Rb < I

129. Two elements whose eletronegativities are 1.2 and 3.0, the bond formed between them would be ......

(a) Ionic   (b) Covalent   (c) Coordinate   (d) Metallic

130. Which of the following is the least electronegative element?

(a) F   (b) Ga   (c) Os   (d) Ra

131. Which of the following is most electronegative ?

(a) Oxygen   (b) Nitrogen   (c) Fluorine   (d) Chlorine

132. Which is the most electronegative element?

(a) O   (b) La   (c) Rb   (d) Mg

133. If the difference in electronegativities of two elements is very large, then ......

(a) The bond is 50% ionic

(b) The bond is 100% covalent

(c) The bond is more covalent than ionic

(d) The bond is more ionic than covalent

134. Nature of the bond formed between two elements depends on the ......

(a) Oxidation potential   (b) Electronegativity

(c) Ionization potential   (d) Electron affinity

135. Which of the following elements will have the lowest electron affinity?

(a) Nitrogen   (b) Fluorine   (c) Chlorine   (d) Phosphorus

136. The correct order of electron gain enthalpy of halogen is

(a) F > Cl > F > I   (b) F > Cl > Br > I   (c) I > Br > Cl > F   (d) Cl > F > Br > I

137. Which one of the following is an incorrect statement?

(a) The ionization potential of nitrogen is greater than that of chlorine

(b) The electron affinity of fluorine is greater than that of chlorine

(c) The ionization potential of beryllium is greater than that of boron

(d) The electronegativity of fluorine is greater than that of chlorine

138. Electron affinity depends on ......

(a) Atomic size

(b) Nuclear charge

(c) Atomic number

(d) Atomic size and nuclear charge both

139. Among halogens, the correct order of amount of energy released in electron gain (electron gain enthalpy) is ......

(a) $F > Cl > Br > I$

(b) $F < Cl < Br < I$

(c) $F < Cl > Br > I$

(d) $F < Cl < Br < I$

140. Which of the following elements has the most negative electron affinity?

(a) S

(b) Cl

(c) He

(d) CO

141. The electron affinity of F is, in effect, the energy required for which of the following reactions?

(a) $F_{2(g)} \rightarrow 2F_{(g)}$

(b) $F_{(g)} \rightarrow F^+_{(g)} + e^-$

(c) $F_{2(g)} + e^- \rightarrow F^-_{(g)} + F_{(g)}$

(d) $F^-_{(g)} \rightarrow F_{(g)} + e^-$

142. Which of the following has the highest electron affinity?

(a) Cs

(b) Na

(c) Si

(d) F

143. What chemical process would liberate the most energy?

(a) $O_{(g)} + e^- \rightarrow O^-_{(g)}$

(b) $O^-_{(g)} + e^- \rightarrow O^{2-}_{(g)}$

(c) $O^{2-}_{2(g)} + e^- \rightarrow O^{3-}_{3(g)}$

(d) $O_{(g)} \rightarrow O^+_{(g)} + e^-$

144. Which element liberates the most energy during the electron affinity process?

(a) Bromine

(b) Chlorine

(c) Fluorine

(d) Iodine

145. The electron affinity of fluorine is ......

(a) 348.8 kJ/mol

(b) 337 kJ/mol

(c) 337 kJ/mol

(d) 348.8 kJ/mol

146. Which of the following has the largest first electron affinity (ignore sign, just magnitude)?

(a) F

(b) Li

(c) Cs

(d) Na

147. Which one of the elements is most metallic?

(a) P

(b) As

(c) Sb

(d) Bi

148. Which of the following sets contain only isoelectronic ions?

(a) $Zn^{2+}, Ca^{2+}, Ga^{3+}, Al^{3+}$

(b) $K^+, Ca^{2+}, Sc^{3+}, Cl$

(c) P^{3-}, S^{2-}, Cl, K^+

(d) $Ti^{4+}, Ar, Cr^{3+}, V^{5+}$

149. Calculate the lattice energy for NaCl(s) using a Born-Haber cycle and the following information :

$NaCl_{(s)} \rightarrow Na^+_{(g)} + Cl^-_{(g)}$

$Na_{(s)} + 1/2\ Cl_{2(g)} \rightarrow NaCl_{(s)}$ -411.0 kJ/mol

$Na_{(s)} \rightarrow Na_{(g)}$ $+107.3$ kJ/mol

$Na_{(g)} \rightarrow Na^+_{(g)} + e^-$ $+495.8$ kJ/moj

$1/2 Cl_{2(g)} \rightarrow Cl_{(g)}$ $+121.7$ kJ/mol

$Cl_{(g)} + e^- \rightarrow Cl^-_{(g)}$ -348.6 kJ/mol

(a) + 34.8 kJ/mol

(b) + 690.3 kJ/mol

(c) +787.2 kJ/mol

(d) + 1512 kJ/mol

150. Which compound would be expected to have the highest lattice energy?

    (a) LiCl   (b) NaCl

    (c) KCl   (d) RbCl

151. Which element is the odd one out because it does not have a high melting point?

    (a) Caesium   (b) Rhenium   (c) Carbon   (d) Molybdenum

152. Which of the following has the most favourable first electron affinity?

    (a) F   (b) Li   (c) Na   (d) Br

153. The element, which has the highest electron affinity in the 3rd period is ......

    (a) Sodium   (b) Magnesium   (c) Silicon   (d) Chlorine

154. The statement that is not true about electron affinity is ......

    (a) It causes energy to be released   (b) It causes energy to be absorbed

    (c) It is expressed in electron volts   (d) It involves formation of an anion

155. Which of the following pair contains a metalloid element ?

    (a) Cu and Au   (b) As and Sb   (c) Ca and Mg   (d) Na and K

156. Down a group, the electron affinity ......

    (a) Increases   (b) Decreases

    (c) Remains same   (d) Increases and then decreases

157. Number of elements present in the 5th period is ......

    (a) 8   (b) 18   (c) 32   (d) 24

158. What is the general trend in ionization energy and electron affinity values?

    (a) Both decrease as one traverses a period from left to right and both decrease as one descends a group

    (b) Both decrease as one traverses a period from left to right and both increase as one descends a group

    (c) Both increase as one traverses a period from left to right and both decrease as one descends a group

    (d) Both increase as one traverses a period from left to right and both increase as one descends a group

159. What oxidation states do you expect to be associated with elements in group 14?

    (a) +4 and +2, with +2 becoming important nearer the bottom of the group

    (b) +4 only

    (c) +4 and 2, with 2 becoming important nearer the bottom of the group

    (d) +4 and +2, with +4 becoming important nearer the bottom of the group

160. Which of the following elements is most likely to exhibit variable oxidation states?

    (a) F   (b) N   (c) Na   (d) Mg

161. Which of the following factors does not affect the metallic character of an element?

    (a) Atomic size   (b) Ionization potential

    (c) Electronegativity   (d) Atomic radius

162. Which of the following compounds is least likely to exist?

    (a) BaF_2 (b) LaF_3 (c) SrF_3 (d) PbS

163. The atomic number of an element is 18. Which of the following statement is true ?

   (a) It is highly unstable

   (b) It has highly negative electron gain enthalpy

   (c) It is monoatomic

   (d) It has very low ionization enthalpy

164. Which of the following oxides is amphoteric in character?

   (a) CaO   (b) CO_2 (c) SiO_2 (d) SnO_2

165. Which of the following possess maximum hydration power?

   (a) Na^+ (b) K^+ (c) Mg^{+2} (d) Ca^{+2}

166. The electronegative elements form ......

   (a) Acidic oxides   (b) Basic oxides   (c) Neutral oxides   (d) Amphoteric oxide

167. The correct decreasing order of melting points of chlorides of alkali metals ......

   (a) CsCl > LiCl > NaCl > KCl > RbCl   (b) RbCl > CsCl > LiCl > NaCl > KCl

   (c) NaCl > KCl > RbCl > CsCl > LiCl   (d) LiCl > NaCl > KCl > RbCl > CsCl

168. Which of the following salts has the largest lattice energy?

   (a) MgO   (b) CH_4 (c) Na_2O (d) NaI

169. The elements with atomic numbers 35, 53 and 85 are all ......

   (a) Noble gases   (b) Halogens   (c) Heavy metals   (d) Light metals

170. Which of the following is covalent?

   (a) P_2O_5 (b) MgO   (c) Fe_2O_3 (d) Bi_2O_3

171. Which of the following elements would be expected to lose electrons and form positive ions when it reacts?

   (a) Phosphorus   (b) Nitrogen   (c) Iron   (d) Iodine

172. Arrange the following elements in order of increasing metallic character: As, P, Bi, Sb, N.

   (a) As, P, Bi, Sb, N   (b) N, Sb, Bi, P, As   (c) As, Bi, N, P, Sb   (d) Bi, Sb, As, P, N

173. Which of the following oxides is most acidic?

   (a) Cl_2O_7 (b) Al_2O_3 (c) Ga_2O_3 (d) CaO

174. The first ionization potential (eV) of Be and B respectively are ......

   (a) 8.29, 9.32   (b) 9.32, 9.32   (c) 8.29, 8.29   (d) 9.32, 8.29

175. The valency of noble gas in general is ......

   (a) 0   (b) 1   (c) 3   (d) 2

176. Correct order of first ionisation potential among following elements Be, B, C, N, O is ......

   (a) B < Be < C < O < N   (b) B < Be < C < N < O

   (c) Be < B < C < N < O   (d) Be < B < C < O < N

177. For electron affinity of halogens, which of the following is correct?

   (a) Br > F   (b) F > Cl   (c) Br > Cl   (d) F > I

178. Which of the following order is wrong ?

   (a) $NH_3 < PH_3 < AsH_2$ – (acidic)   (b) Li < Be < B < C – (I^{st} IP)

   (c) $Al_2O_3 < MgO < NaO < K_2O$ – (basic)   (d) $Li^+ < Na^+ < K^+ < Cs^+$ – (ionic radius)

179. Which is the correct order of ionic sizes ?

(a) Ce > Sn > Yb > Lu

(b) Sn > Ce > Lu > Yb

(c) Lu > Yb > Sn > Ce

(d) Sn > Yb > Ce > Lu

(At. Nos. Ce = 58, Sn = 50, Yb = 70 and Lu = 71)

180. A reduction in atomic size with increase in atomic number is a characteristic of element of ......

(a) High atomic masses

(b) d-block

(c) f-block

(d) Radioactive series

181. The values of electronegativity of atoms A and B are 1.2 and 4.0 respectively. The % ionic character of the A–B bond is ......

(a) 50%

(b) 72.24%

(c) 55.3%

(d) 43%

182. Which of the following ion will form most water soluble hydroxide?

(a) K^+

(b) Ni^{2+}

(c) Zn^{2+}

(d) Al^{3+}

183. Which of the following has greatest tendency to lose electron?

(a) F

(b) Fr

(c) S

(d) Be

184. The element with the highest first ionization potential is ......

(a) Boron

(b) Carbon

(c) Nitrogen

(d) Oxygen

185. The first ionization potential in electron volts of nitrogen and oxygen atoms are respectively given by ......

(a) 14.6, 13.6

(b) 13.6, 14.6

(c) 13.6, 13.6

(d) 14.6, 14.6

186. Atomic radii of fluorine and neon in Angstrom units are respectively given by ......

(a) 0.72, 1.60

(b) 1.60, 1.60

(c) 0.72, 0.72

(d) None of these

187. The electronegativity of the following elements increases in the order ......

(a) C, N, Si, P

(b) N, Si, C, P

(c) Si, P, C, N

(d) P, Si, N, C

188. Which one of the following is the smallest in size?

(a) N^{3-}

(b) O^{2-}

(c) F^-

(d) Na^+

189. Amongst the following elements (whose electronic configurations are given below), the one having the highest ionization energy is ......

(a) $[Ne]3s^2 3p^1$

(b) $[Ne]3s^2 3p^3$

(c) $[Ne]3s^2 3p^2$

(d) $[Ar]3d^{10}4s^2 4p^3$

190. Arrange these elements in the correct order of the magnitude (without sign) of their electron gain enthalpy?

(i) $2s^2 2p^5$

(ii) $3s^2 3p^5$

(iii) $2s^2 2p^4$

(iv) $3s^2 3p^4$

Select the correct answer using the codes given below:

(a) (i) < (ii) < (iii) < (iv)

(b) (ii) < (i) < (iv) < (iii)

(c) (i) < (iii) < (iv) < (ii)

(d) (iii) < (iv) < (ii) < (i)

191. Which has most stable + 2 oxidation state?

(a) Sn

(b) Pb

(c) Fe

(d) Ag

192. The incorrect statement among the following is ......

(a) The first ionization potential of Al is less than the first ionization potential of Mg

(b) The second ionization potential of Mg is greater than the second ionization potential of Na

(c) The first ionization potential of Na is less than the first ionization potential of Mg

(d) The third ionization potential of Mg is greater than the third ionization potential of Na

193. The correct order of radii is ......

(a) $N < Be < B$　　　　(b) $F^- < O^{2-} < N^{3-}$　　　(c) $Na < Li < K$　　　(d) $Fe^{+3} < Fe^{+2} < Fe^{+4}$

194. The set representing the correct order of first ionization potential is ......

(a) $K > Na > Li$　　　　(b) $Be > Mg > Ca$　　　(c) $B > C > N$　　　(d) $Ge > Si > C$

195. Among the isoelectronic species, K^+, S^{2-}, Cl^- and Ca^{2+} the radii of the ions decreases as ......

(a) $Ca^{2+} > K^+ > Cl^- > S^{2-}$　　　　　　　　(b) $Cl^- > S^{2-} > K^+ > Ca^{2+}$

(c) $S^{2-} > Cl^- > K^+ > Ca^{2+}$　　　　　　　　(d) $K^+ > Ca^{2+} > S^{2-} > Cl^-$

196. With which of the following electronic configuration, an atom has the lowest ionization enthalpy?

(a) $1s^2\,2s^2\,2p^3$　　　　(b) $1s^2\,2s^2\,2p^6\,3s^1$　　　(c) $1s^2\,2s^2\,2p^6$　　　(d) $1s^2\,2s^2\,2p^5$

197. Which of the following orders is wrong?

(a) $NH_3 < PH_3 < AsH_3$ – Acidic　　　　　　(b) $Li < Be < B < C$ – IE_1

(c) $Al_2O_3 < MgO < Na_2O < K_2O$ – Basic　　　　(d) $Li^+ < Na^+ < K^+ < Cs^+$ – Ionic radius

198. Which is true about electronegativity order of the following elements?

(a) $P > Si$　　　　(b) $C > N$　　　(c) $C > Br$　　　(d) $Sr > Ca$

199. Two elements whose electronegativities are 1.2 and 3.0, the bond formed between them would be ......

(a) Ionic　　　　(b) Covalent　　　(c) Coordinate　　　(d) Metallic

200. Chloride ion and potassium ion are isoelectronic. Then ......

(a) Their sizes are same

(b) Cl^- ion is bigger than K^+ ion

(c) K^+ ion is relatively bigger

(d) Their sizes depend on other cation and anion

201. Increasing order of electron affinity is ......

(a) $N < O < Cl < Al$　　(b) $O < N < Al < Cl$　　(c) $Al < N < O < Cl$　　(d) $Cl < N < O < Al$

202. Which of the following sets is of coinage metal?

(a) Cu, Ag, Au　　　　(b) Zn, Cd, Hg　　　(c) Au, Ag, Zn　　　(d) Li, Na, K

203. The electronic configuration of transition elements is exhibited by ......

(a) ns^1　　　　(b) $ns^2 - np^5$　　　(c) $ns^2\,(n-1)d^{10}$　　　(d) $(n-1)d^{1-10}\,ns^{1-2}$

204. General electronic configuration of outermost and penultimate shell is $(n-1)s^2\,(n-1)p^6\,(n-1)d^x\,ns^2$. If $n = 4$ and $x = 5$, then number of protons in the nucleus will be ......

(a) > 25　　　　(b) < 24　　　(c) 25　　　(d) 30

205. Outer electronic configurations of K, Cu and Cr are respectively ......

(a) $4s^1, 3d^{10}$ and $3d^5$ (b) $4s^2, 3d^{10}$ and $3d^4$ (c) $4s^1, 3d^9$ and $3d^4$ (d) $4s^2, 3d^9$ and $3d^4$

206. The formation of the oxide ion, O^{2-} (g) require first an exothermic and then an endothermic step as shown below :

$$O_{(g)} + e \rightarrow O^-_{(g)} \qquad \Delta H° = -142 \text{ kJ mol}^{-1}$$

$$O^-_{(g)} + e \rightarrow O^{2-}_{(g)} \qquad \Delta H° = 844 \text{ kJ mol}^{-1}$$

This is because ......

(a) Oxygen is more electronegative

(b) Oxygen has high electron affinity

(c) O^- ion will tend to resist the addition of another electron

(d) O^- has comparatively larger size than oxygen atom

207. Identify the correct order of the size of the following ......

(a) $Ca^{2+} < K^+ < Ar < Cl^- < S^{2-}$ (b) $Ar < Ca^{2+} < K^+ < Cl^- < S^{2-}$

(c) $Ca^{2+} < Ar < K^+ < Cl^- < S^{2-}$ (d) $Ca^{2+} < K^+ < Ar < S^{2-} < Cl^-$

208. Which one of the following arrangement represents the correct order of electron gain enthalpy (with negative sign) of the given atomic species?

(a) $S < O < Cl < F$ (b) $Cl < F < S < O$ (c) $F < Cl < O < S$ (d) $O < S < F < Cl$

209. The correct order regarding the mobility of the alkali metal ions in aqueous solution is ......

(a) $K^+ > Rb^+ > Na^+ > Li^+$ (b) $Rb^+ > K^+ > Na^+ > Li^+$

(c) $Li^+ > Na^+ > K^+ > Rb^+$ (d) $Na^+ > K^+ > Rb^+ > Li^+$

210. In which of the following arrangements, the order is not according to the property indicated against it?

(a) $Li < Na < K < Rb$ Increasing metallic radius

(b) $I < Br < F < Cl$ Increasing electron gain enthalpy with negative sign

(c) $B < C < N < O$ Increasing first ionisation enthalpy

(d) $Al^{3+} < Mg^{2+} < Na^+ < F^-$ Increasing ionic size

211. The increasing order of first ionisation enthalpies of elements B, P, S and F (lowest first) is ...

(a) $F < S < P < B$ (b) $P < S < B < F$ (c) $B < P < S < F$ (d) $B < S < P < F$

212. Which one of the following sets of ions represents a collection of isoelectronic species?

(a) $K^+, Cl^-, Ca^{2+}, Sc^{3+}$ (b) $Ba^{2+}, Sr^{2+}, K^+, Ca^{2+}$ (c) $N^{3-}, O^{2-}, F^-, S^{2+}$ (d) $Li^+, Na^+, Mg^{2+}, Ca^{2+}$

213. In the following, the element with the highest ionisation energy is ......

(a) $[Ne]\ 3s^2 3p^1$ (b) $[Ne]\ 3s^2 3p^3$ (c) $[Ne]\ 3s^2 3p^2$ (d) $[Ne]\ 3s^2 3p^4$

214. The successive ionisation energies for an element X are given below:

1. 1st IE = 410 kJ/mol   2. 2st IE = 820 kJ/mol

3. 3st IE = 1100 kJ/mol   4. 4st IE = 1500 kJ/mol

5. 5st IE = 3200 kJ/mol

Find the number of valence electrons for the atom X.

(a) 4   (b) 3   (c) 5   (d) 2

PREVIOUS YEAR'S QUESTIONS

1. Which of the following orders of ionic radii is correctly represented? **[AIPMT 2014]**

   (a) $O^{2-} > F^- > Na^+$　　(b) $Al^3 > Mg^{2+} > N^{3-}$　(c) $H^- > H^+ > H$　(d) $Na^+ > F^- > O^{2-}$

2. Reason of the lanthanoid contraction is ...... **[AIPMT 2014]**

   (a) Decreasing nuclear charge　　　　　(b) Decreasing screening effect

   (c) Negligible screening effect of 'f' orbitals　(d) Increasing nuclear charges

3. Which of the following lanthanoid ions is diamagnetic? **[NEET]**

   (At nos. Ce = 58, Sm = 62, Eu = 63, Yb = 70)

   (a) Yb^{2+}　　　　　(b) Ce^{2+}　　　　　(c) Sm^{2+}　　　　　(d) Eu^{2+}

4. Which one of the following does not correctly represent the correct order of the property indicated against it? **[AIPMT 2012]**

   (a) Ti < V < Cr < Mn : increasing melting points

   (b) Ti < V < Mn < Cr : increasing 2nd ionization enthalpy

   (c) $Ti^{3+} < V^{3+} < Cr^{3+} < Mn^{3+}$: increasing number of oxidation states

   (d) $Ti^{3+} < V^{3+} < Cr^{3+} < Mn^{3+}$: increasing magnetic moment

5. Which of the following exhibits only +3 oxidation state?

   (a) N_3H　　　　　(b) NH_2OH　　　　　(c) N_2H_4　　　　　(d) NH_3

6. The correct order of decreasing electronegativity values among the elements I-beryllium, II-oxygen, III-nitrogen and IV-magnesium, is ...... **[Kerala CEE 2011]**

   (a) (II) > (III) > (I) > (IV)　　　　　(b) (III) > (IV) > (II) > (I)

   (c) (I) > (II) > (III) > (IV)　　　　　(d) (II) > (III) > (IV) > (III)

   (e) (II) > (III) > (IV) > (I)

7. The correct order of the decreasing ionic radii among the following isoelectronic species is ...... **[CBSE AIPMT, BVP 2010]**

   (a) $K^+ > Ca^{2+} > Cl^- S^{2-}$　　　　　(b) $Ca^{2+} > K^+ > S^{2-} > Cl^-$

   (c) $Cl^- > S^{2-} Ca^{2-} > K^+$　　　　　(d) $S^{2-} > Cl^- > K^+ Ca^{2+}$

8. Which of the following represents the correct order of increasing electron gain enthalpy with negative sign for the elements O, S, F and Cl ? **[CBSE AIPMT 2010]**

   (a) S < O < Cl < F　　(b) Cl < F < O < S　　(c) O < S < F < Cl　(d) F < S < O < Cl

9. The electronegativity of the following elements increases in the order ...... **[AFMC 2010]**

   (a) C, N, Si, P　　　　　(b) N, Si, C, P　　　　　(c) Si, P, C, N　　　　　(d) P, Si, N, C

10. Generally, the first ionization energy increases along a period. But there are some exceptions. One which is not an exception is ...... **[KCET 2010]**

    (a) N and O　　　　　(b) Na and Mg　　　　　(c) Mg and Al　　　　　(d) Be and B

11. Electron affinity is maximum for ...... **[Manipal, CPMT 2010]**

    (a) Cl　　　　　(b) F　　　　　(c) Br　　　　　(d) I

12. Which represents the correct order of first ionization potential of third period elements? **[AFMC 2009]**

    (a) Na > Mg > Al > Si　　　　　(b) Na < Mg < Al < Si

    (c) Na < Si < Al < Mg　　　　　(d) Na < Al < Mg < Si

13. The correct order of the electron affinities of N, O, S and Cl is ...... **[AIMS 2009]**

(a) N < O < S < Cl   (b) O < N < Cl < S   (c) O < Cl < N < S   (d) O < S < Cl < N

14. Which of the following pairs has almost same atomic radii? **[AIIMS 2009]**

(a) Al, Ga   (b) Be, Mg   (c) Mg, Al   (d) B, Be

15. The value of electronegativity of atoms A and B are 1.2 and 4.0 respectively. The % ionic character of the A-B bond is ...... **[DUMET 2009]**

(a) 50%   (b) 72.24%   (c) 55.3%   (d) 43%

16. Which one of the following order is correct for the first ionization energies of the elements? **[EAMCET 2009]**

(a) B < Be < N < O   (b) Be < B < N < O   (c) B < Be < O < N   (d) B < O < Be < N

17. The correct order of electron affinity of halogens is ...... **[Manipal 2009]**

(a) F > Cl > Br > I   (b) I > Br > Cl > F   (c) Cl > F > Br > I   (d) Cl > F < Br < I

18. In which of the following arrangements, the order is not according to the property indicated after it in bracket? **[Manipal 2009]**

(a) $Al^{3+} < Mg^{2+} < Na^+ < F^-$ (Increasing electron gain enthalpy)

(b) B < C < N < O (Increasing first ionization energy)

(c) I < Br < F < Cl (Increasing electron gain enthalpy)

(c) Li < Na < K < Rb (Increasing metallic radius)

19. The first ionization energies of the elements of the first transition series (Ti – Cu) ......

(a) increase as the atomic number increases **[Manipal 2009]**

(b) decrease as the atomic number increases

(c) do not show any change as the addition of electrons takes place in the inner (n – 1) d-orbital

(d) increase from Ti to Mn and then decrease from Mn to Cu

20. The correct order of decreasing second ionization enthalpy of Ti (22), V (23), Cr (24) and Mn (25) is ...... **[CBSE AIPMT 2008]**

(a) Cr > Mn > V > Ti   (b) V > Mn > Cr > Ti   (c) Mn > Cr > Ti > V   (d) Ti > V > Cr > Mn

21. Diagonal relationship is not shown by ...... **[BHU 2008]**

(a) Li and Mg   (b) Be and Al   (c) B and Si   (d) C and P

22. **Assertion :** The ionic size of $Mg^{2+} > Al^{3+}$ **[AIIMS 2008]**

Reason : In isoelectronic species, greater the nuclear charge, less is the size.

(a) Both Assertion and Reason are true and Reason is the correct explanation of Assertion.

(b) Both Assertion and Reason are true but Reason is not the correct explanation of Assertion.

(c) Assertion is true but Reason is false

(d) Both Assertion and Reason are false

23. An element with configuration $1s^2, 2s^2, 2p^6, 2p^2\, 3s^2\, 3p^5$ will form a compound of highest ionic character with the element having configuration ...... **[DUMET 2008]**

(a) $1s^2, 2s^2, 2p^6$ (b) $[Ar]\, 4s^1, 3d^{10}$ (c) $[Ar]\, 4s^1$ (d) $1s^2, 2s^1$

24. The correct order in which the first ionization potential increase is ......　　　**[KCET 2008]**

(a) Na, K, Be　　　　　(b) K, Na, Be　　　　　(c) K, Be, Na　　　　(d) Be, Na, K

25. The elements 'X', 'Y' and 'Z' form oxides which are acidic, basic and amphoteric respectively. The correct order of their electronegativity is ......　　　**[EAMCET 2008]**

(a) X > Y > Z　　　　　(b) Z > Y > X　　　　　(c) X > Z > Y　　　　(d) Y > X > Z

26. If the electronegativity difference between two atoms A and R is 2.0, the percentage of covalent character in the molecule is ......　　　**[Manipal 2008]**

(a) 54%　　　　　(b) 46%　　　　　(c) 23%　　　　(d) 72%

27. The atomic number of vanadium (V), chromium (Cr), manganese (Mn) and iron (Fe) are respectively 23, 24, 25 and 26. Which one of these may be expected to have the highest second ionisation enthalpy?　　　**[RPMT 2008]**

(a) V　　　　　(b) Cr　　　　　(c) Mn　　　　(d) Fe

28. Identify the correct order of the size of the following ......　　　**[CBSE AIPMT 2007]**

(a) $Ca^{2+} < K^+ < Ar < S^{2+} < Cl^-$　　　　　(b) $Ca^{2+} < K^+ < Ar < Cl^- < S^{2-}$

(c) $Ar < Ca^{2+} < K^+ < Cl^- < S^{2-}$　　　　　(d) $Ca^{2+} < Ar < K^+ < Cl^- < S^{2-}$

29. Which of the following is the second most electronegative element?　　　**[CPMT 2007]**

(a) Chlorine　　　　　(b) Oxygen　　　　　(c) Sulphur　　　　(d) Fluorine

30. Which of the following has lowest ionization energy?　　　**[CPMT 2007]**

(a) Oxygen　　　　　(b) Nitrogen　　　　　(c) Fluorine　　　　(d) Sulphur

31. Ionisation energy decreases down the group due to ......　　　**[CPMT 2007]**

(a) Increase in charge　　　　　(b) Increase in atomic size

(c) Decrease in atomic size　　　　　(d) Decrease in shielding effect

32. Which of the following order is wrong?　　　**[Punjab PMET 2007]**

(a) $NH_3 < PH_3 < AsH_3$ – acidic　　　　　(b) Li < Be < B < C – first IP

(c) $Al_2O_3 < MgO < Na_2O < K_2O$ – basic　　　　　(d) $Li^+ < Na^+ < K^+ < Cs^+$ – ionic radius

33. The electronic configurations of four elements are given below. Arrange these elements in the correct order of the magnitude (without sign) of their electron affinity.

[Kerala CEE 2007]

(i) $2s^2\,2p^5$　　　　　(ii) $3s^2\,3p^5$　　　　　(iii) $2s^2\,sp^4$　　　　(iv) $3s^2\,sp^4$

Select the correct answer using the codes given below :

(a) (i) < (ii) < (iv) < (iii)　　　　　(b) (ii) < (i) < (iv) < (iii)

(c) (i) < (iii) < (iv) < (ii)　　　　　(d) (iii) < (iv) < (i) < (ii)

34. Which one of the following orders is not in accordance with the property stated against it?

(a) $F_2 > Cl_2 > Br_2 > I_2$: Oxidising power　　　**[CBSE AIPMT 2006]**

(b) HI > HBr > HCl > HF : Acidic property in water

(c) $F_2 > Cl_2 > Br_2 > I_2$: Electronegativity

(d) $F_2 > Cl_2 > Br_2 > L_2$: Bond dissociation energy

35. Which is chemically most active non-metal?　　　**[Manipal 2006]**

(a) S　　　　　(b) O_2　　　　　(c) F_2　　　　(d) N_2

36. Pauling's equation for determining the electronegativity of an element is ...... X_A, X_B = electronegativity values of elements A and B. Δ represents polarity of A–B bond.

[J&K CET 2006]

(a) $X_A - X_B = 0.208 \sqrt{\Delta}$

(b) $X_A + X_B = 0.208 \sqrt{\Delta}$

(c) $X_A - X_B = 0.208 \, \Delta^2$

(d) $X_A - X_B = \sqrt{\Delta}$

37. A natural atom will have the lowest ionization potential when electronic configuration is ...

[KCET 2005]

(a) $2s^2$　　　(b) $1s^2, 2s^2, 2p^2$　　　(c) $1s^2, 2s^2, 2p^6$　　　(d) $1s^2, 2s^2, 2p^6, 3s^1$

38. Identify the correct order in which the ionic radius of the following ions increases ......

[EAMCET 2005]

(i) F^-　　　(ii) Na^+　　　(iii) N^{3-}

(a) III, I, II　　　(b) I, II, III　　　(c) II, III, I　　　(d) II, I, III

39. Among 3rd row element, atomic size is maximum for ......　　　**[MHT CET 2005]**

(a) sodium　　　(b) argon　　　(c) magnesium　　　(d) chlorine

40. Which of these have no unit?

(a) Electronegativity

(b) Electron affinity

(c) Ionisation energy

(d) Excitation potential

41. Which of the following order is correct for the size of Fe^{3+}, Fe and Fe^{2+} ?　　　**[EAMCET 2004]**

(a) $Fe < Fe^{2+} < Fe^{3+}$　　　(b) $Fe^{2+} < Fe^{3+} < Fe$　　　(c) $Fe < Fe^{3+} < Fe^{2+}$　　　(d) $Fe^{3+} < Fe^{2+} < Fe$

42. The first ionization potentials of four consecutive elements, present in the second period of the Periodic Table, are 8.3, 11.3, 14.5 and 13.6 eV respectively. Which one of the following is the first ionization potential (in eV) of nitrogen?　　　**[EAMCET 2004]**

(a) 13.6　　　(b) 11.2　　　(c) 8.3　　　(d) 14.5

43. Whose electron affinity will be less than zero?　　　**[RPMT 2004]**

(a) O^{2-}　　　(b) S^{2-}　　　(c) Both (a) and (b)　　　(d) O^+

44. The ions O^{2-}, F^-, Na^+, Mg^{2-} and Al^{3+} are isoelectronic. Their ionic radii show ......

[CBSE AIPMT 2003]

(a) an increase from ions O^{2-}, F^-, Na^+, Mg^{2+} and Al^{3+} are isoelectronic.

(b) a decrease from ions O^{2-}, F^-, Na^+, Mg^{2+} and Al^{3+} are isoelectronic.

(c) a significant increase from O^{2-} to Al^{3-}

(d) a significant increase from O^{2-} to Al^{3-}

45. Which is the property of non-metal?　　　**[Manipal 2003]**

(a) Electronegativity

(b) Basic nature of oxide

(c) Reducing property

(d) Low ionisation potential

46. Arrange the elements in increasing order of atomic radius – Na, Rb, K, Mg

[CBSE PMT 2006]

(a) Na, K, Mg, Rb　　　(b) K, Na, Mg, Rb　　　(c) Mg, Na, K, Rb　　　(d) Rb, K, Mg, Na

47. What is the correct decreasing order of ionic radii of the following ions ?　　　**[M.P.P.E.T. 2010]**

(a) N and O　　　(b) Na and Mg　　　(c) Mg and Al　　　(d) Be and B

48. Which one of the following sets of ions represents the collection of isoelectronic species ?

[BHU 1995; Orissa JEE 2005]

(a) K^+, Ca^{2+}, Sc^{3+}, Cl^- (b) Na^+, Mg^{2+}, Al^{3+}, Cl^-

(c) K^+, Cl^-, Mg^{2+}, Sc^{3+} (d) Na^+, Ca^{2+}, Sc^{3+}, F^-

(Atomic nos. : F = 9, Cl = 17, Na = 11, Mg = 12, Al = 13, K = 19, Ca = 20, Sc = 21)

49. Which one of the following arrangements represents the correct order of electron gain enthalpy (with negative sign) of the given atomic species ?

[CBSE PMT 1995; CPMT 2002; RPMT 2005]

(a) F < Cl < O < S   (b) S < O < Cl < F

(c) O < S < F < Cl   (d) Cl < F < S < O

50. The charge/size ratio of a cation determines the polarizing power. Which one of the following sequences represents the increasing order of the polarizing power of the cations K^+, Ca^{2+}, Mg^{2+} and Be^{2+} ?   **[MP PMT 2004]**

(a) $Ca^{2+} < Mg^{2+} < Be^{2+} < K^+$ (b) $Mg^{2+} < Be^{2+} < K^+ < Ca^{2+}$

(c) $Be^{2+} < K^+ < Ca^{2+} < Mg^{2+}$ (d) $K^+ < Ca^{2+} < Mg^+ < Be^{2+}$

51. The set representing the correct order of ionic radius is ......   **[CBSE PMT 2006]**

(a) $Li^+ > Be^{2+} > Na^+ > Mg^{2+}$ (b) $Na^+ > Li^+ > Mg^{2+} > Be^{2+}$

(c) $Li^+ > Na^+ > Mg^{2+} > Be^{2+}$ (d) $Mg^{2+} > Be^{2+} > Li^+ > Na^+$

52. Which of the following pair of elements belongs to same period of the periodic table?

[CPMT 2000]

(a) P, Se   (b) Mg, Sb   (c) Ag, Cl   (d) Ca, Zn

53. Pauling's electronegativity values for elements are useful in predicting ... **[CBSE PMT 2000]**

(a) Polarity of bonds in molecules

(b) Position of elements in electromotive series

(c) Co-ordination number

(d) Dipole moment of various molecules

54. Which period of the periodic table contains maximum number of elements?

[RPMT 2000; DPMT 2001]

(a) 7th (b) 6th (c) 4th (d) 5th

55. Alkali metals in each period have ......   **[Kerala PMT 2000]**

(a) Smallest size   (b) Lowest IE

(c) Highest IE   (d) Highest electronegativity

56. Among the elements given below, the one with highest electropositivity is ... **[RPMT 2001]**

(a) Cu   (b) Cs   (c) Cr   (d) Ba

57. Gradual addition of electronic shells in the noble gases causes a decrease in their ......

[DPMT 2001]

(a) Ionisation energy   (b) Atomic radius

(c) Boiling point   (d) Density

58. The element with highest electron affinity among the halogen is ......   **[DPMT 2001]**

(a) F   (b) Cl   (c) Br   (d) I

59. Which of the following does not exhibit the periodicity in properties of elements?

[Kerala CET 2002]

(a) Ionisation energy   (b) N/P ratio

(c) Electronegativity   (d) Atomic radius

60. According to the periodic law of elements, the variation in properties of elements is related to their ......　　　**[Orissa JEE 2005]**
(a) Atomic masses
(b) Nuclear masses
(c) Atomic numbers
(d) Nuclear neutron-proton number ratios

61. Ionic radii are ......　　　**[BCECE 2005]**
(a) Directly proportional to square of effective nuclear charge
(b) Inversely proportional to effective nuclear charge
(c) Inversely proportional to square of effective nuclear charge
(d) Directly proportional to effective nuclear charge

62. Which of the following species has the highest electron affinity?　　　**[AMU 2005]**
(a) F^-
(b) O
(c) O^-
(d) Na^+

63. The IE of hydrogen atom is 13.6 eV. The energy required to remove an electron in the $n = 2$ state of the hydrogen atom is ......
(a) 27.2 eV
(b) 13.6 eV
(c) 6.8 eV
(d) 3.4 eV

64. Correct sequence of increasing order of ionization energy is ...　　　**[Manipur M.B.B.S. 2009]**
(a) $I < Br < Cl$
(b) $Cl < Br < I$
(c) $Cl < I < Br$
(d) $I < Cl < Br$

65. A sudden large jump between the values of second and third ionisation energies of elements would be associated with which of the following electronic configuration ?
　　　[C.B.S.E. 1992, A.F.M.C. 1998 J & K P.M.T. 2004]
(a) $1s^2\,2s^2\,2p^5\,3s^1$
(b) $1s^2\,2s^2\,2p^6\,3s^2\,3p^1$
(c) $1s^2\,2s^2\,2p^6\,3s^1\,3p^2$
(d) $1s^2\,2s^2\,2p^6\,3s^2$

66. Which of the following order for ionization energy is correct ?
　　　[C.P.M.T. 1999, C.B.S.E. Med. 2001]
(a) $Be > B > C > N > O$
(b) $B < Be < C < O < N$
(c) $B < Be < C < N < O$
(d) $B < Be < N < C < O$

67. Among the following are isoelectronic species ?
(a) NO^+, C_2^{2-}, O_2, CO
(b) N_2, C_2^{2-}, CO, NO
(c) $N_2, C_2^{2-}, CN^-, C_2^{2-}$
(d) NO, CN^-, N_2, O_2^-

68. An element of atomic number 29 belongs to which of the following blocks of the periodic table ?　　　**[M.P.P.E.T. 2001]**
(a) s-block
(b) p-block
(c) f-block
(d) d-block

69. Ionisation energy is highest in ......　　　**[B.H.U. 2001]**
(a) $[Ne]3s^1$
(b) $[Ne]3s^2 3p^3$
(c) $[Ne]3d^{10}4s^2 4p^3$
(d) $[Ne]3s^2 3p^4$

70. Which of the following isoelectronic ions has the lowest ionisation energy ?
　　　[Haryana C.E.E.T. 2001]
(a) K^+
(b) Ca^{2+}
(c) Cl^-
(d) S^{2-}

71. Eka-aluminium and Eka-silicon are known as ......　　　**[Kerala P.M.T. 2002]**
(a) Gallium and germanium
(b) Aluminium and silicon
(c) Proton and silicon
(d) Neutron and magnesium

72. Which one of the following statements is correct ?
(a) Ionic radius of Fe^{3+} is greater than Fe^{2+}
(b) Atomic radius of chlorine atom is greater than ionic radius of chloride ion
(c) Electron affinity of phosphorus is greater than nitrogen
(d) Cs_2O is strongly acidic in nature

73. Element with atomic number 56 belongs to which block ?　　　**[A.F.M.C. 2002]**
(a) s　　　　　　　(b) p　　　　　　　(c) d　　　　　　　(d) f

74. Which of the following is correctly matched ?　　　**[Tamil Nadu C.E.T. 2002]**
(a) C–C bond length – 0.077 nm　　　(b) Ionic radius of Na^+ – 0.136 nm
(c) C–Cl bond length – 0.176 nm　　　(d) Ionic radius of F^- – 0.095 nm

75. Which one of the following groups represents a collection of isoelectronic species ?
(Atomic numbers : Cs = 55, Br = 35)　　　　　**[A.I.E.E.E. 2003]**
(a) Na^+, Ca^2, Mg^{2+}　　(b) N^{3-}, F^-, Na^+　　(c) Be, Al^{3+}, Cl^-　　(d) Ca^{2+}, Cs^+, Br

76. What is the general outer electronic configuration of the coinage metals ?

[Orissa J.E.E. 2003]
(a) ns^2np^6　　　　(b) $(n-1)d^{10}\,ns^1$　　(c) $(n-1)d^{10}ns^2$　　(d) $(n-1)d^9\,ns^2$

77. An atom with high electronegativity has ......　　　**[Kerala C.E.T. 2003]**
(a) large size　　　　　　　　(b) high ionization potential
(c) low electron affinity　　　　　(d) low ionization potential

78. For electron affinity of halogens, which of the following is correct ?　　**[A.I.I.M.S. 2004]**
(a) Br > F　　　　(b) F > Cl　　　　(c) Br > Cl　　　　(d) F > I

79. The elements with atomic numbers 9, 17, 35, 53, 85 are all　　**[Karnataka C.E.T. 2004]**
(a) Noble gases　　(b) Halogens　　(c) Heavy metals　　(d) Light metals

80. Among Al_2O_3, SiO_2, P_2O_3 and SO_2 the correct order of acid strength is ...　**[A.I.E.E.E. 2004]**
(a) $SO_2 < P_2O_3 < SiO_2 < Al_2O_3$　　　　(b) $Al_2O_3 < SiO_2 < P_2O_3 < SO_2$
(c) $Al_2O_3 < SiO_2 < SO_2 < P_2O_3$　　　　(d) $SiO_2 < SO_2 < Al_2O_3 < P_2O_3$

81. Which of the following ion has the highest value of ionic radius ?　　**[A.I.E.E.E. 2004]**
(a) Li^+　　　　(b) F^-　　　　(c) O^{2-}　　　　(d) B^{3+}

82. Which of the following oxides is amphoteric in character ?　　**[A.I.E.E.E. 2005]**
(a) CaO　　　　(b) CO_2　　　　(c) SiO_2　　　　(d) SnO_2

83. Lattice energy of an ionic compound depends upon ......　　**[E.A.M.C.E.T. Medical 2009]**
(a) Charge on the ion only　　　　(b) Size of the ion only
(c) Charge on the ion and size of the ion　　(d) Packing of ions only

84. The number of unpaired electrons in gaseous species of Mn^{3+}, Cr^{3+} and V^{3+} respectively are
...... and most stable species is ......　　　　**[D.C.E.T. 2009]**
(a) 4, 3 and 2 and V^{3+} is most stable　　　(b) 3, 3 and 2 and Cr^{3+} is most stable
(c) 4, 3 and 2 and Cr^{3+} is most stable　　　(d) 3, 7 and 3 and Mn^{3+} is most stable

85. The electronic configuration of the element with maximum electron affinity is ......
(a) $1s^2\,2s^2\,2p^3$　　　　(b) $1s^2\,2s^2\,2p^5$　　　　(c) $1s^2\,2s^2\,2p^6\,3s^2\,3p^5$
(d) $1s^2\,2s^2\,2p^6\,3s^2\,3p^3$　　　(e) $1s^2\,2s^2\,2p^6\,3s^1$　**[Kerala P.E.T. 2008]**

86. The sizes of the following species increase in the order ......　　**[D.C.E. 2006]**
(a) $Mg^{2+} < Na^+ < F^- < Al$　　　　(b) $F^- < Al < Na^+ < Mg^{2+}$
(c) $Al < Mg^{2+} < F^- < Na^+$　　　　(d) $Na^+ < Al < F^- < Mg^{2+}$

87. Which electronic configuration of an element has abnormally high difference between
second and third ionization energy ?　　　　**[D.C.E. 2006]**
(a) $1s^2 2s^2 2p^6 3s^1$　　(b) $1s^2 2s^2 2p^6 3s^2 3p^1$　(c) $1s^2 2s^2 2p^6$　　(d) $1s^2 2s^2 2p^6 3s^2$

88. The electronic configuration of four elements are given below. Arrange these elements in
the correct order of the magnitude (without sign) of their electron affinity

[Kerala P.M.T. 2007]
(i) $2s^2 2p^5$　　　(ii) $3s^2 3p^5$　　　(iii) $2s^2 2p^4$　　　(iv) $3s^2 3p^4$
Select the correct answer using the codes given below :
(a) (i) < (ii) < (iv) < (iii)　　　(b) (ii) < (i) < (iv) < (iii)　　　(c) (i) < (iii) < (iv) < (ii)
(d) (iii) < (iv) < (ii) < (i)　　　(e) (iii) < (iv) < (i) < (ii)

ANSWER KEY

1. (c)	2. (d)	3. (b)	4. (a)	5. (c)	6. (b)	7. (b)	8. (b)
9. (d)	10. (c)	11. (a)	12. (c)	13. (b)	14. (c)	15. (a)	16. (b)
17. (b)	18. (b)	19. (a)	20. (c)	21. (d)	22. (b)	23. (a)	24. (a)
25. (d)	26. (a)	27. (b)	28. (b)	29. (d)	30. (b)	31. (d)	32. (c)
33. (b)	34. (c)	35. (c)	36. (a)	37. (b)	38. (c)	39. (b)	40. (b)
41. (c)	42. (d)	43. (b)	44. (b)	45. (c)	46. (d)	47. (d)	48. (a)
49. (c)	50. (a)	51. (b)	52. (b)	53. (a)	54. (c)	55. (a)	56. (b)
57. (a)	58. (b)	59. (d)	60. (d)	61. (c)	62. (a)	63. (d)	64. (d)
65. (d)	66. (a)	67. (d)	68. (c)	69. (a)	70. (b)	71. (c)	72. (c)
73. (c)	74. (a)	75. (b)	76. (a)	77. (c)	78. (c)	79. (c)	80. (a)
81. (c)	82. (c)	83. (b)	84. (c)	85. (b)	86. (c)	87. (d)	88. (d)
89. (a)	90. (a)	91. (c)	92. (a)	93. (c)	94. (a)	95. (d)	96. (b)
97. (d)	98. (b)	99. (d)	100. (d)	101. (a)	102. (d)	103. (a)	104. (b)
105. (c)	106. (a)	107. (c)	108. (d)	109. (d)	110. (c)	111. (a)	112. (b)
113. (d)	114. (b)	115. (c)	116. (b)	117. (d)	118. (b)	119. (b)	120. (d)
121. (a)	122. (a)	123. (c)	124. (c)	125. (a)	126. (b)	127. (a)	128. (c)
129. (a)	130. (d)	131. (c)	132. (a)	133. (d)	134. (b)	135. (d)	136. (d)
137. (b)	138. (d)	139. (c)	140. (b)	141. (c)	142. (d)	143. (a)	144. (b)
145. (a)	146. (a)	147. (d)	148. (b)	149. (c)	150. (a)	151. (a)	152. (a)
153. (d)	154. (b)	155. (b)	156. (b)	157. (b)	158. (c)	159. (a)	160. (b)
161. (c)	162. (c)	163. (c)	164. (c)	165. (c)	166. (a)	167. (d)	168. (a)
169. (b)	170. (a)	171. (c)	172. (d)	173. (a)	174. (d)	175. (a)	176. (b)
177. (d)	178. (b)	179. (a)	180. (c)	181. (b)	182. (a)	183. (b)	184.
185. (c)	186.	187. (c)	188.	189. (b)	190. (b)	191. (b)	192. (b)
193. (b)	194. (b)	195. (c)	196. (b)	197. (b)	198. (a)	199. (a)	200. (b)
201. (c)	202. (a)	203. (d)	204. (c)	205. (a)	206. (c)	207. (a)	208. (d)
209. (c)	210. (d)	211. (d)	212. (a)	213. (b)	214. (c)		

Previous Years Questions

1. (a)	2. (c)	3. (a)	4. (c)	5. (a)	6. (a)	7. (d)	8. (c)
9. 9c)	10. (b)	11. (a)	12. (d)	13. (a)	14. (a)	15. (b)	16. (c)
17. (c)	18. (b)	19. (a)	20. (a)	21. (d)	22. (a)	23. (c)	24. (b)
25. (c)	26. (a)	27. (b)	28. (b)	29. (b)	30. (d)	31. (b)	32. (b)
33. (d)	34. (d)	35. (c)	36. (a)	37. (d)	38. (d)	39. (a)	40. (a)
41. (d)	42. (d)	43. (c)	44. (d)	45. (a)	46. (c)	47. (b)	48. (a)
49. (d)	50. (d)	51. (d)	52. (d)	53. (a)	54. (b)	55. (b)	56. (b)
57. (a)	58. (b)	59. (b)	60. (c)	61. (b)	62. (b)	63. (d)	64. (a)
65. (d)	66. (b)	67. (d)	68. (a)	69. (b)	70. (d)	71. (a)	72. (c)
73. (a)	74. (c)	75. (b)	76. (b)	77. (b)	78. (d)	79. (b)	80. (b)
81. (c)	82. (d)	83. (c)	84. (c)	85. (c)	86. (a)	87. (d)	88. (c)

•••

UNIT 4

CHEMICAL BONDING AND MOLECULAR STRUCTURE

1. Chemical reactivity of elements depends upon their characteristic ......
   (a) Electronic configuration
   (b) Atomic radius
   (c) Enthalpy of atomization
   (d) Number of free electrons

2. During bond formation, potential energy of the system is ......
   (a) Instability
   (b) Stable
   (c) Decreases
   (d) Increases

3. In bond formation, when repulsive force dominates the attractive force, it leads to ...... of the bond.
   (a) Stability
   (b) Instability
   (c) Decreases
   (d) Increases

4. Based on the Lewis structure, the number of electron domains in the valence shell of the boron atom in the BF_3 molecule is ......
   (a) 1
   (b) 2
   (c) 3
   (d) 4

5. Which of the following is the correct electron-dot formula for carbon dioxide?
   (a) $\ddot{O}-\ddot{C}-\ddot{O}$
   (b) $\ddot{O}=\ddot{C}-\ddot{O}$
   (c) $\ddot{O}=C=\ddot{O}$
   (d) $O\equiv C-\ddot{O}$

6. The following electron-dot formulas for carbon dioxide both satisfy the octet rule for all of the atoms. Which of these structures is the better structure and why is this the case?

   $$\ddot{O}=C=\ddot{O} \qquad \qquad O\equiv C-\ddot{O}$$

   A   B

   (a) "A" is the better structure because there is no formal charge on any of the atoms.
   (b) "A" is the better structure because all the bonds and non-bonding electron pairs are arranged in a symmetrical pattern.
   (c) "B" is the better structure because there are opposite formal charges on the two oxygen atoms which attract each other and give the molecule a lower energy.
   (d) "B" is the better structure because the bond energies of a single bond and a triple bond are higher than the bond energies of two double bonds.

7. What is the total number of electrons in the correct Lewis dot formula of the sulfite ion?
   (a) 8
   (b) 24
   (c) 26
   (d) 30

8. In the Lewis structure for OF_2 molecule, the number of lone pairs of electrons around the central oxygen atom is ......
   (a) 0
   (b) 1
   (c) 2
   (d) 3

9. The formal charge of S in SO_3 is ......
   (a) +2
   (b) +1
   (c) 0
   (d) −1

10. What is the formal charge on the oxygen (note: double bonds count as four shared electrons)?

    (a) +1
    (b) −1
    (c) zero
    (d) −2

4.1

11. What is the formal charge on the carbon atom ?

$$H_2C:$$

(a) +1　　　(b) −1　　　(c) zero　　　(d) +4

12. What is the formal charge on the oxygen atom ?

(a) +1　　　(b) −1　　　(c) zero　　　(d) −2

13. In PO_4^{3-} ion, the formal charge on the oxygen atom of P–O bond is ......

(a) + 1　　　(b) − 1　　　(c) − 0.75　　　(d) + 0.756

14. What is the formal charge on oxygen atom of the following compound?

$$H - \overset{\cdot\cdot}{\underset{|}{O}} - H$$
$$H$$

(a) +3　　　(b) +1　　　(c) −2　　　(d) −3

15. Among the following, the electron deficient compound is ......

(a) CCl_4　　　(b) PCl_5　　　(c) $BeCl_2$　　　(d) BCl_3

16. Octet rule is not followed in the formation of ......

(a) CH_4　　　(b) CCl_4　　　(c) NH_3　　　(d) PCl_5

17. CsF is an ionic compound because of ......

(a) High ionization potential of Cs and high electron affinity of F

(b) Low ionization potential of Cs and low electron affinity of F

(c) Low ionization potential of Cs and high electron affinity of F

(d) High ionization potential of Cs and low electron affinity of F

18. Which of the following is a non-conductor of electricity?

(a) Molten NaOH　　　(b) Molten KOH　　　(c) Solid NaCl　　　(d) Aqueous NaCl

19. Which of the following has non-polar covalent bond?

(a) I_2　　　(b) HCl　　　(c) C_2H_2　　　(d) NH_3BF_3

20. Which of the following is a favorable factor for cation formation?

(a) Low ionisation potential　　　(b) High electron affinity

(c) High electronegativity　　　(d) Small atomic size

21. The charge/size ratio of a cation determines its polarizing power. Which one of the following sequences represents the increasing order of the polarizing power of the cationic species K^+, Ca^{2+}, Mg^{2+}, Be^{2+}?

(a) Mg^{2+}, Be^{2+}, K^+, Ca^{2+}　　　(b) Be^{2+}, K^+, Ca^{2+}, Mg^{2+}

(c) K^+, Ca^{2+}, Mg^{2+}, Be^{2+}　　　(d) Ca^{2+}, Mg^{2+}, Be^{2+}, K^+

22. Lattice energy of an ionic compound depends upon ......

(a) Size of the ion only　　　(b) Charge on the ion only

(c) Charge on the ion and size of the ion　　　(d) Packing of ions only

23. Polar covalent bond is ____ than non-polar covalent bond.

(a) Weaker　　　(b) Unstable　　　(c) Stronger　　　(d) None of these

24. An ionic compound will dissolve in water only if ......
    (a) Hydration energy is low and lattice energy is high
    (b) Hydration energy is high and lattice energy is very high
    (c) Hydration energy is high and lattice energy is low
    (d) Hydration energy is low and lattice energy is low

25. Ionic compounds do not show isomerism because bonds are ......
    (a) Directional and rigid
    (b) All
    (c) Non-directional and non-rigid
    (d) Non-directional and rigid

26. Covalent compounds are soluble in water because of ......
    (a) Hydrolysis
    (b) None of these
    (c) Hydration
    (d) Hydrogen bonding

27. Which one of these is weakest?
    (a) Ionic bond
    (b) Covalent bond
    (c) Metallic bond
    (d) Van der Waal's forces

28. Which of the following is a polar covalent compound?
    (a) NH_3BF_3
    (b) HCl
    (c) Al_2O_3
    (d) I_2

29. Which of the following is a coordinate covalent compound?
    (a) Al_2O_3
    (b) HCl
    (c) NH_3BF_3
    (d) C_2H_2

30. Which chloride should exhibit the most covalent type of bond?
    (a) KCl
    (b) $CaCl_2$
    (c) $BeCl_2$
    (d) $BaCl_2$

31. NH_3 and BF_3 form adduct readily through ......
    (a) Ionic bond between BF_3 and NH_3
    (b) Co-ordinate bond between B and N
    (c) Covalent bond between B and N
    (d) H-bond between F atoms of BF_3 and H-atoms of NH_3

32. Which of the following is an electron deficient molecule?
    (a) B_2H_6
    (b) C_2H_6
    (c) PH_3
    (d) SiH_4

33. Which one of the compounds below is most likely to be ionic?
    (a) GaAs
    (b) $ScCl_3$
    (c) NO_2
    (d) CCl_4

34. Malleability and ductility of metals can be accounted due to ......
    (a) the presence of electrostatic force
    (b) the crystalline structure in metal
    (c) the capacity of layers of metal ions to slide over the other
    (d) the interaction of electrons with metal ions in the lattice

35. The ion which is isoelectric with CO is ......
    (a) CN^-
    (b) O_2
    (c) N^{+2}
    (d) O^{+2}

36. In NO_3^- ion, the number of bond pairs and lone pairs of electrons on nitrogen atom are ...
    (a) 2, 2
    (b) 3, 1
    (c) 1, 3
    (d) 4, 0

37. Which of the following species has tetrahedral geometry?
    (a) BH_4^-
    (b) NH_2^-
    (c) CO_3^{2-}
    (d) H_3O^+

38. Which molecule/ion out of the following does not contain unpaired electrons?
    (a) N^{2+}
    (b) O_2
    (c) O_2^{2-}
    (d) B_2

39. Which of the following has the highest dipole moment?
    (a) CO_2 (b) HI   (c) H_2O (d) SO_2

40. Dipole moment is shown by ......
    (a) 1, 4-dichlorobenzene
    (b) cis 1, 2-dichloroethene
    (c) trans 1, 2-dichloroethene
    (b) trans 2, 3-dichloro-2-butene

41. If the bond length and dipole moment of a diatomic molecule are 1.25 A° and 1.0 D respectively, what is the percent ionic character of the bond?
    (a) 10.66   (b) 12.33   (c) 16.66   (d) 19.33

42. The bond length of HCl molecule is 1.275 A° and its dipole moment is 1.03 D. The ionic character of the molecule (in percent) (charge of electron is 4.8×10^{-10} esu) is ......
    (a) 100   (b) 67.3   (c) 33.6   (d) 16.83

43. Which bond is most polar?
    (a) Cl-F   (b) Br-F   (c) I-F   (d) F-F

44. Among the following mixtures, dipole-dipole as the major interaction, is present in ......
    (a) benzene and ethanol
    (b) acetonitrile and acetone
    (c) KCl and water
    (d) benzene and carbon tetrachloride

45. Which of the following compound has dipole moment zero?
    (a) CCl_4 (b) $CHCl_3$ (c) HF   (d) NH_3

46. Which of the following molecules will have a dipole moment?
    (a) CF_4 (b) NF_3 (c) BF_3 (d) None of these

47. The dipole moment is highest for ......
    (a) Trans-2-butene
    (b) 1, 3-Dimethylbenzene
    (c) Acetophenone
    (d) Ethanol

48. The central atom in BrF_5 has bonding pairs of electrons and non-bonding pairs of electrons ......
    (a) 1.5   (b) 0.5   (c) 5.1   (d) 5.0

49. Amongst the following molecules the one with the largest distance between the two adjacent carbon atoms is ......
    (a) Ethane
    (b) Ethene
    (c) Methane
    (d) Benzene

50. The types of bonds present in $CuSO_4 \cdot 5H_2O$ are ......
    (a) Electrovalent and covalent only
    (b) Electrovalent and co-ordinate covalent only
    (c) Electrovalent, covalent, co-ordinate covalent and hydrogen bonds
    (d) Covalent and co-ordinate covalent only

51. Bond angle in water is ......
    (a) 105°.40'   (b) 104°.40'   (c) 104°.50'   (d) 105°.50'

52. The ONO angle is maximum in ......
    (a) NO_3^- (b) NO_2^- (c) NO_2 (d) NO_2^+

53. The number of bonds formed between atoms after the atomic orbitals overlap is called as ......
    (a) Bond number
    (b) Bond strength
    (c) Bond length
    (d) Bond order

54. Which of the following bonds have lowest bond energy?

(a) C-C (b) N-N (c) H-H (d) O-O

55. Bond energy is a measure of …… of a bond.

(a) Polarity (b) Length (c) Angle (d) Strength

56. The energy required to break a molecule is ……

(a) Bond enthalpy (b) Electronegativity (c) Electron affinity (d) Ionization potential

57. Bond energies of multiple bonds are ……

(a) Stronger than single bonds (b) Weaker than single bonds

(c) Greater than single bonds (d) None of these

58. Which one of the following halogens has the highest bond energy?

(a) F_2 (b) Cl_2 (c) Br_2 (d) I_2

59. In the anion $HCOO^-$ the two carbon–oxygen bonds are found to be of equal length. What is the reason for it?

(a) Electronic orbitals of carbon atom are hybridised

(b) The $C = O$ bond is weaker than $C - O$ bond

(c) The anion $HCOO^-$ has two resonating structures

(d) The anion is obtained by removal of a proton from the acid molecule

60. Out of these, which theory is related to shapes of molecules?

(a) Valence bond theory (b) VSEPR

(c) Molecular orbital theory (d) Dipole moment

61. Total number of lone pair of electrons in $XeOF_4$ is ……

(a) 0 (b) 1 (c) 2 (d) 3

62. Which of the following has square planar structure?

(a) NH_4 (b) BF_4 (c) XeF_4 (d) CCl_4

63. Given electronic configuration of four elements as

(I) $1s^2$ (II) $1s^2\,2s^2\,2p^2$ (III) $1s^2\,2s^2\,2p^5$ (IV) $1s^2\,2s^2\,2p^6$

The one which is capable of forming ionic as well as covalent bonds is ……

(a) I (b) II (c) III (d) IV

64. XeF_4 has a shape of ……

(a) Sphere (b) Trigonal bipyramidal

(c) Tetrahedral (d) Square planar

65. BCl_3 molecule is planar while NCl_3 is pyramidal because ……

(a) BCl_3 does not have lone pair but NCl_3 has

(b) B-Cl bond is more polar than NCl_3 bond

(c) N atom is smaller than B

(d) NCl_3 bond is more covalent than BCl_3 bond

66. Which of the following pairs contains isostructural species?

(a) CH_3^- and CH_3^+ (b) NH_4^- and NH_3 (c) SO_4^{-2} and BF_4^- (d) NH_2^- and BeF_2

67. The structure of ICl_2^- is ……

(a) Trigonal (b) Trigonal bipyramidal

(c) Octahedral (d) Linear

68. The shape of ClO_3 according to valence shell electron pair repulsion theory will be ......
    (a) Planar triangle   (b) Pyramidal   (c) Tetrahedral   (d) Square planar

69. The octahedral shape is associated with ......
    (a) PF_5 (b) SF_4 (c) TeF_6 (d) ClF_3

70. An atom of an element A has three electrons in its outermost orbit and that of B has six electrons in its outermost orbit. The formula of the compound between these two will be ......
    (a) A_3B_3 (b) A_2B_3 (c) A_3B_2 (d) A_2B

71. In OF_2, number of bond pairs and lone pairs of electrons are respectively ......
    (a) 2, 6   (b) 2, 8   (c) 2, 10   (d) 2, 9

72. Based on VSEPR theory, the number of 90 degree F — Br — F angles in BrF_5 is ......
    (a) 0   (b) 2   (c) 4   (d) 8

73. In BrF_3 molecule, the lone pairs occupy equatorial positions to minimize ......
    (a) Lone pair-lone pair repulsion only   (b) Lone pair-bond pair repulsion only
    (c) Bond pair-bond pair repulsion only
    (d) Lone pair-lone pair repulsion and lone pair-bond pair repulsion

74. In XeF_2, XeF_4 and XeF_6, the number of lone pairs of Xe is ...... respectively
    (a) 2, 3, 1   (b) 1, 2, 3   (c) 4, 1, 2   (d) 3, 2, 1

75. Which one of the following has the regular tetrahedral structure?
    (a) XeF_4 (b) $[Ni(CN)_4]^{2-}$ (c) BF_4^- (d) SF_4

76. The structure of IF_7 is ......
    (a) Pentagonal bipyramid   (b) Square pyramid
    (c) Trigonal bipyramid   (d) Octahedral

77. Which of the following has maximum number of lone pairs associated with Xe?
    (a) XeF_2 (b) XeO_3 (c) XeF_4 (d) XeF_6

78. Which of the following is a linear molecule?
    (a) $BeCl_2$ (b) H_2O (c) SO_2 (d) CH_4

79. In which of the following molecules are all bonds not equal ?
    (a) AlF_3 (b) NF_3 (c) ClF_3 (d) BF_3

80. In which of the following molecule/ion all the bonds are not equal?
    (a) XeF_4 (b) BF_4^- (c) C_2H_4 (d) SiF_4

81. In NH_3, the covalent bonds are due to ......
    (a) None of these   (b) s-sp^2 overlap   (c) s-sp^3 overlap   (d) s-sp overlap

82. BCl_3 is a planar molecule, because in this molecule, boron is ......
    (a) sp^3 hybridized   (b) sp^2 hybridized   (c) sp hybridized   (d) unhybridized

83. Which overlap is involved in HCl molecule ?
    (a) s-s overlap   (b) p-p overlap   (c) s-d overlap   (d) s-p overlap

84. How many sigma and pi bonds are present in tetra cyano ethylene ?
    (a) Nine σ and nine π (b) Five σ and nine π
    (c) Nine σ and seven π (d) Eight σ and eight π

85. A molecule in which sp^2 hybrid orbitals are used by the central atom in forming covalent bonds is ......
    (a) He_2 (b) SO_2 (c) PCl_5 (d) N_2

86. The AsF_5 molecule is trigonal bipyramidal. The orbitals used for hybridisation are ......
    (a) d_z^2, s, p_x, p_y, p_z
    (b) $d_x^2 y2s, p_x, p_y, p_z^2$
    (c) s, p_x, p_y, p_z, d_{xz}
    (d) None of these
87. In the resonating structure of benzene, the number of σ and π bonds are ......
    (a) 3σ and 12π
    (b) 3σ and 12π
    (c) 6σ and 6π
    (d) 12σ and π
88. The order of O-O bond length in O_2, H_2O_2, O_3 is ......
    (a) $O_2 > O_3 > H_2O_2$
    (b) $O_3 > H_2O_2 > O_2$
    (c) $H_2O_2 > O_3 > O_2$
    (d) $O_2 > H_2O_2 > O_3$
89. For which of the following compounds, hybridization and VSEPR concept predict the same structure?
    (a) CH_4
    (b) H_2O
    (c) NH_3
    (d) None of these
90. Molecular orbitals are filled with the available electrons according to ......
    (a) Aufbau's principle
    (b) Pauli's exclusion principle
    (c) Hund's rule
    (d) All of these
91. The calculated bond order in H_2 ion is ......
    (a) 0
    (b) 1/2
    (c) –1/2
    (d) 1
92. The number of anti-bonding electron pairs in O_2 ion on the basis of MO theory is ......
    (a) 4
    (b) 3
    (c) 2
    (d) 5
93. Which of the following hydrides has the lowest boiling point?
    (a) H_2O
    (b) H_2S
    (c) H_2Se
    (d) H_2Te
94. The hydrogen bond is strongest in ......
    (a) OH...S
    (b) SH...O
    (c) FH...F
    (d) FH...O
95. The bond order in O_2 is ......
    (a) 2
    (b) 2.5
    (c) 1.5
    (d) 3
96. Polarization of electrons in acrolein may be written as
    (a) $CH_2 = CH_2 - CH = O$
    (b) $+ : CH_2 = CH - CH = + : O$
    (c) $CH_2 = CH + CH_2 = O$
    (d) $: -CH_2 = CH_2 - CH = : +O$
97. Which one of the following molecules have unpaired electrons in the bonding molecular orbital?
    (a) F_2
    (b) N_2
    (c) B_2
    (d) O_2
98. Which one of the following molecules will form a linear polymeric structure due to hydrogen bonding?
    (a) HCl
    (b) HF
    (c) H_2O
    (d) NH_3
99. The bond length between C-C bonds in sp^2 hybridized molecule is ......
    (a) 1.2 A°
    (b) 1.32 A°
    (c) 1.54 A°
    (d) 1.4 A°
100. The most efficient overlapping is ......
    (a) $sp^2 - sp^2$
    (b) $s - s$
    (c) $sp^3 - sp^3$
    (d) $sp - sp$
101. The main axis of diatomic molecule is Z. The orbitals p_x and p_y overlap to form ......
    (a) p molecular orbital
    (b) s molecular orbital
    (c) d molecular orbital
    (d) No bond will be formed
102. Which atomic orbitals are responsible for the formation of a square planar complex?
    (a) s, p_x, p_y, p_z
    (b) $s, p_x, p_y, d_{x^2-y^2}$
    (c) s, p_x, p_y, d_z^2
    (d) s, p_x, p_z, d_{xy}

103. The bond order of O_2^{-2} is ......

    (a) 1   (b) 1.5   (c) 2.5   (d) 3

104. Which of the following has pπ – dπ bonding?

    (a) NO_3^- (b) SO_3^{-2} (c) BO_3^{-3} (d) CO_3^{-2}

105. The correct order of bond angles (smallest first) in H_2S, NH_3, BF_3 and SiH_4 is ......

    (a) $H_2S < SiH_4 < NH_3 < BF_3$ (b) $H_2S < NH_3 < BF_3 < SiH_4$

    (c) $H_2 < NH_3 < SiH_4 < BF_3$ (d) $NH_3 < H_2S < SiH_4 < BF_3$

106. The bond order of O_2^- is ......

    (a) 0.5   (b) 1.5   (c) 3.5   (d) 2.5

107. Which is most viscous ?

    (a) CH_3OH (b) C_2H_5OH (c) $CH_2OH - CH_2OH$ (d) None of these

108. In an octahedral structure, the pair of d orbitals involved in d^2sp^3 hybridization is ......

    (a) d_{xy}, d_{yz} (b) $d_{x^2-y^2}$, d_z^2 (c) d_{xz}, $d_{x^2-y^2}$ (d) d_{z2}, d_{xz}

109. The number of sigma bonds in P_4O_{10} is ......

    (a) 6   (b) 7   (c) 17   (d) 16

110. Atomic orbital hybridization is explained by ......

    (a) Molecular orbital theory   (b) VSEPR

    (c) Dipole moment   (d) Valence bond theory

111. Which of the following molecules has three fold axis of symmetry?

    (a) NH_3 (b) C_2H_4 (c) CO_2 (d) SO_2

112. In O_3, there are ......

    (a) 2σ, 1π bond   (b) 1σ, 2π bonds

    (c) 2σ, 2π bonds   (d) 1σ, 1π, one lone pair

113. The sequence that correctly describes the relative bond strengths pertaining to the oxygen molecule and its cation or anion is ......

    (a) $O_2^2 > O_3^- > O_2 > O_2^+$ (b) $O_2 > O_2^+ > O_2 > O_2^{+2}$ (c) $O_2^+ > O_2 > O_2^{-2} > O_2^-$

    (d) $O_2^+ > O_2 > O_2^- > O_2^{-2}$ (e) $O_2 > O_2 > O_2^{-2} > O_2^+$

114. What is the bond order of nitric oxide?

    (a) 1   (b) 2.5   (c) 2   (d) 1.5

115. Oxygen molecule is paramagnetic because ......

    (a) Bonding electrons are more than antibonding electrons

    (b) It contains unpaired electrons

    (c) Bonding electrons are less than antibonding electrons

    (d) Bonding electrons are equal to antibonding electrons

116. The compound in which C uses its sp^3 hybrid orbital for bond formation is ......

    (a) HCOOH   (b) $(NH_2)_2CO$ (c) HCOH   (d) CH_3CHO

117. The maximum possible number of hydrogen bonds in which a water molecule can participate is ......

    (a) 4   (b) 3   (c) 2   (d) 1

118. Which of the following represents the given mode of hybridization $sp^2 - sp^2 - sp - sp$ from left to right?

(a) $H_2C = CH - C \equiv N$ 　　　　　　(b) $HC \equiv C - C \equiv CH$

(c) $H_2C = C = C = CH_2$ 　　　　　　(d) None of these

119. Which of the following is not isostructural with $SiCl_4$?

(a) PO_3^{-4} 　　　　(b) NH_4^+ 　　　　(c) SCl_4 　　　　(d) SO_2^{-4}

120. Which of the following are arranged in an increasing order of their bond strength ?

(a) $O_2^- < O_2 < O_2^+ < O_2^{-2}$ 　　　　　　(b) $O_2^{-2} < O_2^- < O_2 < O_2^+$

(c) $O_2^- < O_2^{-2} < O_2 < O_2^+$ 　　　　　　(d) $O_2^+ < O_2 < O_2^- < O_2^{-2}$

121. Among the given species identify the isostructural pairs ......

(a) $[NF_3$ and $BF_3]$ 　　　　　　(b) $[BF_4^-$ and $NH_4^+]$

(c) $[BCl_3$ and $BrCl_3]$ 　　　　　　(d) $[NH_3$ and $NO_3^-]$

122. The types of hybrid orbitals of nitrogen in NO_2^+, NO_3^- and NH_4^+ respectively are expected to be

(a) sp, sp^3 and sp^2 　　(b) sp, sp^2 and sp^3 　　(c) sp^2, sp and sp^3 　　(d) sp^2, sp^3 and sp

123. The correct decreasing order of the boiling points of below compounds is :

(a) $HF > H_2O > NH_3$ 　　(b) $H_2O > HF > NH_3$ 　　(c) $NH_3 > HF > H_2O$ 　　(d) $NH_3 > H_2O > HF$

124. In which of the following substances will hydrogen bond be strongest?

(a) HCl 　　　　(b) H_2O 　　　　(c) HI 　　　　(d) H_2S

125. If the electronic configuration of an element is $1s^2\ 2s^2,\ 2p^6\ 3s^2\ 3p^6\ 3d^2\ 4s^2$, the four electrons involved in chemical bond formation will be ......

(a) $3p^6$ 　　　　(b) $3p^6, 4s^2$ 　　　　(c) $3p^6, 3d^2$ 　　　　(d) $3d^2, 4s^2$

126. Which of the following angle correspond to sp^2 hybridization?

(a) $90°$ 　　　　(b) $120°$ 　　　　(c) $180°$ 　　　　(d) $109°$

127. Which of the following order of energies of molecular orbitals of N_2 is correct?

(a) $(\pi 2p_y) < (\sigma 2p_z) < (\pi^*2p_x) \approx (\pi^*2p_y)$ 　　　　(b) $(\pi 2p_y) > (\sigma 2p_z) > (\pi^*2p_x) \approx (\pi^*2p_y)$

(c) $(\pi 2p_y) < (\sigma 2p_z) > (\pi^*2p_x) \approx (\pi^*2p_y)$ 　　　　(d) $(\pi 2p_y) > (\sigma 2p_z) < (\pi^*2p_x) \approx (\pi^*2p_y)$

128. Which of the following statement is not correct from the view point of molecular orbital theory?

(a) Be_2 is not a stable molecule.

(b) He_2 is not stable but He^{2+} is expected to exist.

(c) Bond strength of N_2 is maximum amongst the homonuclear diatomic molecules belonging to the second period.

(d) The order of energies of molecular orbitals in N_2 molecule is

$\sigma 2s < \sigma^*2s < \sigma 2p_z < (\pi 2p_x = \pi 2p_y) < (\pi^*2p_x = \pi^* 2p_y) < \sigma^*2p_z$

129. Which of the following options represent the correct bond order ......

(a) $O_2^- > O_2 > O_2^+$ 　　(b) $O_2^- < O_2 < O_2^+$ 　　(c) $O_2^- > O_2 < O_2^+$ 　　(d) $O_2^- < O_2 > O_2^+$

130. With regard to the species $^{16}O^{2-}$, $^{19}F^-$ and ^{20}Ne, which of the following statements is correct?
   (a) All three species contain 10 electrons.
   (b) The sum of the neutrons in all three species is 27.
   (c) The sum of the protons in all three species is 28.
   (d) Both $^{19}F^-$ and ^{20}Ne contain 20 neutrons.

131. Which of the following does not have a noble gas electron configuration ? (or Which of the following is not isoelectronic with a noble gas ?)
   (a) S^{2-} (b) Ba^+ (c) Al^{3+} (d) Sb^{3-}

132. The correct electron-dot formulation for hydrogen cyanide shows ......
   (a) 2 double bonds and 2 lone pairs of electrons on the N atom.
   (b) 1 C-H bond, 1C=N bond, 1 lone pair of electrons on the C atom and 1 lone pair of electrons on the N atom.
   (c) 1 C-H bond, 1 C-N bond, 2 lone pairs of electrons on the C atom and 3 lone pairs of electrons on the N atom.
   (d) 1 triple bond between C and N, 1 C-H bond and 1 lone pairs of electrons on the N atom.

133. The correct dot formulation for nitrogen trichloride has ......
   (a) 3N-Cl bonds and 10 lone pairs of electrons.
   (b) 3N=Cl bonds and 6 lone pairs of electrons.
   (c) 1N-Cl bond, 2N=Cl bonds and 7 lone pairs of electrons.
   (d) 2N-Cl bonds, 1 N=Cl bond and 8 lone pairs of electrons.

134. The electronic structure of SO_2 molecule is best represented as a resonance hybrid of ...... equivalent structures.
   (a) 2   (b) 3   (c) 4   (d) 5

135. Consider the bicarbonate ion (also called the hydrogen carbonate ion). After drawing the correct Lewis dot structure(s), you would see ......
   (a) two double bonds around the central carbon atom.
   (b) three single bonds around the central carbon atom.
   (c) three equivalent resonance forms.
   (d) two equivalent resonance forms.

136. Which statement is false? A sigma molecular orbital ......
   (a) may result from overlap of p atomic orbitals perpendicular to the molecular axis (side-on).
   (b) may result from overlap of p atomic orbitals along the molecular axis (head-on).
   (c) may result from overlap of two s atomic orbitals.
   (d) may result from overlap of one s and one p atomic orbitals.

137. Carbon monoxide has ten bonding electrons and four antibonding electrons. Therefore it has a bond order of ......
   (a) 3   (b) 7   (c) 1   (d) 5/2

138. Which of the following is the correct electron configuration for C_2?
   (a) $\sigma_{1s}^2\,\sigma_{2s}^2\,\pi_{2py}^2\,\sigma^*_{1s}^2\,\sigma^*_{2s}^2\,\pi^*_{2py}^2$ (b) $\sigma_{2s}^2\,\sigma^*_{1s}^2\,\sigma_{2s}^2\,\sigma_{2s}^2\,\pi_{2py}^2\,\pi^*_{2pz}^1\,\sigma_{2p}^1$
   (c) $\sigma_{1s}^2\,\sigma^*_{1s}^2\,\sigma_{2s}^2\,\sigma^*_{2s}^2\,\pi_{2py}^2\,\pi_{2pz}^2$ (d) $\sigma_{1s}^2\,\sigma^*_{1s}^2\,\sigma_{2s}^2\,\sigma^*_{2s}^2\,\pi_{2py}^1\,\pi_{2pz}^1$

139. The number of electrons in σ_{2p} molecular orbital molecular ion, N_2^+ is ......

(a) 0   (b) 1   (c) 2   (d) 3

140. What is the bond order in O_2^+ ?

(a) 3.5   (b) 2.0   (c) 1.5   (d) 2.5

141. The number of unpaired electrons in the molecular orbital diagram for B_2 molecule is ......

(a) 0   (b) 1   (c) 2   (d) 3

142. Which one of the following statements is false?

(a) Valence bond theory and molecular orbital theory can be described as two different views of the same thing.

(b) When one considers the molecular orbitals resulting from the overlap of any two specific atomic orbitals, the bonding orbitals are always lower in energy than the antibonding orbitals.

(c) Molecular orbitals are generally described as being more delocalized than hybridized atomic orbitals.

(d) One of the shortcomings of molecular orbital theory is its inability to account for a triple bond in the nitrogen molecule, N_2.

143. Antibonding molecular orbitals are produced by ......

(a) constructive interaction of atomic orbitals.

(b) destructive interaction of atomic orbitals.

(c) the overlap of atomic orbitals of two negative ions

(d) all of these

144. Which statement regarding stable heteronuclear diatomic molecules is false?

(a) All have bond orders greater than zero.

(b) The antibonding molecular orbitals have more of the character of the more electropositive element than those of the more electronegative element.

(c) Their molecular orbital diagrams are more symmetrical than those of homonuclear diatomic molecules.

(d) The bonding molecular orbitals have more of the character of the more electronegative element than those of the less electronegative element.

145. The state of hybridization of the central atom and the number of lone pairs over the central atom in $POCl_3$ are ......

(a) sp, 0   (b) sp^2, 0   (c) sp^3, 0   (d) dsp^2, 1

146. When O_2 is converted into O_2^+ ......

(a) both paramagnetic character and bond order increase

(b) bond order decreases

(c) paramagnetic character increases

(d) paramagnetic character decreases and the bond order increases

147. Which one of the following conversions involve change in both hybridization and shape ?

(a) $NH_3 \rightarrow NH_4^+$ (b) $CH_4 \rightarrow C_2H_6$ (c) $H_2O \rightarrow H_3O^+$ (d) $BF_3 \rightarrow BF_4^-$

148. Assuming that Hund's rule is violated, the bond order and magnetic nature of the diatomic molecule B_2 is ......

(a) 1 and diamagnetic

(b) 0 and diamagnetic

(c) 1 and paramagnetic

(d) 0 and paramagnetic

149. Based on VSEPR theory, the number of 90 degree F — Br — F angles in BrF_5 is ......

(a) 0　　　　(b) 2　　　　(c) 4　　　　(d) 8

150. Using MO theory predict which of the following species has the shortest bond length?

(a) O^{2+}　　　　(b) O^{2-}　　　　(c) O_2^{2-}　　　　(d) O_2^{2+}

151. The number of nodal planes present in σ^*s antibonding orbitals is ......

(a) 1　　　　(b) 2　　　　(c) 0　　　　(d) 3

152. One of the following constitutes a group of the isoelectronic species?

(a) CO_2^{2-}, O_2^-, CO, NO

(b) $NO^+, C_2^{2-}, CN^-, N_2$

(c) $CN^-, N_2, O_2^{2-}, C_2^{2-}$

(d) N_2, O_2^-, NO^+, CO

153. Which one of the following pairs of species have the same bond order?

(a) CN^- and NO^+　　(b) CN^- and CN^+　　(c) O_2^- and CN^-　　(d) NO^+ and CN^+

154. For a stable molecule, the value of bond order must be ......

(a) negative　　　　(b) positive　　　　(c) zero

(d) there is no relationship between stability and bond order

155. The species having bond order different from that in CO is ......

(a) NO^-　　　　(b) NO^+　　　　(c) CN^-　　　　(d) N_2

156. In which of the following ionization processes, the bond order has increased and the magnetic behaviour has changed?

(a) $C_2 \rightarrow C_2^+$　　(b) $NO \rightarrow NO^+$　　(c) $O_2 \rightarrow O_2^+$　　(d) $N_2 \rightarrow N_2^+$

157. Which of the following hydrogen bonds is the strongest?

(a) $O - H \bullet\bullet\bullet N$　　(b) $F - H \bullet\bullet\bullet F$　　(c) $O - H \bullet\bullet\bullet O$　　(d) $O - H \bullet\bullet\bullet F$

158. (I)　1, 2-dihydroxy benzene

(II)　1, 3-dihydroxy benzene

(III)　1, 4-dihydroxy benzene

(IV) Hydroxy benzene

The increasing order of boiling points of above mentioned alcohols is ......

(a) I < II < III < IV　　(b) I < II < IV < III　　(c) IV < I < II < III　　(d) IV < II < I < III

159. A molecule (X) has ......

(i)　four sigma bonds formed by the overlap of sp^2 and s orbital.

(ii)　one sigma bond formed by the overlap of sp^2 and sp^2 orbitals and

(iii)　one p bond is formed by p_x and p_x orbitals.

Which of the following molecules is X?

(a) C_2H_6　　　　(b) C_2H_3Cl　　　　(c) $C_2H_2Cl_2$　　　　(d) C_2H_4

160. Which of the following contains maximum number of lone pairs on the central atom?

(a) ClO_3^-　　　　(b) XeF_4　　　　(c) SF_4　　　　(d) I_3^-

161. Which one of the following species is diamagnetic in nature?

(a) He^{2+} (b) H_2 (c) H_2^+ (d) H_2^-

162. The number of lone pair(s) in $XeOF_4$ is/are ......

(a) 0   (b) 1   (c) 2   (d) 3

163. The states of hybridization of boron and oxygen atoms in boric acid (H_3BO_3) are respectively ......

(a) sp^2 and sp^2 (b) sp^2 and sp^3 (c) sp^3 and sp^2 (d) sp^3 and sp^3

164. Which one of the following does not have sp^2 hybridized carbon?

(a) Acetone   (b) Acetic acid   (c) Acetonitrile   (d) Acetamide

165. The correct order of bond angles (smallest first) in H_2S, NH_3, BF_3 and SiH_4 is ......

(a) $H_2S < SiH_4 < NH_3 < BF_3$ (b) $NH_3 < H_2S < SiH_4 < BF_3$

(c) $H_2S < NH_3 < SiH_4 < BF_3$ (d) $H_2S < NH_3 < BF_3 < SiH_4$

166. According to MO theory ......

(a) O_2^+ is paramagnetic and bond order greater than O_2

(b) O_2^+ is paramagnetic and bond order less than O_2

(c) O_2^+ is diamagnetic and bond order is less than O_2

(d) O_2^+ is diamagnetic and bond order is more than O_2

167. Which one of the following pairs of molecules will have permanent dipole moments for both members?

(a) SiF_4 and NO_2 (b) NO_2 and CO_2 (c) NO_2 and O_3 (d) SiF_4 and CO_2

168. In which of the following molecules/ions all the bonds are not equal?

(a) SF_4 (b) SiF_4 (c) XeF_4 (d) BF_4^-

169. Which of the following molecules/ions does not contain unpaired electrons?

(a) O_2^{2-} (b) B_2 (c) N_2^+ (d) O_2

170. An atom of an element A has three electrons in its outermost orbit and that of B has six electrons in its outermost orbit. The formula of the compound between these two will be ......

(a) A_3B_6 (b) A_2B_3 (c) A_3B_2 (d) A_2B

171. Which one of the following has the regular tetrahedral structure?
(Atomic numbers of B = 5, S = 16, Ni = 28, Xe = 54)

(a) XeF_4 (b) SF_4 (c) BF_4^- (d) $[Ni(CN)_4]^{2-}$

172. Which one of the following is a correct set?

(a) H_2O, sp^3, angular   (b) H_2O, sp^2, linear

(c) NH_4^+, dsp^2, square planar   (d) CH_4, dsp^2, tetrahedral

173. In the anion $HCOO^-$ the two carbon–oxygen bonds are found to be of equal length. What is the reason for it?

(a) Electronic orbitals of carbon atom are hybridized

(b) The C=O bond is weaker than C – O bond

(c) The anion $HCOO^-$ has two resonating structures

(d) The anion is obtained by removal of a proton from the acid molecule

174. In allene (C_3H_4), the type(s) of hybridization of the carbon atoms is (are) ......

    (a) sp and sp^3　　　　(b) sp and sp^2　　　　(c) only sp^2　　　　(d) sp^2 and sp^3

175. The sp^3d^2 hybridization of central atom of a molecule would lead to ......

    (a) Square planar geometry　　　　　　　　(b) Tetrahedral geometry

    (c) Trigonal bipyramidal geometry　　　　(d) Octahedral geometry

PREVIOUS YEAR'S QUESTIONS

1. Which of the following substances has giant covalent structure ?　　　　**[DPMT 1985]**

    (a) Loading crystal　　(b) Solid CO_2　　(c) Silica　　(d) White phosphorus

2. The correct sequence of increasing covalent character is represented by ......

    [CBSE PMT 2005]

    (a) $LiCl < NaCl < BeCl_2$　　　　　　　　(b) $BeCl_2 < NaCl < LiCl$

    (c) $NaCl < LiCl < BeCl_2$　　　　　　　　(d) $BeCl_2 < LiCl < NaCl$

3. Which of the following would have a permanent dipole moment ?　　　　**[CBSE PMT 2005]**

    (a) BF_3　　　　(b) SiF_4　　　　(c) SF_4　　　　(d) XeF_4

4. N_2 is less reactive than CN due to ......　　　　**[UPSEAT 2003]**

    (a) Presence of more electrons in orbitals　　(b) Absence of dipole moment

    (c) Difference in spin quantum number　　(d) None of these

5. In a polar molecule, the ionic charge is 4.8×10^{-10} e.s.u. If the interionic distance is one A° unit then the dipole moment is ......　　　　**[MHCET 2003]**

    (a) 41.8 debye　　　　(b) 4.18 debye　　　　(c) 4.8 debye　　　　(d) 0.48 debye

6. If HCl molecule is completely polarized, so expected value of dipole moment is 6.12D (deby), but experimental value of dipole moment is 1.03D. Calculate the percentage ionic character.　　　　**[Kerala CET 2005]**

    (a) 17　　　　(b) 83　　　　(c) 50　　　　(d) 0

7. The number and type of bonds between two carbon atoms in calcium carbide are ......

    [AIEEE 2005]

    (a) One sigma, one pi　　　　　　　　(b) One sigma, two pi

    (c) Two sigma, one pi　　　　　　　　(d) Two sigma, two pi

8. Which of the following has $p\pi - d\pi$ bonding ?　　　　**[CBSE 2002]**

    (a) NO_3　　　　(b) CO_3^{-2}　　　　(c) BO_3^{-3}　　　　(d) SO_3^{-2}

9. The correct order of O – O bond length in O_2, H_2O_2 and O_3 is ......　　　　**[CBSE PMT 1995]**

    (a) $O_2 < O_3 > H_2O_2$　　(b) $O_3 > H_2O_2 > O_2$　　(c) $H_2O_2 > O_3 > O_2$　　(d) $O_2 > H_2O_2 > O_3$

10. The smallest bond angle is found in ......　　　　**[AIIMS 2001]**

    (a) IF_7　　　　(b) CH_4　　　　(c) BeF_2　　　　(d) BF_3

11. In which of the following species is the interatomic bond angle 109° 28' ?　　　　**[AIEEE 2002]**

    (a) $BeCl_2$, sp^2, linear　　　　　　　　(b) $BeCl_2$, sp^2, triangular planar

    (c) BCl_3, sp^2, triangular planar　　　　(d) BCl_3, sp^3, tetrahedral

12. In a regular octahedral molecule, MX_6, the number of $X - M - X$ bonds at $180°$ is ......
[CBSE PMT 2004]

    (a) Six (b) Four (c) Three (d) Two

13. In an octahedral structure, the pair of d orbitals involved in $d^2 sp^3$ hybridization is ......
[CBSE PMT 2004]

    (a) d_{x2}, d_{xz} (b) d_{xy}, d_{yz} (c) d_{x2-y2}, d_{z2} (d) d_{yz}, d_{x2-y2}

14. The states of hybridization of boron and oxygen atoms in boric acid (H_3BO_3) are respectively ...... **[AIEEE 2001]**

    (a) sp^3 and sp^2 (b) sp^2 and sp^3 (c) sp^2 and sp^2 (d) sp^3 and sp^3

15. The bond angle of water is $104.5°$ due to ...... **[CPMT 2002]**
    (a) Repulsion between lone pair and bond pair
    (b) sp^3 hybridization of O
    (c) Bonding of H_2O
    (d) Higher electronegativity of O

16. Among the following pairs in which the two species are not isostructural with ......
[CBSE PMT 2004]

    (a) BH_4^- and NH_4^+ (b) PF_6^- and SF_6 (c) SiF_4 and SF_4 (d) IO_3^- and XeO_3

17. Which concept best explain that o-nitrophenol is more volatile than p-nitrophenol ?
[AIMS 1980]

    (a) Resonance (b) Hyperconjugation
    (c) Hydrogen bonding (d) Steric hindrance

18. Of the following hydrides, which has the lowest boiling point ? **[CBSE PMT 1987)**
    (a) NH_3 (b) PH_3 (c) SbH_3 (d) AsH_3

19. NH_3 has a much higher boiling point then PH_3 because ...... **[UPSEAT 2002]**
    (a) NH_3 has a larger molecular weight
    (b) NH_3 undergoes umbrella inversion
    (c) NH_3 forms hydrogen bond
    (d) NH_3 contains ionic bonds whereas PH_3 contains covalent bonds

20. Structure of IF_4 and hybridization of iodine in this structure are ...... **[UPSEAT 2001]**
    (a) $sp^3 d$, linear (b) $sp^3 d^2$, T-shaded
    (c) $sp^3 d$, irregular tetrahedral (d) sp^3, d^2, octahedral

21. A compound contains atoms x, Y, Z. The oxidation number of X in $sp - sp^2$ is $+5$ and Z is -2. Therefore, a possible formula of the compound is ......
    (a) XYZ_2 (b) $X_2(YZ_3)_2$
    (c) $X_3(YZ_4)_2$ (d) $X_3(Y_4Z)_2$

22. The correct order regarding the electronegativity of hybrid orbital of carbon is ......
[CBSE 2006]

    (a) $sp > sp^2 > sp^3$ (b) $sp < sp^2 > sp^3$ (c) $sp < sp^2 < sp^3$ (d) $sp > sp^2 < sp^3$

23. The electronegativity difference between N and F is greater than that between N and H yet the dipole moment of NH_3 (1.5 D) is larger than that of NH_3 (0.2 D). This is because ......   **[CBSE 2005]**
    (a) in NH_3 the atomic dipole and bond dipole are in the same direction whereas in NF_3, the same in opposite directions.
    (b) in NH_3 as well as NF_3 the atomic dipole and bond dipole are in opposite direction.
    (c) in NH_3 the atomic dipole and bond dipole are in the opposite directions whereas in NF_3 these are in the same direction.
    (d) in NH_3 as well as in NF_3 the atomic dipole and bond dipole are in the same direction.

24. In which of the following pairs, the two species are isostructural ......   **[CBSE 2007]**
    (a) BrO_3 and XeO_3 (b) SF_4 and XeF_4 (c) SO_3^{2-} and NO_3^- (d) BF_3 and NF_3^-

25. The correct order of C – O bond length among CO, CO_3^{2-} and CO_2 is ......   **[CBSE 2007]**
    (a) $CO < CO_2 < CO_3^{2-}$ (b) $CO_2 < CO_3^{2-} < CO$
    (c) $CO < CO_3^{2-} < CO_2$ (d) $CO_3^{2-} < CO_2 < CO$

26. What is the dominant intermolecular force or bond that must be overcome in converting liquid CH_3OH to a gas?   **[CBSE 2009]**
    (a) Dipole-diople interactions   (b) Covalent bonds
    (c) London dispersion force   (d) Hydrogen bonding

27. Which one of the following species does not exist under normal conditions?   **[CBSE 2010]**
    (a) B_2 (b) Li_2 (c) Be_2^+ (d) Be_2

28. Which of the following has minimum bond length?   **[AIPMT 2011]**
    (a) O_2^+ (b) O_2^- (c) O_2^{2-} (d) O_2

29. Which of the two ions from the list given below have the geometry that is explained by the same hybridization of orbitals : NO_2^-, NO_3^-, NH_4^+, SCN^- ?   **[AIPMT 2011]**
    (a) NO_2^- and NO_3^- (b) NH_4^+ and NO_3^- (c) SCN^- and NH_2^- (d) NO_2^- and NH_2^-

30. During change of O_2 to O_2^- ion, the electron adds on which one of the following orbitals?   **[AIPMT 2012]**
    (a) σ^* orbital   (b) σ orbital   (c) π^* orbital   (d) π orbital

31. Four diatomic species are listed below. Identify the correct order in which the bond order is increasing in them :   **[AIPMT 2012]**
    (a) $C_2^{2-} < He_2^+ < O_2^- < NO$ (b) $He_2^+ < O_2^- < NO < C_2^{2-}$
    (c) $NO < O_2^- < C_2^{2-} < He_2^+$ (d) $O_2^- < NO < C_2^{2-} < He_2^+$

32. Which of the following exhibits only +3 oxidation state?   **[AIPMT 2012]**
    (a) Ac   (b) Pa
    (c) U   (d) Th

33. Which are of the following pairs is isostructural ?   **[CBSE 2012]**
    (a) [NF_3 and BF_3]   (b) [BF_4 and NH_4^+]   (c) [BCl_3 and $BrCl_3$]   (d) [NH_3 and NO_3^-]

34. In which of the following compounds, nitrogen exhibits highest oxidation state?

[CBSE 2012]

(a) N_3H (b) NH_2OH (c) N_2H_4 (d) NH_3

35. The pair of species with the same bond order is ......   **[CBSE 2012]**

(a) NO, CO   (b) N_2, O_2 (c) O_2^{2-}, B_2 (d) O_2^+, NO^+

36. Which one of the following molecules contains no π bonds ?   **[NEET 2013]**

(a) NO_2 (b) CO_2 (c) H_2O (d) SO_2

37. XeF_2 is isostructural with ......   **[NEET 2013]**

(a) $BaCl_2$ (b) TeF_2 (c) ICl_2^- (d) $SbCl_3$

38. Dipole-induced dipole interactions are present in which of the following pairs: **[NEET 2013]**

(a) SiF_4 and He atoms   (b) H_2O and alcohol   (c) Cl_2 and CCl_4 (d) HCl and He atom

39. Which of the following is paramagnetic?   **[NEET 2013]**

(a) NO^+ (b) CO   (c) O_2^- (d) CN^-

40. Which of the following orders of ionic radii is correctly represented?   **[AIPMT 2014]**

(a) $H^- > H^+ > H$ (b) $Na^+ > F > O^{2-}$ (c) $O^{2-} > F > Na^+$ (d) $Al^{3+} > Mg^{2+} > N^{3-}$

41. The pair of compounds that can exist together is ......   **[AIPMT 2014]**

(a) $FeCl_3, SnCl_2$ (b) $HgCl_2, SnCl_2$ (c) $FeCl_2, SnCl_2$ (d) $FeCl_3, KI$

42. Be^{2+} is isoelectronic with which of the following ions?   **[AIPMT 2014]**

(a) H^+ (b) Li^+ (c) Na^+ (d) Mg^{2+}

43. Acidity of diprotic acids in aqueous solutions increases in the order ......   **[AIPMT 2014]**

(a) $H_2S < H_2Se < H_2Te$ (b) $H_2Se < H_2S < H_2Te$

(c) $H_2Te < H_2S < H_2Se$ (d) $H_2Se < H_2Te < H_2S$

44. Decreasing order of stability of O_2, O_2^-, O_2^+ and O_2^{2-} is ......   **[NEET 2015]**

(a) $O_2 > O_2^+ > O_2^{2-} > O_2^-$ (b) $O_2^- > O_2^{2-} > O_2^+ > O_2$

(c) $O_2^+ > O_2 > O_2^- > O_2^{2-}$ (d) $O_2^{2-} > O_2^- > O_2 > O_2^+$

45. In which of the following pairs both the species are not isostructural ......

(a) NH_3, PH_3 (b) XeF_4, XeO_4 (c) $SnCl_4, PCl_4^+$ (d) diamond, SiC

46. Which of the following statement given below is incorrect ?   **[NEET 2015]**

(a) ONF is isoelectronic with O_2N^- (b) OF_2 is an oxide of fluorine

(c) Cl_2O_6 is anhydride of perchloric acid   (d) O_3 molecule is bent

47. Predict the correct order among the following ......   **[NEET 2016]**

(a) $bp - bp > lp - bp > lp - lp$ (b) $lp - bp > bp - bp > lp - lp$

(c) $lp - lp > lp - bp > bp - bp$ (d) $lp - lp > bp > lp - bp$

48. Consider the molecules CH_4, NH_3 and H_2O. Which of the given statements is false ?

[NEET 2010]

(a) the H–O–H bond angle in H_2O is smaller than H-N-H in NH_3

(b) H–C–H bond angle in CH_4 is larger than H–N–H in NH_3

(c) the H–C–H bond angle in CH_4, the H–N–H angle in NH_3 and H–O–H in H_2O are all greater than 90°

(d) the H–O–H bond angle in H_2O is larger than H–C–H in CH_4

ANSWER KEY

1. (a)	2. (c)	3. (b)	4. (c)	5. (c)	6. (b)	7. (c)	8. (c)
9. (a)	10. (a)	11. (c)	12. (b)	13. (b)	14. (b)	15. (d)	16. (d)
17. (c)	18. (c)	19. (a)	20. (a)	21. (c)	22. (c)	23. (c)	24. (c)
25. (c)	26. (d)	27. (d)	28. (b)	29. (c)	30. (c)	31. (b)	32. (a)
33. (b)	34. (c)	35. (a)	36. (d)	37. (d)	38. (d)	39. (c)	40. (b)
41. (c)	42. (d)	43. (c)	44. (b)	45. (a)	46. (b)	47. (c)	48. (c)
49. (a)	50. (c)	51. (c)	52. (d)	53. (d)	54. (d)	55. (d)	56. (a)
57. (a)	58. (b)	59. (c)	60. (b)	61. (d)	62. (c)	63. (c)	64. (d)
65. (a)	66. (c)	67. (d)	68. (a)	69. (c)	70. (b)	71. (b)	72. (b)
73. (d)	74. (d)	75. (c)	76. (a)	77. (a)	78. (a)	78. (c)	80. (c)
81. (c)	82. (b)	83. (d)	84. (a)	85.	86. (b)	87. (a)	88. (c)
89. (a)	90. (d)	91. (b)	92. (a)	93. (b)	94. (c)	95. (a)	96. (b)
97. (c)	98. (b)	99. (c)	100. (c)	101. (d)	102. (b)	103. (a)	104. (d)
105. (c)	106. (b)	107. (c)	108. (b)	109. (d)	110. (d)	111. (c)	112. (a)
113. (d)	114. (b)	115. (b)	116. (d)	117. (a)	118. (a)	119. (c)	120. (b)
121. (b)	122. (b)	123. (b)	124. (b)	125. (d)	126. (b)	127. (a)	128. (d)
129. (b)	130. (a)	131. (b)	132. (d)	133. (a)	134. (b)	135. (c)	136. (a)
137. (a)	138. (c)	139. (c)	140. (d)	141. (b)	142. (d)	143. (b)	144. (c)
145. (c)	146. (d)	147. (d)	148. (a)	149. (c)	150. (d)	151. (c)	152. (b)
153. (a)	154. (b)	155. (a)	156. (c)	157. (b)	158. (c)	159. (d)	160. (d)
161. (b)	162. (b)	163. (a)	164. (c)	165. (c)	166. (a)	167. (c)	168. (a)
169. (a)	170. (b)	171. (c)	172. (a)	173. (c)	174. (b)	175. (d)	

Previous Years Questions

1. (c)	2. (c)	3. (c)	4. (b)	5. (c)	6. (a)	7. (b)	8. (d)
9. (c)	10. (a)	11. (a)	12. (c)	13. (c)	14. (b)	15. (a)	16. (c)
17. (c)	18. (b)	19. (c)	20. (c)	21. (c)	22. (a)	23. (a)	24. (a)
25. (a)	26. (d)	27. (d)	28. (a)	29. (a)	30. (c)	31. (b)	32. (b)
33. (b)	34. (a)	35. (c)	36. (c)	37. (c)	38. (d)	39. (c)	40. (c)
41. (c)	42. (b)	43. (a)	44. (c)	45. (c)	46. (b)	47. (c)	48. (d)

❑❑❑

STATES OF MATTER

1. Which of the following is an incorrect statement?
   (a) Gases do not have a definite shape and volume
   (b) Gases exert uniform pressure on the wall of the container in all directions
   (c) Volume of a gas is equal to the volume of the container having gas
   (d) Mass of a gas cannot be measured by weighing a container in which it is kept

2. Torr is a unit of ......
   (a) Pressure   (b) Temperature   (c) Volume   (d) Refractive index

3. Pressure of a gas is due to ......
   (a) Space between the gas molecules
   (b) Molecular impact on the wall of the container
   (c) Intermolecular collisions
   (d) High kinetic energy of the gas molecule

4. 2 litre volume is equal to ......
   (a) $2m^3$ (b) $2 \times 10^3 \, cm^3$ (c) $2 \times 10^3 \, dm^3$ (d) $2 \, dm^3$

5. $-20°C$ is equal to ......
   (a) 253 K   (b) -293 K   (c) $-32°F$ (d) $-40°F$

6. The volume of a gas at STP is equal to ......
   (a) $24.0 \, dm^3$ (b) $22.4 \, dm^3$ (c) $11.2 \, dm^3$ (d) $24.8 \, dm^3$

7. At zero Kelvin, which statement is correct ?
   (a) All molecular motion ceases
   (b) Volume of an ideal gas is zero
   (c) The average kinetic energy which is translation of molecules is zero
   (d) All are correct

8. If the absolute temperature and pressure of gas are doubled, its volume becomes ......
   (a) Halved   (b) Four times
   (c) Remains the same   (d) Doubled

9. If a gas at $0°C$ is cooled at constant pressure, then the volume is found to be reduced to one half. The temperature at this stage is ......
   (a) -136.5 A   (b) $-136.5 \, °C$ (c) $-273 \, °C$ (d) $+136.5 \, °C$

10. 380 Torr gas pressure is equal to ......
    (a) 5 atm   (b) 0.5 atm   (c) 2 atm   (d) 0.2 atm

11. The pressure of 2 moles of ideal gas at 546 K having volume 448 litre is ......
    (a) 2 atm   (b) 4 atm   (c) 3 atm   (d) 1 atm

12. What is the pressure of 380.0 mm Hg column of a gas in pascal ?
    (a) 0.505×10^5 pascal   (b) 5.06×10^5 pascal   (c) 0.50^5 pascal   (d) 1.013×10^5 pascal

13. 0.912 bar pressure is equal to ......
    (a) 680 mm Hg   (b) 684 mm Hg   (c) 6.84 mm Hg   (d) 1.824×10^5 pascal

14. One gram molecule of a gas at NTP occupies 22.4 litres. This is based upon ......
    (a) Law of gaseous volume   (b) Avogadro's hypothesis
    (c) Dalton's theory   (d) Berzelius hypothesis

15. A chemist observed that the pressure exerted by a sample of water vapour at 200°C was 1268 Torr. What is the pressure in kilo pascals ?
    (a) 1.690×10^2 kPa   (b) 1690 kPa   (c) 16.9×10^2 kPa   (d) 17×10^2 kPa

16. A gas is initially at 1 atm pressure. To compress it to 14th of its initial volume, the pressure to be applied is ......
    (a) 1 atm   (b) 2 atm   (c) 14th of 4 atm   (d) 1/4 atm

17. A sample of a given mass of a gas at a constant temperature occupied 95 cm^3 under a pressure of 9.962×10^4 Nm^{-2}. At the same temperature, its volume at a pressure of 10.13×10^4 Nm^{-2} is ......
    (a) 190 cm^3 (b) 93 cm^3 (c) 465 cm^3 (d) 47.5 cm^3

18. Which of the following graphs represents Boyle's law?

(a) 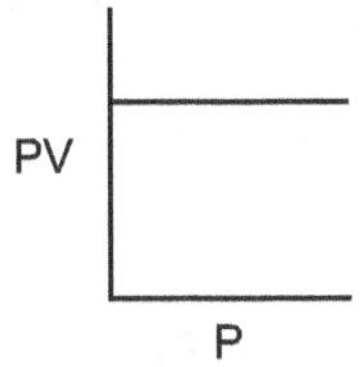 PV vs P   (b) 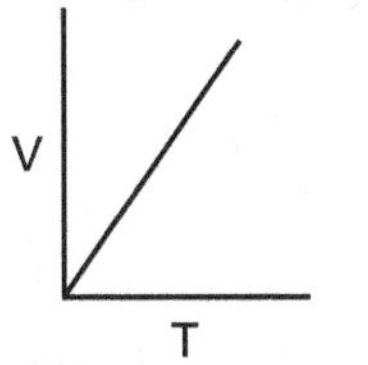 V vs T   (c) 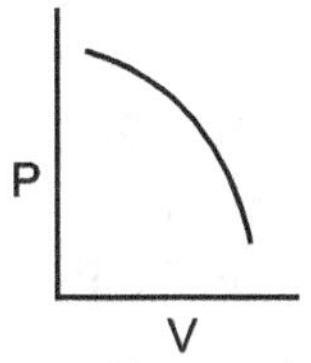 P vs V   (d) 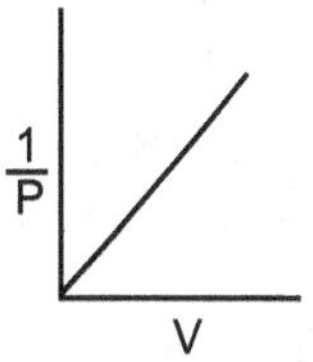 $\frac{1}{P}$ vs V

19. If the pressure of 1 V m^3 of a gas is reduced to half at constant temperature, the final volume of the gas is ......
    (a) 2V   (b) 2V^2 (c) 0.50 V   (d) 0.25 V

20. At 450 K Argon gas is transferred from 500 cm^3 flask to 1000 cm^3 flask, the pressure of the gas becomes ......
    (a) Doubled   (b) Half   (c) Four times   (d) Remains the same

21. 16 gm of oxygen and 3 gm of hydrogen are mixed and kept under 760 mm pressure at 0°C. The total volume of the mixture is ......
    (a) 448 litres   (b) 22.4 litres   (c) 22400 ml   (d) 44800 ml

22. The kinetic energy of two moles of N_2 at 270°C is (R = 8.324 J K^{-1} mol^{-1}) ......
    (a) 54916 J   (b) 6491.6 J   (c) 7491.6 J   (d) 8882.4 J

23. One litre of gas weighing 2g at 300 K and 1 atm pressure is subjected to a volume change to 80 ml at 740 mm pressure. The temperature of the gas is ......
    (a) 90.5°C   (b) 340°C   (c) –33°C   (d) 21.6°C

24. 300 ml of a gas at 27°C is cooled to –3°C at constant pressure, the pressure of the gas is ...
    (a) 270 ml   (b) 540 ml   (c) 135 ml   (d) 67.5 ml

25. Which of the following volume-temperature plots represents the behaviour of one mole of an ideal gas at atmospheric pressure?

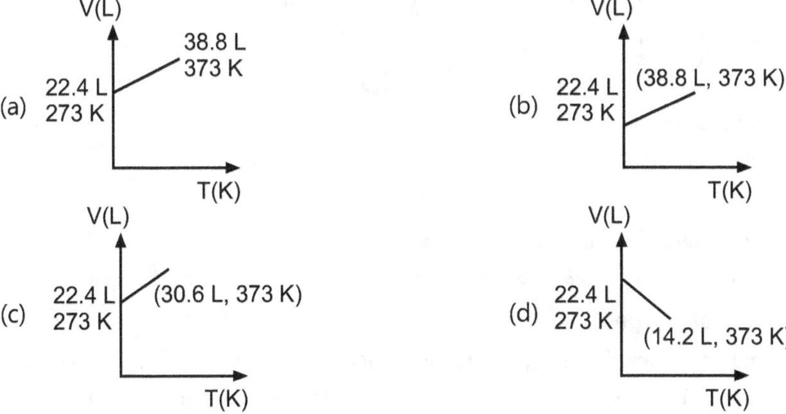

26. The vapour density of a gas is 11.2, the volume occupied by 11.2 g of the gas at NTP is ......
    (a) 1 litre   (b) 11.2 litres   (c) 22.4 litres   (d) 44.8 litres

27. Helium gas is compressed to half of the volume at 303 K. It should be heated to which temperature for its volume to increase to double of its original volume ?
    (a) 303 K   (b) 606 K   (c) 1212 K   (d) 30°C

28. When a gas is heated from 298 K to 323 K at a constant pressure of 1 atmosphere, its volume ......
    (a) Increases from V to 1.8 V   (b) Increases from V to 1.08 V
    (c) Increases from V to 1.5 V   (d) Increases from V to 2V

29. In the equation PV = nRT, what is the value of 'R' if the pressure is measured in atmosphere and the temperature in Kelvin ?
    (a) 26.6   (b) 0.0821   (c) 2.66×10^{23} (d) 3.14

30. Gay Lussac's law relates to which of these following gas properties :
    (a) P, T and V   (b) P and V   (c) P and T   (d) T and V

31. The combined gas law is $P_1V_1 / T_1 = P_2V_2 / T_2$. What must remain constant for this to be right?
    (a) Volume   (b) Pressure   (c) Temperature   (d) Number of moles

32. The pressure in a car tyre is 1.88 atm at 25°C. What will be the new pressure if the temperature warms up to 37°C?
    (a) 1.96 atm   (b) 2.78 atm   (c) 3.01 atm   (d) 30.1 atm

33. The volume occupied by 4.4 g of CO_2 at STP is ......
    (a) 0.1 L   (b) 22.4 L   (c) 0.224 L   (d) 2.24 L

34. The pressure of a gas is 750.0 torr when volume is 400.4 m^3. Calculate the pressure in atm if the gas is allowed to expand to 600.0 ml at constant temperature.
    (a) 1125 atm   (b) 500.0 atm   (c) 1.48 atm   (d) 0.660 atm

35. A gas has a volume of 250.9 litres at 17.0°C and 3 atm of pressure. To what volume must the gas be increased for the gas to be under STP conditions ?
    (a) 797 L   (b) 771 L   (c) 706 L   (d) 78.4 L

36. How many moles of helium gas are contained in a 4.0 L flask at STP?
    (a) 0.045 mol   (b) 0.17 mol   (c) 0.089 mol   (d) 89 mol

37. The volume of 1.4 mol of a gas at 40°C and 2.00 atm is ......
    (a) 1.8 L   (b) 180 L   (c) 3.6 L   (d) 22.4 L

38. Select one correct statement.
    In the gas equation PV = nRT
    (a) n is the number of molecules of a gas
    (b) n moles of a gas have a volume V
    (c) V denotes volume of one mole of a gas
    (d) P is the pressure of the gas when only one mole of gas is present

39. What is the number of molecules in 1.12 litre of carbon dioxide gas at 273 K and 1 atm?
    (a) 2.5×10^{22} (b) 3×10^{22} (c) 2.5×10^{23} (d) 3×10^{23}

40. The pressure exerted by 12 g of an ideal gas at temperature $t°C$ in a vessel of volume V litres is 1 atm. When the temperature is increased by 10 degrees at the same volume, the pressure increase is by 10%. The volume V is (molecular mass of gas = 120) ......
    (a) 0.82 L   (b) 0.41 L   (c) 0.28 L   (d) 1.28 L

41. The density of carbon monoxide gas at STP is ......
    (a) 0.625 g L^{-1} (b) 1.25 g L^{-1} (c) 2.5 g L^{-1} (d) 0.125 g L^{-1}

42. For a fixed mass of a gas at constant temperature, which of the following statements is correct ?
    (a) Plot of P versus V is linear
    (b) Plot of P versus V is non-linear with zero intercept
    (c) Plot of PV versus P is linear with positive slope
    (d) Plot of PV versus P is linear with zero slope

43. Two separate vessels contain ideal gases M and N at the same temperature. If the density of N is twice the density of M and MR of M is twice of MR of N, the ratio of M and N would be ......
    (a) 2   (b) 4   (c) 14   (d) 12

44. The total pressure of the mixture of hydrazine and ammonia gas at 300 K is 0.5 atm. When it is heated to 1500 K, gases decompose to give nitrogen and hydrogen gas and the pressure is 5.0 atm. What was the mole percent of hydrazine in the original mixture?
    (a) 20   (b) 25   (c) 40   (d) 60

45. The density of phosphorus vapour at 600 K and 1 atm is 2.52 g dm^{-3}. The molecular formula of phosphorus is ......
    (a) P   (b) P_2 (c) P_3 (d) P_4

46. According to Charles' law the volume at temperature 40°C and pressure 1 bar will be ......
    (a) $40 V_0$ (b) $1/273 (V_0 + 40)$ (c) $313/273 V_0$ (d) $V_0 + 40/273$

47. The volume of oxygen required by 1 litre of SO_2 at 298 K and 1 atm during the formation of SO_3 is ......
    (a) 1 L   (b) 2 L   (c) 0.5 L   (d) 1.5 L

48. The pressure coefficient for all gases is ......
    (a) $\alpha = 273$ (b) $\alpha = 1273$ (c) $\alpha = 1298$ (d) $\alpha = 1/t (P^0/P - 1)$

49. The volume coefficient for all gases is ......
    (a) $\mu = 273$ (b) 1273
    (c) $v_0 = v_t - 1 + \alpha (-) - P^0 = P (1 + \alpha t)$ (d) $\alpha = 1/t (V_0/V - 1)$

50. What will be the pressure inside the meteorological balloon when the temperature is −23°C ? The balloon of radius 2.0 m was released at sea level at 27°C and expanded to 4.0 m at higher sea level.
    (a) 0.0104   (b) 0.104 atm   (c) 104 atm   (d) 10.4 atm

51. What will be the total pressure of the mixture of helium, argon and oxygen gas in the container, if the partial pressure of gases are P_1, P_2 and P_3 respectively at T Kelvin ?
    (a) $P_1 + P_2 + P_3$ (b) Less than $P_1 + P_2 + P_3$
    (c) More than $P_1 + P_2 + P_3$ (d) Equal to $P_1 + P_2 + P_3$ for non-reacting gas

52. Flask X contains 1 dm^3 of helium at 2 kPa pressure and flask Y contains 2 dm^3 of neon at 1 kPa pressure. If the flasks are connected at constant temperature, what is the final pressure?

(a) 1.33 kPa　　　(b) 1.5 kPa　　　(c) 1.66 kPa　　　(d) 13.3 kP

53. A helicopter of capacity 10 m^3 is connected to another of capacity 30 m^3 and have pressures 50 kPa and 100 kPa respectively before connection. The pressure after the connection of two is ......

(a) 75 kPa　　　(b) 87.5 kPa　　　(c) 100 kPa　　　(d) 125 kPa

54. The partial pressure of hydrogen gas in a flask having 2 gm of H_2 and 8 gm of CH_2 is ......

(a) P/8　　　(b) P/4　　　(c) P/2　　　(d) P/1.5

55. The mole fraction of water vapour in the air at 25°C is 0.0287. What is the partial pressure of dry air if total pressure is 0.977 atm?

(a) 0.028 atm　　　(b) 0.056 atm　　　(c) 0.949 atm　　　(d) 0.474 atm

56. A flask contains gas of density 6 g dm^{-3} and another flask contains gas B of density 3 g dm^{-3}. The molecular mass of gas A is half of molecular mass of gas B, then the ratio of pressures P_A/P_B exerted by gases is ......

(a) 1　　　(b) 2　　　(c) 3　　　(d) 4

57. A glass bulb contains equal number of helium and argon molecules at a total pressure of 700 atm. What will be the pressure if argon is completely removed from the glass bulb ?

(a) 700 atm　　　(b) 350 atm　　　(c) 760 atm　　　(d) 380 atm

58. 0.4 g of helium, 1.6 g of oxygen and 1.4 g of nitrogen at 27°C are taken in a 10 litre cylinder. The partial pressure of helium gas in the cylinder is ......

(a) 0.492 atm　　　(b) 0.246 atm　　　(c) 0.984 atm　　　(d) 0.123 atm

59. Equal weights of methane and hydrogen are mixed in an empty container at 25°C. The fraction of total pressure exerted by hydrogen is ......

(a) 1/2　　　(b) 8/9　　　(c) 1/9　　　(d) 16/17

60. The glass bulbs of capacity 500 ml having 2 g of H_2 exert pressure P atm and 16 g of methane gas are taken. The total pressure when the stopcock is opened will be ......

(a) P　　　(b) 2P　　　(c) P/2　　　(d) P/4

61. Helium diffuses twice as fast as another gas B, if the vapour density of helium is 2, the molecular mass of B is ......

(a) 4　　　(b) 8　　　(c) 16　　　(d) 24

62. The atomic weight of helium is four times that of hydrogen. Its rate of diffusion as compared to hydrogen is ......

(a) Twice　　　(b) $1/\sqrt{2}$ times　　　(c) $\sqrt{2}$ times　　　(d) 1/4th

63. The rate of diffusion of methane at a given temperature is twice that of a gas X. The molecular weight of gas is ......

(a) 8.0　　　(b) 4.0　　　(c) 32.0　　　(d) 64.0

64. A gas diffuses four times faster than another gas B. The ratio of densities of these gases $D_A : D_B$ is ......

(a) $\dfrac{1}{4}$　　　(b) $\dfrac{1}{8}$　　　(c) $\dfrac{1}{16}$　　　(d) $\dfrac{1}{12}$

65. The rate of diffusion of a gas is proportional to ......

(a) $p/\sqrt{d}$　　　(b) $\sqrt{p/d}$　　　(c) p/d　　　(d) $\sqrt{p/d}$

66. Under similar conditions of temperature and pressure, the ratio of rates of effusion of O_2 and CO_2 gases is given by ......

(a) Rate of effusion of O_2/Rate of effusion of CO_2 = 0.87

(b) Rate of effusion of O_2/Rate of effusion of CO_2 = 1.16

(c) Rate of effusion of O_2/Rate of effusion of CO_2 = 11.7

(d) Rate of effusion of O_2/Rate of effusion of CO_2 = 87

67. If 4 g of oxygen diffuses through a narrow hole, how much hydrogen would diffuse under identical conditions?

(a) 16 g　　　(b) 64 g　　　(c) 1 gm　　　(d) 1/4 gm

68. The rate of diffusion of hydrogen is about ......

(a) 1/2 times that of He　　　　　　(b) 1/4 times that of He

(c) Twice that of He　　　　　　(d) Four times that of He

69. Hydrogen diffuses six times faster than gas A. The molar mass of gas is ......

(a) 72　　　(b) 6　　　(c) 24　　　(d) 36

70. Among the following pairs of gases, which pair will diffuse at the same rate if atomic weight of C, N, O are 12, 14 and 16 respectively ......

(a) Carbon dioxide and nitrous oxide　　　(b) Carbon dioxide and sodium peroxide

(c) Carbon dioxide and carbon monoxide (d) Carbon dioxide and nitric oxide

71. Which of the following properties has the same order for H_2 and for D_2, when compared under similar conditions of pressure and temperature ?

(a) Density　　　　　　(b) Relative molecular mass

(c) Average molecular kinetic energy　　　(d) Average molecular speed

72. The ratio of average kinetic energy of ozone to that of hydrogen both at 300 K is ......

(a) 1 : 1　　　(b) 3 : 1　　　(c) 3 : 2　　　(d) 24 : 1

73. The internal energy of one mole of an ideal gas is given by ......

(a) 3/2 RT　　　(b) 1/2 KT　　　(c) 1/2 RT　　　(d) 3/2 KT

74. The molecules of helium, argon, carbon monoxide will have kinetic energy at 530 K if ......

(a) Ar > He, CO　　(b) Ar, He < CO　　(c) CO < He, Ar　　(d) He = Ne = Ar

75. At what temperature, the K.E of 0.30 mole of helium will be the same as the K.E of 0.40 mol of Argon at 400 K ?

(a) 300 K　　　(b) 375 K　　　(c) 400 K　　　(d) 533 K

76. The average K.E of an ideal gas molecule at 25°C is ......

(a) 6.17×10^{-20} J　　(b) 6.17×10^{-21} J　　(c) 6.17×10^{-21} KJ　　(d) 617×10^{-20} J

77. Ideal gas equation in terms of kinetic energy per unit volume is

(a) $\dfrac{2}{3}E$　　　(b) $\dfrac{3}{2}RT$　　　(c) $\dfrac{2}{3}RT$　　　(d) $\dfrac{3}{2}E$

78. The K.E of 16 gm of oxygen gas at 500 K is ......

(a) 2.3 J　　　(b) 3.1 J　　　(c) 4.5 J　　　(d) 8.3 J

79. The K.E of hydrogen molecules in 1 mole of a gas is ......

(a) 3 KT　　　(b) 3/2 RT　　　(c) 3RT　　　(d) 3/2 KT

80. Which of the following is the same for all ideal gases at the same temperature?
   (a) Number of molecules is 1 g
   (b) Kinetic energy of 1 molecule
   (c) Kinetic energy of 1 g
   (d) Kinetic energy of 1 mole

81. Which of the following graphs correctly represent the Maxwell-Boltzmann distribution of molecular speeds at temperatures T_1 and T_2 if $T_2 > T_1$

(a) 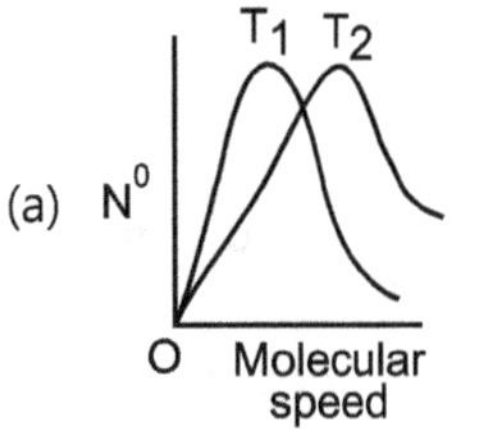

(b) 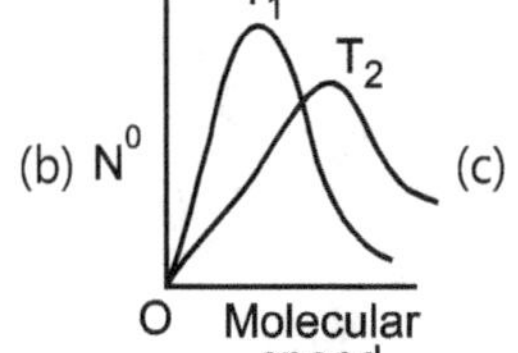

(c) 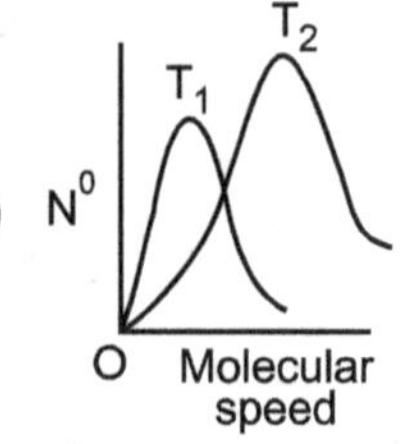

(d) 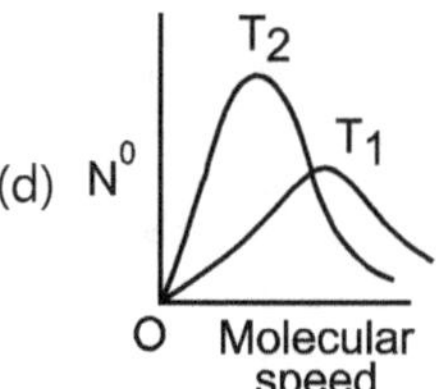

82. The RMS velocity of an ideal gas at constant pressure varies with density as ......
   (a) d
   (b) $\sqrt{d}$
   (c) d^2
   (d) $1/\sqrt{d}$

83. The RMS velocity of hydrogen is $\sqrt{7}$ times the RMS velocity of nitrogen. If T is the temperature of the gas, then
   (a) $T_{H_2} = T_{N_2}$
   (b) $T_{H_2} > T_{N_2}$
   (c) $T_{H_2} < T_{N_2}$
   (d) $T_{H_2} = \sqrt{7T_{N_2}}$

84. The graph for N_2 gas at 273 K is

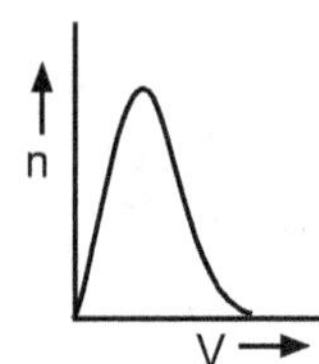

Which of the following graphs is applicable to N_2 at 473 K ?

(a) 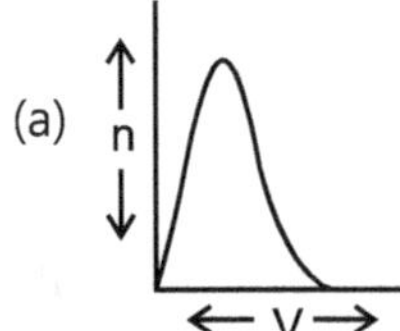

(b) 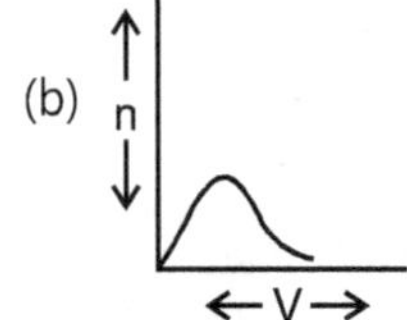

(c) 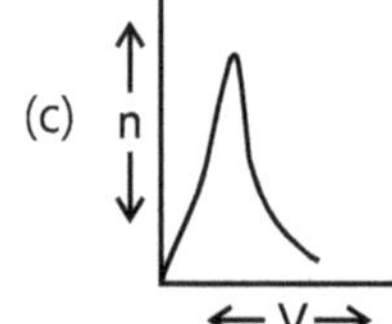

(d) 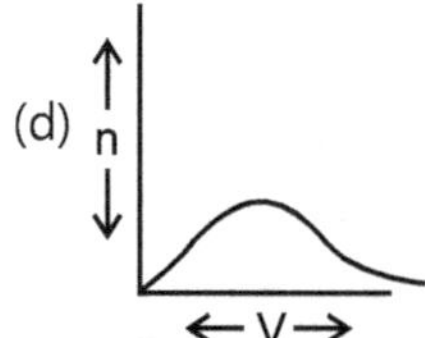

85. The average velocity of an ideal gas molecule at 27°C is 0.3 m/s. The average velocity at 92.7°C will be ......
   (a) 0.6 m/s
   (b) 0.3 m/s
   (c) 0.9 m/s
   (d) 3.0 m/s

86. The ratio of RMS velocity to average velocity of a gas molecule at a given temperature is ...
   (a) $1.086 : 1$
   (b) $1 : 1.086$
   (c) $2 : 1.086$
   (d) $1.086 : 2$

87. For a gas at a given temperature, which of the following is true ?
   (a) $\mu > v < \alpha$
   (b) $\mu < v < \alpha$
   (c) $\mu < v < \alpha$
   (d) $\alpha < v < \mu$

88. The ratio of most probable velocity (v), root mean square velocity (m) and average velocity (v) is ......
   (a) $\sqrt{2} : \sqrt{\dfrac{8}{\pi}} : \sqrt{3}$
   (b) $\sqrt{2} : \sqrt{3} : \sqrt{\dfrac{8}{\pi}}$
   (c) $1 : \sqrt{2} : \sqrt{3}$
   (d) $1 : \sqrt{8\pi} : \sqrt{3}$

89. For two different gases the ratio of root mean square velocities is ......

(a) $\dfrac{\bar{v_1}}{\bar{v_2}} = \sqrt{\dfrac{M_2}{m_1}}$

(b) $\dfrac{m_1}{\sqrt{M_2}} = \dfrac{m_2}{\sqrt{M_1}}$

(c) $\dfrac{\alpha_1}{\sqrt{M_2}} = \dfrac{\alpha_2}{\sqrt{M_1}}$

(d) $\dfrac{\sqrt{M_2}}{m_1} = \dfrac{\sqrt{M_1}}{m_2}$

90. The ratio of RMS mean square velocities for the same gas at two different temperatures is ...

(a) $\dfrac{m_1}{m_2} = \sqrt{\dfrac{T_1}{T_2}}$

(b) $\dfrac{m_1}{m_2} = \sqrt{\dfrac{T_2}{T_1}}$

(c) $\dfrac{m_1}{m_2} = \sqrt{\dfrac{T_1}{T_2}}$

(d) $\bar{v}_1 / \bar{v}_2 = \sqrt{\dfrac{T_1}{T_2}}$

91. The ratio of RMS velocity (m), average velocity (−v) and most probable velocity (v) of an ideal gas is ......

(a) $(3)^{1/2} : \left(\dfrac{8}{\pi}\right)^{1/2} : (2)^{1/2}$

(b) $(8)^{1/2} : (3)^{1/2} : (2)^{1/2}$

(c) $(3)^{1/2} : (2)^{1/2} : 1$

(d) $(3)^{1/2} : (8\pi)^{1/2} : 1$

92. The ratio between the root mean square velocity of hydrogen gas at 50 K and that of oxygen gas at 800 K is ......

(a) 4　　　　(b) 2　　　　(c) 1　　　　(d) 1/4

93. At what temperature will the average speed of CH_4 molecules have the same value as oxygen gas has at 300 K ?

(a) 1200 K　　　　(b) 150 K　　　　(c) 600 K　　　　(d) 300 K

94. The temperature of the gas is raised from 27°C to 927°C. The RMS velocity will become ...

(a) $\dfrac{\pi}{2}$　　　　(b) Same as before　(c) Halved　　　　(d) Doubled

95. The ratio of most probable velocity to that of average velocity is ......

(a) $\dfrac{\pi}{2}$　　　　(b) $\dfrac{2}{\pi}$　　　　(c) $\dfrac{\sqrt{\pi}}{2}$　　　　(d) $\dfrac{2}{\sqrt{\pi}}$

96. The collision frequency is ......
(a) It is the number of collisions of molecules with other molecules per second
(b) It is the total number of collisions between gas molecules per unit volume per second
(c) Number of collisions
(d) Number of collisions between the molecules

97. At constant pressure, the collision frequency is ......

(a) $CF \propto T^2$　　　　(b) $CF \propto \dfrac{1}{T}$　　　　(c) $CF \propto T^{2/3}$　　　　(d) $CF \propto \dfrac{3}{2}$

98. At constant temperature, the collision frequency is ......

(a) $CF \propto P_2$　　　　(b) $CF \propto \dfrac{1}{P^2}$　　　　(c) $CF \propto \sqrt{P}$　　　　(d) $CF \propto \dfrac{1}{\sqrt{P}}$

99. Collision diameter (σ) is given by the expression ......

(a) $\sigma = \dfrac{4}{9}\eta$

(b) $\sigma = \dfrac{9}{4}\eta b \sqrt{\dfrac{\pi}{RTM}}$

(c) $\sigma = \eta b \sqrt{\dfrac{\pi}{RTM}}$

(d) $\sigma = \dfrac{9}{4}\eta b \sqrt{\dfrac{RTM}{\pi}}$

100. Which statement is true for mean path?
   (a) The distance travelled by various collisions
   (b) The path covered by different types of gas molecules
   (c) The average distance travelled by the molecules between the successive collisions
   (d) Larger the path travelled, longer is the mean free path

101. If the collision frequency is Z at the 760 mm of Hg then the collision frequency at 2 atm is ......
   (a) 1 Z   (b) 4 Z   (c) 2 Z   (d) Z

102. With increase in pressure, mean free path at constant temperature ......
   (a) Decreases   (b) Increases   (c) Remains the same   (d) Becomes zero

103. With increase in temperature, mean free path at constant pressure ......
   (a) Decreases   (b) Increases   (c) Remains the same   (d) Becomes zero

104. Most probable velocity gets doubled when the temperature is ......
   (a) Halved   (b) Doubled
   (c) Quadrupled   (d) Increased by 10 degrees

105. If collision diameter s is linear at constant temperature and pressure, the mean free path λ is ......
   (a) Less   (b) More
   (c) Remains the same   (d) Unpredictable

Van der Waal's Equation, Critical Phenomenon

106. Real gases are those ......
   (a) Which obey ideal gas equation under all conditions of pressure and temperature
   (b) Which do not obey ideal gas equation at high temperature and low pressure
   (c) Which deviate from ideal gas behaviour at low temperature and high pressure
   (d) Which deviate from ideal gas behaviour at high temperature and high pressure

107. Compressibility factor Z is mathematically represented as ......
   (a) PV = nRT   (b) Pn = VRT   (c) $\dfrac{PV}{nRT}$ (d) $\dfrac{nRT}{PV}$

108. If Z > 1, the gas is ......
   (a) More compressible   (b) Less compressible
   (c) Not compressible   (d) Liquifiable

109. The expression for Van der Waal's equation of states is ......
   (a) $\left(P + \dfrac{a}{n^2V^2}\right)(V - nb) = nRT$ (b) $\left(P + \dfrac{an^3}{V^2\,(V - nb)}\right) = \Delta nRT$
   (c) $\left(P + \dfrac{an^2}{V^2}\right)(V - nb) = nRT$ (d) $\left(P + \dfrac{an^2}{V^2}\right)(V - b) = nRT$

110. The Van der Waal's equation reduces itself to the ideal gas equation at ......
   (a) Low pressure, high temperature   (b) High pressure, low temperature
   (c) Low pressure, low temperature   (d) High pressure, high temperature

111. At low pressure, the Van der Waal's equation is written as $\left(P + \dfrac{a}{V^2}\right) V = RT$, the compressibility factor Z is then equal to ......

(a) $\left(1 + \dfrac{RTV}{a}\right)$　　(b) $\left(1 + \dfrac{a}{RTV}\right)$　　(c) $\left(1 - \dfrac{RTV}{a}\right)$　　(d) $\left(1 - \dfrac{a}{RTV}\right)$

112. In Van der Waal's equation, which term provides correction for intermolecular forces of attraction ?

(a) $1/RT$　　　　(b) RT　　　　(c) b　　　　(d) a/V^2

113. The constant 'b' in Van der Waal's equation signifies ......

(a) Pressure correction　　　　　(b) Volume correction

(c) Nature of gas　　　　　(d) Temperature correction

114. Unit of 'a' is ......

(a) $atm\ L^2\ mol^{-2}$　　(b) $atm\ L^2\ mol^{-1}$　　(c) $atm\ L\ mol^{-1}$　　(d) $atm^{-1}\ L^2\ mol^{-2}$

115. Unit of 'b' is ......

(a) L^{-1}　　(b) $L\ mol^{-1}$　　(c) $L^2\ mol^{-1}$　　(d) L

116. If the value of 'b' remains constant for wide range of pressure and temperature, it indicates

(a) The gas is highly compressible　　(b) Almost incompressible

(c) No effect on compressibility　　(d) The gas is less compressible

117. A real gas which obeys Van der Waal's equation resembles ideal gas if ......

(a) a is large, b is small　　　　(b) a is small, b is large

(c) a and b both are small　　　　(d) a and b both are large

118. At high pressure, the Van der Waal's equation becomes ......

(a) $P(V - b) = RT$　　(b) $PV = RT - Pb$　　(c) $PV = RT - \dfrac{a}{V^2}$　　(d) $PV = RT - \dfrac{a}{V}$

119. At low pressure, the Van der Waal's equation becomes ......

(a) $\left(P - \dfrac{a}{V^2}\right)$　　(b) $P.(V - b) = RT$　　(c) $PV = RT$　　(d) $\left(P - \dfrac{a}{V}\right) V = RT$

120. In case of hydrogen and helium gas, the Van der Waal's equation reduces to ......

(a) $PV = RT$　　(b) $PV = RT + Pb$　　(c) $PV = RT - Pb$　　(d) $PV = Pb$

121. The Van der Waal's equation holds good for ......

(a) Ideal gas　　　　(b) Real gas

(c) Any gaseous substance　　　　(d) None of these

122. If radius of nitrogen molecule is 100 dm, volume of molecule in one mole of a gas is ......

(a) $3 \times 10^{-3}\ dm^3\ mol^{-1}$　　　　(b) $2.53 \times 10^{-3}\ dm^3\ mol^{-1}$

(c) $2.52\ dm^3\ mol^{-1}$　　　　(d) $2.52 \times 10^{-23}\ dm^3\ mol^{-1}$

123. If volume of one mole of a gas is $3 \times 10^{-3}\ dm^3\ mol^{-1}$ then the value of Van der Waal's constant 'b' is ......

(a) $1.2 \times 10^{-3}\ dm^3\ mol^{-1}$　　　　(b) $0.12 \times 10^{-3}\ dm^3\ mol^{-1}$

(c) $12 \times 10^{-3}\ dm^3\ mol^{-1}$　　　　(d) $3 \times 10^{-3}\ dm^3\ mol^{-1}$

124. The compressibility factor Z at low pressure for 1 mole of a gas at 400 K in vessel of 30.0 L. If Van der Waal's constant 'a' is $20\ L^2\ atm\ mol^{-2}$ is ......

(a) 1.00　　　　(b) 98　　　　(c) 1.98　　　　(d) 0.98

125. If Van der Waal's constant 'b' is 0.15, the compressibility factor for a gas which occupies 20.0 L at 300 K under high pressure is ......
  (a) 1.00   (b) 1.0075   (c) 0.0075   (d) 0.0175

126. The volume occupied by one mole of a gas at critical temperature and pressure is ......
  (a) b   (b) 2b   (c) 3c   (d) 4b

127. The minimum pressure required to liquify the gas at critical temperature is
  (a) $\dfrac{2.7\,b^2}{a}$ (b) $\dfrac{a}{2.7\,b^2}$ (c) $\dfrac{a}{b^2}$ (d) $\dfrac{a}{27\,b^2}$

128. A gas can be liquified at ......
  (a) Its critical temperature   (b) Below its critical temperature
  (c) Above its critical temperature   (d) Only temperature

129. The critical temperature is ......
  (a) $\dfrac{8a}{27\,Rb}$ (b) $\dfrac{27\,Rb}{8a}$ (c) $\dfrac{Rb}{8a}$ (d) $\dfrac{2.7\,Rb}{8a}$

130. The critical temperature of the gas is the temperature ......
  (a) Above which it cannot be liquified
  (b) Below which it cannot be liquified
  (c) At which one mole of gas occupies 22.4 L
  (d) At which it occupies 22.4 L

131. The behaviour of carbon dioxide gas approaches that of permanent gas N_2 ......
  (a) Below critical temperature   (b) Above critical temperature
  (c) Above absolute zero   (d) Below absolute zero

132. At Boyle's temperature, compressibility factor 'Z' for a real gas is ......
  (a) Z = 1   (b) Z > 1   (c) Z < 1   (d) Z = 0

133. The values of Van der Waal's constant 'a' for the gases N_2, H_2, NH_3 and SO_2 are 3.5, 0.25, 4.9 and 6.9 respectively. Which will show the highest case of liquification?
  (a) N_2 (b) H_2 (c) SO_2 (d) NH_3

134. Boyle's temperature (T_b) is the temperature at which ......
  (a) Ideal gas behaves like real gas
  (b) Real gas shows ideal behaviour for a range of pressure
  (c) Ideal gas liquifies
  (d) Real gas liquifies

135. The relationship between Boyle's temperature and Van der Waal's constants 'a' and 'b' is ......
  (a) $T_C = \dfrac{a}{b}$ (b) $T_C = \dfrac{a}{Rb}$ (c) $T_C = \dfrac{Rb}{a}$ (d) $b = \dfrac{T_C a}{R}$

136. The relationship between critical temperature, critical pressure and critical volume is ......
  (a) $P_C V_C = \dfrac{3}{8} RT_C$ (b) $P_C V_C = RT_C$ (c) $P_C V_C = 3RT_C$ (d) $P_C V_C = \dfrac{8}{3} RT_C$

137. Normal boiling point of a liquid is ......
  (a) $\dfrac{1}{3}$ of T_C (b) 3 times of T_C (c) $\dfrac{2}{3}$ of T_C (d) $\dfrac{3}{2}$ of T_C

138. Critical volume is ......
    (a) Volume occupied by a gas at STP
    (b) Volume occupied by 1 mole of a gas at critical pressure and critical temperature
    (c) 22.4 L of volume of gas at 298 K
    (d) Volume of a gas at RTP

139. Joule Thomson effect is ......
    (a) Rise in temperature when a gas under pressure is allowed to expand
    (b) Fall in temperature when a gas under pressure is allowed to expand adiabatically through a small aperture
    (c) Fall in temperature when a gas is allowed to expand isothermally through a small orifice
    (d) Rise in temperature when a gas is allowed to expand adiabatically through a small aperture

140. The Joule-Thomson coefficient is zero at ......
    (a) Absolute temperature
    (b) Critical temperature
    (c) Inversion temperature
    (d) Boyle's temperature

141. Inversion temperature is the temperature at which ......
    (a) Gas shows Joule-Thomson effect
    (b) Gas does not show Joule-Thomson effect
    (c) Gas expands isothermally
    (d) Gas expands adiabatically

142. A gas does not cause cooling effect when allowed to expand is ......
    (a) Gas is an ideal gas
    (b) Gas is an inert gas
    (c) Boiling point of the gas is very low
    (d) Inversion temperature of the gas is very low

143. Oxygen gas cannot be liquified at ordinary temperature like ammonia gas because ......
    (a) Critical temperature of oxygen is low
    (b) Critical temperature of oxygen is very high
    (c) Critical temperature of oxygen is moderate
    (d) Critical temperature of oxygen is higher than ammonia

144. One mole of monoatomic gas is mixed with 1 mole of diatomic gas, the molar specific heat of the reaction mixture at constant volume becomes ......
    (a) 4 cal   (b) 6 cal   (c) 8 cal   (d) 10 cal

145. The relationship between C_p and C_v for triatomic gas is ......
    (a) $\dfrac{C_p}{C_v} = 1.66$ (b) $\dfrac{C_p}{C_v} = 1.40$ (c) $\dfrac{C_p}{C_v} = 1.33$ (d) $\dfrac{C_p}{C_v} = 1.20$

146. Density of methane at 250°K and 6 atm pressure is ...... (R = 0.0821 L atm)
    (a) 4 g/l (b) 8 m/l (c) 12 g/l (d) 16 g/l

147. The compressibility factor of an ideal gas is ......
    (a) 0   (b) 1   (c) 2   (d) 4

148. The volume occupied by 4.4 g of CO_2 is ......
    (a) 2.24 litres   (b) 22.4 litres   (c) 224 litres   (d) None of these

149. In the equation

$$4HNO_{3(g)} + 5O_2 \rightarrow 4NO_{(g)} + 6H_2O_{(e)}$$

when 1 mole of ammonia and 1 mole of O_2 are made to react to completion, what will happen?

(a) 1.0 mole of H_2O will be produced　　(b) 1.0 mole of NO will be produced

(c) All the oxygen will be consumed　　(d) All the ammonia will be produced

150. One mole of Argon gas will have least density at ......

(a) STP　　(b) 0°C and 2 atm

(c) 273°C and 2 atm　　(d) 273°C and 1 atm.

151. At 25°C and 730 mm pressure, 380 ml of dry oxygen was collected. What will be the volume of oxygen at 760 mm pressure at constant temperature?

(a) 96 ml　　(b) 449 ml　　(c) 569 ml　　(d) 621 ml

152. Which one of the following statements is wrong for gases ?

(a) Gases do not have a definite shape and volume

(b) Volume of the gas is equal to the volume of container confining the gas

(c) Confined gas exerts uniform pressure on the walls of the container in all directions

(d) Mass of the gas cannot be determined by weighing a container in which it is enclosed

153. The value of universal gas constant 'R' depends upon ......

(a) Temperature of the gas　　(b) Volume of the gas

(c) Number of moles of gas　　(d) None of these

154. Mass of one litre of a gas is 1g at 27°C and pressure 76 cm. The molecular weight of the gas will be ......

(a) 60.2　　(b) 41.3　　(c) 24.6　　(d) 31.7

155. Gas equation, PV = nRT is obeyed by ......

(a) Only isothermal process　　(b) Only adiabatic process

(c) Both (a) and (b)　　(d) None of these

156. One litre of a gas weighs 2 g at 300 K and 1 atm pressure. If the pressure is made 0.75 atm, at which one of the following temperatures will one litre of the same gas weigh one gram ?

(a) 450 K　　(b) 800 K　　(c) 600 K　　(d) 650 K

157. The rate of diffusion of a gas is twice that of the other. If first gas has molecular weight 16, the molecular weight of the second is ......

(a) 8　　(b) 16　　(c) 32　　(d) 64

158. The density of a gas at 27° C and 1 atm is d, pressure remaining constant. At which of the following temperature, will its density become 0.75 d ?

(a) 20°C　　(b) 80°C　　(c) 400 K　　(d) 300 K

159. The rate of diffusion of a gas having molecular weight just double of nitrogen gas is 56 ml s^{-1}. The rate of diffusion of nitrogen will be ......

(a) 79.19 ml s^{-1}　　(b) 56 ml s^{-1}　　(c) 112.0 ml s^{-1}　　(d) 90.00 ml s^{-1}

160. At 100°C and 1 atm, if the density of liquid water is 1.0 gm cm^{-3} and that of water vapour is 0.0006 gm cm^{-3}, then the volume occupied by water molecules in one litre of steam at that temperature is ......

(a) 6 cm^3　　(b) 60 cm^3　　(c) 0.6 cm^3　　(d) 0.06 cm^3

161. 'n' moles of an ideal gas at temperature T Kelvin occupies 'V' litres volume, exerting a pressure P atmosphere. What is the concentration in mol lit^{-1}?

(a) $\dfrac{P}{RT}$　　　(b) $\dfrac{PT}{R}$　　　(c) $\dfrac{RT}{P}$　　　(d) $\dfrac{R}{PT}$

162. The value of Van der Waal's gas constant 'a' for gases O_2, N_2, NH_3 and CH_4 are 1.360, 1.390, 4.170 and 2.253 lit^2 atm mol^{-2}. The gas which can be most easily liquified is as follows ......

(a) O_2　　　(b) N_2　　　(c) NH_3　　　(d) CH_4

163. Van der Waal's real gas will act as an ideal gas under which conditions ?

(a) High temperature, low pressure　　　(b) Low temperature, high pressure

(c) High temperature, high pressure　　　(d) Low temperature, low pressure

164. The value of gas constant R is ......

(a) 0.082 litre atm　　　(b) 0.987 ml mol^{-1} K^{-1}

(c) 8.3 J mol^{-1} K^{-1}　　　(d) 83 erg mol^{-1} K^{-1}

165. Kinetic theory of gases proves ......

(a) Only Boyle's law　　　(b) Only Charles' law

(c) Only Avogadro's law　　　(d) All of these

166. For an ideal gas, number of moles per litre in terms of its pressure P, gas constant R and temperature T is ......

(a) PT/R　　　(b) PRT　　　(c) P/RT　　　(d) RT/P

167. If pressure P and density r are for a gas, then P and r are related as ......

(a) $P \propto r$　　　(b) $P \propto \rho^2$　　　(c) $P \propto \dfrac{1}{\rho}$　　　(d) $P \propto \dfrac{1}{\rho^2}$

168. The ratio of rate of diffusion of SO_2 (M = 64) and oxygen (M = 32) is ......

(a) 1 : 1　　　(b) 2 : 1　　　(c) 1 : 2　　　(d) 1 : 1.414

169. 'X' litres of carbon monoxide is present at STP. It is completely oxidized to CO_2. The volume of CO_2 formed is 11.20 litres at STP. What is the value of 'X' in litres ?

(a) 22.414　　　(b) 11.207　　　(c) 5.6035　　　(d) 44.828

170. 4 gm of an ideal gas occupies 5.6035 litres of volume at 546 K and 2 atm pressure. What is the molecular weight ?

(a) 4　　　(b) 16　　　(c) 32　　　(d) 64

171. According to kinetic theory of gases, in an ideal gas between two successive collisions a gas molecule travels

(a) In a circular path　　　(b) In a wavy path

(c) In a straight line path　　　(d) With an accelerated velocity

172. Two gas cylinders with the same capacity have been filled with 44 gm of H_2 and 44 g of CO_2 respectively. If the pressure in CO_2 cylinder is 1 atmosphere at a particular temperature, pressure in the hydrogen cylinder at the same temperature is ......

(a) 22 atmosphere　　(b) 44 atmosphere　　(c) 2 atmosphere　　(d) 1 atmosphere

173. Kinetic energy of one mole of an ideal gas at 300 K is ......

(a) 34.8 kJ　　　(b) 3.48 kJ　　　(c) 3.74 kJ　　　(d) 348

174. Critical temperature is the highest temperature at which ......

(a) Liquification of gas occurs　　　(b) Solid changes to liquid

(c) Liquid changes to gas　　　(d) None of these

175. Absolute temperature is the temperature at which ......
(a) All molecular motion ceases
(b) Volume becomes zero
(c) Mass becomes zero
(d) None of these

176. Maximum number of molecules are present in ......
(a) 15 litre of H_2 gas of STP
(b) 5 litre of N_2 gas at STP
(c) 0.5 g of H_2 gas
(d) 10 g of O_2 gas

177. The pressure and temperature of 4 dm^3 of CO_2 gas are doubled, then the volume of CO_2 gas would be ......
(a) 2 dm^3
(b) 3 dm^3
(c) 4 dm^3
(d) 8 dm^3

178. As the temperature is raised from 20°C to 40°C, the average kinetic energy of neon atom changes by a factor of ......
(a) 1/2
(b) 2
(c) 313/293
(d) $\sqrt{(313/293)}$

179. In Van der Waal's equation of the state of the gas law, the constant 'b' is a measure of ......
(a) Intermolecular repulsion
(b) Intermolecular collisions per unit volume
(c) Volume occupied by the molecule
(d) Intermolecular attraction

180. The ratio of the rate of diffusion of helium and methane under identical conditions of pressure and temperature will be ......
(a) 4
(b) 2
(c) 0.2
(d) 0.5

181. For the formation of 3.65 g hydrogen chloride gas, what volumes of hydrogen gas and chlorine gas are required at NTP conditions ?
(a) 1.12 lit., 1.12 lit.
(b) 1.12 lit., 2.24 lit.
(c) 3.65 lit., 1.88 lit.
(d) 1 lit., 1 lit.

182. The molar heat capacity of a monoatomic gas for which ratio of pressure and volume is one
(a) 2 R
(b) 3/2 R
(c) 5/2 R
(d) Zero

183.

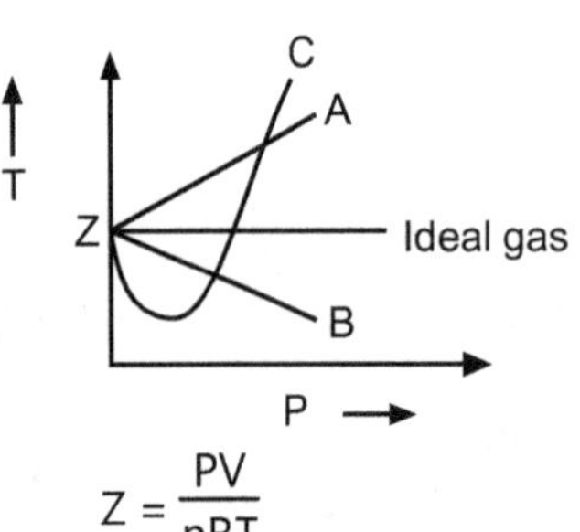

$$Z = \frac{PV}{nRT}$$

a – Van der Waal's constant for pressure correction.

b – Van der waal's constant for volume correction. Pick up the incorrect statement.

(a) For gas A, if a = 0, the compressibility factor is directly proportional to pressure.

(b) For gas B, if b = 0, the compressibility factor is directly proportional to pressure.

(c) For gas C, a = 0, b = 0, it can be used to calculate a and b by giving lowest P value and its intercept with $Z_1 = 1$.

(d) Slope for the three gases at high pressure is positive.

184. A and B are ideal gases and their molecular weights are in the ratio of $1 : 4$. The pressure of a gas mixture containing equal weights of A and B is P atm. What is the partial pressure of B in the mixture?

(a) P/5   (b) P/2   (c) P/2.5   (d) 3P/4

185. Dominance of strong repulsive forces among the molecules of the gas (Z-compressibility factor) ......

(a) Depends upon Z and indicated by $Z = 1$

(b) Depends upon Z and indicated by $Z > 1$

(c) Depends upon Z and indicated by $Z < 1$

(d) Is independent of Z

186. Which pair of gases diffuses with the same rate at same temperature and pressure ?

(a) CO and NO (b) NO_2 and CO_2 (c) NH_3 and PH_3 (d) NO and C_2H_6

187. Steam distillation is based on ......

(a) Boyle's law   (b) Charles' law

(c) Dalton's law of partial pressure   (d) Avagadro's law

188. Equal mass of methane and oxygen are mixed in an empty container at 25°C. The fraction of the total pressure extended by oxygen is ......

(a) 1/2   (b) 2/3   (c) $\dfrac{1}{3} \times \dfrac{273}{298}$ (d) 1/3

189. If the ratio of mass of SO_2 and O_2 gases in a vessel is $1 : 1$, then the ratio of their partial pressures would be ......

(a) $5 : 2$ (b) $2 : 5$ (c) $2 : 1$ (d) $1 : 2$

190. A $4 : 1$ mixture of helium and methane are present in a vessel at 10 bar pressure. The composition of mixture effusing out at the beginning is ......

(a) $1 : 8$ (b) $2 : 8$ (c) $8 : 3$ (d) $3 : 8$

191. The volume-temperature graph of a given mass of ideal gas at constant pressure is shown below

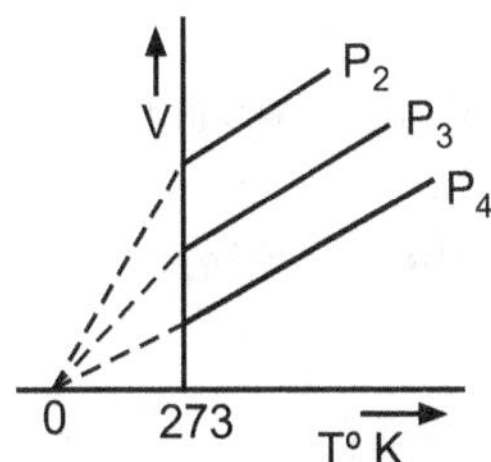

What is the correct order of pressure ?

(a) $P_1 > P_3 > P_2$ (b) $P_1 > P_2 > P_3$ (c) $P_2 > P_3 > P_1$ (d) $P_2 > P_1 > P_3$

192. If a gas expands at constant temperature, it indicates that ......

(a) Pressure of the gas increases

(b) Kinetic energy of molecules remains the same

(c) Number of molecules of the gas increases

(d) Kinetic energy of molecules decreases

193. The most probable velocity in cm/s of hydrogen molecule at 27°C will be ......

(a) 19.3×10^4 (b) 17.8×10^4 (c) 24.93×10^9 (d) 17.8×10^6

194. The temperature at which real gases obey the ideal gas law over a wide range of pressures is called ......

(a) Critical temperature

(b) Inversion temperature

(c) Boyle temperature

(d) Reduced temperature

195. The term that corrects for the attractive forces present in a real gas in Van der Waal's equation is ......

(a) nb
(b) n^2a/V^2
(c) $-(n^2 a/V^2)$
(d) – nb

196. Molar volume of CO_2 is maximum at ......

(a) NTP

(b) 0°C and 2.0 atm

(c) 127°C and 1 atm

(d) 273°C and 2.0 atm

197. Density of air is 0.00130 gm cm at STP. The vapour density of air will be ......

(a) 0.065
(b) 14.56
(c) 14.48
(d) 0.0065

198. If 300 ml of a gas weighs 0.368 g at STP, what is its molecular weight ?

(a) 30.16
(b) 2.55
(c) 27.5
(d) 37.5

199. If 400 ml of a gas weighs 0.486 g at STP, what is its molecular weight ?

(a) 27.2
(b) 37.2
(c) 2.8
(d) 47.2

200. If one mole of an ideal gas expands isothermally at 37°C from 15 litres to 25 litres, the maximum work obtained is ......

(a) – 12.76 J
(b) 6.43 J
(c) 8.57 J
(d) 2.92 J

201. What will happen to the volume of a bubble of air found under water in a lake, where the temperature is 15°C and the pressure is 1.5 atm. If the bubble then rises to the surface where the temperature is 25°C and the pressure 1.0 atm ......

(a) Its volume will become greater by a factor of 2.5

(b) Its volume will become greater by a factor of 1.5

(c) Its volume will become greater by a factor of 1.1

(d) Its volume will become smaller by a factor of 0.70

202. Two separate bulbs contain ideal gases P and Q respectively maintained at the same temperature. The density of gas P is twice that of Q and the molecular weight of gas P is half of that of gas Q. The ratio of the pressure of gas P to that of gas Q is ......

(a) 2
(b) 1/2
(c) 4
(d) 1/4

PREVIOUS YEAR'S QUESTIONS

1. Equal masses of H_2, O_2 and methane have been taken in a container of volume V at temperature 27°C in identical conditions. The ratio of the volumes of gases H_2, O_2 and methane would be ......   **[AIPMT 2014]**

(a) 16 : 1 : 2
(b) 8 : 1 : 2
(c) 8 : 16 : 1
(d) 16 : 8 : 1

2. Maximum deviation from ideal gas is expected from ......   **[NEET 2013]**

(a) NH_3 (g)
(b) H_2 (g)
(c) N_2 (g)
(d) CH_4 (g)

3. A certain gas take three times as long to effuse out as Helium. Its molecular mass will be ...

(a) 27u
(b) 36u
(c) 64u
(d) 9u   **[CBSE 2012]**

4. For real gases, Van der Waals' equation is written as $\left(P + \dfrac{an^2}{V^2}\right)(V - nb) = nRT$ **[CBSE 2012]**

Where 'a' and 'b' are Van der Waals' constants.

The sets of gases are :

O_2, CO_2, H_2 and He (11) CH_4, O_2 and H_2

The gases given in set-I in increasing order of 'b' and gases given in set – II in decreasing order of 'a' are arranged below. Select the correct order from the following:

(a) (I) He $<$ H_2 $<$ CO_2 $<$ O_2 (II) CH_4 $>$ H_2 $>$ O_2

(b) (I) O_2 $<$ He $<$ H_2 $<$ CO_2 (II) H_2 $>$ O_2 $>$ CH_4

(c) (I) H_2 $<$ He $<$ O_2 $<$ CO_2 (II) CH_4 $>$ O_2 $>$ H_2

(d) (I) H_2 $<$ O_2 $<$ He $<$ CO_2 (II) O_2 $>$ CH_4 $>$ H_2

5. 50 mL of each gas A and of gas B takes 150 and 200 seconds respectively for effusing through a pin hole under the similar condition. If molecular mass of gas A is 36, the molecular mass of gas B will be ......   **[CBSE 2012]**

(a) 96   (b) 128   (c) 32   (d) 64

6. Two gases A and B having the same volume diffuse through a porous partition in 20 and 10 s respectively. The molecular mass of A is 49 u. Molecular mass of B will be ......

(a) 25.00 u   (b) 50.00 u   (c) 12.25 u   (d) 6.50 u **[AIPMT 2011]**

7. By what factor does the average velocity of a gaseous molecule increase, when the temperature (in Kelvin) is doubled?   **[AIPMT 2011]**

(a) 1.4   (b) 2.0   (c) 2.8   (d) 4.0

8. A gaseous mixture was prepared by taking equal moles of CO and N_2. If the total pressure of the mixture was found to be 1 atm, the partial pressure of the nitrogen (N_2) in the mixture is ......   **[AIPMT 2011]**

(a) 1 atm   (b) 0.5 atm   (c) 0.8 atm   (d) 0.9 atm

9. Equal weights of CH_4 and H_2 are mixed in a container at 25°C. Fraction of total pressure exerted by methane is ......   **[AIPMT 2011]**

(a) $\dfrac{1}{2}$ (b) $\dfrac{1}{3}$ (c) $\dfrac{1}{9}$ (d) $\dfrac{8}{9}$

10. What will be the partial pressure of He and O_2 respectively, if 200 mL of He at 0.66 atm and 400 mL of O_2 at 0.52 atm pressure are mixed in 400 mL vessel at 20°C ?   **[AFMC 2010]**

(a) 0.33 and 0.56   (b) 0.33 and 0.52   (c) 0.38 and 0.52   (d) 0.25 and 0.45

11. Which of the following expression is true regarding gas laws?   **[CPMT 2010]**

(w = weight; M = molecular mass)

(a) $\dfrac{T_1}{T_2} = \dfrac{M_1 w_2}{M_2 w_1}$ (b) $\dfrac{T_1}{T_2} = \dfrac{M_2 w_1}{M_1 w_2}$ (c) $\dfrac{T_1}{T_2} = \dfrac{M_1 w_1}{M_2 w_2}$ (d) $\dfrac{T_2}{T_1} = \dfrac{M_1 w_1}{M_2 w_2}$

12. A mixture of gases having different molecular weights is separated by which method?

(a) Atmolysis   (b) Metathesis   **[CPMT 2010]**

(c) Ostwald and Walker method   (d) Reverse osmosis

13. For one mole of an ideal gas, increasing the temperature from 10°C to 20°C

(a) increases the average kinetic energy by two times

(b) increases the rms velocity by $\sqrt{2}$ times

(c) increases the rms velocity by two times

(d) increases both the average kinetic energy and rms velocity, but not significantly

14. In which one of the following, does the given amount of chlorine exert least pressure in a vessel of capacity 1 dm^3 at 273 K ? **[KCET 2010]**
(a) 0.0335 g
(b) 0.071 g
(c) 6.023×10^{21} molecules
(d) 0.02 mol

15. Two grams of hydrogen diffuse from a container in 10 minutes. How many gram of oxygen would diffuse through the same container in the same time under similar conditions?
(a) 0.5 g
(b) 4 g
(c) 6 g
(d) 8 g **[Manipal 2010]**

16. Van der Waals' equation of state is obeyed by real gases. For n moles of a real gas, the expression will be **[Manipal 2010]**
(a) $\left(\dfrac{P}{n} + \dfrac{na}{V^2}\right)\left(\dfrac{V}{n-b}\right) = RT$
(b) $\left(P + \dfrac{an^2}{V^2}\right)(V - nb) = nRT$
(c) $\left(P + \dfrac{na}{V^2}\right)(nV - b) = nRT$
(d) $\left(P + \dfrac{na}{V^2}\right)(nV - b) = nRT$

17. In Van der Waals' equation of state of gas, the constant 'b' is a measure of ......
(a) intermolecular repulsions
(b) intermolecular attraction **[JCECE 2010]**
(c) volume occupied by molecules
(d) intermolecular collisions per unit volume

18. The density of gas A is twice that of B. Molecular mass of A is half of molecular mass of B. The ratio of partial pressures of A and B is ...... **[OJEE 2010]**
(a) 1/4
(b) 1.2
(c) 4/1
(d) 2/1

19. By the ideal gas law, the pressure of 0.60 mole NH_2 gas in a 3.00 L vessel at 25°C is ...
(a) 48.9 atm
(b) 4.89 atm
(c) 0.489 atm
(d) 489 atm **[AFMC 2009]**

20. A gas can be liquefied ...... **[CPMT 2009]**
(a) at its critical temperature
(b) above its critical temperature
(c) below its critical temperature
(d) at 0°C

21. If a gas expands at constant temperature, it indicates that it is ...... **[AIPMT 2008]**
(a) CH_4
(b) C_2H_6
(c) CO_2
(d) Xe .

22. The most probable velocity of a gas molecule at 298 K is 300 m/s. Its rms velocity (in m/s) is ...... **[PMT 2008]**
(a) 420
(b) 245
(c) 402
(d) 367

23. The volume-temperature graphs of a given mass of an ideal gas at constant pressure are shown below. What is the correct order of pressure? **[DUMET 2008]**

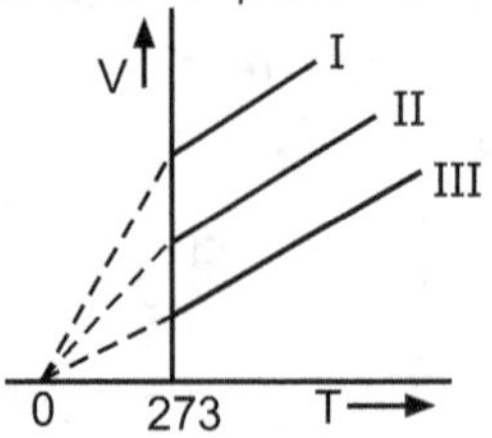

(a) $P_3 > P_2 > P_1$
(b) $P_1 > P_2 > P_3$
(c) $P_2 > P_3 > P_1$
(d) $P_2 > P_1 > P_3$

24. If X is the total number of collisions which a gas molecule register with other per unit time under particular conditions, then the collision frequency of the gas containing N molecules per unit volume is ...... **[Manipal 2008]**
(a) $\dfrac{X}{N}$
(b) NX
(c) 2NX
(d) $\dfrac{NX}{2}$

25. **Assertion :** At high pressure, the compressibility factor Z is $\left(1 + \dfrac{Pb}{RT}\right)$.　　**[AIIMS 2007]**

    Reason : At high pressure Van der Waals' equation is modified as $P(V - b) = RT$
    (a) Both Assertion and Reason are true and Reason is the correct explanation of Assertion.
    (b) Both Assertion and Reason are true but Reason is not the correct explanation of Assertion.
    (c) Assertion is true but Reason is false.
    (d) Both Assertion and Reason are false.

26. Graph between P and V at constant temperature is ......　　**[CPMT 2007]**
    (a) straight　　　　　　　　　　　(b) curved increasing
    (c) straight line with slope　　　　(d) none of these

27. Dominance of strong repulsive forces among the molecules of the gas (Z = compressibility factor)　　**[AIIMS 2006]**
    (a) depends on Z and indicated by Z = 1　(b) depends on Z and indicated by Z > 1
    (c) depends on Z and indicated by Z < 1　(d) is independent of Z

28. The CO_2 gas does not follow gaseous laws at all ranges of pressure and temperature because　　**[MHTCET 2006]**
    (a) it is triatomic gas
    (b) its internal energy is quite high
    (c) there is attraction between its molecules
    (d) it solidify at low temperature

29. **Assertion :** Compressibility factor for hydrogen varies with pressure with positive slope at all pressures.　　**[AIIMS 2005]**
    Reason : Even at low pressure, repulsive forces dominate hydrogen gas.
    (a) Both Assertion and Reason are true and Reason is the correct explanation of Assertion.
    (b) Both Assertion and Reason are true but Reason is not the correct explanation of Assertion.
    (c) Assertion is true but Reason is false.
    (d) Both Assertion and Reason are false.

30. What is the ratio of kinetic energies of 3 g of hydrogen and 4 g of oxygen at T (K) ?
    (a) $12 : 1$　　　(b) $6 : 1$　　　(c) $1 : 6$　　　(d) $24 : 1$　　**[PMT 2005]**

31. The temperature at which the most probable speed of CO_2 molecules is twice that at 50°C will be nearly ......　　**[BHU 2000]**
    (a) 1000°C　　　(b) 1019°C　　　(c) 509°C　　　(d) 590°C

32. For a real gas, $\left(\dfrac{\partial u}{\partial v}\right)$ is ......　　**[AMU 2005]**

    (a) Zero　　　(b) Positive　　　(c) Negative　　　(d) Infinity

33. Ten moles of an ideal gas expand into a vacuum. The work done is ......　　**[EAMCET 2009]**
    (a) Infinity　　　(b) 10 J　　　(c) Zero　　　(d) 5 J

34. The compressibility factor of an ideal gas is ......　　**[CET 2000]**
    (a) 0　　　(b) 1　　　(c) 2　　　(d) 4

35. One mole of an ideal gas is allowed to expand freely and adiabatically into vacuum until its volume has doubled. A statement which is not true related to this is ...... **[AMU 2000]**
    (a) $\Delta H = 0$ (b) $\Delta S = 0$ (c) $\Delta E = 0$ (d) $W = 0$

36. One mole of oxygen gas will have least density at ...... **[CBSE PMT 2000]**
    (a) STP   (b) $0°C$ and 2 atm   (c) 273 K and l atm   (d) $273°C$

37. Densities of two gases are in the ratio 1 : 2 and their temperatures are in the ratio 2 : 1, then ratio of their respective pressures is ...... **[AIIMS 2000]**
    (a) $1 : 1$ (b) $1 : 2$ (c) $2 : 1$ (d) $4 : 1$

38. The density of a gas at $27°C$ and 1 atmosphere is d, pressure remaining constant, at which of the following temperature will its density become 0.75 d ? **[Kerala 2000]**
    (a) $20°C$ (b) $80°C$ (c) $400\ °K$ (d) $300\ °K$

39. The vapour density of a gas is 11.2. The volume occupied by 11.2 gm of the gas at STP is ...
    [CPMT 2000; BHU 2006]
    (a) 1 litre   (b) 11.2 litre   (c) 22.4 litre   (d) 44.8 litre

40. A gas is initially at 1 atm pressure. To compress it to $1/4^{th}$ of its initial volume, pressure to be applied is ...... **[EAMCET 2009]**
    (a) 1 atm   (b) 2 atm   (c) 4 atm   (d) 1/4 atm

41. The Van der Waal's equation explains the behaviour of ...... **[BHU 2001]**
    (a) Real gas   (b) Ideal gas   (c) Non-ideal gas   (d) Non-real gas

42. The $C_p - C_v$ for an ideal gas is ...... **[HP PMT 2005; Orissa JEE 2008]**
    (a) RT   (b) R   (c) R/2   (d) R/1

43. The volume of PV for 5.6 litre of an ideal gas at NTP is ...... **[Karnataka CET 2006]**
    (a) RT   (b) 3 RT   (c) 0.25 RT   (d) 0.56 RT

44. The root mean square velocity of an ideal gas at constant pressure varies with density (d) as
    ...... **[AMU 2001]**
    (a) d^2 (b) d   (c) $\sqrt{d}$ (d) $1/\sqrt{d}$

45. The root mean square velocity of one mole of monoatomic gas having molar mass M is μ_{rms}. The relation between average kinetic energy (E) of gas μ_{rms} is ...... **[J & K CET 2008]**
    (a) $\mu_{rms} = \sqrt{\dfrac{3E}{2M}}$ (b) $\mu_{rms} = \sqrt{2E / 3M}$
    (c) $\mu_{rms} = \sqrt{\dfrac{2E}{M}}$ (d) $\mu_{rms} = \sqrt{\dfrac{E}{3M}}$

46. Use of hot air balloons in meteorological and sports is based upon ...... **[WB JEE 2008]**
    (a) Boyle's law   (b) Charles' law   (c) Avogadro's law   (d) Newton's law

47. The Van der Waal's equation of a gas reduces itself to the ideal gas equation at
    [Kerala PMT 2009]
    (a) High pressure and low temperature   (b) Low pressure and low temperature
    (c) Low pressure and high temperature   (d) High pressure and high temperature

48. Which of the following liquids will distill first ?
    (a) Liquid CO_2 (b) Liquid N_2 (c) Liquid O_2 (d) Liquid H_2

49. Kinetic energy of 1 mole of an ideal gas at 300 K in kJ is ......
    (a) 34.8   (b) 3.48   (c) 3.74   (d) 348

50. What is the kinetic energy of 1 gm of O_2 at $47°C$?
    (a) 2.17×10^2 J   (b) 2.24×10^2 J   (c) 1.24×10^2 J   (d) None of these

ANSWER KEY

1. (d)	2. (a)	3. (b)	4. (d)	5. (a)	6. (b)	7. (b)	8. (c)
9. (b)	10. (b)	11. (a)	12. (a)	13. (a)	14. (b)	15. (a)	16. (c)
17. (a)	18. (a)	19. (a)	20. (b)	21. (d)	22. (c)	23. (c)	24. (a)
25. (b)	26. (b)	27. (c)	28. (b)	29. (b)	30. (c)	31. (d)	32. (a)
33. (d)	34. (d)	35. (c)	36. (d)	37. (b)	38. (b)	39. (b)	40. (a)
41. (b)	42. (d)	43. (c)	44. (a)	45. (d)	46. (c)	47. (c)	48. (b)
49. (b)	50. (b)	51. (d)	52. (a)	53. (b)	54. (d)	55. (c)	56. (d)
57. (b)	58. (b)	59. (b)	60. (c)	61. (c)	62. (b)	63. (d)	64. (c)
65. (b)	66. (b)	67. (c)	68. (b)	69. (a)	70. (a)	71. (c)	72. (a)
73. (d)	74. (d)	75. (d)	76. (b)	77. (a)	78. (b)	79. (c)	80. (d)
81. (b)	82. (d)	83. (c)	84. (d)	85. (a)	86. (a)	87. (d)	88. (a)
89. (b)	90. (a)	91. (a)	92. (c)	93. (b)	94. (d)	95. (c)	96. (b)
97. (c)	98. (a)	99. (b)	100. (c)	101. (b)	102. (a)	103. (b)	104. (c)
105. (a)	106. (c)	107. (c)	108. (b)	109. (c)	110. (a)	111. (d)	112. (d)
113.(b)	114. (a)	115. (b)	116. (b)	117. (c)	118. (a)	119. (c)	120. (b)
121. (c)	122. (b)	123. (c)	124. (d)	125. (b)	126. (c)	127. (d)	128. (b)
129. (a)	130. (a)	131. (b)	132. (c)	133. (c)	134. (b)	135. (b)	136. (a)
137. (c)	138. (b)	139. (b)	140. (c)	141. (b)	142. (d)	143. (a)	144. (a)
145. (c)	146. (a)	147. (b)	148. (a)	149. (c)	150. (a)	151. (a)	152. (d)
153. (d)	154. (a)	155. (a)	156. (a)	157. (a)	158. (c)	159. (a)	160. (c)
161. (a)	162. (c)	163. (a)	164. (c)	165. (d)	166. (c)	167. (a)	168. (d)
169. (b)	170. (b)	171. (c)	172. (c)	173. (a)	174. (a)	175. (a)	176. (a)
177. (c)	178. (c)	179. (c)	180. (b)	181. (a)	182. (a)	183. (c)	184. (a)
185. (b)	186. (d)	187. (c)	188. (d)	189. (b)	190. (c)	191. (a)	192. (b)
193. (b)	194. (c)	195. (b)	196. (c)	197. (b)	198. (c)	199. (a)	200. (a)
201. (b)	202. (c)						

Previous Year's Questions

1. (a)	2. (a)	3. (b)	4. (d)	5. (d)	6. (c)	7. (a)	8. (b)
9. (c)	10. (b)	11. (a)	12. (a)	13. (d)	14. (a)	15. (d)	16. (b)
17. (c)	18. (c)	19. (b)	20. (c)	21. (c)	22. (d)	23. (a)	24. (d)
25. (a)	26. (d)	27. (b)	28. (c)	29. (a)	30. (a)	31. (b)	32. (a)
33. (c)	34. (b)	35. (d)	36. (a)	37. (a)	38. (c)	39. (b)	40. (c)
41. (a)	42. (b)	43. (c)	44. (a)	45. (c)	46. (b)	47. (c)	48. (d)
49. (c)	50. (c)						

❑❑❑

THERMODYNAMICS

1. Thermodynamics can be used to determine all of the following except ......
   (a) The direction in which a reaction is spontaneous
   (b) The extent to which a reaction occurs
   (c) The rate of reaction
   (d) The temperature at which a reaction is spontaneous

2. A system is said to be ...... if it can neither exchange matter nor energy with the surroundings ......
   (a) Open   (b) Closed   (c) Isolated   (d) Insulated

3. The heat content of the products is more than that of the reactants in an ____ reaction.
   (a) Exothermic   (b) Endothermic
   (c) Both exothermic and endothermic   (d) None of these

4. Enthalpy is an ...... property.
   (a) Intensive   (b) Extensive
   (c) Both extensive and intensive   (d) Additive

5. What happens to the water in a calorimeter when an exothermic reaction occurs in it?
   (a) It absorbs heat, and a drop in temperature is observed
   (b) It absorbs heat, and a rise in temperature is observed
   (c) It releases heat, and a drop in temperature is observed
   (d) It releases heat, and a rise in temperature is observed

6. Of the following, which one is a state function?
   (a) H enthalpy   (b) w   (c) Heat   (d) q

7. Which one of the following statements is true?
   (a) Enthalpy is a state function
   (b) Enthalpy is an intensive property
   (c) The enthalpy change for a reaction is independent of the state of reactants and products
   (d) H is the value of q measured under conditions of constant temperature

8. The total energy of one mole of an ideal monoatomic gas at 27°C is ......
   (a) 894.15 kJ   (b) 894.15 cal   (c) 0.0012 cal   (d) 399.38 cal

9. When a gas undergoes adiabatic expansion, it gets cooled due to ......
   (a) Loss of kinetic energy   (b) Fall in temperature
   (c) Decrease in velocity   (d) Energy used in doing work

10. To calculate the amount of work done in joules during reversible isothermal expansion of an ideal gas, the volume must be expressed in ......
    (a) m^3 only   (b) dm^3 only   (c) cm^3 only   (d) Any one of them

11. If one mole of ammonia and one mole of hydrogen chloride are mixed in a closed container to form ammonium chloride gas, then ......

(a) $\Delta H > \Delta u$

(b) $\Delta H = \Delta u$

(c) $\Delta H < \Delta u$

(d) There is no relationship

12. The heat content of a system is called ......

(a) Internal energy   (b) Entropy   (c) Free energy   (d) Enthalpy

13. Heat of reaction at constant volume is measured in the apparatus ......

(a) Bomb calorimeter   (b) Calorimeter   (c) Pyknometer   (d) Pyrometer

14. The temperature of the system decreases in an ....

(a) Adiabatic compression

(b) Isothermal expansion

(c) Isothermal compression

(d) Adiabatic expansion

15. A Beckmann thermometer is used to measure ......

(a) High temperature

(b) Low temperature

(c) Normal temperature

(d) All temperatures but not absolute temperature

16. 200 J of energy was applied to a 10 g sample of copper. If the temperature of copper is increased by 50°C, what is the specific heat capacity of copper?

(a) $0.25 \, J \, g^{-1} \, °C^{-1}$ (b) $0.40 \, J \, g^{-1} \, °C^{-1}$ (c) $2.5 \, J \, g^{-1} \, °C^{-1}$ (d) $4.0 \, J \, g^{-1} \, °C^{-1}$

17. The heat required to raise the temperature of a body by 1 K is called ......

(a) Specific heat

(b) Thermal capacity

(c) Water equivalent

(d) None of these

18. Mechanical work is specially important in system that contain ......

(a) Solid-liquid   (b) Liquid-liquid   (c) Solid-solid   (d) Gases

19. In thermodynamics, a process is called reversible when ......

(a) Surroundings and system change into each other

(b) There is no boundary between system and surroundings

(c) The surroundings are always in equilibrium with the system

(d) The system changes into surroundings spontaneously

20. Which of the following unit represents largest amount of energy ?

(a) Calorie   (b) Joule   (c) Erg   (d) Electron volt

21. In thermodynamic processes which of the following statements is not true?

(a) In an isochoric process, pressure remains constant

(b) In an isothermal process, the temperature remains constant

(c) In an adiabatic process, PV = constant

(d) In an adiabatic process, the system is insulated from the surroundings

22. What is 4.18 J?

(a) The heat required to raise the temperature of one gram of water by one degree celsius

(b) The heat required to raise the temperature of one mole of water by one degree celsius

(c) The heat required to raise the temperature of one gram of substance by one degree celsius

(d) The heat required to raise the temperature of one mole of substance by one degree celsius

23. The internal energy change in a system that has absorbed 2 kcals of heat and done 500 J of work is ......

(a) 6400 J (b) 5400 J (c) 7900 J (d) 8900 J

24. When Fe (solid) is dissolved in aqueous hydrochloric acid in a closed vessel, the work done is ......

(a) Zero (b) More than zero (c) Less than zero (d) Negative

25. The first law of thermodynamics can be given as ......

(a) For any spontaneous process, the entropy of the universe increases

(b) The entropy of a pure crystalline substance at absolute zero is zero

(c) $U = q + w$

(d) $S = q_{rev}/T$ at constant temperature

26. Enthalpy of solution of NaOH (solid) in water is -41.6 kJ mol^{-1}. When NaOH is dissolved in water, the temperature of water ......

(a) Increases (b) Decreases

(c) Does not change (d) Fluctuates indefinitely

27. In an electrochemical cell, if E° is the e.m.f. of the cell involving 'n' moles of electrons, then $\Delta G°$ is ......

(a) $\Delta G° = nFE°$ (b) $\Delta G° = -nFE°$ (c) $E° = nF\Delta G°$ (d) $\Delta G° = nF/E°$

28. If the enthalpy of vaporisation of water is 136.5 J mol^{-1}, then entropy of its vaporisation will be ......

(a) 0.5 J K^{-1} mol^{-1} (b) 1.0 J K^{-1} mol^{-1} (c) 1.5 J K^{-1} mol^{-1} (d) 2.0 J K^{-1} mol^{-1}

29. 6 g of ammonium nitrate was dissolved in 745.3 ml of water. The temperature of water rises from 18.4°C to 21.3°C. Calculate the molar enthalpy of solution of formation of NH_4NO_3.

(a) 25 kJ/mol (b) -2.5×10^4 J/mol

(c) $+2.5 \times 10^4$ J/mol (d) 0.25 kJ/mol

30. When 3.6 g of butanal (relative formula mass = 72) was burned, 134 kJ of energy was released. From this result, what is the enthalpy of combustion in kJ mol^{-1}?

(a) -6.7 (b) $+6.7$ (c) -2680 (d) $+2680$

31. The ΔH value for reaction

$$C_{(s)} + \frac{1}{2} O_{2(g)} \rightarrow CO_{(g)} \text{ and } CO_{(g)} + \frac{1}{2} O_{2(g)} \rightarrow CO_{2(g)}$$

are 100 and 200 kJ respectively. The heat of reaction for $C_{(s)} + O_{2(g)} \longrightarrow CO_{2(g)}$ will be

(a) 50 kJ (b) 100 kJ (c) 150 kJ (d) 300 kJ

32. The law of Lavoisier and Laplace illustrates ......
 (a) The principle of conservation of energy
 (b) Equivalence of mechanical and thermal energy
 (c) The principle of conservation of matter
 (d) Equivalence of mechanical and chemical energy

33. The unit of specific heat is ......
 (a) J/g°C   (b) g°C/J   (c) J/°C   (d) °C/J

34. Gibb's free energy is defined as ....

 (a) $\Delta G = \Delta H - T\Delta S$ (b) $\Delta G = \Delta H + \dfrac{T}{\Delta S}$

 (c) $\Delta H = \Delta G = T\Delta S$ (d) $\Delta G = \Delta H + T.C_P$

35. A substance has a molar heat combustion of 810.4 kJ/mol. When 0.285 mol of the substance is burned in a calorimeter containing 8.60 kg of water, what is the increase in water temperature?
 (a) 0.156°C   (b) 6.41°C   (c) 7.89°C   (d) 12.8°C

36. The addition of 9.54 kJ of heat is required to raise the temperature of 225.0 g of a liquid hydrocarbon from 20.5°C to 45.0°C. What is the heat capacity of this hydrocarbon?
 (a) 0.94 J/g°C   (b) 1.73 J/g°C   (c) 1.88 J/g°C   (d) 9.42 J/g°C

37. The temperature of a 15 g sample of lead metal increases from 22°C to 37°C upon the addition of 29.0 J of heat. The specific heat capacity of lead is ...... J/g°C.
 (a) 29   (b) 0.13   (c) –29   (d) 1.9

38. If the heat of fusion of a substance is 20 kJ/mol, how much heat is released when 1.0 mol of liquid at the melting point freezes?
 (a) 10 kJ   (b) 20 kJ   (c) 40 kJ   (d) 80 kJ

39. The amount of 2.00 mol of a solid ionic compound was dissolved in 225 ml of water in an insulated container. The initial temperature of the water was 20.0°C and the final temperature of the water was 47.8°C. What is enthalpy of the solution ?
 (a) –27.8 kJ/mol   (b) –26.2 kJ/mol   (c) –13.1 kJ/mol   (d) –6.26 kJ/mol

40. In a constant volume calorimeter, 3.5 g of a gas with molecular weight 28 was burnt in excess oxygen at 298.0 K. The temperature of the calorimeter was found to increase from 298.0 K to 298.45 K due to the combustion process. Given that the heat capacity of the calorimeter is 2.5 kJ K^{-1}, the numerical value for the enthalpy of combustion of gas in kJ mol^{-1} is ......
 (a) 3   (b) 7   (c) 8   (d) 9

41. Use the equations to answer the question :
 $2A + B \rightarrow A_2B$ $\Delta H = 217.3$ kJ
 $B + C \rightarrow BC$ $\Delta H = 867.5$ kJ
 What is the value of ΔH for the reaction ?
 $2A + BC \rightarrow A_2B + C$
 (a) +1084.8 kJ   (b) +650.2 kJ   (c) 650.2 kJ   (d) 1084.8 kJ

42. During the production of a small amount of material, there is a large decrease in the temperature of the water in the calorimeter. What is ΔH for the reaction?
   (a) Large and positive   (b) Small and negative
   (c) Small and positive   (d) Large and negative

43. The free energy change $\Delta G = 0$, when ......
   (a) The system is at equilibrium   (b) Catalyst is added
   (c) Reactants are initially mixed thoroughly   (d) The reactants are completely consumed

44. A 2.200 g sample of quinine ($C_6H_4O_2$) is burned in a bomb calorimeter whose total heat capacity is 7.854 kJ/°C. The temperature of the calorimeter increases from 23.44°C to 57°C. What is the heat of combustion per mole of quinine?
   (a) -55.99 kJ/gram   (b) -25.45 kJ/mol   (c) -2750 kJ/mol   (d) -27.50 kJ/mol

45. Standard enthalpy and standard entropy changes for the oxidation of ammonia at 298 K are -382.64 kJ mol^{-1} and -145.6 kJ^{-1} mol^{-1}, respectively. Standard Gibbs energy change for the same reaction at 298 K is ......
   (a) -439.3 kJ mol^{-1} (b) -523.2 kJ mol^{-1}
   (c) -221.1 kJ mol^{-1} (d) -339.3 kJ mol^{-1}

46. Use these thermochemical equations to answer the question.

$$C_2H_{4(g)} + 3O_{2(g)} \rightarrow 2CO_{2(g)} + 2H_2O_{(g)} \quad \Delta H^o_{comb} = 1410.1 \text{ kJ}$$

$$C_4H_{8(g)} + 6O_{2(g)} \rightarrow 4CO_{2(g)} + 4H_2O_{(g)} \quad \Delta H^o_{comb} = 2698.3 \text{ kJ}$$

What is the heat of reaction,
$$2C_2H_{4(g)} \rightarrow C_4H_{8(g)} \text{ ?}$$
   (a) -5518.5 kJ   (b) -3986.5 kJ   (c) -1288.3 kJ   (d) -121.9 kJ

47. 12.6 ml of 0.10 M HCl (aq) completely neutralized 6.3 ml of 0.20 M NaOH (aq) in a coffee-cup calorimeter. The molar enthalpy of neutralization is -8.9 kJ/mol. Calculate the temperature change in the calorimeter.
   (a) 14°C   (b) 0.14°C   (c) 1.4°C   (d) 0.28°C

48. In order for 10.0 g of NH_4Cl to dissociate in water, 2.77 kJ of energy is required. What is the molar enthalpy of solution for NH_4Cl?
   (a) 0.277 kJ/mol   (b) 2.77 kJ/mol   (c) 14.8 kJ/mol   (d) 19.8 kJ/mol

49. The value of heat generated when 36.5 gm HCl and 40 gm of NaOH reacts during neutralization is ......
   (a) 76.5 kcal   (b) 13.7 kcal
   (c) More than 13.7 kcal   (d) 108 kcal

50. Hess's law states that ......
   (a) The standard enthalpy of an overall reaction is the sum of the enthalpy changes in individual reactions.
   (b) Enthalpy of formation of a compound is same as the enthalpy of decomposition of the compound into its constituent elements, but with opposite sign.
   (c) At constant temperature the pressure of a gas is inversely proportional to its volume.
   (d) The mass of a gas dissolved per litre of a solvent is proportional to the pressure of the gas in equilibrium with the solution.

51. In thermodynamics, which one of the following is not an intensive property?

(a) Pressure   (b) Density   (c) Volume   (d) Temperature

52. A reaction occurs spontaneously if ......

(a) $T\Delta S < \Delta H$ and both ΔH and ΔS are +ve   (b) $T\Delta S > \Delta H$ and both ΔH and ΔS are +ve

(c) $T\Delta S = \Delta H$ and both ΔH and ΔS are +ve   (d) $T\Delta S < \Delta H$ and ΔH is +ve and ΔS is –ve

53. Which of the following gas has the highest heat of combustion ?

(a) Methane   (b) Ethane   (c) Ethylene   (d) Acetylene

54. The amount of heat measured for a reaction in a bomb calorimeter is ......

(a) ΔG (b) ΔH (c) ΔU (d) $P\Delta V$

55. The enthalpies of combustion of carbon and carbon monoxide are –393.5 and –283 kJ mol^{-1} respectively. The enthalpy of formation of carbon monoxide per mole is

(a) 110.5 kJ   (b) –110.5 kJ   (c) – 676.5 kJ   (d) + 676.5 kJ

56. For the reaction $N_2. + 3H_2 \rightleftharpoons 2NH_3$; $\Delta H = ?$

(a) $\Delta U + 2RT$ (b) $\Delta U - 2RT$ (c) $\Delta U + RT$ (d) $\Delta U - RT$

57. $C_{(graphite)} + O_{2(g)} \rightarrow CO_{2(g)}$

$\Delta H = -94.05$ kcal mol^{-1}

$C_{(diamond)} + O_{2(g)} \rightarrow CO_{2(g)}$;

$\Delta H = -94.50$ kcal mol^{-1}

(a) $C_{(graphite)} \rightarrow C_{(diamond)}$; $\Delta H^{o}_{298K} = - 450$ cal mol^{-1}

(b) $C_{(diamond)} \rightarrow C_{(graphite)}$; $\Delta H^{o}_{298K} = - 450$ cal mol^{-1}

(c) Graphite is the stable allotrope

(d) Diamond is harder than graphite

58. Enthalpy of formation of two compounds x and y are –84 kJ and –156 kJ respectively. Which of the following statements is correct ?

(a) x is more stable than y   (b) x is less stable than y

(c) Both x and y are unstable   (d) x and y are endothermic compounds

59. Heat capacity is ......

(a) $\dfrac{dQ}{dT}$ (b) $dQ \times dT$ (c) $\Sigma Q \cdot \dfrac{1}{dt}$ (d) None of these

60. An adiabatic expansion of an ideal gas always has ......

(a) Decrease in temperature   (b) $q = 0$

(c) $W = 0$ (d) $\Delta H = 0$

61. The law formulated by Nernst is ......

(a) First law of thermodynamics   (b) Second law of thermodynamics

(c) Third law of thermodynamics   (d) Both (b) and (c)

62. "The quantity of heat which must be supplied to decompose a compound into its element is equal to the heat evolved during the formation of that compound from the elements." This statement is known as ......

    (a) Hess's law
    (b) Joule's law
    (c) Le Chatelier's principle
    (d) Lavoiser and Laplace law

63. The value of $\Delta H°$ for the reaction below is $+128.1$ kJ

    $$CH_3OH_{(l)} \rightarrow CO_{(g)} + 2H_{2(g)}$$

    How many kJ of heat are released when 5.10 g of $H_{2(g)}$ is formed as shown in the equation?

    (a) 62.0 kJ   (b) 162 kJ   (c) 128 kJ   (d) 326 kJ

64. When graphite and diamond burn, the reactions can be represented by the thermochemical equations:

    $C_{(graphite)} + O_{2(g)} \rightarrow CO_{2(g)}$ $\Delta H = -393$ kJ

    $C_{(graphite)} + O_{2(g)} \rightarrow CO_{2(g)}$ $\Delta H = -395$ kJ

    If 1.0 mol of graphite is converted into 1.0 mol of diamond under the same conditions, what is the heat energy change?

    (a) 2 kJ of heat are absorbed from the surroundings
    (b) 2 kJ of heat are given off to the surroundings
    (c) 788 kJ of heat are absorbed from the surroundings
    (d) 788 kJ of heat are given off to the surroundings

65. If 1.0 mol of ammonia reacts to form nitrogen and hydrogen,

    $N_{2(g)} + 3H_{2(g)} \rightarrow 2NH_{3(g)}$ $\Delta H = 92$ kJ

    what heat energy is associated with the reaction?

    (a) 46 kJ and the reaction is endothermic
    (b) 46 kJ and the reaction is exothermic
    (c) 92 kJ and the reaction is endothermic
    (d) 92 kJ and the reaction is exothermic

66. For the reaction ΔH

    $2H_{2(g)} + O_{2(g)} \rightarrow 2H_2O_{(g)}$ -483.6 kJ

    $3O_{2(g)} \rightarrow 2O_{3(g)}$ $+284.6$ kJ

    Calculate the heat of the reaction

    $3H_{2(g)} + O_{3(g)} \rightarrow 3H_2O_{(g)}$

    (a) $+876$ (b) -867.7 kJ   (c) $+583.1$ kJ   (d) 583.1 kJ

67. Calculate the standard reaction enthalpy for the reaction of calcite with hydrochloric acid.

    $$CaCO_{3(s)} + 2HCl_{(aq)} \rightarrow CaCl_{2(aq)} + H_2O_{(l)} + CO_{2(g)}$$

    The standard enthalpies of formation are

    for $CaCl_{2(aq)}$: -877.1 kJ/mol;

    for $H_2O_{(l)}$: -285.83 kJ/mol;

    for $CO_{2(g)}$: -393.51 kJ/mol;

    for $CaCO_{3(s)}$: -1206.9 kJ/mol;

    and for $HCl_{(aq)}$: 167.16 kJ/mol.

    (a) -165 kJ/mol   (b) -116 kJ/mol   (c) -215 kJ/mol   (d) -15.2 kJ/mol

68. Using the thermochemical equation:

$$2Al_{(s)} + 23O_{2(g)} \rightarrow Al_2O_{3(s)} \quad \Delta H = 1676 \text{ kJ}$$

What is ΔH for the following reaction:

$$2Al_2O_{3(a)} \rightarrow 4Al_{(s)} + 3O_{2(g)} \text{ ?}$$

(a) -3352 kJ   (b) -838 kJ   (c) $+838$ kJ   (d) $+3352$ kJ

69. The following decomposition reaction may occur in an air bag.

$$2NaN_{3(s)} \rightarrow 3N_{2(g)}\uparrow + 2Na_{(s)} \quad \Delta H = -43.5 \text{ kJ}$$

What is the heat of formation, ΔH_f for NaN_3?

(a) -43.5 kJ   (b) -21.8 kJ   (c) 21.8 kJ   (d) 43.5 kJ

70. Use the thermochemical equations:

$$Fe_2O_{3(s)} + 3CO_{(g)} \rightarrow 2Fe(s) + 3CO_{2(g)} \quad \Delta H = 26.8 \text{ kJ}$$

$$FeO_{(s)} + CO_{(g)} \rightarrow Fe(s) + CO_{2(g)} \quad \Delta H = 16.5 \text{ kJ}$$

to calculate ΔH for this reaction:

$$Fe_2O_{3(s)} + CO_{(g)} \rightarrow 2FeO_{(s)} + CO_{2(g)}$$

(a) 59.8 kJ   (b) 43.3 kJ   (c) -10.3 kJ   (d) $+6.2$ kJ

71. For spontaneity of a cell, which of the following is correct

(a) $\Delta G = 0, \Delta U = 0$ (b) $\Delta G = -ve, \Delta U = 0$

(c) $\Delta G = +ve, \Delta U = +ve$ (d) $\Delta G = -ve, \Delta U = +ve$

72. Calculate $\Delta G°$ for $CaCO_3$ given the following information.

$$C_{(s)} + O_{2(g)} \rightarrow CO_{2(g)} \qquad \Delta G° = -394.4 \text{ kJ}$$

$$CaO_{(g)} + CO_{2(g)} \rightarrow CaCO_{3(s)} \quad \Delta G° = -130.4 \text{ kJ}$$

$$Ca_{(s)} + O_{(g)} \rightarrow CaO_{(s)} \qquad \Delta G° = -604.0 \text{ kJ}$$

(a) 1128.8 kJ   (b) 340.0 kJ   (c) 130.4 kJ   (d) $+868.0$ kJ

73. When 0.1 mole of a gas absorbs 41.75 J of heat, the rise in temperature occurs equal to 20°C. The gas must be ......

(a) Triatomic   (b) Diatomic

(c) Polyatomic   (d) Monoatomic

74. In a gas phase reaction, what is the effect of increasing reactant or product pressure on the standard Gibbs free energy?

(a) It increases due to decreased entropy   (b) It decreases due to decreased entropy

(c) It increases due to increased enthalpy   (d) It may either increase or decrease

75. The enthalpy of formation of ammonia is -46.2 kJ mol^{-1}. The enthalpy change for the reaction $2NH_{3(g)} \longrightarrow N_{2(g)} + 3H_{2(g)}$ is ......

(a) 42.0 kJ   (b) 64.0 kJ   (c) 80.0 kJ   (d) 92.0 kJ

76. What is the entropy change (in J K^{-1} mol^{-1}) when one mole of ice is converted into water at 0°C? $[\Delta H_f^o = 6000 \text{ JK}^{-1}\text{mol}^{-1}]$

(a) 21.98 (b) 20.13 (c) 2.013 (d) 2.198

77. Consider the reactions

    $C_{(s)} + 2H_{2(g)} \rightarrow CH_{4(g)}$, $\Delta H = -x$ kcal

    $C_{(s)} + 4H_{(g)} \rightarrow CH_{4(g)}$, $\Delta H = -x_1$ kcal

    $CH_{4(g)} \rightarrow CH_{3(g)} + H_{(g)}$, $\Delta H = +y$ kcal

    The bond energy is ......

    (a) y kcal mol^{-1}
    (b) x_1 kcal mol^{-1}
    (c) $x/4$ kcal mol^{-1}
    (d) $x/4$ kcal mol^{-1}

78. In order to decompose 9g of water, 142.5 kJ of heat is required. Hence enthalpy of formation of water is incomplete

    (a) -142.5 kJ
    (b) $+142.5$ kJ
    (c) -285 kJ
    (d) $+285$ kJ

79. Heat liberated when 100 ml of 1 N NaOH is neutralized by 300 ml of 1 N HCl is ......

    (a) 22.92 kJ
    (b) 17.19 kJ
    (c) 11.46 kJ
    (d) 5.73 kJ

80. The third law of thermodynamics can be given as ......

    (a) For any spontaneous process, the entropy of the universe increases

    (b) $\Delta S = q_{rev}/T$ at constant temperature

    (c) $\Delta H_f (x_n) = \sum_n HF_{(reactants)} - \sum_n HF_{(products)}$

    (d) The entropy of a pure crystalline substance is zero at absolute zero

81. If a chemical reaction has a positive change in entropy, S, then ......

    (a) The disorder of the system increases

    (b) The reaction is exothermic

    (c) Heat goes from the system into the surroundings

    (d) The Gibbs free energy is negative

82. Which of the following involves a decrease in entropy?

    (a) The sublimation of carbon dioxide
    (b) The dissolution of NaCl in water
    (c) The decomposition of $N_2O_{4(g)}$ to $NO_{2(g)}$
    (d) The freezing of liquid water into ice

83. A gas can expand from 100 ml to 250 ml under a constant pressure of 2 atm. The work done by the gas is ......

    (a) 30.38 joule
    (b) 25 joule
    (c) 5 kJ
    (d) 16 joule

84. Enthalpy of formation of two compounds x and y are 84 kJ and 156 kJ respectively. Which of the following statements is correct ?

    (a) x is more stable than y
    (b) x is less stable than y
    (c) both x and y are unstable
    (d) x and y are endothermic compounds

85. If for a given substance melting point is T_B and freezing point is T_A, then correct variation shown by graph between entropy change and temperature is

(a) 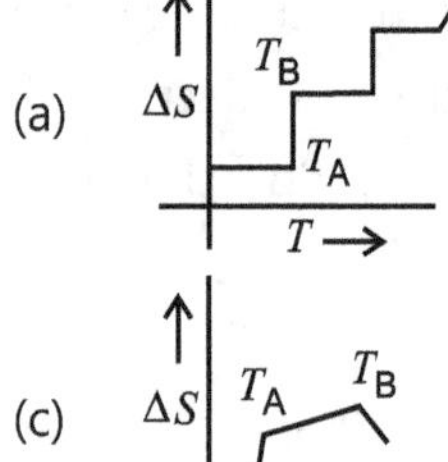

(b) 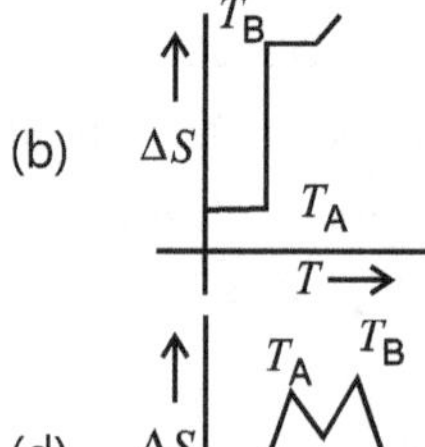

(c)

(d)

86. Which of the following substances is likely to have the highest standard entropy in the liquid state?

    (a) CH_2Cl_2 (b) CCl_4 (c) CH_3OH (d) C_8H_{18}

87. All of the following statements concerning entropy are true except ......

    (a) Entropy is zero for elements under standard conditions

    (b) Entropy is a state function

    (c) A positive change in entropy denotes a change toward greater disorder

    (d) Entropy values are greater than or equal to zero

88. Calculate the standard molar entropy change for the combustion of methane.

    $$CH_{4(g)} + 2O_{2(g)} \rightarrow CO_{2(g)} + 2\,H_2O_{(g)}$$

    Species S° (J/K·mol)

Species	S° (J/K·mol)
$CH_{4(g)}$	186.3
$O_{2(g)}$	205.1
$CO_{2(g)}$	213.7
$H_2O_{(g)}$	188.8

    (a) -5.2 J/K   (b) -1.0 J/K   (c) $+1.0$ J/K   (d) $+5.2$ J/K

89. For an ideal gas expanding adiabatically in vacuum

    (a) $\Delta H = 0$ (b) $\Delta H > 0$ (c) $\Delta H < 0$ (d) None of these

90. The lattice enthalpy and hydration enthalpy of four compounds are given below :

Compounds	Lattice enthalpy (in kJ mol^{-1})	Hydration enthalpy (in kJ mol^{-1})
P	+780	-920
Q	+1012	-812
R	+828	-878
S	+632	-600

    The pair of compounds which is soluble in water is ......

    (a) P and Q   (b) Q and R   (c) R and S   (d) Q and S

    (e) P and R

91. If an endothermic reaction occurs spontaneously at constant T and P, then which of the following is true?

    (a) $\Delta G > 0$ (b) $\Delta H > 0$ (c) $\Delta S > 0$ (d) $\Delta S > 0$

92. Calculate the standard entropy change for the following reaction,

    $$2Ag_2O_{(s)} \rightarrow 4Ag_{(s)} + O_{2(g)}$$

    Given $S°[Ag_2O] = 121.3$ J/K.mol,

    $S°[Ag_{(s)}] = 42.6$ J/K.mol,

    and $S°[O_{2(g)}] = 205.1$ J/K.mol.

    (a) -205.1 J/K   (b) -126.4 J/K   (c) $+126.4$ J/K   (d) $+132.9$ J/K

93. The standard entropy of formation of $CCl_4(l)$ is 235.48 J/Kmol. Calculate the standard molar entropy of $CCl_4(l)$ given $S°[C(s)] = 5.74$ J/kmol and $S°[Cl_{2(g)}] = 223.07$ J/kmol.

    (a) 687.36 J/K   (b) +6.67 J/K   (c) +216.40 J/K   (d) +465.02 J/K

94. Calculate the work done when 1 mole of an ideal gas is compressed reversibly from 1.0 bar to 5.00 bar at constant temperature of 300 K.

    (a) 4.01 kJ   (b) −8.02 kJ   (c) 18.02 kJ   (d) −14.01 kJ

95. For the following reaction at 25°C,

$$N_{2(g)} + O_{2(g)} \rightarrow 2\,NO_{(g)}$$

Calculate ΔS.

Given $\Delta S = 24.8$ J/K and $\Delta H = 181.8$ kJ.

    (a) −585 J/K   (b) +24.2 J/K   (c) +157 J/K   (d) +174 J/K

96. Predict the signs of ΔH and ΔS for the evaporation of water at 35°C.

    (a) $\Delta H > 0$ and $\Delta S > 0$ (b) $\Delta H > 0$ and $\Delta S < 0$

    (c) $\Delta H < 0$ and $\Delta S > 0$ (d) $\Delta H < 0$ and $\Delta S < 0$

97. An endothermic reaction has a positive internal energy change ΔU. In such a case, what is the minimum value that activation energy can have?

    (a) ΔU (b) $\Delta U = \Delta H + \Delta nRT$

    (c) $\Delta U = \Delta H - \Delta nRT$ (d) $\Delta U = E_a + RT$

98. If a chemical reaction has a positive change in entropy, S, then

    (a) The disorder of the system increases

    (b) The reaction is exothermic

    (c) Heat goes from the system into the surroundings

    (d) The Gibbs free energy is negative

99. Given that

$$C_{(s)} + O_{2(g)} \rightarrow CO_{2(g)} \quad \Delta G° = -394.4 \text{ kJ}$$
$$CO_{(g)} + O_{2(g)} \rightarrow CO_{2(g)} \quad \Delta G° = -257.2 \text{ kJ}$$

calculate $\Delta G°$ for the following reaction.

$$C_{(s)} + O_{2(g)} \rightarrow CO_{(g)}$$

    (a) 651.6 kJ   (b) 137.2 kJ   (c) +1.53 kJ   (d) +45.3 kJ

100. A chemical reaction cannot occur at all if its

    (a) ΔH is (+ve) and ΔS is −ve   (b) ΔH is (−ve) and ΔS is +ve

    (c) ΔH and ΔS are +ve but $\Delta H > \Delta S$ (d) ΔH and ΔS are −ve and $\Delta H > \Delta S$

101. The standard Gibbs free energy of formation of _____ is zero.

    (i) $H_2O_{(l)}$ (ii) $O_{(g)}$ (iii) $H_{2(g)}$

    (a) (i) only   (b) (ii) only   (c) (iii) only   (d) (ii) and (iii)

    (a) $\Delta G = -nF/ERT$ (b) $\Delta G = -E/nF$ (c) $\Delta G = -nF/E$ (d) $\Delta G = -nFE$

102. Ten moles of an ideal gas expand into a vacuum. The work done is ......

    (a) Inifinity   (b) 10 J   (c) Zero   (d) 5 J

103. The standard cell potential of the reaction below is +0.126 V.

The value of G for the reaction is _____ kJ/mol.

$Pb_{(s)} + 2H_{(aq)} \rightarrow Pb_{(aq)} + H_2$

(a) −24   (b) +24   (c) −12   (d) +12

104. Consider the reaction:

$FeO_{(s)} + Fe_{(s)} + O_{2(g)} \rightarrow Fe_2O_{3(s)}$

Given the following table of thermodynamic data at 298 K:

Substance	ΔS (kJ/mol)	ΔS (J/K.mol)
$FeO_{(s)}^{-}$	−271.9	60.75
$Fe_{(s)}$	0	27.15
$2O_{(g)}$	0	205.0
$Fe_2O_{3(s)}$	−822.16	89.96

The value of K for the reaction at 25°C is

(a) 3.8×10^{-14} (b) 370   (c) 7.1×10^{85} (d) 8.1×10^{19}

105. For a given reaction, $\Delta H = -19.9$ kJ/mol and $\Delta S = -55.5$ J/K.mol. The reaction will have $\Delta G = 0$ at ___ K.

Assume that ΔH and ΔS do not vary with temperature.

(a) 2.79   (b) 359   (c) 2789   (d) 298

106. Predict the signs of ΔH, ΔS, and ΔG for the combustion of hydrogen gas at 25°C.

$2H_{2(g)} + O_{2(g)} \rightarrow 2 H_2O$

(a) $\Delta H < 0$, $\Delta S < 0$, $\Delta G < 0$ (b) $\Delta H < 0$, $\Delta S > 0$, $\Delta G < 0$

(c) $\Delta H < 0$, $\Delta S > 0$, $\Delta G < 0$ (d) $\Delta H > 0$, $\Delta S < 0$, $\Delta G < 0$

107. Predict the signs of ΔH, ΔS and ΔG for the melting of ice at 50°C

(a) $\Delta H < 0$, $\Delta S < 0$, $\Delta G < 0$ (b) $\Delta H < 0$, $\Delta S > 0$, $\Delta G < 0$

(c) $\Delta H < 0$, $\Delta S > 0$, $\Delta G < 0$ (d) $\Delta H > 0$, $\Delta S > 0$, $\Delta G < 0$

108. If $\Delta G < 0$ for a reaction at all temperatures, then ΔS is _____ and ΔH is ______

(a) Positive, positive   (b) Positive, negative

(c) Zero, positive   (d) Negative, positive

109. The dissolution of ammonium nitrate occurs spontaneously in water. As NH_4NO_3 dissolves, the temperature of water decreases. What are the signs of H, S, and G for this process?

(a) $\Delta H < 0$, $\Delta S < 0$, $\Delta G < 0$ (b) $\Delta H < 0$, $\Delta S > 0$, $\Delta G < 0$

(c) $\Delta H < 0$, $\Delta S > 0$, $\Delta G < 0$ (d) $\Delta H > 0$, $\Delta S > 0$, $\Delta G < 0$

110. Diluting concentrated sulphuric acid with water can be dangerous. The temperature of the solution can increase rapidly. What are the signs of H, S, and G for this process?

(a) $\Delta H < 0$, $\Delta S < 0$, $\Delta G < 0$ (b) $\Delta H < 0$, $\Delta S > 0$, $\Delta G < 0$

(c) $\Delta H < 0$, $\Delta S > 0$, $\Delta G < 0$ (d) $\Delta H > 0$, $\Delta S > 0$, $\Delta G < 0$

111. Above what temperature would you expect a reaction to become spontaneous if $\Delta H = +322$ kJ and $\Delta S = +531$ J/K?

(a) 171 K   (b) 209 K   (c) 606 K

(d) The reaction will be spontaneous at any temperature

112. At what temperature would you expect a reaction to become spontaneous if ΔH = +67.0 kJ and ΔS = −131 J/K?

(a) The reaction will NOT be spontaneous at any temperature

(b) T > 238 K

(c) T > 511 K

(d) The reaction will be spontaneous at any temperature

113. For a reaction, ΔH = +265 kJ and ΔS = +271.3 J/K. At what temperature will ΔG = 0?

(a) 6.30 K　　　　(b) 977 K　　　　(c) 359 K　　　　(d) 719 K

114. If a process is endothermic and spontaneous, which of the following must be true?

(a) $\Delta G > 0$ and $\Delta H < 0$　　　　　　(b) $\Delta G < 0$ and $\Delta H < 0$

(c) $\Delta G < 0$ and $\Delta S > 0$　　　　　　(d) $\Delta H < 0$ and $\Delta S > 0$

115. Calculate ΔG for the reaction below at 25.0°C

$2H_2S_{(g)} + O_{2(g)} \rightarrow 2H_2O_{(g)} + S_{(s)}$

Given ΔH = −442.4 kJ, and ΔS = −175.4 J/K.

(a) −438.0 kJ　　　　(b) −390.1 kJ　　　　(c) −321.9 kJ　　　　(d) +3943 kJ

116. Calculate ΔG for the reaction below at 25.0°C

$Mg_{(s)} + O_{2(s)} \rightarrow 2MgO$

Given ΔH = −1203.4 kJ, and ΔS = −216.6 J/K.

(a) −2076 kJ　　　　(b) −1421 kJ　　　　(c) −1139 kJ　　　　(d) +2888 kJ

117. An ideal gas expands in volume from 1×10^{-3} m^3 to 1×10^{-2} m^3 at 300 K against a constant pressure at 1×10^5 Nm^{-1}. The work done is ......

(a) 110.5 kJ　　　　(b) − 110.5 kJ　　　　(c) − 676.5 kJ　　　　(d) 676.5 kJ

118. Calculate G for the reaction below at 25.0°C.

$$PCl_{3(g)} + Cl_{2(g)} \rightarrow PCl_{5(g)}$$

Species	ΔH (kJ/mol)	ΔS (J/K·mol)
$PCl_{3(g)}$	−287.0	311.8
$Cl_{2(g)}$	0	223.1
$PCl_{5(g)}$	−374.9	364.5

(a) −1432.6 kJ　　　　(b) −930.1 kJ　　　　(c) −879.0 kJ　　　　(d) −37.1 kJ

119. Calculate $\Delta G°$ for the reaction below at 25.0°C.

$C_2H_5OH + 3O_{2(g)} \rightarrow 2CO_{2(g)} + 3 H_2O$

	ΔH (kJ/mol)	S (J/K.mol)
C_2H_5OH	−277.7	160.7
$O_{2(g)}$	0	205.1
$CO_{2(g)}$	−393.5	213.7
$H_2O_{(l)}$	−285.8	69.1

(a) 1325 kJ　　　　(b) 365.1 kJ　　　　(c) 141.3 kJ　　　　(d) +1038 kJ

120. If $\Delta G° < 0$, then

   (a) $K > 1$ (b) $K = 0$ (c) $K < 1$ (d) $K = 1$

121. All of the following substances have a free energy of zero EXCEPT ......

   (a) $He_{(g)}$ (b) $O_{(g)}$ (c) $S_{8(s)}$ (d) $Cu_{(s)}$

122. For a chemical system, $\Delta G°$ and ΔG are equal when

   (a) The equilibrium constant, K, equals 1

   (b) The equilibrium constant, K, equals 0

   (c) A system is at equilibrium

   (d) The reactants and products are in standard state concentrations

123. The free energy change for a given reaction is +15.0 kJ. What is the equilibrium constant for the reaction at 75°C? (R = 8.314 J/K·mol)

   (a) 5.60×10^{-3} (b) 6.82×10^{-1} (c) 1.01 (d) 5.18×10^{-6}

124. The free energy change for the formation of the complex ion AlF_6^{3-} is −140 kJ at 25°C. What is the equilibrium constant for the reaction?

   (a) 2.9×10^{-25} (b) 5.65×10^{-1} (c) 3.5×10^{24} (d) 5.2×10^{29}

125. What is the equilibrium constant for formation of carbon dioxide at 25°C?

   (R = 8.314 J/K·mol)

   $C_{(s)} + O_{2(g)} \rightarrow CO_{2(g)}$ $\Delta G = 3.90 \times 10^{2}$ kJ/mol

   (a) 5.7×10^{1} (b) 5.4×10^{13} (c) 2.9×10^{24} (d) 2.3×10^{68}

126. The equilibrium constant for a reaction at 298 K is 9.3×10^{-12}. What is G°?

   (R = 8.314 J/K.mol)

   (a) 2.54 kJ   (b) $+2.54$ kJ   (c) $+5.28$ kJ   (d) $+62.9$ kJ

127. Calculate $\Delta G°$ for the following reaction at 298 K,

   $N_2O_{4(g)} \rightarrow 2NO_{2(g)}$

   Given K = 0.15. (R = 8.314 J/K.mol)

   (a) $+1.15$ kJ   (b) $+4.70$ kJ   (c) $+8.13$ kJ   (d) $+38.1$ kJ

128. The standard enthalpy of formation of NH_3 is − 46.0 kJ mol^{-1}. If the enthalpy of formation of H_2 from its atoms is − 436 kJ mol^{-1} and that of N is −712 kJ mol^{-1}, the average bond enthalpy of N − H bond in NH_3 is

   (a) − 1102 kJ mol^{-1} (b) − 964 kJ mol^{-1} (c) + 352 kJ mol^{-1} (d) + 1056 kJ mol^{-1}

129. Standard enthalpy of vaporization ΔH_{vap} for water at 100°C is 40.66 kJmol^{-1}. The internal energy of vaporization of water at 100°C (in kJmol^{-1}) is

   (Assume water vapour to behave like an ideal gas)

   (a) $+43.76$ (b) $+40.66$ (c) $+37.56$ (d) 43.76

130. Consider the reaction :

   $4NO_{2(g)} + O_{2(g)} \rightarrow 2N_2O_{5(g)},$ $\Delta_r H = 111$ kJ.

   If $N_2O_{5(s)}$ is formed instead of $N_2O_{5(g)}$ in the above reaction, the ΔH value will be ......

   (given, ΔH of sublimation for N_2O_5 is 54 kJ/mol)

   (a) -219 kJ   (b) -165 kJ   (c) $+ 54$ kJ   (d) $+ 219$ kJ

131. Based on the first law of thermodynamics, which one of the following is correct?

(a) For an isothermal process, $q = +w$

(b) For an isochoric process, $\Delta = -q$

(c) For an adiabatic process, $\Delta U = -w$

(d) For a cyclic process, $q = -w$

132. The amount of heat released when 20 ml 0.5 M NaOH is mixed with 100 ml 0.1 M HCl is x kJ. The heat of neutralization is ......

(a) $-100\ x$ kJ/mol   (b) $-50\ x$ kJ/mol   (c) $+100\ x$ kJ/mol (d) $+50\ x$ kJ/mol

133. The bond energy (in kcal mol^{-1}) of a C–C single bond is approximately ......

(a) 1   (b) 10   (c) 100   (d) 1000

134. The amount of heat evolved when 500 cm^3 of 0.1 M HCl is mixed with 200 cm^3 of 0.2 M NaOH is

(a) 1.292 kJ   (b) 2.292 kJ   (c) 3.392 kJ   (d) 0.292 kJ

135. 40 grams of a sample of carbon on combustion left 10% of it unreacted. The volume of oxygen required at STP for this combustion reaction is

(a) 22.4 l (b) 67.2 l (c) 11.2 l (d) 44.8 l

136. Standard free energies of formation (in kJ/mol) at 298 K are -237.2, -394.4 and -8.2 for $H_2O_{(l)}$, $CO_{2(g)}$ and pentane (g), respectively. The value of E° cell for the pentane-oxygen fuel cell is ......

(a) 2.0968 V   (b) 1.0968 V   (c) 0.0968 V   (d) 1.968 V

137. Which of the following is an intensive property?

(a) Temperature   (b) Surface tension   (c) Viscosity   (d) All of these

138. The standard enthalpy of formation (ΔH_f°) at 298 K for methane, $CH_{4(g)}$, is 74.8 kJ mol^{-1}. The additional information required to determine the average energy for C–H bond formation would be

(a) The dissociation energy of H_2 and enthalpy of sublimation of carbon

(b) Latent heat of vaporization of methane

(c) The first four ionization energies of carbon and electron gain enthalpy of hydrogen

(d) The dissociation energy of hydrogen molecule, H_2

139. In a fuel cell, methanol is used as a fuel and oxygen gas is used as an oxidizer. The reaction is :

$$CH_3OH_{(l)} + 3/2O_{2(g)} \longrightarrow CO_{2(g)} + H_2O_{(l)}$$

At 298 K standard Gibb's energies of formation for $CH_3OH_{(l)}$, $H_2O_{(l)}$ and $CO_{2(g)}$ are -166.2, -237.2 and -394.4 kJ mol^{-1} respectively. If the standard enthalpy of combustion of methanol is -726 kJ mol^{-1}, efficiency of the fuel cell will be ......

(a) 80%   (b) 87%   (c) 90%   (d) 97%

140. In view of the signs of $\Delta G°$ for the following reactions

$PbO_2 + Pb \rightarrow 2PbO,\ \Delta G° < 0$

$SnO_2 + Sn \rightarrow 2SnO,\ \Delta G° > 0,$

Which oxidation states are more characteristic for lead and tin?

(a) For lead +2, for tin +4   (b) For lead +4, for tin +2

(c) For lead +2, for tin +2   (d) For lead +4, for tin +4

141. The Gibbs energy for the decomposition of Al_2O_3 at 500°C is as follows

$$\frac{2}{3}Al_2O_3 \rightarrow \frac{4}{3}Al + O_2, \Delta G = +966 \text{ kJ mol}$$

The potential difference needed for electrolytic reduction of Al_2O_3 at 500°C is at least ......
(a) 5.0 V   (b) 4.5 V   (c) 3.0 V   (d) 2.5 V

142. On the basis of the following thermochemical data:

$$H_2O_{(l)} \rightarrow H^+_{(aq)} + OH^-_{(aq)}; \Delta H = 57.32 \text{ kJ}$$

$$H_{2(g)} + \frac{1}{2}O_{2(g)} \rightarrow H_2O_{(l)}; \Delta H = -286.20 \text{ kJ}$$

The value of enthalpy of formation of OH^- ion at 25°C is ......
(a) −22.88 kJ   (b) −228.88 kJ   (c) +228.88 kJ   (d) −343.52 kJ

143. One mole of which of the following has the highest entropy?
(a) Liquid nitrogen   (b) Hydrogen gas   (c) Mercury   (d) Diamond

144. Standard entropy of X_2, Y_2 and XY_3 are 60, 40 and 50 JK^{-1} mol^{-1}, respectively.
For the reaction, $X_2 + Y_2 \rightarrow XY_3$, $\Delta H = -30$ kJ, to be at equilibrium, the temperature will be
(a) 1250 K   (b) 500 K   (c) 750 K   (d) 1000 K

145. In which of the following process, a maximum increase in entropy is observed?
(a) Dissolution of salt in water   (b) Condensation of water
(c) Sublimation of naphthalene   (d) Melting of ice

146. $\Delta H_{vap} = 30$ kJ/mole and $\Delta S_{vap} = 75$ J.mol/K. Find temperature of vapour at one atmosphere
(a) 400 K   (b) 350 K   (c) 298 K   (d) 250 K

147. The enthalpy change of a reaction does not depend on ......
(a) The state of reactants and products
(b) Nature of reactants and products
(c) Different intermediate reaction
(d) Initial and final enthalpy change of a reaction

148. For which of the processes ΔS is negative ?
(a) $H_{2(g)} \rightarrow 2H_{(g)}$ (b) N_2 (g, 1 atm) $\rightarrow N_2$ (g, 8 atm)
(c) $2SO_{3(g)} \rightarrow 2SO_{2(g)} + O_{2(g)}$ (d) $C_{(diamond)} \rightarrow C_{(graphite)}$

149. Standard molar heat of formation of ethane, CO_2 and liquid water is − 21.1, −94.1 and −68.3 kilo calories. The value of standard molar heat of combustion of ethane will be
(a) 372 kilo calorie   (b) 272 kilo calorie
(c) 172 kilo calorie   (d) 472 kilo calorie

150. What is the enthalpy change for

$$2H_2O_{2(l)} \rightarrow 2H_2O_{(l)} + O_{2(g)}$$

if heat of formation of $H_2O_{2(l)}$ and $H_2O_{(l)}$ are − 188 and − 286 kJ/mol respectively ?
(a) − 196 kJ/mol   (b) + 196 kJ/mol   (c) + 948 kJ/mol   (d) − 948 kJ/mol

151. Heat of combustion ΔH for $C_{(s)}$, $H_{(g)}$ and $CH_{4(g)}$ are –94, –68 and –213 kcal/mol, then ΔH for

$C_{(s)} + 2H_{2(g)} \rightarrow CH_{4(g)}$ is ......

(a) – 17 kcal (b) – 111 kcal (c) – 170 kcal (d) – 85 kcal

152. The enthalpy change for the following processes are listed below :

$Cl_{2(g)} \rightarrow Cl_{2(g)}$, 242.3 kJ mol^{-1}

$I_{2(g)} \rightarrow 2I_{(g)}$, $Cl_{2(g)}$, 211.3 kJ mol^{-1}

$ICl_{2(s)} \rightarrow I_{(g)}$, $Cl_{2(g)}$, 211.3 kJ mol^{-1}

$I_{2(s)} \rightarrow I_{(g)}$, 62.76 mol^{-1}

Given that the standard states for iodine and chlorine are $I_{2(s)}$ and $Cl_{2(g)}$, the standard enthalpy of formation for $ICl_{(g)}$ is

(a) + 244.8 kJ mol^{-1} (b) – 14.6 kJ mol^{-1} (c) – 16.8 kJ mol^{-1} (d) + 16.8 kJ mol^{-1}

153. The heat of neutralization of strong base and a strong acid is 57 kJ. The heat released when 0.5 mole of HNO_3 solution is added to 0.20 moles of NaOH solution is

(a) 11.4 kJ (b) 23.5 kJ (c) 34.7 kJ (d) 58.8 kJ

154. In an irreversible process taking place at constant T and P and in which only pressure-volume work is being done, the change in Gibbs free energy (dG) and change in entropy (dS), satisfy the criteria ......

(a) $\Delta S < 0$, $\Delta G < 0$ (b) $\Delta S > 0$, $\Delta G < 0$

(c) $\Delta S = 0$, $\Delta G = 0$ (d) $\Delta S = 0$, $\Delta G > 0$

155. A cylinder of gas supplied by Bharat Petroleum is assumed to contain 14 kg of butane. If a normal family requires 20000 kg of energy per day for cooking, butane gas in the cylinder lasts for ...... days. (ΔH_c of C_4H_{10} = – 2658 kJ per mole)

(a) 15 days (b) 32 days (c) 20 days (d) 40 days

156. $\Delta G = \Delta H - T\Delta S$ was given by ......

(a) Faraday (b) Kirchhoff (c) Einstein (d) Gibbs-Helmholtz

157. The reaction : $N_{2(g)} + 3H_{2(g)} \rightarrow 2NH_{3(g)}$ carried out at constant temperature and pressure. If ΔH and ΔU are the enthalpy and internal energy changes for the reaction, which of the following expressions is true ?

(a) $\Delta H = 0$ (b) $\Delta H = \Delta U$ (c) $\Delta H < \Delta U$ (d) $\Delta H > \Delta U$

158. Given

$NH_{3(g)} + 3Cl_{2(g)} \rightleftharpoons NCl_{3(g)} + 3HCl_{(g)}; -\Delta H_1$

$NH_{2(g)} + 3H_{2(g)} \rightleftharpoons 2NH_{3(g)}; -\Delta H_2$

$NH_{2(g)} + Cl_{2(g)} \rightleftharpoons 2HCl_{(g)}; -\Delta H_3$

The heat of formation of $NCl_{3(g)}$ in terms of ΔH_1, ΔH_2 and ΔH_3 is ......

(a) $\Delta H_f = -\Delta H_1 + \dfrac{\Delta H_2}{2} - \dfrac{3}{2}\Delta H_3$ (b) $\Delta H_f = -\Delta H_1 + \dfrac{\Delta H_2}{2} - \dfrac{3}{2}\Delta H_3$

(c) $\Delta H_f = -\Delta H_1 + \dfrac{\Delta H_2}{2} - \dfrac{3}{2}\Delta H_3$ (d) None of these

159. The entropy change involved in the isothermal reversible expansion of 2 moles of an ideal gas from a volume of 10 dm^3 to a volume of 100 dm^3 at 27°C is ......

    (a) 42.3 J mol K^{-1} (b) 38.3 J mol K^{-1} (c) 35.8 J mol K^{-1} (d) 32.3 J mol K^{-1}

160. For a particular reversible reaction at temperature T, ΔH and ΔS were found to be both +ve. If T_e is the temperature at equilibrium, the reaction would be spontaneous when ......

    (a) $T = T_c$ (b) $T_c > T$ (c) $T > T_c$ (d) T_c is 5 times T

161. The standard molar heat of formation of ethane, CO_2 and water are respectively −21.0, −94.1 and −68.3 kcal. The standard molar heat of combustion of ethane will be

    (a) −372 kcal   (b) 162 kcal   (c) −340 kcal   (d) 183.5 kcal

162. For the reaction, $N_{2(g)} + 3H_{2(g)} \rightleftharpoons 2NH_{3(g)}$ + Heat when temperature increases, equilibrium concentration of ......

    (a) NH_3 increases   (b) NH_3 decreases   (c) N_2 decreases   (d) H_2 decreases

163. ΔH for solid to liquid transitions for proteins A and B are 2.73 kcal/mol and 3.0 kcal/mol. The two melting points are 0°C and 30°C respectively. The entropy changes ΔS_A and ΔS_B at two transition temperatures are related as ......

    (a) $\Delta S_A = \Delta S_B$ (b) $\Delta S_A < \Delta S_B$ (c) $\Delta S_B < \Delta S_A$ (d) $\Delta S_B = \dfrac{300\ \Delta S_A}{273}$

    (e) $\Delta S_A = \dfrac{300}{273} \Delta S_A$

164. The heat absorbed at constant volume is equal to the system's change in ......

    (a) Enthalpy   (b) Entropy

    (c) Entropy × temperature   (d) Free energy

    (e) Internal energy

165. The heat of neutralization is maximum when ......

    (a) Sodium hydroxide is neutralised by acetic acid

    (b) Ammonium hydroxide is neutralized by acetic acid

    (c) Ammonium hydroxide is neutralized by hydrochloric acid

    (d) Sodium hydroxide is neutralized by formic acid

    (e) Sodium hydroxide is neutralized by hydrochloric acid

166. The law of thermodynamics that provides the basis for the determination of absolute entropy of a substance is ......

    (a) Zeroth law   (b) First law   (c) Second law   (d) Third law

167. A heat engine absorbs heat Q_1 at temperature T_1 and heat Q_2 at temperature T_2. Work done by the engine is $(Q_1 + Q_2)$. This data

    (a) Violates first law of thermodynamics

    (b) Violates first law of thermodynamics if Q_1 is negative

    (c) Violates first law of thermodynamics if Q_2 is negative

    (d) Does not violate first law of thermodynamics

168. If an endothermic reaction is non-spontaneous at freezing point of water and becomes feasible at its boiling point, then

    (a) ΔH is −ve, ΔS is +ve   (b) ΔH and ΔS both are +ve

    (c) ΔH and ΔS both are −ve   (d) ΔH is +ve and ΔS is −ve

169. Compounds with high heat of formation are less stable because

(a) It is difficult to synthesize them

(b) Energy rich state leads to instability

(c) High temperature is required to synthesize them

(d) Molecules of such compounds are disturbed

170. If a reaction involves only solids and liquids, which of the following is true ?

(a) $\Delta H < \Delta U$　　　　(b) $\Delta H = \Delta U$　　　　(c) $\Delta H > \Delta U$　　　(d) $\Delta H = \Delta U + RT\Delta n$

171. Heat of combustion (ΔH) for C(s), H_2(g) and CH_4(g) are -94, -68 and -213 kcal/mol. Then ΔH for $C(s) + 2H_2(g) \rightarrow CH_4(g)$ is ......

(a) -17 kcal　　　　(b) -111 kcal　　　　(c) -170 kcal　　　(d) -85 kcal

172. The internal energy change when a system goes from state A to B is 40 kJ/mole. If the system goes from A to B by a reversible path and returns to state A by an irreversible path, what would be the net change in internal energy ?

(a) 40 kJ　　　　(b) > 40 kJ　　　　(c) < 40 kJ　　　(d) 0

173. The correct relationship between free energy change in a reaction and the corresponding equilibrium constant K is ......

(a) $\Delta G = RT \ln K_c$　　　(b) $-\Delta G = RT \ln K_c$　　(c) $\Delta G° = RT \ln K_c$　(d) $-\Delta G° = RT \ln K_c$

174. The enthalpies of formation of Al_2O_3 and Cr_2O_3 are -1596 kJ and -1134 kJ respectively. ΔH for the reaction

$2Al + Cr_2O_3 \longrightarrow 2Cr + Al_2O_3$ is ......

(a) -1365 kJ　　　　(b) $+ 2730$ kJ　　　　(c) -2730 kJ　　　(d) -462 kJ

175. The value of $\Delta H - \Delta U$ for the following reaction at 27°C will be ......

$$2NH_{3(g)} \longrightarrow N_{2(g)} + 3H_{2(g)}$$

(a) $8.314 \times 273 \times (-2)$　　　　　　　(b) $8.314 \times 300 \times (-2)$

(c) $8.314 \times 27 \times (-2)$　　　　　　　(d) $8.314 \times 300 \times (2)$

(e) $8.314 \times 273 \times (1)$

176. The enthalpy of the reaction

$H_{2(g)} + \dfrac{1}{2} O_{2(g)} \longrightarrow H_2O_{(g)}$ is ΔH_1 and that of

$H_{2(g)} + \dfrac{1}{2} O_{2(g)} \longrightarrow H_2O_{(l)}$ is ΔH_2, then

(a) $\Delta H_1 < \Delta H_2$　　　　(b) $\Delta H_1 + \Delta H_2 = 0$　　(c) $\Delta H_1 > \Delta H_2$　　(d) $\Delta H_1 = \Delta H_2$

177. 1 mole of H_2SO_4 is mixed with 2 moles of NaOH. The heat evolved will be ......

(a) 57.3 kJ　　　　　　　　　　(b) 2×57.3 kJ

(c) 57.3/2 kJ　　　　　　　　　(d) Cannot be predicted

PREVIOUS YEAR'S QUESTIONS

1. Which of the following unit represents largest amount of ...... **[AMU 2001]**

(a) Calorie (b) Joule (c) Erg (d) Electron volt

2. Enthalpy of formation of two compounds x and y are -84 kJ and -156 kJ respectively. Which of the following statements is correct ? **[CBSE PMT 2001]**

(a) x is more stable than y (b) x is less stable than y

(c) Both x and y are unstable (d) x and y are endothermic compounds

3. The heat required to raise the temperature of a body by 1 K is called ...... **[AIEEE 2002]**

(a) Specific heat (b) Thermal capacity (c) Water equivalent (d) None of these

4. The molar heat capacity of water at constant pressure, C_p is 75 J mole^{-1}. When 1.0 kJ of heat is supplied to 100 g of water which is free to expand, the increase in temperature of water is ...... **[CBSE AIPMT 2003]**

(a) 4.8 K (b) 6.6 KA (c) 1.2 K (d) 2.4 K

5. Formation of a solution from two components can be considered as ...**[CBSE AIPMT 2003]**

(1) pure solvent $\to$ separated solvent molecules, ΔH_1

(2) pure solute $\to$ separated solvent molecules, ΔH_2

(3) separated solvent and solute molecules $\to$ solution, ΔH_3

Solution so formed will be ideal if

(a) $\Delta H_{Soln} = \Delta H_1 - \Delta H_2 - \Delta H_3$ (b) $\Delta H_{Soln} = \Delta H_3 - \Delta H_1 - \Delta H_2$

(c) $\Delta H_{Soln} = \Delta H_1 + \Delta H_2 + \Delta H_3$ (d) $\Delta H_{Soln} = \Delta H_1 + \Delta H_2 - \Delta H_3$

6. For the reaction : C_3H_8 (g) $+ 5O_2$ (g) $\to 3CO_2$ (g) $+ 4H_2O(l)$ **[CBSE AIPMT 2003]**

at constant temperature, $\Delta H - \Delta E$ is ......

(a) $+3RT$ (b) $-RT$ (c) $+RT$ (d) $-3RT$

7. The enthalpies of formation of Al_2O_3 and Cr_2O_3 are -1596 kJ and -1134 kJ respectively. ΔH for the reaction $2Al + Cr_2O_3 \to 2Cr + Al_2O_3$ is ...... **[KCET 2003]**

(a) -2730 kJ (b) -462 kJ (c) -1265 kJ (d) $+2730$ kJ

8. The enthalpy change for the reaction of 50.00 ml of ethylene with 50.00 ml of H_2 at 1.5 atm pressure is $\Delta H = -0.31$ kJ. The value of ΔE will be **[DPMT 2004]**

(a) -0.3024 kJ (b) 0.3024 kJ (c) 2.567 kJ (d) -0.0076 kJ

9. When 50 cm^3 of 0.5 N H_2SO_4 is mixed with 50 cm^3 of 1 N KOH, the heat liberated is **[KCET 2004]**

(a) 11.46 kJ (b) 57.3 kJ (c) 573 kJ (d) 573 J

10. How much energy is released when 6 moles of octane is burnt in air? ΔH_f^o for CO_2 (g), H_2O (g) and C_8H_{18} (l) respectively are $-490, -240$ and $+160$ J/mol **[AIIMS 2004]**

(a) -6.2 kJ (b) -37.4 kJ (c) -35.5 kJ (d) -20.0 kJ

11. $\Delta G = \Delta H - T\Delta S$ was given by **[AFMC 2004]**

(a) Faraday (b) Kirchhoff (c) Einstein (d) Gibbs-Helmholtz

12. For the equilibrium, **[CBSE AIPMT-2004]**

$$H_2O\ (l) \rightleftharpoons H_2O\ (g) \text{ at 1 atm and 298 K}$$

    (a) standard free energy change is equal to zero ($\Delta G^\circ - 0$)

    (b) free energy change is less than zero ($\Delta G < 0$)

    (c) standard free energy change is less than zero ($\Delta G^\circ > 0$)

13. For the reaction of one mole of zinc dust with one mole of sulphuric acid in a bomb calorimeter, ΔU and W corresponds to **[AIIMS 2005]**

    (a) $\Delta U < 0,\ W = 0$ (b) $\Delta U < 0,\ W < 0$ (c) $\Delta U < 0,\ W = 0$ (d) $\Delta U > 0,\ W > 0$

14. The absolute enthalpy of neutralization of the reaction

    $MgO\ (s) + 2HCl\ (aq) \rightarrow MgCl_2\ (aq) + H_2O\ (l)$ **[CBSE AIPMT-2005]**

    will be

    (a) Less than $-57.33\ kJ\ mol^{-1}$ (b) $-57.33\ kJ\ mol^{-1}$

    (c) greater than $-57.33\ kJ\ mol^{-1}$ (d) $57.33\ kJ\ mol^{-1}$

15. ΔH_f° (298 K) of methanol is given by the chemical equation, **[AIIMS 2005]**

    (a) $CH_4\ (g) + \dfrac{1}{2}O_2\ (g) \rightarrow CH_3OH\ (g)$

    (b) $C\ (graphite) + \dfrac{1}{2}O_2\ (g) + 2H_2(g) \rightarrow CH_3OH\ (l)$

    (c) $C\ (diamond) + \dfrac{1}{2}O_2\ (g) + 2H_2(g) \rightarrow CH_3OH\ (l)$

    (d) $CO\ (g) + 2H_2\ (g) \rightarrow CH_3OH\ (l)$

16. Minimum work is obtained when 1 kg of ...... gas expanded under 500 kPa to 200 kPa pressure at 0°C. **[MHT CET 2005]**

    (a) chlorine   (b) oxygen   (c) nitrogen   (d) methane

17. Which of the following pairs of a chemical reaction is certain to result in a spontaneous reaction? **[CBSE AIPMT 2005]**

    (a) Exothermic and decreasing disorder (b) Endothermic and increasing disorder

    (c) Exothermic and increasing disorder (d) Endothermic and decreasing disorder

18. One mole of an ideal gas is initially at 0°C and 1 atm pressure. If it absorbs 1000 cal heat during a reversible isothermal expansion, what will be its final volume? **[MHT CET 2006]**

    (a) 102.5 L   (b) 242.5 L   (c) 22.4 L   (d) 140 L

19. The enthalpy change ΔH for the reaction

    $$N_2(g) + 3H_2\ (g) \rightarrow 2NH_3(g)$$ **[AIIMS 2006]**

    is -92.38 kJ at 298 K. The internal energy change ΔU at 298 K is ......

    (a) -92.83 kJ   (b) -87.42 kJ   (c) -97.34 kJ   (d) -89.8 kJ

20. Assume each reaction is carried out in an open container. For which reaction will be $\Delta H = \Delta E$? **[CBSE AIPMT 2006]**

    (a) $H_2\ (g) + Br_2\ (g) \rightarrow 2HBr\ (g)$ (b) $C(s) + 2H_2O\ (g) \rightarrow 2H_2\ (g) + CO_2\ (g)$

    (c) $PCl_5\ (g) \rightarrow PCl_3\ (g) + Cl_2\ (g)$ (d) $2COO\ (g) + O_2\ (g) \rightarrow 2CO_2\ (g)$

21. Identify the correct statement for change of Gibbs energy for a system ΔG_{system} at constant temperature and pressure.   **[CBSE AIPMT-2006]**

(a) If $\Delta G_{system} > 0$, the process is spontaneous

(b) If $\Delta G_{system} = 0$, the system has attained equilibrium

(c) If $\Delta G_{system} = 0$, the system is still moving in a particular direction

(d) If $\Delta G_{system} < 0$, the process is not spontaneous

22. A cylinder of gas supplied by Bharat petroleum is assumed to contain 14 kg of butane. If anormal family requires 20,000 kJ of energy per day for cooking, butane gas in the cylinder last for ... days, (ΔH_c of $C_4H_{10} = -2658$ kJ per mole).   **[BHU 2006]**

(a) 15 days   (b) 20 days   (c) 32 days   (d) 40 days

23. Which of the following is combustion reaction?   **[CPMT 2007]**

(a) $C + O_2 \rightarrow CO_2$ (b) $CH_4 + O_2 \rightarrow CO_2 + H_2O$

(c) $Mg + O_2 \rightarrow MgO$ (d) All of these

24. The enthalpy of hydrogenation of cyclohexene is -119.5 kJ mol^{-1}. If resonance energy of benzene is -150.4 kJ mol^{-1}, its enthalpy of hydrogenation would be ......   **[AIIMS 2007]**

(a) -2018.1 kJ mol^{-1} (b) -269.9 kJ mol^{-1}

(c) -358.5 kJ mol^{-1} (d) -508.9 kJ mol^{-1}

25. One mole of methanol when burnt in O_2, gives out 723 kJ mol^{-1} heat. If one mole of O_2 is used, what will be the amount of heat evolved?   **[AIIMS 2007]**

(a) 723 kJ   (b) 924 kJ   (c) 482 kJ   (d) 241 kJ

26. Which of the following is a path function?   **[MHT CET 2007]**

(a) Internal energy   (b) Enthalpy   (c) Work   (d) Entropy

27. Hess's law deals with ......   **[AFMC 2007]**

(a) change in heat of reaction   (b) rate of reaction

(c) equilibrium constant   (d) influence of pressure on volume of gas

28. Calculate the difference between ΔE and ΔH for the following reaction at 27° C (in kcal)

C (graphite) $+ H_2$ (g) $\rightarrow CH_4$ (g)   **[EAMCET 2007]**

(a) -0.6 (b) -1.2 (c) $+0.5$ (d) $+1.2$

29. The bond energy is the energy required to   **[MHT CET 2007]**

(a) dissociate one mole of the substance   (b) dissociate bond in 1 kg of the substance

(c) break one mole of similar bonds   (d) break bonds in one mole of substance

30. For the reaction,   **[MHT CET 2007]**

$2H_2(g) + O_2$ (g) $\rightarrow 2H_2O$ (g); $\Delta H° = -573.2$ kJ

The heat of decomposition of water per mole is

(a) 286.6 kJ   (b) 573.2 kJ   (c) -28.66 kJ   (d) Zero

31. For the gas phase reaction, PCl_5 (g) $\rightleftharpoons PCl_3$ (g) $+ Cl_2$ (g)

Which of the following conditions are correct?   **[CBSE AIPMT 2008]**

(a) $\Delta H = 0$ and $\Delta S < 0$ (b) $\Delta H > 0$ and $\Delta S > 0$

(c) $\Delta H < 0$ and $\Delta S < 0$ (d) $\Delta H > 0$ and $\Delta S < 0$

32. Identity the reaction for which $\Delta H \neq \Delta E$　　　　　**[AFMC 2008]**

(a) S (rhombic) $+ O_2$ (g) $\rightarrow SO_2$ (g)

(b) N_2 (g) $+ O_2$ (g) $\rightarrow 2NO$ (g)

(c) H_2 (g) $+ Cl_2$ (g) $\rightarrow 2HCl$ (g)

(d) CO (g) $+ \dfrac{1}{2} O_2$ (g) $\rightarrow CO_2$ (g)

33. If one mole of ammonia and one mole of hydrogen chloride are mixed in a closed container to form ammonium chloride gas, then ......　　　　　**[KCET 2008]**

(a) $\Delta H > \Delta U$　　　　(b) $\Delta H = \Delta U$　　　　(c) $\Delta H < \Delta U$　　　　(d) there is no relationship

34. 100 cm^3 of 0.1 M HCl and 100 cm^3 of 0.1 M NaOH solutions are mixed in a calorimeter. If the heat liberated is "Q" kcal, the heat of neutralization (ΔH) (in kcal) of HCl (aq) and NaOH (aq) is ......　　　　　**[EAMCET 2008]**

(a) -10 Q　　　　(b) -100 Q　　　　(c) -1000 Q　　　　(d) $-$Q

35. From the following bond energies,　　　　　**[CBSE AIPMT 2009]**

$C_2H_4 + H_2 \rightarrow C_2H_6$

$H - H$ bond energy; 431.37 kJ mol^{-1}

$C - C$ bond energy; 606.10 kJ mol^{-1}

$C - C$ bond energy; 336.49 kJ mol^{-1}

$C - H$ bond energy; 410.50 kJ mol^{-1}

Enthalpy for the reaction is ......

(a) 1523.6 kJ mol^{-1}　　　(b) -243.6 kJ mol^{-1}　　　(c) -120.0 kJ mol^{-1}　　　(d) 553.0 kJ mol^{-1}

36. The value of ΔH and ΔS for the reaction C (graphite) $+ CO_2$ (g) $\rightarrow CO$ (g) are 170 kJ and 170 JK^{-1} respectively. This reaction will be spontaneous at　　　　　**[CBSE AIPMT 2009]**

(a) 710 K　　　　(b) 910 K　　　　(c) 1110 K　　　　(d) 510 K

37. Consider the following reactions :　　　　　**[CPMT 2009]**

I.　$C(s) + \dfrac{1}{2} O_2$ (g) $\rightarrow CO$ (g);　　　$\Delta H_1 = a$

II.　CO (g) $+ \dfrac{1}{2} O_2$ (g) $\rightarrow CO$ (g);　　$\Delta H_2 = b$

III.　$C(s) + CO_2$ (g) $\rightarrow 2CO$ (g);　　$\Delta H_3 = c$

Select the correct statement

(a) Heat of formation of CO_2 is $(a + b)$

(b) Heat of combustion of C is $(a + b)$

(c) $\Delta H_3 = \Delta H_1 - \Delta H_2$

(d) All the above are correct statement

38. Given that ΔH_f (H) = 218 kJ/mol, express $H - H$ bond energy in kcal/mol　　　**[EAMCET 2009]**

(a) 52.15　　　　(b) 911　　　　(c) 104　　　　(d) 52153

39. The heat change for the following reaction at 298 K and constant pressure is +7.3 kcal

A_2B (s) $\rightarrow 2A(s) + \dfrac{1}{2} B_2$ (g);　　$\Delta H = +7.3$ kcal　　　　　**[Manipal 2009]**

The heat change at constant volume would be ......

(a) +7.3 kcal

(b) more than 8.3 kcal

(c) less than 7.3 kcal

(d) zero

40. For endothermic reaction, energy of activation is E_a and enthalpy of the reaction is ΔH (both of these in kJ/mol). Minimum value of E_a will be ......   **[CBSE AIPMT 2010]**

(a) equal to zero   (b) less than ΔH (c) equal to ΔH (d) more than ΔH

41. Standard entropies of X_2, Y_2 and XY_3 and are 60, 40 and 50 $JK^{-1}\ mol^{-1}$ respectively. For the reaction $\frac{1}{2}X_2 + \frac{3}{2}Y_2 \rightleftharpoons XY_3$, $\Delta H = -30$ kJ to be at equilibrium, the temperature should be ......   **[CBSE AIPMT 2010]**

(a) 500 K   (b) 750 K   (c) 1000 K   (d) 1250 K

42. If 1 mole of an ideal gas expands isothermally at 37°C from 15 L to 25 L, the maximum work obtained is ......   **[AFMC 2010]**

(a) 12.87   (b) 6.43   (c) 8.57   (d) 2.92

43. The heat liberated when 1.89 g of benzoic acid is burnt in a bomb calorimeter at 25°C increase the temperature of 18.94 kg of water by 0.632°C. If the specific heat of water at 25°C is 0.998 cal/g deg, the value of the heat of combustion of benzoic acid is ......

   [AFMC 2010]

(a) 881.1 kcal   (b) 771.4 kcal   (c) –249.2 kcal   (d) +871.2 kcal

44. The heat of combustion of methane, if the heat of formation of CH_4, CO_2 and H_2O are respectively –18.4 kcal, –94.0 kcal, –68.4 kcal is   **[CPMT 2010]**

(a) –212.4 kcal   (b) +212.4 kcal   (c) –249.2 kcal   (d) +249.2 kcal

45. The bond energies of $C - C$, $C = C$, $H - H$ and $C - H$ linkages are 350, 600, 400 and 410 kJ/mol respectively. The heat of hydrogenation of ethylene is   **[BVP 2010]**

(a) 170 kJ/mol   (b) –400 kJ/mol   (c) –260 kJ/mol   (d) –450 kJ/mol

46. According to second law of thermodynamics, a process (reaction) is spontaneous, if during the process   **[Manipal 2010]**

(a) $\Delta S_{universe} > 0$ (b) $\Delta S_{universe} = 0$ (c) $\Delta H_{system} > 0$ (d) $\Delta S_{universe} = \Delta S_{system}$

47. Calculate the free energy change for the following reaction at 300 K   **[Manipal 2010]**

$$2CuO(s) \rightarrow Cu_2O(s) + \frac{1}{2}O_2\ (g)$$

Given, $\Delta H = 145.6$ kJ mol^{-1} and $\Delta S = 116$ $JK^{-1}\ mol^{-1}$

(a) 110.8 kJ/mol^{-1} (b) 1221.5 kJ mol^{-1} (c) 55.4 kJ mol^{-1} (d) 145.6 kJ mol^{-1}

48. Which of the following is the correct option for free expansion of an ideal gas under adiabatic condition ?   **[CBSE AIPMT 2011]**

(a) $q = 0, \Delta T < 0, w \neq 0$ (b) $q = 0, \Delta T \neq 0, w = 0$

(c) $q \neq 0, \Delta T = 0, w = 0$ (d) $q = 0, \Delta T = 0, w = 0$

49. Enthalpy change for the reaction $4H\ (g) \rightarrow 2H_2\ (g)$ is –869.5 kJ. The dissociation energy of $H - H$ bond is ......   **[CBSE AIPMT 2011]**

(a) +217.4 kJ   (b) –434.5 kJ   (c) –869.6 kJ   (d) +434.8 kJ

50. The enthalpy of vaporization of benzene is $+35.3$ kJ/mol at its boiling point of $80°C$. The entropy change in the transition of vapour to liquid at its boiling point is... (in $J\ mol^{-1}\ K^{-1}$).

    (a) -100 (b) $+100$ (c) $+342$ (d) -342 **[KCET 2011]**

51. For the reversible reaction   **[KCET 2011]**

$$A(s) + B\ (g) \rightleftharpoons C\ (g) + D\ (g),\ \Delta G° = -350\ kJ.$$

which of the following statement is true?

    (a) The reaction is thermodynamically non-feasible

    (b) The entropy change is negative

    (c) Equilibrium constant is negative

    (d) Equilibrium constant is greater than one

    (e) The reaction should be instantaneous

52. A reaction having equal energies of activation for forward and reverse reactions has ......

    (a) $\Delta H = \Delta G \equiv \Delta S = 0$ (b) $\Delta S = 0$

    (c) $\Delta G \equiv 0$ (d) $\Delta H = 0$

53. Which of the following statement is correct for the spontaneous adsorption of a gas ?

    (a) ΔS is positive and therefore ΔH should be negative   **[NEET 2013]**

    (b) ΔS is positive and therefore ΔH should also be highly positive

    (c) ΔS is negative and therefore ΔH should be highly positive

    (d) ΔS is negative and therefore ΔH should be highly negative

54. For the reaction :   **[AIPMT 2014]**

$$X_2O_4\ (l) \rightarrow 2XO_2\ (g)$$

$\Delta U = 2.1$ kcal, $\Delta S = 20$ cal K^{-1} at 300 K. Hence, ΔG is ......

    (a) 9.3 kcal   (b) -9.3 kcal   (c) 2.7 kcal   (d) -2.7 kcal

55. The species which by definition has ZERO standard molar enthalpy of formation at 298 K is ...

    (a) $Br_{2(g)}$ (b) $Cl_{2(g)}$ (c) $H_2O_{(g)}$ (d) $CH_{4(g)}$ **[CBSE 2000]**

56. Identify the correct statement from the following in a chemical reaction.   **[CBSE 2000]**

    (a) The entropy always increases

    (b) The change in entropy along with suitable change in enthalpy decides the fate of a reaction

    (c) The enthalpy always decreases

    (d) Both the enthalpy and the entropy remain constant

57. For the reversible reaction,   **[AIIMS 2000]**

$$A_{(s)} + B_{(g)} \rightleftharpoons C_{(g)} + \Delta_{(g)} \Delta G° = -350\ kJ$$

which one of the following statements is true?

    (a) The reaction is thermodynamically non-feasible

    (b) The entropy change is negative

    (c) Equilibrium constant is greater than one

    (d) The reaction should be instantaneous

58. The enthalpy of vaporization of benzene is +35.3 kJ/mol at its boiling point of 80°C. The entropy change in the transition of vapour to liquid at its boiling point is .... (in $J\ mol^{-1}\ K^{-1}$)

   (a) −100   (b) +100   (c) +342   (d) −342 **[DPMT 2001]**

59. For a particular reversible reaction at temperature T, ΔH and ΔS were found to be both +ve. If T_e is the temperature at equilibrium, the reaction would be spontaneous when ......

                                                                 [Manipal 2001]

   (a) $T = T_c$ (b) $T_c > T$ (c) $T > T_c$ (d) T_c is 5 times T

60. In a fuel cell, methanol is used as fuel and oxygen gas is used as an oxidizer. The reaction is ......

$$CH_3OH_{(l)} + \frac{3}{2}O_{2(g)} \rightarrow CO_{2(g)} + 2H_2O_{(l)}$$

At 298 K standard Gibb's energies of formation for $CH_3OH_{(l)}$, $H_2O_{(l)}$ and $CO_{2(g)}$ are 166.2, 237.2 and 394.4 kJ mol respectively. If standard enthalpy of combustion of methanol is 726 kJ/mol, efficiency of the fuel cell will be ......   **[Manipal 2001]**

   (a) 87%   (b) 90%   (c) 97%   (d) 80%

61. The molar heat capacity of a monoatomic gas of which ratio of pressure and volume is one is ......   **[CBSE 2005]**

   (a) 4/2 R   (b) 3/2 R   (c) 5/2 R   (d) Zero

62. C–H bond energy is about 101 kcal/mol for methane, ethane and other alkanes but is only 77 kcal/mol for C–H bond of CH_3 in toluene. This is because ......   **[CBSE 2006]**

   (a) Of the presence of benzene ring in toluene

   (b) Of inductive effect due to – CH_3 in toluene

   (c) Of resonance

   (d) Aromaticity of toluene

63. The standard molar heat of formation of ethane, CO_2 and water respectively are −21.0, −94.1 and −68.3 lcal. The standard molar heat of combustion of ethane will be

   (a) −372 kcal   (b) 162 kcal   (c) −340 kcal   (d) 183.5 kcal

64. 0.5 g mixture of $NaHCO_3$ and Na_2CO_3 titrated with HCl. The change of colour of indicator appears at pH = 9 and pH = 5, the reaction corresponding to pH = 9 will be as

                                                                   [AIPMT 2009]

   (a) $CO_3^{2-} + HCO_3^- \rightarrow 2CO_2 + H_2O + 3e^-$ (b) $HCO_3^- + H^+ \rightarrow H_2O + CO_2$

   (c) $CO_3^{2-} + 2H^+ \rightarrow H_2CO_3$ (d) $CO_3^{2-} + H^+ \rightarrow HCO_3^{-2}$

65. Standard entropy of X_2, Y_2 and XY_3 are 60, 40 and 50 $JK^{-1}\ mol^{-1}$, respectively. For the reaction $\frac{1}{2}X_2 + \frac{3}{2}Y_2 \rightarrow XY_3$, $\Delta H = -30$ kJ, to be at equilibrium, the temperature will be

   (a) 1000 K   (b) 1250 K   (c) 500 K   (d) 750 K

66. The heat of formation of $CO_{(g)}$ and $CO_{2(g)}$ are $\Delta H = -110$ and $\Delta H = -393$ $kJ\ mol^{-1}$ respectively. What is the heat of reaction (ΔH) (in $kJ\ mol^{-1}$) for the following reaction ?

$$CO_{(g)} + \frac{1}{2}O_{2(g)} \rightarrow CO_{2(G)}$$

                                                                     [AIPMT 2007]

   (a) − 504   (b) − 142.5   (c) − 283   (d) 504

67. Which of the following holds good to the laws of thermodynamics for the reaction

$C_2H_{4(g)} + 3O_{2(g)} \longrightarrow 2CO_{2(g)} + 2H_2O_{(l)}$ **[C.B.S.E. 2000]**

(a) $\Delta H = \Delta E + RT$ (b) $\Delta H = \Delta E - RT$

(c) $\Delta H = \Delta E + 2RT$ (d) $\Delta H = \Delta E - 2RT$

68. For melting of a solid at 25°C, the fusion process requires energy equivalent to 2906 joules to be added to a system considering the process to be reversible at fusion point, the entropy change of the process is ...... **[C.B.S.E. 2000]**

(a) $9.75\ JK^{-1}$ (b) $11.272\ JK^{-1}$ (c) $2.33\ JK^{-1}$ (d) Insufficient data

69. In a closed insulated container a liquid is stirred with a paddle to increase the temperature. Which of the following is true ? **[C.B.S.E. 2002]**

(a) $\Delta E = W \neq 0,\ q = 0$ (b) $\Delta E = W = q \neq 0$

(c) $\Delta E = 0,\ W = q \neq 0$ (d) $W = 0,\ \Delta E = q \neq 0$

70. If a reaction involves only solids and liquids, which of the following is true ?

[Tamil Nadu C.E.T. 2002]

(a) $\Delta H < \Delta E$ (b) $\Delta H = \Delta E$ (c) $\Delta H > \Delta E$ (d) $\Delta H = \Delta E + RT\ \Delta n$

71. Heat of combustion ΔH for C(s), H_2(g) and CH_4(g) are −94, −68 and −213 kcal/mol. Then ΔH for $C(s) + 2H_2(g) \rightarrow CH_4(g)$ is ...... **[Pb. P.M.T. 2002]**

(a) −17 kcal (b) −111 kcal (c) −170 kcal (d) −85 kcal

72. The molar heat capacity of water at constant pressure, C_p is $75\ JK^{-1}\ mol^{-1}$. When 1.0 kJ of heat is supplied to 100 g of water which is free to expand, the increase in temperature of water is ...... **[C.B.S.E. 2003]**

(a) 6.6 K (b) 1.2 K (c) 2.4 K (d) 4.8 K

73. For which one of the following equations is ΔH^{o}_{react} equal to ΔH^{o}_{f} for the product ?

[C.B.S.E. 2003]

(a) $2CO(g) + O_2(g) \longrightarrow 2CO_2(g)$ (b) $N_2(g) + O_2(g) \longrightarrow N_2O_3(g)$

(c) $CH_4(g) + 2Cl_2(g) \longrightarrow CH_2Cl_2(l) + 2HCl(g)$ (d) $Xe(g) + 2F_2(g) \longrightarrow XeF_4(g)$

74. Which one of the following has $\Delta S°$ greater than zero? **[A.I.I.M.S. 2003]**

(a) $CaO_{(s)} + CO_{2(g)} \rightleftharpoons CaCO_{3(s)}$ (b) $NaCl_{(aq)} \rightleftharpoons NaCl_{(s)}$

(c) $NaNO_{3(s)} \rightleftharpoons Na^{+}_{(aq)} + NO^{3-}_{(aq)}$ (d) $N_{2(g)} + 3H_{2(g)} \rightleftharpoons 2NH_{3(g)}$

75. Considering entropy (S) as a thermodynamic parameter, the criterion for the spontaneity of any process is ...... **[C.B.S.E. P.M.T. 2004]**

(a) $\Delta S_{surroundings} > 0$ only (b) $\Delta S_{system} + \Delta S_{surroundings} > 0$

(c) $\Delta S_{system} + \Delta S_{surroundings} < 0$ (d) $\Delta S_{system} > 0$ only

76. How much energy is released when 6 moles of octane is burnt in air ? Given ΔH^{o}_{f} for $CO_{2(g)}$, $H_2O_{(g)}$ and $C_8H_{18(l)}$ respectively are −490, −240 and +160 kJ/mol . **[A.I.I.M.S. 2004]**

(a) −6.2 MJ (b) −37.4 MJ (c) −35.5 MJ (d) −20.0 MJ

ANSWER KEY

1. (c)	2. (c)	3. (b)	4. (b)	5. (b)	6. (a)	7. (a)	8. (b)
9. (d)	10. (d)	11. (c)	12. (d)	13. (b)	14. (d)	15. (d)	16. (d)
17. (a)	18. (d)	19. (c)	20. (a)	21. (a)	22. (a)	23. (c)	24. (a)
25. (c)	26. (a)	27. (b)	28. (a)	29. (b)	30. (c)	31. (d)	32. (a)
33. (a)	34. (a)	35. (b)	36. (b)	37. (b)	38. (b)	39. (c)	40. (d)
41. (b)	42. (a)	43. (a)	44. (c)	45. (d)	46. (d)	47. (b)	48. (c)
49. (b)	50. (a)	51. (c)	52. (b)	53. (b)	54. (c)	55. (b)	56. (b)
57. (c)	58. (b)	59. (a)	60. (b)	61. (c)	62. (d)	63. (b)	64. (a)
65. (a)	66. (b)	67. (d)	68. (d)	69. (c)	70. (d)	71. (d)	72. (a)
73. (d)	74. (a)	75. (d)	76. (a)	77. (a)	78. (c)	79. (d)	80. (d)
81. (a)	82. (d)	83. (a)	84. (d)	85. (a)	86. (d)	87. (a)	88. (a)
89. (a)	90. (e)	91. (c)	92. (d)	93. (c)	94. (a)	95. (a)	96. (a)
97. (c)	98. (a)	99. (b)	100. (c)	101. (c)	102. (c)	103. (a)	104. (c)
105. (b)	106. (a)	107. (d)	108. (b)	109. (d)	110. (b)	111. (c)	112. (a)
113. (b)	114. (c)	115. (b)	116. (c)	117. (a)	118. (d)	119. (a)	120. (a)
121. (b)	122. (d)	123. (a)	124. (c)	125. (d)	126. (d)	127. (b)	128. (d)
129. (c)	130. (a)	131. (d)	132. (a)	133. (c)	134. (b)	135. (b)	136. (b)
137. (d)	138. (a)	139. (d)	140. (a)	141. (d)	142. (b)	143. (b)	144. (c)
145. (c)	146. (a)	147. (c)	148. (b)	149. (a)	150. (a)	151. (a)	152. (d)
153. (a)	154. (b)	155. (b)	156. (d)	157. (c)	158. (a)	159. (b)	160. (c)
161. (a)	162. (b)	163. (c)	164. (e)	165. (e)	166. (d)	167. (d)	168. (b)
169. (b)	170. (b)	171. (a)	172. (d)	173. (d)	174. (d)	175. (d)	176. (d)
177. (b)							

Previous Years Questions

1. (a)	2. (b)	3. (b)	4. (d)	5. (c)	6. (d)	7. (b)	8. (a)
9. (b)	10. (c)	11. (d)	12. (b)	13. (a)	14. (a)	15. (b)	16. (a)
17. (c)	18. (d)	19. (b)	20. (a)	21. (b)	22. (c)	23. (d)	24. (a)
25. (c)	26. (c)	27. (a)	28. (c)	29. (c)	30. (a)	31. (b)	32. (d)
33. (c)	34. (b)	35. (c)	36. (c)	37. (d)	38. (c)	39. (c)	40. (d)
41. (b)	42. (a)	43. (b)	44. (a)	45. (a)	46. (a)	47. (a)	48. (d)
49. (d)	50. (a)	51. (c)	52. (d)	53. (d)	54. (d)	55. (b)	56. (b)
57. (c)	58. (a)	59. (c)	60. (c)	61. (b)	62. (b)	63. (a)	64. (c)
65. (d)	66. (c)	67. (d)	68. (a)	69. (a)	70. (b)	71. (a)	72. (c)
73. (d)	74. (c)	75. (b)	76. (c)				

❑❑❑

EQUILIBRIUM

Chemical Equilibrium

1. Chemical equilibrium establishes if a reaction takes place in ......

   (a) A closed system   (b) An open system   (c) Gaseous state   (d) Liquid state

2. Which of the following statements is TRUE?

   (a) Equilibrium is a static state in which both the forward and reverse reactions no longer occur.

   (b) Equilibrium is a state in which the net reactant and product concentrations remain constant with time.

   (c) Equilibrium is a state in which the rates of forward and reverse reactions are equal.

   (d) (b) and (c) are true.

3. Which of the following statements correctly describe(s) chemical equilibrium?

   (a) State in which the concentrations of reactants and products are always equal.

   (b) State in which the concentrations of all reactants and products remain constant with time.

   (c) State in which the rates of forward and reverse reactions are not equal.

   (d) State in which all chemical reactions no longer occur.

4. For which of the following reactions will the equilibrium constants K_c and K_p have the same value?

   (a) $2CO_{2(g)} \rightleftharpoons 2CO_{(g)} + O_{2(g)}\uparrow$ 	(b) $H_2O_{(l)} + CO_{(g)} \rightleftharpoons H_{2(g)} + CO_{2(g)}$

   (c) $3O_{2(g)} \rightleftharpoons 2O_{3(g)}$ 	(d) $CO_{(g)} + Cl_{2(g)} \rightleftharpoons COCl_{2(g)}$

5. Assume the equilibrium constant for the following reaction

   $$2NO_{2(g)} \rightleftharpoons 2NO_{(g)} + O_{2(g)}$$

   $$K_1 = 7.4 \times 10^{-16} \text{ (at 25°C)}$$

   What is the correct value of equilibrium constant (K_2) for the opposite reaction?

   $$2NO_{(g)} + O_{2(g)} \rightleftharpoons 2NO_{2(g)}$$

   (a) Impossible to determine from this information.

   (b) $K_2 = K_1 = 7.4 \times 10^{-16}$

   (c) $K_2 = 1/K_1 = 1.4 \times 10^{15}$

   (d) $K_2 = K_1(RT) = 1.8 \times 10^{-14}$

6. Assume that the equilibrium constants for the following reactions are known:

   $$2SO_{2(g)} + O_{2(g)} \rightleftharpoons 2SO_{3(g)}, K_1$$
   $$2CO_{(g)} + O_{2(g)} \rightleftharpoons 2CO_{2(g)}, K_2$$

   What is the equilibrium constant for the following reaction?

   $$SO_{2(g)} + 2CO_{2(g)} \rightleftharpoons 2SO_{3(g)} + 2CO_{(g)}$$

   (a) $K = K_1 \times K_2$ 	(b) $K = K_1/K_2$ 	(c) $K = K_2/K_1$ 	(d) $K = K_1 + K_2$

7. The partial pressure of a component in a gas-phase reaction is 0.452 atm. What is the activity of the component?

    (a) 0.452 bar   (b) 0.458   (c) 0.458 bar   (d) 0.452 atm

8. The equilibrium constant for the reaction,

    $2NO + O_2 \rightleftharpoons 2NO_2$ at 500 K is $K_c = 7.7 \times 10^7$. For a reaction mixture containing 1.0×10^{-3} mol/l of each of the three components

    (a) The reaction is at equilibrium.

    (b) The concentration of NO_2 must decrease, and the concentration of NO must increase to reach equilibrium.

    (c) The concentration of NO must decrease, and the concentration of NO_2 must increase to reach equilibrium.

    (d) The reaction is not at equilibrium, but it is not possible to predict which direction the reaction must go to reach equilibrium without calculating equilibrium concentrations

9. If the following reaction was at equilibrium in a closed vessel at a controlled temperature, what would be the effect of adding more CO_2 to the reaction vessel and permitting the reaction to approach equilibrium again

    $CO_{(g)} + H_2O_{(g)} \rightleftharpoons CO_{2(g)} + H_{2(g)}$

    (a) The concentrations of CO, H_2O and H_2 would all increase.

    (b) The concentrations of CO, H_2O and H_2 would all decrease.

    (c) The concentrations of CO and H_2O would decrease and the concentration of H_2 would increase.

    (d) The concentrations of CO and H_2O would increase and the concentration of H_2 would decrease.

10. Consider the following reaction initially at equilibrium

    $$4NO_{2(g)} + 6H_2O_{(g)} \rightleftharpoons 4NH_{3(g)} + 7O_{2(g)}$$

    If the concentration of $NH_{3(g)}$ were suddenly increased, which of the following best describes, what would happen to the concentrations of the other species?

    (a) $NO_{2(g)}$, $H_2O_{(g)}$ and $O_{2(g)}$ would all increase.

    (b) $NO_{2(g)}$, $H_2O_{(g)}$ and $O_{2(g)}$ would all decrease.

    (c) $NO_{2(g)}$ and $H_2O_{(g)}$ would decrease and $O_{2(g)}$ would increase.

    (d) $NO_{2(g)}$ and $H_2O_{(g)}$ would increase and $O_{2(g)}$ would decrease.

11. Calcium carbonate undergoes thermal decomposition

    $CaCO_{3(s)} \rightleftharpoons CaO_{(s)} + CO_{2(s)}$

    at high temperatures. The equilibrium constant for the reaction is 0.0120 at 900 K. Calculate the partial pressure of carbon dioxide, calcium carbonate $(CaCO)_3$ is heated at 900 K.

    (a) 120 Pa   (b) 1.20 kPa   (c) 1.20 bar   (d) 1.20 atm

12. What is the correct equilibrium constant expression for the reaction ?

$$2NOCl_{(g)} \rightleftharpoons 2NO_{(g)} + Cl_{2(g)}$$

(a) $K_c = [NO][Cl_2]/[NOCl]$

(b) $K_c = ([NO] + [NO] + [Cl_2])/([NOCl] + [NOCl])$

(c) $K_c = [NO_2][Cl_2]/[NOCl]^2$

(d) $K_c = ([NOCl] + [NOCl])/([NO] + [NO] + [Cl_2])$

13. At 1800 K, molecular oxygen dissociates slightly to give small amounts of atomic oxygen as follows :

$$O_{2(g)} \rightleftharpoons 2O_{(g)}$$
$$K_c = 1.7 \times 10^{-8}$$

What is the value of the equilibrium constant, K_C for the reaction,

$$1/2\ O_{(g)} \rightleftharpoons 1/4O_{2(g)} \text{ at 1500 K ?}$$

(a) $K_c = 4.3 \times 10^{-9}$ (b) $K_c = 1.1 \times 10^{-2}$ (c) $K_c' = 8.8 \times 10^{1}$ (d) $K_c' = 7.7 \times 10^3$

14. For $3H_{2(g)} + N_{2(g)} \rightleftharpoons 2NH_{3(g)}$, $K_c = 60$

The equilibrium constant expressed as partial pressure would be ......

(a) $K_p = 60(RT)^{-1}$ (b) $K_p = 60(RT)''$ (c) $K_p = 60(RT)^{-2}$ (d) $K_p = (RT)^{-1}/60$

15. Consider the following reaction and equilibrium constant,

$$CO_{(g)} + H_2O_{(g)} \rightleftharpoons CO_{2(g)} + 2H_2O_{(g)}, K_{c2} = 0.72\ @\ 800°C$$

Which of the following is the correct expression for the equilibrium constant at 800°C

$$2CO_{2(g)} + 2H_{2(g)} \rightleftharpoons 2CO_{(g)} + 2H_2O_{(g)}, K_{c2} = ?$$

(a) $K_{c2} = 0.72$ (b) $K_{c2} = (0.72)^2$ (c) $K_{c2} = 1/0.72$ (d) $K_{c2} = (1/0.72)^2$

16. For which of the following reactions would the equilibrium constants not be affected by a change in total pressure?

(a) $N_{2(g)} + 3H_{2(g)} \rightleftharpoons 2NH_{3(g)}$ (b) $PCl_{3(g)} + Cl_{2(g)} \rightleftharpoons PCl_{5(g)}$

(c) $2NO_{2(g)}O \rightleftharpoons N_{2(g)} + 2O_{2(g)}$ (d) $CO_{(g)} + H_2O_{(g)} \rightleftharpoons CO_{2(g)} + H_{2(g)}$

17. Given the following reactions and associated equilibrium constants, select the correct expression for the third equilibrium constant in terms of the first two.

(1) $2CO_{(g)} + O_{2(g)} \rightleftharpoons 2CO_{2(g)}\ K_{c1}$

(2) $H_{2(g)} + 1/2O_{2(g)} \rightleftharpoons H_2O_{(g)}\ K_{c2}$

(3) $CO_{(g)} + H_2O_{(g)} \rightleftharpoons CO_{2(g)} + H_{2(g)}\ K_{c3}$

(a) $K_{c3} = K_{c1} \times K_{c2}$ (b) $K_{c3} = K_{(g)} \times K_{c2}$

(c) $K_{c3} = (K_{c1})^{1/2}/K_{c2}$ (d) $K_{c3} = K_{c1} \times (K_{c2})^{1/2}$

18. Given the following reaction and equilibrium constant, which statement is correct for this reaction at equilibrium.

$$CO_2 \rightleftharpoons CO + 1/2O_2, K_1 = 9.1 \times 10^{-12}$$

(a) The forward rate will be the same as the reverse rate.

(b) The forward rate will be larger than the reverse rate.

(c) The forward rate will be smaller than the reverse rate.

(d) The concentration of CO_2 must be much smaller than the concentrations of both CO and O_2

19. At 200°C, nitrogen oxide reacts with oxygen to form nitrogen dioxide as follows

$$2NO + O_2 \rightarrow 2NO_2, \ K_c = 3 \times 10^6$$

In a mixture of three species at equilibrium, we can accurately predict that ......

(a) The concentrations of both NO & O_2 will be much larger than the concentration of NO_2.

(b) The concentrations of both NO & O_2 will be much smaller than the concentration of NO_2.

(c) The concentrations of either NO or O_2 (and possibly both) will be much smaller than the concentration of NO_2.

(d) The concentration of O_2 will be exactly one half the concentration of NO.

20. At 200°C, nitrogen oxide reacts with oxygen to form nitrogen dioxide as follows,

$$2NO + O_2 \rightleftharpoons 2NO_2, \ K_c = 3 \times 10^6$$

If a mixture of these three gases contains 0.10 M NO, 0.10 M NO_2, and 0.01 M O_2, then we can accurately predict that the reaction

(a) Is at equilibrium.

(b) Is not at equilibrium and must proceed from left to right to reach the equilibrium.

(c) Is not at equilibrium and must proceed from right to left to reach the equilibrium.

(d) Is not at equilibrium but insufficient information is given to predict in which direction the reaction must go to reach the equilibrium.

21. Consider the following gas-phase reaction, at equilibrium, at 298 K.

$$2SO_{2(g)} + O_{2(g)} \rightleftharpoons 2SO_{3(g)}, \ \Delta H = -196.6 \ kJ$$

Which one of the following, when applied to this system initially at equilibrium, would increase the equilibrium concentration of $SO_{3(g)}$?

(a) Decreasing the pressure by increasing the volume of the reaction vessel

(b) Increasing the temperature

(c) Decreasing the concentration of $O_{2(g)}$

(d) Decreasing the temperature

22. The reaction of nitrogen, $N_2(g)$, with hydrogen, $H_2(g)$, to produce ammonia, $NH_3(g)$, is a commercially important gas-phase reaction because huge amounts of ammonia are used for fertilization

$$N_{2(g)} + 3H_{2(g)} \rightleftharpoons 2NH_{3(g)}$$

This reaction is generally performed at high pressure and high temperature. Which of the following statements best explains why high pressure is used?

(a) Increasing the pressure will lead to the production of more $N_{2(g)}$ and $NH_{3(g)}$.

(b) Increasing the pressure will lead to the production of more $N_{2(g)}$ and $H_{2(g)}$.

(c) Increasing the pressure will lead to the production of more $NH_{3(g)}$.

(d) Increasing the pressure will lead to the production of more $H_{2(g)}$ and $NH_{3(g)}$.

23. The Haber-Bosch process is used to prepare ammonia

$$N_{2(g)} + 3H_{2(g)} \rightleftharpoons 2NH_{3(g)}, \Delta H = -92.4 \text{ kJ}$$

Industrially, this reaction is performed at temperatures ranging from 400°C to 650°C. The high temperatures used in the process cause ......

(a) The value for K_c to increase, and the rate of the reaction to decrease.

(b) The value for K_c to increase, and the rate of the reaction to increase.

(c) The value for K_c to decrease, and the rate of the reaction to decrease.

(d) The value for K_c to decrease, and the rate of the reaction to increase.

24. If the reaction $3H_2 + N_2 \rightarrow 2NH_3$, is at equilibrium, decreasing the volume of the reaction vessel by a factor of two at constant temperature, it will cause ......

(a) The amount of ammonia to increase.

(b) The amount of ammonia to decrease.

(c) The concentrations of all species to decrease.

(d) The amounts of hydrogen and nitrogen to increase.

25. For two reactions with the same stoichiometry (e.g. $2A + B \rightarrow 2D$) and the same initial concentrations of all reactants, then at equilibrium, the reaction with the smallest equilibrium constant will ......

(a) Have the largest reaction quotient.

(b) Have a reaction quotient the same as the other reaction.

(c) Have the highest concentration of species D.

(d) Have the highest concentration of species A.

26. If the reaction quotient for a reaction is larger than the equilibrium constant (i.e. $Q_c > K_c$) then the reaction ......

(a) Will always proceed to equilibrium very rapidly.

(b) Must shift from right to left to reach equilibrium.

(c) Must shift from left to right to reach equilibrium.

(d) Is at equilibrium.

27. Consider the following gas-phase reaction and equilibrium constant at 25°C,

$$4HCl_{(g)} + O_{2(g)} \rightarrow 2Cl_{2(g)} + 2H_2O_{(g)}, \quad K = 1.1 \times 10^{13}$$

The concentrations of all species were measured at a particular moment in time and the following data were obtained

$$[HCl] = 0.00050 \text{ M} \qquad\qquad [O_2] = 0.0010 \text{ M}$$
$$[Cl_2] = 2.30 \text{ M} \qquad\qquad [H_2O] = 1.22 \text{ M}$$

Which of the following statements is true at this moment in time?

(a) The reaction is at equilibrium.

(b) The reaction is not at equilibrium, the reaction must proceed from left to right to reach the equilibrium.

(c) The reaction is not at equilibrium, the reaction must proceed from right to left to reach the equilibrium.

(d) The reaction is not at equilibrium, but the concentrations of all species will no longer change with time.

28. At 450 K, phosphorus pentachloride (PCl_5) decomposes to produce phosphorus trichloride (PCl_3) and chlorine (Cl_2).

$$PCl_{5(g)} \rightleftharpoons PCl_{3(g)} + Cl_{2(g)}, \ K = 1.3 \times 10^{-3} \text{ at } 450 \text{ K}$$

At a particular moment in time, the following concentrations are determined :

$$(PCl_5) = 0.80 \text{ M}; \ (PCl_3) = 0.0064 \text{ M}; \ (Cl_2) = 0.55 \text{ M}$$

Which of the following statements is true ?

(a) The reaction is not at equilibrium; the concentration of PCl_3 will increase as the reaction proceeds towards equilibrium.

(b) The reaction is not at equilibrium; the concentration of PCl_5 will decrease as the reaction proceeds towards equilibrium.

(c) The reaction is not at equilibrium; the concentration of PCl_5 will not change as the reaction proceeds towards equilibrium.

(d) The reaction is at equilibrium.

29. The correct value for the equilibrium constant K_p, for the reaction

$$2NO_{(g)} + O_2 \rightleftharpoons 2NO_{(g)} + O_2, \ K_c = 7.4 \times 10^{-16}$$

would be ......

(a) $K_p = K_c = 7.4 \times 10^{-16}$

(b) $K_p = 1/K_c = 1.4 \times 10^{15}$

(c) $K_p = K_c (RT) = 1.8 \times 10^{-14}$

(d) $K_p = K_c(RT)^{-1} = 3.0 \times 10^{-17}$

30. Assuming that the reaction quotient (Q_c) for the following reaction at 25°C is 1.0×10^{-8}

$$2NO_{(g)} \rightleftharpoons 2NO_{(g)} + O_{2(g)}, \ K_c = 7.4 \times 10^{-16} \text{ (at 25°C)}$$

From this it can be concluded that

(a) The reaction is at equilibrium.

(b) Without any reaction taking place, equilibrium could be reached by adding enough NO or O_2 to the system.

(c) The reaction must proceed from left to right to reach equilibrium.

(d) The reaction must proceed from right to left to reach equilibrium.

31. The equilibrium constant for the reaction

$$PCl_{3(g)} + Cl_{2(g)} \rightarrow PCl_{5(g)} \text{ is } K = 3.29 \times 10^6 \text{ at } 298 \text{ K.}$$

Calculate the value of K_c, the equilibrium constant expressed in terms of concentration.

(a) 8.15×10^3　　　(b) 8.15×10^4　　　(c) 8.15×10^5　　　(d) 8.15×10^6

32. For the equilibrium

$$4HCl_{(g)} + O_{2(g)} \rightleftharpoons 2Cl_{2(g)} + 2H_2O_{(g)}, \ (K_c = 885 \text{ lit/mol at 500°C})$$

If 0.030 mol HCl, 0.020 mol O_2, 0.085 mol Cl_2 and 0.090 mol H_2O are mixed in a one-litre container at 500°C, in what direction will the reaction proceed?

(a) Left　　　　　　　　　　　　　(b) Right

(c) Already at equilibrium　　　　　(d) Not enough information

33. The equilibrium constant for the gas-phase reaction $N_2O_4(O) \rightleftharpoons 2NO_2(O)$ is 0.1179. Calculate the mole fraction of nitrogen dioxide (NO_2) in the equilibrium reaction mixture when the total pressure is exactly 1 bar.

(a) 0.466   (b) 0.289   (c) 0.943   (d) 0.407

34. When equal amounts of hydrogen (H_2) and iodine (I_2) are mixed together at a total pressure of 1 bar, the partial pressure of hydrogen iodide (HI) vapour produced from by the reaction $H_{2(g)} + I_{2(g)} \rightleftharpoons 2HI_{(g)}$ is 22.8 kPa. Calculate the equilibrium constant for the reaction.

(a) 0.349   (b) 0.055   (c) 0.591   (d) 0.295

35. Initially, a mixture of 0.100 M NO, 0.050 M H_2, 0.100 M H_2O was allowed to reach equilibrium (initially there was no N_2). At equilibrium the concentration of NO was found to be 0.062 M. Equilibrium moles of NO, H_2 and H_2O are

Option	O	H_2	N_2	H_2O
(a)	0.062	0.012	0.019	0.138
(b)	0.062	0.024	–	0.138
(c)	0.138	0.012	0.019	0.276
(d)		0.024	–	0.138

36. In the reaction

$$4NH_{3(g)} + 5O_{2(g)} \rightarrow 4NO_{(g)} + 6H_2O_{(l)}$$

when 1 mole of ammonia and 1 mole of O_2 are made to react to completion, what will happen ?

(a) 1.0 mole of H_2O will be produced   (b) 1.0 mole of NO will be produced

(c) All the oxygen will be consumed   (d) All the ammonia will be consumed

37. The law of mass action was given by ......

(a) Guldberg and Waage   (b) Bodenstein

(c) Berthelot   (d) Graham

38. What is the equation for the equilibrium constant (K_c) for the following reaction ?

$$\frac{1}{2} A_{(g)} + \frac{1}{3} B_{(g)} \xrightleftharpoons{T(K)} \frac{2}{3} C_{(g)}$$

(a) $K_c = \dfrac{[A]^{1/2} [B]^{1/3}}{[C]^{3/2}}$ (b) $K_c = \dfrac{[C]^{3/2}}{[A]^2 [B]^3}$ (c) $K_c = \dfrac{[C]^{2/3}}{[A]^{1/2} [B]^{1/3}}$ (d) $K_c = \dfrac{[C]^{2/3}}{[A]^{1/2} [B]^{1/3}}$

Ionic Equilibrium

39. Which of the following is a general characteristic of Arrhenius acids?

(a) They produce H^+ ions in solution.   (b) They accept H^+ ions from water.

(c) They donate a proton.   (d) They accept a proton.

40. Which of the following is a general characteristic of Arrhenius bases?

(a) They produce OH^- ions in solution.   (b) They produce H_3O^+ ions in water.

(c) They donate a proton.   (d) They accept a proton.

41. Which of the following is a general characteristic of Bronsted acids?

(a) They produce H^+ ions in solution.

(b) They accept H^+ ions from water.

(c) They donate a proton.

(d) They accept a proton.

42. A Bronsted-Lowry base is defined as ......

(a) A proton acceptor

(b) A hydroxide donor

(c) A proton donor

(d) An electron pair acceptor

43. One major difference between Bronsted-Lowry and Arrhenius definitions of acids and bases is which of the following?

(a) In the Arrhenius definition, acids release protons while in the Bronsted-Lowry definition, they donate protons.

(b) Arrhenius said that, bases donate electron pairs whereas, Bronsted and Lowry said that bases accept protons.

(c) The solvent dependence i.e. aqueous medium is essential for Arrhenius theory of acids and bases.

(d) There is no difference.

44. Identify two substances that act as Bronsted-Lowry bases in the equation

$$HS^- + SO_4^{2-} \rightleftharpoons S^{2-} + HSO_4^-$$

(a) HS^- and S^{2-}
(b) SO_4^{2-} and S^{2-}
(c) HS^- and HSO_4^-
(d) SO_4^{2-} and HSO_4^-

45. In the equilibrium system ......

$$H_2BO_{3(aq)}^- + HCO_{3(aq)}^- \rightleftharpoons H_2CO_{3(aq)} + HBO_{3\,(aq)}^{2-}$$

The two species acting as Bronsted-Lowry acids are ......

(a) HCO_3^- and H_2CO_3

(b) $H_2BO_3^-$ and H_2CO_3

(c) HCO_3^- and HBO_3^{2-}

(d) $H_2BO_3^-$ and HBO_3^{2-}

46. If reactants are favoured in the following equilibrium, the stronger base must be ......

$$HCN + HS^- \rightleftharpoons H_2S + CN^-$$

(a) H_2S
(b) HS^-
(c) CN^-
(d) HCN

47. Which of the following has most impact on the acidity of halogen acid, HX ?

(a) The electronegativity of X

(b) The strength of H-X bond

(c) The electron affinity of X

(d) The ionization potential of H

48. $H_2C_3H_2O_4 + 2H_2O \rightleftharpoons 2H_3O^+ + C_3H_2O_4^{2-}$

As shown above, malonic acid is a diprotic acid. The successive equilibrium constants are 1.5×10^{-3} (K_{a1} and K_{a2}) and 2.0×10^{-6} (K_{a2}). What is the equilibrium constant for the above reaction?

(a) 1.0×10^{-14}
(b) 2.0×10^{-6}
(c) 4.0×10^{-12}
(d) 3.0×10^{-9}

49. If K_a of sulphurous acid is 1.54×10^{-2}, what is the K_b of its conjugate base?

(a) 1.54×10^{-12}
(b) 6.49×10^{-13}
(c) 1.30×10^{-12}
(d) 6.17×10^{-10}

50. Which Bronsted acid (H_2O or $H_2S_{(aq)}$) is the stronger acid and why is it the stronger acid?

(a) H_2O is the stronger acid because oxygen has a greater electronegativity than sulfur, which gives the attached hydrogen atom more proton character.

(b) H_2O is the stronger acid, because H_2S is a gas and gases are not acids.

(c) H_2S is the stronger acid because the hydrogen-sulfur bond is much weaker than the hydrogen-oxygen bond due to a greater difference in atomic orbital energy levels.

(d) H_2S is the stronger acid because it is a heavier molecule and therefore has more energetic collisions.

51. Which one of the following substances is/are amphiprotic?

(1) H_3PO_4　　　(2) $H_2PO_4^-$　　　(3) HPO_4^{2-}

(a) 2 only　　　　(b) 3 only　　　　(c) 1 and 2　　　　(d) 2 and 3

52. In the following Bronsted-Lowry acid-base equation,

$$NH_{4(aq)}^+ + H_2O_{(l)} \rightleftharpoons NH_{3(aq)} + H_3O_{(aq)}^+$$

The stronger base is ......

(a) NH_4^+　　　　(b) H_2O　　　　(c) NH_3　　　　(d) H_3O

53. What is K_a expression for H_3PO_4 ?

(a) $K_a = \dfrac{[H^+]^3}{[PO_4^{3-}]}$　　　　　　(b) $K_a = \dfrac{[H^+]^3}{[H_3PO_4]}$

(c) $K_a = \dfrac{[H^+]\,[H_2PO_4^-]}{[H_3PO_4]}$　　　　　　(d) $K_a = \dfrac{[H^+]^3\,[H_2PO_4^{2-}]}{[H_3PO_4]}$

54. The conjugate acid of OH^- is ......

(a) H^+　　　　　　(b) O^{2-}

(c) H_2O　　　　　　(d) H_3O^+

55. The amphoteric ion $HSeO_3^-$ can undergo hydrolysis according to the following equations,

$$HSeO_3^- + H_2O \rightleftharpoons H_2SeO_3 + OH^-$$

$$HSeO_3^- + H_2O \rightleftharpoons SeO_3^{2-} + H_3O^+$$

An aqueous solution of HSeO is found to be acidic. This observation indicates that when it is added to water, $HSeO_3^-$ behaves mainly as a ......

(a) Proton donor and K_b is less than K_a

(b) Proton donor and K_b is greater than K_a

(c) Proton acceptor and K_b is less than K_a

(d) Proton acceptor and K_b is greater than K_a

56. Arrange NH_4^+, H_2O, H_3O and OH^- in increasing order of acidic nature.

(a) $H_3O^+, < NH_4^+ < HF < OH^- < H_2O$　　　　(b) $NH_4^+ < HF < H_3O^+ < H_2O < OH^-$

(c) $OH^- < H_2O < NH_4^+ < HF < H_3O^+$　　　　(d) $< H_3O > HF > H_2O > NH_4^+ > OH^-$

57. The K_b expression for HPO_4^{2-} is ......

    (a) $[PO_4^{3-}]\,[H_3O^+]\,[HPO_4^{2-}]$ (b) $[PO_4^{2-}]\,[OH^-]\,[H_2PO_4^-]$

    (c) $[H_2PO_4^-]\,[OH^-]\,[HPO_4^{2-}]$ (d) $[HPO_4^{2-}]\,[H_3O^+]\,[PO_4^{3-}]$

58. Given the equilibrium:

$$H_2BO_3^- + H_2PO_4^- \rightleftharpoons H_3BO_3 + HPO_4^{2-}$$

Which is the strongest acid?

    (a) HPO_4^{2-} (b) H_3BO_3 (c) $H_2PO_4^-$ (d) $H_2BO_3^-$

59. $H_3PO_4 + HCO_3^- \rightleftharpoons H_2PO_4^- + H_2CO_3$ [K >> 1]

The conjugate ____ of HCO_3^- is ....

    (a) Base; $H_2PO_4^-$ (b) Acid; H_3PO_4 (c) Acid; CO_3^{-2} (d) Base; H_2CO_3

60. $H_3PO_4 + HCO_3^- \rightleftharpoons H_2PO_4^- + H_2CO_3$ [K>>1]

The strongest base is

    (a) HCO_3^- (b) $H_2PO_4^-$ (c) H_2CO_3 (d) H_3PO_4

61. If water were added to 0.25 M $C_2H_5NH_2$ solution ($K_b = 4.3 \times 10^{-4}$), the amount of OH^- (number of moles) would ... and the OH^- concentration would ... amount of OH^-, $[OH^-]$.

    (a) Increase, decrease   (b) Increase, increase

    (c) Decrease, increase   (d) Decrease, decrease

62. Given three separate solutions containing equal concentrations of formic acid ($K_a = 1.7 \times 10^{-4}$), phenol ($K_a = 1.3 \times 10^{-10}$), and acetic acid ($K_a = 1.8 \times 10^{-5}$). Select the response below that has the acids arranged in order of increasing percent dissociation at equilibrium.

    (a) Formic acid < phenol < acetic acid   (b) Formic acid < acetic acid < phenol

    (c) Acetic acid < formic acid < phenol   (d) Phenol < acetic acid < formic acid

63. From the following choices, select the one that would be most basic (least acidic).

    (a) 0.1 M hydrochloric acid (a strong acid)

    (b) 0.1 M acetic acid (a weak acid)

    (c) 0.1 M sodium acetate (the salt of a weak acid)

    (d) 0.1 M ammonium chloride (the salt of a weak base)

64. Which of the following is true ?

    (a) Acetic acid is a stronger acid than perchloric acid.

    (b) Acetate ion is a weaker base than perchlorate ion.

    (c) Acetate ion is a stronger base than perchlorate ion.

    (d) Water is a very strong acid.

65. Consider the following data for the series of hydrogen halide Bronsted acids,

Acid	K_a
HF	7.2×10^{-4}
HCl	1×10^{6}
HBr	1×10^{9}
HI	3×10^{9}

Which of these Bronsted acids would have the weakest conjugate base?

(a) HF　　　　　　(b) HCl　　　　　　(c) HBr　　　　　　(d) HI

66. Why is it necessary to take the acid-base properties of water into account when computing the hydronium ion concentration of very dilute solutions of strong acids?

(a) The hydroxide ion produced from the dissociation of water reacts with most of the hydronium ion produced from the acid.

(b) The dissociation constant for water is larger in dilute solution rather than in concentrated solution of acids.

(c) The acids do not dissociate completely in dilute solutions.

(d) The amount of hydronium ion produced by the dissociation of water is significant compared to that produced by the acid.

67. For a weak diprotic acid, H_2A, for which $K_{a1} = 2.1 \times 10^{-7}$ and $K_{a2} = 4.3 \times 10^{-13}$, the A^{2-} ion concentration at equilibrium will be ......

(a) Approximately equal to the initial concentration of H_2A.

(b) Roughly equal to K_{a2}

(c) Roughly equal to $[HA^-]$

(d) Much larger than $[HA^-]$

68. Which of the following anions would be the strongest base?

(a) $CH_3CO_2^-$ ($CH_3CO_2H : K_a = 1.8 \times 10^{-5}$)　　　(b) HCO_2^- ($HCO_2H : K_a = 1.8 \times 10^{-4}$)

(c) $ClCH_2CO_2^-$ ($ClCH_2CO_2H : K_a = 1.4 \times 10^{-3}$)　　(d) $Cl_2CHCO_2^-$ ($Cl_2CHCO_2H : K_a = 5.1 \times 10^{-2}$)

69. Which of the following solutions would be the most basic ?

(a) 0.10 M $NaNO_3$ (K_a for HNO_3 = 28)

(b) 0.10 M $NaNO_2$ (K_a for HNO_2 = 5.1×10^{-4})

(c) 0.10 M $NaOCl$ (K_a for $HOCl$ = 2.9×10^{-8})

(d) 0.10 M $NaCN$ (K_a for HCN = 6.0×10^{-10})

70. Which of the following base is weakest ?

(a) NH_4OH ($K_b = 1.6 \times 10^{-6}$)　　　　　　(b) $C_6H_5NH_2$ ($K_b = 3.8 \times 10^{-10}$)

(c) $C_2H_5NH_2$ ($K_b = 5.6 \times 10^{-4}$)　　　　　(d) C_6H_7N ($K_b = 6.3 \times 10^{-10}$)

71. The following equilibrium exists in aqueous solution $CH_3COOH \rightleftharpoons CH_3OO^- + H^+$. If dilute HCl is added without a change in temperature, then the ......

(a) concentration of CH_3COO^- will increase　　(b) concentration of CH_3COO^- will decrease

(c) equilibrium constant will increase　　　　　　(d) equilibrium constant will decrease

72. A monoprotic acid in a 0.1 M solution ionizes to 0.001%. Its ionisation constant is ......

(a) 1.0×10^{-3} (b) 1.0×10^{-6} (c) 1.0×10^{-8} (d) 1.0×10^{-11}

73. K_{a_1}, K_{a_2} and K_{a_3} are the respective ionization constants for the following reactions.

$$H_2S \rightleftharpoons H^+ + HS^- \qquad HS^- \rightleftharpoons H^+ + S^{2-} \qquad H_2S \rightleftharpoons 2H^+ + S^{2-}$$

The correct relationship between K_{a_1}, K_{a_2} and K_{a_3} is ......

(a) $K_{a_3} = K_{a_1} \times K_{a_2}$ (b) $K_{a_3} = K_{a_1} + K_{a_2}$ (c) $K_{a_3} = K_{a_1}\, K_{a_2}$ (d) $K_{a_3} = K_{a_1} / K_{a_2}$

74. The ionization constant of an acid, K_a is the measure of strength of an acid.

The K_a values of acetic acid, hypochlorous acid and formic acid are 1.74×10^{-5}, 3.0×10^{-8} and 1.8×10^{-4} respectively. Which of the following orders of pH of 0.1 mol dm^{-3} solutions of these acids is correct?

(a) acetic acid > hypochlorous acid > formic acid

(b) hypochlorous acid > acetic acid > formic acid

(c) formic acid > hypochlorous acid > acetic acid

(d) formic acid > acetic acid > hypochlorous acid

75. The pH of neutral water at 25°C is 7.0. As the temperature increases, ionization of water increases, however, the concentration of H$^+$ ions and OH$^-$ ions are equal. What will be the pH of pure water at 60°C?

(a) Equal to 7.0   (b) Greater than 7.0   (c) Less than 7.0   (d) Equal to zero

76. $HSO_4^- + OH^- \rightleftharpoons SO_4^{2-} + H_2O$. Which is correct about conjugate acid-base pair ?

(a) HSO_4^{2-} is conjugate acid of base SO_4^{2-} (b) HSO_4^- is conjugate base of acid SO_4^{2-}

(c) SO_4^{2-} is conjugate acid of base HSO_4^- (d) None of these

77. NH$_4$Cl is acidic, because ......

(a) On hydrolysis NH$_4$Cl gives weak base NH$_4$OH and strong acid HCl

(b) Nitrogen donates a pair of electron

(c) It is a salt of weak acid and strong base

(d) On hydrolysis NH$_4$Cl gives strong base and weak acid

78. Which of the following concepts explain the acidity of BF$_3$?

(a) Arrhenius concept   (b) Bronsted-Lowry concept

(c) Lewis concept   (d) Bronsted-Lowry as well as Lewis concept

79. What is produced when CH$_3$NH$_2$ acts as a base in water?

(a) CH_3NH^- (b) $CH_3NH_3^+$ (c) $CH_3NH_2^+$ (d) $CH_2NH_2^-$

80. Which of the following K_a values represents the acid that is strongest?

(a) $K_a = 2.8 \times 10^{-18}$ (b) $K_a = 8.2 \times 10^{-18}$ (c) $K_a = 4.4 \times 10^{-22}$ (d) $K_a = 6.4 \times 10^{-22}$

81. What will be the value of pH of 0.01 mol dm^{-3} CH$_3$COOH ($K_a = 1.74 \times 10^{-5}$) ?

(a) 3.4   (b) 3.6   (c) 3.9   (d) 3.0

82. Which of the following K_a values represents the acid with the strongest conjugate base?

(a) $K_a = 2.8 \times 10^{-18}$ (b) $K_a = 8.2 \times 10^{-18}$ (c) $K_a = 4.4 \times 10^{-22}$ (d) $K_a = 6.4 \times 10^{-22}$

83. Consider the following equilibrium expression

$$K = \frac{[H_2S]\,[OH^-]}{[HS^-]}$$

This expression represents the ......

(a) K_b for H_2S　　　　(b) K_a for H_2S　　　　(c) K_b for H_2S^-　　　　(d) K_a for HS^-

84. Which of the following is a conjugate acid-base pair?

(a) H_3PO_4 and PO_4^{3-}　　　　　　　　　(b) $H_2PO_4^-$ and PO_4^{3-}

(c) H_3PO_4 and HPO_4^{2-}　　　　　　　　(d) $H_2PO_4^-$ and HPO_4^{2-}

85. HClO is a weak acid. The concentration of H^+ ions in 0.1 M solution of HClO ($K_a = 5 \times 10^{-8}$) will be equal to

(a) 7.07×10^{-5} M　　　(b) 5×10^{-9} M　　　(c) 5×10^{-7} M　　　(d) 7×10^{-4} M

86. For the following reaction of hypochlorous acid (HOCl) with water,

$$HOCl + H_2O \rightleftharpoons H_3O^+ + OCl^-$$

What would be the effect of adding sodium hypochlorite (NaOCl) to the reaction at equilibrium?

(a) The concentrations of both HOCl and H_3O^+ would increase.

(b) The concentrations of both HOCl and H_3O^+ would decrease.

(c) The concentration of HOCl would increase and the concentration of H_3O^+ would decrease.

(d) The concentration of HOCl would decrease and the concentration of H_3O^+ would increase

87. According to Lewis definition, a base is a ......

(a) Proton donor　　　　　　　　　(b) Electron pair donor

(c) Hydroxide ion donor　　　　　　(d) Electron pair acceptor

88. Which of the following is not a Lewis base?

(a) NH_3　　　　　(b) H^-　　　　　(c) BF_3　　　　　(d) H_2O

89. Which of the following is not a true statement?

(a) All Lewis bases are also Bronsted-Lowry bases

(b) All Lewis acids contain hydrogen

(c) All Bronsted-Lowry acids contain hydrogen

(d) All Lewis acids are electron deficient

(e) According to Bronsted-Lowry theory, water is both an acid and a base

90. Which of these is not a Lewis acid ?

(a) $AlCl_3$　　　　　(b) H_3O^+　　　　　(c) $FeCl_3$　　　　　(d) C_4H_{10}

91. This species is a carbon-based Lewis acid ......

(a) CH_4　　　　　(b) CCl_3　　　　　(c) CH_3^+　　　　　(d) CH_3^-

92. Which of the following is a Lewis acid?

(a) H_3O^+　　　　　(b) BF_3　　　　　(c) NF_3　　　　　(d) OH^-

93. At 25°C, the equation representing the ionization of water is ......

    (a) $H_2O + H_2O \rightleftharpoons 2H_2 + O_2$ (b) $H_2O + H_2O \rightleftharpoons H_2O_2 + H_2$

    (c) $H_2O + H_2O \rightleftharpoons 4H^+ + 2O_2^-$ (d) $H_2O + H_2O \rightleftharpoons H_3O^+ + OH^-$

94. Consider the following equilibrium

$$H_2O_{(l)} \rightleftharpoons H_2O_{(l)} \rightleftharpoons H_3O^+_{(aq)} + OH^-_{(aq)}$$

The equilibrium constant for this system is referred to as ......

    (a) K_w (b) K_a (c) K_b (d) K_{sp}

95. The pH scale is ......

    (a) Direct   (b) Inverse   (c) Logarithmic   (d) Exponential

96. What is pH?

    (a) $\log [H^+]$ (b) A measure of basicity of a solution

    (c) $-\log [H^+]$ (d) $-\log [K_a]$

97. Which of the following equations correctly relate pH and $[H_3O^+]$?

    (a) $pH = \log [H_3O^+]$ (b) $pH = 14 - [H_3O^+]$

    (c) $pH = -\log [H_3O^+]$ (d) $pH = pK_w [H_3O^+]$

98. Which of the following is a definition of pH?

    (a) $pH = +\log [H_3O]^+$ (b) $pH = -\log [OH]^-$

    (c) $pH = -\log [H_3O^+]$ (d) $pH = pOH + pK_w$

99. What is the value of pK_w for water at 25°C ?

    (a) 1.0×10^{-14} (b) 10×10^{-7} (c) 7.00   (d) 14.00

100. Which of the following is true?

    (a) $pH + pK_a = 14$ (b) $pK_b + pOH = 14$ (c) $pH + pOH = K_w$ (d) $pK_a + pK_b = pK_w$

101. If the pOH of a solution is 6, what is the pH?

    (a) 8   (b) 6   (c) 10^6 (d) 10^8

102. Consider the ionization of water,

$$2H_2O \rightleftharpoons H_3O^+ + OH^-$$

What happens to the pH when KOH is added to water?

    (a) pH increases, since $[H_3O^+]$ increases.   (b) pH increases, since $[H_3O^+]$ decreases.

    (c) pH decreases, since $[H_3O^+]$ increases.   (d) pH decreases, since $[H_3O^+]$ decreases.

103. A 0.1 aqueous solution of a weak acid is 2% ionised. If the ionic product of water is 1×10^{-4} then $[OH^-]$ is ......

    (a) 5×10^{-12} M   (b) 2×10^{-3} M   (c) 1×10^{-14} M   (d) None of these

104. The approximate pH of "normal" rain water is ......

    (a) 0   (b) 6   (c) 7   (d) 8

105. What pH would most likely result when CO_2 dissolves naturally in rain water?

    (a) 3.5   (b) 6.5   (c) 7.2   (d) 7.8

106. The pH of salt of weak acid and strong base can be calculated using ......

    (a) $pH = 1/2pK_w - 1/2pK_a + 1/2log\ C$ (b) $pH = 1/2pK_w + 1/2pK_a - 1/2log\ C$

    (c) $pH = pK_w + pK_a + log\ C$ (d) $pH = 1/2pK_w + 1/2pK_a + 1/2log\ C$

107. The pH of a 0.3 M solution of NH_3 is approximately ......

    (a) 14.0   (b) 11.0   (c) 6.0   (d) 3.0

108. The pH of an aqueous solution is 4.32. The pH of $[OH^-]$ is ......

    (a) 6.4×10^{-1} M   (b) 4.8×10^{-5} M   (c) 2.1×10^{-10} M   (d) 1.6×10^{-14} M

109. The pH of an aqueous solution is 10.32. The pH of $[OH^-]$ is

    (a) 5.0×10^{-12} M   (b) 2.0×10^{-11} M   (c) 4.8×10^{-11} M   (d) 2.1×10^{-4} M

110. When 0.1 mole of an acid is added to 2 litres of a buffer solution, the pH of the buffer decreases by 0.5. The buffer capacity of the solution is ......

    (a) 0.6   (b) 0.4   (c) 0.2   (d) 0.1

111. The pH of salt of a weak acid and a weak base can be calculated using ......

    (a) $pH = 1/2pK_a + 1/2pK_w - 1/2pK_b$ (b) $pH = 1/2pK_a + 1/2pK_w + 1/2pK_b$

    (c) $pH = pK_a + pK_w - pK_b$ (d) $pH = 1/2pK_a - 1/2pK_w - 1/2pK_b$

112. The $[H_3O^+]$ in a solution of pH 0.60 is ......

    (a) 4.0×10^{-14} M   (b) 2.2×10^{-1} M   (c) 2.5×10^{-1} M   (d) 6.0×10^{-1} M

113. Given,

$Ag^+ + NH_3 \rightleftharpoons Ag(NH_3)^+; K_1 = 1.6 \times 10^1$

$Ag_2(NH)_4 + NH_3 \rightleftharpoons [Ag(NH_3)_2]^+; K_2 = 6.8 \times 10^3$

The equilibrium constant for the reaction

$Ag^+ + 2NH_3 \rightleftharpoons [Ag(NH_3)_2]^+$ is ......   **[Pb. PMT 2001]**

    (a) 6.8×10^3 (b) 1.088×10^7 (c) 1.088×10^6 (d) 1.6×10^3

114. If OH^- is added to a solution, then $[H_3O^+]$ will ......

    (a) remain constant   (b) adjust, such that $[H_3O^+] = [OH^-] = K_w$

    (c) increase, such that $[H_3O^+] [OH^-] = K_w$ (d) decrease, such that $[H_3O^+] [OH^-] = K_w$

115. The concentration of benzoic acid and benzoate in a solution whose pH = 5.2. The pK_a of benzoic acid is 4.20 and the solution was prepared to be 0.005 M benzoic acid.

    (a) 4.5×10^{-3} M   (b) 4.5×10^{-4} (c) 0.45 M   (d) 4.5 M

116. Calculate pH of 0.05 M sodium acetate, given that acetic acid pK_a = 4.66.

    (a) 6.86   (b) 6.68   (c) 12   (d) 8.68

117. The concentration of acetic acid needed to be added to a 0.1 M solution of sodium acetate to give a buffer of pH 5 (pK_a of acetic acid = 4.66) ......

    (a) 0.45   (b) 0.045   (c) 4.5   (d) 0.00045

118. Which of the following could typically be used to prepare a buffer solution?

    (a) $NaHS$ and H_2S (b) H_2S and Na_2S

    (c) HNO_3 and $NaNO_3$ (d) HNO_3 and $NaNO_2$

119. Which of the following pairs of substances form a buffer system for human blood?

    (a) HCl and Cl^- (b) NH_3 and NH_2^-

    (c) H_2CO_3 and HCO_3^- (d) $H_2C_6H_5O_7$ and $HC_6H_5O_7^{2-}$

120. The pH of a buffer is 4.745. When 0.01 mole of NaOH is added to 1 litre of it, the pH changes to 4.832. Calculate its buffer capacity.

(a) 0.087　　　　　(b) 0.115　　　　　(c) 1.15　　　　　(d) 11.5

121. How much of sodium acetate is required to be added to 1 litre of N/10 acetic acid to form buffer solution of pH 4 ?

(a) 2.252 g　　　　(b) 0.2252 g　　　　(c) 1.47g　　　　(d) 1.47 moles

122. What does a chemical indicator and a buffer solution typically contain?

(a) A strong acid and its conjugate acid　　　　(b) A strong acid and its conjugate base

(c) A weak acid and its conjugate acid　　　　(d) A weak acid and its conjugate base

123. Consider the following buffer equilibrium

$$HF + H_2O \rightleftharpoons H_3O^+ + F^-$$

What concentration would limit the buffering action if base were added?

(a) $[F^-]$　　　　(b) $[HF]$　　　　(c) $[H_2O]$　　　　(d) $[H_3O^+]$

124. The pH of the buffer solution containing 0.15 mole of NH_4OH and 0.25 moles of NH_4Cl

(K_b for $NH_4OH = 1.98 \times 10^{-5}$)

(a) 9.03　　　　(b) 4.96　　　　(c) 10　　　　(d) 9.3

125. For a sparingly soluble salt A_pB_q the relationship of its solubility product (L_s) with its solubility (S) is ......

(a) $L_s = S^{p+q}, p^p\, q^q$　　(b) $L_s = S^{p+q}, p^q\, q^p$　　(c) $L_s = S^{pq}, p^p\, q^q$　　(d) $L_s = S^{pq}, (pq)^{p+q}$

126. Consider the following equilibrium

$$CaCO_{3(s)} \rightleftharpoons Ca^{2+}_{(aq)} + CO^{2-}_{3(aq)}$$

Which of the following reagents, when added to the equilibrium system, would cause more $CaCO_3$ to dissolve ?

(a) $KNO_{3(s)}$　　(b) $CaCO_{3(s)}$　　(c) $H_2C_2O_{4(s)}$　　(d) $Na_2CO_{3(s)}$

127. The solubility product of CuS, Ag_2S, HgS are 10^{-31}, 10^{-51}, 10^{-54} respectively. The solubilities of these sulphides are in the order

(a) $Ag_2S > CuS > HgS$　　　　(b) $Ag_2S > HgS > CuS$

(c) $HgS > Ag_2S > CuS$　　　　(d) $CuS > Ag_2S > HgS$

128. Consider the following solubility equilibrium: $MgCO_{3(s)} \rightleftharpoons Mg^{2+}_{(aq)} + CO^{2-}_{3(aq)}$

The addition of which of the following substances would decrease the solubility of $MgCO_3$?

(a) H_2O　　(b) NaCl　　(c) NaOH　　(d) Na_2CO_3

129. Sodium iodide is added to a saturated solution of lead (II) iodide. The net change is ......

(a) $[I^-]$ increases and $[Pb^{2+}]$ increases　　　　(b) $[I^-]$ decreases and $[Pb^{2+}]$ decreases

(c) $[I^-]$ increases and $[Pb^{2+}]$ decreases　　　　(d) $[I^-]$ decreases and $[Pb^{2+}]$ increases

130. Consider the following equilibrium

$AgCl_{(s)} \rightleftharpoons Ag^+_{(aq)} + Cl^-_{(aq)}$ sodium chloride is added to a saturated solution of AgCl. The amount of solid AgCl will ......

(a) Increase as the equilibrium shifts to the left

(b) Decrease as the equilibrium shifts to the left

(c) Increase as the equilibrium shifts to the right

(d) Decrease as the equilibrium shifts to the right

131. What will be the effect of adding some solid $AgNO_3$ to a saturated solution of AgCl ?

(a) The $AgNO_3$ will not dissolve

(b) More solid AgCl will dissolve

(c) More solid AgCl will be produced

(d) There will be no effect on AgCl equilibrium

132. The solubility product of AgI at 25°C is 1.0×10^{-16} mol^2 L^{-2}. The solubility of AgI in the solution is approximately (in mol l^{-1}).

(a) 1.0×10^{-8} (b) 1.0×10^{-16} (c) 1.0×10^{-12} (d) 1.0×10^{-10}

133. An equal number of moles of Na_2CO_3 is added to four different samples that contain the cations below in low concentration.

Sample 1	Sample 2	Sample 3	Sample 4
Ba^{2+}	Ca^{2+}	Mg^{2+}	Sr^{2+}

A precipitate forms in three of the samples. Identify the cation. Which is present in sample that does not precipitate ?

(a) Ba^{2+} (b) Ca^{2+} (c) Mg^{2+} (d) Sr^{2+}

134. Consider the following equilibrium,

$$Mg(OH)_{2(s)} \rightleftharpoons Mg^{2+} + 2OH^-$$

Adding which of the following would cause the solid to dissolve?

(a) HCl   (b) KOH   (c) $Mg(OH)_2$ (d) $Mg(NO_3)_2$

135. Consider the following equilibrium,

$$Mg(OH)_{2(s)} \rightleftharpoons Mg^{2+} + 2OH^-$$

Adding which of the following would cause the solid to precipitate?

(a) 1.0 M HCl   (b) 1.0 M KOH   (c) 1.0 M $Sr(OH)_2$ (d) 1.0 M $Mg(NO_3)_2$

136. Which one of the following equilibrium systems is described by K_{sp}?

(a) $MgCO_{3(s)} \rightleftharpoons CaO_{(s)} + CO_{2(g)}$

(b) $MgCO_{3(s)} \rightleftharpoons Mg^{2+}_{(aq)} + CO^2_{3(aq)}$

(c) $Ca^{2+}_{(aq)} \rightleftharpoons CO^{2-}_{(aq)} \rightleftharpoons CaCO_{3(s)}$

(d) $Ca(OH)_{2(aq)} + H_2CO_{3(aq)} \rightleftharpoons CaCO_{3(s)} + 2H_2O_{(l)}$

137. How many grams of CaC_2O_4 (molecular weight = 128), on dissolving in distilled water will give a saturated solution ?

(a) 0.0064 g (b) 0.1280 g (c) 0.0128 g (d) 1.2800 g

138. In a saturated solution of manganese (II) hydroxide, $Mn(OH)_2$, and $[Mn^{2+}]$ equals -4.5×10^{-5} M. Therefore, the K_{sp} of $Mn(OH)_2$ is ......

(a) 9.1×10^{-14} (b) 3.6×10^{-13} (c) 2.0×10^{-9} (d) 4.1×10^{-9}

139. The compound Ag_2S has a solubility of 1.3×10^{-4} moles per litre at 25°C. The K_{sp} for this compound is

(a) 2.2×10^{-12} (b) 8.8×10^{-12} (c) 1.7×10^{-8} (d) 3.4×10^{-8}

140. The solubility of MnS is 4.8×10^{-7} M at 25°C. The K_{sp} value is ......

(a) 2.3×10^{-13} (b) 4.8×10^{-7} (c) 9.6×10^{-7} (d) 6.9×10^{-4}

141. The solubility of barium fluoride is 3.6×10^{-3} M. The solubility product constant is ......

(a) 4.7×10^{-8} (b) 1.9×10^{-7} (c) 1.3×10^{-5} (d) 2.6×10^{-5}

142. In an experiment, 20.0 ml of 0.0060 M $CaCl_2$ and 20.0 ml of 0.0050 M Na_2SO_4 are mixed together. K_{sp} of calcium sulphate is 4.9×10^5 $mol^2 lit^2$.

The ionic product of $CaSO_4$ in this mixture is ......

(a) 7.5×10^{-6} and a precipitate will form (b) 7.5×10^{-6} and a precipitate will not form

(c) 3.0×10^{-5} and precipitate will form (d) 3.0×10^{-5} and a precipitate will not form

143. When solutions of $Pb(NO_3)_2$ and NaCl are mixed, the ionic product is 9.8×10^{-6}. Which of the following statements is true? (K_{sp} of $PbCl_2$ at 25°C is 1.70×10^{-5})

(a) A precipitate forms because $K_{sp} > 9.8 \times 10^{-6}$

(b) A precipitate forms because $K_{sp} < 9.8 \times 10^{-6}$

(c) A precipitate does not form because $K_{sp} < 9.8 \times 10^{-6}$

(d) A precipitate does not form because $K_{sp} > 9.8 \times 10^{-6}$

144. The K_{sp} for AgCl is 1.8×10^{-10} M^2. What is the molar solubility of AgCl in pure water?

(a) 1.3×10^{-5} (b) 0.13 (c) 1.3×10^{-4} (d) 2.6×10^{-5}

145. The K_{sp} for Ag_2CrO_4 is 9×10^{-12} M. What is the molar solubility of Ag_2CrO_4 in pure water ?

(a) 2.6×10^{-4} (b) 1.3×10^{-4} (c) 3.9×10^{-4} (d) 1.3×10^{-3}

146. If K_{sp} of silver chromate is 1.12×10^{-12}, then solubility of it will be

(a) 0.28×10^{-3} (b) 6.54×10^{-5} (c) 0.654 (d) 0.28×10^{-5}

147. Calculate the solubility of $PbSO_4$ in 0.100 M Na_2SO_4 if $K_{sp} = [Pb^{2+}] [SO_4^{2-}] = 1.96 \times 10^{-8}$

(a) 1.96×10^{-7} (b) 1.40×10^{-4} (c) 1.96×10^{-8} (d) 1.40×10^{-8}

148. The solubility product of silver chloride is 1.5625×10^{-10} at 25°C, then its solubility in g/L^{-1} is ......

(a) 1.57×10^{-10} (b) 1.25×10^{-5} (c) 1.6×10^{-3} (d) 1.8×10^{-5}

149. The solubility product constant K_{sp} of $Mg(OH)_2$ is 9.0×10^{-12}. If a solution is 0.010 M with respect to Mg^{2+} ion, what is the maximum hydroxide ion concentration which could be present without causing the precipitation ?

(a) 1.5×10^{-7} M (b) 3.0×10^{-7} M (c) 1.5×10^{-5} M (d) 3.0×10^{-5} M

150. The solubility product of $BaSO_4$ is 1.5×10^{-9}. Find out the solubility of barium sulphate in 0.1 M $BaCl_2$ solution.

(a) 3.87×10^{-5} (b) 1.5×10^{-8} (c) 0.15×10^{-5} (d) 1.5×10^{-4}

151. The K_{sp} for $Cr(OH)_3$ is 1.2×10^{-15} M. What is the molar solubility of $Cr(OH)_3$ in pure water?

(a) 8.2×10^{-5} (b) 0.0082 (c) 8×10^{-15} (d) 3×10^{-5}

152. Consider the titration of 30.0 ml of 0.20 ml nitrous acid by adding 0.0500 M aqueous ammonia to it. The pH at the equivalence point is ....

(**Note:** This is the titration of a weak acid with a weak base.)

(a) Greater than 7   (b) Equal to 7   (c) Less than 7

(d) Cannot be determined without more data (not including K_a and K_b)

153. The following titration curve is the kind of curve expected for the titration of a ...... acid with a ...... base.

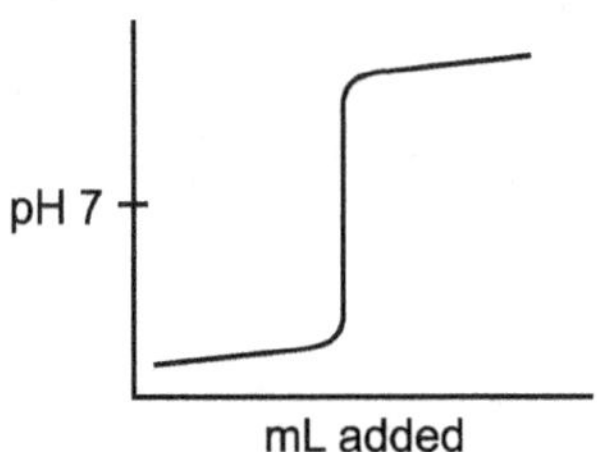

Fig. 1

(a) Strong, strong   (b) Weak, strong   (c) Strong, weak   (d) Weak, weak

154. What is the pH at the equivalence point in the titration of 100.0 mL of 0.20 M ammonia with 0.10 M hydrochloric acid?

(a) 4.6   (b) 5.2   (c) 7.0   (d) 5.5

155. Consider the titrations of pairs of aqueous acids and bases listed on the left. For which pair is the pH at the equivalence point stated incorrectly?

	Acid-Base Pair	pH at Equivalence Point
(a)	$HCl + NH_3$	less than 7
(b)	$HNO_3 + Ca(OH)_2$	equal to 7
(c)	$HClO_4 + NaOH$	equal to 7
(d)	$HClO + NaOH$	less than 7

156. Which indicator (identified by a letter) could be used to titrate aqueous NH_3 with HCl solution?

Indicator	Acid Range Colour	Colour-Change pH	Basic Range Colour
(a)	Pink	1.2 – 2.8	Yellow
(b)	Blue	3.4 – 4.6	Yellow
(c)	Yellow	6.5 – 7.8	Purple
(d)	Colourless	8.3 – 9.9	Red

157. Consider an indicator that is ionized as shown below for which its $K_a = 1.0 \times 10^{-4}$

$$HIn + H_2O \rightleftharpoons H_3O^+ + In^-$$

yellow　　　　　　　　　　　　　red

Which of the responses contain all the true statements and no others?

(1) The predominant colour in its acid range is yellow.

(2) In the middle of the pH range of its colour change a solution containing the indicator will probably be orange.

(3) At pH = 7.00, a solution containing this indicator (and no other coloured species) will be red. (Hint: Write the equilibrium constant expression for the indicator.)

(4) At pH = 7.00, most of the indicator is in the unionized form.

(5) The pH at which the indicator changes its colour is pH = 4.

(a) 1, 3, 5　　　　　　(b) 2, 4　　　　　　(c) 3, 4, 5　　　　　　(d) 1, 2, 3, 5

158. The solubility product of CuS, Ag_2S and HgS are 10^{-31}, 10^{-44}, 10^{-54} respectively. The solubility of these sulphides are in the order ......

(a) $AgS > HgS > CuS$

(b) $HgS > Ag_2S > CuS$

(c) $Ag_2S > CuS > HgS$

(d) $CuS > Ag_2S > HgS$

159. The hydride ion H^- is a stronger base than its hydroxide ion OH^-. Which of the following reactions will occur if sodium hydride (NaH) is dissolved in water ?

(a) $2H^-_{(aq)} + H_2O \rightarrow H_2O + H_2 + e^-$

(b) $2H^-_{(aq)} + H_2O_{(l)} \rightarrow OH^- + H_2$

(c) $H^- + H_2O \rightarrow$ No reaction

(d) None of these

160. Arrange the following in order of increasing acidity H_3PO_4, H_2CO_3, HCl, HI

(a) H_3PO_4, HCl, H_2CO_3, HI

(b) H_3PO_4, H_2CO_3, HCl, HI

(c) H_2CO_3, H_3PO_4, HCl, HI

(d) None of these

161. If α is the degree of ionization, C the concentration of a weak electrolyte and K_a the acid ionization constant, then the correct relationship between a, C and K_a is

(a) $\alpha^2 = \sqrt{\dfrac{K_a}{C}}$　　　　(b) $\alpha^2 = \sqrt{\dfrac{C}{K_a}}$　　　　(c) $\alpha = \sqrt{\dfrac{K_a}{C}}$　　　　(d) $\alpha = \sqrt{\dfrac{C}{K_a}}$

162. What will be the percentage quantity of the decomposition of H_2S on passing 1 mole of H_2S gas at 1000 K in 1.10 litre capacity vessel ? The value of K_c of the reaction $2H_2S \rightleftharpoons 2H_2 + 2SV$ is 1.0×10^{-6}.

(a) 1.2　　　　　　(b) 1.3　　　　　　(c) 1.4　　　　　　(d) 1.5

163. Which solutions are mixed to form a buffer solution ?

(a) A strong acid and its salt of strong base

(b) Strong acid and its salt of weak base

(c) Weak acid and its salt of strong base

(d) Weak acid and its salt of weak base

164. Solubility of a M_2S salt is 3.5×10^{-6} then find out solubility product.

(a) 1.7×10^{-6}　　　　(b) 1.7×10^{-16}　　　　(c) 1.7×10^{-18}　　　　(d) 1.7×10^{-12}

165. Which has highest pH ?

(a) CH_3COOK　　　　(b) Na_2CO_3　　　　(c) NH_4Cl　　　　(d) $NaNO_3$

166. Among the following the dissociation constant is highest for ......

(a) C_6H_5OH　　　(b) $C_6H_5CH_2OH$　　　(c) $CH_3C \equiv CH$　　　(d) C_3HNH_3Cl

167. The conjugate base of $H_2PO_4^-$ is ......

(a) PO_4^{3-}　　　(b) HPO_4^{2-}　　　(c) H_3PO_4　　　(d) P_2O_5

168. The correct order of acid strength is ......

(a) $HClO_4 < HClO_3 < HClO_2 < HClO$

(b) $HClO_2 < HClO_3 < HClO_4 < HClO$

(c) $HClO_4 < HClO < HClO_2 < HClO_3$

(d) $HClO < HClO_2 < HClO_3 < HClO_4$

169. If on addition of NH_3, pH of solution rises to 11, then which of the electrode is affected by change in pH ?

(a) $E_{oxidation}$ increases over $E°$, by 0.65 V

(b) $E_{reduction}$ increases over $E°$, by 0.65 V

(c) $E_{oxidation}$ decreases over $E°$, by 0.65 V

(d) $E_{reduction}$ decreases over $E°$, by 0.65 V

170. The pK_a of a weak acid, HA, is 4.80. The pK_b of a weak base BOH is 4.78. The pH of an aqueous solution of the corresponding salt, BA, will be

(a) 9.22　　　(b) 9.58　　　(c) 4.79　　　(d) 7.01

171. A solution of colourless salt H on boiling with excess NaOH produces non-flammable gas. The gas evolution ceases after some time. Upon addition of Zn dust to the same solution, the gas evolution restarts. The colourless salt(s) of H is (are) ......

(a) NH_4NO_3　　　(b) NH_4NO_2　　　(c) NH_4Cl　　　(d) $(NH_4)_2SO_4$

172. On adding 0.1 M solution each of $[Ag^+]$, $[Ba^{2+}]$, $[Ca^{2+}]$ in a Na_2SO_4 solution, species first precipitated will be ......

$$(K_{sp} \text{ of } BaSO_4 = 10^{-11}, CaSO_4 = 10^{-6}, K_{sp} \text{ of } Ag_2SO_4 = 10^{-5})$$

(a) Ag_2SO_4　　　(b) $BaSO_4$　　　(c) $CaSO_4$　　　(d) All of these

173. The equilibrium constants K_{p1} and K_{p2} for the reactions $X \rightleftharpoons 2Y$ and $Z \rightleftharpoons P + Q$, respectively are in the ratio of 1 : 9. If the degree of dissociation of X and Z be equal then the ratio of total pressures at these equilibria is ......

(a) $1:9$　　　(b) $1:36$　　　(c) $1:1$　　　(d) $1:3$

For answering questions 174 ...... 177 consider the following titration curve.

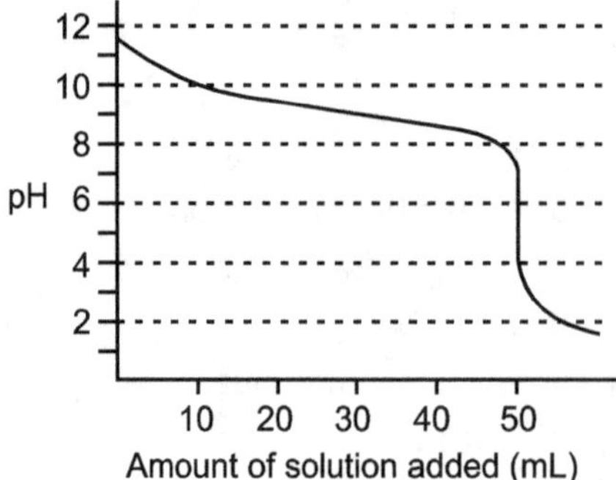

Fig. 2

174. Which one of the following combinations does the titration curve represent?

    (a) Addition of a strong base to a weak acid

    (b) Addition of a weak base to a strong acid

    (c) Addition of a strong acid to a weak base

    (d) Addition of a weak acid to a strong base

175. What is the value of pK_a that can be obtained from this titration curve?

    (a) 11.3   (b) 10.0   (c) 9.3   (d) 5.3

176. What is the pH of the solution at the point of maximum buffering?

    (a) 11   (b) 10.0   (c) 9.3   (d) 5.3

177. What is the pH of solution at the equivalence point?

    (a) 11.3   (b) 10.0   (c) 9.3   (d) 5.3

178. At 25°C, the dissociation constant of a base, BOH, is 1.0×10^{-12}. The concentration of hydroxyl ions in 0.01 M aqueous solution of the base would be ......

    (a) 1.0×10^{-6} mol L^{-1} (b) 1.0×10^{-7} mol L^{-1}

    (c) 1.0×10^{-8} mol L^{-1} (d) 1.0×10^{-5} mol L^{-1}

179. What is the correct relationship between the pH of isomolar solutions of sodium oxide (pH_1), sodium sulphide (pH_2), sodium selenide (pH_1) and sodium telluride (pH_4) ?

    (a) $pH_1 < pH_2 < pH_3 < pH_4$ (b) $pH_1 < pH_2 < pH_3 > pH_4$

    (c) $pH_1 < pH_2 < pH_3 = pH_4$ (d) $pH_1 < pH_2 = pH_3 > pH_4$

PREVIOUS YEAR'S QUESTIONS

1. For the reversible reaction: **[AIPMT 2014]**

$N_{2(g)} + 3H_{2(g)} \rightleftharpoons 2NH_{2(g)} + heat$

The equilibrium shifts in forward direction ......

    (a) by decreasing the concentrations of $N_{2(g)}$ and $H_{2(g)}$

    (b) by increasing pressure and decreasing temperature

    (c) by increasing the concentration of $NH_{3(g)}$

    (d) by decreasing the pressure

2. For a given exothermic reaction, K_p and K_p' are the equilibrium constants at temperatures T_1 and T_2 respectively. Assuming that heat of reaction is constant in the temperature range between T_1 and T_2, it is readily observed that ......   **[AIPMT 2014]**

    (a) $K_p = K_p'$ (b) $K_p = 1/K_p'$ (c) $K_p > K_p'$ (d) $K_p < K_p'$

3. For the reaction, $N_{2(g)} + O_{2(g)} \rightleftharpoons 2NO_{(g)}$, the equilibrium constant is K_1. The equilibrium constant is K_2 for the reaction $2NO_{(g)} + O_{2(g)} \rightleftharpoons 2NO_{2(g)}$. What is K for the reaction

$$NO_{2(g)} \rightleftharpoons \frac{1}{2} N_{2(g)} + O_{2(g)} \ ?$$

    (a) $\dfrac{1}{(K_1 K_2)}$ (b) $\dfrac{1}{(2K_1 K_2)}$ (c) $\dfrac{1}{(4K_1 K_2)}$ (d) $\left[\dfrac{1}{(K_1 K_2)}\right]^{1/2}$

4. For the reactions, $I_{2(aq)} \rightleftharpoons I_{2\ (oil)}$, equilibrium constant is K_1.

$I_{2(oil)} \rightleftharpoons I_2$ (ether) $= K_3$, Equilibrium constant is K_2 for the reaction.

$I_{2(aq)} \rightleftharpoons I_{2(ether)} = K_3$

The relation between K_1, K_2, K_3 is   **[DUMET 2011]**

(a) $K_3 = K_1 + K_2$ (b) $K_3 = K_1 K_2$ (c) $K_3 = K_1/K_2$ (d) $K_3 = K_2/K_1$

5. For a chemical reaction of the type $A \rightleftharpoons B$, $K = 2.0$ and $B \rightleftharpoons C$, $K = 0.01$. Equilibrium for the reaction $2C \rightleftharpoons 2A$ is ......   **[DUMET 2011]**

(a) 25   (b) 50   (c) 2500   (d) 4×10^{-4}

6. Given a gas phase reaction $2A_{(g)} + B_{(g)} \rightleftharpoons C_{(g)} + D_{(g)}$, which one of the following changes will affect the value of K_c ?   **[DUMET 2011]**

(a) Addition of inert gas   (b) Addition of catalyst

(c) Addition of reactants   (d) Increase in temperature

7. Consider the following gaseous equilibria with equilibrium constants K_1 and K_2 respectively

$$SO_{2(g)} + \frac{1}{2} O_{2(g)} \rightleftharpoons SO_{3(g)} \; ; \; 2SO_{3(g)} \rightleftharpoons 2SO_{2(g)} + O_{2(g)}$$

The equilibrium constants are related as ......   **[KCET 2011]**

(a) $2K_1 = K_2^2$ (b) $K_2^2 = \dfrac{1}{K_2}$ (c) $K_2^2 = \dfrac{1}{K_1}$ (d) $K_2 = \dfrac{2}{K_1^2}$

8. In which of the following equilibrium, K_c and K_p are not equal?   **[CBSE, AIPMT 2010]**

(a) $2C_{(s)} + O_{2(g)} \rightleftharpoons 2CO_{2(g)}$ (b) $2NO_{(g)} \rightleftharpoons N_{2(g)} + O_{2(g)}$

(c) $SO_{2(g)} + NO_{2(g)} \rightleftharpoons SO_{3(g)} + NO_{(g)}$ (d) $H_{2(g)} + I_{2(g)} \rightleftharpoons 2H_{(g)}$

9. In which of the following reaction, $K_p > K_c$?   **[CPMT 2011]**

(a) $N_{2(g)} + 3H_{2(s)} \rightleftharpoons 2NH_{3(g)}$ (b) $H_{2(g)} + I_{2(g)} \rightleftharpoons 2H_{(g)}$

(c) $PCl_{3(g)} + Cl_{2(g)} \rightleftharpoons PCl_{5(g)}$ (d) $2SO_{3(g)} \rightleftharpoons 2SO_{2(g)} + O_{2(g)}$

10. Two moles of each reactant A and B are taken in a reaction flask. They react in the following manner.

$$A_{(g)} + B_{(g)} \rightleftharpoons C_{(g)} + D_{(g)}$$

At equilibrium, it was found that the concentration of C is triple to that of B. The equilibrium constant for the reaction is ......   **[AIIMS 2010]**

(a) 4.5   (b) 6   (c) 9   (d) 1/6

11. 5 moles of SO_2 and 5 moles of O_2 are allowed to react. At equilibrium, it was observed that 60% of SO_2 is used up. If the partial pressure of the equilibrium mixture is one atmosphere, then the partial pressure of O_2 is ......   **[KCET 2010]**

(a) 0.52 atm   (b) 0.21 atm   (c) 0.41 atm   (d) 0.82 atm

12. Consider the reaction where $K_p = 0.497$ at 500 K.
$$PCl_{5(g)} \rightleftharpoons PCl_{3(g)} + Cl_{2(g)}$$
If the three gases are mixed in a rigid container so that the partial pressure of each gas is initially 1 atm, which is true? **[OJEE 2010]**
(a) More PCl_5 will be produced
(b) More PCl_3 will be produced
(c) Equilibrium will be established when 50% reaction is complete.
(d) None of the above.

13. If the concentration of OH^- ions in the reaction $Fe(OH)_{3(s)} \rightleftharpoons Fe^{3+}_{(aq)} + 3OH^-_{(aq)}$ is decreased by 1/4 times, then the equilibrium concentration of Fe^{3+} will increase by ......

[CBSE AIPMT 2008]

(a) 8 times
(b) 16 times
(c) 64 times
(d) 4 times

14. The dissociation equilibrium of a gas AB_2 can be represented as
$$2AB_{2(g)} \rightleftharpoons 2AB_{(g)} + B_{2(g)}$$
The degree of dissociation is 'x' and is small compared to 1. The expression relating the degree of dissociation (x) with equilibrium constant K_p and total pressure p is ......

[CBSE AIPMT 2008]

(a) $\left(\dfrac{2K_p}{p}\right)$
(b) $\left(\dfrac{2K_p}{p}\right)^{1/3}$
(c) $\left(\dfrac{2K_p}{p}\right)^{1/2}$
(d) $\left(\dfrac{K_p}{p}\right)$

15. The values of K_{p1} and K_{p2} for the reactions :
$$X \rightleftharpoons Y + Z \quad ... \text{ (i)} \quad \text{and} \quad A \rightleftharpoons 2B \quad ... \text{ (ii)}$$
are in the ratio of 9 : 1. If degree of dissociation of X and A be equal, then total pressure at equilibrium (i) and (ii) are in the ratio **[CBSE AIPMT 2008]**
(a) 3 : 1
(b) 1 : 9
(c) 36 : 1
(d) 1 : 1

16. In which of the following reactions, the concentrations of the product is higher than the concentration of reactant at equilibrium ? (K = equilibrium constant) **[AIIMS 2008]**
(a) $A \rightleftharpoons B$; K = 0.001
(b) $M \rightleftharpoons N$; K = 10
(c) $X \rightleftharpoons Y$; K = 0.005
(d) $R \rightleftharpoons P$; K = 0.01

17. Assertion : For the reaction $N_{2(g)} + 3H_{(g)} \rightleftharpoons 2NH_{3(g)}$, unit of $K_c = L^2\,mol^{-2}$
Reason : For the reaction, $N_{2(g)} + 3H_{2(g)} \rightleftharpoons 2NH_{3(g)}$, Equilibrium constant,
$$K_c = \frac{[NH_3]^2}{[N_2]\,[H_2]^3}$$

[AIIMS 2008]

(a) Both Assertion and Reason are true and Reason is the correct explanation of the Assertion.
(b) Both Assertion and Reason are true but Reason is not the correct explanation of the Assertion.
(c) Assertion is true but Reason is false
(d) Both Assertion and Reason are false.

18. In the equilibrium $2NH_3 \rightleftharpoons N_2 + 3H_2$, 6 moles of NH_3 is taken in 10 L flask. If concentration of N_2 at equilibrium is x then concentration of NH_3 at equilibrium is ......

[DUMET 2008]

(a) $0.6 - x$
(b) $0.6 - 2x$
(c) $0.6 - x/2$
(d) None is correct

19. Three moles of PCl_5, three moles of PCl_3 and two moles of Cl_2 are taken in a closed vessel. If at equilibrium the vessel has 1.5 moles of PCl_5, the number of PCl_3 present in it is ......

[Kerala CEE 2008]

(a) 5　　　　(b) 3　　　　(c) 6　　　　(d) 4.5

20. Formaldehyde polymerizes to form glucose according to the reaction,
$$6HCHO \rightleftharpoons C_6H_{12}O_6$$
The theoretically computed equilibrium constant for this reaction is found to be 6×10^{22}. If 1 M solution of glucose dissociates according to the above equilibrium, the concentration of formaldehyde in the solution will be ...... **[Manipal 2008]**

(a) 1.6×10^{-2} M　　(b) 1.6×10^{-4} M　　(c) 1.6×10^{-6} M　　(d) 1.6×10^{-8} M

21. Which of the following is irreversible reaction? **[CBSE AIPMT 2007]**

(a) $2NH_3 \rightarrow N_2 + 3H_2$　　　　　　(b) $PCl_5 \rightarrow PCl_3 + Cl_2$

(c) $KClO_3 \rightarrow KNI + O_2$　　　　　　(d) $SO_3 \rightarrow SO_2 + O_2$

22. The following equilibrium constants are given :
$$N_2 + 3H_2 \rightleftharpoons 2NH_3; \ K_1$$
$$N_2 + 3H_2 \rightleftharpoons 2NH_3; \ K_1$$
$$H_2 + \frac{1}{2}O_2 \rightleftharpoons H_2O; \ K_3$$

The equilibrium constant for the oxidation of NH_3 by oxygen to give NO is ... **[CPMT 2007]**

(a) $\dfrac{K_2 K_3^3}{K_1}$　　　　(b) $\dfrac{K_2 K_3^2}{K_1}$　　　　(c) $\dfrac{K_2^2 K_3}{K_1}$　　　　(d) $\dfrac{K_1 K_2}{K_1}$

23. Which has equilibrium constant as one? **[DUMET 2006]**

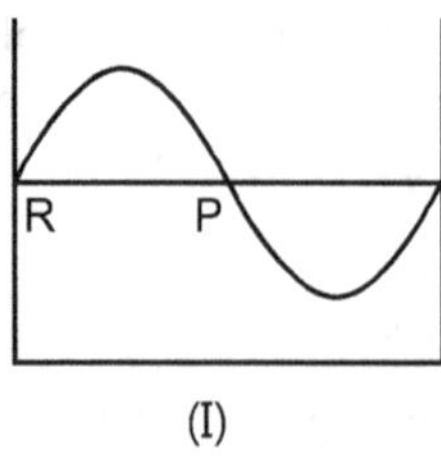
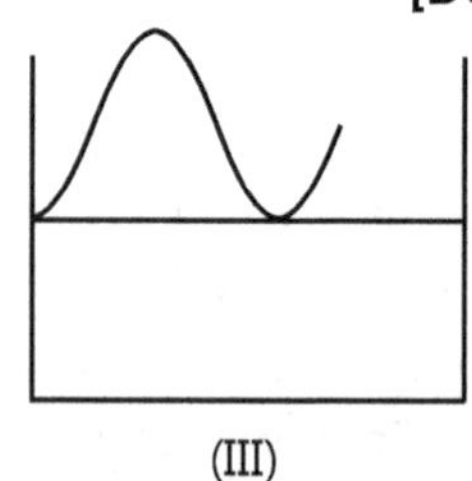

Fig. 3

(a) I only　　　　(b) II only　　　　(c) Both II and III　　(d) Both I and III

24. Equilibrium constants K_1 and K_2 for the following equilibria **[CBSE AIPMT 2005]**
$$NO_{(g)} + \frac{1}{2}O_2 \rightleftharpoons NO_{2(g)} \ \text{and} \ 2NO_{2(g)} \rightleftharpoons 2NO_{(g)} + O_{2(g)}$$

(a) $K_2 = 1/K_1$　　　(b) $K_2 = K_1^2$　　　(c) $K_2 = \dfrac{K_1}{2}$　　　(d) $K_2 = \dfrac{1}{K_1^2}$

25. $NH_4COONH_{2(s)} \rightleftharpoons 2NH_{3(g)} + CO_{2(g)}$. If equilibrium pressure is 3 atm for the above reaction, K_p for the reaction is ...... **[DUMET 2005]**

(a) 4　　　　(b) 27　　　　(c) $\dfrac{4}{27}$　　　　(d) $\dfrac{1}{27}$

26. If in the reaction, $N_2O_4 \rightleftharpoons 2N$, x is that part of N_2O_4 which dissociates, then the number of molecules at equilibrium will be ...... **[KCET 2005]**

(a) 1 (b) 3 (c) $(1 + x)$ (d) $(1 + x)^2$

27. At 600°C, K_p for the following reaction is 1 atm.

$$X_{(g)} \rightleftharpoons Y_{(g)} + Z_{(g)}$$

At equilibrium, 50% of X(g) is dissociated. The total pressure of the equilibrium system is p atm. What is the partial pressure (in atm) of X(g) at equilibrium ? **[EAMCET 2005]**

(a) 1 (b) 4 (c) 2 (d) 0.5

28. The value of ΔH for the reaction, $X_{2(g)} + 4Y_{2(g)} \rightleftharpoons 2XY_{4(g)}$ is less than zero. Formation of $XY_{4(g)}$ will be favoured at ...... **[CBSE AIPMT 2011]**

(a) high pressure and low temperature

(b) high temperature and high pressure

(c) low pressure and low temperature

(d) high temperature and low pressure.

29. Which reaction is not affected by change in pressure? **[AFMC 2009]**

(a) $H_2 + I_2 \rightleftharpoons 2HI$

(b) $2C + O_2 \rightleftharpoons 2CO$

(c) $N_2 + 3H_2 \rightleftharpoons 2NH_3$

(d) $PCl_3 \rightleftharpoons PCl_3 + Cl_2$

30. Assertion : For the reaction, $2NO_{(g)} + O_{2(g)} \rightleftharpoons 2NO_{2(g)}$, increace in pressure favour the formation of NO_2.

Reason : The reaction is exothermic **[AIIMS 2009]**

(a) Both Assertion and Reason are true and Reason is the correct explanation of the Assertion.

(b) Both Assertion and Reason are true and Reason is not the correct explanation of the Assertion.

(c) Assertion is true but Reason is false

(d) Both Assertion and Reason are false.

31. For the equilibrium, $2NO_{2(g)} \rightleftharpoons N_2O_{4(g)} + 14.6$ kcal, increase in temperature ...... **[CPMT 2009]**

(a) favour the formation of N_2O_4

(b) favour the decomposition of N_2O_4

(c) does not effect equilibrium

(d) stop the reaction.

32. $N_2 + 3H_2 \rightleftharpoons 2NH_3$ + heat. What is the effect of increase of temperature on the equilibrium of the reaction? **[KCET 2008]**

(a) Equilibrium is shifted to the left.

(b) Equilibrium is shifted to the right.

(c) Equilibrium is unaltered.

(d) Reaction rate does not change.

33. For the reaction, $CH_{4(g)} + 2O_{2(s)} \rightleftharpoons CO_{2(g)} + 2H_2O_{(l)}$; $\Delta H = -170.8$ kJ mol^{-1}

Which of the following statements is not true? **[CBSE AIPMT 2006]**

(a) At equilibrium, the concentration of $CO_{2(g)}$ and $H_2O_{(l)}$ are not equal.

(b) The equilibrium constant for the reaction is given by $K_p = \dfrac{[CO_2]}{[CH_4]\,[O_2]}$

(c) Addition of $CH_{4(g)}$ or $O_{2(g)}$ at equilibrium will cause a shift to the right.

(d) The reaction is exothermic.

34. In a gaseous reversible reaction, $N_2 + O_2 \rightleftharpoons 2NO + heat$, if pressure is increased then the equilibrium ...... **[Manipal 2006]**

    (a) Unchanged

    (b) Increased

    (c) Decreased

    (d) Sometimes increased, sometimes decreased

35. $CaCO_3 \rightleftharpoons CaO + CO_2$ reaction in lime kiln goes to completion because ... **[AFMC 2005]**

    (a) CaO does not react with CO_2 to give $CaCO_3$

    (b) Backward reaction is very low

    (c) CO_2 formed escapes out

    (d) None of the above

36. Of the following which change will shift the reaction towards the product?

    $$I_{2(g)} \rightleftharpoons 2I_{(g)}, \quad \Delta H_t^o \ (298 \ K) = +150 \ kJ$$ **[AIIMS 2004]**

    (a) Increase in concentration of I

    (b) Decrease in concentration of I_2

    (c) Increase in temperature

    (d) Increase in total pressure.

37. For the reaction : $CH_{4(g)} + 2O_{2(g)} \rightleftharpoons CO_{2(g)} + 2H_2O_{(l)}$, $\Delta_rH = -170.8 \ J \ mol^{-1}$. Which of the following statements is not true?

    (a) At equilibrium, the concentrations of $CO_{2(g)}$ and $H_2O_{(l)}$ are not equal.

    (b) The equilibrium constant for the reaction is given by $K_p = \dfrac{[CO_2]}{[CH_4] \ [O_2]}$

    (c) Addition of $CH_{4(g)}$ or $O_{2(g)}$ at equilibrium will cause a shift to the right

    (d) The reaction is exothermic **[AIPMT 2006]**

38. If the value of an equilibrium constant for a particular reaction is 1.6×10^{12}, then at equilibrium the system will contain ...... **[AIPMT 2015]**

    (a) mostly reactants

    (b) mostly products

    (c) similar amounts of reactants and products (d) all reactants

Ionic Equilibrium

39. A buffer solution contains 0.1 mole of sodium acetate dissolved in 100 cm^3 of 0.1 M acetic acid. To the active buffer solution, 0.1 mole of sodium acetate is further added and dissolved. The pH of the resulting solution is ...... **[KCET 2011]**

    (a) pK_a　　　(b) $pK_a + 2$　　　(c) $pK_a + log \ 2$　　(d) $pK_a + log \ 2$

40. In a buffer solution containing equal concentrations of B^- and HB, then K_b for B^- is 10^{-10}. Then pH of the buffer solution is ...... **[CBSE AIPMT 2010]**

    (a) 4　　　　　(b) 10　　　　　(c) 7　　　　　(d) 6

41. What is $[H^+]$ in mol/L of a solution that is 0.20 in CH_3COONa and 0.10 M in CH_3COOH ? K_a for $CH_3COOH = 1.8 \times 10^{-5}$ **[CBSE AIPMT 2010]**

    (a) 9.0×10^{-6}　　(b) 3.5×10^{-4}　　(c) 1.1×10^{-5}　　(d) 1.8×10^{-5}

42. If 100 mL of HCl + 35 mL of NaOH, then the colour of methyl orange in the solution will be
...... **[AFMC 2010]**
    (a) Red   (b) Yellow
    (c) Cannot be predicted   (d) Methyl orange is not suitable indicator

43. The pH of an acidic buffer mixture is ......   **[Manipal 2010]**
    (a) 6.8   (b) 7
    (c) 7.5   (d) depends upon K_a of the acid

44. The dissociation contant for acetic acid and HCN at 25°C are 1.5×10^{-5} and 4.5×10^{-10}
respectively. The equilibrium, $CN^- + CH_3COOH \rightleftharpoons HCN + CH_3COO^-$ would be ......
[CBSE AIPMT 2009]
    (a) 3.0×10^5 (b) 3.0×10^{-5} (c) 3.0×10^{-4} (d) 3.0×10^4

45. A buffer solution is used in ......   **[Manipal 2009]**
    (a) preparation of potash alum.   (b) the removal of PO_4^{3-} ions
    (c) increasing the pH value of a solution   (d) precipitation of $Cr(OH)_3$ from $CrCl_3$

46. When 0.1 mole of an acid is added to 2L of a buffer solution, then pH of the buffer
decreases by 0.5. The buffer capacity of the solution is ......   **[EAMCET 2008]**
    (a) 0.6   (b) 0.4   (c) 0.2   (d) 0.1

47. The pH value of gastric juice in human stomach is about 1.8 and in the small intestine it is
about 7.8. The pK_a value of aspirin is 3.5. Aspirin will be ......   **[KCET 2003]**
    (a) completely ionized in the small intestine and in the stomach .
    (b) unionised in the small intestine and in the stomach
    (c) ionised in the small intestine and almost unionised in the stomach
    (d) ionised in the stomach and almost unionised in the small intestine

48. How many times a solution of pH = 2 has higher acidity than the solution of pH = 6 ?
[RPMT 2003]
    (a) 4   (b) 12   (c) 400   (d) 10000

49. A buffer solution is prepared in which the concentration of NH_3 is 0.30 M and the
concentration of NH_4^+ is 0.20 M. If the equilibrium constant, K_b for NH_3 equal to 1.8×10^{-5},
what is the pH of the solution ?   **[CBSE AIPMT 2011]**
    (a) 8.73   (b) 9.08   (c) 9.43   (d) 11.72

50. What is the pH of 0.01 M glycine solution ? For glycine, $K_{a1} = 4.5 \times 10^{-3}$ and $K_{a2} = 1.7 \times 10^{-10}$
at 298 K ?   **[AIIMS 2004]**
    (a) 3.0   (b) 10.0   (c) 6.1   (d) 7.1

51. Assertion : Addition of silver ions to a mixture of aqueous sodium chloride and sodium
bromide solution will first precipitate AgBr rather than AgCl.   **[AAIIS 2004]**
    Reason : K_{sp} of AgCl < K_{sp} of AgBr.
    (a) Both assertion and Reason are true and Reason is the correct explanation of the
        Assertion
    (b) Both Assertion and Reason are true but Reason is not correct explanation of Assertion
    (c) Assertion is true but Reason is false
    (d) Both Assertion and Reason are false.

52. Select the pK_a value of the strongest acid for the following. **[KCET 2004]**
 (a) 1.0 (b) 3.0 (c) 2.0 (d) 4.5

53. The pH value of an acid is 5 and its concentration is 1 M. What is the value of K_a for the acid ? **[Manipal 2004]**
 (a) 10^{-7} (b) 10^{-5} (c) 10^{-10} (d) 10^{-8}

54. Which of the following has highest pH ? **[Manipal 2006]**
 (a) M/4 KOH (b) M/4 NaOH (c) M/4 NH_4OH (d) M/4 $Ca(OH)_2$

55. The solubility of AgI in NaI solution is less than that in pure water because ......
 (a) the temperature of the solution decreases **[Manipal 2006]**
 (b) solubility product of AgI is less than that of NaI
 (c) of common ion effect
 (d) AgI forms complex with NaI

56. 0.005 M acid solution has 5 pH. The percentage ionization of acid is ...... **[RPMT 2006]**
 (a) 0.8% (b) 0.6% (c) 0.4% (d) 0.2%

57. The solubility of Sb_2S_3 in water is 1.0×10^{-5} mol L^{-1} at 298 K. What will be its solubility product ? **[RPMT 2006]**
 (a) 108×10^{-25} (b) 1.0×10^{-25} (c) 144×10^{-25} (d) 126×10^{-28}

58. Some chemists at ISRO wished to prepare a saturated solution of a silver compound and they wanted it to have the highest concentration of silver ion possible, Which of the following compounds, would they use ? **[BCECE 2006]**
$$K_{sp\ (AgCl)} = 1.8 \times 10^{-10},\ K_{sp\ (AgBr)} = 5.0 \times 10^{-13},\ K_{sp(Ag_2CrO_4)} = 2.4 \times 10^{-12}$$
 (a) AgCl (b) AgBr (c) Ag_2CrO_4 (d) None of these

59. At 25°C, the dissociation constant of a base BOH, is 1.0×10^{-12}. The concentration of hydroxyl ions in 0.01 M aqueous solution of the base would be ...... **[CBSE AIPMT 2005]**
 (a) 2.0×10^{-6} (b) 1.0×10^{-5} mol L^{-1}
 (c) 1.0×10^{-6} mol L^{-1} (d) 1.0×10^{-7} mol L^{-1}

60. A solution has pH = 5, it is diluted to 100 times, then it will become ...... **[AFMC 2005]**
 (a) neutral (b) basic (c) unaffected (d) more acidic

61. Assertion: On mixing 500 mL of 10^{-6} M Ca^{2+} ion and 500 mL of 10^{-6} M F^- ion, the precipitate of CaF_2 will be obtained, K_{sp} ($CaF_2 = 10^{-18}$) **[AIIMS 2007]**
 Reason : If K_{sp} is greater than ionic product, a precipitate will develop.
 (a) Both Assertion and Reason are true and Reason is the correct explanation of Assertion.
 (b) Both Assertion and Reason are true but Reason is not the correct explanation of Assertion.
 (c) Assertion is true but Reason is false
 (d) Both Assertion and Reason are false

62. Assertion : NaCl is precipitated when CHI gas is passed in a saturated solution of NaCl.
 Reason : HCl is strong acid. **[AIIMS 2007]**
 (a) Both Assertion and Reason are true and Reason is the correct explanation of Assertion.
 (b) Both Assertion and Reason are true but Reason is not the correct explanation of Assertion.
 (c) Assertion is true but Reason is false
 (d) Both Assertion and Reason are false

63. 100 mL of 0.1 M H_2SO_4 is added to 200 mL of 0.1 M NaOH. What is the pH of the resulting mixture? **[EAMCET 2007]**

(a) 2 	(b) 7 	(c) 10 	(d) 12

64. The solubility of AgCl is 1×10^{-5} mol/L. Its solubility in 0.1 molar sodium chloride solution is **[MHT CET 2007]**

(a) 1.50×10^{22} 	(b) 1.50×10^{23} 	(c) 1.506×10^{20} 	(d) 3.012×10^{21}

65. When ammonium chloride is added to ammonia solution, the pH of the resulting solution will be ...... **[MHT CET 2007]**

(a) increased 	(b) seven 	(c) decreased 	(d) unchanged

66. The hydrogen ion concentration of a 10^{-8} M HCl aqueous solution at 298 K ($K_w = 10^{-14}$) is ... **[CBSE AIPMT 2006]**

(a) 1.0×10^{-6} M 	(b) 1.0525×10^{-7} M 	(c) 9.525×10^{-8} M 	(d) 1.0×10^{-8} M

67. Solubility product of salt AB is 1×10^{-8} M in a solution ...... in which the concentration of A^+ ions is 10^{-3} M. Its concentration is ...... **[AFMC 2008]**

(a) between 10^{-8} M to 10^{-7} M 	(b) between 10^{-7} M to 10^{-8} M

(c) $> 10^{-5}$ M 	(d) $< 10^{-8}$ M

68. On adding 0.1 M solution each of $[Ag^+]$, $[Ba^{2+}]$, $[Ca^{2+}]$ in a Na_2SO_4 species first precipitated is ...... $[K_{sp\ (BaSO_4)} = 10^{-11}, K_{sp\ (CaSO_4)} = 10^{-4}, K_{sp\ (Ag_2SO_4)} = 10^{-5}]$ **[AIIMS 2008]**

(a) Ag_2SO_4 	(b) $BaSO_4$ 	(c) $CaSO_4$ 	(d) All of these

69. Which of the following is correct? **[CPMT 2008]**

(a) The pH of 1 L solution containing 0.49 g of H_2SO_4 is 2.0

(b) The conjugate base of H_2S is S^{2-}

(c) BF_3 is a Lewis base.

(d) Phenolphthalein is colourless in basic medium

70. Number of H^+ ions present in 250 mL of lemon juice of pH = 3 is ...... **[Keral CEE 2008]**

(a) 1.50×10^{22} 	(b) 1.50×10^{23} 	(c) 1.506×10^{20} 	(d) 3.012×10^{21}

(e) 2.008×10^{23}

71. An aqueous solution contains Ni^{2+}, Co^{2+} and Pb^{2+} ions at equal concentrations. The solubility product of NiS, PbS and CoS in water at 25°C are 1.4×10^{-24}, 3.4×10^{-28}, respectively, indicate which of these ions will be precipitated first and last when sulphide concentration is progressively increased from zero? **[J&K CET 2008]**

(a) NiS and PbS 	(b) NiS and CoS 	(c) CoS and NiS 	(d) PbS and NiS

72. A weak acid, HA, has a K_a of 1.00×10^{-5}. If 0.100 mole of this acid is dissolved in 1 L of water, the percentage of acid dissociated at equilibrium is closest to ...... **[CBSE AIPMT 2007]**

(a) 99.0% 	(b) 1.00% 	(c) 99.9% 	(d) 0.100%

73. 30 cc of M/3 HCl, 200 cc of M/2 NO_3 and 40 cc of M/4 NaOH solution are mixed and the volume was made up to 1 dm^3. The pH of the resulting solution is ...... **[KCET 2009]**

(a) 2 	(b) 1 	(c) 3 	(d) 8

74. 10^{-6} M NaOH is diluted to 100 times. The pH of the diluted base is **[KCET 2009]**

(a) between 5 and 6 	(b) between 6 and 7

(c) between 10 and 11 	(d) between 7 and 8

75. 20 mL of 0.1 M acetic acid is mixed with 50 mL of potassium acetate. K_a of acetic acid = 1.8×10^{-5} at 27°C. The concentration of potassium acetate if pH of the mixture is 4.8 ...... **[EAMCET 2009]**

(a) 0.1 M   (b) 0.04 M   (c) 0.4 M   (d) 0.02 M

76. If 20 ml of an acidic solution of pH 3 is diluted to 100 mL, then H^+ ion concentration will be ...... **[MHT CET 2009]**

(a) 1×10^{-3} M   (b) 2×10^{-3} M   (c) 2×10^{-4} M   (d) 0.02×10^{-4} M

77. The degree of dissociation of a 0.01 M week acid is 10^{-3}. Its pOH is ... **[MHT CET 2009]**

(a) 5   (b) 3   (c) 9   (d) 11

78. Both HCOOH and CH_3COOH solutions have equal pH. If K_1/K_2 (ratio of acid ionization constants) of these acids is 4, their molar concentration ratio will be ......**[Manipal 2009]**

(a) 2   (b) 0.5   (c) 4   (d) 0.25

79. Equal volumes of three acid solutions of pH 3, 4 and 5 are mixed in a vessel. What will be the H^+ ion concentration in the mixture? **[CBSE AIPMT 2008]**

(a) 1.11×10^{-4} M   (b) 3.7×10^{-4} M   (c) 3.7×10^{-3} M   (d) 1.11×10^{-3} M

80. The pH value of 1×10^{-4} M NaOH solution is ...... **[AFMC 2009]**

(a) 4   (b) 10   (c) 6   (d) Between 6-7

81. If the solubility of calcium fluoride in pure water is x mol/L, its solubility product is ...... **[AFMC 2009]**

(a) $\sqrt{2}\,x$ (b) $2x^2$ (c) $4x^3$ (d) x^2

82. If the dissociation constant of 5×10^{-4} M aqueous solution of diethylamine is 2.5×10^{-5}, its pH value is ...... **[AIIMS 2009]**

(a) 8   (b) 3.95   (c) 10.05   (d) 2

83. The number of hydroxyl ions in 100 mL of a solution having pH 10 is **[AIIMS 2009]**

(a) 1×10^4 (b) 3.012×10^4 (c) 6.02×10^{18} (d) 6.023×10^{19}

84. The solubility product of a salt having formula M_2X_3 is 2.2×10^{-20}. If the solubility of another salt having formula M_2X is twice the molar solubility of M_2X_3, the solubility product of M_2X is ...... **[AIIMS 2009]**

(a) 3×10^{-12} (b) 9.16×10^{-5} (c) 4.58×10^{-5} (d) 2.76×10^{-18}

85. When equal volumes of $AgNO_3$ and NaCl solution are mixed, the precipitation of AgCl ($K_{sp} = 1.81 \times 10^{-10}$) will occur with ...... **[AMU 2009]**

(a) 10^{-3} M (Ag^+) and 10^{10} M (Cl^-) (b) 10^{-5} M (Ag^+) and 10^{-5} (Cl^-)

(c) 10^{-6} M (Ag^+) and 10^{-5} M (Cl^-) (d) 10^{-4} M (Ag^+) and 10^{-4} M (Cl^-)

86. If pK_a of acetic acid and pK_b of ammonium hydroxide are 4.76 each, then pH of ammonium acetate is ...... **[AMU 2009]**

(a) 7   (b) less than 7   (c) more than 7   (d) zero

87. Solubility (S) of CaF_2 in terms of its solubility product is given as ...... **[AMU 2009]**

(a) $S = (K_{sp})^{1/3}$ (b) $S = \left(\dfrac{K_{sp}}{2}\right)^{1/3}$ (c) $S = \left(\dfrac{K_{sp}}{4}\right)^{1/3}$ (d) $S = \left(\dfrac{K_{sp}}{2}\right)^{1/2}$

88. Two acids A and B have pK_a 4 and 6, then **[CPMT 2009]**

(a) A is 4/6 times stronger than B   (b) A is 10 times stronger than B

(c) A is 6/4 times stronger than B   (d) B is 10 times stronger than B

89. Ammonium acetate which is 0.01 M, is hydrolysed to 0.001 M concentration. Calculate the change in pH in 0.001 M solution, if initially pH = pK_a. **[MHT CET 2010]**

(a) 5　　　　(b) 10　　　　(c) 100　　　　(d) 1

90. Which is not an example of common ion effect? **[MHT CET 2010]**

(a) $NaCl + AgCl$

(b) $H_2S + HCl$

(c) $CH_3COOH + NaOH$

(d) $NH_4OH + NH_4Cl$

91. 0.023 g of sodium metal is reacted with 100 cm^3 of water. The pH of the resulting solution is ...... **[KCET 2010]**

(a) 10　　　　(b) 11　　　　(c) 9　　　　(d) 12

92. pH value of which one of the following is not equal to one? **[KCET 2010]**

(a) 0.1 M CH_3COOH

(b) 0.1 M HNO_3

(c) 0.05 M H_2SO_4

(d) 50 cm^3 0.4 M CHI + 50 cm^3 0.2 M NaOH

93. The concentration of Ag^+ ion in a given saturated solution of AgCl at 25°C is 1.06×10^{-5} g ion per litre. Thus, the solubility product of AgCl is ...... **[Manipal 2010]**

(a) 0.353×10^{-10}　　　(b) 0.530×10^{-10}　　　(c) 1.12×10^{-10}　　　(d) 2.12×10^{-10}

94. If pH of a saturated solution of $Ba(OH)_2$ is 12, then the value of its K_{sp} is ......

[CBSE AIPMT 2010]

(a) 5.00×10^{-7} M^3　　(b) 4.00×10^{-6} M^3　　(c) 4.00×10^{-7} M^3　　(d) 5.00×10^{-6} M^3

95. The pH of a solution prepared by mixing 2.0 mL of HCl solution of pH 3.0 and 3.0 mL of NaOH of pH 10.0 is ...... **[AMU 2010]**

(a) 2.5　　　　(b) 3.5　　　　(c) 5.5　　　　(d) 6.5

96. The pH of a solution obtained by mixing equal volumes of N/10 NaOH and N/20 HCl is ...

[AMU 2010]

(a) 13.4　　　　(b) 12.4　　　　(c) 7.6　　　　(d) 1.6

97. The pH value of 0.01 N NaOH solution is **[CPMT 2010]**

(a) 2　　　　(b) 6　　　　(c) 12　　　　(d) 11

98. A monoprotic acid in 1.00 M solution is 0.01% ionised. The dissociation constant of this acid is ...... **[BCECE 2006]**

(a) 1×10^{-8}　　　(b) 1×10^{-4}　　　(c) 1×10^{-6}　　　(d) 1×10^{-5}

99. If 0.1 M of weak acid is taken and its percentage of degree of ionization is 1.34%, then its ionization constant will be ...... **[AFMC 2005]**

(a) 0.8×10^{-5}　　　(b) 1.79×10^{-5}　　　(c) 0.182×10^{-5}　　　(d) None of these

100. The pair of amphoteric hydroxides is ...... **[AIIMS 2005]**

(a) $Al(OH)_3$, LiOH　　(b) $Be(OH)_2$, $Mg(OH)_2$　(c) $B(OH)_3$, $Be(OH)_2$　(d) $Be(OH)_2$, $Zn(OH)_2$

101. The values of dissociation constant of bases are given below. Which is the weakest base?

[MHT CET 2005]

(a) 1.8×10^{-5}　　　(b) 4.8×10^{-10}　　　(c) 7.2×10^{-11}　　　(d) 7.07×10^{-7}

102. The dissociation constant of two acids HA_1 and HA_2 are 3.0×10^{-4} and 1.8×10^{-5} respectively. The relative strengths of acids are ...... **[RPMT 2005]**

(a) 1 : 16　　　　(b) 1 : 4　　　　(c) 4 : 1　　　　(d) 16 : 1

103. Among the following the dissociation constant is highest for ...... **[AIIMS 2004]**

(a) C_6H_5OH (b) $C_6H_5CH_2OH$ (c) $CH_3C = CH$ (d) $CH_3NH_3^+Cl^-$

104. Boron halides behave as Lewis acid, because of their ...... **[BHU 2004]**

(a) ionic nature

(b) acidic nature

(c) covalent nature

(d) electron deficient nature

105. Strong conjugate base is ...... **[DUMET 2004]**

(a) Cl^- (b) Br^- (c) F^- (d) I^-

106. The Ostwald dilution law is expressed as ...... **[Manipal 2004]**

(a) $K_a = \dfrac{C\alpha^2}{(1-\alpha)}$ (b) $K_a = \dfrac{C\alpha}{(1-\alpha)}$ (c) $K_a = \dfrac{1-\alpha}{C\alpha^2}$ (d) $K_a = \dfrac{C(1-\alpha)}{\alpha^2}$

107. Which of the following easily accept proton? **[RPMT 2004]**

(a) F^- (b) Br^- (c) OH^- (d) NH_2^-

108. Which of the oxide of manganese is amphoteric? **[Manipal 2008]**

(a) MnO_2 (b) Mn_2O_3 (c) Mn_2O_7 (d) MnO

109. Which one of the following species act as both Bronsted acid base? **[MHT CET 2008]**

(a) $H_2PO_2^-$ (b) HPO_3^{2-} (c) HPO_4^{2-} (d) All of these

110. The correct order of basic strength is ...... **[AIIMS 2007]**

(a) $H_2O < OH^- < CH_3OH < CH_3O^-$

(b) $CH_3OH < H_2O < CH_3O^- < OH^-$

(c) $H_2O < CH_3OH < OH^- < CH_3O^-$

(d) $CH^- < H_2O < CH_3OH^- < CH_3OH$

111. Lemon gives sour taste because of ...... **[MHT CET 2007]**

(a) citric acid   (b) tartaric acid   (c) oxalic acid   (d) acetic acid

112. Which of the following is not Lewis acid? **[CPMT 2006]**

(a) $AlCl_3 6H_2O$ (b) $AlCl_3$ (c) $SnCl_4$ (d) $FeCl_3$

113. Degree of dissociation of 0.1 N CH_3COOH is ($K_{acid} = 1 \times 10^{-5}$) **[CPMT 2006]**

(a) 10^{-5} (b) 10^{-4} (c) 10^{-3} (d) 10^{-2}

114. Conjugate acid of $S_2O_8^{2-}$ is ...... **[MHT CET 2006]**

(a) $H_2S_2O_8$ (b) H_2SO_4 (c) $HS_2O_8^-$ (d) HSO_4^-

115. Which acid is present in vinegar? **[RPMT 2010]**

(a) Hydrochloric acid   (b) Acetic acid   (c) Citric acid   (d) Tartaric acid

116. The conjugate base of $H_2PO_4^-$ is **[Manipal 2010]**

(a) PO_4^{3-} (b) P_2O_5 (c) H_3PO_4 (d) HPO_4^{2-}

117. Which of the following molecules act as Lewis acid? **[CBSE AIPMT 09]**

(a) $(CH_3)_3B$ (b) $(CH_3)_2O$ (c) $(CH_3)_3P$ (d) $(CH_3)_3N$

118. Ammonium ion is ...... **[AFMC 2009]**

(a) a conjugate acid

(b) a conjugate base

(c) neither an acid nor a base

(d) both an acid and a base

119. 0.1 M solution of which of the following has almost unity degree of dissociation?

[MHT CET 2009]

(a) Ammonium chloride (b) Potassium chloride

(c) Sodium acetate (d) All of these

120. The number of hydroxyl ions in 10 cm^3 of 0.2 M CHI solution is ...... **[MHT CET 2009]**

(a) 5×10^{-14} (b) 3×10^8 (c) 3×10^{12} (d) 5×10^{-12}

121. In a solution, 0.02 M acetic acid is 4% dissociated. The [OH] in the solution is ......

[MHT CET 2009]

(a) 8×10^{-4} (b) 2×10^{-14} (c) 99×10^{10} (d) 1.25×10^{-11}

122. BOH is weak base. Molar concentration of BOH that provides a [OH] of 1.5×10^{-3} M is ...... ($K_{b(BOH)} = 1.5 \times 10^{-5}$) **[Manipal 2009]**

(a) 1.5×10^{-5} M (b) 0.015 M (c) 0.0015 M (d) 0.15 M

123. Assertion : $[Al(H_2O)_6]^{3+}$ is stronger acid than $[Mg(H_2O)_6]^{2+}$ **[AIIMS 08]**

Reason : Size of $[Al(H_2O)_6]^{3+}$ is smaller than $[Mg(H_2O)_6]^{2+}$ and possesses more effective nuclear charge.

(a) Both Assertion and Reason are true and Reason is the correct explanation of Assertion.

(b) Both Assertion and Reason are true but Reason is not the correct explanation of Assertion.

(c) Assertion is true but Reason is false

(d) Both Assertion and Reason are false

124. Using the Gibbs energy change, $\Delta G° = +63.3$ kJ, for the following reaction,

$Ag_2CO_{3(s)} \rightleftharpoons 2Ag^+_{(aq)} + CO_3^{2+}{}_{(aq)}$ the K_{sp} of $Ag_2CO_{3(s)}$ in water at 25°C is ...... ($R = 8.314$ JK^{-1} mol^{-1}) **[AIPMT 2014]**

(a) 2.9×10^{-1} (b) 7.9×10^{-2} (c) 3.2×10^{-26} (d) 8.0×10^{-12}

125. Which of the following salts will give highest pH in water? **[AIPMT 2014]**

(a) Na_2CO_3 (b) $CuSO_4$ (c) KCl (d) NaCl

126. Which of these is least likely to act as a Lewis base? **[NEET 2013]**

(a) PF_3 (b) CO (c) F^- (d) BF_3

127. Which of the following is least likely to behave as Lewis base? **[CBSE AIPMT 2011]**

(a) OH^- (b) H_2O (c) NH_3 (d) BF_3

128. Which one of the following molecular hydrides act as a Lewis acid? **[CBSE AIPMT 2010]**

(a) CH_4 (b) NH_3 (c) H_2O (d) B_2H_6

129. How many gram-equivalents of NaOH are required to neutralize 25 cm^3 of decinormal HCl solution? **[MHT CET 2010]**

(a) 0.00125 (b) 0.0025 (c) 0.0050 (d) 0.025

130. Conjugate acid-base pair differ by ...... **[MHT CET 2010]**

(a) electron (b) proton (c) neutron (d) hydroxyl group

131. Which of the following is not buffer solution? **[JCECE 2004]**

(a) $CH_3COOH + CH_3COONa$ (b) $H_3BO_3 + Na_3BO_3$

(c) $HClO_4 + NaClO_4$ (d) $NH_4OH + (NH_4)SO_4$

132. Which one of the following is not a buffer solution? **[AIIMS 2003]**

(a) 9.8 M H_2S + 0.8 M KHS

(b) 2 M $C_6H_5NH_2$ + 2 M C_6NH_3Br

(c) 3 M H_2CO_3 + 3M $KHCO_3$

(d) 0.05 M $KClO_4$ + 0.05 M $CHIO_4$

133. In which of the following acid-base titrations, pH is greater than 8 at equivalence point?

(a) Acetic acid versus ammonia **[AIIMS 2003]**

(b) Acetic acid versus sodium hydroxide

(c) Hydrochloric acid versus ammonia

(d) Hydrochloric acid versus sodium hydroxide

134. Buffer solution is prepared by mixing ...... **[MHT CET 2003]**

(a) strong acid + its salt of strong base

(b) weak acid + its salt of weak base

(c) strong acid + its salt of weak base

(d) weak acid + its salt of strong base

135. NH_4Cl is acidic due to ...... **[MHT CET 2011]**

(a) cationic hydrolysis

(b) anionic hydrolysis

(c) its ionic nature

(d) pH > 7

136. The ionization constant of ammonium hydroxide is 1.77×10^{-5} at 298 K. Hydrolysis constant of ammonium chloride is ...... **[CBSE AIPMT 2009]**

(a) 5.65×10^{-10}　　(b) 6.50×10^{-12}　　(c) 5.65×10^{-13}　　(d) 5.65×10^{-2}

137. Which one of the following aqueous solutions of salts has the lowest pH value?

[J&K CET 2009]

(a) CH_3COONa　　(b) NaCl　　(c) NH_4OOCCH_3　　(d) NH_4Cl

138. Hydrolysis of sodium acetate will give ...... **[AFMC 2008]**

(a) acidic solution　　(b) basic solution　　(c) neutral solution　(d) normal solution

139. The rapid changes of P_x near the equivalence point of an acid-base titration is the base of indicator detection pH of the equivalence is related to the ratio of the concentrations of the conjugate acid (HIn) and base (In$^-$) form of the indicator given by the expression

[Manipal 2007]

(a) $\log \dfrac{[In^-]}{[HIn]} = pK_{In} - pH$

(b) $\log \dfrac{[HIn]}{[In^-]} = pK_{In} - pH$

(c) $\log \dfrac{[HIn]}{[In^-]} = pH - pK_{In}$

(d) $\log \dfrac{[In^-]}{[HIn]} = pH - pK_{In}$

140. Which of the following pairs constitute a buffer? **[CBSE AIPMT2006]**

(a) HNO_2 and $NaNO_2$

(b) NaOH and NaCl

(c) HNO_3 and NH_4NO_3

(d) HCl and KCl

141. Consider following solutions of equal concentrations : **[J&K CET 2006]**

(a) A = NH_4Cl　　(b) B = CH_3COONa　　(c) C = NH_4OH　　(d) D = CH_3COOH

A buffer solution can be obtained by mixing equal volumes of ......

(a) C and D　　(b) A and B　　(c) A and C　　(d) C and D

142. When 10 ml of 0.1 M acetic acid (pK_1 = 5.0) is titrated against 10 mL of 0.1 M ammonia solution (pK_b = 5.0), the equivalence point occurs at pH ...... **[AIIMS 2005]**

(a) 5.0　　(b) 6.0　　(c) 7.0　　(d) 9.0

143. In a mixture of acetic acid and sodium acetate the ratio of concentrations of the acid is increased ten times. Then the pH of the solution ......   **[KCET 2004]**
    (a) increases by one   (b) decreases by one
    (c) decreases ten fold   (d) increases ten fold

144. The degree of hydrolysis of 0.01 M NH_4Cl is ...... ($K_h = 2.5 \times 10^{-9}$)   **[JCECE 2003]**
    (a) 5×10^{-5} (b) 5×10^{-4} (c) 5×10^{-3} (d) 5×10^{-7}

145. The K_{sp} of Ag_2CrO_4, AgCl, AgBr and AgI are respectively, 1.1×10^{-13}, 8.3×10^{-17}. Which one of the following salts will precipitate last if $AgNO_3$ solution is added to the solution containing equal moles of NaCl, NaBr, NaI and Na_2CrO_4 ?   **[AIPMT 2015]**
    (a) AgCl   (b) AgBr   (c) Ag_2CrO_4 (d) AgI

146. Which of the following salt does not get hydrolysed in water?   **[RPMT 2006]**
    (a) $KClO_4$ (b) NH_4Cl (c) CH_3COONa (d) None of these

147. Which is the basic salt?   **[CPMT 2005]**
    (a) PbS   (b) $2PbCO_3 \cdot Pb(OH)_2$ (c) $PbSO_4$ (d) $PbCO_3$

148. The relation between hydrolysis constant and dissociation constant are given. Which is the correct formula for $MgCl_2$?   **[MHT CET 2005]**
    (a) $K_h = \dfrac{K_2}{K_a}$ (b) $K_h = \dfrac{K_w}{K_b}$ (c) $K_h = \dfrac{K_w}{K_a \times K_b}$ (d) $K_w = \dfrac{K_h}{K_b}$

149. 0.5 M ammonium benzoate is hydrolysed to 0.25%. Hence its hydrolysis constant is   **[MHT CET 2004]**
    (a) 2.5×10^{-5} (b) 1.5×10^{-4} (c) 3.125×10^{-6} (d) 6.25×10^{-6}

150. Ionic hydrides react with water to give ......   **[Manipal 2003]**
    (a) hydride ions   (b) acidic solutions   (c) protons   (d) basic solutions

151. The hydrolysis constant of a salt of weak acid and weak base is inversely proportional to ...
    (a) ionic product of water   **[Manipal 2003]**
    (b) dissociation constant of both weak acid and weak base
    (c) dissociation constant of weak acid
    (d) dissociation constant of weak base

152. pH of water is ......   **[A.F.M.C. 2003]**
    (a) Pressure dependent   (b) Pressure independent
    (c) Temperature dependent   (d) Temperature independent

153. Which is an amphoteric oxide ?   **[Orissa J.E.E. 2004]**
    (a) CaO   (b) BaO   (c) SrO   (d) ZnO

154. The solubility product of a sparingly soluble salt AX_2 is 3.2×10^{-11}. Its solubility (in moles/litre) is ......   **[C.B.S.E. Med. 2004]**
    (a) 4×10^{-4} (b) 5.6×10^{-6} (c) 3.1×10^{-4} (d) 2×10^{-4}

155. At 90°C, pure water has $[H_3O^+] = 10^{-6}$ moles/litre. The value of K_w at 90°C is ......   **[J & K Med. 2004]**
    (a) 10^{-6} (b) 10^{-8} (c) 10^{-12} (d) 10^{14}

ANSWER KEY

1. (a)	2. (d)	3. (b)	4. (b)	5. (c)	6. (b)	7. (b)	8. (c)
9. (d)	10. (d)	11. (b)	12. (c)	13. (c)	14. (c)	15. (d)	16. (d)
17. (c)	18. (a)	19. (b)	20. (b)	21. (d)	22. (c)	23. (d)	24. (a)
25. (d)	26. (c)	27. (c)	28. (a)	29. (c)	30. (d)	31. (d)	32. (b)
33. (b)	34. (a)	35. (a)	36. (c)	37. (a)	38. (c)	39. (a)	40. (a)
41. (c)	42. (a)	43. (c)	44. (b)	45. (b)	46. (c)	47. (b)	48. (d)
49. (b)	50. (a)	51. (d)	52. (c)	53. (c)	54. (c)	55. (a)	56. (c)
57. (c)	58. (c)	59. (d)	60. (b)	61. (a)	62. (d)	63. (c)	64. (c)
65. (d)	66. (d)	67. (b)	68. (a)	69. (d)	70. (b)	71. (b)	72. (d)
73. (a)	74. (d)	75. (c)	76. (a)	77. (a)	78. (c)	79. (b)	80. (b)
81. (a)	82. (c)	83. (c)	84. (d)	85. (a)	86. (c)	87. (b)	88. (c)
89. (b)	90. (d)	91. (c)	92.(b)	93. (d)	94. (a)	95. (c)	96. (c)
97. (c)	98. (c)	99. (d)	100. (d)	101. (a)	102. (b)	103. (a)	104. (b)
105. (b)	106. (d)	107. (b)	108. (c)	109. (d)	110. (d)	111. (a)	112. (c)
113. (b)	114. (d)	115. (a)	116. (d)	117. (b)	118. (a)	119. (c)	120. (b)
121. (c)	122. (d)	123. (b)	124. (a)	125. (a)	126. (c)	127. (d)	128. (d)
129. (c)	130. (a)	131. (c)	132. (c)	133. (c)	134. (a)	135. (c)	136. (b)
137. (a)	138. (b)	139. (b)	140. (a)	141. (b)	142. (d)	143. (a)	144. (b)
145. (b)	146. (a)	147. (c)	148. (c)	149. (b)	150. (a)	151. (c)	152. (a)
153. (b)	154. (d)	155. (b)					

Previous Year's Questions

1. (b)	2. (c)	3. (d)	4. (b)	5. (c)	6. (d)	7. (b)	8. (a)
9. (d)	10. (c)	11. (c)	12. (a)	13. (c)	14. (b)	15. (c)	16. (b)
17. (a)	18. (b)	19. (d)	20. (b)	21. (c)	22. (a)	23. (b)	24. (d)
25. (b)	26. (c)	27. (a)	28. (a)	29. (a)	30. (b)	31. (b)	32. (a)
33. (b)	34. (a)	35. (c)	36. (c)	37. (b)	38. (b)	39. (d)	40. (a)
41. (a)	42. (a)	43. (d)	44.(d)	45. (b)	46. (d)	47. (c)	48. (d)
49. (c)	50. (d)	51. (c)	52. (a)	53. (c)	54. (d)	55. (c)	56. (d)
57. (a)	58. (c)	59. (d)	60. (a)	61. (d)	62. (b)	63. (b)	64. (c)
65. (c)	66. (b)	67. (c)	68. (b)	69. (a)	70. (c)	71. (d)	72. (b)
73. (a)	74. (d)	75. (b)	76. (c)	77. (c)	78. (d)	79. (b)	80. (b)
81. (c)	82. (c)	83. (c)	84. (a)	85. (d)	86. (a)	87. (c)	88. (d)
89. (d)	90. (c)	91. (d)	92. (c)	93. (c)	94. (a)	95. (b)	96. (b)
97. (c)	98. (a)	99. (a)	100. (d)	101. (c)	102.(c)	103. (d)	104. (d)
105. (c)	106. (a)	107. (d)	108. (a)	109. (c)	110. (c)	111. (a)	112. (a)
113. (d)	114. (c)	115. (b)	116. (d)	117. (a)	118. (a)	119. (b)	120. (b)
121. (d)	122. (d)	123. (a)	124. (d)	125. (a)	126. (d)	127. (d)	128. (d)
129. (b)	130. (b)	131. (d)	132. (d)	133. (b)	134. (d)	135. (a)	136. (a)
137. (d)	138. b)	139. (d)	140. (a)	141. (c)	142. (c)	143. (a)	144. (b)
145. (c)	146. (a)	147. (b)	148. (b)	149. (c)	150. (d)	151. (b)	152. (c)
153. (d)	154. (d)	155. (c)					

❑❑❑

REDOX REACTIONS

1. Which statement correctly describes a redox reaction?
   (a) The oxidation half reaction occurs before the reduction half reaction
   (b) The oxidation half reaction and the reduction half reaction occur simultaneously
   (c) The oxidation half reaction occurs after the reduction half reaction
   (d) The oxidation half reaction occurs spontaneously but the reduction half reaction does not

2. Oxidation is _______
   (a) Gain of electrons   (b) Gain of hydrogen   (c) Loss of oxygen   (d) Loss of electrons

3. Which change is reduction?
   (a) Increase in oxidation state   (b) Gain of electrons
   (c) Loss of electrons   (d) Loss of hydrogen

4. The species which gains electrons in a redox reaction ......
   (a) Looses mass   (b) Is oxidised
   (c) Is the oxidising agent   (d) Increase in oxidation number

5. When an element is oxidised, its oxidation number ......
   (a) Increases, as electrons are lost   (b) Decreases, as electrons are lost
   (c) Increases, as electrons are gained
   (d) Decreases, as electrons are gained

6. Which of the following rules is not correct in this respect?
   (a) The oxidation number of hydrogen is always +1
   (b) The algebraic sum of all the oxidation numbers in a compound is zero
   (c) An element in the free or the uncombined state bears oxidation number zero
   (d) In all its compounds, the oxidation number of fluorine is 1

7. The strongest oxidising agent is ......
   (a) Ca^{2+} (b) Ca^+ (c) Au^{3+} (d) H^+

8. The strongest reducing agent is ......
   (a) Ca^{2+} (b) Cu^{2+} (c) Au^{3+} (d) H^+

9. In a redox reaction, the species that loses electrons ......
   (a) Is oxidised   (b) Is called the cathode
   (c) Gains mass at the electrode   (d) Decrease in oxidation number

10. What kind of reaction is $Cl_2 \rightarrow Cl^- + ClO_2$?
    (a) An oxidation   (b) A reduction
    (c) A disproportionate   (d) None of these

11. Consider the following redox reaction

$Hg^{2+} + Cu \rightarrow Hg + Cu^{2+}$

In this reaction, Hg^{2+} is a ......

(a) Weaker reducing agent than Cu^{2+}

(b) Weaker oxidising agent than Cu^{2+}

(c) Stronger reducing agent than Cu^{2+}

(d) Stronger oxidising agent than Cu^{2+}

12. Which of the following sets is present in increasing oxidation number of the central atom?

(a) $CrO_2^-, ClO_3^-, CrO_4^{2-}, MnO_4^-$

(b) $ClO_3^-, CrO_4^{2-}, MnO_4^-, CrO_2$

(c) $CrO_2^-, ClO_3^-, MnO_4^-, CrO_4^{2-}$

(d) $CrO_4^{2-}, MnO_4^-, CrO_2^-, ClO_3^-$

13. Which of the following is not an example of a redox reaction?

(a) $CuO + H_2 \rightarrow Cu + H_2O$

(b) $Fe_2O_3 + 3CO \rightarrow 2Fe + 3CO_2$

(c) $2K + F_2 \rightarrow 2KF$

(d) $BaCl_2 + H_2SO_4 \rightarrow BaSO_4 + 2HCl$

14. Hydrogen peroxide (H_2O_2) reacts with silver oxide according to the following equation

$Ag_2O_{(s)} + H_2O_{2(l)} \rightarrow 2Ag_{(s)} + H_2O_{(l)} + O_{2(g)}$

In this reaction, hydrogen peroxide behaves as ......

(a) A dehydrating agent

(b) Catalyst

(c) A reducing agent

(d) An oxidising agent

15. What will happen when liquid bromine (Br_2) is poured into a beaker containing aluminium metal?

(a) Br_2 will be reduced; Al will be oxidised

(b) Br_2 will be oxidised; Al will be reduced

(c) Br_2 will function as the reducing agent; Al will function as the oxidising agent

(d) A reaction will not occur

16. What is the oxidation number of copper in Cu^{+2}?

(a) 0   (b) 1   (c) +2   (d) −2

17. What is the oxidation number of Br in BrO_3^- ion?

(a) −1   (b) +5   (c) −5   (d) +7

18. What are the oxidation numbers of V, O and Cl atoms in $VOCl_3$?

(a) −5, −2, −1   (b) −5, +2, −1   (c) +5, −2, +1   (d) +5, −2, −1

19. What are the oxidation states of Na, Cr and O atoms, respectively, in sodium dichromate, $Na_2Cr_2O_7$?

(a) +2, +2, −2   (b) +1, +3, −2   (c) +2, +6, +2   (d) +1, +6, −2

20. What are the oxidation numbers of H, S and O atoms, respectively, in sulfurous acid, H_2SO_3?

(a) +1, −6, −2   (b) +1, +6, −2   (c) −1, +6, −1   (d) +1, +4, −2

21. In the reaction $HNO_2 + I^- \rightarrow NO + I_3^-$, what atoms are being oxidised and reduced, respectively?

(a) O, I   (b) O, I   (c) I, N   (d) N, I   N, O

22. An oxidising agent is ......

(a) Reduced as it loses electrons

(b) Reduced as it gains electrons

(c) Oxidised as it loses electrons

(d) Oxidised as it gains electrons

23. Which of the following reactions involved in airbag chemistry is not a reduction-oxidation reaction?

(a) $2NaN_{3(s)} \rightleftharpoons 2Na_{(s)} + 3N_{2(g)}$

(b) $2Na_{(s)} + 2H_2O_{(l)} \rightleftharpoons 2NaOH_{(s)} + H_{2(g)}$

(c) $6Na_{(s)} + Fe_2O_{3(s)} \rightleftharpoons 3Na_2O_{(s)} + 2Fe_{(s)}$

(d) $OH^-_{(aq)} + H_3O^+_{(aq)} \rightleftharpoons 2H_2O_{(l)}$

24. If a silver strip is immersed in an aqueous solution containing Cu^{2+} ions, what would you expect to happen?

(a) Copper would be deposited on the silver strip

(b) Cu^{2+} ions would be reduced

(c) No reaction would occur

(d) Ag would be oxidised

25. Given is the lead-acid battery reaction.

Which species is oxidised during battery discharge?

$$Pb + PbO_2 + H_2SO_4 \underset{\text{Charge}}{\overset{\text{Discharge}}{\rightleftharpoons}} 2PbSO_4 + 2H_2O$$

(a) Pb

(b) PbO_2

(c) SO_4^{2-}

(d) $2H_2O$

26. Given is the reaction for the nickel-cadmium battery

$2NiOH + Cd + 2H_2O \rightarrow 2Ni(OH)_2 + Cd(OH)_2$

What species is oxidised during the discharge of the battery?

(a) Ni^{3+}

(b) Ni^{2+}

(c) Cd

(d) Cd^{2+}

27. Given the redox reaction $2I^-_{(aq)} + Br_{2(l)} \rightarrow 2Br^-_{(aq)} + I_{2(s)}$

What occurs during this reaction?

(a) The I^- ion is oxidised, and its oxidation number increases

(b) The I^- ion is oxidised, and its oxidation number decreases

(c) The I^- ion is reduced, and its oxidation number increases

(d) The I^- ion is reduced, and its oxidation number decreases

28. Which half reaction correctly represent reduction?

(a) $Cr^{3+} + 3e^- \rightarrow Cr_{(s)}$

(b) $Cr^{3+} \rightarrow Cr_{(s)} + 3e^-$

(c) $Cr_{(s)} \rightarrow Cr^{3+} + 3e^-$

(d) $Cr_{(s)} + 3e^- \rightarrow Cr^{3+}$

29. Which of the following is a redox reaction?

(a) $Mg(OH)_2 + 2NH_4Cl \rightarrow MgCl_2 + 2NH_4OH$

(b) $CaC_2O_4 + 2HCl \rightarrow CaCl_2 + H_2C_2O_4$

(c) $NaCl + KNO_3 \rightarrow NaNO_3 + KCl$

(d) $Zn + 2AgCN \rightarrow 2Ag + Zn(CN)_2$

30. Metallic platinum reacts spontaneously with $Au^{3+}_{(aq)}$ but does not react with $Ag^+_{(aq)}$. The metals in order of increasing strength as reducing agents, are ......

(a) Ag, Pt, Au

(b) Pt, Au, Ag

(c) Au, Ag, Pt

(d) Au, Pt, Ag

31. Uranium, Vanadium and Yttrium (U, V, Y) were placed in solutions containing the metallic ions U^{3+}, V^{2+}, and Y^{3+}. The following observations were recorded.

Expt. No.	Ion	Metal	Observation
1	U^{3+}	Y	reaction
2	V^{2+}	U	reaction
3	V^{2+}	Y	reaction
4	Y^{3+}	V	no reaction

The oxidising agents from the strongest to the weakest are

(a) V^{2+}, U^{3+}, Y^{3+} (b) U^{3+}, V^{2+}, Y^{3+} (c) Y^{3+}, U^{3+}, V^{2+} (d) V^{2+}, Y^{3+}, U^{3+}

32. In the reaction

$$Cu_{(s)} + 2Ag^{+}_{(aq)} \rightarrow Cu^{2+}_{(aq)} + 2Ag_{(s)}$$

(a) $Cu_{(s)}$ is reduced by the oxidising agent

(b) $Ag^{+}_{(aq)}$ is the reducing agent and $Cu_{(s)}$ is reduced

(c) $Cu_{(s)}$ is the reducing agent and $Ag^{+}_{(aq)}$ is reduced

(d) $Cu_{(s)}$ is the oxidising agent and $Ag^{+}_{(aq)}$ is oxidised

33. Consider the following redox equation $12H^{+}_{(aq)} + 2IO^{-}_{3(aq)} + 10Fe^{2+}_{(aq)} \rightarrow 10Fe^{3+}_{(aq)} + I_{2(s)} + 6H_2O_{(l)}$

The reducing agent is ......

(a) I_2 (b) H^{+} (c) Fe^{2+} (d) IO^{-}_3

34. The oxidation number of nitrogen increases in ......

(a) $NO^{-}_3 \rightarrow NO$ (b) $N_2O_4 \rightarrow NI_3$ (c) $NH_3 \rightarrow NH^{+}_4$ (d) $NO_2 \rightarrow N_2O_5$

35. Hydrogen has an oxidation number of -1 in ......

(a) H_2 (b) NaH (c) H_2O (d) KOH

36. What is the next step in balancing the half reaction? $Cr_2O_7^{-2} \rightarrow 2Cr^{+3}$?

(a) Add $7H_2O$ to the right   (b) Add $7H_2O$ to the left

(c) Add $3.5O_2$ to the left   (d) Add 8 electrons to the left

37. What is the next step in balancing the reaction $SO_3^{-2} + H_2O \rightarrow SO_4^{-2} + 2H^{+}$?

(a) Add $3\ H_2O$ to the left   (b) Add 2 electrons to the left

(c) Add 2 electrons to the right   (d) Multiply throughout by 2

38. What is the next step in balancing the redox reaction having the two half reactions ?

$$Cr(OH)^{-}_4 \rightarrow CrO_4^{-2} + 4H^{+} + 3e^{-}$$

$$ClO^{-} + 2H^{+} + 2e^{-} \rightarrow Cl^{-} + H_2O$$

(a) Add the two half reactions

(b) Multiply both by 3

(c) Multiply the oxidation part by 2 and the reduction part by 3

(d) Multiply the oxidation part by 3 and the reduction part by 2

39. In a redox reaction, ClO^- was converted to Cl^- in a basic solution. The balanced half-reaction for this process is ......

(a) $ClO^- + H_2O + 2e^- \rightarrow Cl^- + 2OH^-$

(b) $ClO^- + 2OH^- \rightarrow Cl^- + 2e^- + H_2O$

(c) $ClO^- + H_2O \rightarrow Cl^- + 2e^- + 2OH^-$

(d) $ClO^- + 2OH^- + 2e^- \rightarrow Cl^- + H_2O$

40. When the balanced reaction

$$2MnO_4^- + SO_3^{-2} + H_2O \rightarrow 2\,MnO_4^{-2} + SO_4^{-2} + 2H^+$$

is changed to be balanced in basic solution, the result will be ......

(a) $2\,MnO_4^- + SO_3^{-2} \rightarrow 2\,MnO_4^{-2} + SO_4^{-2} + H_2O$

(b) $2\,MnO_4^- + SO_3^{-2} + 2\,OH^- \rightarrow 2\,MnO_4^{-2} + SO_4^{-2} + H_2O$

(c) $2\,MnO_4^- + SO_3^{-2} \rightarrow 2\,MnO_4^{-2} + SO_4^{-2} + H_2O + 2\,OH^-$

(d) $2\,MnO_4^- + SO_3^{-2} + 2\,OH^- \rightarrow 2\,MnO_4^{-2} + SO_4^{-2} + H_2O + 2\,OH^-$

41. The following reaction occurs in aqueous acid solution

$$MnO_4^- + Fe^{2+} \rightarrow Mn^{2+} + Fe^{3+}$$

When the equation is balanced with smallest whole numbers, the coefficient of H_2O is ......

(a) 2   (b) 6   (c) 4   (d) 3

42. What are the coefficients, x and y respectively, for bromine and water when the following oxidation/reduction equation is balanced (in acid solution)?

$$IO_3^- + Br^- + H^+ \rightarrow x\,Br_2 + y\,H_2O + I_2$$

(a) 2 and 3   (b) 3 and 4   (c) 5 and 6   (d) 7 and 8

43. Given the balanced equation : $2Al_{(s)} + 6H^+_{(aq)} \rightarrow 2Al^{3+}_{(aq)} + 3H_2$

When 2 moles of Al(s) completely react, what is the total number of moles of electrons transferred from $Al_{(s)}$ to $H^+_{(aq)}$?

(a) 5   (b) 6   (c) 3   (d) 4

44. Which of the following equations is not predicted to represent a redox reaction?

(a) $2H_2O_{(l)} + O_{2(g)} \rightarrow 2H_2O_{2(l)}$

(b) $2Sn^{2+}_{(aq)} \rightarrow Sn_{(s)} + Sn^{4+}_{(aq)}$

(c) $Ag^+_{(aq)} + Cl^-_{(aq)} \rightarrow AgCl_{(s)}$

(d) $C_2H_{4(g)} + 3O_{2(g)} \rightarrow 2CO_{2(g)} + 2H_2O_{(g)}$

45. The substances H_2O_2, H_3PO_4 and H_2SO_3 in order of increasing strength of oxidising agents are ......

(a) H_2O_2, H_3PO_4, H_2SO_3

(b) H_2SO_3, H_3PO_4, H_2O_2

(c) H_3PO_4, H_2SO_3, H_2O_2

(d) H_2O_2, H_2SO_3, H_3PO_4

46. Use the following unbalanced redox reaction to answer this question.

$$\_O_{2(g)} + \_H^+_{(aq)} + \_Ag(s) \rightarrow \_Ag^+_{(aq)} + \_H_2O_{(l)}$$

The coefficients for the balanced equation are ......

(a) 1, 4, 4, 4, 2   (b) 1, 4, 1, 1, 2   (c) 1, 2, 1, 1, 1   (d) 1, 1, 1, 1, 1

47. Which of the following elements does not show disproportionation tendency?

(a) Cl　　　　　(b) Br　　　　　(c) F　　　　　(d) I

48. Acidified potassium dichromate (VI) can be used to detect the presence of ethanol vapour in the breath of a person who consumed alcohol. A colour change from orange to green is observed if ethanol is present. This shows that ethanol is ......

(a) An alkali　　　　　(b) An indicator

(c) An oxidising agent　　　　　(d) A reducing agent

49. Using the standard electrode potential of redox couples given below find out which of the following is the strongest oxidising agent

$E°$ values : $Fe^{3+}/Fe^{2+} = + 0.77$; $I_2(s)/I^- = + 0.54$;

$Cu^{2+}/Cu = + 0.34$; $Ag^+/Ag = + 0.80$ V

(a) Fe^{3+}　　　　　(b) Ag^+　　　　　(c) I^2　　　　　(d) Cu^{2+}

50. On the basis of ET values of redox couples, predict whether copper can reduce elements having the following ET values

$Br_2/Br = + 1.90$; $Ag^+/Ag(s) = + 0.80$

$Cu^{2+}/Cu(s) = + 0.34$; $I_2(s)/I = + 0.54$

(a) Cu will reduce Br_2　　　　　(b) Cu will reduce I^-

(c) Cu will reduce Br^-　　　　　(d) Cu will reduce Ag

51. Which of the reactions is not feasible? ET values

$Fe^{3+}/Fe^{2+} = + 0.77$; $I_2/I = + 0.54$;

$Cu^{2+}/Cu = + 0.34$; $Ag^+/Ag = + 0.80$ V

(a) Fe^{3+} and I　　(b) Ag and Fe^{3+}　　(c) Ag^+ and Cu　　(d) Fe^{3+} and Cu

52. Thiosulphate reacts differently with iodine and bromine in the reactions given below

$$2S_2O_3^{2-} + I_2 \rightarrow S_4O_6^{2} + 2I^-$$

$$S_2O_3^{2-} + 2Br_2 + 5H_2O \rightarrow 2SO_4^{2-} + 2Br^- + 10H^+$$

Which of the following statements explain both reactions of thiosulphate ion?

(a) Bromine is a weaker oxidant than iodine.

(b) Thiosulphate undergoes oxidation by bromine and reduction by iodine in these reactions

(c) Bromine is a stronger oxidant than iodine

(d) Bromine undergoes oxidation and iodine undergoes reduction in these reactions

53. On the basis of the following E° values, the strongest oxidising agent is,

$$[Fe(CN)_6]^{4-} \rightarrow [Fe(CN)_6]^{3-} + e^{-1}; E° = 0.35 \text{ V}$$

$$Fe^{2+} \rightarrow Fe^{3+} + e^{-1}; E° = 0.77 \text{ V}$$

(a) Fe^{2+}　　　　(b) Fe^{3+}　　　　(c) $[Fe(CN)_6]^{3-}$　　　　(d) $[Fe(CN)_6]^{4-}$

54. When $KMnO_4$ acts as an oxidising agent and ultimately forms MnO_4^{2-}, MnO_2, Mn_2O_3 and Mn^{2+}, then the number of electrons transferred in each case is ?

(a) 1, 3, 4, 5　　　　(b) 1, 5, 3, 7　　　　(c) 4, 3, 1, 5　　　　(d) 3, 5, 7, 1

55. The oxidation state of Cr in $K_2Cr_2O_7$ is ......

(a) $+8$　　(b) $+6$　　(c) -7　　(d) -6

56. The colour of $K_2Cr_2O_7$ changes from red orange to lemon yellow on treatment with aqueous KOH because of ......

(a) Reduction of Cr(VI) to Cr(III)

(b) Formation of chromium hydroxide

(c) Conversion of dichromate ion to chromate

(d) Oxidation of potassium hydroxide to potassium peroxide

57. Which of the following halogen acid is a better reducing agent ?

(a) HCl　　(b) HBr　　(c) HI　　(d) HF

58. For the redox reaction

$$MnO_4^- + CrO_4^{2-} + H^+ \longrightarrow Mn^{2+} + CO_2 + H_2O$$

Correct stoichiometric coefficients of Mn_4^-, $Cr_2O_4^{2-}$, H^+ are ......

(a) 2, 5, 16　　(b) 16, 5, 2　　(c) 5, 16, 2　　(d) 2, 16, 5

59. The oxidation number of P in $Mg_2P_2O_7$ is ......

(a) $+3$　　(b) $+2$　　(c) $+5$　　(d) 3

60. The oxidation number of S in SO_4^{2-} is ......

(a) $+8$　　(b) $+6$　　(c) $+4$　　(d) 0

61. A 2.5 mol of hydrazine N_2H_4 loses 25 moles of electrons on being converted to a new compound X. Assuming that all of the nitrogen appears in the new compound, what is the oxidation state of nitrogen in compound X ?

(a) 1　　(b) 2　　(c) $+3$　　(d) $+4$

62. $N_{2(g)} + 3H_{2(g)} \longrightarrow 2NH_{3(g)}$

In the above reaction, equivalent weight of N_2 is ......

(a) 4.67　　(b) 28　　(c) 14　　(d) 2.33

63. In a certain reaction, KCl is converted into $KClO_3$. Change in oxidation number is ......

(a) $+3$　　(b) $+6$　　(c) $+7$　　(d) $+8$

64. 1 mole of $FeCr_2O_4$ is oxidized by x mole of $Cr_2O_7^{2-}$ in acidic medium. x is ......

(a) 3　　(b) 1.5　　(c) 0.5　　(d) 1.0

65. The oxidation number of covalency of phosphorus in phosphorus molecule (P_4) are ......

(a) 0 and 2　　(b) $+6$ and 8　　(c) 0 and 8　　(d) $+6$ and 2

66. Which of the following is redox reaction ?

(a) HCl reacts with NaOH

(b) Formation of O_3 in atmosphere from O_2 by lightening

(c) Formation of oxides of nitrogen from nitrogen and oxygen by lightening

(d) Evaporation of water

67. In the following redox reaction,

$5Fe^{2+} + MnO_4^- + 8H^+ \rightleftharpoons Mn^{2+} + 5Fe^{3+} + 4H_2O$

Given : $Fe^{3+} + e^- \longrightarrow Fe^{2+}$

$MnO_4^- + 8H^+ + 5e^- \longrightarrow Mn^{2+} + 4H_2O$

Potential at the equivalence point is ......

(a) $E = (E_1^o + E_2^o) - 0.08$ pH

(b) $E = \dfrac{E_1^o + 5E_2^o}{6} - 0.08$ pH

(c) $E = (E_1^o - E_2^o) - 0.08$ pH

(d) $E = \dfrac{E_1^o - 5E_2^o}{6} + 0.08$ pH

68. A drunken person was asked to blow a glass tube packed with acidified potassium dichromate. The change in colour of the material from orange to green was observed due to consumption of alcohol. This is because of ......

(I) the oxidation of alcohol with the reduction of dichromate to chromium (III).

(II) complex formation of alcohol and dichromate.

(III) change in coordination number of chromium.

Which of the statements given above is/are correct ?

(a) I only   (b) II only   (c) III only   (d) II and III

First option is correct. In this CH_3CH_2OH is oxidized to CH_3CHO and $Cr_2O_7^{2-}$ is reduced to Cr^{3+} (green)

69. $H_2S_2O_8$ and $H_2S_2O_5$ both have + 6 oxidation state of sulphur. It is due to presence of ......

(a) Peroxy group

(b) Superoxo group

(c) Neutral O_2

(d) Presence of ozone

70. In the redox reaction,

$x\,KMnO_4 + NH_3 \rightarrow y\,KNO_3 + MnO_2 + KOH + H_2O$

x and y in the above reaction are ......

(a) x = 4, y = 6   (b) x = 3, y = 8   (c) x = 8, y = 6   (d) x = 8, y = 3

71. The photographic paper is developed with alkaline hydroquinone and is shown by following

reaction $2AgBr_{(s)} + 2OH^-_{(aq)} + $ [hydroquinone] $\longrightarrow 2Ag + 2H_2O + 2Br^- + $ [quinone]

the above reaction, which statement is correct ?

(a) Hydroquinone is oxidant

(b) Ag^+ is the oxidant

(c) Br^- is the oxidant

(d) Ag^+ is the reductant

72. Oxidation number of Fe in Fe_2O_3 is ......

(a) + 3   (b) + 2   (c) – 3   (d) – 2

73. Fluorine reacts with ice and gave following result

$H_2O_{(s)} + F_{2(g)} \rightarrow HF_{(g)} + HOF_{(g)}$

Justify that this reaction is .... reaction.

(a) Oxidation   (b) Reduction   (c) Redox   (d) Displacement

74. Cl_2 changes to Cl^- and ClO^- in cold NaOH. Equivalent weight of Cl_2 will be ......

(a) M   (b) $\dfrac{M}{2}$ (c) $\dfrac{M}{3}$ (d) $\dfrac{2M}{3}$

75. The complex $[Fe(H_2O)_5NO]^{2+}$ is formed in the ring test for nitrate when freshly prepared $FeSO_4$ solution is added to the aqueous solution of NO_3^- followed by addition of conc. H_2SO_4. This complex is formed by charge transfer in which ......

(a) Fe^{2+} changes to Fe^{3+} and NO^+ changes to NO

(b) Fe^{2+} changes to Fe^{3+} and NO changes to NO^+

(c) Fe^{2+} changes to Fe^+ and NO changes to NO^+

(d) No charge transfer takes place

76. Which of the given acids is strongest ?

(a) $HBrO_4$ (b) HOCl   (c) HNO_2 (d) H_3PO_3

77. To test presence of sugar in urine sample, it is to be treated with silver ions in aqueous ammonia (Tollen's test) with glucose, reaction is

$$C_6H_{12}O_{6(aq)} + 2Ag^+_{(aq)} + 2OH^-_{(aq)} \longrightarrow CH_2OH - (CHOH)_4 - COO^- + 2Ag + H_2O$$

In this reaction ......

(a) Glucose is oxidized   (b) Silver ion is reduced

(c) A silver mirror is formed   (d) All of the above are correct

78. NH_3 is oxidized to NO by O_2 (air) in basic medium. Number of equivalent of NH_3 oxidised by 1 mole of O_2 is ......

(a) 4   (b) 5   (c) 6   (d) 7

79. Which has least number of equivalent per mole of the reactant ?

(a) MnO_4^- changes to MnO_2 (b) MnO_4^- changes to Mn^{2+}

(c) MnO_4^- changes to MnO_4^{2-} (d) MnO_4^- changes to Mn_2O_3

80. For a titration of 100 cm^3 of 0.1 M Sn^{2+} to Sn^{4+}, 50 cm^3 and 0.40 M Ce^{4+} solution was required. The oxidation state of cerium in the reduction product is ......

(a) + 1   (b) + 2   (c) + 3   (d) 0

81. I^- reduces IO_3^- to I_2 and itself oxidized to I_2 in acidic medium.

(a) I^- reduces $IO_3^- + 6H^+ \longrightarrow I_2 + 3H_2O$ (b) $I^- + IO_3^- \longrightarrow I_2 + O_3$

(c) $5I^- + IO_3^- + 6H^+ \longrightarrow 3I_2 + 3H_2O$ (d) None of these

82. When Br_2 is passed in hot aqueous solution of Na_2CO_3 ......

(a) Br^- is formed by reduction   (b) BrO_3^- is formed by oxidation

(c) CO_2 is evolved   (d) All of the above is correct

83. If CO_2 gas is passed into waste water containing CrO_4^{2-} (yellow) then ......

(a) Solution turns green due to formation of Cr^{3+}

(b) Solution turns blue due to formation of CrO_3

(c) Solution turns orange due to formation of $Cr_2O_7^{2-}$

(d) No effect takes place

84. One mole of ferric oxalate is titrated with acidified potassium permanganate solution. In this ......

(a) 1.2 mol of potassium permanganate are required

(b) Oxalate ion is oxidized to carbon dioxide

(c) Oxalate ion is reduced

(d) (a) and (b) are correct

85. 0.5 mole of $Ca(OH)_2$ can neutralize H_2SO_4. This H_2SO_4 can be neutralised by ......

(a) 0.05 moles of NaOH   (b) 0.10 moles of NaOH

(c) 0.05 moles of $POH(OH)_2$ (d) None of these

86. Match the half reactions (in column I) with change in oxidation number (in column II)

	Column I		Column II
(A)	$Cl^- \longrightarrow ClO_4^-$	1.	2
(B)	$Cr^{3+} \longrightarrow Cr_2O_6$	2.	8
(C)	$H_2O_2 \longrightarrow O_2$	3.	0
(D)	$CrO_2^{2+} \longrightarrow CrO_4^{2-}$	4.	3

(a) (A) - 1, (B) - 2, (C) - 3, (D) - 4   (b) (A) - 2, (B) - 4, (C) - 3, (D) - 1

(c) (A) - 2, (B) - 4, (C) - 1, (D) - 3   (d) (A) - 3, (B) - 1, (C) - 4, (D) - 2

87. The oxidation state of sulphur in $Na_2S_4O_6$ is ......

(a) $\dfrac{3}{2}$ (b) $\dfrac{2}{3}$ (c) $\dfrac{5}{2}$ (d) $\dfrac{2}{5}$

88. In which of the following transformations, oxygen is not the reducing agent ?

(a) $Ag_2O \rightarrow 2Ag + \dfrac{1}{2}O_2$ (b) $4NH_3 + 3O_2 \rightarrow 2N_2 + 6H_2O$

(c) $2F_2 + 2H_2O \rightarrow 4HF + O_2$ (d) $2AgNO_3 + H_2O_2 \rightarrow 2Ag + 2HNO_3 + O_2$

89. One mole of ferrous oxalate is oxidized by x moles of MnO_4^- in acidic medium x is ......

(a) 0.6   (b) 0.1   (c) 0.3   (d) 1.00

90. Consider the following reaction,

$Br_2 + OH^- \longrightarrow BrO_3^- + Br^- + H_2O$ (unbalanced)

Select the incorrect statement.

(a) Equivalent weight of Br_2 when it is reduced to Br^- is 80.

(b) Equivalent weight of Br_2 when it is oxidized to BrO_3^- is 96.

(c) Net equivalent weight of Br_2 is 96.

(d) It is a disproportionate reaction.

91. A reaction in which same substance is oxidized and reduced is known as ......

(a) Disproportionation

(b) Dehydrogenation

(c) Amphoteric reaction

(d) Replacement reaction

92. Select the incorrect statements ......

(a) Equivalent weight of $Ca(HC_2O_4)_2$ is $\dfrac{M}{2}$ when it is a reducing agent.

(b) Equivalent weight of $Ca(HC_2O_4)_2$ is M when it behaves as an acid.

(c) $Ca(HC_2O_4)_2$ can be estimated by MnO_4^-/H^+.

(d) $Ca(HC_2O_4)_2$ can be estimated by an acid

93. Equivalent weight of H_3PO_2 in a reaction is found to be half of its molecular weight. It can be due to its ......

(a) Reaction of its two H^+ ions

(b) Oxidation of H_3PO_3

(c) Both (a) and (b)

(d) None of these

94. In the following unbalanced redox reaction,

$$Cu_3P + Cr_2O_7^{2-} \rightarrow Cu^{2+} + H_3PO_4 + Cr^{3+}$$

Equivalent weight of H_3PO_4 is ......

(a) $\dfrac{M}{3}$

(b) $\dfrac{M}{6}$

(c) $\dfrac{M}{7}$

(d) $\dfrac{M}{8}$

95. Which of the following is a disproportionate reaction?

(a) $CaCO_3 + 2H^+ \longrightarrow Ca^{2+} + H_2O + CO_2$

(b) $2CrO_4^{2-} + 2H^+ \longrightarrow Cr_2O_7^{2-} + H_2O$

(c) $Cr_2O_7^{2-} + 2OH^- \longrightarrow 2Cr_2O_4^{2-} + H_2O$

(d) $Cu_2O + 2H^+ \longrightarrow Cu + Cu^{2+} + H_2O$

96. If a small amount of $KMnO_4$ is added to conc. H_2SO_4, a green coloured solution with oxidation number of Mn as +7 is formed, probable compound is ......

(a) $MnO_3.HSO_4$

(b) K_2MnO_4

(c) $MnO_2.HSO_4$

(d) MnO_2

97. In the following redox reaction,

$$Zn_{(s)} + NO_{3(aq)}^- + H_{(aq)}^+ \longrightarrow Zn_{(aq)}^{2+} + NH_{4(aq)}^+$$

$Zn_{(s)}$ and $NO_{3(aq)}^-$ respectively are ......

(a) Oxidant, reductant

(b) Reductant, oxidant

(c) Both oxidant

(d) Both reductant

98. In an experiment 20 gms of vanadium (V) oxide (molar mass = 182) was reduced by excess of zinc dust in acidic solution to vanadium (II) ions. The required number of moles of iodine to reoxidise vanadium (III) to VO^{2+} is ......

(a) 0.22

(b) 0.11

(c) 0.30

(d) 0.23

99. 1 mole of N_2H_4 loses 10 moles of electrons to form a new compound Y. Assuming that all the nitrogen appear in the new compound, what is the oxidation state of nitrogen in Y ? (no change in oxidation state of H)

(a) −1

(b) −3

(c) + 3

(d) + 5

100. Equivalent weight of Mn^{3+} in the following reaction is .... (Mn = 55)

$$Mn^{3+} \longrightarrow Mn^{2+} + MnO_2$$

(a) 27.5　　　　(b) 55　　　　(c) 110　　　　(d) 165

101. In cyanide method, silver metal is obtained as,

$$2K[Ag(CN)_2] + Zn \longrightarrow K_2[Zn(CN)_4] + 2Ag$$

In this ......

(a) Ag has been oxidized and Zn has been reduced

(b) Ag^+ has been reduced and Zn has been oxidized

(c) Both the metals have been oxidized

(d) Both the metals have been reduced

102. Which one of the following cannot act as a reducing agent ?

(a) CO_2　　　　(b) SO_2　　　　(c) NO_2　　　　(d) ClO_2

103. In the following reaction

$$Zn + 2OH^- + 2H_2O \longrightarrow Zn(OH)_4^{2-} + H_2$$

Species which has been reduced is ......

(a) Zn　　　　(b) OH^-　　　　(c) H_2O　　　　(d) None of these

104. Oxidation number of Cr is +5 in ......

(a) K_3CrO_8　　　　(b) $(NH_3)CrO_4$　　　　(c) K_2CrO_4　　　　(d) $[Cr(NH_3)_5(H_2O)]Cl_3$

105. The oxidation number of P in $Ba(H_2PO_2)$ is ......

(a) + 3　　　　(b) + 2　　　　(c) + 1　　　　(d) −1

106. In the reaction,

$$Cu + H_2SO_4 \longrightarrow CuSO_4 + H_2O + SO_2$$

(a) H^+ is the oxidizing agent

(b) SO_4^{2-} is the oxidizing agent

(c) Both H^+ and SO_4^- act as oxidizing agent

(d) None of the above is correct

107. In the following unbalanced redox reaction,

$$H_2S_{(g)} + SO_{2(g)} \longrightarrow S_{(s)} + H_2O_{(g)}$$

Total number of equivalents of SO_2 is .....

(a) + 4　　　　(b) + 3　　　　(c) + 2　　　　(d) + 1

108. Which of the following is the strongest oxidizing agent?

(a) Mn　　　　(b) Mn^{+2}　　　　(c) acidified MnO_2　　(d) acidified MnO_4^-

109. Metallic platinum reacts spontaneously with $Au_{(aq)}^{+3}$ but does not react with $Ag_{(aq)}^+$. The metals, in order of increasing strength as reducing agents, are ......

(a) Ag, Pt, Au　　　　(b) Pt, Au, Ag　　　　(c) Au, Ag, Pt　　　　(d) Au, Pt, Ag

110. When NO_2 reacts to form N_2O_4 the oxidation number of nitrogen ......

(a) increases by 2　　　(b) increases by 4　　　(c) increases by 8　　(d) does not change

111. The oxidation number of sulphur in S_8, S_2F_2, H_2S respectively, are ......

(a) 0, + 1 and –2   (b) +2, +1 and –2   (c) 0, +1 and + 2   (d) –2, +1 and –2

112. An aqueous solution of 6.3 g oxalic acid dehydrate is made up to 250 mL. The volume of 0.1 N NaOH required completely to neutralize 10 mL of this solution is ......

(a) 40 mL   (b) 20 mL   (c) 4 mL   (d) 10 mL

113. In the standardization of $Na_2S_2O_3$ using $K_2Cr_2O_7$ by iodometry, the equivalent weight is ...

(a) (Molecular weight)/2   (b) (Molecular weight)/6

(c) (Molecular weight)/3   (d) Same as molecular weight

114. Consider a titration of potassium dichromate solution with acidified Mohr's salt required per mole of dichromate is ......

(a) 3   (b) 4   (c) 5   (d) 6

115. A colourless solution of chlorine is mixed with a colourless solution of potassium bromide (KBr). What colour does the resultant mixture turn?

(a) yellow   (b) red   (c) green   (d) colourless

PREVIOUS YEAR'S QUESTIONS

1. $H_2O_2 + O_3 \rightarrow H_2O + 2O_2$, $H_2O + Ag_2O \rightarrow 2A + H_2O + O_2$

Role of hydrogen peroxide in the above reactions is respectively ......   **[AIPMT 2014]**

(a) reducing in (a) and (b)   (b) oxidizing in (a) and (b)

(c) oxidizing in (a) and reducing in (b)   (d) reducing in (a) and oxidizing in (b)

2. The pair of compounds that can exist together is ......   **[AIPMT 2014]**

(a) $FeCl_2$, $SnCl_2$ (b) $FeCl_3$, KI   (c) $FeCl_3$, $SnCl_2$ (d) $HgCl_2$, $SnCl_2$

3. The reaction of aqueous $KMnO_4$ with H_2O_2 in acid conditions gives :   **[AIPMT 2014]**

(a) Mn^{2+} and O_2 (b) Mn^{4+} and MnO_2 (c) Mn^{4+} and O_2 (d) Mn^{2+} and O_2

4. In acidic medium, H_2O_2 changes $Cr_2O_7^{-2}$ to CrO_5 which has two (–O – O–) bonds. Oxidation state of Cr in CrO_5 is ......   **[AIPMT 2014]**

(a) +6   (b) –10   (c) +5   (d) +3

5. When Cl_2 gas reacts with hot and concentrated sodium hydroxide solution, the oxidation number of chlorine charges from ......   **[CBSE Pre 2012]**

(a) Zero to –1 and zero to +3   (b) Zero to +1 and zero to –3

(c) Zero to+1 and zero to –5   (d) Zero to –1 and zero to +5

6. In which of the following compounds, nitrogen exhibits highest oxidation state?

[CBSE Pre 2012]

(a) N_3H (b) NH_2OH (c) N_2H_4 (d) NH_3

7. A mixture of potassium chlorate, oxalic acid and sulphuric acid is heated. During the reaction which element undergoes maximum change in the oxidation number?   **[CBSE Pre 2012]**

(a) Cl   (b) C   (c) S   (d) H

8. Which one of the following reactions involves oxidation-reduction?　　　**[Manipal 2010]**

    (a) $H_2 + Br_2 \rightarrow 2HBr$

    (b) $NaBr + HCl \rightarrow NaCl + HBr$

    (c) $HBr + AgNO_3 \rightarrow AgBr + HNO_3$

    (d) $2NaOH + H_2SO_4 \rightarrow Na_2SO_4 + 2H_2O$

9. Strongest reducing agent is ......　　　　　　**[AFMC 2009]**

    (a) K　　　　　(b) Mg　　　　　(c) Al　　　　　(d) Ba

10. $I_2 + 2S_2O_3^{2-} \rightarrow S_4O_6^{2-} + 2I^-$　　　　　　**[CPMT 2009]**

    In the above reaction ......

    (a) iodine is reduced; sulphur is reduced

    (b) iodine is reduced; sulphur is oxidised

    (c) iodine is oxidised; sulphur is reduced

    (d) iodine is oxidised; sulphur is oxidized

11. Which of the following molecules can act as an oxidizing as well as a reducing agent?

    (a) H_2S　　　　　(b) SO_3　　　　　(c) H_2O_2　　　　　(d) F_2　　　**[AIIMS 2008]**

12. Which is the best description of behavior of bromine in the reaction given below?

    $H_2O + Br_2 \rightarrow HBr + HOBr$　　　　　　**[Manipal 2007]**

    (a) Proton accepted only

    (b) Both oxidized and reduced

    (c) Oxidized only

    (d) Reduced only

13. Which of the following chemical reactions depicts the oxidizing behavior of H_2SO_4 ?

    　　　　　　[RPMT 2005]

    (a) $Ca(OH)_2 + H_2SO_4 \rightarrow CaSO_4 + 2H_2O$

    (b) $NaCl + H_2SO_4 \rightarrow NaHSO_4 + HCl$

    (c) $2HI + H_2SO_4 \rightarrow I_2 + SO_2 + 2H_2O$

    (d) $2PCl_5 + H_2SO_4 \rightarrow 2POCl_3 + 2HCl + SO_2Cl_2$

14. In one of the following reactions, HNO_3 does not behave as an oxidizing agent. Identify it.

    (a) $I_2 + 10HNO_3 \rightarrow 2HIO_3 + 10NO_2 + 4H_2O$　　　　　　**[JCECE 2005]**

    (b) $3Cu + 8HNO_3 \rightarrow 3Cu(NO_3)_2 + 2NO + 4H_2O$

    (c) $4Zn + 10HNO_3 \rightarrow 4Zn(NO_3)_2 + NH_4NO_3 + 3H_2O$

    (d) $2HNO_3 + P_2O_5 \rightarrow 2HPO_3 + N_2O_5$

15. In the reaction $Ag_2O + H_2O_2 \rightarrow 2Ag + H_2O + O_2$　　　　　　**[BHU 2004]**

    H_2O_2 acts as a ......

    (a) reducing agent

    (b) oxidizing agent

    (c) bleaching agent

    (d) none of these

16. Which of the following reaction is disproportionation?　　　　　　**[RPMT 2004]**

    (a) $2H_2S + SO_2 \rightarrow 2H_2O + 3S$

    (b) $Ca + H_2 \rightarrow CaH$

    (c) $4P + 3NaOH + 3H_2O \rightarrow PH_3 + 3NaH_2PO_2$

    (d) All of these

17. In the reaction　　　　　　**[DUMET 2003]**

    $HAsO_2 + Sn^{2+} \rightarrow As + Sn^{4+} + H_2O$

    Oxidizing agent is ......

    (a) Sn^{2+}　　　　　(b) Sn^{4-}　　　　　(c) As　　　　　(d) $HAsO_2$

18. In chromite ore, the oxidation number of iron and chromium respectively, are ......

[KCET 2001]

(a) $+3, +2$ (b) $+3, +6$ (c) $+2, +6$ (d) $+2, +3$

19. Oxidation states of P in $H_4P_2O_5$, $H_4P_2O_6$, $H_4P_2O_7$, are respectively ......   **[CBSE AIPMT 2010]**

(a) $+3, +4, +5$ (b) $+3, +5, +4$ (c) $+5, +3, +4$ (d) $+5, +4, +3$

20. Highest oxidation state of Mn is present in ......   **[AFMC 2010]**

(a) $KMnO_4$ (b) K_2MnO_4 (c) Mn_2O_3 (d) MnO_2

21. Which gives $+7$ oxidation state?   **[MHTCET 2010]**

(a) Mn (25)   (b) Cr (24)   (c) Cu (2)   (d) Fe (26)

22. Oxidation number of N in HNO_3 is ......   **[Manipal 2010]**

(a) -3.5 (b) $+3.5$ (c) $-3, +5$ (d) $+5$

23. The oxidation number and covalency of sulphur in sulphur molecule (S_8) are ... **[BVP 2010]**

(a) 0 and 2   (b) $+6$ and 8   (c) 0 and 8   (d) $+6$ and 2

24. Oxidation number of P in PO_4^{-3}, of S in SO_4^{2-} and that of Cr in $Cr_2O_7^{2-}$ are respectively ......

[CBSE AIPMT 2009]

(a) $+5, +6$ and $+6$ (b) $+3, +6$ and $+5$ (c) $+5, +3$ and $+6$ (d) $-3, +6$ and $+6$

25. The oxidation state of Fe in the brown ring complex $[Fe(H_2O)_5NO]SO_4$ is ......   **[KCET 2009]**

(a) 0   (b) $+2$ (c) $+1$ (d) $+3$

26. Oxidation number of S in $H_2S_2O_8$ is ......   **[Manipal 2009]**

(a) $+2$ (b) $+4$ (c) $+3$ (d) $+6$

27. The oxidation number of sulphur atoms in peroxomonosulphuric acid (H_2SO_5) and peroxodisulphuric acid ($H_2S_2O_8$) are respectively ......   **[J&K CET 2009]**

(a) $+8$ and $+7$ (b) $+3$ and $+3$ (c) $+6$ and $+6$ (d) $+4$ and $+6$

28. The oxidation states of S atoms in $S_4O_6^{2-}$ from left to right respectively, are ......

(a) $+6, 0, 0, +6$ (b) $+3, 1, +1, +3$ (c) $+5, 0, 0, +5$ (d) $+4 + 1 + 1 + 4$

29. In the conversion of Br_2 to BrO_3^-, the oxidation number of Br changes from ... **[AFMC 2008]**

(a) zero to $+5$ (b) $+1$ to $+5$ (c) zero to -3 (d) $+2$ to $+5$

30. The oxidation states of iodine in HIO_4, H_3IO_5 and H_5IO_6 respectively, are ...... **[AIIMS 2008]**

(a) $+1, +3, +7$ (b) $+7, +7, +3$ (c) $+7, +7, +7$ (d) $+7, +5, +3$

31. Oxidation state of oxygen in F_2O is ......   **[CPMT 2008]**

(a) $+1$ (b) -1 (c) $+2$ (d) -2

32. When sulphur dioxide is passed in an acidified $K_2Cr_2O_7$ solution, the oxidation state of sulphur is changed from ......   **[KCET 2008]**

(a) $+4$ to 0   (b) $+4$ to $+2$ (c) $+4$ to $+6$ (d) $+6$ to $+4$

33. Which of the following oxidation states are the most characteristics for lead and tin respectively?

(a) +4, +2　　　　(b) +2, +4　　　　(c) +4, +4　　　　(d) +2, +2

34. +3 oxidation state is most common in ......　　　　**[AFMC 2007]**

(a) Ni (28)　　　　(b) Fe (26)　　　　(c) Zn (3)　　　　(d) Cu (29)

35. The oxidation number of nitrogen in $NaNO_2$ is ......　　　　**[AFMC 2006]**

(a) +3　　　　(b) +5　　　　(c) −3　　　　(d) −5

36. Carbon is in the lowest oxidation state in　　　　**[Punjab PMET 2006]**

(a) CO_2　　　　(b) CF_4　　　　(c) CCl_4　　　　(d) CH_4

37. CrO_5 has a structure as shown

$$:O\diagdown \underset{Cr}{\overset{\overset{\displaystyle O}{\parallel}}{\diagup \diagdown}} \diagup O$$

The oxidation number of chromium in the above compound is ......　　　　**[Kerala CCE 2006]**

(a) 4　　　　(b) 5　　　　(c) 6　　　　(d) 10　　　　(e) 0

38. Oxidation number of 'N' in N_3H (Hydrazoic acid) is ......　　　　**[Manipal 2006]**

(a) −1/3　　　　(b) +3　　　　(c) 0　　　　(d) −1

39. Oxidation number of carbon in CH_2Cl_2 is ......　　　　**[J&K CET 2005]**

(a) 0　　　　(b) 2　　　　(c) 3　　　　(d) 5

40. The oxidation states of sulphur in the anions SO_3, $S_2O_4^{2-}$ and $S_2O_6^{2-}$ follow the order

[CBSEAIPMT 2003]

(a) $S_2O_4^{2-} < S_2O_6^{2-} < SO_3^{2-}$　　　　(b) $S_2O_4^{2-} < S_2O_4^{2-} < SO_3^{2-}$

(c) $S_2O_4^{2-} < SO_3^{2-} < S_2O_6^{2-}$　　　　(d) $SO_3^{2-} < S_2O_4^{2-} < S_2O_6^{2-}$

41. Nitrogen shows different oxidation states in the range ......　　　　**[Kerala CEE 2003]**

(a) 0 to +5　　　　(b) −3 to +5　　　　(c) −5 to +3　　　　(d) −3 to +3

42. How many moles of iodine are liberated when 1 mole of potassium dichromate reacts with potassium iodide?　　　　**[AFMC 2010]**

(a) 1　　　　(b) 2　　　　(c) 3　　　　(d) 4

43. In the following redox equation $I^- + IO_3^- + H^+ \rightarrow I_2 + H_2O$

coefficients are in the balanced form respectively are ......　　　　**[CMC Ludhiyana 2010]**

(a) 5, 1, 6　　　　(b) 1, 5, 6　　　　(d) 6, 1, 5　　　　(d) 5, 6, 1

44. In the redox reaction,

$xKMnO_4 + NH_3 \rightarrow yKNO_3 + MnO_2 + KOH + H_2O$

x and y are ......　　　　**[DUMET 2009]**

(a) x = 4, y = 6　　　　(b) x = 3, y = 8　　　　(c) x = 8, y = 6　　　　(d) x = 8, y = 3

45. For the redox reaction,　　　　**[Manipal 2009]**

$Zn + NO_3^- \rightarrow Zn^{2+} + NH_4^+$

In basic medium, coefficients of Zn, NO_3^- and OH^- in the balanced equation respectively, are ......

(a) 4, 1, 7　　　　(b) 7, 4, 1　　　　(c) 4, 1, 10　　　　(d) 1, 4, 10

46. The equivalent weight of potassium permanganate in strong alkaline medium is its

(a) $\dfrac{\text{Molar mass}}{5}$　　(b) $\dfrac{\text{Molar mass}}{3}$　　(c) $\dfrac{\text{Molar mass}}{2}$　　(d) Molar mass itself

47. In the ionic equation, $BiO_3^- + 6H^+ + xe^- \rightarrow Bi^{3+} + 3H_2O$　　**[J & K CET 2009]**
the value of x is ......　　**[KCET 2007]**

(a) 6　　　　(b) 2　　　　(c) 4　　　　(d) 3

48. In alkaline medium, ClO_2 oxidises H_2O_2 in O_2 and reduced itself in Cl^- then how many moles of H_2O_2 will oxidize by one mole of ClO_2 ?　　**[BHU 2006]**

(a) 1.0　　　　(b) 1.5　　　　(c) 2.5　　　　(d) 3.5

49. How many moles of nitrogen produced by the oxidation of one mole of N_2H_4 by $\dfrac{2}{3}$ moles of BrO_3^- ion ?

$$3N_2H_4 + 2BrO_3^- \rightarrow 3N_2 + 2Br^- + 6H_2O$$

(a) $\dfrac{1}{3}$　　　　(b) 1　　　　(c) $\dfrac{1}{2}$　　　　(d) $\dfrac{2}{3}$

50. How many moles of $Cr_2O_7^{2-}$ are reduced by 1 mole of HCOOH ?

$$Cr_2O_7^{2-} + 8H^+ + 3HCOOH \rightarrow 2Cr^{3+} + 3CO_2 + 7H_2O$$
$$\phantom{Cr_2O_7^{2-}}\ 1\ \text{mol}3\ \text{mol}$$

(a) $\dfrac{1}{3}$　　　　(b) 1　　　　(c) $\dfrac{2}{3}$　　　　(d) $\dfrac{5}{3}$

51. What is the oxidation number of Fe in $Fe(CO)_5$?　　**[C.P.M.T. 2000]**

(a) Zero　　　　(b) 5　　　　(c) 5　　　　(d) +3

52. In the balanced equation $5H_2O_2 + xClO_2 + 2OH^- \longrightarrow xCl^- + yO_2 + 6H_2O$　　**[DCE 2000]**
The reaction is balanced if

(a) x = 5, y = 2　　(b) x = 2, y = 5　　(c) x = 4, y = 10　　(d) x = 5, y = 5

53. A, B and C are three elements forming a part of a compound in oxidation states of +2, +5 and –2 respectively. What could be the compound ?　　**[C.B.S.E. P.M.T. 2000]**

(a) $A_2(BC)_2$　　(b) $A_2(BC)_2$　　(c) $A_3(BC_4)_2$　　(d) ABC

54. Oxidation number of iron in Fe_3O_4 is ......　　**[C.B.S.E. P.M.T. 1999; Haryana C.E.T. 2000]**

(a) + 2　　　　(b) + 3　　　　(c) 8/3　　　　(d) 2/3

55. HNO_3 acts as a/an　　**[Manipal 2001]**

(a) Acid　　(b) Oxidising agent　(c) Reducing agent　(d) Both (a) and (b)

56. The chemical that undergoes self oxidation and self reduction in the same reaction is ......

[Tamil Nadu C.E.T. 2001]

(a) Benzyl alcohol　　(b) Acetone　　(c) Formaldehyde　(d) Acetic acid.

57. Which of the following is a redox reaction ?　　**[A.I.E.E.E. 2002]**

(a) $NaCl + KNO_3 \longrightarrow NaNO_3 + KCl$
(b) $CaC_2O_4 + 2HCl \longrightarrow CaCl_2 + H_2C_2O_4$
(c) $Mg(OH)_2 + 2NH_4Cl \longrightarrow MgCl_2 + NH_2OH$
(d) $Zn + 2AgCN \longrightarrow 2Ag + Zn(CN)_2$

58. Oxidation number of S in $H_2S_2O_8$ is ......   **[M.P.C.E.T. 2002]**
(a) + 2   (b) + 4   (c) + 6   (d) +7

59. MnO_4^{2-} (1 mole) in neutral aqueous medium is disproportionate to   **[A.I.I.M.S. 2003]**

(a) 2/3 mole of MnO_4^- and 1/3 mole of MnO_2

(b) 1/3 mole of MnO_4^- and 2/3 mole of MnO_2

(c) 1/3 mole of Mn_2O_7 and 2/3 mole of MnO_2

(d) 2/3 mole of Mn_2O_7 and 1/3 mole of MnO_2

60. $P_4 + NaOH + H_2O \longrightarrow NaH_2PO_3 + PH_3$ is ......   **[Wardha 2003]**
(a) Oxidation reaction   (b) Reduction reaction
(c) Both oxidation and reduction   (d) None of these

61. How many electrons are involved in oxidation by $KMnO_4$ in basic medium ?
          [Orissa J.E.E. 2003]
(a) 1   (b) 2   (c) 5   (d) 3

62. In acidic medium, dichromatic ion oxidises ferrous ion to ferric ion. If the gram molecular weight of potassium dichromate is 294 grams, its gram equivalent weight is .... grams.
          [E.A.M.C.E.T. 2003]
(a) 294   (b) 127   (c) 49   (d) 24.5

63. In the following redox reaction $xUO^{2-} + Cr_2O_7^{2-} + YH^+ \rightarrow aUO_2^{2+} + zCr^{3+} + bH_2O$
The values of coefficients x, y, z respectively are
(a) 3, 8, 2   (b) 3, 8, 7   (c) 3, 2, 4   (d) 3, 1, 8

64. Oxidation state of oxygen in H_2O_2 is ......   **[Orissa J.E.E. 2004]**
(a) 2   (b) –1   (c) 0   (d) +2

65. KI and $CuSO_4$ solution when mixed gives ......   **[J & K Med. 2004]**
(a) $CuI_2 + K_2SO_4$ (b) $Cu_2I_2 + K_2SO_4$
(c) $K_2SO_4 + Cu_2I_2 + I_2$ (d) $K_2SO_4 + CuI_2 + I_2$

66. Which of the following is the strongest oxidising agent ?   **[J & K Med. 2004]**
(a) HOCl   (b) $HClO_2$ (c) $HClO_3$ (d) $HClO_4$

67. Oxidation number of carbon in CH_2Cl_2 is ......   **[A.F.M.C. 2004]**
(a) 0   (b) 2   (c) 3   (d) 5

68. For decolourisation of 1 mole of acidified $KMnO_4$, the moles of H_2O_2 required are ......
          [A.I.I.M.S. 2004]
(a) 1/2   (b) 3/2   (c) 5/2   (d) 7/2

69. Among the properties (a) reducing (b) oxidising (c) complexing, the set of properties shown by CN ion towards metal species is ......   **[A.I.I.E.E.E. 2004]**
(a) a, b   (b) a, b, c   (c) c, a   (d) b, c

70. In the balanced chemical reaction   **[A.I.I.M.S. 2005]**

$O_3^- + aI^- + bH^+ \longrightarrow cH_2O + dI_2$

a, b, c and d respectively correspond to ......
(a) 5, 6, 3, 3   (b) 5, 3, 6, 3   (c) 3, 5, 3, 6   (d) 5, 6, 5, 5

71. One mole of acidified $K_2Cr_2O_7$ on reaction with excess KI will liberate .... moles of I_2.
          [Kerala P.M.T. 2006]

(a) 6   (b) 1   (c) 3   (d) 2

72. Oxidation state of Cl_2 in $CaOCl_2$ is /are ......   **[D.C.E. 2006]**
   (a) Zero   (b) $+1$ (c) 1   (d) $+1,\ 1$

73. In the reaction   **[Orissa J.E.E. 2006]**
   $As_2S_5 + xHNO_3 \longrightarrow 5H_2SO_4 + yNO_2 + 2H_3AsO_4 + 12H_2O$
   The values of x and y are ......
   (a) 40, 40   (b) 10, 10   (c) 30, 30   (d) 20, 20

74. Oxidation state of Cl in HOCl is/are ......   **[D.C.E. 2006]**
   (a) Zero   (b) $+1$ (c) 1   (d) -1

75. Which of the following is a set of reducing agents?   **[Orissa J.E.E. 2007]**
   (a) HNO_3, Fe^{2+}, F_2 (b) F, Cl^-, MnO_4^- (c) I^-, Na, Fe^{2+} (d) $CrO_7^{2-}, CrO_4^{2-}, Na$

76. Oxidation number of iodine in IO_3^-, IO_4^-, KI and I_2 respectively are ...   **[Kerala P.M.T. 2008]**
   (a) 1, 1, 0, $+1$ (b) $+3, +5, +7, 0$ (c) $+5, +7,\ -1, 0$ (d) 1, 5, 1, 0
   (e) 2, 5, 1, 0

77. Which of the following reactions involve disproportionation ?   **[Kerala P.M.T. 2006]**
   (a) $2H_2SO_4 + Cu \longrightarrow CuSO_4 + 2H_2O + SO_2$ (b) $As_2O_3 + 3H_2S \longrightarrow As_2S_3 + 3H_2O$
   (c) $2KOH + Cl_2 \longrightarrow KCl + KOCl + H_2O$ (d) $Ca_3P_2 + 6H_2O \longrightarrow 3Ca(OH)_3 + 2PH_3$
   (e) $NH_3 + 3O_2 \longrightarrow 2N_2 + 6H_2O$

78. Oxidation number of S in S, S_2F_2 and H_2S respectively will be ...... **[Manipur M.B.B.S. 2009]**
   (a) 0, $+1$, 2   (b) $+2, +1$ and 2   (c) 0, $+1$ and -2 (d) 2, $+1$ and $+2$

79. The equivalent mass of potassium permanganate in the alkaline medium is
                                                                     [J & K.C.E.T. 2009]
   (a) Molar mass/5   (b) Molar mass/3   (c) Molar mass/2   (d) Molar mass/1

80. In which of the following reactions, there is no change in valency ?   **[D.P.M.T. 2009]**
   (a) $SO_2 + 2H_2S \longrightarrow 2H_2O + 3S$ (b) $2Na + O_2 \longrightarrow 2Na_2O_2$
   (c) $Na_2O_2 + H_2SO_4 \longrightarrow Na_2SO_4 + H_2O_2$ (d) $3KClO_3 \longrightarrow 3KClO_4 + KCl$

81. Small quantities of compounds TX, TY and TZ are put into separate test tubes containing X, Y and Z solutions. TX does not react with any of these. TY reacts with both X and Z. TZ reacts only with X. The decreasing order of ease of oxidation of the anions X, Y and Z is
   (a) Y, Z, X   (b) Z, X, Y   (c) Y, X, Z   (d) X, Z, Y **[D.C.E. 2009]**

82. The oxidation state of sulphur in peroxomono sulphuric acid H_2SO_5 is ... **[U.P.C.P.M.T. 2010]**
   (a) $+5$ (b) $+6$ (c) $+7$ (d) $+8$

83. When $KMnO_4$ acts as an oxidising agent and ultimately forms MnO_4^{2-}, MnO_2, Mn_2O_2, Mn_2O_3 and Mn^{2+}, then the number of electrons transferred in each case respectively are ......
                                                                     [A.I.E.E.E. 2002]
   (a) 4, 3, 1, 5   (b) 1, 5, 3, 7   (c) 1, 3, 4, 5   (d) 3, 5, 7, 1

84. The strongest reducing agent among the following is ......   **[J & K Med. 2004]**
   (a) F^- (b) Cl^- (c) Br^- (d) I^-

85. In the balanced chemical reaction $IO_3^- + aI^- + bH^+ \longrightarrow cH_2O + dI_2$ **[A.F.M.C. 2009]**
   a, b, c and d respectively correspond to ......
   (a) 5, 6, 3, 3   (b) 5, 3, 6, 3   (c) 3, 5, 3, 6   (d) 5, 6, 5, 5

86. Amongst the following, identify the species with an atom in +6 oxidation state.
   (a) MnO_4^- (b) $Cr(CN)_6^{3-}$ (c) NiF_6^{2-} (d) CrO_2Cl_2

87. The reaction $3Cl^-_{(aq)} \rightarrow ClO^-_{3\ (aq)} + 2Cl^-_{(aq)}$ is an example of ......

    (a) Oxidation reaction   (b) Reduction reaction

    (c) Disproportionation reaction   (d) Decomposition reaction

88. The pair of compounds in which both the metals are in the highest possible oxidation state is ......

    (a) $[Fe(CN)_6]^{3-}$, $[Co(CN)_6]^{3-}$ (b) CrO_2Cl_2, MnO_4^-

    (c) TiO_3, MnO_2 (d) $[Co(CN)_6]^{3-}$, MnO_2

89. Which of the following chemical reactions depicts the oxidising behaviour of H_2SO_4 ?

    (a) $NaCl + H_2SO_4 \longrightarrow NaHSO_4 + HCl$

    (b) $2PCl_5 + H_2SO_4 \longrightarrow 2POCl_3 + 2HCl + SO_2Cl_2$

    (c) $2HI + H_2SO_4 \longrightarrow I_2 + SO_2 + 2H_2$ (d) $Ca(OH)_2 + H_2SO_4 \longrightarrow CaSO_4 + 2H_2O$

90. Number of moles of MnO_4^- required to oxidise one mole of ferrous oxalate completely in acidic medium will be ......   **[A.I.P.M.T. 2008]**

    (a) 7.5 mol   (b) 0.2 mol   (c) 0.6 mol   (d) 0.4 mol

91. Oxidation states of P in $H_4P_2O_5$, $H_4P_2O_6$, $H_4P_2O_7$ are respectively   **[A.I.P.M.T. Prelim. 2010]**

    (a) +3, +5, +4   (b) +5, +3, +4   (c) +5, +4, +3   (d) +3, +4, +5

ANSWER KEY

1. (b)	2. (d)	3. (b)	4. (c)	5. (a)	6. (a)	7. (c)	8. (b)
9. (a)	10. (c)	11. (d)	12. (a)	13. (d)	14. (c)	15. (a)	16. (c)
17. (b)	18. (d)	19. (d)	20. (d)	21. (c)	22. (b)	23. (d)	24. (c)
25. (a)	26. (c)	27. (a)	28. (a)	29. (d)	30. (d)	31. (a)	32. (c)
33. (c)	34. (d)	35. (b)	36. (a)	37. (c)	38. (c)	39. (a)	40. (b)
41. (c)	42. (c)	43. (b)	44. (c)	45. (c)	46. (a)	47. (c)	48. (d)
49. (b)	50. (a)	51. (b)	52. (c)	53. (b)	54. (a)	55. (b)	56. (c)
57. (c)	58. (a)	59. (c)	60. (b)	61. (c)	62. (a)	63. (b)	64. (c)
65. (a)	66. (c)	67. (a)	68. (a)	69. (a)	70. (d)	71. (b)	72. (a)
73. (c)	74. (a)	75. (c)	76. (a)	77. (d)	78. (a)	79. (c)	80. (a)
81. (c)	82. (d)	83. (c)	84. (d)	85. (b)	86. (c)	87. (c)	88. (b)
89. (a)	90. (b)	91. (a)	92. (d)	93. (c)	94. (d)	95. (d)	96. (a)
97. (b)	98. (a)	99. (c)	100. (b)	101. (b)	102. (a)	103. (b)	104. (b)
105. (c)	106. (b)	107. (a)	108. (a)	109. (d)	110. (d)	111. (a)	112. (d)
113. (b)	114. (d)	115. (b)					

Previous Years Questions

1. (a)	2. (a)	3. (d)	4. (a)	5. (d)	6. (a)	7. (a)	8. (a)
9. (a)	10. (b)	11. (c)	12. (b)	13. (c)	14. (d)	15. (a)	16. (c)
17. (d)	18. (d)	19. (a)	20. (a)	21. (a)	22. (d)	23. (a)	24. (a)
25. (c)	26. (d)	27. (c)	28. (c)	29. (a)	30. (c)	31. (c)	32. (c)
33. (b)	34. (b)	35. (a)	36. (d)	37. (c)	38. (a)	39. (a)	40. (c)
41. (b)	42. (c)	43. (a)	44. (d)	45. (c)	46. (b)	47. (b)	48. (c)
49. (b)	50. (a)	51. (a)	52. (b)	53. (c)	54. (c)	55. (b)	56. (c)
57. (d)	58. (c)	59. (a)	60. (c)	61. (d)	62. (c)	63. (a)	64. (b)
65. (c)	66. (a)	67. (a)	68. (c)	69. (c)	70. (a)	71. (c)	72. (a)
73. (a)	74. (b)	75. (c)	76. (c)	77. (c)	78. (c)	79. (d)	80. (c)
81. (a)	82. (b)	83. (c)	84. (d)	85. (a)	86. (d)	87. (c)	88. (b)
89. (c)	90. (c)	91. (d)					

❑❑❑

HYDROGEN

1. Which of the following evolve hydrogen by reacting with cold dilute hydrochloric acid?

   (a) Mg   (b) Al   (c) Fe   (d) Cu

2. Hydrogen accepts an electron to form inert gas configuration. In this it resembles ......

   (a) Halogen   (b) Alkali metals

   (c) Chalcogens   (d) Alkaline earth metals

3. Which of the following is correct for hydrogen?

   (a) It can form bonds in +1 as well as in −1 oxidation state

   (b) It is always collected at the cathode

   (c) It has a very high ionisation potential

   (d) Insecticide preparation

4. What is heavy water?

   (a) H_2O^{17} (b) H_2O^{18} (c) D_2O (d) H_2O

5. Which of the following will not displace hydrogen?

   (a) Ba   (b) Pb   (c) Hg   (d) Sn

6. The absorption of hydrogen by palladium is called as ......

   (a) Hydration   (b) Reduction   (c) Occlusion   (d) Hydrogenation

7. The alum used for purifying water is ......

   (a) Ferric alum   (b) Chrome alum   (c) Potash alum   (d) Ammonium alum

8. The boiling point of water is exceptionally high because of ......

   (a) There is covalent bond between H and O

   (b) Water molecule is linear

   (c) Water molecules associate due to hydrogen bonding

   (d) Water molecule is not linear

9. The percentage by weight of hydrogen in H_2O_2 is ......

   (a) 5.88   (b) 6.25   (c) 25   (d) 50

10. The metal which cannot displace hydrogen from dilute HCl is ......

    (a) Al   (b) Fe   (c) Cu   (d) Zn

11. The process used for the removal of hardness of water is ......

    (a) Calgon   (b) Baeyer   (c) Serpeck   (d) Hope

12. Pure water can be obtained from sea water by ......

    (a) Centrifugation   (b) Plasmolysis   (c) Reverse osmosis   (d) Sedimentation

13. Metal which does not react with cold water but evolves H_2 with steam is ......

    (a) Na   (b) K   (c) Pt   (d) Fe

14. Which of the following could act as a propellant for rocks?
    (a) Liquid hydrogen + Liquid nitrogen   (b) Liquid oxygen + Liquid argon
    (c) Liquid hydrogen + Liquid oxygen   (d) Liquid nitrogen + Liquid oxygen

15. Shape of H_2O_2 molecule is ......
    (a) Non-polar   (b) Linear   (c) Circular   (d) Planar

16. Which of the properties of interstitial hydrides is correct?
    (a) They generally form non-stoichiometric species
    (b) The hydrogen dissolved improves its mechanical properties
    (c) They give rise to metals fit for fabrication
    (d) On thermal decomposition they afford a source of pure hydrogen
    (e) They can be used as hydrogenation catalysts.

17. Hydrogen resembles ......
    (a) Alkali metals   (b) Noble gases   (c) Halogens   (d) Carbon

18. Hydrogen can be obtained from water by ......
    (a) Reaction with metal oxides   (b) Reaction with non-metal oxides
    (c) Reaction with metals   (d) Reaction with metal hydrides

19. Hydrogen can be obtained from water, by the action of water on ......
    (a) Calcium carbide   (b) Calcium hydride   (c) Calcium oxide   (d) Calcium

20. The metal(s) which react with $NaOH_{(aq)}$ to give H_2, under ordinary conditions is ......
    (a) Zn   (b) Al   (c) Fe   (d) Both (a) and (b)

21. The acid not suitable for the preparation of H_2 by action with metals is ......
    (a) HCl   (b) CH_3COOH (c) HNO_3 (d) H_2SO_4

22. Hydrogen ......
    (a) Is a highly reactive chemical substance   (b) Has pungent smell
    (c) Has green colour in gaseous state   (d) Is acidic in nature

23. These do not form hydrides with hydrogen ......
    (a) Noble gases   (b) All actinides   (c) All lanthanides   (d) Coolants

24. Heavy water is ......
    (a) Radioactive   (b) Non-radioactive   (c) Stoichiometric   (d) Hard water

25. Which of the following is an important use of hydrogen peroxide?
    (a) To reduce BOD and COD of waste water   (b) Drinking
    (c) Cooling   (d) Neutralisation

26. Which of the following is a universal solvent ?
    (a) Hydrochloric acid   (b) Nitric acid   (c) Water   (d) Sulphuric acid

27. Which of the following is the anion of hydrogen ?
    (a) Hydride   (b) Hydrogen peroxide
    (c) Heavy water   (d) Hard water

Assertion and Reasons

Direction : In the following question, a statement of Assertion (A) is given followed by a corresponding statement of Reason (R) just below it. Of the statements, mark the correct answer as

(a) If both A and R are true and R is correct explanation of A

(b) If both A and R are true but R is not the correct explanation of A

(c) If A is true but reason is false.

(d) If A is false but reason is true.

(e) If both A and R are false.

28. Assertion   : Ortho- and para-dihydrogen are nuclear spin isomers.

    Reason   : They have same nuclear spins.

29. Assertion   : Saline hydrides are non-volatile, non-conducting and crystalline solids.

    Reason   : Saline hydrides are compounds of hydrogen with most of the p-block elements.

30. Assertion   : Ammonia and water are electron rich hydrides.

    Reason   : They have electrons more than required for bonding.

31. Assertion   : H_2O_2 is stored in wax-lined glass.

    Reason   : Presence of metal surfaces, traces of alkali (present in glass) etc. increases its decomposition.

32. Assertion   : Heavy water is used as a moderator in nuclear reactors.

    Reason   : Heavy water is made up of an isotope of helium.

33. Assertion   : H_2O_2 reduces Cl_2 to HCl.

    Reason   : H_2O_2 is also called antichlor.

34. Assertion   : Calgon is used for removing Ca^{2+} and Mg^{2+} ions from hard water.

    Reason   : Calgon forms precipitate with Ca^{2+} and Mg^{2+}ions.

35. Arrange LiH, NaH, KH, RbH, CsH, in the correct order of increasing ionic character

(a) LiH > NaH > CsH > KH>RbH   (b) LiH < NaH < KH < RbH < CsH

(c) RbH > CsH > NaH > KH > LiH   (d) NaH > CsH > RbH > LiH > KH

36. Which of the following hydrides is an electron-precise hydride?

(a) NH_3 (b) H_2O (c) CH_4 (d) B_2H_6

37. The radioactive isotope of hydrogen is ......

(a) Protium   (b) Deuterium   (c) Tritium   (d) Hydronium

38. Consider the reactions

(A) $H_2O_2 + 2HI \rightarrow I_2 + 2H_2O$

(B) $HOCl + H_2O_2 \rightarrow H_3O^+ + Cl^- + O^2$

Which of the following statements is correct ?

Hydrogen peroxide is ______.

(a) an oxidising agent in both (A) and (B)

(b) an oxidising agent in (A) and reducing agent in (B)

(c) a reducing agent in (A) and oxidising agent in (B)

(d) a reducing agent in both (A) and (B)

39. Hydrogen resembles halogens in many respects. Which of the following factors is the most important reason for this similarity?

(a) Its small size.

(b) Its tendency to lose an electron to form a cation.

(c) Its tendency to gain a single electron in its valence shell to attain stable electronic configuration.

(d) Its low negative electron gain enthalpy value.

40. Which oxide give H_2O_2 on treatment with dilute H_2SO_4 ?

(a) PbO_2 (b) $BaO_2 \cdot 8H_2O + O_2$ (c) MnO_2 (d) TiO_2

41. Which of the following equations show the oxidising nature of H_2O_2?

(a) $2MnO_4^- + 6H^+ + 5H_2O_2 \rightarrow 2Mn^{2+} + 8H_2O + 5O_2$

(b) $2Fe^{3+} + 2H^+ + H_2O_2 \rightarrow 2Fe^{2+} + 2H_2O + O_2$

(c) $2I^- + 2H^+ + H_2O_2 \rightarrow I^2 + 2H_2O$

(d) $KIO_4 + H_2O_2 \rightarrow KIO_3 + H_2O + O_2$

42. Which of the following equation depicts reducing nature of H_2O_2?

(a) $2[Fe(CN)_6]^{4-} + 2H^+ + H_2O_2 \rightarrow 2[Fe(CN)_6]^{3-} + 2H_2O$

(b) $I_2 + H_2O_2 + 2OH^- \rightarrow 2I^- + 2H_2O + O_2$

(c) $Mn^{2+} + H_2O_2 \rightarrow Mn^{4+} + 2OH^-$

(d) $PbS + 4H_2O_2 \rightarrow PbSO_4 + 4H_2O$

43. Hydrogen peroxide is a/an________.

(a) Oxidising agent   (b) Reducing agent

(c) Oxidising and a reducing agent   (d) None of the above

44. Why does H^+ ion always get associated with other atoms or molecules?

(a) Loss of an electron from hydrogen atom results in a nucleus of very small size due to which it cannot exist in free state.

(b) Ionisation enthalpy of hydrogen is similar to that of alkali metals.

(c) Its reactivity is similar to halogens.

(d) It resembles both alkali metals and halogens.

45. When sodium peroxide reacts with dilute sulphuric acid, the products are ......

(a) Sodium sulphate and water   (b) Sodium sulphate and oxygen

(c) Sodium sulphate, hydrogen and oxygen   (d) Sodium sulphate and hydrogen peroxide

46. Which of the following is used for water softening?

(a) $Ca_3(PO_4)_2$ (b) Na_3PO_4 (c) $Na_6P_6O_{18}$ (d) Na_2HPO_4

47. Elements of which of the following group(s) of periodic table do not form hydrides ?
    (a) Groups VII, VIII, IX
    (b) Group XIII
    (c) Groups XV, XVI, XVII
    (d) Group XIV

48. Hydrogen peroxide is obtained by the electrolysis of _____.
    (a) Sodium hydroxide   (b) Sulphuric acid   (c) Hydrochloric acid   (d) Sodium peroxide

49. Only one element of _______ forms hydride.
    (a) Group VI   (b) Group VIII   (c) Group II   (d) Group IX

50. What will cause hardness in water sample?
    (a) Ca^{2+} (b) Na^{+} (c) Pb   (d) K^{+}

51. Which of the following statements are not true for hydrogen?
    (a) It exists as a diatomic molecule.
    (b) It has one electron in the outermost shell.
    (c) It can lose an electron to form a cation which cannot exist in a free state.
    (d) It forms a large number of ionic compounds by losing an electron.

52. In the preparation of dihydrogen by the action of steam on hydrocarbons, a mixture of CO and H_2 gas is formed. It is known as __________.
    (a) Coal gas   (b) Syngas   (c) Producer gas   (d) Gobar gas

53. Which of the following statements about water is incorrect?
    (a) Water is a universal solvent.
    (b) Hydrogen bonding is present to a large extent in liquid water.
    (c) There is no hydrogen bonding in the frozen state of water.
    (d) Frozen water is lighter than liquid water.

54. Choose the correct statements from the following :
    (a) Hydrogen has three isotopes of which protium is the most uncommon.
    (b) Hydrogen never acts as cation in ionic salts.
    (c) Hydrogen ion, H^{+}, exists in solution in free state.
    (d) Dihydrogen is not a reducing agent.

55. Permanent hardness of water is due to the presence of ......
    (a) Carbonates of Ca and Mg in water
    (b) Sulphates of Ca and Mg in water
    (c) Hydrogen carbonates of Ca and Mg in water
    (d) Presence of radioactive elements in water

56. Choose the correct statement.
    (a) Electron rich hydrides can act as Lewis acids.
    (b) Elements of group 15 form electron deficient hydrides.
    (c) All elements of group 16 form electron precise hydrides.
    (d) Electron precise hydrides have tetrahedral geometries.

57. Choose the correct statements from the following :
   (a) Hydrides of group 13 act as Lewis acids.
   (b) Hydrides of group 14 are electron rich hydrides.
   (c) Hydrides of group 14 act as Lewis acids.
   (d) Hydrides of group 15 act as Lewis bases.

58. Which of the following statements is correct?
   (a) Metallic hydrides are rich in hydrogen.
   (b) Metallic hydrides are not good conductors of heat and electricity.
   (c) Ionic hydrides are not good conductors of electricity in solid state.
   (d) Ionic hydrides are very good conductors of electricity in solid state.

59. Which of the following statement(s) is/are correct in the case of heavy water?
   (a) Heavy water is used as a moderator in nuclear reactor.
   (b) Heavy water is a better solvent than ordinary water.
   (c) Heavy water has more hydrogen bonding than ordinary water.
   (d) Heavy water has lower boiling point than ordinary water.

60. Hydrogen is evolved by the action of cold dil. HNO_3 on ......
   (a) Fe   (b) Mn   (c) Cu   (d) Al

61. HCl is added to following oxides. Which one would give H_2O_2 ?
   (a) MnO_2 (b) PbO_2 (c) BaO   (d) None of these

62. Hydrogen will not reduce ......
   (a) Heated cupric oxide   (b) Heated ferric oxide
   (c) Heated tannic oxide   (d) Heated aluminium oxide

63. When zeolite, which is hydrated sodium aluminium silicate, is treated with hard water, the sodium ions are exchanged with ......
   (a) H^+ ions   (b) Ca^{2+} ions   (c) Mg^{2+} ions   (d) Both Ca^{2+} and Mg^{2+}

64. The amount of H_2O_2 present in 1L of 1.5 N H_2O_2 solutions is ......
   (a) 2.5 g   (b) 25.5 g   (c) 3.0 g   (d) 8.0 g

65. The critical temperature of water is higher than of O_2 because H_2O molecule has ......
   (a) Fewer electrons than oxygen   (b) Two covalent bonds
   (c) V-shape   (d) Dipole moment

66. Hydrogen directly combines with ......
   (a) Au   (b) Cu   (c) Ni   (d) Ca

67. When same amount of zinc is treated separately with excess of sulphuric acid and excess of sodium hydroxide solution, the ratio of volumes of hydrogen evolved is ......
   (a) $1:1$ (b) $1:2$ (c) $2:1$ (d) $9:4$

68. If an isotope of hydrogen has two neutrons in its atom, its atomic number and mass number will respectively be ......
   (a) 2 and 1   (b) 3 and 1   (c) 1 and 1   (d) 1 and 3

69. Which is the lightest gas ?

(a) Nitrogen   (b) Helium   (c) Oxygen   (d) Hydrogen

70. Which of the following on oxidation gives H_2O_2 ?

(a) 2-Ethyl anthraquinol   (b) 2-Ethyl anthraquinone

(c) Anthracene   (d) 2-Ethyl anthracene

71. Hydrogen behaves as an oxidising agent in its reaction with ......

(a) Chlorine   (b) Nitrogen   (c) Sodium   (d) Sulphur

72. Water is said to be permanently hard when it contains ......

(a) Sulphates of Mg and Ca   (b) Bicarbonates of Mg and Ca

(c) Sulphates of Cu and Hg

73. The composition of tritium is ......

(a) 1 electron, 1 proton, 1 neutron   (b) 1 electron, 2 proton, 1 neutron

(c) 1 electron, 1 proton, 2 neutron   (d) 1 electron, 1 proton, 3 neutron

74. Which one of the following substances is used in the laboratory for a fast drying of neutral gases ?

(a) Active charcoal   (b) Anhydrous calcium chloride

(c) Anhydrus calcium chloride   (d) Na_3PO_4

75. Sodium sulphate is soluble in water but barium sulphate is insoluble because ......

(a) The hydration energy of Na_2SO_4 is more than its lattice energy

(b) The lattice energy of $BaSO_4$ is more than its hydration energy

(c) The lattice energy has no role to play in solubility

(d) The hydration energy of Na_2SO_4 is less than its lattice energy

(e) Both (a) and (b)

76. In absence of hydrogen bonding, boiling point of water would have been ......

(a) 100°C   (b) 0°C   (c) – 100°C   (d) 373°C

77. Temporary hardness and permanent hardness in water can be removed respectively by the oxidation of ......

(a) $CaO, CaCO_3$ (b) CaO, Na_2CO_3 (c) Na_2CO_3, CaO (d) $NaHCO_3, CaCl_2$

78. Which of the following are oxidized by water ? Which are reduced by water ? Which undergoes a disproportionation reaction when treated with water ?

(a) Cl_2 (b) F_2 (c) K   (d) Br_2

79. Hydride ion is a ......

(a) Strong conjugate acid of H_2 (b) Strong conjugate base of H_2

(c) Strong conjugate acid of H^+ (d) Strong conjugate acid of H^-

80. Fuel used for rocket propulsion is a mixture of ......

(a) Hydrazine and hydrogen peroxide   (b) Hydrazine and TNT

(c) Hydroxyl amine and TNT   (d) Hydroxyl amine and hydrogen peroxide

81. H_2, D_2 and T_2 do not differ in ......

(a) Freezing point   (b) Boiling point   (c) Critical temperature (d) Bond energy

82. Steam is passed over hot carbon and the gaseous products cooled and passed first through a solution of alkali, then through ammonical cuprous chloride and then through water. What is finally collected ?

(a) CO_2 (b) A mixture of hydrocarbons

(c) $CO + H_2$ (d) H_2

83. Which one of the following processes will produce hard water ?

(a) Saturation of water with $CaCO_3$ (b) Saturation of water with $MgCO_3$

(c) Saturation of water with $CaSO_4$ (d) Addition of Na_2SO_4 to water

84. Calgon used as water softner is ......

(a) $Na_2[Na_4(PO_3)_6]$ (b) $Na_4[Na_2(PO_3)_6]$ (c) $Na_2[Na_4(PO_4)_5]$ (d) None of these

85. Abundance of H_2 in the earth's atmosphere is very small. This is because ......

(a) The earth's gravitational field is too small to hold so light an element

(b) H_2 exists in ortho and para form

(c) H_2 is a diatomic gas

(d) H_2 is not a metal

86. Which among the following is a hydride ?

(a) Rongalite   (b) Nitrolim   (c) Hydrolith   (d) Minium

87. Select the correct statement(s) about lime light.

(a) Oxy-hydrogen flame

(b) Used in welding

(c) Temperature of limelight is sufficient to melt even platinum

(d) All of the above are correct.

88. Which is a source of nascent hydrogen ?

I : Zn + dil HCl   II : $CH_3OH + Na$

III : Electrolysis of H_2O

IV : Silent electric discharge

(a) I, II   (b) II, III   (c) I, II, III, IV   (d) IV

89. H_2 gas is liberated at cathode and anode both by electrolysis of the following aqueous solution except in ......

(a) NaH   (b) HCOONa   (c) NaCl   (d) LiH

90. Spin isomerism is shown by ......

(a) Dichloro benzene   (b) Hydrogen   (c) Dibasic acid   (d) n-butane

91. SiH_4 is an example of which of the following type of hydrides ?

(a) Ionic   (b) Interstitial   (c) Metallic   (d) Covalent

92. Select the correct statements ......

(a) Hydride ion is larger than any of the halide ions except iodide

(b) Hydride ions are reducing agents

(c) Boranes are electron deficient hydrides

(d) All of the above are correct statements

93. Metallic hydrides ....

(a) Are also called interstitial hydrides

(b) Are non-stoichiometric being deficient in hydrogen

(c) Are poor conductors of electricity, exhibit less paramagnetism

(d) Have all the above properties

94. Which statements is/are correct ?

(a) Boiling point of H_2O, NH_3, HF are maximum in their respective group due to intermolecular hydrogen bonding.

(b) Boiling point of CH_4, out of CH_4, SiH_4, GeH_4 and SnH_4 is least due to lack of hydrogen bonding.

(c) Formic acid forms dimer by hydrogen bonding.

(d) All the above statements are correct.

95. Bond angles H–O–H and H–O–O– in water and hydrogen peroxide respectively are ......

(a) $104.5°$ and $104.5°$ (b) $94.8°$ and $94.8°$ (c) $104.5°$ and $94.8°$ (d) $94.8°$ and $104.5°$

96. H_2 reacts much faster with Cl_2 than D_2, because ......

(a) Rate of diffusion of H_2 is greater than D_2

(b) H_2 has lower energy of activation than D_2

(c) Both statements are correct

(d) Both statements are incorrect.

97. On burning hydrogen in air, the colour of flame is ....

(a) Green   (b) Light bluish   (c) Yellow   (d) None of these

98. Assertion (A) : NaCl is less soluble in heavy water than in ordinary water.

Reason (R) : Dielectric constant of ordinary water is more than that of heavy water.

The correct answer is

(a) Both (A) and (R) are true and (R) is the correct explanation of (A)

(b) Both (A) and (R) are true but (R) is not the correct explanation of (A)

(c) (A) is true, but (R) is not true

(d) (R) is true, but (A) is not true

99. The decomposition of hydrogen peroxide can be slowed by the addition of acetamide. The latter acts as a ......

(a) Detainer   (b) Stopper   (c) Promoter   (d) Inhibitor

100. The hardness of water sample containing 0.002 mole of magnesium sulphate dissolved in a litre of water is expressed as ......

(a) 20 ppm   (b) 200 ppm   (c) 120 ppm   (d) 240 ppm

101. H^- is a ......

    (a) Lewis base   (b) Lowry-Bronsted base

    (c) Both (a) and (b)   (d) None of these

102. Consider the following statements :

    I : Rate of transfer of D^+ from D_2O is slower than that of H^- from H_2O

    II : K_a for $CH_3COOH \rightleftharpoons CH_3COO^- + H^+$ is smaller than that of K_a for $CH_3COOD \rightleftharpoons CH_3OO^\ominus + D^+$

    III: Tritium is a radioactive isotope.

    Select the correct statements.

    (a) I, II   (b) II, III   (c) I, III   (d) I, II, III

103. The hydride ion H^- is stronger base than its hydroxide ion (OH^-). Which of the following reactions will occur if sodium hydride (NaH) is dissolved in water?

    (a) $2H^+_{(aq)} \longrightarrow H_2 + 2e^-$ (b) $H^+_{(aq)} + H_2O_{(l)} \longrightarrow OH^- + H_2$

    (c) $H^- + H_2O_{(l)} \longrightarrow$ No reaction   (d) None of these

104. Zn gives H_2 gas with H_2SO_4 and HCl but not with HNO_3 because ......

    (a) Zn acts as an oxidizing agent, when react with HNO_3

    (b) HNO_3 is a weaker acid than H_2SO_4 and HCl

    (c) In electrochemical series, Zn is above hydrogen

    (d) NO_3^- is reduced in preference to hydronium ion

105. Dilute H_2SO_4 and oxide react to produce hydrogen peroxide. The oxide is ......

    (a) MnO_2 (b) PbO_2 (c) TiO_2 (d) Na_2O_2

106. Mass of one atom is 6.66×10^{-23} gms. Its percentage in an hydride is 95.24. Thus hydride is ......

    (a) MH   (b) MH_2 (c) MH_3 (d) MH_4

107. Which is true about the different forms of hydrogen?

    (a) Ortho hydrogen has some spins of two nuclei clockwise and anticlockwise

    (b) Para hydrogen has different spins of two nuclei

    (c) At absolute zero there is 100% para form and at high temperature, there is 75% ortho form.

    (d) All of the above are correct.

108. Which of the following pairs of substances would give some gaseous product on reaction with water ?

    (a) Na and Na_2O_2 (b) Ca and CaH_2 (c) Ca and CaO   (d) Ba and BaO_2

109. H_2O_2 used in rocket has the concentration ......

    (a) 50%   (b) 70%   (c) 30%   (d) 90%

110. H, D and T (isotopes and hydrogen) have nuclear spin quantum number respectively as ...

    (a) $\frac{1}{2}, 1, \frac{1}{2}$ (b) $\frac{1}{2}, \frac{1}{2}, 1$ (c) $\frac{1}{2}, 1, \frac{3}{2}$ (d) $\frac{1}{2}, \frac{1}{2}, \frac{1}{2}$

111. There are three isotopes of hydrogen and three naturally occurring isotopes of oxygen (^{16}O, ^{17}O and ^{18}O). How many kinds of water are possible ?

    (a) 18　　　　　(b) 16　　　　　(c) 8　　　　　(d) 4

112. H_2O_2 can also be obtained by the partial oxidation of 2-propanol.

$$(CH_3)_2CHOH + O_2 \longrightarrow (CH_3)_2CO + H_2O_2$$

Intermediate in this reaction is,

(a) $(CH_3)_2C\underset{\displaystyle OH}{\overset{\displaystyle OH}{<}}$ 　　　　　(b) $(CH_3)_3C^{\oplus}$

(c) $(CH_3)_2C\underset{\displaystyle O\text{–}O\text{–}H}{\overset{\displaystyle OH}{<}}$ 　　　　　(d) None of these

113. Water gas is a mixture of ......

    (a) $CO + H_2O$　　　(b) $CO + N_2$　　　(c) $CO + H_2O$　　　(d) $CO + CH_4$

114. Hydrogen gas is not liberated when the following metal is added to dil HCl.

    (a) Ag　　　　　(b) Zn　　　　　(c) Mg　　　　　(d) Sn

115. The salt responsible for permanent hardness of H_2O is ......

    (a) Na_2SO_4　　　(b) $MgHCO_3$　　　(c) $NaCl$　　　(d) $MgCl_2$

116. In the following compounds, H is covalently bonded in case of ......

    (a) BaH_2　　　(b) CaH_2　　　(c) SiH_4　　　(d) NaH

117. The acid that is not suitable for preparation of hydrogen by the action of metals is ......

    (a) HCl　　　(b) CH_3COOH　　　(c) HNO_3　　　(d) H_2SO_4

118. Which is true statement about D_2O and H_2O ?

    (a) D_2O has lower dielectric constant than H_2O

    (b) NaCl is more soluble in D_2O than in H_2O

    (c) Both (a) and (b) are correct.

    (d) None of the above are correct.

119. Hydrogen gas can be fused to form helium at ......

    (a) High temperature and high pressure　　　(b) High temperature and low pressure

    (c) Low temperature and high pressure　　　(d) Low temperature and low pressure

120. Hydrogen gas is produced by the reaction ......

    (a) $Na_2O_2 + 2HCl$　　　(b) $Mg + H_2O$　　　(c) $BaO_2 + HCl$　　　(d) $H_2S_4O_8 + H_2O$

121. H_2 can be obtained from ......

    (a) Water gas ($CO + H_2$) by liquefication of CO at low temperature under pressure

    (b) Water gas by oxidation of CO into CO_2 (by steam) which can be easily removed by dissolving in H_2O

    (c) Electrolysis of water

    (d) All of the above methods.

122. Which is true statement about H_2O ?

    (a) Hardness can be removed by passing through ion exchange resin.

    (b) Its presence can be detected by anhydrous $CuSO_4$.

    (c) It is amphiprotic.

    (d) All the above are correct.

123. Polyphosphates are used as water softening agents because they ......

    (a) Form soluble complexes with anionic species

    (b) Precipitate anionic species

    (c) Forms soluble complexes with cationic species

    (d) Precipitate cationic species

124. Consider the following statements :

    I.   Atomic hydrogen is obtained by passing hydrogen through an electric arc.

    II.   Hydrogen gas will not reduce heated aluminium oxide.

    III.   Finely divided palladium absorbs large volume of hydrogen gas.

    IV.   Pure nascent hydrogen is best obtained by reacting Na with C_2H_2OH.

    Which of the above statements is/are correct ?

    (a) I alone   (b) II alone   (c) I, II and III   (d) II, III and IV

125. A metal which does not liberate $H_2(g)$ from acids is ......

    (a) Cu   (b) Fe   (c) Mn   (d) Zn

126. Match list I with list II and select the correct answer using the codes given below the lists

Sr. No.	List I		List II
1.	Heavy water	(a)	Bicarbonates of Mg and Ca in water
2.	Temporary hard water	(b)	No foreign ions in water
3.	Soft water	(c)	D_2O
4.	Permanent hard water	(d)	Sulphates and chlorides of Mg and Ca in water

    (a) 1-c, 2-d, 3-b, 4-a   (b) 1-b, 2-a, 3-c, 4-d

    (c) 1-b, 2-d, 3-c, 4-a   (d) 1-c, 2-a, 3-b, 4-d

PREVIOUS YEAR'S QUESTIONS

1.   (a) $H_2O_2 + O_3 \rightarrow H_2O + 2O_2$ **[AIPMT 2014]**

    (b) $H_2O_2 + Ag_2O \rightarrow 2Ag + H_2O + O_2$

    Role of hydrogen peroxide in the above reaction is respectively ......

    (a) Oxidizing in (a) and reducing in (b)   (b) Reducing in (a) and oxidizing in (b)

    (c) Reducing in (a) and (b)   (d) Oxidizing in (a) and (b)

2. Which of the following is electron-deficient ?   **[NEET 2013]**

(i) $(SiH_3)_2$ (b) $(H_3)_2$ (c) PH_3 (d) $(CH_3)_2$

3. The degree of hardness of water is usually expressed in ......   **[DUMET 2011]**

(a) ppm by weight of $MgSO_4$

(b) g/L of $CaCO_3$ and $MgSO_4$ present

(c) ppm by weight of $CaCO_3$ irrespective of whether it is actually present.

(d) ppm of $CaCO_3$ actually present in water.

4. Ortho-and para-hydrogens have ......   **[WB JEET 2010]**

(a) identical chemical properties but different physical properties.

(b) identical physical and chemical properties.

(c) identical physical properties but different chemical properties.

(d) different physical and chemical properties

5. Which of the following statements is correct ?   **[CPMT 2009]**

(a) Zeolites have more closed structure then feldspar

(b) $H_4As_2O_7$ is an ortho acid.

(c) pseudo-alum does not have Na^+ and K^+

(d) superphosphate of lime is $4Ca(H_2PO_4)_2$

6. How many 'mL' of perhydrol is required to produce sufficient oxygen which can be used to completely convert 2L of SO_2 gas to SO_3 gas ?   **[EAMCET 2009]**

(a) 10 mL   (b) 5 mL   (c) 20 mL   (d) 30 mL

7. Blackened oil painting can be restored into original form by the action of...**[WB JEET 2009]**

(a) chlorine   (b) BaO_2 (c) H_2Se (d) H_2O

8. Which of the following is not correct regarding the electrolytic preparation of H_2O_2 ?

[AIIMS 2008]

(a) lead is used as cathode   (b) 50% H_2SO_4 is used

(c) Hydrogen is liberated at anode   (d) Sulphuric acid undergoes oxidation.

9. Match the following.   **[CPMT 2008]**

	Column I		Column II
(A)	10 vol H_2O_2	1.	Perhydrol
(B)	20 vol H_2O_2	2.	5.358 N
(C)	30 vol H_2O_2	3.	1.785 M
(D)	100 vol H_2O_2	4.	3.03%

The correct match is ......

(a) A-4, B-3, C-2, D-1   (b) A-1, B-2, C-3, D-4

(c) A-1, B-3, C-2, D-4   (d) A-4, B-2, C-3, D-1

10. Which of the following statements is correct? **[Manipal 2008]**

Dielectric constant of H_2O_2 ......

(a) increases with dilution   (b) decreases with dilution

(c) is unaffected on dilution   (d) none of these

11. Hydrogen can be prepared by the action of dil H_2SO_4 on ...... **[AIIMS 2007]**

(a) copper   (b) iron   (c) lead   (d) mercury

12. Radioactive isotope of hydrogen is ...... **[RPMT 2007]**

(a) uranium   (b) deuterium   (c) tritium   (d) none of these

13. When CO_2 is bubbled through a solution of barium peroxide in water, **[AFMC 2005]**

(a) O_2 is released   (b) carbonic acid is formed

(c) H_2O_2 is formed   (d) no reaction occurs

14. Hydrogen peroxide when added to a solution of potassium permanganate acidified with sulphuric acid ...... **[JCECE 2005]**

(a) forms water only   (b) acts as an oxidizing acid

(c) acts as a reducing agent   (d) reduces sulphuric acid

15. Water is oxidized to oxygen by ...... **[JCECE 2005]**

(a) ClO_2 (b) $KMnO_4$ (c) H_2O_2 (d) fluorine

16. On burning hydrogen in air, the colour of flame is ...... **[AFMC 2003]**

(a) green   (b) light bluish   (c) yellow   (d) none of these

17. Assertion increasing pressure on pure water decreases its freezing point. Reason density of water is maximum at 44°C. **[AIIMS 2003]**

(a) Both Assertion and Reason are true and Reason is the correct explanation of Assertion

(b) Both Assertion and Reason are true but Reason is not correct explanation of Assertion

(c) Assertion is true but Reason is false

(d) Both Assertion and Reason are false

18. What is the volume of "20 volume H_2O_2" required to get 5000 cm^3 of oxygen at STP? **[KCET 2003]**

(a) 250 cm^3 (b) 50 cm^3 (c) 100 cm^3 (d) 125 cm^3

19. The H-O-H angle in water molecule is about ...... **[A.F.M.C. 2001]**

(a) 10° and 35'   (b) 180°   (c) 102°   (d) 105°

20. One mole of magnesium nitride on reaction with excess of water gives ...... **[A.I.E.E.E. 2004]**

(a) One mole of ammonia   (b) One mole of nitric acid

(c) Two moles of ammonia   (d) Two moles of nitric acid.

21. Which of the following is not correct regarding electrolytic preparation of H_2O_2 ? **[E.A.M.C.E.T. Med. 2005]**

(a) Lead is used as cathode   (b) 50% H_2SO_4 is used

(c) Hydrogen is liberated at anode   (d) Sulphuric acid undergoes oxidation

22. Which one of the following reactions does not form gaseous product ? **[E.A.M.C.E.T. Engg. 2005]**

(a) $PbO_2 + H_2O_2$ (b) Acidified $KMnO_4 + H_2O_2$

(c) $PbS + H_2O_2$ (d) $Cl_2 + H_2O_2$

23. The percentage by weight of hydrogen in H_2O is ......   **[A.I.I.M.S. 2001]**
(a) 5.88   (b) 6.25   (c) 25   (d) 50

24. When two ice cubes are passed over each other, they unite to form one cube. Which of the following forces is responsible to hold them together ?   **[A.F.M.C. 2001]**
(a) Hydrogen bond formation   (b) van der Waals forces
(c) Covalent attraction   (d) Ionic interaction

25. The metal that cannot displace hydrogen from dil. HCl is ......   **[Kerala C.E.T. 2001]**
(a) Al   (b) Fe   (c) Cu   (d) Zn
(e) Mg

26. In which of the following reactions, H_2O_2 acts as a reducing agent ?   **[E.A.M.C.E.T. 2001]**
(a) $PbO_{2(s)} + H_2O_{2(aq)} \rightarrow PbO_{(s)} + H_2O_{(l)} + O_{2(g)}$
(b) $Na_2SO_{3(aq)} + H_2O_{2(aq)} \rightarrow Na_2SO_{4(aq)} + H_2O_{(l)}$
(c) $2KI_{(aq)} + H_2O_{2(aq)} \rightarrow 2KOH_{(aq)} + I_{2(s)}$
(d) $KNO_{2(aq)} + H_2O_{2(aq)} \rightarrow KNO_{3(aq)} + H_2O_{(l)}$

27. Which of the following acts as both reducing and oxidizing agents ?   **[C.P.M.T. 2001]**
(a) H_2SO_4 (b) H_2O_2 (c) KOH (d) $KMnO_4$

28. What is formed when calcium carbide reacts with heavy water ?   **[NEET 2003]**
(a) C_2D_2 (b) CaD_2 (c) Ca_2D_2O (d) CD_2

29. Action of water or dilute mineral acids on metals can give ......
(a) Monohydrogen   (b) Tritium   (c) Dihydrogen   (d) Trihydrogen

30. Which of the following is correct about heavy water ?
(a) Water at 40°C having maximum density is known as heavy water
(b) It is heavier than water (H_2O)
(c) It is formed by the combination of heavier isotope of hydrogen and oxygen
(d) None of these

31. The reagent commonly used to determine hardness of water titrimetrically is ......
          [A.I.I.M.S. 2003]
(a) Oxalic acid   (b) Sodium thiosulphate
(c) Disodium salt of EDTA   (d) Sodium citrate

32. Which one of the following statements about the zeolite is false ?
(a) They are used as cation exchangers
(b) They have open structure which enables them to take up small molecules
(c) Zeolites are aluminosilicates having three dimensional network
(d) None of the SiO_4^{4-} units are replaced by AlO_4^{5-} and AlO_6^{9-} ions in zeolites

33. By which of the following process permanent hardness of water can be removed ?
          [A.F.M.C. 2005]
(a) Soda lime   (b) Sodium bicarbonate
(c) Washing soda   (d) Sodium chloride

34. A commercial sample of hydrogen peroxide is labelled as 10 volume. Its percentage strength is nearly ......   **[Karnataka C.E.T. 2005]**
(a) 3%   (b) 1%   (c) 90%   (d) 10%

ANSWER KEY

1. (a)	2. (a)	3. (a)	4. (c)	5. (c)	6. (c)	7. (c)	8. (c)
9. (a)	10. (c)	11. (a)	12. (c)	13. (d)	14. (c)	15. (a)	16. (a)
17. (a)	18. (c)	19. (a)	20. (d)	21. (b)	22. (a)	23. (a)	24. (b)
25. (a)	26. (c)	27. (a)	28. (c)	29. (c)	30. (a)	31. (a)	32. (c)
33. (b)	34. (e)	35. (b)	36. (c)	37. (c)	38. (b)	39. (c)	40. (b)
41. (c)	42. (b)	43. (c)	44. (a)	45. (d)	46. (c)	47. (a)	48. (b)
49. (a)	50. (a)	51. (d)	52. (b)	53. (c)	54. (b)	55. (b)	56. (d)
57. (a)	58. (c)	59. (a)	60. (b)	61. (d)	62. (d)	63. (d)	64. (b)
65. (d)	66. (d)	67. (a)	68. (d)	69. (d)	70. (a)	71. (c)	72. (a)
73. (c)	74. (a)	75. (a)	76. (c)	77. (b)	78. (a)	79. (b)	80. (c)
81. (d)	82. (d)	83. (c)	84. (a)	85. (a)	86. (c)	87. (d)	88. (a)
89. (c)	90. (b)	91. (d)	92. (d)	93. (d)	94. (d)	95. (c)	96. (b)
97. (b)	98. (a)	99. (d)	100. (b)	101. (c)	102. (d)	103. (b)	104. (d)
105. (d)	106. (b)	107. (d)	108. (b)	109. (d)	110. (a)	111. (a)	112. (c)
113. (c)	114. (a)	115. (d)	116. (c)	117. (c)	118. (a)	119. (a)	120. (b)
121. (d)	122. (d)	123. (c)	124. (d)	125. (a)	126. (d)		

Previous Year's Questions

1. (c)	2. (b)	3. (c)	4. (a)	5. (c)	6. (a)	7. (c)	8. (c)
9. (a)	10. (a)	11. (b)	12. (c)	13. (c)	14. (c)	15. (d)	16. (b)
17. (b)	18. (a)	19. (d)	20. (a)	21. (a)	22. (a)	23. (a)	24. (a)
25. (c)	26. (b)	27. (b)	28. (a)	29. (c)	30. (c)	31. (c)	32. (d)
33. (a)	34. (d)						

❑❑❑

s-BLOCK ELEMENTS

1. In the modern periodic table, s-block elements are placed in which of the groups ?

   (a) IA and IIA   (b) IA and IVA   (c) IIIA and IA   (d) VI and VII

2. Elements of group IA except hydrogen are called as ......

   (a) Transition elements (b) Alkali metals   (c) Carbides   (d) Hydrocarbons

3. Elements of Group IIA are called as ......

   (a) Transition elements   (b) Alkali metals

   (c) Carbides   (d) Alkaline earth metals

4. In nature alkali metal occurs in ......

   (a) Alumino silicates   (b) Combined form   (c) Free state   (d) Magnesium

5. Most of the earth crust is composed of ......

   (a) Magnesium   (b) Reducing

   (c) Alumino silicates   (d) Sodium

6. The most abundant mineral of sodium is ......

   (a) Lithium nitride   (b) Rock salt (Halite) (c) Mg_3N_2 (d) Magnesium

7. Two important minerals of magnesium are ......

   (a) Magnesite and Dolomite   (b) Carbide

   (c) Gibsite   (d) Boracite

8. Lithium shows anomalous behaviour because of its ......

   (a) Least radius   (b) Higher radius   (c) Small radius   (d) Normal radius

9. Lithium on burning in air forms ......

   (a) Higher oxides   (b) Smaller oxides   (c) Normal oxides (d) Least oxides

10. Lithium reacts with nitrogen to form ......

    (a) Perchlorate   (b) Carbides   (c) Nitrate   (d) Lithium nitride

11. Alkali metals except lithium do not form .... when they react with carbon.

    (a) Carbides   (b) Super oxides   (c) Magnesium   (d) Reducing

12. An alkali metals are powerful ......

    (a) Reducing agents   (b) Oxidising agents (c) Catalysts   (d) Metallic agents

13. Melting point and boiling point of beryllium are ......

    (a) Same as alkaline earth metals   (b) Smaller than alkaline earth metals

    (c) Lower than alkaline earth metals   (d) Higher than alkaline earth metals

14. $Be + 2NaOH \rightarrow Na_2BeO_2 + ?$

    (a) H_3 (b) H_2 (c) H_1 (d) H_5

15. Potassium, rubidium and cesium react with oxygen to form ......

    (a) H^- (Hydride ion)   (b) Nitrates   (c) Super oxides   (d) Alkanes

16. Ionic hydrides of alkali metals are used as powerful reducing agent, because of the presence of ......

    (a) I^-　　　　　(b) H^- (Hydride ion)　(c) K^+　　　　　(d) Na

17. Beryllium is ......

    (a) Higher reactive metal in group IIA　　　(b) Least reactive metal in group IIA

    (c) Normal reactive metal in group IIA　　　(d) H_2 reactive metal in group IIA

18. On reaction with water, magnesium liberates ......

    (a) Water gas　　(b) Magnesite　　(c) Oxygen　　(d) Hydrogen gas

19. $3Mg + N_2 \rightarrow$?

    (a) Mg_3N_2　　(b) $(CaSO_4)_2 \cdot H_2O$　(c) NH_3　　(d) H_2

20. $Mg_3N_2 + 6H_2O \rightarrow 2\ ? + 3Mg(OH)_2$

    (a) N　　　　(b) H_2　　　　(c) NH_3　　　　(d) NO_3

21. The reaction of KO_2 and CO_2 can be written as ......

    (a) $CO_2 + 2KO_2 \rightarrow 2K_2CO_3$　　　　(b) $KO_2 + 3CO_2 \rightarrow 2K_2CO_3 + O_2$

    (c) $3KO_2 + CO_2 \rightarrow 3K_2CO_3 + O_2$　　(d) $4KO_{2(s)} + 2CO_{2(g)} \rightarrow 2K_2CO_3 + 3O_{2(g)}$

22. What is the chemical formula for Plaster of Paris ?

    (a) $CaSO_4 \cdot \frac{1}{2} H_2O$　　(b) $K_2Cr_2O_7 \cdot H_2O$　　(c) $Mg_2SO_4 \cdot H_2O$　　(d) $BaSO_4 \cdot H_2O$

23. The reaction of an alkali metal oxide is ......

    (a) An acid-base reaction　　　　(b) Displacement reaction

    (c) Hydrogenation reaction　　　　(d) An oxidation-reduction reaction

24. The allkali metal whose carbonate is relatively less stable and decomposes giving its oxide is ......

    (a) Lithium　　(b) Francium　　(c) Sodium　　(d) Potassium

25. This alkali chloride shows exothermic heat of solution ......

    (a) Lithium chloride　　　　(b) Potassium chloride

    (c) Sodium chloride　　　　(d) None of these

26. This is the only alkaline earth metal, which reacts with alkalies releasing hydrogen

    (a) Beryllium　　(b) Calcium　　(c) Barium　　(d) Strontium

27. Beryllium oxide is ......

    (a) Acidic in nature　　　　(b) Basic in nature

    (c) Neither of these　　　　(d) Amphoteric in nature

28. In Nelson's cell method for the preparation of NaOH, at cathode ......

    (a) Sodium reduces　　　　(b) Chlorine oxidizes

    (c) H_2O reduces　　　　(d) None of these reactions occur

29. The only alkaline earth metal which on reaction with oxygen at 500 to 600°C forms peroxide is ......

    (a) Iron　　(b) Magnesium　　(c) Barium　　(d) Calcium

30. Which alkali metal explodes, spontaneously when it comes in contact with air or oxygen ?

(a) Sodium　　　　　(b) Lithium　　　　　(c) Cesium　　　　　(d) Potassium

31. In Nelson's cell method for the preparation of NaOH, Cl_2 produced during the process may react with hydroxide ions in cold giving ......

(a) Perchlorate ion　　　(b) Hypochlorite　　　(c) Chlorate ion　　　(d) None of these

32. Radium is a ......

(a) A rare radioactive metal　　　　　(b) Unstable

(c) $CaSO_4 \cdot H_2O$　　　　　(d) $CaSO_4 \cdot 2H_2O$

33. Sodium metal is used in ......

(a) Ceramic industry　　　　　(b) Acetylene preparation

(c) Down's cell method　　　　　(d) Fertilizer industry

34. Sodium hydroxide is a ......

(a) Down's cell method　　　　　(b) Nelson's method

(c) Hall's process　　　　　(d) Acetylene preparation

35. Lime is useful in ......

(a) Fertilizer industry　　　　　(b) Ceramic industry

(c) Acetylene preparation　　　　　(d) Down's cell method

36. Gypsum is an important material used in ......

(a) Hall's process　　　　　(b) Fertilizer industry

(c) Ceramic industry　　　　　(d) Nelson's method

37. Calcium carbide is used in ......

(a) Nelson's method　　　　　(b) Down's cell method

(c) Acetylene preparation　　　　　(d) Hall's process

38. Rock salt is a mineral of ......

(a) Magnesium　　　(b) Calcium　　　(c) Sodium　　　(d) None of these

39. Oxidation state of ionic compounds formed by s-block element is ......

(a) +1　　　　　(b) −1　　　　　(c) +2　　　　　(d) −2

40. Stable complex compounds are formed by ......

(a) Lithium　　　(b) Calcium　　　(c) Magnesium　　　(d) Sodium

41. Mineral of magnesium is ......

(a) Gypsum　　　(b) Borax　　　(c) Magnetite　　　(d) None of these

42. The elements of IIA group are called ......

(a) Metalloids　　　　　(b) Non-metals

(c) Alkaline earth metals　　　　　(d) Alkali metals

43. Lithium produces _____ when burnt in air.

(a) Methyl oxides　　　(b) Peroxides　　　(c) Super oxides　　　(d) Normal oxides

44. Mineral of barium is ......

(a) Asbestos　　　(b) Barite　　　(c) Dolomite　　　(d) Borax

45. Artificially prepared metal is ......

(a) Calcium　　(b) Barium　　(c) Francium　　(d) Rubidium

46. Lithium has the following characteristics ......

(a) Complex compound　　(b) Covalently bonded

(c) Much harder　　(d) All of these

47. The elements of IA and IIA groups are ......

(a) Less reactive　　(b) Most reactive　　(c) Rare metals　　(d) Inert metals

48. Which compound provides exothermic heat ?

(a) $MgCl$　　(b) KCl　　(c) $NaCl$　　(d) $LiCl$

49. This metal does not react vigorously with halogens to form halides ......

(a) Cesium　　(b) Calcium　　(c) Rubidium　　(d) Potassium

50. Sodium beryllate is formed by the reaction of beryllium and ......

(a) $NaOH$　　(b) Na　　(c) $NaCl$　　(d) $NaBr$

51. On hydrolysis sodium gives an ......

(a) Exothermic reaction　　(b) Endothermic reaction

(c) Redox reaction　　(d) None of these

52. The exceptional trend in boiling and melting points from its group is of ......

(a) Boron　　(b) Nitrogen　　(c) Beryllium　　(d) Calcium

53. Alkali metals are ......

(a) Highly electropositive　　(b) Highly electronegative

(c) Highly ionizable　　(d) Higher reducing agents

54. Potassium and rubidium forms ......

(a) Peroxides　　(b) Normal oxides　　(c) Oxy oxides　　(d) Super oxides

55. Ionic hydrides are used as

(a) Reducing agents　　(b) Hygroscopic agents

(c) None of these　　(d) Oxidizing agents

56. The only alkali formed by direct reaction is ......

(a) Barium carbide　　(b) Sodium carbide　　(c) Lithium carbide　　(d) Calcium carbide

57. The solubility of alkaline earth metals ......

(a) Increases down the group　　(b) Decreases across the period

(c) Remains the same　　(d) Decreases down the group

58. The basic character of alkali metals ......

(a) Decreases down the group　　(b) First increases and then decreases

(c) Increases down the group　　(d) Remains the same

59. The only alkaline earth metal which forms peroxide is ......

(a) Barium　　(b) Magnesium　　(c) Calcium　　(d) None of these

60. The metal that does not react with water even at red-hot temperature is ......

    (a) Barium   (b) Calcium   (c) Beryllium   (d) Magnesium

61. Another name of magnesium metal solution is ......

    (a) None of these   (b) Milk of magnesia   (c) Lime water   (d) Soda water

62. Sodium carbonate is .... in nature.

    (a) Acidic   (b) Amphoteric   (c) All of these   (d) Basic

63. On dissolution in water, alkali metals form ......

    (a) Strong acidic solution   (b) To give neutralization reactions

    (c) Strong alkaline solution   (d) All of these

64. The increase in solubility of alkaline earth metals is due to ......

    (a) High lattice energy   (b) High electron affinity

    (c) Low lattice energy   (d) Low ionization energy

65. Setting of cement is an ......

    (a) Exothermic reaction   (b) Endothermic reaction

    (c) Neither exothermic nor endothermic   (d) None of these

66. Setting of Plaster of Paris involves ......

    (a) Oxidation with atmospheric oxygen   (b) Combination with atmospheric CO_2

    (c) Pine oil   (d) Hydration to yield another hydrate

67. Calcium cyanamide on treatment with steam under pressure gives NH_3 and ......

    (a) Calcium carbonate   (b) Calcium hydroxide

    (c) Calcium oxide   (d) Calcium bicarbonate

68. Which of the following is commonly used as a laboratory desiccator?

    (a) Anhydrous Na_2CO_3 (b) Anhydrous $CaCl_2$

    (c) Dry NaCl   (d) None of these

69. Which of the following ion forms a hydroxide highly soluble in water?

    (a) Ni^{2+} (b) K^+ (c) Zn^{2+} (d) Al^{2+}

70. The wire in flash bulbs is made up of ......

    (a) Mg   (b) Ba   (c) Cu   (d) Ag

71. Dolomite has the composition ......

    (a) $KCl \cdot MgCl_2 \cdot 6H_2O$ (b) Na_3AlF_6

    (c) $CaCO_3 \cdot MgCO_3$ (d) $CaCl_2 \cdot MgCl_2 \cdot 6H_2O$

72. Plaster of Pairs hardens by ......

    (a) Giving off CO_2 (b) Changing into $CaCO_3$

    (c) Combining with water   (d) Giving out water

73. Which one of the following statements is correct for alkaline earth metals?

    (a) They are diatomic and form ions of the type M^+

    (b) They are monoatomic and form ions of the type M^{2+}

    (c) They are monoatomic and form ions of the type $2M^{2+}$

    (d) They are diatomic and form ions of the type M^{2+}

74. Which of the following is true for magnesium ?
    (a) It is more electropositive than sodium
    (b) It is manufactured by electrolysis of aqueous magnesium chloride.
    (c) It is a strong reducing agent
    (d) It resembles in chemical properties, with its diagonally placed element Boron in III group of the periodic table.

75. Which of the following on heating at 125°C gives Plaster of Paris?
    (a) Borax   (b) Gypsum   (c) Alum   (d) Calomel

76. Identify the correct statement.
    (a) Gypsum contains a lower percentage of calcium than Plaster of Paris
    (b) Gypsum is obtained by heating Plaster of Paris
    (c) Plaster of Paris can be obtained by hydration of gypsum
    (d) Plaster of Paris is obtained by partial oxidation of gypsum

77. Which of the following is super phosphate of lime?
    (a) $Ca_3(PO_4)_3$ (b) $CaHPO_4$
    (c) $Ca(PO_4)_2$ (d) $Ca(H_2PO_4)_2 + 2CaSO_4 \cdot 2H_2O$

78. Which of the following represents calcium chlorite?
    (a) $CaClO_2$ (b) $Ca(ClO_4)_2$ (c) $Ca(ClO_3)_2$ (d) $Ca(ClO_2)_2$

79. What is X in the following reaction?
    $MgCl_2 + H_2O \rightarrow X + 2HCl$
    (a) MgO (b) Mg (c) $Mg(OH)_2$ (d) $Mg(OH)Cl$

80. For two ionic solids CaO and KI, identify the wrong statement among the following?
    (a) Lattice energy of CaO is much higher than that of KI
    (b) KI is soluble in benzene
    (c) CaO has high m.p
    (d) KI has high m.p

81. One which is not dissolved by dilute hydrochloric acid is ......
    (a) ZnS (b) MnS (c) $BaCO_3$ (d) $BaSO_4$

82. The one which does not show variable valency is ......
    (a) Barium   (b) Titanium   (c) Copper   (d) Lead

83. Lithophone used as white pigment is a mixture of ......
    (a) $CaSO_4 + ZnS$ (b) $BaSO_4 + ZnS$ (c) $BaSO_4 + CaSO_4$ (d) $CaSO_4 + ZnS$

84. Metals belonging to the same group in the periodic table are ......
    (a) Magnesium and Sodium   (b) Magnesium and Copper
    (c) Magnesium and Barium   (d) Magnesium and Potassium

85. Which of the following is incorrect?
    (a) Mg burns in air releasing dazzling light rich in UV rays
    (b) $CaCl_2 \cdot 6H_2O$ when mixed with ice gives freezing mixture
    (c) Mg cannot form complexes
    (d) Be can form complexes due to its very small size

86. Which of the following substances is used for drying gases?
    (a) Calcium carbonate
    (b) Sodium carbonate
    (c) Sodium bicarbonate
    (d) Calcium oxide

87. Among the alkaline earth metals, the element forming predominantly covalent compound is ......
    (a) Barium
    (b) Strontium
    (c) Calcium
    (d) Beryllium

88. Plaster of Paris is used ......
    (a) As a plaster for walls
    (b) In dentistry and surgery
    (c) In metallurgical process
    (d) As a drying agent

89. Among alkali metal salts, the lithium salts are poorest conductors of electricity in aqueous solution because of ......
    (a) Easy diffusion of Li^+ ions
    (b) Lower ability of Li^+ ions to polarize the water molecules
    (c) Lowest charge to radius ratio
    (d) Higher degree of hydration of Li^+ ions

90. Which of the following sets can be called iso-electronic species?
    (a) Na^+, Mg^+
    (b) Na^+, Mg^{2+}
    (c) Na, Mg
    (d) Na, Mg^{++}

91. The correct sequence of alkali metals in the group is ......
    (a) Fr, Na, K, Rb, Cs, Li
    (b) Li, Na, K, Rb, Cs, Fr
    (c) Na, K, Rb, Cs, Fr, Li
    (d) Rb, Cs, Li, Na, K

92. Which of the following compounds is used in gun powder?
    (a) $NaNO_3$
    (b) KNO_3
    (c) $LiNO_3$
    (d) None of these

93. Microcosmic salt is ......
    (a) $Na(NH_4) HPO_4 \cdot 4H_2O$
    (b) $Na(NH_4) \cdot H_2O$
    (c) $Na(NH_3) HPO_4 \cdot 4H_2O$
    (d) $K(NH_4) HPO_3 \cdot 2H_2O$

94. Fusion mixture is ......
    (a) $K_2CO_3 + Na_2CO_3$
    (b) $KHSO_4 + NaHSO_4$
    (c) $K_2CO_3 + NaHSO_4$
    (d) $KHSO_4 + Na_2SO_3$

95. Which of the following has the highest melting point?
    (a) NaCl
    (b) NaF
    (c) NaBr
    (d) NaI

96. Baking soda is ......
    (a) $NaHCO_3$
    (b) $NaHOCO_3 \cdot 6H_2O$
    (c) Na_2CO_3
    (d) $Na_2CO_3 \cdot 10H_2O$

97. The halide which can be extracted with ether is
    (a) LiCl
    (b) NaCl
    (c) $MgCl_2$
    (d) KCl

98. Ammoniated solutions of alkali metals are .....
    (a) Reducing agents
    (b) Paramagnetic
    (c) Good conductor of electricity
    (d) All of these

99. Washing soda has the formula ......

(a) $Na_2CO_3 \cdot 10H_2O$ (b) $Na_2CO_3 \cdot 7H_2O$ (c) $Na_2CO_3 \cdot 5H_2O$ (d) Na_2CO_3

100. Baking powder is ......

(a) $NaHCO_3$ and citric acid (b) Na_2CO_3

(c) Mixture of $NaHCO_3$ and $Ca(H_2PO_4)_2$ (d) $Ca(HCO_3)_2$

101. Lithium perchlorate is ....

(a) A double salt (b) Desiccant (c) Air purifier (d) Medicine

102. Which is incorrect statement ?

(a) The heat of hydration of the dipositive alkaline earth metal ions decrease with an increasing ionic size.

(b) $NaNO_3$ forms Na_2O on heating.

(c) Hydration of alkali metal ion is less than that of IIA.

(d) Alkaline earth metals ions, because of their much larger charge to size ratio, exert a much stronger electrostatic attraction on the oxygen of water molecule surrounding them.

103. Match the following :

	A		B
(i)	Liquid sodium metal	(I)	Breathing apparatus submarine
(ii)	Potassium stearate	(II)	Explosive
(iii)	Potassium nitrate	(III)	Content in nuclear reaction
(iv)	Potassium superoxide	(IV)	Soft soap

(a) (i - I), (ii - III), (iii - II), (iv - IV) (b) (i - III), (ii - IV), (iii - II), (iv - I)

(c) (i - II), (ii - I), (iii - III), (iv - IV) (d) (i - IV), (ii - II), (iii - III), (iv - I)

104. Which is a pair of paramagnetic species ?

(a) KO_2, NO_2 (b) K_2O_2, KO_2 (c) K_2O, NO_2 (d) NO_2, N_2O_2

105. Which is the major constituent of gun powder ?

(a) Nitre (b) Sulphur (c) Charcoal (d) Chile saltpetre

106. Which is used to treat acid indigestion ?

(a) $Be(OH)_2$ (b) KOH (c) $Mg(OH)_2$ (d) $Ca(OH)_2$

107. Which does not exist in solid state ?

(a) $NaHCO_3$ (b) $NaHSO_3$ (c) $LiHCO_3$ (d) $CaCO_3$

108. Nitrate can be converted into metal oxide on heating in case of ......

(a) Li (b) Na (c) Both (a) and (b) (d) None of these

109. Following compounds are used in fire works ......

(a) $LiNO_3$ (b) $BaCl_2$ (c) $(NH_4)_2Cr_2O_7$ (d) All of these

110. Glauber's salt is ....

(a) $Na_2SO_4 \cdot 10H_2O$ (b) $Na_2SO_4 \cdot 7H_2O$ (c) Na_2SO_4 (d) $MgSO_4 \cdot 7H_2O$

111. The enamel of teeth is ....

(a) CaF_2

(b) $Ca_3(PO_4)_2$

(c) $3Ca_3(PO_4)_2 \cdot CaF_2$

(d) $CaSO_4$

112. Correct increasing order of solubility of sulphates of alkaline earth elements are ......

(a) $BeSO_4 < MgSO_4 < CaSO_4 < SrSO_4 < BaSO_4$

(b) $BeSO_4 > MgSO_4 > CaSO_4 > SrSO_4 > BaSO_4$

(c) $MgSO_4 > CaSO_4 > SrSO_4 > BeSO_4 > BaSO_4$

(d) $MgSO_4 > CaSO_4 > SrSO_4 > BeSO_4 > BaSO_4$

113. Arrange carbonates of group 2 elements in the decreasing order of thermal stability :

(a) $BeCO_3 < MgCO_3 < CaCO_3 < SrCO_3 < BaCO_3$

(b) $BeCO_3 > MgCO_3 > CaCO_3 > SrCO_3 > BaCO_3$

(c) $BaCO_3 > SrCO_3 > CaCO_3 > MgCO_3 > BeCO_3$

(d) $MgCO_3 < CaCO_3 < SrCO_3 < BaCO_3 < BeCO_3$

114. Solubility of carbonates of alkaline earth elements are ......

(a) $BeCO_3 < MgCO_3 < CaCO_3 < SrCO_3 < BaCO_3$

(b) $BeCO_3 > MgCO_3 > CaCO_3 > SrCO_3 > BaCO_3$

(c) $BaCO_3 > SrCO_3 > CaCO_3 > MgCO_3 > BeCO_3$

(d) $MgCO_3 < CaCO_3 < SrCO_3 < BaCO_3 < BeCO_3$

115. Basic nature of hydroxides group 2 elements are in increasing order ......

(a) $Be(OH)_2 > Mg(OH)_2 > Ca(OH)_2 > Sr(OH)_2 > Ba(OH)_2$

(b) $Be(OH)_2 < Mg(OH)_2 < Ca(OH)_2 < Sr(OH)_2 < Ba(OH)_2$

(c) $Ca(OH)_2 < Sr(OH)_2 < Mg(OH)_2 < Be(OH)_2 < Ba(OH)_2$

(d) $Ca(OH)_2 > Sr(OH)_2 > Mg(OH)_2 < Be(OH)_2 < Ba(OH)_2$

116. The decreasing order of melting points of halides of lithium are ......

(a) fluorides < chloride < bromide < iodide

(b) fluorides > chloride > bromide > iodide

(c) chloride < bromide < iodide < fluoride

(d) chloride < fluoride < bromide < iodide

117. The melting point of chlorides for different alkali metals follow the order :

(a) $LiCl > NaCl > KCl > RbCl > CsCl$

(b) $LiCl < NaCl > KCl > RbCl > CsCl$

(c) $LiCl < NaCl < KCl < RbCl < CsCl$

(d) $LiCl > NaCl < KCl > RbCl > CsCl$

118. Chile saltpeter had the chemical formula ......

(a) $NaNO_3$ (b) KNO_3 (c) $Na_2B_4O_7$ (d) $Na_2CO_3H_2O$

119. The carbonates and phosphates of which elements are insoluble in water ?

(a) Na and K   (b) Na and Be   (c) Li and Mg   (d) All of these

120. All alkaline earth metals react with water at room temperature to release hydrogen and give basic solutions except ......

(a) Be and Ca   (b) Be and Mg   (c) Ca and Mg   (d) Mg and Sr

121. Potassium super oxide (KO_2) is used in breathing equipments for mountaineers and space craft because it absorb ......

(a) Oxygen and giving out CO_2 at the same time

(b) N_2 and giving out CO_2 at the same time

(c) CO_2 and giving out O_2 at the same time

(d) Pollutants and giving out O_2 at the same time

122. Which of the following alkaline earth metal hydroxides is the strongest base?

(a) $Be(OH)_2$　　　(b) $Mg(OH)_2$　　　(c) $Ca(OH)_2$　　　(d) $Ba(OH)_2$

123. The ionic halides in order of decreasing m.p. and b.p. can be arranged as ......

(a) Iodide > bromide > chloride > fluoride　　(b) Bromide > chloride > fluoride > iodide

(c) Chloride > bromide > iodide > fluoride　　(d) Fluoride > chloride > bromide > iodide

124. Which one of the following orders presents the correct sequence of the increasing basic nature of the given oxides?

(a) $K_2O < Na_2O < Al_2O_3 < MgO$　　　　(b) $Al_2O_3 < MgO < Na_2O < K_2O$

(c) $MgO < K_2O < Al_2O_3 < Na_2O$　　　　(d) $MgO < K_2O < Na_2O < Al_2O_3$

125. The correct order of stability for the following super oxides is :

(a) $KO_2 > RbO_2 > CsO_2$　　　　(b) $RbO_2 > CsO_2 > KO_2$

(c) $CsO_2 > RbO_2 > KO_2$　　　　(d) $KO_2 > CsO_2 > RbO_2$

PREVIOUS YEAR'S QUESTIONS

1. $CaCl_2$ is used as a ......　　　　　　　　　　　　**[MHT CET 2005]**

(a) disinfectant　　　　　　　　(b) desiccating agent

(c) medicine　　　　　　　　　(d) none of these

2. The product obtained on fusion of $BaSO_4$ and Na_2CO_3 is ......　　**[MHT CET 2005]**

(a) $BaCO_3$　　　(b) BaO　　　(c) $Ba(OH)_2$　　　(d) $BaHSO_4$

3. Photoelectric effect is maximum in ......　　　　　　　**[AFMC 2004]**

(a) Cs　　　(b) Na　　　(c) K　　　(d) Li

4. The electrolyte used in Castner's process of sodium extraction is ......　　**[EAMCET 2004]**

(a) aqueous Na_2CO_3　　　　　　(b) aqueous $NaOH$

(c) $NaCl + CaCl_2$　　　　　　　(d) fused anhydrous $NaOH$

5. On dissolving moderate amount of sodium metal in liquid NH_3 at temperature, which one of the following does not occur?　　　　　　　　**[AIIMS 2003]**

(a) Blue coloured solution is obtained.

(b) Na^+ ions are formed in the solution.

(c) Liquid NH_3 becomes good conductor of electricity

(d) Liquid ammonia remains diamagnetic.

6.   **Assertion :** Barium is not required for normal biological function in human.   **[AIIMS 2003]**
     Reason : Barium does not show variable state.
     (a) Both Assertion and Reason are true and the correct explanation of Assertion.
     (b) Both Assertion and Reason are true but not the correct explanation of Assertion.
     (c) Assertion is true but Reason is false.
     (d) Both Assertion and Reason are false.

7.   The substance used in smoke screen is ......   **[Kerala CEE 2003]**
     (a) sodium chloride   (b) zinc phosphate   (c) calcium phosphide (d) calcium fluoride
     (e) calcium phosphate

8.   Solubility of alkaline earth metal sulphates in water decreases in the sequence ......
                                                                     [AIPMT 2015]
     (a) Ca > Sr > Ba > Mg   (b) Sr > Ca > Mg > Ba
     (c) Ba > Mg > Sr > Ca   (d) Mg > Ca > Sr > Ba

9.   The function of "Sodium pump' is a biological process operation in each and every cell of all
     animals. Which of the following biological important ions is also a constituent of this pump?
     (a) Mg^{2+} (b) K^+ (c) Fe^{2+} (d) Ca^{2+} **[AIPMT 2015]**

10. Lower melting point chloride is ......   **[JCECE 2006]**
     (a) LiCl   (b) NaCl   (c) KCl   (d) CsCl

11. When washing soda is heated ......   **[AFMC 2005]**
     (a) CO is released   (b) $CO + CO_2$ is released
     (c) CO_2 is released   (d) water vapour is released

12. In photography, sodium thiosulphate is used as a ......   **[DUMET 2005]**
     (a) complexing agent   (b) oxidizing agent   (c) reducing agent (d) none of these

13. The solubilities of carbonates decrease down the magnesium group due to decrease in ...
                                                                     [RPMT 2009]
     (a) lattic energies of solids   (b) hydration energies of cations
     (c) interionic attraction   (d) entropy of solution formation

14. Sodium hypohalite when dissolved in water will turn   **[DUMET 2007]**
     (a) blue litmus red   (b) red litmus blue   (c) red litmus green (d) no change

15. Lithopene is   **[RPMT 2007]**
     (a) $ZnSO_4 + PbS$ (b) $BaSO_4 + ZnS$ (c) PbO_2 (d) $ZnSO_4$

16. Aluminium reacts with caustic soda to form ......   **[AMU 2006]**
     (a) aluminium hydroxide   (b) aluminium oxide
     (c) sodium meta-aluminate   (d) sodium tetra-aluminate

17. Dead burnt plaster is ......   **[Kerala CEE 2006]**
     (a) $CaSO_4 \cdot 2H_2O$ (b) $MgSO_4 \cdot 7H_2O$ (c) $CaSO_4 \cdot \frac{1}{2} H_2O$ (d) $CaSO_4$

18. Excess of sodium hydroxide reacts with zinc to form ......   **[Manipal 2009]**
     (a) ZnH_2 (b) Na_2ZnO_2 (c) ZnO   (d) $Zn(OH)_2$

19. Among the following, the least thermally stable is ...... **[J & K CET 2009]**

    (a) K_2CO_3 (b) Na_2CO_3 (c) $BaCO_3$ (d) Li_2CO_3

20. Correct order of stability of group IIA metal carbonates is ...... **[OJEE 2009]**

    (a) $MgCO_3 > CaCO_3 > SrCO_3 > BaCO_3$ (b) $BaCO_3 > SrCO_3 > CaCO_3 > MgCO_3$

    (c) $SrCO_3 > BaCO_3 > CaCO_3 > MgCO_3$ (d) $CaCO_3 > MgCO_3 > BaCO_3 > SrCO_3$

21. Equimolar solution of the following were prepared in water separately. Which one of the solutions will record the highest pH? **[CBSE AIPMT 2009]**

    (a) $SrCl_2$ (b) $BaCl_2$ (c) $MgCl_2$ (c) $CaCl_2$

22. Select correct statement(s) ...... **[AIMS 2009]**

    (a) Cyanamide ion (CN_2^{2-}) is isoelectronic with CO_2 and has the same linear structure.

    (b) Mg_2C_2 reacts with water to form propyne.

    (c) CaC_2 has NaCl type lattice.

    (d) All of these

23. For alkali metals, which one of the following is incorrect? **[KCET 2010]**

    (a) Hydration energy : Li > Na > K > Rb   (b) Ionisation energy : Li > Na > K > Rb

    (c) Density : Li > Na > K > Rb   (d) Atomic size : Li > Na > K > Rb

24. Which of the following oxides is not expected to react with sodium hydroxide?

    [CBSE AIPMT 2009]

    (a) B_2O_2 (b) CaO   (c) SiO_2 (d) BeO

25. In the case of alkali metals, the covalent character decreases in the order :

    [CBSE AIPMT 2009]

    (a) MCl > MI > MBr > MF   (b) MF > MCl > MBr > MI

    (c) MF > MCl > MI > MBr   (d) MI > MBr > MCl > MF

26. Which of the following compounds does not give a precipitate with excess of H ?

    (a) $ZnSO_4$ (b) $FeSO_4$ (c) $AgNO_3$ (d) $HgCl_2$ **[AFMC 2009]**

27. **Assertion :** Among the alkali metals, lithium salts exhibit least electrical conductance in aqueous solution.

    Reason : Smaller the radius of the hydrated cation, lower is the electrical conductance in the aqueous solution. **[AIIMS 2009]**

    (a) Both Assertion and Reason are true and Reason is the correct explanation of Assertion.

    (b) Both Assertion and Reason are true but Reason is not the correct explanation of Assertion.

    (c) Assertion is true but Reason is false.

    (d) Both Assertion and Reason are false.

28. Which physical property in the alkali metal group increase with atomic number?

    [AMU 2010]

    (a) Melting point   (b) Electronegativity   (c) Hydration enthalpy   (d) Density

29. Which of the following will give H_2 gas with dilute HNO_3 ?   **[CPMT 2009]**
    (a) Mg   (b) Zn   (c) Cu   (d) Hg

30. The ease of adsorption of hydrates of alkali metal ions on an ion-exchange resin follows the order :   **[CBSE Premi 2012]**
    (a) $K^+ < Na^+ < Rb^+ < Li^+$ (b) $Na^+ < Li^+ < K^+ < Rb^+$
    (c) $Li^+ < K^+ < Na^+ < Rb^+$ (d) $Rb^+ < K^+ < Na^+ < Li^+$

31. Which one of the following is present as an active ingredient in bleaching powder for bleaching action ?   **[CBSE AIPMT 2011]**
    (a) $CaCl_2$ (b) $CaOCl_2$ (c) $Ca(OCl)_2$ (d) CaO_2Cl_2

32. Which of the following compounds has the lowest melting point ?   **[CBSE AIPMT 2011]**
    (a) CaF_2 (b) $CaCl_2$ (c) $CaBr_2$ (d) CaI_2

33. The property of alkaline earth metals that increase with their atomic number is ......
    [CBSE AIPMT 2010]
    (a) electronegativity   (b) solubility of their hydroxides in water
    (c) solubility of their sulphates in water   (d) ionization energy

34. Which of the following alkaline earth metal sulphates has hydration enthalpy higher than the lattice enthalpy?   **[CBSE AIPMT 2010]**
    (a) $SrSO_4$ (b) $CaSO_4$ (c) $BeSO_4$ (d) $BaSO_4$

35. The solubilities of Na_2SO_4, $BeSO_4$, $MgSO_4$ and $BaSO_4$ will follow the order :   **[AMU 2010]**
    (a) $BeSO_4 > MgSO_4 > Na_2SO_4 > BaSO_4$ (b) $BeSO_4 > Na_2SO_4 > MgSO_4 > BaSO_4$
    (c) $MgSO_4 > BeSO_4 > Na_2SO_4 > BaSO_4$ (d) $Na_2SO_4 > BeSO_4 > MgSO_4 > BaSO_4$

36. In aqueous solution, the most stable sulphate is ......   **[CPMT 2010]**
    (a) $BeSO_4$ (b) $MgSO_4$ (c) $CaSO_4$ (d) $BaSO_4$

37. The highly reactive alkali metals are kept in ......   **[CPMT 2010]**
    (a) air   (b) water   (c) kerosene   (d) all of these

38. Washing soda is ......   **[MP PMT 2010]**
    (a) Na_2CO_3 (b) $Na_2CO_3 \cdot H_2O$ (c) $Na_2CO_3 \cdot 5H_2O$ (d) $Na_2CO_3 \cdot 10H_2O$

39. Epsom salt's chemical formula is ......   **[Karnataka CET 2007]**
    (a) $MgSO_4 \cdot 7H_2O$ (b) $Mg(OH)_2$ (c) $2CaSO_4 \cdot H_2O$ (d) $CaSO_4 \cdot 2H_2O$

40. Which of the following compounds of cement sets at the slowest rate?   **[BHU 2000]**
    (a) Dicalcium silicate   (b) Tricalcium silicate
    (c) Tricalcium aluminate   (d) Tetracalcium aluminoferrite

41. A sudden large jump between the values of second and third ionisation energies of an element would be associated with the electronic configuration ......
    [PMT 1994; MP PMT 1996; WB JEE 2008]
    (a) $1s^2\, 2s^2\, 2p^6\, 3s^1$ (b) $1s^2\, 2s^2\, 2p^6\, 3s^2\, 3p^1$
    (c) $1s^2\, 2s^2\, 2p^6\, 3s^2\, 3p^2$ (d) $1s^2\, 2s^2\, 2p^6\, 3s^2$

42. Which of the following has correct increasing basic strength?   **[BVP 2000]**
    (a) $MgO < BeO < CaO < BaO$ (b) $BeO < MgO < CaO < BaO$
    (c) $BaO < CaO < MgO < BeO$ (d) $CaO < BaO < BeO < MgO$

43. Plaster of Paris is a hydrate of ...... **[BHU 2000]**

    (a) $BaSO_4$　　　(b) $CaSO_4$　　　(c) $MgSO_4$　　　(d) $ZnSO_4$

44. The atomic numbers of four elements are given below. Which one is an alkaline earth metal? **[AFMC 2003]**

    (a) 10　　　(b) 20　　　(c) 30　　　(d) 40

45. A major constituent of Portland cement (except lime) is ......

[Manipal MEE 1995; MP PMT 2009]

    (a) Silica　　　(b) Alumina　　　(c) Iron oxide　　　(d) Magnesia

46. Among the following NaOH, $Ca(OH)_2$, KOH and $Zn(OH)_2$, the weakest base is ......

[MDAT Bihar 1995; MP PMT 2005]

    (a) NaOH　　　(b) $Ca(OH)_2$　　　(c) KOH　　　(d) $Zn(OH)_2$

47. Electrolysis of fused anhydrous $MgCl_2$ gives ...... **[M.P. P.M.T. 2004]**

    (a) Potassium only　　　　　(b) Magnesium only

    (c) Magnesium and chlorine　　　　　(d) Potassium and magnesium

48. Beryllium is placed above magnesium in the second group. Beryllium dust, therefore, when added to $MgCl_2$ solution will ...... **[BVP 2001; AFMC 2002; Pb PMT 2004]**

    (a) Have no effect　　　　　(b) Precipitate Mg metal

    (c) Precipitate Mg

    (d) Leads to the dissolution of Beryllium metal

49. Among the metals Be, Mg, Ca and Sr of group II of the periodic table, the least ionic chloride would be formed by ...... **[WB JEE 2009]**

    (a) Mg　　　(b) Be　　　(c) Ca　　　(d) Sr

50. The presence of which of the following salts increases the rate of setting of Plaster of Paris?

[AIIMS 2008]

    (a) NaCl　　　(b) KCl　　　(c) $BaSO_4$　　　(d) $CuSO_4$

51. Which of the following will liberate hydrogen by its reaction with hydrochloric acid?

[DUMET 2007]

    (a) Copper　　　(b) Phosphorus　　　(c) Mercury　　　(d) Magnesium

52. Which of the following is true peroxide? **[Manipal 2005]**

    (a) NO_2　　　(b) MnO_2　　　(c) BaO_2　　　(d) SO_2

53. Sodium sulphate is solute in water but barium sulphate is insoluble because ......

    (a) The hydration energy of Na_2SO_4 is more than its lattice energy　　**[Kerala 2009]**

    (b) The lattice energy of $BaSO_4$ is more than its hydration energy

    (c) The lattice energy of Na_2SO_4 is less than its hydration energy

    (d) Both (a) and (b) are correct

54. The compounds of alkaline earth metals have the following magnetic nature ......

[EAMCET 2009]

    (a) Diamagnetic　　　(b) Paramagnetic　　　(c) Ferromagnetic　　　(d) Anti-ferromagnetic

55. Which of the following is the smallest cation? **[M.P.P.M.T. 2000]**

    (a) Na^+　　　(b) Mg^{2+}　　　(c) Ca^{2+}　　　(d) Al^{3+}

56. The correct formula of Plaster of Paris is ......　　　　　　　**[Kerala 2000]**
   (a) $CaSO_4 \cdot 2H_2O$　　　　　(b) $CaSO_4$
   (c) $CaSO_4 \cdot 1/2H_2O$　　　(d) $CaSO_4 \cdot H_2O$　　　(e) $CaSO_4 \cdot MgSO_4$

57. The nitride salt of Ca when treated with H_2O gives ......　　**[Kerala P.M.T. 2000]**
   (a) N_2　　　　　　(b) CaO　　　　　　(c) CaH_2　　　　　(d) NH_3

58. When one mole of bleaching powder is completely decomposed, then the mass of chlorine gas that is liberated will be ......　　　　　　　**[S.C.R.A. 2001]**
   (a) 35.45 g　　　　(b) 70.90 g　　　　(c) 17.72 g　　　　(d) 88.60 g

59. In the presence of cobalt chloride, bleaching powder decomposes to form ......
   　　　　　　　　　　　　　　　　　　　　　　　　　[E.A.M.C.E.T. 2001]
   (a) $CaCO_3$ and O_3　　(b) ClO_2 and CaO　　(c) Cl_2O and CaO　(d) $CaCl_2$ and O_2

60. Limestone is not used in which of the following manufacturing process ?
   　　　　　　　　　　　　　　　　　　　　　　　　　[Kerala P.M.T. 2001]
   (a) Phosphorus from phosphorite　　　　(b) Ordinary (Soda lime) glass
   (c) Iron from haematite　　　　　　　　(d) Solvay process of sodium carbonate

61. Magnesium can be obtained by ......　　　　　　　　　**[B.V.P. Pune 2002]**
   (a) Reducing MgO with coke
   (b) Reducing magnesium salt solution with Fe
   (c) Electrolysis of fused magnesium salt
   (d) Electrolysis of $Mg(NO_3)_2$ solution

62. A solution of $MgCl_2$ in water has pH ......　　　　　　**[M.P.M.E.T. 2002]**
   (a) < 7　　　　　　(b) > 7　　　　　　(c) 7　　　　　　(d) 14.2

63. Which element gives green colour in fire works?　　　　**[M.P.C.E.T. 2002]**
   (a) Sodium　　　　(b) Potassium　　　(c) Barium　　　(d) Calcium

64. Bleaching powder is obtained by the interaction of Cl_2 and ......　**[E.A.M.C.E.T 2003]**
   (a) Dry slaked lime　(b) Hot $Ca(OH)_2$　(c) Cold $Ca(OH)_2$　(d) Mg and Cl_2

65. The substance not likely to contain $CaCO_3$ is ......　　　　**[A.I.E.E.E. 2003]**
   (a) Dolomite　　　　　　　　　　　(b) A marble statue
   (c) Calcined gypsum　　　　　　　　(d) Sea shells

66. In curing cement plaster, water is spinkled from time to time. This helps in ......
   　　　　　　　　　　　　　　　　　　　　　　　　　[J & K CET 2005]
   (a) Converting sand into silicic acid
   (b) Keeping it cool
   (c) Developing interlooking needle like crystals of hydrated silicates
   (d) Hydrating sand and gravel mixed with cement.

67. The correct order of solubility of sulphates of alkaline metals in water is ...... **[MHCET 2002]**
   (a) Be > Ca > Mg > Ba > Sr　　　　　(b) Mg > Be > Ba > Ca > Sr
   (c) Be > Mg > Ca > Sr > Ba　　　　　(d) Mg > Ca > Ba > Be > Sr

68. Which halide has highest melting point?　　　　　　　　**[AIEEE 2004]**
   (a) NaCl　　　　　(b) NaBr　　　　　(c) NaF　　　　　(d) NaI

69. Which of the following imparts violet coloration to the non-luminous flame of Bunsen burner? **[BVP 2003]**

(a) NaCl   (b) $BaCl_2$ (c) $CaCl_2$ (d) KCl

70. Causticisation process is used for the preparation of ......

[CPMT 1994; MP PMT 1996; WB JEE 2008]

(a) Caustic soda   (b) Caustic potash

(c) Baryata solution   (d) Slaked lime

71. When CO_2 is bubbled into an aqueous solution of Na_2CO_3, the following is formed ......

(a) NaOH   (b) $NaHCO_3$ (c) H_2O (d) OH^-

72. Which of the following does not liberate O_2 in Bunsen burner?   **[Orissa JEE 2004]**

(a) MgO   (b) $NaNO_3$ (c) Pb_3O_4 (d) $KClO_3$

73. When sodium chloride is dissolved in water, sodium ion is ......   **[RPMT 2006]**

(a) Oxidised   (b) Reduced   (c) Hydrolysed   (d) Hydrated

74. Which of the following oxides is formed when potassium metal is burnt in excess air?

(a) K_2O (b) KO   (c) KO_2 (d) K_2O_2 **[BVP 2000]**

75. The gas evolved on heating Na_2CO_3 is ......   **[AMU 2000]**

(a) CO_2 (b) CO   (c) Water vapour   (d) No gas

76. Strongest bond is between ......   **[BVP 2001; AFMC 2002; Pb PMT 2004]**

(a) CsF   (b) NaCl

(c) Both (a) and (b)   (d) None of these

77. Which is the most basic of the following?   **[WB JEE 2007]**

(a) Na_2O (b) BaO   (c) As_2O_3 (d) Al_2O_3

78. In the preparation of sodium carbonate (Na_2CO_3) which of the following is used?

(a) Slaked lime   (b) Quick lime   **[RPMT 2002]**

(c) Limestone   (d) Sodium hydroxide

79. The chloride of an element A gives a neutral soution in water. In the periodic table, the element A belongs to ......   **[BHU 2000]**

(a) First group   (b) Third group

(c) Fifth group   (d) First transition series

80. Which of the following does not illustrate the anomalous properties of Li?

(a) The m.p. and b.p. of Li are comparatively high   **[Kerala PMT 2001]**

(b) Li forms a nitride Li_3N unlike group I metals

(c) Li is much softer than the other I group metals

(d) Li^+ ion and its compounds are more heavily hydrated than those of the rest of the groups.

81. Which of the following has largest size ?   **[EAMCET 2007]**

(a) Li^+ (b) Cs^+ (c) Na^+ (d) None of these

82. Which of the following properties is not true for an alkali metal?   **[AMU 2004]**

    (a) Low atomic volume   (b) Low ionization energy

    (c) Low density   (d) Low electronegativity

83. Which of the following is known as fusion mixture?   **[MP PMT 2000]**

    (a) Mixture of Na_2CO_3 + $NaHCO_3$ (b) $Na_2CO_3 \cdot 10H_2O$

    (c) Mixture of K_2CO_3 + Na_2CO_3 (d) $NaHCO_3$

84. The reactivity of alkali metal sodium with water, is made use of ......   **[BHU 2008]**

    (a) In drying of alcohols   (b) In drying of benzene

    (c) In drying of ammonia solution   (d) As a general drying agent

85. Which of the following imparts violet coloration to the Bunsen burner non-luminous flame?

    (a) NaCl   (b) $BaCl_2$ (c) $CaCl_2$ (d) KCl **[CPMT 2000]**

86. Alkali metals displace hydrogen from water forming bases due to the reasons that ......

                                                 [AMU 1991; CPMT 2000]

    (a) They are far above the hydrogen in electro-chemical series based on oxidation potential

    (b) They are far below the hydrogen in electrochemical series based on oxidation potential

    (c) Their ionization potential is less than that of the other elements

    (d) They contain only one electron in their outermost shell

87. Which of the following reacts with water at a high rate?   **[BHU 2000]**

    (a) Li   (b) K   (c) Na   (d) Rb

88. The strongest reducing agent out of Na, K, Rb and Cs is ......   **[DPMT 2000]**

    (a) Na   (b) Cs   (c) Rb   (d) K

89. Which of the following is a man-made element?   **[CPMT 2000]**

    (a) Ra   (b) K   (c) Rn   (d) Lr

90. Which one of the following is most reactive?   **[AFMC 2000]**

    (a) Na   (b) K   (c) Pb   (d) Mg

91. Which of the following statements is incorrect?   **[BHU 2000]**

    (a) Sodium is not the most abundant metal in earth's crust

    (b) Sodium is most abundant metallic element in sea water

    (c) Melting and boiling points of alkali metals decrease down the group

    (d) Ionic character of alkali metal halides decrease down the group

92. Which one of the following has highest electropositive character?   **[AMU 2000]**

    (a) MO   (b) M_2O (c) M_2O_3 (d) MO_2

93. In view of their low ionization energies, the alkali metals are ......   **[MHCET 2005]**

    (a) Weak oxidizing agents   (b) Strong reducing agents

    (c) Strong oxidizing agents   (d) Weak reducing agents

94. Which of the following has least ionization potential?   **[WB JEE 2000]**

(a) Li   (b) He   (c) N   (d) Zn

95. Smallest among these species is ......   **[MP PMT 2006]**

(a) Hydrogen   (b) Helium   (c) Lithium   (d) Iodine

96. If electrolysis of NaCl with Pt electrode is taken then H_2 is liberated at cathode while with Hg cathode it forms sodium amalgam. The reason for this is ......   **[J & K CET 2009]**

(a) Hg is more inert than Pt

(b) More voltage is required to reduce H^+ at Hg than at Pt

(c) Na is dissolved in Hg while it does not dissolve in Pt

(d) Concentration of H^+ ions is larger when Pt electrode is taken

97. Aqueous NaCl solution is electrolysed using platinum electrodes. What is the product formed at cathode?   **[AIEEE 2010]**

(a) Na   (b) H_2 (c) O_2 (d) Cl_2

98. Sodium metal reacts with Al_2O_3 at high temperature to give a sodium compound X. X reacts with carbon dioxide in water to form Y. Y is ......   **[Orissa JEE 2011]**

(a) Na_2O_2 (b) Na_2O (c) Na_2CO_3 (d) $NaAlO_2$

99. When washing soda is heated ......   **[KCET 2001]**

(a) CO is released   (b) $CO + CO_2$ is released

(c) CO_2 is released   (d) Water vapour is released

100. Which of the following is not correct?   **[EAMCET 2011]**

(a) SiO_2 is used as acid flux

(b) The distance between the layers in graphite is 3.35×10^{-8} cm

(c) SiO_2 reacts with Na_2CO_3 and liberates CO

(d) The hybridization of C in graphite is sp^2

ANSWER KEY

1. (b)	2. (b)	3. (d)	4. (b)	5. (c)	6. (b)	7. (a)	8. (c)
9. (a)	10. (d)	11. (a)	12. (a)	13. (d)	14. (b)	15. (c)	16. (b)
17. (b)	18. (d)	19. (a)	20. (b)	21. (d)	22. (a)	23. (a)	24. (a)
25. (a)	26. (a)	27. (c)	28. (c)	29. (c)	30. (c)	31. (b)	32. (a)
33. (c)	34. (b)	35. (b)	36. (b)	37. (c)	38. (c)	39. (a)	40. (a)
41. (c)	42. (c)	43. (d)	44. (b)	45. (c)	46. (d)	47. (b)	48. (d)
49. (b)	50. (a)	51. (a)	52. (c)	53. (a)	54. (d)	55. (a)	56. (c)
57. (d)	58. (c)	59. (a)	60. (c)	61. (c)	62. (d)	63. (c)	64. (c)
65. (a)	66. (d)	67. (a)	68. (b)	69. (b)	70. (a)	71. (c)	72. (c)
73. (b)	74. (c)	75. (b)	76. (a)	77. (d)	78. (d)	79. (a)	80. (b)
81. (d)	82. (a)	83. (b)	84. (c)	85. (c)	86. (d)	87. (d)	88. (b)

89. (d)	90. (b)	91. (b)	92. (b)	93. (a)	94. (a)	95. (b)	96. (a)
97. (a)	98. (d)	99. (a)	100. (a)	101. (b)	102. (b)	103. (b)	104. (d)
105. (c)	106. (c)	107. (c)	108. (c)	109. (d)	110. (a)	111. (c)	112. (b)
113. (c)	114. (a)	115. (b)	116. (b)	117. (a)	118. (a)	119. (c)	120. (b)
121. (c)	122. (d)	123. (d)	124. (b)	125. (c)			

Previous Years Questions

1. (b)	2. (a)	3. (a)	4. (d)	5. (d)	6. (b)	7. (c)	8. (d)
9. (b)	10. (a)	11. (d)	12. (a)	13. (b)	14. (b)	15. (b)	16. (c)
17. (d)	18. (b)	19. (d)	20. (b)	21. (b)	22. (d)	23. (c)	24. (b)
25. (d)	26. (a)	27. (c)	28. (d)	29. (a)	30. (c)	31. (c)	32. (d)
33. (b)	34. (c)	35. (d)	36. (d)	37. (c)	38. (d)	39. (a)	40. (b)
41. (d)	42. (b)	43. (b)	44. (b)	45. (a)	46. (d)	47. (c)	48. (a)
49. (b)	50. (a)	51. (d)	52. (c)	53. (d)	54. (a)	55. (d)	56. (c)
57. (d)	58. (b)	59. (a)	60. (a)	61. (c)	62. (d)	63. (c)	64. (a)
65. (c)	66. (c)	67. (c)	68. (c)	69. (d)	70. (a)	71. (b)	72. (a)
73. (d)	74. (d)	75. (a)	76. (a)	77. (b)	78. (b)	79. (a)	80. (c)
81. (c)	82. (a)	83. (c)	84. (b)	85. (d)	86. (b)	87. (d)	88. (b)
89. (c)	90. (b)	91. (d)	92. (b)	93. (b)	94. (a)	95. (a)	96. (b)
97. (b)	98. (c)	99. (d)	100. (c)				

❑❑❑

ORGANIC CHEMISTRY : SOME BASIC PRINCIPLES AND TECHNIQUES

1. The IUPAC name of $(CH_3)_2CHCH_3$ is ......

   (a) Dimethylethane

   (b) Trimethyl methane

   (c) Iso-propylmethane

   (d) 2-methylpropane

2. The IUPAC name of $(CH_3)_2CHCH_2CH_2Br$ is ......

   (a) 1-Bromopentane

   (b) 2-Methyl-4-bromopentane

   (c) 1-Bromo-3-methylbutane

   (d) 2-Methyl-3-bromopropane

3. The IUPAC name of $(CH_3)_2CHCH_2CH_2Cl$ is ......

   (a) 1-chloropentane

   (b) 1-chloro-3-methylbutane

   (c) 2-methyl-3-chloropropane

   (d) none of these

4. The IUPAC name for the compound given below is

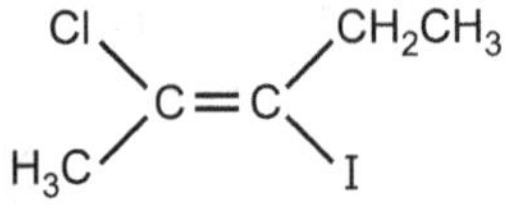

$$\underset{H_3C}{\overset{Cl}{>}}C=C\underset{I}{\overset{CH_2CH_3}{<}}$$

   (a) trans-2-chloro-3-iodo pent-2-ene

   (b) cis-2-chloro-3-iodo pent-2-ene

   (c) trans-3-iodo-4-chloro-3-pentene

   (d) cis-3-iodo-4-chloro-3-pentane

5. The compound ⬡ is known by which of the following names ?

   (a) Bi-cyclo [2, 2, 2] octane

   (b) Bi-cyclo [2, 2, 1] octane

   (c) Bi-cyclo [1, 2, 1] octane

   (d) Bi-cyclo [1, 1, 1] octane

6. The IUPAC name of the formula

$$^4CH_3-^3C=^2C-^1COOH \quad \text{is} \quad ......$$

with H on C-2 and CH_3 on C-3

   (a) 2-methyl but-2-enoic acid

   (b) 3-methyl but-3-enoic acid

   (c) 3-methyl but-2-enoic acid

   (d) 2-methyl but-3-enoic acid

7. 2-methylbut-2-ene can be represented as ......

   (a) $CH_3-\underset{CH_3}{C}=CH_2CH_3$

   (b) $CH_3-C=CH_2CH_3$ with CH_3 substituent

   (c) $CH_3-CH_2-\underset{CH_3}{C}=CH_2$

   (d) $CH_3-CH_2-\underset{CH_3}{C}=CH_2$

8. The IUPAC name of the compound

$$CH_3-CH-C-CH_2-CH_3 \quad is \ldots\ldots$$

with CH_3 (single bond) and CH_2 (double bond) substituents

(a) 2-ethyl-3-methylbut-1-ene

(b) 2-isopropylbut-1-ene

(c) 2-methyl-3-ethyl-3-butene

(d) 2-(1-methylethyl)but-1-ene

9. Which of the following IUPAC name is correct?

(a) 2-methyl-3-ethyl pentane

(b) 3-ethyl-2-methyl pentane

(c) 2-ethyl-3-methyl pentane

(d) 3-methyl-3-ethyl pentane

10. Which of the following represents the systematic name of the compound $CH_2 = CH - CH_2Cl$?

(a) Allyl chloride

(b) 1-chloroprop-3-ene

(c) 3-chloroprop-1-ene

(d) Vinyl chloride

11. The IUPAC name of

$$CH_3-{}^{2}C-{}^{3}CH_2-{}^{4}CH_2 \quad is \ldots\ldots$$

with OH on C_2, ${}^{1}CH_3$ on C_2, and CH_3 on C_3

(a) 2-methyl pentan-2-ol

(b) 2, 4-dimethyl pentan-4-ol

(c) 2, 2-dimethyl butan-2-ol

(d) Butanol-2

12. The rate of sublimation .... if the process is carried out under reduced pressure.

(a) increases

(b) decreases

(c) remains constant

(d) none of these

13. When the boiling point difference between two liquids is very near to each other, then .... is used for separation of two liquids.

(a) simple distillation

(b) fractional distillation

(c) steam distillation

(d) filtration process

14. The correct IUPAC name of the compound with molecular formula $(CH_3)_3C - CH_3$ is ......

(a) Pentane

(b) 1, 1, 1-trimethylethane

(c) 2, 2-dimethylpropane

(d) Neo-pentane

15. The IUPAC name of the compound having the molecular formula $Cl_3C - CH_2CHO$ is ......

(a) 3, 3, 3-trichloropropanal

(b) 1, 1, 1-trichloropropanal

(c) 2, 2, 2-trichloropropanal

(d) 4-hydroxy-4-methyl-3-ene pentenoic acid

16. The IUPAC name of

$$CH_3-C-CH_2-C-CHO \quad is \ldots\ldots$$

with O (double bond) on first C, OH and H on second C

(a) 5-oxo-4-hydroxy-2-pentanone

(b) 4-hydroxy-5-al-2-pentanone

(c) 2-hydroxy-4-oxopentanal

(d) 1-3-oxo-2-pentanol

17. The IUPAC name of $CH_3OC_2H_5$ is ......

  (a) Methyl ethyl ether   (b) Ethyl methyl ether

  (c) Methoxy ethane   (d) Ethoxy methane

18. The IUPAC name of tert-butyl chloride is ......

  (a) 4-Chlorobutane   (b) 2-Chlorobutane

  (c) 1-Chloro-2-methylpropane   (d) 2-Chloro-2-methylpropane

19. The IUPAC name of

$$CH_3-C = C - CHCH_2-C \equiv CH \text{ is ......}$$
$$\quad\quad | \quad\quad | \quad\quad |$$
$$\quad\quad Cl \quad CH_3 \; C_2H_5$$

  (a) 6-chloro-4-ethyl-5-methylhept-5-en-1-yne

  (b) 6-chloro-4-ethyl-5-methylhept-1-yn-5-ene

  (c) 2-chloro-4-ethyl-3-methylhept-2-yn-6-yne

  (d) 2-chloro-4-ethyl-3-methylhept-6-yn-5-ene

20. The size of naphthalene balls goes on decreasing day by day when kept in open test tube. This is due to ..... process.

  (a) Reduction   (b) Sublimation   (c) Vaporisation   (d) None of these

21. The IUPAC name of

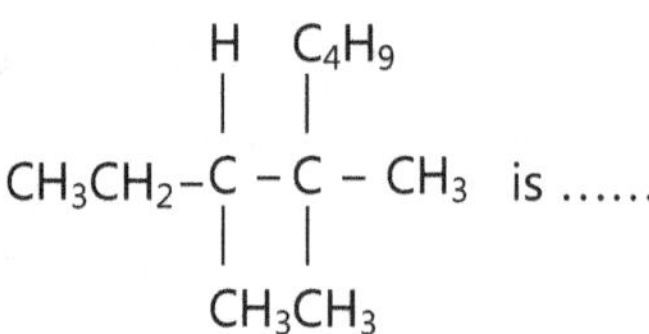

  is ......

  (a) 3, 4, 4-trimethylheptane   (b) 3, 4, 4- trimethyloctane

  (c) 2-Butyl-2-methyl-3-ethylbutane   (d) 2-Ethyl-3, 3-dimethylheptane

22. During Carius method for the estimation of sulphur in 0.2 gm of the compund which gave 0.6 gm of $BaSO_4$ [M_R of $BaSO_4$ = 233], the percentage of sulphur is ......

  (a) 36.7   (b) 40.2   (c) 44   (d) 20.1

23. The IUPAC name of 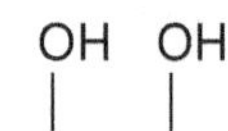 is ......

  (a) Formaldehyde   (b) 1, 2-Ethane dione   (c) Formyl methanoate   (d) Ethane-1, 2-diol

24. The IUPAC name of the following compound is ......

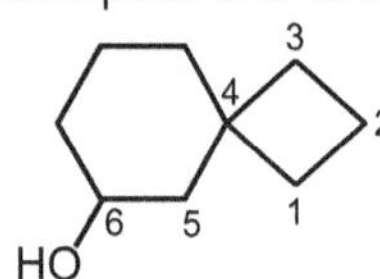

  (a) spiro [3, 5] nonan-6-ol   (b) spiro [3, 5] nonan-8-ol

  (c) 3-cyclobutyl cycloobexanol   (d) 5-cycllobutyl cycloehexanol

25. The structural formula of the following compound is

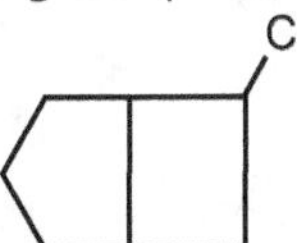

(a) 1-chlorobicydo [2, 2, 5] heptane   (b) 6-chlorobicyclo [3, 2, 0] heptane

(c) 6- chlorobicydo [1, 5, 3] heptane   (d) 1- chlorobicydo [3, 2, 0] heptane

26. The IUPAC name of

$$CH_3-\underset{\underset{OH}{|}}{\overset{\overset{H}{|}}{C}}-CH_2-CH_2-CH_2-\underset{\underset{Br}{|}}{\overset{\overset{Br}{|}}{C}}-CH_3 \text{ is ......}$$

(a) 6, 6-dibromoheptane-2-ol   (b) 2, 2-dibromoheptan-2-ol

(c) 6, 6-dibromoheptan-2-ol   (d) None of these

27. The IUPAC name of the following $CH_3C(CH_3)_2CH_2CH = CH_2$ is ......

(a) 2, 2-dimethyl-4-pentene   (b) 4, 4-dimethyl-1-pentene

(c) 1, 1, 1-trimethyl-3-butene   (d) 4, 4, 4-trimethyl-1-butene

28. The IUPAC nomenclature of the given organic compound $(CH_3)_2C(CH_2CH_3)CH_2CH(Cl)CH_3$ will be ......

(a) 5-chloro-3, 3-dimethylhexane   (b) 4-chloro-2-ethyl-2-methylpentane

(c) 2-chloro-4-ethyl-4-methylpentane   (d) 2-chloro-4, 4-dimethylhexane

29. Which of the following compound has wrong IUPAC name?

(a) $CH_3CH_2CH_2COOCH_2CH_3$ (Ethyl butanoate)

(b) $CH_3 — \underset{\underset{CH_3}{|}}{CH} — CH_2CHO$ (3-Methylbutanal)

(c) $CH_3 — \underset{\underset{OH}{|}}{CH} — \underset{\underset{CH_3}{|}}{CH} — CH_3$ (2-Methyl-3-butanal)

(d) $CH_3 — \underset{\underset{CH_3}{|}}{CH} — \underset{\overset{||}{O}}{C} — CH_2 — CH_3$ (2-Methyl-3-pentanone)

30. The IUPAC name of 3-isopropyl-o-xylene is ......

(a) 1-isopropyl-2, 4-dimethylbenzene   (b) 4-isopropyl-m-xylene

(c) 1-isopropyl-2, 3-dimethylbenzene   (d) 4-isopropyl-3, 5-dimethylbenzene

31. The decreasing order of C–C bond length is ......

(I) C_2H_4 (II) C_2H_2 (III) C_6H_6 (IV) C_2H_6

(a) IV > III > I > II   (b) I > II > IV > III   (c) II > I > IV > III   (d) IV > I > III > II

32. The IUPAC name of $CH_3COCH(CH_3)_2$ is ......

(a) isopropyl methyl ketone   (b) 4-methyl isopropyl ketone

(c) 4-methyl isopropyl ketone   (d) 3-methyl-2-butanone

33. In Duma's method, 0.112 gm of an organic compound gave 22.4 ml of N_2 gas at STP. The percentage of nitrogen is ......

    (a) 25   (b) 20.5   (c) 15.5   (d) 50

34. Pick out the most stable carbonium ion

    (a) $C_6H_5-\overset{+}{C}H-C_6H_5$ (b) $CH_3-\overset{+}{C}HCH_3$

    (c) $CH_3-\overset{\oplus}{C}H-CH_3$ (d) $CH_3-\overset{\oplus}{C}H-C_2H_5$

35. Electrophilic reagents are ......

    (a) Electron pair donors   (b) Lewis acids

    (c) Odd electron molecules   (d) None of these

36. The reaction

    $CH_3CH_2Br + OH^- \rightarrow CH_3CH_2OH + Br^-$ is an example of ......

    (a) Electrophilic addition   (b) Electrophilic substitution

    (c) Nucleophilic addition   (d) Nucleophilic substitution

37. The most stable carbonium ion is ......

    (a) Methyl carbonium ion   (b) Primary carbonium ion

    (c) Secondary carbonium ion   (d) Tertiary carbonium ion

38. The typical reaction of olefinic bond is ......

    (a) Electrophilic substitution reactions   (b) Electrophilic addition reactions

    (c) Nucleophilic substitution reactions   (d) Nucleophilic addition reactions

39. Which of the following is an example of elimination reaction?

    (a) Chlorination of methane   (b) Dehydration of ethanol

    (c) Nitration of benzene   (d) Hydroxylation of ethylene

40. Which of the following is the most stable carbocation?

    (a) $CH_3CH_2^+$ (b) $(CH_3)_2\overset{+}{C}H$ (c) $(CH_3)_3\overset{+}{C}$ (d) $C_6H_5\overset{+}{C}H_2$

41. Which of the following is not a nucleophile?

    (a) CN^- (b) OH^- (c) NH_3 (d) BF_3

42. Which of the following statement is false about resonance contribution structures?

    (a) Contribution structures contribute to the resonance hybrid in proportion of their relative energies.

    (b) Equivalent contributing structures make the resonance very important

    (c) Contributing structures represent molecules having no real existence

    (d) Contributing structures are less stable than the resonance hybrid

43. The most stable carbonium ion among the following is ......

    (a) $C_6H_5\overset{\oplus}{C}HC_6H_5$ (b) $C_6H_5\overset{\oplus}{C}HC_2H_5$ (c) $CH_3^+CH_2$ (d) $C_6H_5\overset{\oplus}{C}HCH_3$

44. Which of the following is correct regarding the I-effect of the substituent?

    (a) $\overset{+}{N}R_3 > NO_2 > OR > OH > F$ (b) $NO_2 > \overset{+}{N}R_3 > OR > OH > F$

    (c) $\overset{+}{N}R_3 > NO_2 > F > OR > OH$ (d) $F > \overset{+}{N}R_3 > NO_2 > OH > OR$

45. Which species represents the electrophile in aromatic nitration?

   (a) NO_2^- (b) NO_2^+ (c) NO_2 (d) NO_3^-

46. Which of the following behave both as a nucleophile and as an electrophile ?

   (a) $H_3C — C \equiv N$ (b) H_3COH (c) $H_2C = CH — CH_3$ (d) H_3CNH_2

47. Among the following alkenes :

   1-Butene; cis-2-Butene; trans-2-Butene

      I   II   III

   the decreasing order of stability is ......

   (a) III > II > I   (b) III > I > II   (c) I > II > III   (d) II > I > III

48. The addition of HCN to a carbonyl compound is an example of ......

   (a) Nucleophilic substitution   (b) Electrophilic addition
   (c) Nucleophilic addition   (d) Electrophilic substitution

49. The inductive effect ......

   (a) decreases with increase of distance

   (b) its extent increases with increase of distance

   (c) indicates the transfer of π pair of electron from less electronegative atom to more electronegative atom in a molecule

   (d) shows the transfer of lone pair of electrons

50. Hybridisation of carbon in CH_3^+, CH_3^- and $CH_2 = CH - \overline{C}H_2$ carbons are ......

   (a) sp^2, sp^3, sp respectively   (b) sp, sp^2, sp^3 respectively
   (c) sp^2, sp^3, sp^2 respectively   (d) sp^2, sp^2, sp^3 respectively

51. Which of the following carbocation is least stable ?

   (a) $CH_2 = CH - CH_2^+$ (b) $(CH_3)_3C^+$ (c) $C_6H_5CH_2^+$ (d) $CH_2 = CH - \overset{\oplus}{C}HR$

52. Which of the following statements is correct ?

   (a) + I group stabilizes a carbanion   (b) + I group stabilizes a carbocation
   (c) – I group stabilizes a carbocation   (d) – I group destabilizes a carbanion

53. The compound which gives the most stable carbonium ion on dehydration is ......

   (a) $CH_3CH(CH_3)CH_2OH$ (b) $(CH_3)_3COH$
   (c) $CH_2 = CHCH_2CH_2OH$ (d) $CH_3CHOH·CH_2·CH_3$

54. The systematic name of $(CH_3)_2CH–COOH$ is ......

   (a) 2-Propanoic acid   (b) Isobutanoic acid
   (c) 2-Methylpropanoic acid   (d) 2-Methylbutanoic acid

55. The IUPAC name of $(CH_3)_3C – CH = CH_2$ is ......

   (a) 2, 2-Dimethylbut-2-ene   (b) 2, 2-Dimethylpent-3-ene
   (c) 3, 3-Dimethylbut-1-ene   (d) Hex-1-ene

56. What is the IUPAC name of

$$\overset{\displaystyle O}{\overset{\displaystyle \|}{H - C}} - CH_2 - CH_2 - OCH_3 \,?$$

   (a) 2-Formylmethoxyethane   (b) Methoxypropanal
   (c) 2-Methoxypropanal   (d) 3-Methoxypropanal

57. The stationary phase in partition chromatography is ......

(a) Solid   (b) Liquid   (c) Gas   (d) (b) and (c) both

58. Molar mass of acetic acid in benzene solvent determined using cryoscopic method is just twice of the theoretical valve. This is due to ....

(a) Its ionisation into CH_3COO^- and H^+ ions

(b) Its association as dimer $(CH_3COOH)_2$ by van der Waal's forces

(c) Its association as dimer by hydrogen bonding

(d) Its molar mass of acetic acid is just twice of theoretical value is not correct

59. The name of $\underset{\underset{CHO}{|}}{CH} = \underset{\underset{NH_2}{|}}{CH}$ is ......

(a) 1-aminoprop-2-enal   (b) 3-aminoprop-2-enal

(c) 1-amino-2-formylethene   (d) 3-amino-1-oxoprop-2-ene

60. The IUPAC name of the following compound is ......

(a) Bicyclo [2, 1, 0] pentane   (b) 1, 2-cyclopropyl cyclobutane

(c) Cyclopentane [4, 3] annulene   (d) 1, 2-methylene cyclobutane

61. The IUPAC name of $CH_3 - \underset{\underset{OH}{|}}{CH} - CH = \underset{\underset{CH_3}{|}}{C} - CHO$ is ......

(a) 4-Hydroxy-1-methylpentanal   (b) 4-Hydroxy-2-methylpent-2-en-1-al

(c) 2-Hydroxy-4-methylpent-3-en-5-al   (d) 2-Hydroxy-3-methylpent-2-en-5-al

62. Indicate the wrongly named compound

(a) $CH_3\underset{\underset{CH_3}{|}}{CH}CH_2CH_2CHO$

(4-Methyl-1-pentanal)

(b) $CH_3 - \underset{\underset{CH_3}{|}}{CH} - C \equiv C - COOH$

(4-Methyl-2-pentyn-1-oic acid)

(c) $CH_3CH_2CH_2 - \underset{\underset{CH_3}{|}}{CH} - COOH$

(2-Methyl-1-pentanoic acid)

(d) $CH_3CH_2 - CH = CH - \overset{\overset{O}{\|}}{C} - CH_3$

(3-Hexen-5-one)

63. Silver salt of a dibasic acid has 27% silver. Molar mass $(g\ mol^{-1})$ of dibasic acid is ....

(a) 400   (b) 200   (c) 293   (d) 586

64. The IUPAC name of the compound $CH_3 - CH - CH_2CH_2CH_3$ is ......

$\quad\quad\quad CH(CH_3)_2$

  (a) 2-isopropyl pentane   (b) 2, 3-dimethylhexane

  (c) Isononane   (d) 2, 4-dimethylhexane

65. The IUPAC name of $CH_3–C \equiv C–CH(CH_3)_2$ is ......

  (a) 4-Methyl-pent-2-yne   (b) 4, 4-Dimethyl-but-2-yne

  (c) Isopropylmethylacetylene   (d) 2-Methylpent-2-yne

66. The IUPAC name of the compound, $CH_3CH = CHCH_2CHCH_2COOH$ is ......

$\quad\quad\quad NH_2$

  (a) 5-aminohept-2-enoic acid   (b) β-amino-δ-heptanoic acid

  (c) 5-aminohex-2-enecarboxylic acid   (d) 3-aminohept-5-enoic acid

67. The IUPAC name of

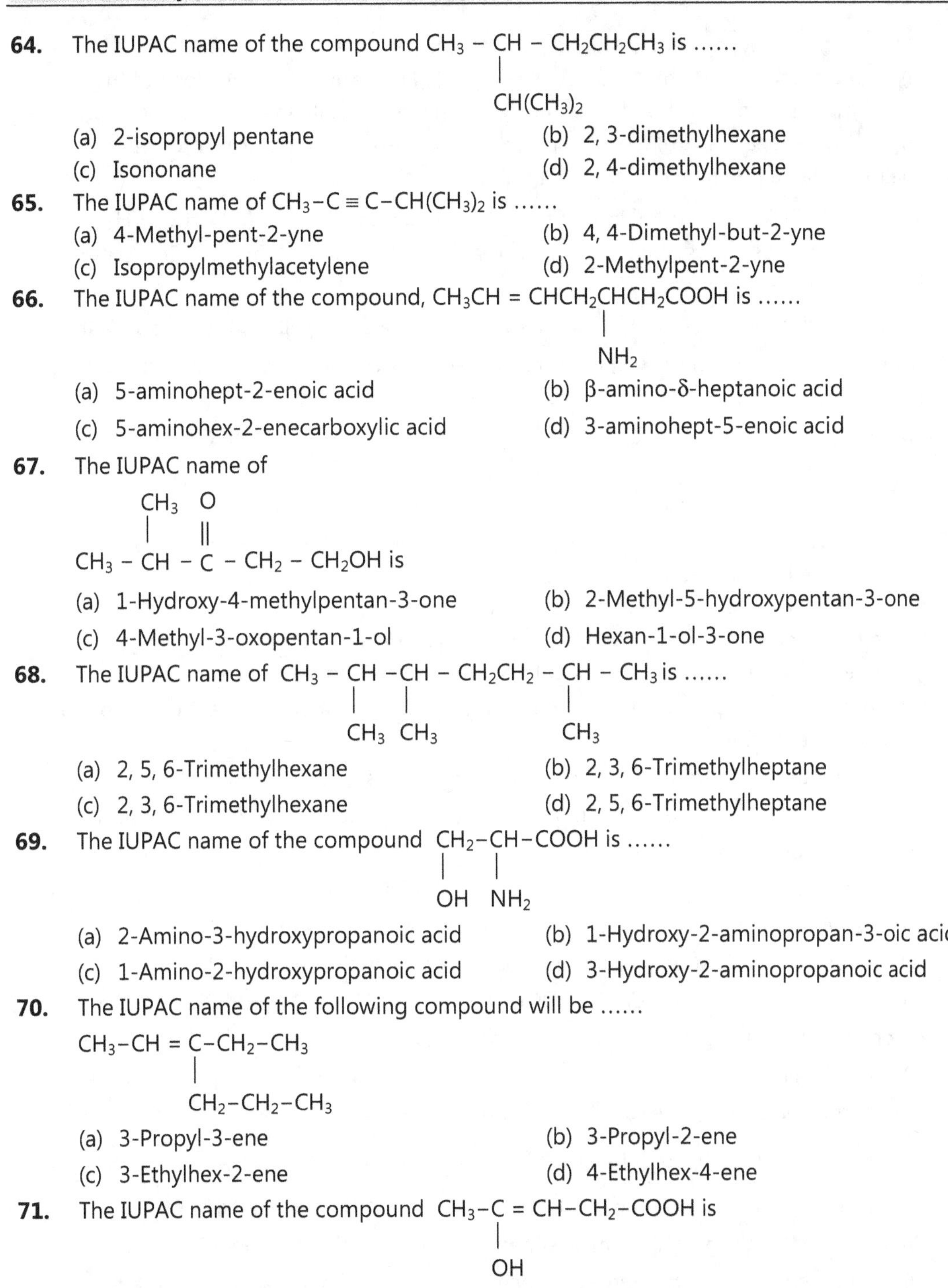

  (a) 1-Hydroxy-4-methylpentan-3-one   (b) 2-Methyl-5-hydroxypentan-3-one

  (c) 4-Methyl-3-oxopentan-1-ol   (d) Hexan-1-ol-3-one

68. The IUPAC name of $CH_3 - CH –CH - CH_2CH_2 - CH - CH_3$ is ......

$\quad\quad\quad CH_3 \ \ CH_3 \quad\quad\quad CH_3$

  (a) 2, 5, 6-Trimethylhexane   (b) 2, 3, 6-Trimethylheptane

  (c) 2, 3, 6-Trimethylhexane   (d) 2, 5, 6-Trimethylheptane

69. The IUPAC name of the compound $CH_2–CH–COOH$ is ......

$\quad\quad\quad OH \ \ NH_2$

  (a) 2-Amino-3-hydroxypropanoic acid   (b) 1-Hydroxy-2-aminopropan-3-oic acid

  (c) 1-Amino-2-hydroxypropanoic acid   (d) 3-Hydroxy-2-aminopropanoic acid

70. The IUPAC name of the following compound will be ......

$CH_3–CH = C–CH_2–CH_3$

$\quad\quad\quad CH_2–CH_2–CH_3$

  (a) 3-Propyl-3-ene   (b) 3-Propyl-2-ene

  (c) 3-Ethylhex-2-ene   (d) 4-Ethylhex-4-ene

71. The IUPAC name of the compound $CH_3–C = CH–CH_2–COOH$ is

$\quad\quad\quad OH$

  (a) Hydroxypentenoic aci   (b) 4-Hydroxypent-3-enoic acid

  (c) 4-Hydroxypent-4-enoic acid

  (d) 4-Hydroxy-4-methyl-3-enepentenoic acid

72. Which of the following contains three pairs of electrons in the valence shell ?
(a) Carbocations   (b) Carbanions   (c) Free radicals   (d) None of these

73. Homolytic fission of C–C bond in ethane gives an intermediate in which carbon is ......
(a) sp^3-hybridized   (b) sp^2-hybridized   (c) sp-hybridized   (d) sp^3d hybridized

74. The most stable free radical among the following is ......
(a) $C_6H_5CH_2\overset{\bullet}{C}H_2$ (b) $C_6H_5\overset{\bullet}{C}HCH_3$ (c) $CH_3\overset{\bullet}{C}H_2$ (d) $CH_3\overset{\bullet}{C}HCH_3$

75. The correct order of stability of the carbanions $(CH_3)_3C^-$ (I); $(CH_3)_2CH^-$ (II); $CH_3CH_2^-$ (III); $C_6H_5CH_2^-$ (IV) is ......
(a) I > II > III > IV   (b) IV > III > II > I   (c) IV > I > II > III   (d) I > II > IV > III

76. Hydrocarbon X contains 3 gms carbon per gm of hydrogen. Simplest formula of hydrocarbon X is ......
(a) CH   (b) CH_2 (c) CH_3 (d) CH_4

77. In which of the following, resonance will be possible?
(a) $CH_2 = CH – CH_2 – CHO$
(b) $CH_2 = CH – CH = O$
(c) CH_3COCH_3
(d) $CH_2 = CH – CH_2 – CH = CH_2$

78. Point out the incorrect statement about resonance ?
(a) Resonance structures should have equal energy
(b) In resonance structures, the constituent atoms must be in the same position
(c) In resonance structures, there should not be same number of electron pairs
(d) Resonance structures should differ only in the location of electrons around the constituent atoms

79. The intermediate involved in Reimer-Tiemann reaction is ......
(a) Carbocation   (b) Carbanion   (c) Carbene   (d) Free radical

80. The correct IUPAC name of C_6H_5–NC is ......
(a) Phenyl carbylamine
(b) Phenyl isonitrile
(c) Phenyl isocyanide
(d) None of these

81. Which one of the following acids would you expect to be the strongest ?
(a) $I–CH_2COOH$ (b) $Cl–CH_2COOH$ (c) $Br–CH_2COOH$ (d) $F-CH_2COOH$

82. Amongst the following the most basic compound is ......
(a) Benzylamine   (b) Aniline   (c) Acetanilide   (d) p-nitroaniline

83. What is the decreasing order of strength of bases ?
(a) $\overset{-}{O}H > \overset{-}{N}H_2 > H–C \equiv C^- > CH_3–CH_2^-$
(b) $CH_3CH_2^- > NH_2^- > H–C \equiv C^- > OH^-$
(c) $OH^- > NH_2^- > H–C \equiv C^- > CH_3–CH_2^-$
(d) $NH_2^- > H–C \equiv C^- > OH^- > H_3C–CH_2^-$

84. Which of the following has the smallest heat of hydrogenation per mole ?
(a) 1-butene   (b) trans-2-butene   (c) cis-2-butene   (d) 1, 3-butadiene

85. The intermediate during the addition of HCl to propene in the presence of peroxide is ......
(a) $CH_3\overset{\bullet}{C}HCH_2Cl$ (b) $CH_3\overset{\oplus}{C}HCH_3$ (c) $CH_3CH_2\overset{\bullet}{C}H_2$ (d) $CH_3CH_2\overset{\oplus}{C}H_2$

86. The formation of cyanohydrin from a ketone is an example of ......
    (a) Electrophilic addition　　　　　　　　(b) Nucleophilic addition
    (c) Nucleophilic substitution　　　　　　(d) Electrophilic substitution

87. Among the following which is aromatic ?

    (a) ☐　　　　　(b) △　　　　　(c) ⬠⁺　　　　　(d) △⁺

88. Which of the following has highest nucleophilicity ?
    (a) OH^-　　　　(b) NH_2^-　　　　(c) CH_3^-　　　　(d) F^-

89. Nucleophilicity order is correctly represented by ......
    (a) $CH_3^- < NH_2^- < HO^- < F^-$　　　　　(b) $CH_3^- \approx NH_2^- > HO^- \approx F^-$
    (c) $CH_3^- > NH_2 > HO^- > F^-$　　　　　(d) $NH_2^- > F^- > HO^- > CH_3^-$

90. The kind of delocalization involving sigma bond orbitals is called ......
    (a) Inductive effect　　　　　　　　(b) Hyperconjugation effect
    (c) Electromeric effect　　　　　　　(d) Mesomeric effect

91. For the reaction of phenol with $CHCl_3$ in the presence of KOH, the electrophile is ......
    (a) $\overset{+}{C}HCl_2$　　　　(b) $:CCl_2$　　　　(c) $\overset{\bullet}{C}HCl_2$　　　　(d) CCl_4

92. In which of the following, homolytic bond fission takes place ?
    (a) Alkaline hydrolysis of ethyl chloride　　　(b) Addition of HBr to double bond
    (c) Photochlorination of methane　　　　　　(d) Nitration of benzene

93. Which of the following is not a nucleophile ?
    (a) H_2O　　　　(b) CH_3OH　　　　(c) H_2　　　　(d) NH_3

94. The reaction of trans-but-2-ene with Br_2/CH_4 gives ......
    (a) ± 2, 3-Di　　　　　　　　　　(b) meso-2, 3-dibromo butane
    (c) 1-bromo-trans-but-2-ene　　　　(d) 1, 4-dibromo-trans-but-2-ene

95. The IUPAC name of the compound $CH_3CH_2-\overset{\overset{\displaystyle CH_3}{|}}{C}H-CH_2COCl$ is ......
    (a) 3-Methylpentanoyl chloride　　　　(b) 3-Methylbutanoyl chloride
    (c) 1-Chloro-3-ethylbutanone　　　　　(d) 1-Chloro-3-methylpentanone

96. Identify correct order of reactivity in electrophilic substitution reactions of the following compounds :

    　　1　　　　2　　　　3　　　　4

    (a) 1 > 2 > 3 > 4　　(b) 4 > 3 > 2 > 1　　(c) 2 > 1 > 3 > 4　　(d) 2 > 3 > 1 > 4

97. Purification of a substance can be done by sublimation under the condition such that ......
(a) Substance to be purified must have relatively high vapour pressure
(b) Impurities must have vapour pressure lower than the substance to be purified
(c) Both (a) and (b)
(d) None of these

98. When the difference in boiling points of two liquids is not too much, then separation can be carried out by using .....
(a) Steam distillation
(b) Fractional distillation
(c) Vacuum distillation
(d) Simple distillation

99. In adsorption chromatography, absorbent and adsobate are respectively .....
(a) Solid, liquid
(b) Liquid, solid
(c) Solid, solid
(d) Liquid, liquid

100. Colourless spots can be made visible by ......
(a) U.V light in case of aromatic compounds
(b) Ninhydrin in case of amino acids
(c) Both (a) and (b)
(d) None of these

101. In the detection of N and S both in the compound by Lassaigne fusion test, blood red colour is due to the formation of ......
(a) $[Fe(CN)_6]^{3-}$
(b) $[Fe(SCN)_2]^{+}$
(c) $[Fe(SCN)(H_2O)_5]^{2+}$
(d) $Fe(SCN)_2$

102. When CO_2 gas is passed into lime water, solution turns milky due to formation of I but milkyness disappears due to formation of II, I and II are ......
(a) $CaCO_3$, $Ca(HCO_3)_2$
(b) $Ca(HCO_3)_2$, $CaCO_3$
(c) $Ca(OH)_2$, $CaCO_3$
(d) $CaCO_3$, $Ca(OH)_2$

103. Detection of phosphorus in the compound is done by its conversion into phosphate. Reagent to identify phosphate ion is ....
(a) Sodium nitroprusside
(b) Ammonium molybdate
(c) Potassium ferrocyanide
(d) Potassium ferricyanide

104. In Carius method the estimation of ..... is done.
(a) Halogen
(b) Nitrogen
(c) Sulphur
(d) Both (a) and (c)

105. Phosphorus is estimated as .....
(a) $Mg_2P_2O_7$
(b) Na_3HPO_4
(c) P_2O_3
(d) P_2O_5

106. Which method is not correctly matched to determine molecular weight ?
(a) Volatile substance - Victor Meyer
(b) Organic base - Platinum salt
(c) Organic acid - Silver salt
(d) Non-electrolyte (like sucrose) - Carius

107. Which has maximum percentage of chlorine ?
(a) $C_6H_6Cl_6$
(b) CH_3Cl
(c) C_6H_5Cl
(d) $C_2H_4Cl_2$

108. Estimation of nitrogen is done by .....
(a) Kjeldahl's
(b) Carius
(c) Duma's
(d) Both (a) and (c)

109. Which of the organic compound will give red colour in Lassaigne's test ?

(a) NaCNS

(b) $NH_2\!-\!\overset{\overset{\textstyle S}{\|}}{C}\!-\!NH_2$

(c) $NH_2\!-\!\underset{\underset{\textstyle O}{\|}}{C}\!-\!NH_2$

(d) None of these

110. Haemoglobin is a chromoprotein having 4 atoms and Fe in each molecule. Analysis showed 0.35% Fe. Hence its molecular weight is ......

   (a) 64,000   (b) 56,000   (c) 12,000   (d) 1,200

111. Number ofstereaisomers of 3, 5-dibromohexane, 2, 5-diol are   **[Hint :** $2^{n-1} + 2^{(n-2)/2}$**]**

   (a) 4   (b) 6   (c) 8   (d) 10

112. Glycerol can be separated from spent lye in soap industry by ......

   (a) Steam distillation   (b) Fractional distillation

   (c) Distillation under reduced pressure   (d) Ordinary distillation

113. Steam distillation is based on the fact that vaporisation of organic liquid takes place at ....

   (a) Lower temperature than its boiling point

   (b) Higher temperature than its boiling point

   (c) Its boiling point

   (d) Water and organic liquid both undergo distillation

114. Naphthalene has some sand impurity. It can be purified by ....

   (a) Sublimation   (b) Steam distillation

   (c) TLC   (d) Column chromatography

115. Mixture of amino acids can be separated by ....

   (a) Sublimation   (b) Chromatography

   (c) Distillation under steam   (d) Distillation under reduced pressure

116. Sprayer used in detection of amino acids is ....

   (a) Iodine   (b) Benedict's solution

   (c) Fehling's solution   (d) Ninhydrin solution

117. The relative adsorption of each component of the mixture is expressed as ......

   (a) Adsorption factor   (b) Retention factor   (c) Co-factor   (d) Sorption factor

118. Adsorption is made up of .... in TLC.

   (a) Silica gel   (b) Alumina   (c) Both (a) and (b) (d) None of these

119. Number of enantiomeric pairs of tartaric acid is ...... **[Hint :** 2^{n-2}**]**

   (a) 1   (b) 2   (c) 3   (d) 4

120. In the detection of nitrogen, blue/green colour is due to the formation of prussian blue. It is ....

   (a) $NaFe^{III}[Fe^{II}(CN)_6]$ (b) $NaFe^{II}[Fe^{III}(CN)_6]$ (c) $Na_4[Fe(CN)_6]$ (d) $Na_3[Fe(CN)_6]$

121. Which factor is most important in determining chemistry of an organic compound ?

   (a) Melting point   (b) Functional group

   (c) Branching of carbon atoms   (d) None of these

122. Aniline is separated from water-aniline mixture by ......

   (a) Fractional distillation   (b) Steam distillation

   (c) Distillation under reduced pressure   (d) None of these

123. Partition coefficient of an organic compound (A) is 20 between ether and water. 5 gms of (A) in 50 ml water is shaken with 50 ml ether. (A) extracted into ether is ....
  (a) 4.0 gms　　(b) 4.2 gms　　(c) 4.6 gms　　(d) 4.8 gms

124. Solubility of an organic compound is 10 gms/100 ml water at 20°C and 60 gms/100 ml water at 70°C. 30 gms of an impure organic compound is dissolved in 50 ml water at 70°C and cooled to 20°C. Crystals formed weigh ....
  (a) 5 gms　　(b) 20 gms　　(c) 25 gms　　(d) 30 gms

125. An organic compound A contains 20% C, 46.66% N, 6.66% H. It gave NH_3 gas on heating with NaOH. A can be ....
  (a) CH_3CONH_2　　(b) $C_6H_5CONH_2$　　(c) NH_2CONH_2　　(d) $CH_3NHCONH_2$

126. The sulphur content of cysteine is 26.7%. Given that cysteine contains two sulphur atoms, molecular weight of cysteine is approximately ....
  (a) 120　　(b) 240　　(c) 100　　(d) 60

127. $R-Mg-Br + H_2O \longrightarrow RH_{(g)}$. Gas occupies 1.4 litre per gm of RH at STP. Hence $R-Mg-Br$ is ....
  (a) CH_3CH_2MgBr　　(b) C_6H_5MgBr　　(c) $CH_3CH_2CH_2MgBr$　　(d) CH_3MgBr

128. $A \xrightarrow[Cu]{\Delta} \underset{B}{RCl + N_2}$ 1 gm of A gave 0.2 gms of B. Hence A is ......
  (a) $CH_3CH_2N_2Cl$　　(b) $C_6H_5N_2Cl$　　(c) CH_3N_2Cl　　(d) None of these

129. The detection of sulphur in sodium extract is done by ......
  (a) Lead acetate　　(b) Sodium nitroprusside
  (c) Both (a) and (b)　　(d) None of these

130. Glycerol is the compound having .... hydroxyl groups in it.
  (a) 1　　(b) 2　　(c) 3　　(d) 4

131. Which of the following decolourise Br_2 water and also give colour with $FeCl_3$ solution ?
  (a) $CH_3CH = CH_2$　　(b)　　(c)　　(d)

132. 6 gms of organic compound on heating with NaOH gave NH_3 which is neutralised by 200 ml of 1 M HCl. Percentage of nitrogen is ....
  (a) 12%　　(b) 60%　　(c) 46.67%　　(d) 22.67%

133. Solubility of benzoic acid in benzene is twice than that in water. 100 ml of benzene is added to 100 ml of aqueous solution containing 2 gms of water. Thus, when equilibrium is attained, benzoic acid extracted into benzene is ....
  (a) 2.0 gms　　(b) 1.0 gm　　(c) 0.67 gm　　(d) 1.33 gms

134. Sulphur is converted into Na_2S in Lassaigne's fusion test. Na_2S can be detected by ......
  (I) CH_3COOH　　(II) $(CH_3COO)_2Pb$　　(III) $Na_2[Fe(CN)_5NO]$
  Correct codes are :
  (a) (I), (II)　　(b) (II), (III)　　(c) (I), (III)　　(d) (III) only

135. In Carius method for the estimation of sulphur, precipitate is of ....
  (a) $BaSO_4$　　(b) $Ba(HSO_4)_2$　　(c) BaS　　(d) Ag_2S

136. 0.63 gms of a dibasic acid neutralizes 100 ml of 0.1 N NaOH solution. Molar mass (g mol^{-1}) of dibasic acid is ....
  (a) 63　　(b) 126　　(c) 31.5　　(d) 12.6

PREVIOUS YEAR'S QUESTIONS

1. Among the following compounds the one which is most reactive towards electrophilic nitration is ...... **[CBSE AIPMT 2012]**

    (a) Benzoic acid   (b) Nitrobenzene   (c) Toluene   (d) Benzene

2. The correct order of decreasing acid strength of trichloroacetic acid (A), trifluoroacetic acid (B), acetic acid (C) and formic acid (D) is ...... **[CBSE AIPMT 2012]**

    (a) B > A > D > C   (b) B > D > C > A   (c) A > B > C > D   (d) A > C > B > D

3. Which nomenclature is not according to IUPAC system ? **[CBSE AIPMT 2012]**

    (a) $Br–CH_2–CH = CH_2$ 1-bromo prop-2-ene

    (b) $CH_3–CH_2–C(CH_3)(Br)CH_2CH(CH_3)_2$ 4-bromo-2, 4-dimethylhexane

    (c) $(CH_3)_2CH(C_6H_6)–CH_2–CH_3$ 2-methyl-3-phenyl pentane

    (d) $CH_3CO–CH_2–CH_2COOH$ 5-oxohexanoic acid

4. Which of the following acids does not exhibit optical isomerism ? **[CBSE AIPMT 2012]**

    (a) Maleic acid   (b) α-amino acids   (c) Lactic acid   (d) Tartaric acid

5. Consider the reaction **[CBSE AIPMT 2012]**

    $RCHO + NH_2NH_2 \rightarrow RCH = N – NH_2$

    What type of reaction is it ?

    (a) Electrophilic addition elimination reaction

    (b) Free radical addition elimination reaction

    (c) Electrophilic substitution elimination reaction

    (d) Nucleophilic addition elimination reaction

6. The well known compounds, (+) – lactic acid and (–) – lactic acid, have the same molecular formula $C_3H_6O_3$. The correct relationship between them is ...... **[WBJEE 2012]**

    (a) constitutional isomers   (b) geometrical isomers

    (c) identicalness   (d) optical isomers

7. Which of the following does not show electromerism effect ? **[AFMC 2012]**

    (a) Alkene   (b) Ethers   (c) Aldehydes   (d) Ketones

8. In which of the following compounds, one of the structural isomers is also capable of showing enantiomorphism ? **[AFMC 2012]**

    (a) C_3H_8 (b) $C_3H_6Br_2$ (c) C_5H_{12} (d) C_6H_{14}

9. The radical ⬡–$\overset{\bullet}{C}H_2$ is aromatic because it has ...... **[NEET 2013]**

    (a) 6p-orbitals and 7 unpaired electrons   (b) 6p-orbitals and 6 unpaired electrons

    (c) 7p-orbitals and 6 unpaired electrons   (d) 7p-orbitals and 7 unpaired electrons

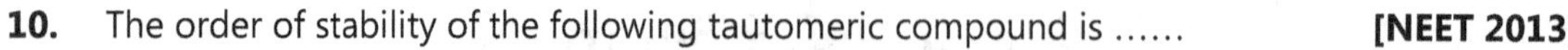

10. The order of stability of the following tautomeric compound is ......   **[NEET 2013]**

$$CH_2 = \overset{\overset{\displaystyle OH}{|}}{C} - CH_2 - \overset{\overset{\displaystyle O}{||}}{C} - CH_3 \;\rightleftharpoons\; CH_2 = \overset{\overset{\displaystyle OH}{+}}{C} - CH_2 - \overset{\overset{\displaystyle O}{||}}{C} - CH_3 \;\longrightarrow\; CH_3 - \overset{\overset{\displaystyle OH}{|}}{C} = CH_2 - \overset{\overset{\displaystyle O}{||}}{C} - CH_3$$

$$\quad\quad\quad\quad I \quad\quad\quad\quad\quad\quad\quad\quad\quad\quad\quad II \quad\quad\quad\quad\quad\quad\quad\quad\quad III$$

(a) II > III > I   (b) I > II > III   (c) III > II > I   (d) II > I > III

11. The structure of isobutyl group in an organic compound is :   **[NEET 2013]**

(a) $CH_3 - \overset{\overset{\displaystyle CH_3}{|}}{\underset{\underset{\displaystyle CH_3}{|}}{C}} -$

(b) $\overset{\overset{\displaystyle CH_3}{|}}{CH_3 - CH - CH_2}$

(c) $CH_3 - CH_2 - CH_2CH_3$ (d) $CH_3 - CH_2 - CH_2 - CH_2 -$

12. Structure of the compound whose IUPAC name is

3 – ethyl – 2 hydroxy – 4 – methylhex – 3 en – 5 ynoic acid is ......   **[NEET 2013]**

(a)

(b)

(c)

(d)

13. Which of the following will not be soluble in sodium hydrogen carbonate ?   **[AIPMT 2014]**

(a) o-Nitrophenol   (b) Benzenesulphonic acid

(c) 2, 4, 6-trinitrophenol   (d) Benzoic acid

14. In Duma's method for estimation of nitrogen, 0.25 g of an organic compound gave 43 litre of nitrogen collected at 300 K temperature and 725 mm pressure. If the aqueous tension at 300 K is 25, the percentage of nitrogen in the compound is ......   **[AIPMT 2015]**

(a) 18.20   (b) 16.76   (c) 15.76   (d) 17.36

15. Which of the following is the most correct electron displacement for a nucleophilic reaction to take place ?   **[AIPMT 2015]**

(a) $CH_3 \leftarrow C = \underset{\underset{\displaystyle H}{}}{C} - CH_2 - Cl$

(b) $CH_3 \rightarrow C = \underset{\underset{\displaystyle H}{}}{C} - CH_2 - Cl$

(c) $CH_3 \rightarrow C = \underset{\underset{\displaystyle H}{}}{C} - CH_2 - Cl$

(d) $CH_3 \rightarrow C = \underset{\underset{\displaystyle H}{}}{C} - CH_2 - Cl$

16. The most reactive nucleophile among the following is ......   **[A.I.I.M.S. 2003]**

(a) $CH_3\bar{O} :$ (b) $C_6H_5\bar{O} :$ (c) $(CH_3)_2CH\bar{O} :$ (d) $(CH_3)_3C\bar{O} :$

17. In which of the following compounds, the C – Cl bond ionization shall give most stable carbonium ion ?   **[AIPMT 2015]**

(a)
$$CH_3-\underset{\underset{CH_3}{|}}{\overset{\overset{CH_3}{|}}{C}}-Cl$$

(b) Ph—$\overset{\overset{H}{|}}{C}H$—Cl

(c) $NO_2CH_2-\overset{\overset{H}{|}}{C}H-Cl$

(d) $CH_3-\underset{\underset{H}{|}}{\overset{\overset{CH_3}{|}}{C}}-Cl$

18. Consider the following compounds

$$CH_3-\underset{\underset{CH_3}{|}}{\overset{\overset{CH_3}{|}}{C}}-\overset{*}{C}H-\bigcirc$$

I

$$Ph-\underset{*}{\overset{\overset{Ph}{|}}{C}}\cdots Ph$$

II

III

Hyperconjugation occurs in ......

(a) II only   (b) III only   (c) I and III   (d) I only

19. Given :   **[AIPMT 2015]**

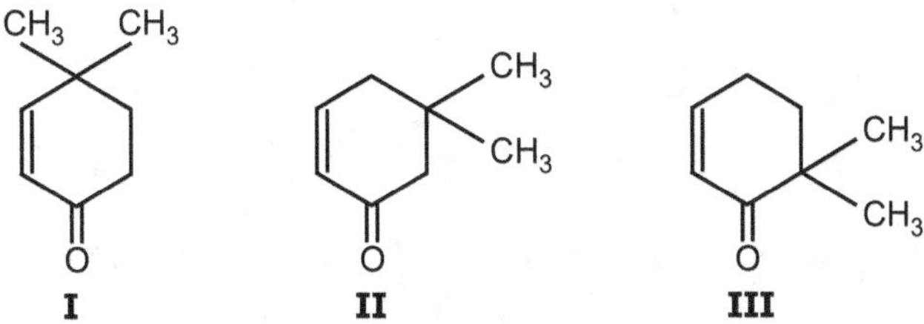

I   II   III

The enthalpy of hydrogenation of these compounds will be in the order as ......

(a) III > II > I   (b) III > I > II   (c) II > I > III   (d) I > II > III

20. The enolic form of ethyl acetoacetate below has   **[AIPMT 2015]**

$$\underset{\text{keto}}{H_3C-\overset{\overset{O}{\|}}{C}-CH_2-\overset{\overset{O}{\|}}{C}-O-C_2H_5} \rightleftharpoons \underset{\text{enol}}{H_3C-\overset{\overset{OH}{|}}{C}=CH-\overset{\overset{O}{\|}}{C}-O-C_2H_5}$$

(a) 16 sigma bonds and 1 pi-bond   (b) 9 sigma bonds and 2 pi-bonds

(c) 0 sigma bond and 1 pi-bond   (d) 18 sigma bonds and 2 pi-bonds

21. Given :

I   II   III

Which of the given compounds can exhibit tautomerism ?   **[AIPMT 2015]**

(a) I and III   (b) II and III   (c) I, II and III   (d) I and II

22. The number of structural isomers possible from the molecular formula C_3H_9N is ......

(a) 2   (b) 3   (c) 4   (d) 5 **[RE AIPMT 2015]**

23. Of the following the compound in which optical isomerism is present is ......

[Kerala, med. 2003]

(a) CH_3CH_2OH (b) $CH_3CHClBr$ (c) CCl_2BrF (d) CCl_2F_2

24. Which of the following statement is wrong ?   **[EAMCET 2003]**

(a) Diethyl ketone and methyl propyl ketone are position isomers

(b) 2-chloro pentane and 1-chloro pentane are position isomers

(c) n-butane and 2-methyl propane are chain isomers

(d) Acetone and propionaldehyde are functional isomers

25. How many chiral isomers can be drawn from 2-bromo, 3-chlorobutane ?   **[Dec. 2003]**

(a) 2   (b) 3   (c) 4   (d) 5

26. Carbocation which is most stable   **[BHU 2003]**

(a) $CH_3CH_2^+$ (b) CH_3^+ (c) $C_6H_5CH_2^+$ (d) $CH_3CH_2CH_2^+$

27. In a reaction of C_6H_5Y, major product (> 60%) is m-isomer, so the group Y is ......

[AIIMS 1997, UPSEAT 2003]

(a) –COOH   (b) –NH_2 (c) –OH   (c) –Cl

28. Which of the following compounds are not arranged in order of decreasing reactivity towards electrophilic substitution ?   **[Dec. 2003]**

(a) Fluorobenzene > chlorobenzene > bromobenzene

(b) Phenol > n-propyl benzene > benzoic acid

(c) Chlorotoluene > para - nitrotoluene > 2 – chloro nitrotoluene

(d) Benzoic acid > phenol > n-propyl benzene

29. With a change in hybridization of the carbon bearing the charge, the stability of a carbanion increases in the order ......

(a) $sp < sp^2 < sp^3$ (b) $sp < sp^3 < sp^2$ (c) $sp^3 < sp^2 < sp$ (d) $sp^2 < sp < sp^3$

30. Cyclic hydrocarbon molecule 'A' has all the carbon and hydrogen in a single plane. All the carbon – carbon bonds are of same length less than 1.54 A°, but more than 1.34 A°. The C – C bond angle will be ......   **[BVP 2003]**

(a) 109° 28'   (b) 100°   (c) 180°   (d) 120°

31. The dipole moment is highest for ......   **[AIIMS 2004]**

(a) Trans-2-butane   (b) 1, 3-dimethylbenzene

(c) Acetophenone   (d) Ethanol

32. Orbital interaction between sigma bond of a substituent group and a neighbouring pi orbital is known as ......   **[Kerala PMT 2004]**

(a) Hyperconjugation   (b) Inductive effect

(c) Steric effect   (d) Dipole dipole interactions

33. Which of the following is the most stable compound ?   **[BHU 2004]**

  (a) Ph_3C^+ (b) Ph_2C^+H (c) $Ph_3C^+H_2$ (d) PhC^+H_2

34. Which of the following cannot be used in Friedel Craft's reaction ?   **[AFMC 2004]**

  (a) $FeCl_3$ (b) $FeBr_2$ (c) $AlCl_2$ (d) $NaCl$

35. Dehydrohalogenation of an alkyl halide is a/an ......   **[MHT CET 2004]**

  (a) Nucleophilic substitution reaction

  (b) Elimination reaction

  (c) Both nucleophilic substitution and elimination reaction

  (d) Rearrangement reaction

36. Which one of the following is least reactive in a nucleophilic substitution reaction ?

                                                    [CBSE PMT 2004]

  (a) CH_3CH_2Cl (b) $CH_2 = CHCH_2Cl$ (c) $(CH_3)_3C - Cl$ (d) $CH_2 = CHCl$

37. Which of the following will have a meso isomer also ......   **[AIEEE 2004]**

  (a) 2, 3-dichloropentane   (b) 2, 3-dichlorobutane

  (c) 2-chlorobutane   (d) 2-hydroxypropanoic acid

38. For which of the following parameters, the structural isomers C_2H_5OH and CH_3OCH_3 would be expected to have the same value ?   **[AIEEE 2004]**

  (a) Boiling points

  (b) Vapour pressure at the same temperature

  (c) Heat of vaporization

  (d) Gaseous densities at the same temperature and pressure

39. The geometrical isomerism is shown by   **[AIIMS 2004]**

  (a)   (b)

  (c)   (d)

40. $CH_3CH(OH)COOH$ shows ......   **[BVP 2004]**

  (a) Geometrical isomerism   (b) Optical isomerism

  (c) Both of these   (d) None of these

41. Which will have enantiomers ?   **[BVP 2004]**

  (a) $CH_3CH_2CH(Cl) - CH_3$ (b) $CH_3CH_2CH_2CH_2Cl$

  (c) $CH_3CH_2CH_2CHCl_2$ (d) None of these

42. The number of possible enantiomeric pairs that can be produced during monochlorination of 2-methylbutane is ......   **[Pb. CET 2004]**

  (a) 3   (b) 4   (c) 1   (d) 2

43. In the given conformation, if C_2 is rotated about $C_2 - C_3$ bond anticlockwise by an angle of 120° then the conformation obtained is ...... **[AIIMS 2004]**

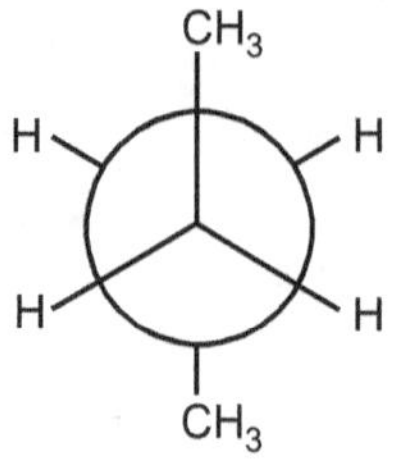

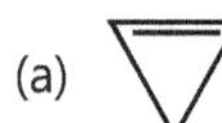

(a) Fully eclipsed conformation

(b) Partially eclipsed conformation

(c) Gauche conformation

(d) Staggered conformation

44. The molecular formula of diphenyl methane is **[CBSE PMT 2004]**

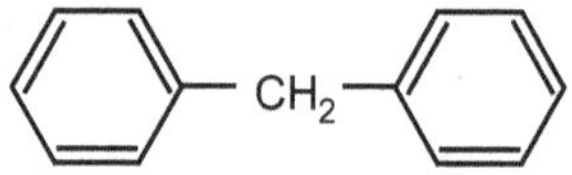

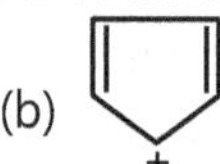

How many structural isomers are possible when one of the hydrogen is replaced by a chlorine atom ?

(a) 8 (b) 7 (c) 6 (d) 4

45. Among the following compounds which can be dehydrated very easily is ...... **[AIEEE 2004]**

(a) $CH_3CH_2\overset{\overset{\displaystyle OH}{|}}{\underset{\underset{\displaystyle CH_3}{|}}{C}}CH_2CH_3$

(b) $CH_3CH_2CH_2\overset{\overset{\displaystyle OH}{|}}{C}HCH_3$

(c) $CH_3CH_2CH_2CH_2CH_2OH$

(d) $CH_3CH_2\overset{}{C}HCH_2CH_2OH$
$|$
CH_3

46. Among the following the dissociation constant is highest for ...... **[AIIMS 2004]**

(a) C_6H_5OH (b) $C_6H_5CH_2OH$ (c) $CH_3C \equiv CH$ (d) $CH_3NH_3^+Cl^-$

47. A compound has 3 chiral carbon atoms. The number of possible optical isomers it can have is ...... **[Dec. 2004]**

(a) 3 (b) 2 (c) 8 (d) 4

48. Among the following the aromatic compound is ...... **[AIIMS 2004]**

(a) ▽   (b) ⬠⁺   (c)  ▢   (d)  ▽⁻

49. The correct IUPAC name of phenetole is ...... **[A.I.I.M.S. 2004]**

(a) Methoxybenzene

(b) Ethoxybenzene

(c) Diphenyl ether

(d) Benzoxybenzene

50. Which gives monosubstituted product ? **[DPMT 2005]**

(a) o-dinitrobenzene

(b) m-dinitrobenzene

(c) p-dinitrobenzene

(d) nitrobenzene

51. Among the following the strongest nucleophile is ......   **[AIIMS 2005]**

    (a) C_2H_5SH (b) CH_3COO^- (c) CH_3NH_2 (d) $NCCH_2^-$

52. The chirality of the following compound is   **[CBSE PMT 2005]**

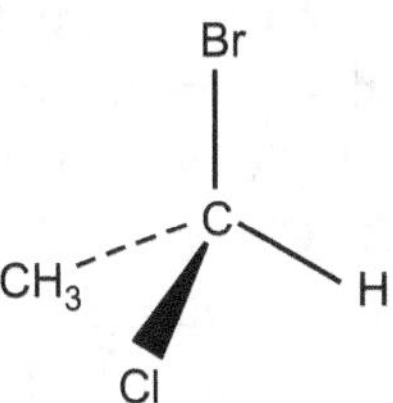

    (a) R   (b) S   (c) Z   (d) E

53. Which one of the following pairs represents stereoisomerism ?   **[CBSE PMT 2005]**

    (a) Chain isomerism and rotational isomerism

    (b) Structural isomerism and geometric isomerism

    (c) Linkage isomerism and geometric isomerism

    (d) Optical isomerism and geometrical isomerism

54. Among the following the most stable compound is ......   **[AIIMMS 2005]**

    (a) cis – 1, 2 – cyclohexanediol   (b) trans – 1, 2 – cyclohexanediol

    (c) cis – 1, 3 – cyclohexanediol   (d) trans – 1, 3-cyclohexanediol

55. Which will give chiral molecule ?   **[DPMT 2005]**

    (a) $CH_3OCl \xrightarrow{4AlH_4}$ (b) $C_2H_5CHO \xrightarrow[H_2O/H^+]{CH_3MgBr}$

    (c) $(CH_3)_2CHC_2H_5 \xrightarrow{Cu}$ (d) $\underset{CH_3}{\overset{H}{>}}C=C\underset{CH_3}{\overset{CH_3}{<}} \xrightarrow{Cl_2}$

56. Which of the following is not a chiral?   **[CBSE AIMPMT 2006]**

    (a) 2-butanol   (b) 2, 3-dibromopentane

    (c) 3-bromopentane   (d) 2-hydroxypropanoic acid

57. Among the following which one can have a meso form ?   **[AIIMS 2006]**

    (a) $CH_3CH(OH)CH(Cl)C_2H_5$ (b) $CH_3CH(OH)CH(OH)CH_3$

    (c) $C_2H_5CH(OH)CH(OH)CH_3$ (d) $HOCH_2CH(Cl)CH_3$

58. The type of isomerism observed in urea molecule is ......   **[AIIMS 2007]**

    (a) chain   (b) position   (c) geometrical   (d) tautomerism

59. $CH_3 - CHCl - CH_2 - CH_3$ has a chiral centre. Which one of the following represents its R configuration ?   **[CBSE AIPMT 2007]**

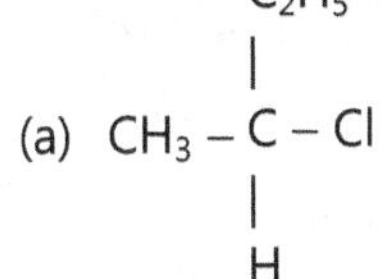
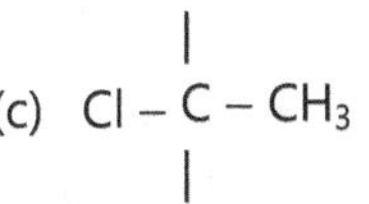
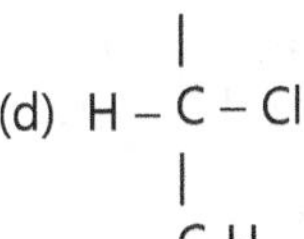

60. If there is no rotation of plane polarized light by a compound in a specific solvent, thought to be chiral, it may mean that   **[CBSE AIPT 2007]**
   (a) the compound is certainly a chiral
   (b) the compound is certainly meso
   (c) there is no compound in the solvent
   (d) the compound may be racemic mixture

61. Which of the following represents the correct order of the acidity in the given compound ?
   (a) $CH_3COOH > BrCH_2COOH > ClCH_2COOH > FCH_2COOH$ **[CBSE AIPMT 2007]**
   (b) $FCH_2COOH > CH_3COOH > BrCH_2COOH > ClCH_2COOH$
   (c) $BrCH_2COOH > ClCH_2COOH > FCH_2COOH > CH_3COOH$
   (d) $FCH_2COOH > ClCH_2COOH > BrCH_2COOH > CH_3COOH$

62. For the following ......
   (1) I^- (2) Cl^- (3) Br^-

   the increasing order of nucleophilicity would be ......   **[CBSE AIPMT 2007]**
   (a) $I^- < Br^- < Cl^-$ (b) $Cl^- < Br^- < I^-$ (c) $I^- < Cl^- < Br^-$ (d) $Br^- < Cl^- < I^-$

63. The decreasing order of stability of the ions is ......   **[AIIMS 2007]**
   (I) $CH_3 - CH^+ - CH_3$ (II) $CH_3 - CH^+ - OCH_3$ (III) $CH_3 - C^+H - COCH_3$
   (a) I > II > III   (b) III > II > I   (c) II > III > I   (d) II > I > III

64. The order of decreasing reactivity towards an electrophilic reagent for the following
          [CBSE AIPMT 2007]
   (I) Benzene   (II) Toluene   (III) Chlorobenzene   (IV) Phenol
   would be ......
   (a) (I) > (II) > (III) > (IV)   (b) (II) > (IV) > (I) > (III)
   (c) (IV) > (III) > (II) > (I)   (d) (IV) > (II) > (I) > (III)

65. Maximum enol content is in ......   **[AIIMS 2008]**

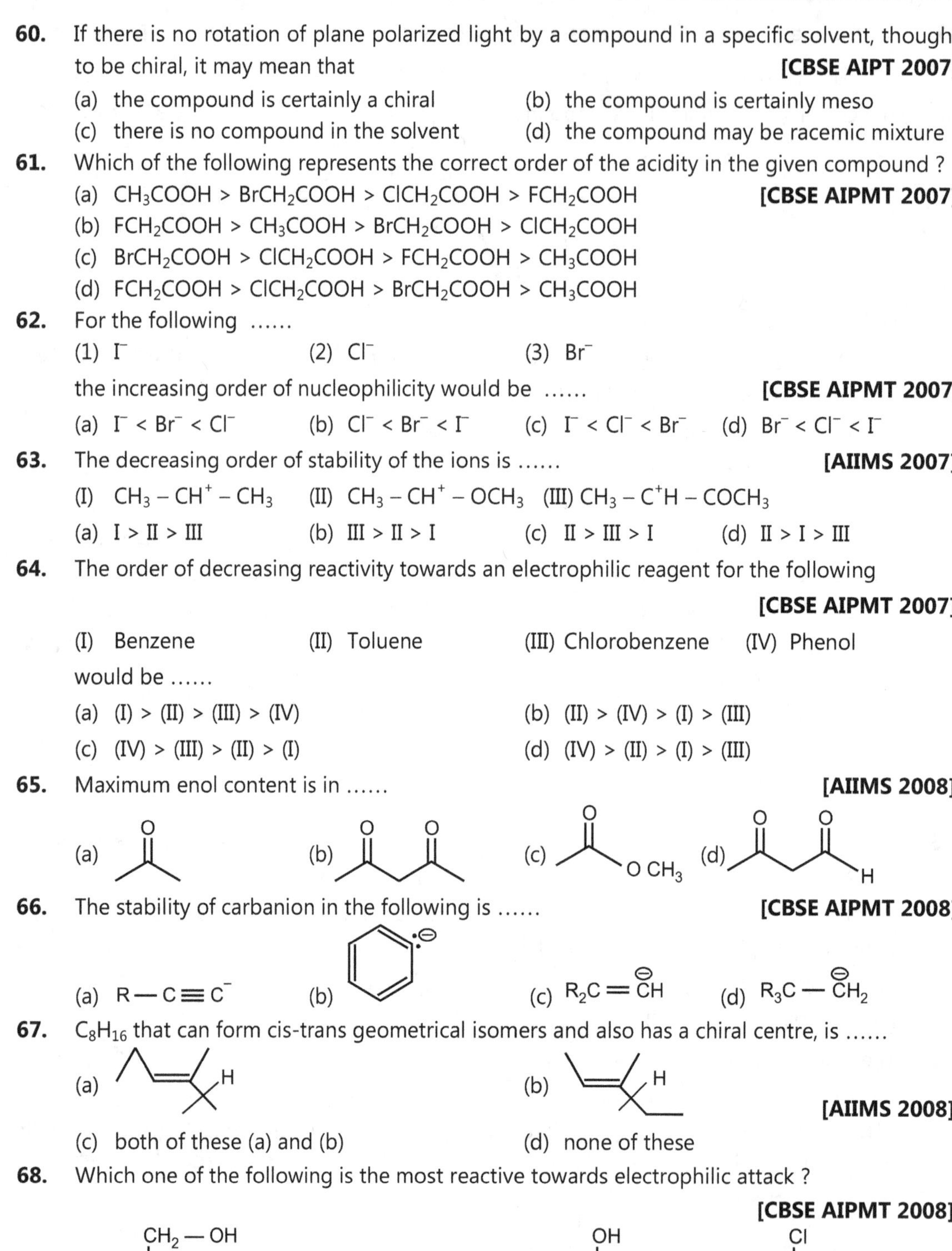

66. The stability of carbanion in the following is ......   **[CBSE AIPMT 2008]**

   (a) $R - C \equiv C^-$ (b)   (c) $R_2C = \overset{\ominus}{C}H$ (d) $R_3C - \overset{\ominus}{C}H_2$

67. C_8H_{16} that can form cis-trans geometrical isomers and also has a chiral centre, is ......
   (a)   (b)
                                                                      [AIIMS 2008]
   (c) both of these (a) and (b)   (d) none of these

68. Which one of the following is the most reactive towards electrophilic attack ?
          [CBSE AIPMT 2008]

69. Which of the following compounds will exhibit cis-trans (geometrical) isomerism ?

[CBSE AIPMT 2009]

(a) 2- butane   (b) Butanol   (c) 2-butyne   (d) 2-butenol

70. Which will not show geometrical isomerism?   **[CBSE AIPMT 2009]**

(a) $CH_3CH = NOH$ (b) 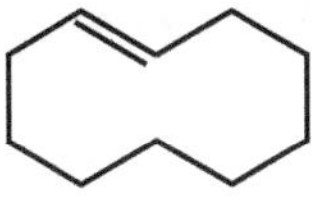   (c) $HO - N = N - OH$ (d) $(CH_3)_2C = NOH$

71. Which is the strongest acid ?   **[CPMT 2009]**

(a) C_6H_6 (b) C_6H_4 (c) $CH \equiv CH$ (d) CH_3OH

72. Which of the following reactions is an example of nucleophilic substitution reaction?

[CBSE AIPMT 2009]

(a) $RX + KOH \rightarrow ROH + KX$ (b) $2RX + 2Na \rightarrow R - R + 2NaX$

(c) $RX + H_2 \rightarrow RX + HX$ (d) $RX + Mg \rightarrow RMgX$

73. The total number of isomers of C_4H_7OH is ......   **[CPMT 2010]**

(a) 3   (b) 4   (c) 6   (d) 7

74. In the following the most stable conformation of n-butane is ......   **[CBSE AIPMT 2010]**

(a) 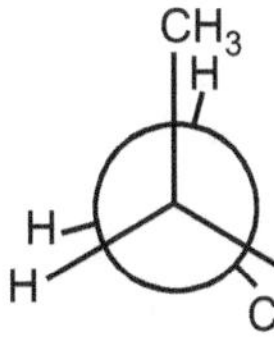   (b) 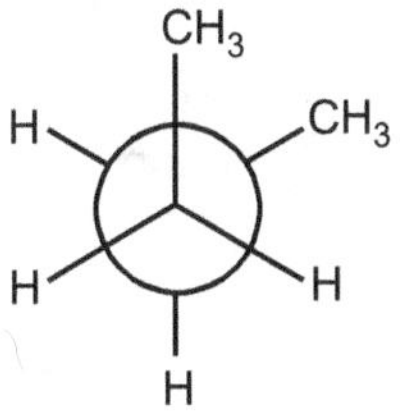   (c) 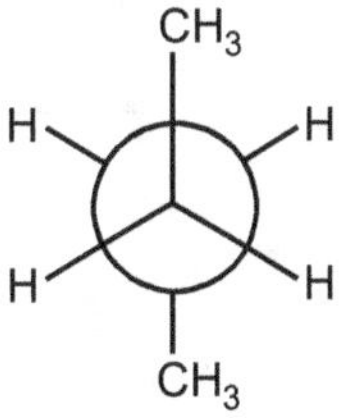   (d)

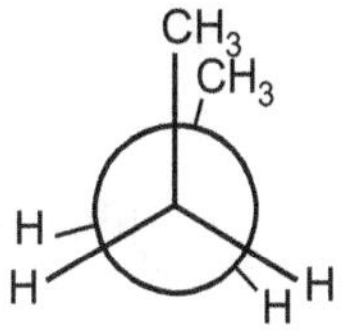

75. The correct order of acidity of the following compounds is ......   **[CPMT 2010]**

(a) $RCOOH > C_2H_2 > H_2O > ROH$ (b) $RCOOH > ROH > H_2O > C_2H_2$

(c) $RCOOH > ROH > C_2H_2 > H_2O$ (d) $RCOOH > H_2O > ROH > C_2H_2$

76. Among the given compounds, the most susceptible to nucleophilic attack at the carbonyl group is :   **[CBSE AIPMT 2010]**

(a) CH_3COCl (b) CH_3COOCH_3 (c) CH_3CONH_2 (d) $CH_3COOCOCH_3$

77. Which of the following is the most stable carbocation ?   **[CPMT 2010]**

(a) $C_6H_5CH_2^+$ (b) $CH_3CH_2^+$ (c) $(CH_3)_2C^+H$ (d) $(CH_3)_3C^+$

78. The correct order of the increasing reactivity of C – X bond towards nucleophile in the following compound is   **[CBSE AIPMT 2010]**

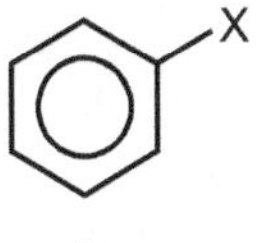

I 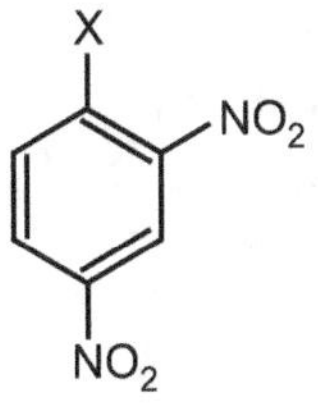   II $(CH_3)_3 - X$ $(CH_3)_2CH - X$

     III   IV

(a) III < II < I < IV   (b) I < II < IV < III   (c) II < III < I < IV   (d) IV < III < I < II

79. Which of the following is the most reactive towards electrophilic reagent ?

[CBSE AIPMT 2011]

(a) $CH_3CHO + HCN \rightarrow CH_3CH(OH)CN$

(b) $CH_3 - CH = CH_2 + H_2O \xrightarrow{H^+} CH_3 - \underset{\underset{OH}{|}}{CH} - CH_3$

(c) $RCHO + R'MgX \dashrightarrow R - \underset{\underset{OH}{|}}{CH} - R'$

(d) $CH_3 - CH_2 - \underset{\underset{CH_3}{|}}{CH} - CH_2 - Br + NH_3 \longrightarrow CH_3 - CH_2 - \underset{\underset{CH_3}{|}}{CH} - CH_2 - NH_2$

80. Considering the state of hybridization of carbon atoms, find out the molecule among the following which is linear?

[AIPMT 201]

(a) $CH_3 - CH = CH - CH_3$　　　　　　(b) $CH_3 - C \equiv C - CH_3$

(c) $CH_2 = CH - CH_2 - C \equiv CH$　　　　(d) $CH_3 - CH_2 - CH_2 - CH_3$

81. In the following reactions

[AIPMT 2011]

(I) $CH_3 - \underset{\underset{CH_3}{|}}{\overset{\overset{H}{|}}{C}} - \overset{\overset{OH}{|}}{CH} - CH_3 \xrightarrow{H^+/heat} \underset{major}{A} + \underset{minor}{B}$

(II) $A \xrightarrow{HBr/dark} \underset{major}{C} + \underset{minor}{D}$

(a) $CH_2 = \underset{\underset{CH_3}{|}}{C} - CH_2 - CH_3$ and $\underset{\underset{Br}{|}}{CH_2} - \underset{\underset{CH_3}{|}}{CH} - CH_2 - CH_3$

(b) $CH_3 - \underset{\underset{CH_3}{|}}{C} = CH - CH_3$ and $CH_3 - \underset{\underset{Br}{|}}{\overset{\overset{CH_3}{|}}{C}} - CH_2 - CH_3$

(c) $CH_3 - \underset{\underset{CH_3}{|}}{C} = CH - CH_3$ and $CH_3 - \underset{\underset{Br}{|}}{\overset{\overset{CH_3}{|}}{CH}} - CH - CH_3$

(d) $CH_2 = \underset{\underset{CH_3}{|}}{C} - CH_2 - CH_3$ and $CH_3 - \underset{\underset{Br}{|}}{\overset{\overset{CH_3}{|}}{C}} - CH_2 - CH_3$

82. The number of structural isomers possible from the molecular formula C_3H_9N is ......

[RE AIPMT 2015]

   (a) 2   (b) 3   (c) 4   (d) 5

83. In the mechanism of Hoffmann reaction, which intermediate rearranges to alkyl isocyanate?

[C.B.S.E. 2005]

   (a) Bromoamide   (b) Nitrene   (c) Nitroso   (d) Amide

84. The compound having only primary hydrogen atoms is ......   **[J.I.P.M.E.R. 2006]**

   (a) Isobutene   (b) 2, 3-dimethylbutene

   (c) Cyclohexane   (d) Propyne

85. The number and type of bond between two carbon atoms in calcium carbide are ......

[C.B.S.E. 2006]

   (a) One sigma, one pi   (b) One sigma, two pi

   (c) Two sigma, one pi   (d) Two sigma, one pi

86. The compound which has one isopropyl group is ......   **[P.M.T. M.P. 2001]**

   (a) 2, 2, 3, 3-tetramethylpentane   (b) 2, 2-dimethylpentane

   (c) 2, 2, 3-trimethylpentane   (d) 2-methylpentane

87. The IUPAC name of $OHCCH = CH-CH - CH = CH_2$ is ......

$$\underset{\displaystyle CH_2CH_2CH_2CH_3}{|}$$

   (a) 5-vinyl ocit-3-en-1-al   (b) 4-butyl hexa-2, 5-dien-1-al

   (c) 5-vinyl oct-5-en-8-al   (d) 3-butyl hexa 1-4-dien-8-al

88. The correct IUPAC name for $CH_3-CH - CHO$ is ......   **[C.P.M.T. 2000]**

$$\underset{\displaystyle CH_2CH_3}{|}$$

   (a) Butan-2-aldehyde   (b) 2-methylbutanal

   (c) 3-methyl isobutyraldehyde   (d) 2-ethylpropanal

89. Which of the following has the highest nucleophilicity?   **[BHU 2005]**

   (a) F^- (b) OH^- (c) CH_3^- (d) NH_2^-

90. Which is most stable?   **[CBSE Pre. 2010]**

   (a) $CH_2 = CHCl$ (b) $CH_2 = CH - CH_2Cl$

   (c) $C_6H_5CH_2Cl$ (d) $C_6H_5CH_2CH_2Cl$

91. The IUPAC name of the compound $CH_3-\overset{\displaystyle \overset{OH}{|}}{C}H -CH_2-\overset{\displaystyle \overset{CH_3}{|}}{C}H-CHO$ is ......   **[J.I.P.M.E.R. 2000]**

   (a) 4-Hydroxyl-1-methylpentanal   (b) 4-Hydroxy-2-methylpentanal

   (c) 2-Hydroxy-4-methylpentanal   (d) 2-Hydroxy-2-methylpentanal

92. $CH_3CH_2CH_2CH(CH = CH_2)CH_2CH_2CH_3$ is ......   **[Kerala E.E.E. 2000]**
(a) 4-Ethylheptane
(b) 3-Propylhex-1-ene
(c) 4-Ethylhexane
(d) 3-Ethyenylheptane

93. The IUPAC name of $CH_3CH = CHCOOC_2H_5$ is ......   **[Haryana C.E.E.T. 2000]**
(a) Ethyl but-1-enoate
(b) Ethyl but-2-enoate
(c) Ethyl prop-2-enoate
(d) None of these

94. IUPAC name of $CH_2 = CH - CN$ is ......   **[N.S.E. 2001]**
(a) Ethynenitrile
(b) Vinyl cyanide
(c) Cyanoethene
(d) 2-Propenenitrile

95. IUPAC name of 4-isopropyl-m-xylene is ......   **[D.P.M.T. 2001]**
(a) 1-Isopropyl-2, 4-dimethylbenzene
(b) 4-Isopropyl-m-xylene
(c) 4-Isopropyl-3, 5-dimethylbenzene
(d) 4-Isopropyl-3, 5-dimethylbenzene

96. The correct nomenclature (IUPAC) for the following alcohol   **[U.P.S.E.A.T. 2002]**

$$CH_3CH_2 \diagdown \quad \diagup CH_3$$
$$C$$
$$CH_3CH_2 \diagup \quad \diagdown OH$$

is ......

(a) 2-Ethyl-2-butanol
(b) 3-Methyl-3-pentanol
(c) 3-Ethyl-3-methyl-2-pentanol
(d) 1, 1-Dimethylanol

97. The name of $ClCH_2-C = C - CH_2Cl$ according to IUPAC nomenclature system is ......

$$\underset{Br \quad Br}{| \quad |}$$

[M.P.P.M.T. 2001]

(a) 2, 3-dibromo-1, 4-dichlorobutene-2
(b) 1, 4-dichloro-2, 3-dibromo but-2-ene
(c) Dichlorodibromobutene
(d) Dichlorodibromobutane

98. The IUPAC name of the following compound
$CH_3-C(CH_3)_2-CH = C(CH_3)_2$ is ......   **[A.I.I.M.S. 2002**
(a) 1, 1, 3, 3-Tetramethylbut-1-ene
(b) 1, 3, 3-Trimethylpent-2-ene
(c) 2, 2, 4-Trimethylbut-4-ene
(d) 2, 4, 4-Trimethylpent-2-ene

99. The name of the compound given below is   **[C.B.S.E. 2003]**

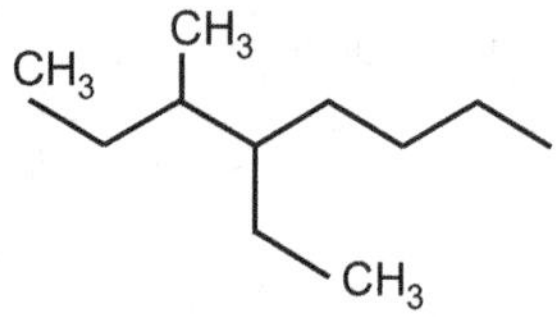

(a) 5-Ethyl-6-methyloctane
(b) 4-Ethyl-3-methyloctane
(c) 3-Methyl-4-ethyloctane
(d) 2, 3-Dimethylheptane

100. The IUPAC name of   **[Orissa J.E.E. 2004]**
$CH_2 = CH - CH(CH_3CH_2)C = CH_2$ is

$$|$$
$$Br$$

(a) 4-Bromo-3-ethyl-1, 4-pentadiene
(b) 2-Bromo-3-ethyl-1, 4-pentadiene
(c) 2-Bromo-3-ethyl-1, 5-pentadiene
(d) None of these

101. The IUPAC name of given compound is

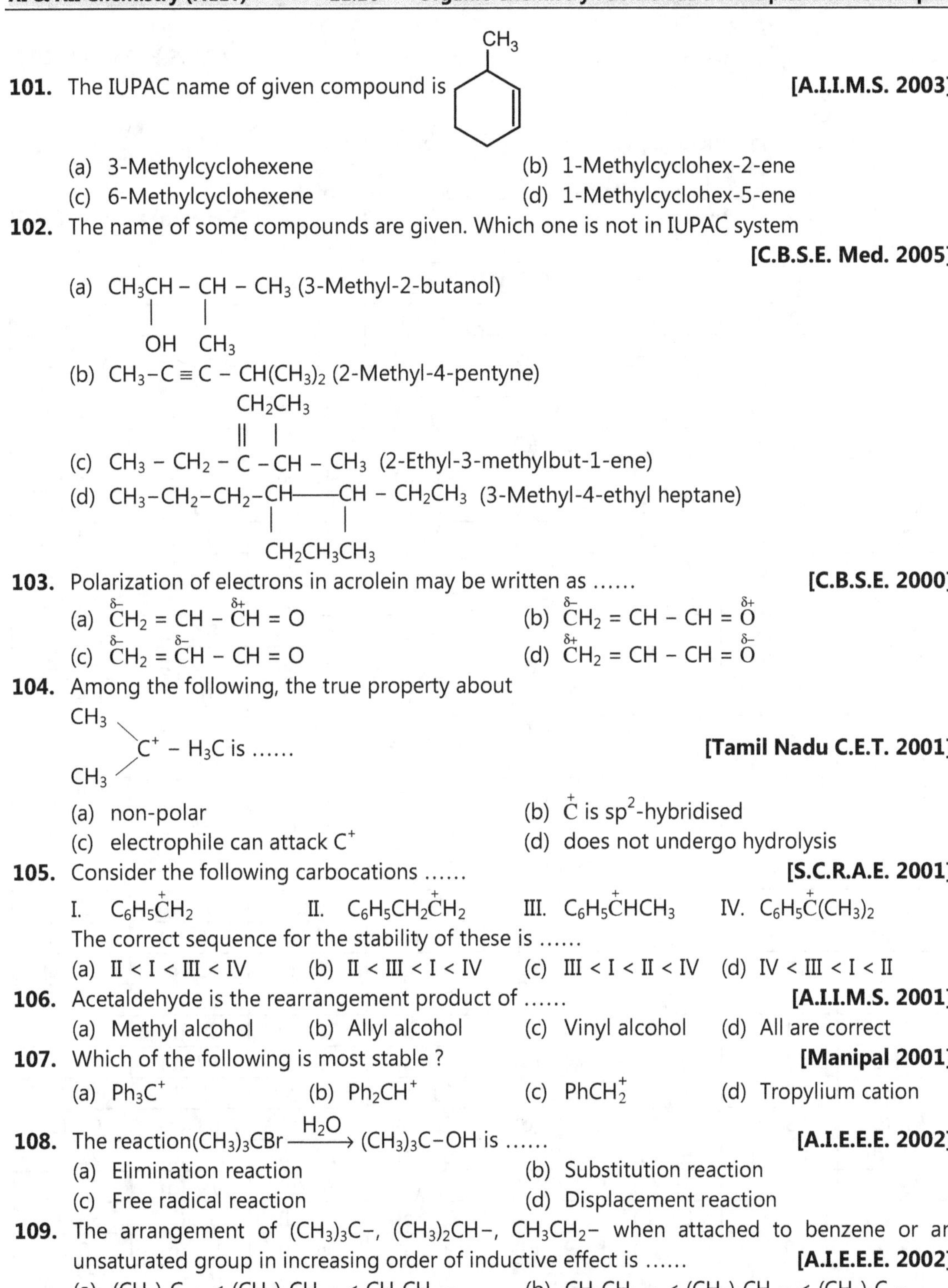

[A.I.I.M.S. 2003]

(a) 3-Methylcyclohexene
(b) 1-Methylcyclohex-2-ene
(c) 6-Methylcyclohexene
(d) 1-Methylcyclohex-5-ene

102. The name of some compounds are given. Which one is not in IUPAC system

[C.B.S.E. Med. 2005]

(a) $CH_3CH - CH - CH_3$ (3-Methyl-2-butanol)
　　　　　|　　|
　　　　OH　CH_3

(b) $CH_3 - C \equiv C - CH(CH_3)_2$ (2-Methyl-4-pentyne)

(c) $CH_3 - CH_2 - C - CH - CH_3$ (2-Ethyl-3-methylbut-1-ene)
　　　　　　　||　|
　　　　　　CH_2CH_3

(d) $CH_3 - CH_2 - CH_2 - CH \!-\!\!-\!\! CH - CH_2CH_3$ (3-Methyl-4-ethyl heptane)
　　　　　　　　　　|　　|
　　　　　　　　$CH_2CH_3CH_3$

103. Polarization of electrons in acrolein may be written as ...... [C.B.S.E. 2000]

(a) $\overset{\delta-}{C}H_2 = CH - \overset{\delta+}{C}H = O$
(b) $\overset{\delta-}{C}H_2 = CH - CH = \overset{\delta+}{O}$
(c) $\overset{\delta-}{C}H_2 = \overset{\delta-}{C}H - CH = O$
(d) $\overset{\delta+}{C}H_2 = CH - CH = \overset{\delta-}{O}$

104. Among the following, the true property about

CH_3
　　　$\diagdown$
　　　　　$C^+ - H_3C$ is ......　　[Tamil Nadu C.E.T. 2001]
　　　$\diagup$
CH_3

(a) non-polar
(b) $\overset{+}{C}$ is sp^2-hybridised
(c) electrophile can attack C^+
(d) does not undergo hydrolysis

105. Consider the following carbocations ...... [S.C.R.A.E. 2001]

I. $C_6H_5\overset{+}{C}H_2$　　II. $C_6H_5CH_2\overset{+}{C}H_2$　　III. $C_6H_5\overset{+}{C}HCH_3$　　IV. $C_6H_5\overset{+}{C}(CH_3)_2$

The correct sequence for the stability of these is ......

(a) II < I < III < IV
(b) II < III < I < IV
(c) III < I < II < IV
(d) IV < III < I < II

106. Acetaldehyde is the rearrangement product of ...... [A.I.I.M.S. 2001]

(a) Methyl alcohol
(b) Allyl alcohol
(c) Vinyl alcohol
(d) All are correct

107. Which of the following is most stable ? [Manipal 2001]

(a) Ph_3C^+
(b) Ph_2CH^+
(c) $PhCH_2^+$
(d) Tropylium cation

108. The reaction $(CH_3)_3CBr \xrightarrow{H_2O} (CH_3)_3C-OH$ is ...... [A.I.E.E.E. 2002]

(a) Elimination reaction
(b) Substitution reaction
(c) Free radical reaction
(d) Displacement reaction

109. The arrangement of $(CH_3)_3C-$, $(CH_3)_2CH-$, CH_3CH_2- when attached to benzene or an unsaturated group in increasing order of inductive effect is ...... [A.I.E.E.E. 2002]

(a) $(CH_3)_3C - < (CH_3)_2CH - < CH_3CH_2 -$
(b) $CH_3CH_2 - < (CH_3)_2CH - < (CH_3)_3C -$
(c) $(CH_3)_2CH - < (CH_3)_3C - < CH_3CH_2 -$
(d) $(CH_3)_3C - < CH_3CH_2 - < (CH_3)_2CH -$

110. $\overset{-}{C}H_2 - \overset{\parallel}{\underset{O}{C}} - CH_3$ and $CH_2 = \overset{\mid}{\underset{O}{C}} - CH_3$ are ......   **[C.B.S.E. P.M.T. 2002]**

   (a) Resonating structures   (b) Tautomers
   (c) Geometrical isomers   (d) Optical isomers

111. Pick out the alkane which differs from the other members of the group ......
   (a) 2, 2-Dimethylpropane   (b) Pentane   **[Karnataka C.E.T. 2004]**
   (c) 2-Methylbutane   (d) 2, 2-Dimethylbutane

ANSWER KEY

1. (d)	2. (c)	3. (b)	4. (a)	5. (a)	6. (c)	7. (a)	8. (a)
9. (b)	10. (c)	11. (a)	12. (a)	13. (b)	14. (c)	15. (a)	16. (c)
17. (c)	18. (d)	19. (c)	20. (b)	21. (b)	22. (b)	23. (d)	24. (a)
25. (b)	26. (a)	27. (b)	28. (d)	29. (c)	30. (c)	31. (b)	32. (d)
33. (a)	34. (a)	35. (b)	36. (d)	37. (d)	38. (b)	39. (b)	40. (c)
41. (d)	42. (b)	43. (a)	44. (c)	45. (b)	46. (a)	47. (a)	48. (c)
49. (a)	50. (c)	51. (a)	52. (b)	53. (b)	54. (c)	55. (c)	56. (d)
57. (d)	58. (c)	59. (b)	60. (a)	61. (b)	62. (d)	63. (d)	64. (b)
65. (a)	66. (d)	67. (a)	68. (b)	69. (a)	70. (c)	71. (b)	72. (a)
73. (a)	74. (b)	75. (b)	76. (d)	77. (b)	78. (c)	79. (c)	80. (c)
81. (d)	82. (a)	83. (a)	84. (d)	85. (b)	86. (b)	87. (d)	88. (c)
89. (c)	90. (b)	91. (b)	92. (c)	93. (c)	94. (b)	95. (a)	96. (d)
97. (c)	98. (b)	99. (a)	100. (c)	101. (c)	102. (a)	103. (b)	104. (d)
105. (a)	106. (d)	107. (a)	108. (d)	109. (a)	110. (a)	111. (d)	112. (a)
113. (a)	114. (a)	115. (b)	116. (d)	117. (b)	118. (a)	119. (a)	120. (b)
121. (b)	122. (b)	123. (d)	124. (a)	125. (b)	126. (a)	127. (b)	128. (c)
129. (c)	130. (c)	131. (b)	132. (c)	133. (b)	134. (b)	135. (a)	136. (b)

Previous Year's Questions

1. (c)	2. (a)	3. (b)	4. (a)	5. (d)	6. (d)	7. (b)	8. (b)
9. (d)	10. (c)	11. (b)	12. (c)	13. (a)	14. (b)	15. (b)	16. (a)
17. (a)	18. (b)	19. (a)	20. (d)	21. (c)	22. (c)	23. (b)	24. (a)
25. (c)	26. (c)	27. (a)	28. (d)	29. (c)	30. (d)	31. (c)	32. (a)
33. (a)	34. (d)	35. (b)	36. (d)	37. (b)	38. (d)	39. (d)	40. (b)
41. (a)	42. (d)	43. (c)	44. (d)	45. (a)	46. (d)	47. (c)	48. (a)
49. (b)	50. (b)	51. (a)	52. (a)	53. (d)	54. (d)	55. (b)	56. (c)
57. (b)	58. (d)	59. (a)	60. (d)	61. (d)	62. (a)	63. (d)	64. (d)
65. (d)	66. (a)	67. (b)	68. (c)	69. (a)	70. (d)	71. (d)	72. (a)
73. (d)	74. (c)	75. (d)	76. (a)	77. (d)	78. (b)	79. (d)	80. (b)
81. (b)	82. (c)	83. (b)	84. (b)	85. (b)	86. (d)	87. (b)	88. (b)
89. (c)	90. (c)	91. (b)	92. (d)	93. (a)	94. (d)	95. (d)	96. (b)
97. (b)	98. (d)	99. (b)	100. (b)	101. (a)	102. (b)	103. (d)	104. (b)
105. (d)	106. (c)	107. (a)	108. (b)	109. (b)	110. (b)	111. (d)	

❑❑❑

HYDROCARBONS

1. Petroleum is an .... natural resource.
   (a) Inexhaustible
   (b) Exhaustible
   (c) Both (a) and (b)
   (d) None of these

2. Crude oil is also called as ......
   (a) Petroleum
   (b) Petrol
   (c) Gasoline
   (d) Paraffin

3. Black gold is ......
   (a) Black Au
   (b) Petroleum
   (c) Petrol
   (d) CNG

4. Petroleum is a mixture of ......
   (a) Hydrocarbons
   (b) Unnatural hydrocarbons only
   (c) Phenones
   (d) Ketones

5. CNG is ......
   (a) Cetain number of gas
   (b) Compressed natural gas
   (c) Carbon number in a gas
   (d) CN in gasoline

6. CNG is mainly ......
   (a) Pentane
   (b) Butane
   (c) Propane
   (d) Methane

7. LPG is ......
   (a) Liquid petroleum green
   (b) Liquified petroleum gas
   (c) Low protein grade
   (d) Low petrol gas

8. LPG contains mainly ......
   (a) Ethane
   (b) n-Butane and iso-Butane
   (c) Methane
   (d) Propane

9. Coal is produced in the industry to get ......
   (a) Coke
   (b) Coal tar
   (c) Coal gas
   (d) All of these

10. Carbonization is ......
    (a) Slow conversion of dead vegetation into coal
    (b) Deposition of soil
    (c) Falling of trees
    (d) Formation of carbon dioxide

11. Fisher–Tropsch process produces petroleum from ......
    (a) Carbon dioxide and hydrogen
    (b) Producer gas
    (c) Carbon monoxide and hydrogen
    (d) Carbon monoxide and water

12. The catalyst used in Fisher–Tropsch method is ......
    (a) Cobalt
    (b) Molybdenum
    (c) Iron
    (d) Ferric oxide

13. Crude having higher percentage of cycloalkane is called as ......

(a) Paraffinic   (b) Olefin   (c) Asphaltic   (d) Gasoline

14. Petrochemicals are obtained from ......

(a) Paraffins   (b) Coal   (c) Petroleum   (d) Coal tar

15. Fisher–Tropsch process involves the reaction ......

(a) $2nH_2 + nCO \rightarrow C_nH_{2n} + nH_2O$ (b) $(2n+1) H_2 + nCO \rightarrow C_nH_{2n+2} + nH_2O$

(c) $(2n+1) H_2 + nCO_2 \rightarrow C_nH_{2n+2} + (n+1)H_2O$ (d) $(2n+1) H_2 + 2nCO \rightarrow C_nH_{2n+2} + nH_2O$

16. Octane number is ......

(a) Percentage of octane in petroleum

(b) Percentage of iso-octane in petroleum

(c) Percentage of n-octane and n-heptane which resemble the given fuel

(d) Percentage of iso-octane in a mixture of n-heptane and iso-octane which matches given fuel

17. Branching in alkane results in ......

(a) Decrease in octane number   (b) Decrease in heptane number

(c) Increase in oxidation number   (d) Increase in octane number

18. Octane number is zero for ......

(a) Iso-octane   (b) n-heptane   (c) Iso-heptane   (d) n-octane

19. A fuel has the same knocking property as a mixture of 70% isooctane and 30% n-heptane by volume. The octane number is ......

(a) 100   (b) 70   (c) 50   (d) 30

20. Which of the following has the highest octane number?

(a) 2, 2, 4-dimethyl pentane   (b) 2, 3, 4-trimethyl pentane

(c) n-octane   (d) n-pentane

21. Knocking is due to combustion of fuel in engine ......

(a) Slowly   (b) Fast   (c) Rapidly   (d) Continuously

22. Anti-knocking property is improved by the addition of ......

(a) Methyl lead   (b) Ethyl lead   (c) Tetra ethyl lead   (d) Lead

23. Cetane number is the measure of ......

(a) Fuel's ignition delay   (b) Fuel's ignition fast

(c) Fuel's combustion   (d) Antiknocking

24. Cetane number is calculated by determining which will result in the same ignition delay

(a) Mixture of heptadecane and 2, 3, 4, 4, 6, 8 heptan methyl nonane

(b) Mixture of hexadecane and 2, 2, 4, 4, 6, 8, 8 heptan methyl nonane

(c) Cetane and sec – cetane

(d) Iso-cetane and neo – cetane

25. Cetane number is increased by the addition of ......

(a) n-hexadecane   (b) n-decane   (c) iso-cetane   (d) n-phellation

26. The carbon content is maximum in ......

    (a) Anthracite   (b) Bituminous   (c) Peat   (d) Lignite

27. The reagent required to form ethane from sodium propionate is ......

    (a) Water, electrolysis   (b) Soda lime

    (c) Sodium in dry ethane   (d) Sodium hydroxide

28. When aq. solution potassium butanoate is electrolyzed, the hydrocarbon formed is ......

    (a) Butane   (b) Butene   (c) Octane   (d) Hexane

29. The compound 'A' produces ethyne when treated with water, which is compound A?

    (a) Aluminium carbide   (b) Calcium carbide   (c) Calcium nitride   (d) Beryllium carbide

30. When ethyl chloride reacts with sodium in the presence of dry ether, the hydrocarbon formed is ......

    (a) Butane   (b) Ethane   (c) Propane   (d) Methane

31. Which of the following cannot be produced by Kolbe's electrolytic process?

    (a) CH_4 (b) C_2H_6 (c) C_2H_4 (d) C_2H_2

32. When C_2H_5MgBr reacts with water, the hydrocarbon produced is ......

    (a) CH_4 (b) C_2H_4 (c) C_2H_6 (d) C_4H_{10}

33. Which of the following straight chain hydrocarbons is not obtained on treating ethyl chloride with n-propyl sodium metal in dry ether?

    (a) C_3H_9 (b) C_4H_{10} (c) C_5H_{12} (d) C_6H_{14}

34. When methyl magnesium iodide reacts with 40.2 gm of an unknown alcohol, 1.56 ml of methane gas at STP is released, the molar mass of alcohol is ......

    (a) $76 \ gm \ mol^{-1}$ (b) $59 \ gm \ mol^{-1}$ (c) $44 \ gm \ mol^{-1}$ (d) $28 \ gm \ mol^{-1}$

35. The major product when 2-chlorobutane is treated with ethanolic KOH is ......

    (a) But-2-ene   (b) But-1-ene   (c) Butan-1-ol   (d) Butan-2-ol

36. When ethyl alcohol is heated with conc. H_2SO_4 the product formed is ......

    (a) $CH_3COOC_2H_3$ (b) C_2H_6 (c) C_2H_4 (d) C_2H_2

37. Identify Y in the following reaction

$$CH_3CH_2CH_2OH \xrightarrow{PCl_5} X \xrightarrow{Alc. \ KOH} Y$$

    (a) Propane   (b) Propene   (c) Propan-1-ol   (d) Propyne

38. Which solution, on reaction with sodium in ether gives 2, 3-dimethyl butane ?

    (a) Iso-propyl chloride   (b) Ethyl bromide   (c) n-propyl bromide   (d) 1-bromo butane

39. Identify Y in the reaction

$$CH_3 - CH = CH_2 \xrightarrow{HBr} X \xrightarrow[H_2O]{Mg} Y$$

    (a) $CH_3–CH_3$ (b) $CH_3CH_2CH_2CH_3$ (c) $CH_3CH_2CH_3$ (d) $CH_3CH(Br)CH_3$

40. Among the following compounds the one that is most reactive towards electrophilic nitration is ......

    (a) Toluene   (b) Benzene   (c) Benzoic acid   (d) Nitrobenzene

41. For following reaction, what is X ?

$$CH_3-\overset{\overset{\displaystyle O}{\|}}{C}-CH_2CH_3 \xrightarrow{\ X\ } CH_3CH_2CH_2CH_3$$

    (a) $LiAlH_4$ (b) $NaBH_4$ (c) Bu_3SnH (d) NH_2NH_2 and OH^-

42. By which of the following reagent, propanoic acid can be converted into propane ?

    (a) $LiAlH_4$ (b) Red P | HI   (c) $NaOH/CaO$ (d) CH_3MgBr

43. Which of the following carbide can be used to get an alkane ?

    (a) Al_4C_3 (b) CaC_2 (c) B_2C_3 (d) SiC

44. An unknown carboxylic acid salt on Kolbe's electrolysis forms n-octane, the carboxylic acid is ......

    (a) Formic acid   (b) Adipic acid

    (c) Hydrochloric acid   (d) Sulphuric acid

45. n-hexane can be converted to benzene by the treatment with ......

    (a) Alkaline $KMnO_4$ (b) Alcoholic KOH

    (c) Cr_2O_3 at 770 K   (d) $LiAlH_4$

46. But-2-ene can be obtained by reacting ...

    (a) Butan-1-ol with alcohol   (b) Bromoethane with zinc

    (c) 1, 2-dibromopropane with zinc   (d) 1, 1-dibromo ethane with zinc

47. On electrolysis of potassium succinate solution, the hydrocarbon obtained is ?

    (a) Ethane   (b) Ethene   (c) Ethyne   (d) All of these

48. Terminal ($\alpha, \omega,$) dihalides on heating with zinc or sodium form ......

    (a) Alkanes   (b) Alkenes   (c) Alkynes   (d) Cycloalkanes

49. When chloroform is heated with silver powder, the compound formed is ......

    (a) Ethane   (b) Ethene   (c) Ethyne   (d) Ethanoic acid

50. Ethyne is prepared industrially by passing electric discharge through graphite electrodes in the presence of ......

    (a) N_2 (b) CO_2 (c) O_2 (d) H_2

51. Ethyl benzene cannot be prepared by ______ .

    (a) Clemmensen reduction   (b) Wurtz reaction

    (c) Wurtz-Fittig reaction   (d) Friedel–Crafts reaction

52. Identify (b) and (d) in the following sequence of reactions :

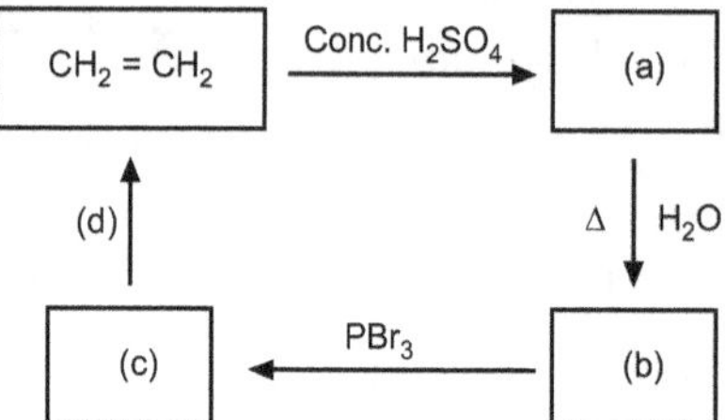

    (a) Ethanol and alcoholic KOH

    (b) Methanol and bromoethane

    (c) Ethyl hydrogen sulphate and alcoholic KOH

    (d) Ethyl hydrogen sulphate and aqueous KOH

53. Ozonolysis of an organic compound 'A' produces acetone and propionaldehyde in equimolar mixture. Identify 'A' from the following compounds :

    (a) 1-Pentene
    (b) 2-Methyl-1-pentene
    (c) 2-Methyl-2-pentene
    (d) 2-Pentene

54. Ozonolysis of an organic compound gives formaldehyde as one of the products. This confirms the presence of ......

    (a) A vinyl group
    (b) Two ethylenic double bonds
    (c) An acetylenic triple bond
    (d) An isopropyl group

55. Heating a mixture of sodium benzoate and soda lime gives ......

    (a) Benzene
    (b) Methane
    (c) Calcium benzoate
    (d) Benzoic acid

56. In the following Corey House synthesis, X is : $(CH_3)_2CHBr \xrightarrow[\ (CH_3)_2CHCH_2Br\ ]{Li/Cu} X$

    (a) $(CH_3)_2CHCH_2CH_2CH_3$
    (b) $(CH_3)_2CHCH_2CH(CH_3)_2$
    (c) $(CH_3)_2CHCH_2CH_2CH_2CH_3$
    (d) $(CH_3)_3CHCH_2CH_2CH_3$

57. Which branched chain isomer of the hydrocarbon with molecular mass 72u gives only one isomer of monosubstituted alkyl halide ?

    (a) Tertiary butyl chloride
    (b) Neopentane
    (c) Isohexane
    (d) Neohexane

58. The reagents for the preparation of ethyne from 1, 2-dibromoethane are ......

    (a) Alcoholic KOH
    (b) Aqueous KOH followed by $NaNH_2$
    (c) Alcoholic KOH followed by $NaNH_2$
    (d) $Zn \mid C_2H_5OH$

59. How many isomeric alkenes are obtained on dehydrohalogenation of 2-bromobutane with hot alcoholic potash ?

    (a) 1
    (b) 2
    (c) 3
    (d) 4

60. Name the reaction

$$CH_3COCH_3 + 4[H] \xrightarrow[HCl]{Zn \mid Hg} C_3H_8 + H_2O$$

    (a) Rosenmund's reduction
    (b) Kolbe's reaction
    (c) Clemmensen reduction
    (d) Sabatier - Senderens reaction

61. Ethanol on treatment with concentrated HI and red phosphorous gives ......

    (a) C_2H_5I
    (b) C_2H_4
    (c) C_2H_6
    (d) C_3H_8

62. Identify 'A' in the following reaction

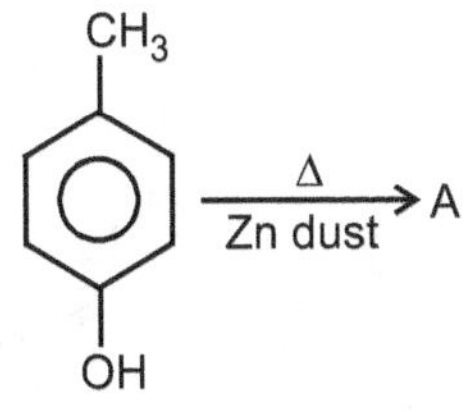

A benzene ring bearing a CH_3 group at the top and an OH group at the bottom, reacting $\xrightarrow[Zn\ dust]{\Delta} A$

    (a) Toluene
    (b) Benzene
    (c) Phenol
    (d) Xylene

63. Identify 'X' in the following reaction :

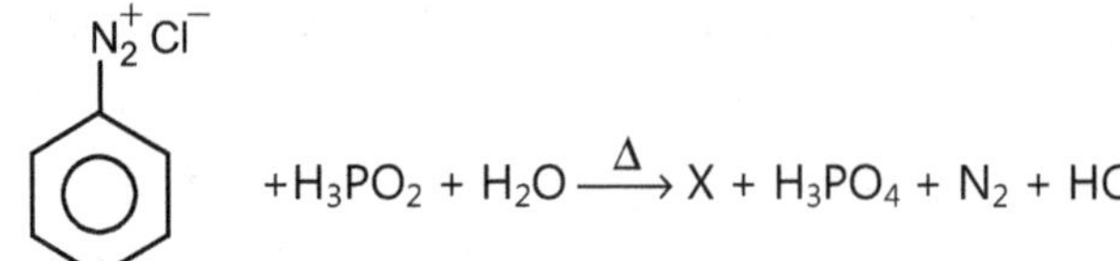

$$+ H_3PO_2 + H_2O \xrightarrow{\Delta} X + H_3PO_4 + N_2 + HCl$$

  (a) Aniline   (b) Phenol   (c) Benzene   (d) Toluene

64. But-2-yne is formed by the reaction of

  (a) CH_3Br with $Na^+C^- \equiv CH$ (b) CH_3I with $Na^+C^- \equiv C^- Na^+$

  (c) CH_3I with $CH_2 \equiv CH_2$ (d) CH_4 with chloroacetylene

65. In the reaction $H_3C - C \equiv CH + H_2 \xrightarrow{X} H_3C - CH = CH_2$, X is ......

  (a) Pure Nickel   (b) Zn|Cu couple   (c) Pd|BaSO$_4$ (d) AlCO$_3$

66. Lindlar's catalyst is ......

  (a) $Pt + C_2H_5OH$ (b) $Pd + BaSO_4$ (c) Pd + ethanol   (d) Na + liquid NH$_3$

67. Bromination of butane produces ......

  (a) 1-bromobutane product

  (b) 2-bromobutane

  (c) Both 1-bromobutane and 2-bromobutane (equal yield)

  (d) iso-butachloride

68. An alkane of molar mass 72 gm mol^{-1} on monochlorosubstitution produces only one product, the alkane is ......

  (a) n-pentane   (b) 2-methyl butane

  (c) 2, 2-dimethyl propane   (d) n-butane

69. Benzene reacts with chlorine in the presence of sunlight to give ......

  (a) CCl_3CHO (b) $C_6H_6Cl_6$ (c) $C_6H_{12}Cl_6$ (d) $C_6H_9Cl_2$

70. The monochlorination of an alkane 'A' of molecular formula C_8H_{18} gives only one product, the name of A is ......

  (a) 2, 2, 3-trimethyl octane   (b) 2, 2, 3, 3-tetramethyl butane

  (c) Octane   (d) 2-methyl heptane

71. 1-bromobutane with alcoholic KOH gives ......

  (a) But-1-ene   (b) But-2-ene   (c) Butan-1-ol   (d) Butan-2-ol

72. The non-aromatic compound among the following is

(A) 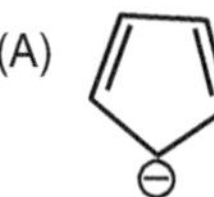   (B) 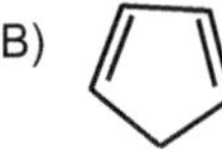

(C) 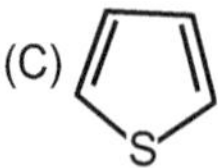   (D) 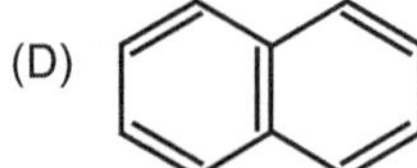

  (a) Option (A)   (b) Option (B)   (c) Option (C)   (d) Option (D)

73. A dibromo derivative of an alkane reacts with sodium metal to form an alicyclic hydrocarbon. The derivative is _____.

(a) 2, 2-dibromobutane

(b) 1, 1-dibromopropane

(c) 1, 4-dibromobutane

(d) 1, 2-dibromoethane

74. Which one of these is NOT TRUE for benzene?

(a) Heat of hydrogenation of benzene is less than the theoretical value

(b) There are three carbon-carbon single bonds and three carbon-carbon double bonds

(c) It forms only one type of monosubstituted product

(d) The bond angle between carbon-carbon bonds is 120°

75. The synthesis of 3-octyne is achieved by adding a bromoalkane into a mixture of sodium amide and an alkyne. The bromoalkane and alkyne respectively are ......

(a) $BrCH_2CH_2CH_2CH_2CH_3$ and $CH_3CH_2C \equiv CH$

(b) $BrCH_2CH_2CH_3$ and $CH_3CH_2CH_2C \equiv CH$

(c) $BrCH_2CH_2CH_2CH_2CH_3$ and $CH_3C \equiv CH$

(d) $BrCH_2CH_2CH_2CH_3$ and $CH_3CH_2C \equiv CH$

76. n-propyl bromide on treating with alcoholic KOH produces ......

(a) propyne　　　(b) propene　　　(c) propane　　　(d) propanol

77. The angle strain in cyclobutane is ......

(a) 24° 44'　　　(b) 29° 16'　　　(c) 19° 22'　　　(d) 9° 44'

78. In the following sequence of reactions, the alkene affords the compound 'B' ......

$$CH_3CH = CHCH_3 \xrightarrow{O_3} A \xrightarrow[Zn]{H_2O} B$$

The compound B is ......

(a) CH_3CH_2CHO　　　(b) CH_3COCH_3　　　(c) $CH_3CH_2COCH_3$　　　(d) CH_3CHO

79. The hydrocarbon which can react with sodium in liquid ammonia is ......

(a) $CH_3CH_2CH_2C \equiv CCH_2CH_2CH_3$

(b) $CH_3CH_2C \equiv CH$

(c) $CH_3CH = CHCH_3$

(d) $CH_3CH_2C \equiv CCH_2CH_3$

80. The treatment of CH_3MgX with $CH_3C \equiv C-H$ produces ......

(a) CH_4　　　(b) $CH_3 - CH = CH_2$　　　(c) $BCH_3 \equiv C - CH_3$　　　(d) $CH_3 - \overset{\overset{H}{|}}{C} = \overset{\overset{H}{|}}{C} - CH_3$

81. The general formula of a cycloalkane is

(a) C_nH_{2n+2}　　　(b) C_nH_{2n-2}　　　(c) C_nH_{2n}　　　(d) C_nH_n

82. Cyclohexene on ozonolysis followed by reaction with zinc dust and water gives compound E. Compound E on further treatment with aqueous KOH yields compound F. Compound F is

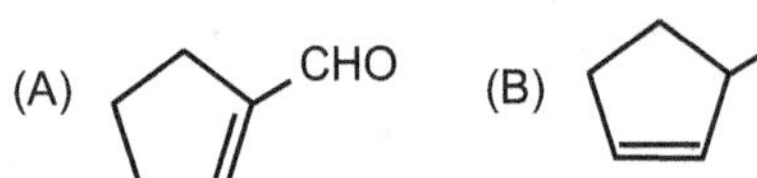

(A)   (B)

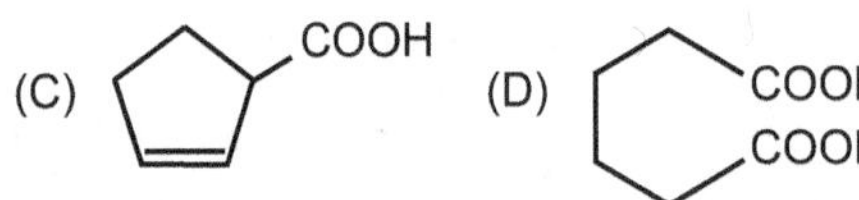

(C)   (D)

   (a) Option (A)   (b) Option (B)   (c) Option (C)   (d) Option (D)

83. The compound formed as a result of oxidation of ethyl benzene by $KMnO_4$ is ......
   (a) benzophenone   (b) acetophenone   (c) benzoic acid   (d) benzyl alcohol

84. Which of the following reactions will yield 2, 2-dibromopropane?
   (a) $CH_3 - C \equiv CH + 2HBr \rightarrow$
   (b) $CH_3CH \equiv CHBr + HBr \rightarrow$
   (c) $CH \equiv CH + 2HBr \rightarrow$
   (d) $CH_3 - CH = CH_2 + HBr \rightarrow$

85. HBr reacts with $CH_2 = CH - OCH_3$ under anhydrous conditions at room temperature to form ......
   (a) CH_3CHO and CH_3Br
   (b) $BrCH_2CHO$ and CH_3OH
   (c) $BrCH_2 - CH_2 - OCH_3$
   (d) $H_3C - CHBr - OCH_3$

86. Phenyl magnesium bromide reacts with methanol to give ......
   (a) a mixture of anisole and Mg(OH)Br
   (b) a mixture of benzene and Mg(OMe)Br
   (c) a mixture of toluene and Mg(OH)Br
   (d) a mixture of phenol and Mg(Me)Br

87. 1-bromobutane with aqueous KOH gives ......
   (a) But-1-ene   (b) But-2-ene   (c) Butan-1-ol   (d) Butan-2-ol

88. The order of dehydrohalogenation of alkyl halide with alcoholic KOH is ......
   (a) $1° < 2° < 3°$ (b) $1° > 2° > 3°$ (c) $3° > 2° < 1°$ (d) $3° < 2° > 1°$

89. Which of the following has the highest boiling point?
   (a) n-pentane
   (b) iso-pentane
   (c) neo-pentane
   (d) 2, 2-dimethyl propane

90. The electrophile in the sulphonation of benzene is ......
   (a) SO_3 (b) SO_3H (c) SO_2 (d) HSO_4^-

91. Which of the carbocations is the most stable?

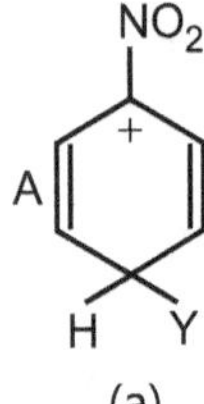

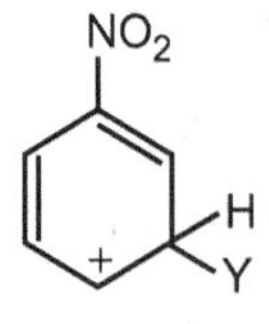

   (a)   (b)   (c)   (d)

92. Among the following which is the most stable carbocation, during the nitration of phenol at ortho position ?

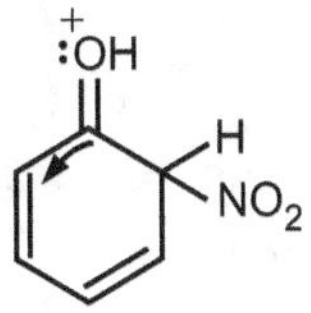

(a) 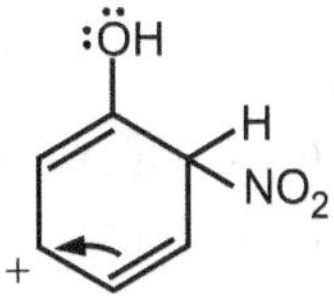   (b) 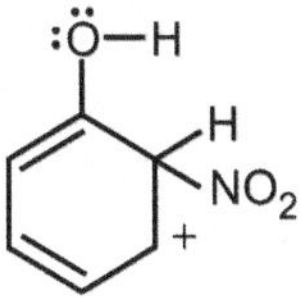   (c) 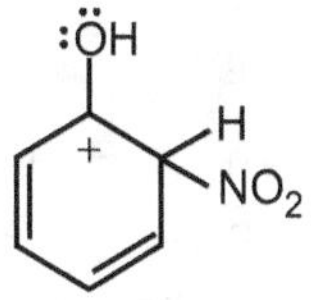   (d)

93. During the nitration of toluene, which is the most stable carbocation intermediate for para substitution ?

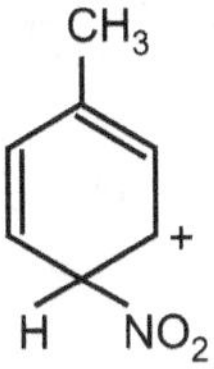

(a) 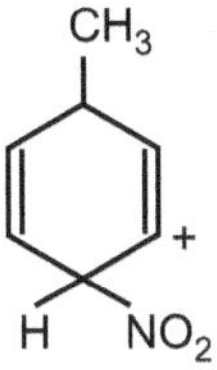   (b) 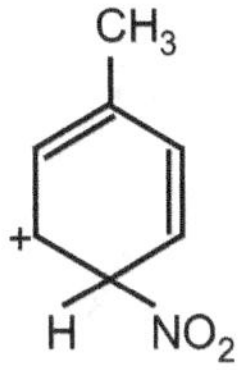   (c) 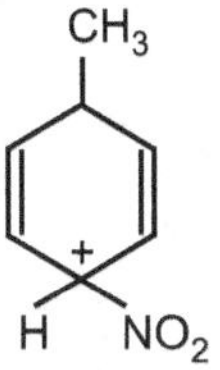   (d)

94. During the nitration of benzaldehyde, what is the least stable carbocation ?

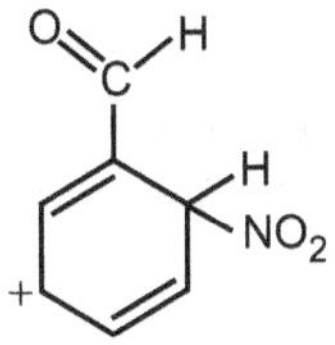

(a) 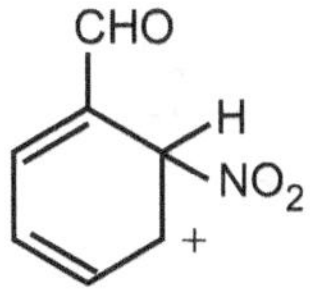   (b) 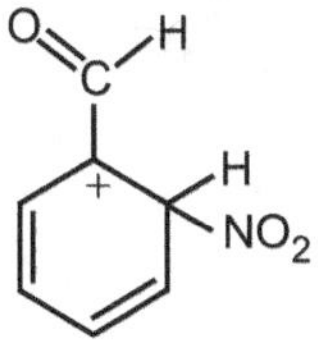   (c) 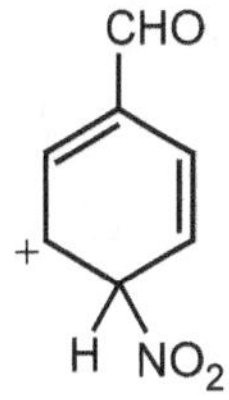   (d)

95. The compound 'A' in the following reaction is ......

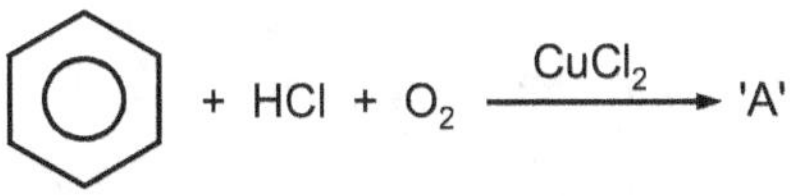

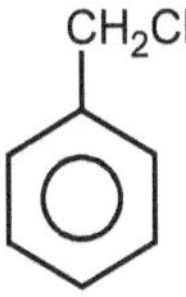

$$\text{C}_6\text{H}_6 + HCl + O_2 \xrightarrow{CuCl_2} \text{'A'}$$

(a) 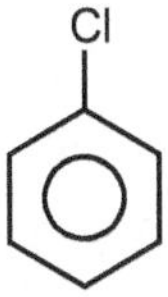   (b) 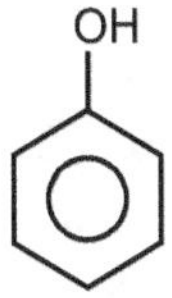   (c) 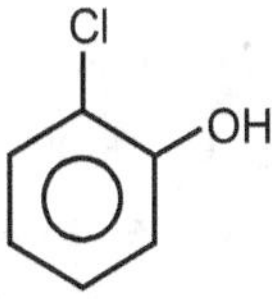   (d)

96. Benzene with 2-methyl propene in the presence of sulphuric acid gives ?

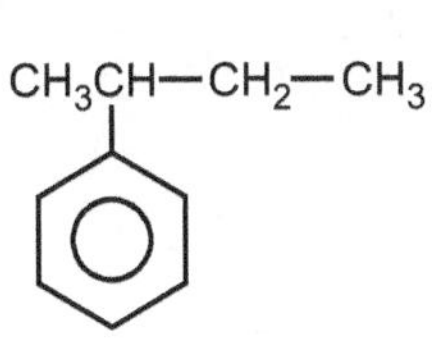

(a) 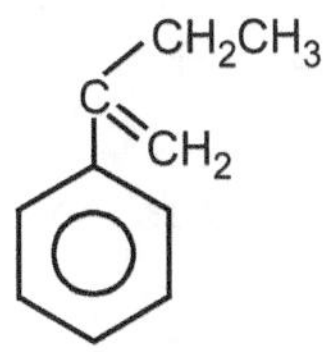   (b) 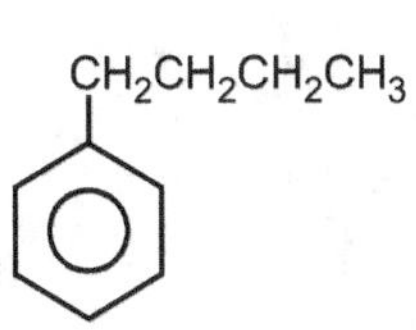   (c) 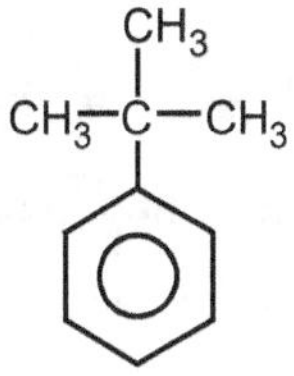   (d)

97. In the following reaction the major product is

$$CH_3—\underset{\underset{CH_3}{|}}{CH}—CH = CH_2 + HCl \rightarrow X$$

(a) 1-chloro-3-methyl butane (b) 2-chloro-3-methyl butane

(c) 3-chloro-2-methyl butane (d) 2-chloro-2-methyl butane

98. X in the following reaction is ......

$$CH_3—C \equiv CH \xrightarrow{H_2O\,|\,Hg^{2+}\,|\,H^+} X$$

(a) CH_3CH_2CHO (b) $CH_3CH_2CH_2OH$ (c) $CH_3\underset{\underset{O}{||}}{C}—CH_3$ (d) $CH_3—\underset{\underset{OH}{|}}{C} = CH_2$

99. In the following reaction

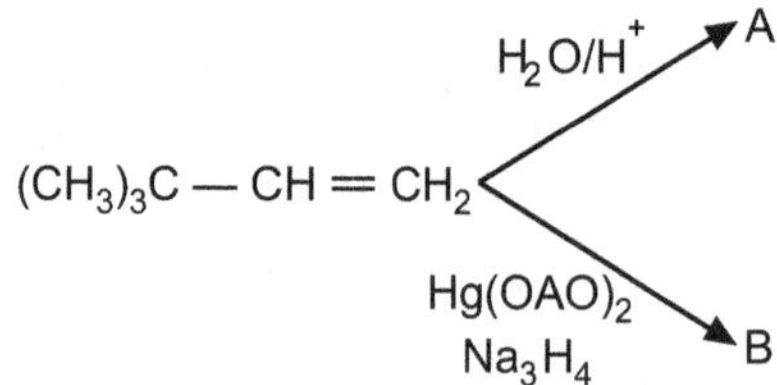

'A' is ......

(a) 1-Bromo-But-2-ene (b) Meso-2, 3-dibromo butane

(c) Racemic mixture of 2, 3-dibromo butane (d) Mesocarb racemic mixture

100. Identify A and B in the following reaction

$$(CH_3)_3C — CH = CH_2 \overset{H_2O/H^+ \nearrow A}{\underset{\underset{Na_3H_4}{Hg(OAO)_2} \searrow B}{}}$$

A or B respectively are ......

(a) 2, 3-Dimethyl butan-1-ol and 3, 3-Dimethyl butan-2-ol

(b) 2, 3-Dimethyl butan-2-ol and 3, 3-Dimethyl butan-1-ol

(c) 2, 3-Dimethyl butan-2-ol and 3, 3-Dimethyl butan-2-ol

(d) 3, 3-Dimethyl butan-2-ol and 2, 3-Dimethyl butan-2-ol

101. Which of the following reactions will not give propane?

(a) $CH_3CH_2CH_2Cl \xrightarrow[H_2O]{Mg\,|\,Ether}$ (b) $CH_2—\underset{\underset{OH}{|}}{CH}—CH_3$

(c) $CH_3—CH = CH_2 \xrightarrow[CH_3COOH]{B_2H_6}$ (d) $CH_3COCl \xrightarrow[H_2O]{CH_3MgX}$

102. Consider the following reaction

$$CH_3—\underset{\underset{D}{|}}{CH}—\underset{\underset{CH_3}{|}}{CH}—CH_3 + \overset{\cdot}{Br} \longrightarrow X + HBr$$

X is ......

(a) 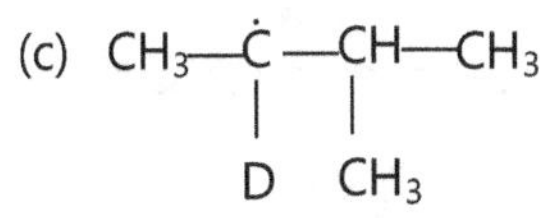

(b) 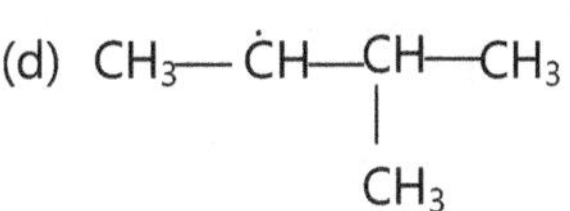

(c) $CH_3-\overset{\cdot}{C}-CH-CH_3$ with D, CH_3

(d) $CH_3-\overset{\cdot}{C}H-CH-CH_3$ with CH_3

103. In the given reaction, X is ......

$CH_3COC_2H_5 \xrightarrow{X} CH_3CH_2C_2H_5I$

(a) $LiAlH_4$　　　(b) $NaBH_4$　　　(c) C_2H_4　　　(d) $NH_2-NH_2|OH^-$

104. Chlorination of propane is carried out in the presence of sunlight. The percent yield of major and minor alkyl halides will be ......

(a) 86%, 14%　　　(b) 80%, 20%　　　(c) 70%, 30%　　　(d) 92%, 8%

105. A hydrocarbon C_4H_{10} on monochlorination gives Y which on Wurtz reaction gives 2, 2, 3, 3-tetramethyl butane. Suggest the structure of compounds X and Y respectively.

(a) n-butane, 1-chlorobutane

(b) 2-methyl propane, 1-chloro-2-methyl propane

(c) 2-methyl propane, 2-chloro-2-methyl propane

(d) Butane, 2-chloro-2-methyl propane

106. Which of the following has dipole moment?

(a) trans-2-pentane　　　　　　(b) trans-3-hexene

(c) 2, 2-methyl propene　　　　　　(d) 2, 2, 3, 3-tetramethyl butene

107. Which of the following alkynes is most acidic?

(a) $CH_3 - C \equiv CH$　　　　　　(b) $CH_3 - C \equiv C - CH_3$

(c) $HC \equiv CH$　　　　　　(d) $HC \equiv C - CH_2CH_2CH_3$

108. The general molecular formula of the product when chloroform reacts with silver metal is ...

(a) C_nH_{2n+2}　　　(b) C_nH_{2n}　　　(c) C_nH_{2n-2}　　　(d) C_nH_{2n+1}

109. Ethyne has the same degree of unsaturation as ......

　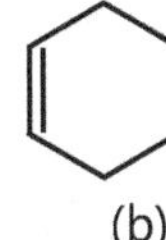　　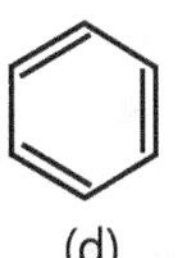

　(a)　　　　　　(b)　　　　　　(c)　　　　　　(d)

110. A compound of molecular formula C_5H_9Br (X) does not decolorize dilute alkaline $KMnO_4$ solution or bromine water but on treatment with alcoholic KOH forms C_5H_8(Y). C_5H_8 which decolorizes dilute alkaline $KMnO_4$ and bromine water. (Y) on ozonolysis followed by hydrolysis forms pentane-1, 5-dial. X is ......

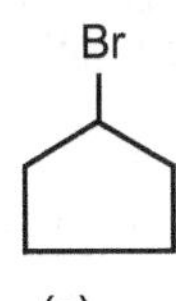

　　　　　$CH_3CH_2CH_2CH_2CH_2Br$　　　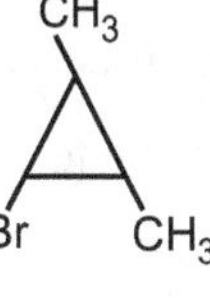

　(a)　　　　　　(b)　　　　　　(c)　　　　　　(d)

111. In a reaction

$$H_2C = CH_2 \xrightarrow[\text{acid}]{\text{hypochlorous}} M \xrightarrow{R} \begin{array}{c} CH_2OH \\ | \\ CH_2OH \end{array}$$

M and R are ......

(a) CH_3CH_2Cl and NaOH

(b) $CH_2Cl—CH_2OH$ and aqueous $NaHCO_3$

(c) CH_3CH_2OH and HCl

(d) $\begin{array}{c} CH_2 - CH_2 \\ \diagdown \diagup \\ O \end{array}$ and heat

112. Which of the following reactions is expected to readily give a hydrocarbon product in good yield?

(a) $RCOOK + H_2O \xrightarrow{\text{Electrolysis}}$

(b) $RCOOAg \xrightarrow{I_2}$

(c) $CH_3CH_3 \xrightarrow{\dfrac{Cl_2}{hr}}$

(d) $(CH_3)_2CCl \xrightarrow{C_2H_5OH}$

113. The cylindrical shape of alkyne is due to ......

(a) 3σ C–C bonds

(b) 3π bonds

(c) 2σ C–C and 1π C–C

(d) $1\sigma ; 2\pi$

114. The oxidation of toluene to benzaldehyde with chromyl chloride is ......

(a) Sandmeyer's reaction

(b) Etard reaction

(c) Perkin's reaction

(d) Fittig reaction

115. 1-Butyne reacts with cold alkaline $KMnO_4$ to produce ......

(a) CH_3CH_2COOH

(b) $CH_3CH_2CH_2COOH$

(c) $CH_3CH_2COOH + CO_2$

(d) $CH_3CH_2COOH + HCOOH$

116. Formation of polythene from calcium carbide takes place as follows ......

$$CaC_2 + 2H_2O \rightarrow Ca(OH)_2 + C_2H_2$$
$$C_2H_2 + H_2 \rightarrow C_2H_4$$
$$n(C_2H_4) \rightarrow (CH_2–CH_2)_n$$

The amount of polyethylene obtained from 64.1 kg CaC_2 is ......

(a) 7 kg (b) 14 kg (c) 21 kg (d) 28 kg

117. Aromatic hydrocarbon shows mostly ......

(a) Addition electrophilic reaction

(b) Addition nucleophilic reaction

(c) Substitution electrophilic reaction

(d) Substitution nucleophilic reaction

118. Which of the following shows geometric isomerism ?

(a) 1-butane (b) 2-butene (c) Propane (d) 1, 1-dichlorobutane

119. Which will undergo Friedel–Craft alkylation reaction?

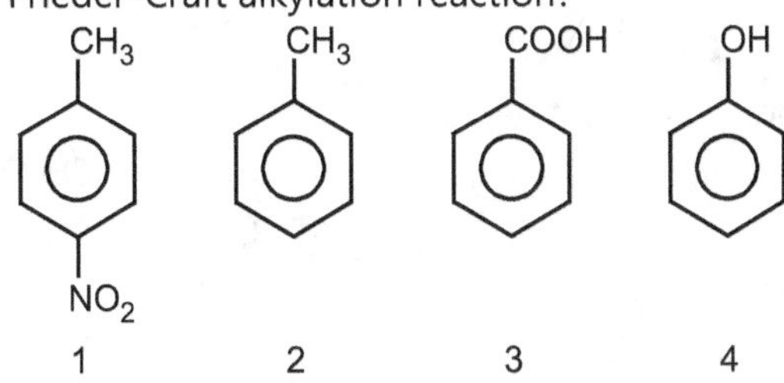

(a) 1, 2, 4　　　　(b) 1 and 3　　　　(c) 2 and 4　　　　(d) 1 and 2

120. Addition of HI on double bond of propene yields isopropyl iodide and not n-propyl iodide as the major product because addition proceeds through ......

(a) A more stable carbonium ion　　　　(b) A more stable carbanion

(c) A more stable free reaction　　　　(d) Homolysis

121. Which of the following deactivates benzene substitution ?

(a) –NHR　　　　(b) –OH　　　　(c) –COOR　　　　(d) –OR

122. Chlorination of toluene in the presence of light and heat followed by treatment with aqueous NaOH gives ......

(a) o–cresol　　　　(b) p-cresol

(c) 2, 4 dihydroxy toluene　　　　(d) Benzoic acid

123. In Friedel-Craft's alkylation, besides $AlCl_3$, the other reactants are ......

(a) $C_6H_6 + NH_2$　　(b) $C_6H_6 + CH_4$　　(c) $C_6H_6 + CH_3Cl$　　(d) $C_6H_6 + CH_3COCl$

124. Propyne on polymerization gives ......

(a) Propylene　　(b) Benzene　　(c) Mesitylene　　(d) Propyl benzene

125. $KMnO_4$ will oxidize acetylene to ......

(a) Ethene glycol　　(b) Ethyl alcohol　　(c) Oxalic acid　　(d) Acetic acid

126. What is the order of stability for ......

(I) But-2-ene　　　　(II) Cis-But-2-ene　　　　(III) Trans-But-2-ene

(a) I < II < III　　(b) I > II > III　　(c) III > I > II　　(d) III > II > I

127. Arrange the following compounds in increasing order of acidity :

$HC \equiv CH$, $CH_2 = CH_2$, $ClCH_2CH_3$, FCH_2CH_3, $CH_3–CH_3$

(a) $HC \equiv CH < CH_2 = CH_2 < CH_3 – CH_3 < ClCH_2CH_3 < FCH_2CH_3$

(b) $CH_3CH_3 < CH_2 = CH_2 < OH \equiv CH < ClCH_2CH_3 < FCH_2CH_3$

(c) $ClCH_2CH_3 < FCH_2CH_3 < CH_2 = CH_2 < CH \equiv CH < CH_3CH_3$

(d) $CH_3–CH_3 < ClCH_2CH_3 < FCH_2CH_3 < CH_2 = CH_2 < CH \equiv CH$

128. Two organic compounds 'A' and 'B' both having carbon and hydrogen only, on quantitative analysis gave the same percentage of C and H. 'A' can decolorize bromine water whereas 'B' cannot. 'A' and 'B' respectively are ......

(a) C_2H_2 and C_6H_6　　(b) C_2H_4 and C_6H_6　　(c) C_2H_6 and C_6H_6　　(d) C_2H_2 and C_2H_6

129. $CaC_2 + H_2O \rightarrow A \xrightarrow[HgSO_4]{H_2SO_4} B$

Identify A and B in the above reaction.

(a) C_2H_2 and CH_3COOH

(b) C_2H_4 and CH_3COOH

(c) CH_4 and $HCOOH$

(d) C_2H_2 and CH_3CHO

130. Which alkene on ozonolysis gives

$CH_3-\overset{\underset{\Vert}{O}}{C}-CH_3$ and CH_3CH_2CHO

(a) $CH_3CH_2CH = C\underset{CH_3}{\overset{CH_3}{<}}$

(b) $CH_3CH_2CH = CH-CH_2CH_3$

(c) $CH_3CH_2CH = CH-CH_3$

(d) $CH_3-\underset{\underset{CH_3}{\vert}}{C} = CH-CH_3$

131. An organic compound 'A' C_4H_9Cl on reaction with sodium/diethyl ether gives a hydrocarbon which on monochlorination gives only one chloro derivative, then 'A' is ......

(a) tert-butyl chloride

(b) sec-butyl chloride

(c) iso-butyl chloride

(d) n-butyl chloride

132. Which one of the following gives a red precipitate with a solution of cuprous chloride ?

(a) H_3C-CH_3 (b) $H_2C = CH_2$ (c) $H_3C-C \equiv CH$ (d) $H_3C \cdot C \equiv C \cdot CH_3$

133. When methyl bromide is heated with Zn, it gives ......

(a) C_2H_2 (b) C_2H_6 (c) C_2H_4 (d) CH_4

134. The empirical formula of an organic compound is CH_2. One mole of this compound has a mass of 42 gm. Its molecular formula is ......

(a) CH_2 (b) C_2H_6 (c) C_2H_2 (d) C_3H_6

135. CH_3COCH_3 can be converted to $CH_3CH_2CH_3$ by the action of ......

(a) HIO_3 (b) HI (c) HNO_3 (d) H_3PO_3

136. The reagent used for converting acetylene to oxalic acid is ......

(a) $HgSO_4 | H_2SO_4(g)$

(b) $HgSO_4 | CH_3COOH$

(c) $KMnO_4 | KOH$

(d) $Cr_2O_3 | H_2SO_4$

137. In the following reaction, A and B respectively are ......

$C_2H_6 \xrightarrow[A]{\Delta} C_2H_5-Cl \xrightarrow{Zn | HCl} \text{(B)}$

(a) $Cl_2 | UV$ light and C_2H_6

(b) PCl_3 and C_2H_4

(c) HCl and C_2H_6

(d) Cl_2 and C_2H_6

138. In the following reaction, X and Y are respectively ......

$C_2H_6 \xrightarrow{X} C_2H_4 \xrightarrow{Y} C_2H_5SO_3H$

(a) Iron tube | heat Na_2SO_4

(b) Zn, conc. H_2SO_4

(c) Red hot iron tube, fuming H_2SO_4

(d) $H_2 | Pd, BaSO_4$, dil H_2SO_4

139. The compound 2-methyl but-2-ene on reaction with $NaIO_4$ in the presence of $KMnO_4$ gives ......

(a) $CH_3CHO + CO_2$

(b) CH_3COCH_3

(c) $CH_3COCH_3 + CH_3COOH$

(d) $CH_3COCH_3 + CH_3CHO$

140. Butene-1 may be converted to butane by reaction with ......

(a) Zn–HCl   (b) Sn–HCl   (c) Zn–Hg   (d) $Pd\,|\,H_2$

141. The reaction of HBr with propene in the presence of peroxide gives ......

(a) Isopropyl bromine

(b) 3-Bromo propane

(c) Alkyl bromide

(d) n-propyl bromide

142. Which of the following is used for the conversion of 2-hexyne to trans-2-hexene ?

(a) $H_2\,|\,Pd\,|\,BaSO_4$ (b) H_2, PtO_2 (c) $NaBH_4$ (d) $Li–NH_3/C_2H_5OH$

143. Which of the following has the minimum boiling point ?

(a) n-Butane   (b) iso-butane   (c) 1-butene   (d) 1-butyne

144. 2-Methyl butane on reaction with bromine in the presence of sunlight gives mainly ......

(a) 1-bromo-2-methyl butane

(b) 2-bromo-2-methyl butane

(c) 2-bromo-3-methyl butane

(d) 1-bromo-3-methyl butane

145. When phenyl magnesium bromide reacts with tertiary butyl alcohol, the product would be ......

(a) Benzene

(b) Phenol

(c) tert-butyl benzene

(d) tert-butyl phenyl ether

146. Which gas is liberated when Al_4C_3 is hydrolyzed?

(a) CH_4 (b) C_2H_2 (c) C_2H_6 (d) CO_2

147. Predict the product C obtained in the following reaction of Butyne-1.

$$CH_3CH_2-C \equiv CH + HCl \rightarrow B \xrightarrow{HI} C$$

(a) 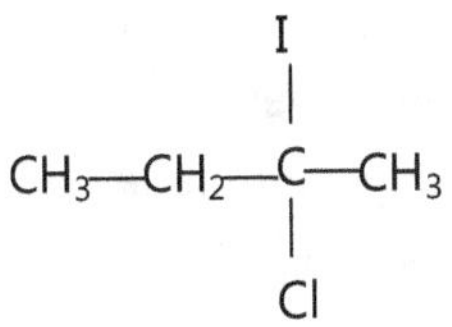
$$CH_3-CH_2-\underset{\underset{Cl}{|}}{\overset{\overset{I}{|}}{C}}-CH_3$$

(b)
$$CH_3-\underset{\underset{Cl}{|}}{CH}-CH_2-CH_2I$$

(c)
$$CH_3CH_2-CH_2-\underset{\underset{Cl}{|}}{\overset{\overset{I}{|}}{C}}-H$$

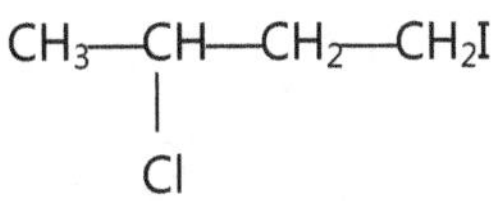

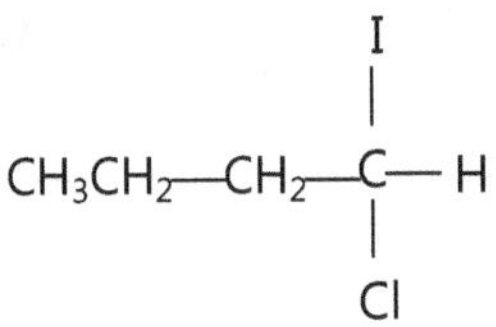

(d) $CH_3CH_2-CH_2Cl$

148. The compound X in the following reaction is ......

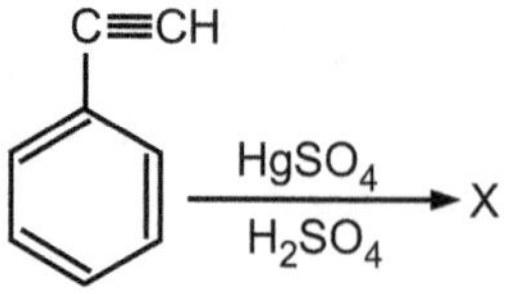

(structure: phenyl–C≡CH) $\xrightarrow[\text{H}_2\text{SO}_4]{\text{HgSO}_4}$ X

(a) 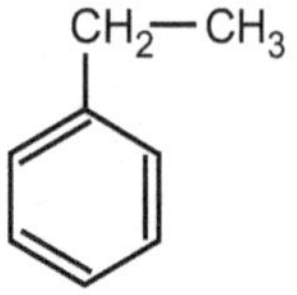 phenyl–CH_2–CH_3

(b) 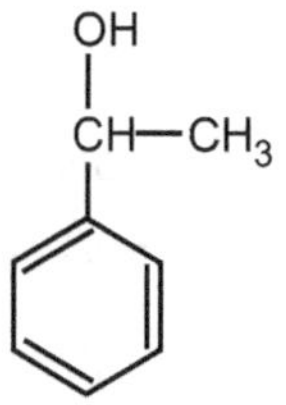 phenyl–$\underset{\underset{OH}{|}}{CH}$–$CH_3$

(c) phenyl–$\underset{\underset{O}{\|}}{C}$–$CH_3$

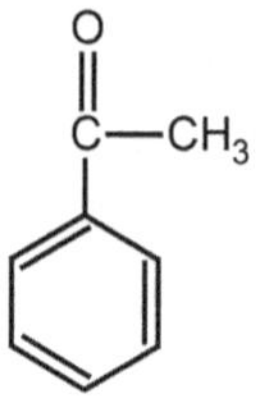

(d) 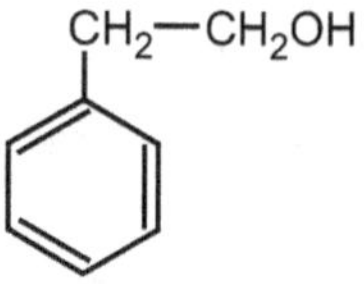 phenyl–CH_2–CH_2OH

149. The product obtained on treating CH_2Cl_2 with excess of benzene in the presence of anhydrous $AlCl_3$ is ......

(a) 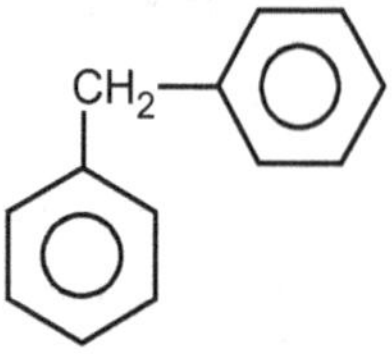 phenyl–CH_2–phenyl

(b) 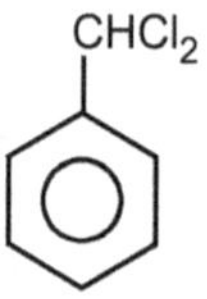 phenyl–$CHCl_2$

(c) 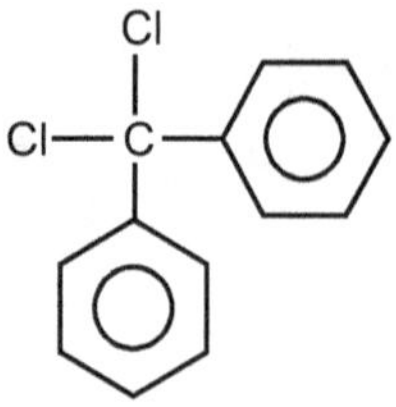 Cl–$\underset{\underset{phenyl}{|}}{\overset{\overset{Cl}{|}}{C}}$–phenyl

(d) 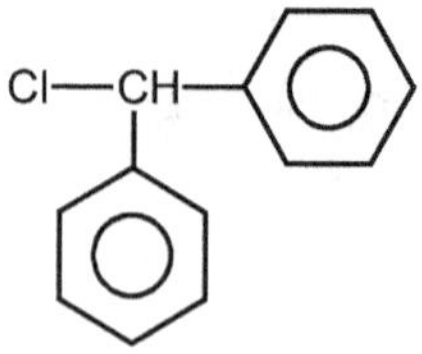 Cl–$\underset{\underset{phenyl}{|}}{CH}$–phenyl

150. $(CH_3)_3CMgCl$ on reaction with D_2O forms ......

(a) $(CH_2)_3CD$ (b) $(CH_3)_3COD$ (c) $(CD_3)_3CD$ (d) $(CD_3)_3OD$

151. The isomers which can be converted into another form by rotation of the molecules around single bond are ......

(a) Geometrical isomers   (b) Conformers

(c) Enantiomers   (d) Diastereomers

152. The IUPAC name of the following $CH_3C(CH_3)_2CH_2CH = CH_2$ is ......

(a) 2, 2-Dimethyl-4-pentene   (b) 4, 4-Dimethyl-1-pentene

(c) 1, 1, 1-Trimethyl-3-butene   (d) 4, 4 4-Trimethyl-1-butene

153. In the presence of peroxide, hydrogen chloride and hydrogen iodide do not give anti-Markownikov addition to alkenes because ......

(a) Both are highly ionic

(b) One is oxidizing and the other is reducing

(c) One of the steps is endothermic in both the cases

(d) All the steps are exothermic in both the cases

154. Identify a reagent from the following list which can easily distinguish between 1-butyne and 2-butyne ......
(a) Bromine, CCl_4
(b) H_2, Lindlar catalyst
(c) Dilute H_2SO_4, $HgSO_4$
(d) Ammoniacal Cu_2Cl_2 solution

155. The most reactive among the following towards sulphonation is ......
(a) Toluene
(b) Chlorobenzene
(c) Nitrobenzene
(d) m-Xylene

156. Number of geometrical isomers for the following structure will be ......
$CH_3 - CH_2 - CH = CH - CH_2 = CH(CH_2)_2$
(a) 2
(b) 3
(c) 4
(d) 5

157. $C_2H_2 \xrightarrow[\text{acid}]{\text{Chromic}} A \xrightarrow{NH_3} B \xrightarrow[H_2O]{\Delta} C$
(a) $CH_3–CH_2NH_2$
(b) $CH_3–CN$
(c) $CH_3–CH_2–NH–CH_3$
(d) CH_3CONH_2

158. IUPAC name of

$$CH_2—CH_2—CH—C = CH_2 \text{ is ......}$$
with CH_2 and CH_3 substituents, and CH_3 below CH_2.

(a) 2-methyl-3-ethyl-1-pentene
(b) 3-methyl-4-methyl-4-pentene
(c) 3-ethyl-2-methyl-1-pentene
(d) 3-methyl-2-ethyl-1-pentene

159. IUPAC nomenclature of

$$H_3C—C—CH = C – CH_3 \text{ is ......}$$
with CH_3 above the second carbon, and CH_3, CH_3 below.

(a) 2, 4, 4-Trimethylpent-2-ene
(b) 2, 4, 4-Trimethylpent-3-ene
(c) 2, 2, 4-Trimethylpent-3-ene
(d) 2, 2, 4-Trimethylpent-2-ene

160. What is the end product of nitration of toluene?
(a) m-nitrotoluene
(b) p-nitrotoluene
(c) 2, 4, 6-trinitrotoluene
(d) 2, 4-dinitrotoluene

161. Gas which is decolourised by $KMnO_4$ solution but gives no precipitate with ammoniacal cuprous chloride is ......
(a) Ethane
(b) Methane
(c) Ethene
(d) Acetylene

162. What would be the product formed when 1-bromo-3-chlorocyclobutane reacts with two equivalents of metallic sodium in ether?

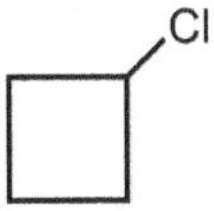

(a) 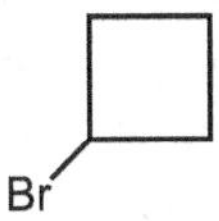 Option (A)
(b) Option (B)
(c) Option (C)
(d) Option (D)

163. 2-methylbutane on reacting with bromine in the presence of sunlight gives mainly ......

(a) 1-bromo 2-methylbutane　　　　　　(b) 2-bromo 2-methylbutane

(c) 2-bromo 3-methylbutane　　　　　　(d) 1-bromo 3-methylbutane

164. Alkyl halides react with dialkyl copper reagents to give ......

(a) alkanes　　　　　　(b) alkyl copper halides

(c) alkenes　　　　　　(d) alkenyl halides

165. Some meta-directing substituents in aromatic substitution are given. Which one is most deactivating ?

(a) $-C \equiv N$　　　　(b) $-SO_3H$　　　　(c) $-COOH$　　　　(d) $-NO_2$

166. When 2-butyne is treated with $Pd\text{-}BaSO_4$; the product formed will be ......

(a) 1-butene　　　(b) trans-2-butene　　　(c) cis-2-butene　　　(d) 2-hydroxy butane

167. Which of the following compounds will not undergo Friedel-Craft's reaction easily?

(a) Cumene　　　(b) Xylene　　　(c) Nitrobenzene　　　(d) Toluene

168. The reaction of one molecule of HBr with one molecule of 1, 3-butadiene at 40°C gives predominantly ......

(a) 3-bromobutene under kinetically controlled conditions

(b) 1-bromo-2-butene under thermodynamically controlled conditions

(c) 3-bromobutene under thermodynamically controlled conditions

(d) 1-bromo-2-butene under kinetically controlled conditions

169. Aqueous solution of an organic compound, 'A' on electrolysis liberates acetylene and CO_2 at anode. 'A' is ......

(a) potassium citrate　　　　　　(b) potassium succinate

(c) potassium acetate　　　　　　(d) potassium maleate

170. Vapours of ethyl alcohol when passed over phosphoric acid at 220°C gives ......

(a) diethyl phosphate　　　　　　(b) methylene

(c) ethyl hydrogen phosphate　　　　　　(d) ethylene

171. Which of the following have maximum boiling point?

(a) n-pentane　　　(b) isopentane　　　(c) isohexane　　　(d) n-hexane

172. Sabatier and Senderen's reaction cannot be used for the preparation of ......

(a) methane　　　(b) ethane　　　(c) n-butane　　　(d) butane

173. The addition reaction of carbon-carbon double bonds are ......

(a) nucleophilic addition　　　　　　(b) free radical addition

(c) electrophilic addition　　　　　　(d) none of these

174. With the increase in branching, the boiling point ......

(a) decreases　　　　　　(b) increases

(c) no regular gradation　　　　　　(d) remains constant

175. Which of the following has minimum boiling point?

(a) isopentane　　　(b) neopentane　　　(c) n-pentane　　　(d) both (a) and (b)

176. Which of the following will show maximum possible isomers?

    (a) Pentene   (b) Pentane   (c) Butane   (d) Butene

177. Propane when treated with conc. nitric acid at 723 K gives ......

    (a) 2-nitropropane

    (b) 1-nitropropane

    (c) a mixture of nitromethane, nitroethane, 1-nitropropane and 2-nitropropane

    (d) nitroethane and nitromethane

178. Vapours of n-hexane when passed over special catalysts under high pressure and temperature give benzene. This process is called as ......

    (a) cyclisation   (b) aromatisation   (c) isomerisation   (d) crystallization

179. Which of the following is an intermediate in the reaction of benzene with CH_3Cl and $AlCl_3$?

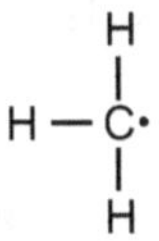

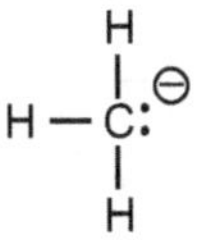

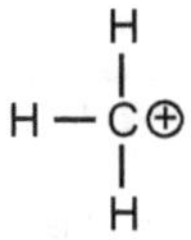

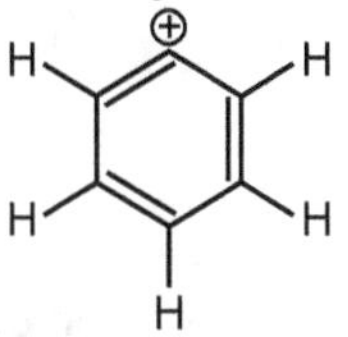

180. Which of the following is an intermediate in the reaction of benzene with Br_2 and $AlBr_3$?

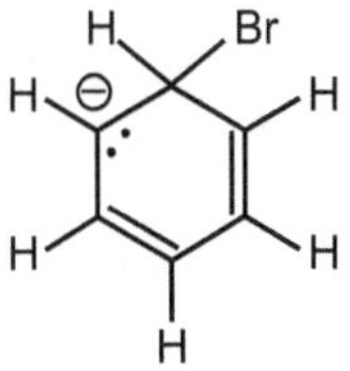

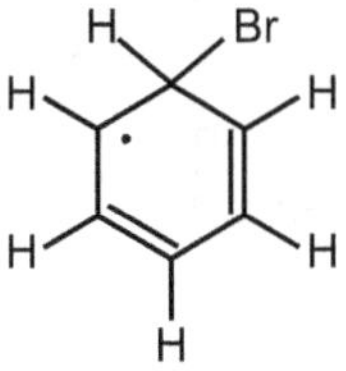

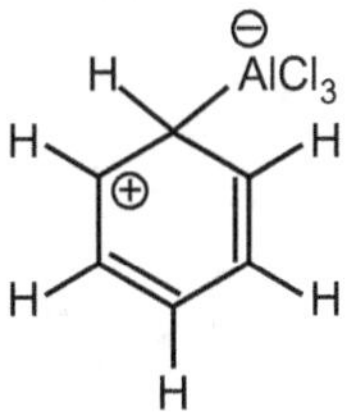

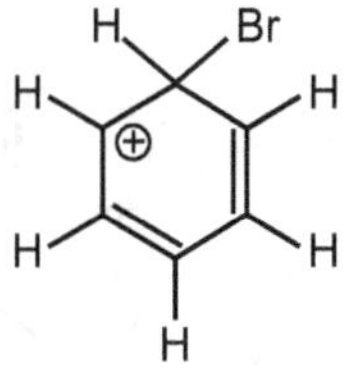

181. Which of these compounds represents the major monochlorination isomer formed in the following reaction?

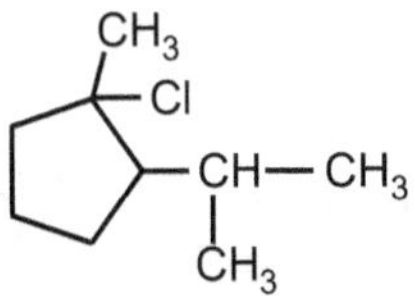

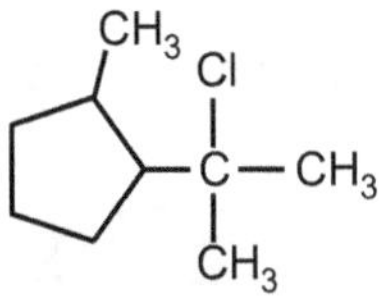

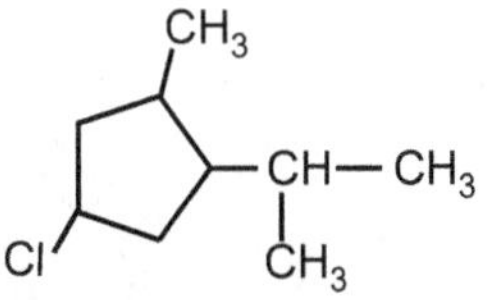

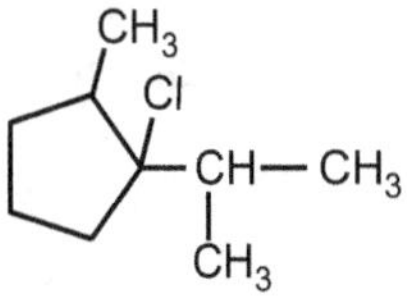

182. What is the major product expected from the following reaction ?

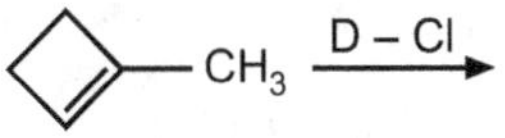

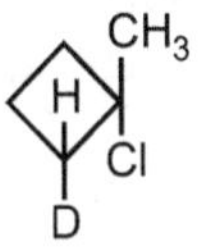

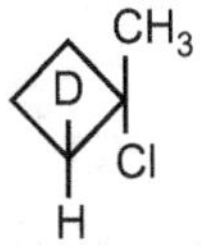

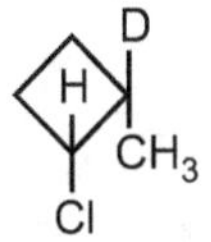

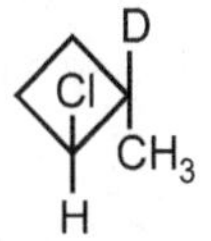

183. What is the major product expected from the following reaction ?

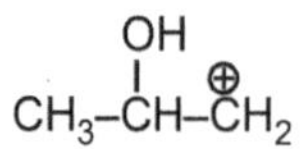

(a) 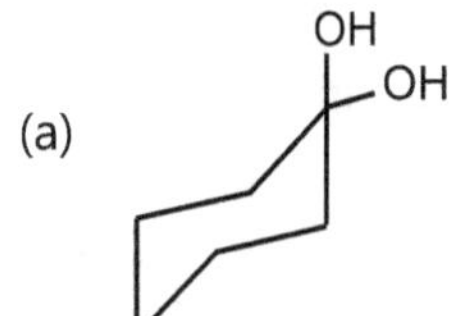   (b) 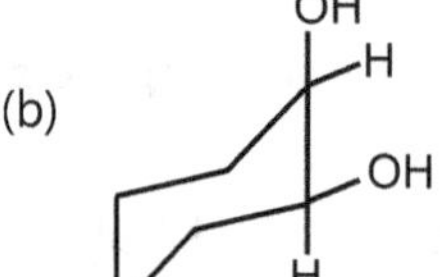   (c) 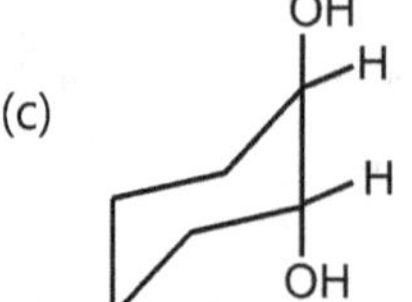   (d) 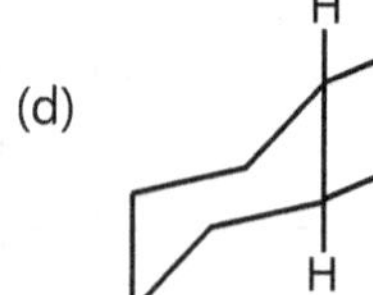

184. The mechanism of the reaction of propene with HOCl ($Cl_2 + H_2O$) will proceed through which of the following intermediates ?

(a) $CH_3-\overset{\oplus}{C}H-CH_2-OH$ (b) $CH_3-\overset{\oplus}{C}H-CH_2-Cl$ (c) $CH_3-\underset{OH}{CH}-\overset{\oplus}{C}H_2$ (d) $CH_3-\underset{Cl}{CH}-$

PREVIOUS YEAR'S QUESTIONS

1. The reaction of $C_6H_5CH = CHCH_3$ with HBr produces ...... **[AIPMT 2015]**

(a) 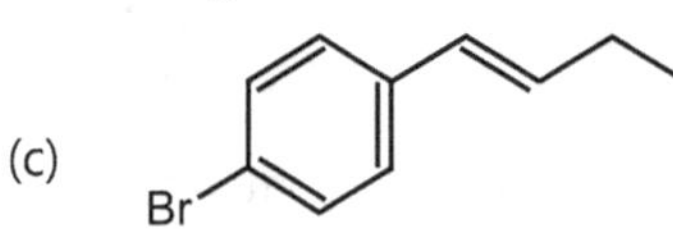

(b) $C_6H_5CH_2CH_2CH_2Br$

(c) 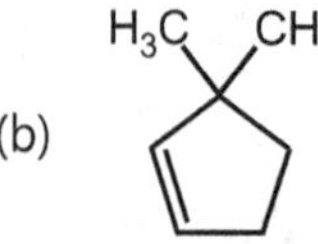

(d) 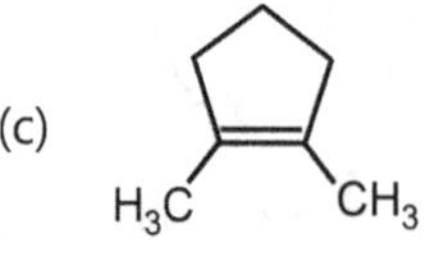

2. A single compound of the structure **[AIPMT 2015]**

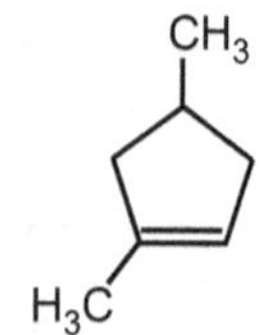

is obtainable from ozonolysis of which of the following cyclic compounds?

(a) (b) (c) (d)

3. 2, 3-Dimethyl-2-butene can be prepared by heating which of the following compounds with a strong acid? **[RE-AIPMT 2015]**

(a) $(CH_3)_2C = NEH - CH_2 - CH_3$

(b) $(CH_3)_2CH - CH_2CH = CH_2$

(c) $(CH_3)_2CH - CH(CH_3) - CH = CH_2$

(d) $(CH_3)_2C - CH = CH_2$

4. In the reaction with HCl, an alkene reacts in accordance with the Markovnikov's rule, to give a product 1-chloro-1-methylcyclohexane   **[RE AIPMT 2015]**

(a) 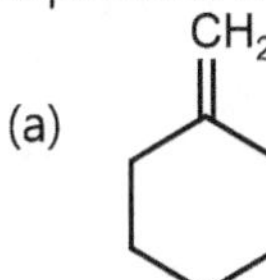   (b) 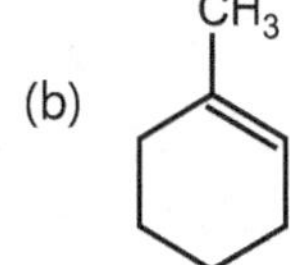   (c) (a) and (b)   (d) 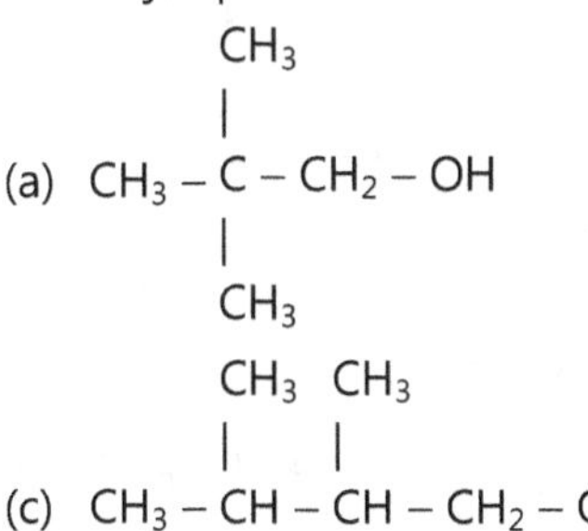

5. The oxidation of benzene by V_2O_5 in the presence of air produces ......
    (a) benzoic acid   (b) benzaldehyde
    (c) benzoic anhydride   (d) maleic anhydride

6. Identify Z in the sequence of reactions :

$$H_3C - CH_2 - CH = CH_2 \xrightarrow[\text{peroxide}]{\text{HBr}} Y \xrightarrow{C_2H_5ONa} Z$$

    (a) $CH_3(CH_2)_4 - O - CH_3$ (b) $CH_3CH_2 - CH(CH_3) - O - CH_2CH_3$
    (c) $CH_3 - (CH_2)_3 - O - CH_2CH_3$ (d) $(CH_3)_2CH_2 - O - CH_2CH_3$

7. Some meta-directing substituents in aromatic substitution are given. Which one is most deactivating?
    (a) $-NO_2$ (b) $-C \equiv N$ (c) $-SO_3H$ (d) $-COOH$

8. Which of the following compounds will not undergo Friedel - Craft's reaction easily ?
    (a) Toluene   (b) Cumene   (c) Xylene   (d) Nitrobenzene

9. In the following reaction : $CH_3 - \overset{\overset{\displaystyle CH_3}{|}}{\underset{\underset{\displaystyle CH_3}{|}}{C}} - CH = CH_2 \xrightarrow{H_2O/H^+}$ **[CBSE AIPMT 2012]**

    the major product is ......

    (a) $CH_3 - \overset{\overset{\displaystyle CH_3}{|}}{\underset{\underset{\displaystyle CH_3}{|}}{C}} - CH_2 - OH$

    (b) $CH_3 - \overset{\overset{\displaystyle CH_3}{|}}{\underset{\underset{\displaystyle CH_3}{|}}{C}} - \overset{\overset{\displaystyle OH}{|}}{\underset{\underset{\displaystyle H}{|}}{C}} - CH_3$

    (c) $CH_3 - \overset{\overset{\displaystyle CH_3}{|}}{C}H - \overset{\overset{\displaystyle CH_3}{|}}{C}H - CH_2 - OH$

    (d) $CH_3 - \overset{\overset{\displaystyle CH_3}{|}}{\underset{\underset{\displaystyle CH_3}{|}}{C}} - CH_2 - OH$

10. Which of the following reagents will be able to distinguish between 1-butyne and 2-butyne?   **[CBSE 2012]**
    (a) $NaNH_2$ (b) HCl   (c) O_2 (d) Br_2

11. Propyne on ozonolysis gives ......   **[OJEE 2012]**
    (a) $CH_3COOH + HCOOH$ (b) $CH_3COOH + HCHO$
    (c) $CH_3CHO + HCHO$ (d) $CH_3CHO + HCOOH$

12. The ozonolysis of an olefin gives only propanone. The olefin is ...... **[AMU 2012]**

(a) but-1-ene (b) but-2-ene
(c) 2, 3-dimethyl but-2-ene (d) propene

13. Acylation of benzene to produce aliphatic aromatic ketones is known as ...... **[AMU 2012]**

(a) Benzoin condensation (b) Hydroformylation
(c) Clemmensen reduction (d) Friedel-Craft's reaction

14. The reaction of propene with diborane followed by alkaline hydrolysis in the presence of hydrogen peroxide gives ...... **[AMU 2012]**

(a) 1-propanol (b) 2-propanol
(c) 1, 2-dihydroxypropane (d) n-propane

15. Identify 'C' in the following reaction **[AFMC 2012]**

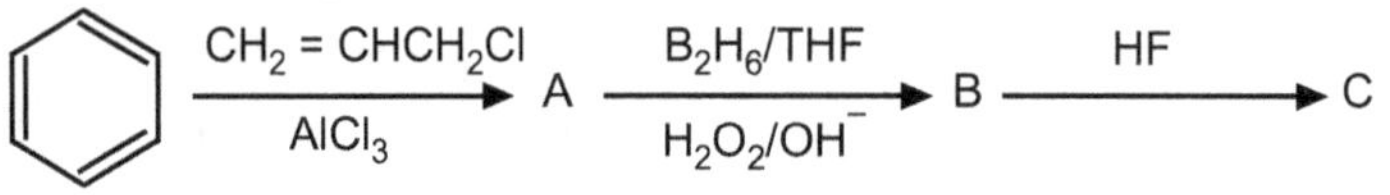

(a) 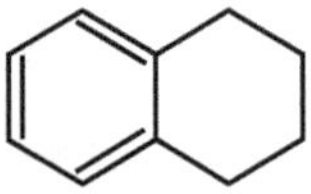 (b) 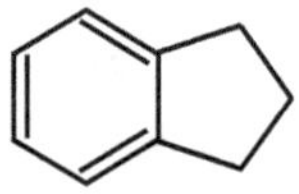 (c) 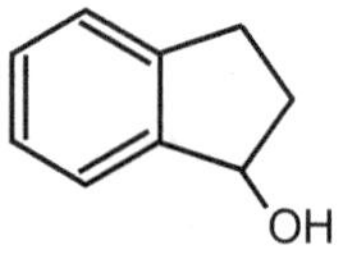

(d) 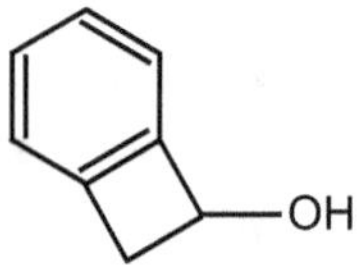

16. Benzene reacts with chlorine in sunlight to give a final product ...... **[UPCPMT 2012]**

(a) CCl_4 (b) $C_6H_6Cl_6$ (c) C_6Cl_6 (d) C_6H_5Cl

17. Which one of the following has the minimum boiling point? **[AIIMS 2012]**

(a) n-butane (b) 1-butyne (c) 1-butene (d) Iso-butene

18. $CaC_2 + H_2O \rightarrow A \rightarrow B$ **[UP CPMT 2012]**
Identify A and B in the given reaction ......

(a) C_2H_2 and CH_3CHO (b) CH_4 and $HCOOH$
(c) C_2H_4 and CH_3COOH (d) C_2H_2 and CH_3COOH

19. Liquid hydrocarbons can be converted to a mixture of gaseous hydrocarbons by ......

(a) hydrolysis (b) oxidation **[CBSE AIPMT 2010]**
(c) cracking (d) distillation under reduced pressure

20. Petrochemicals can be used to prepare ...... **[Manipal 2008]**

(a) synthetic fibres (b) pesticides (c) plastics (d) all of these

21. Which of the following has highest knocking property? **[AFMC 2007]**

(a) Aromatic hydrocarbons (b) Olefins
(c) Branched chain paraffins (d) Straight chain paraffins

22. Which of the following substances is used as an anti-knocking compound? **[BHU 2007]**

(a) Tetraethyl lead (b) Lead tetrachloride (c) Lead acetate (d) Ethyl acetate

23. Which of the following fraction of coal tar distillation is obtained at $270° - 360°C$?

[MHT CET 2006]

(a) Light oil   (b) Middle oil   (c) Green oil   (d) Heavy oil

24. A sample of gasoline contains 80% iso-octane and 20% n-heptane. Its octane number will be ......   **[MP PMT 2006]**

(a) 62   (b) 100   (c) 20   (d) 80

25. Gasoline with an octane number of 80 is equivalent in knocking characteristics to a mixture of heptanes and iso-octane of the following composition ......   **[Manipal 2005]**

(a) 20% heptane + 80% iso-octane   (b) 90% heptane + 10% iso-octane

(c) 80% heptane + 20% iso-octane   (d) 10% heptane + 90% iso-octane

26. Cetane is a compound which has very good ignition property. Chemically, it is ......

[MP PMT 2005]

(a) $CH_3(CH_2)_{14}CH_3$ (b) $(CH_3)_3C(CH_2)_{11}CH_3$

(c) $C_{17}H_{34}$ (d) none of these

27. Gasoline has composition ......   **[AFMC 2004]**

(a) $C_7 - C_{12}$ (b) $C_2 - C_5$ (c) $C_6 - C_n$ (d) none of these

28. On mixing alkane with chlorine and irradiating with ultraviolet light, it forms only one monochloroalkane. The alkane is ......   **[WB JEE 2010]**

(a) propane   (b) pentane   (c) iso-pentane   (d) neo-pentane

29. Which isomer of hexane has only two different sets of structurally equivalent hydrogen atoms?   **[DUMET 2009]**

(a) 2, 2-dimethyl butane   (b) 2-methyl pentance

(c) 3-methyl pentane   (d) 2, 3-dimethyl butane

30. The number of primary, secondary and tertiary carbons in 3,4-dimethylheptane are respectively ......   **[Kerala CEE 2009]**

(a) 4, 3 and 2   (b) 2, 3 and 4   (c) 4, 2 and 3   (d) 3, 4 and 2

31. Which of the following is a 3-methyl butyl group?   **[Kerala CEE 2009]**

(a) $CH_3CH_2CH_2CH_2CH_2 -$ (b) $(CH_3CH_2)_2CH -$

(c) $CH_3CH_2CH(CH_3)CH_2 -$ (d) $(CH_3)_2CHCH_2CH_2 -$

32. The compounds formed at anode in the electrolysis of an aqueous solution of potassium acetate, are ......   **[CPMT 2008]**

(a) C_2H_6 and CO_2 (b) C_2H_4 and CO_2 (c) CH_4 and H_2 (d) CH_4 and CO_2

33. Which of the following reagents convert both acetaldehyde and acetone to alkanes?

(a) Ni/H_2 (b) $LiAlH_4$ (c) $I_2/NaOH$ (d) Zn-Hg/conc. HCl

34. When 2-chloro-2-methylbutane is heated with alcoholic KOH, the possible product/s is/are ......   **[Kerala CEE 2008]**

(i) $(CH_3)_2C = CHCH_3$ (ii) $CH_2 = C(CH_3)CH_2CH_3$ (iii) $(CH_3)_2CHCH = CH_2$

(a) (i), (ii) and (iii)   (b) (i) and (iii)   (c) (ii) and (iii)   (d) (i) and (ii)

35. When 1,1-dichloro propane and 2, 2-dichloro propane are reacted separately with aqueous potassium hydroxide solution, compounds 'A' and 'B' are formed. Both 'A' and 'B' gave the same product 'C' on reduction using amalgamated zinc and HCl. Identify 'C'.

[EAMCET 2008]

(a) propyl alcohol　　　(b) isopropyl alcohol　(c) propyl chloride (d) propane

36. The coal tar fraction which contains phenol is ...... **[KCET 2004]**

(a) middle oil　　　　　(b) green oil　　　　　(c) heavy oil　　　　(d) light oil

37. During the fractional distillation of coal tar, the fraction obtained at 530 K is......

[JJCECE 2004]

(a) light oil　　　　　　(b) anthracene oil　　　(c) heavy oil　　　　(d) middle oil

38. Synthetic petrol is prepared by ...... **[Kerala CEE 2003)]**

(a) Fisher-Tropsch process　　　　　　　(b) Wurtz reaction

(c) distillation　　　　　　　　　　　　(d) fractional distillation

39. The chemical added to leaded petrol to prevent the deposition of lead in the combustion chamber is ...... **[Kerala CEE 2003]**

(a) iso-octane　　　　　　　　　　　　(b) ethylene dibromide

(c) tetraethyl lead　　　　　　　　　　(d) mercaptan

40. The octane number of a sample of petrol is 40. It means that its knocking property is equal to the mixture of ...... **[MP PMT 2003]**

(a) 40% n-heptane + 60% isooctane　　(b) 40% n-heptane + 60% isooctane

(c) 60% n-heptane + 40% isooctane　　(d) 60% n-heptane + 40% isooctane

41. Which compound cannot be formed from Wurtz reaction? **[CPMT 2010]**

(a) Propane　　　　(b) Butane　　　　(c) Ethane　　　　(d) Methane

42. Three products are obtained by the ozonolysis of penta-1, 3-diene. Out of these if two products are formaldehyde and acetaldehyde, the name of the third one is ... **[AFMC 2009]**

(a) formaldehyde　　(b) ethanol　　(c) glyoxal　　(d) propanaldehyde

43. $CH_2 = CH - CH_2 - CH = CH_2$ represents a/an ...... **[AFMC 2009]**

(a) conjugated system　(b) cumulative system　(c) isolated system (d) all of these

44. The compound which is obtained by treating chloropropane with alcoholic KOH, when reacts with BH_3/THF followed by acetic acid gives ...... **[AIIMS 2009]**

(a) $CH_3CH_2CH_2OH$　(b) $CH_3CH_2CH_3$　(c) $CH_3CH(OH)CH_3$ (d) $CH_3CH_2CHOHCH_3$

45. Formation of alcohol by oxymercuration-demercuration of alkenes ...... **[AIIMS 2009]**

(a) involves carbocations and rearrangement

(b) involves carbanions and rearrangement

(c) is stereospecific

(d) does not involve rearrangement and carbocation

46. The order of reactivity of alkenes, $(CH_2)_2C = CH_2$, $CH_3CH = CH_2$, $CH_2 = CH_2$ when subjected to acid catalyzed hydration is ...... **[AMU 2009]**
   (a) I > II > III   (b) I > III > II   (c) III > II > I   (d) II > I > III

47. Products of the following reaction on ozonolysis is ......

$Me_2C = CHCH_3 \rightarrow ?$ are   **[AMU 2009]**
   (a) $CH_3CHO + CH_3COOH$
   (b) $Me_2CO + CH_3CHO$
   (c) $Me_2CO + CH_3COOH$
   (d) $2Me_2CO$

48. One mole of alkene X on ozonolysis gave one mole of acetaldehyde and one mole of acetone. The IUPAC name of X is ...... **[EAMCET 2009]**
   (a) 2-methyl-2-butene
   (b) 2-methyl-1-butene
   (c) 2-butene
   (d) 1-butene

49. The addition of HBr to 2-pentene gives ...... **[WBJEE 2009]**
   (a) 2-bromopentane only
   (b) 3-bromopentane only
   (c) 2-bromopentane and 3-bromopentane
   (d) 1-bromopentane and 3-bromopentane

50. Which of the following hydrocarbons has the lowest dipole moment ?
   (a) H_3C and CH_3 attached to $C = C$ with H and H (cis-2-butene)
   (b) $CH_3C \equiv CCH_3$
   (c) $CH_3CH_2C \equiv CH$
   (d) $CH_2 = CH - C \equiv CH$

51. The best method to prepare cyclohexene from cyclohexanol is by using ......
   (a) Conc. $HCl + ZnCl_2$ (b) Conc. H_3PO_4 (c) HBr   (d) Conc. HCl

52. Ethylene combines with sulphur monochloride to form ...... **[BVP 2010]**
   (a) phosgene
   (b) mustard gas
   (c) methyl isocyanate (MIC)
   (d) lewisite

53. Formation of alkane by the action of zinc on alkyl halide is called ...... **[MHT CET 2004]**
   (a) Wurtz reaction   (b) Kolbe reaction   (c) Ulmann's reaction   (d) Frankland reaction

54. Natural gas is ...... **[RPMT 2004]**
   (a) CH_4
   (b) $CO + H_2 + CH_4$
   (c) $CH_4 + C_2H_6 + C_3H_8$
   (d) all of these

55. Which of the following hydrocarbon is mainly present in gobar gas? **[AFMC 2003]**
   (a) Butane   (b) Propane   (c) Methane   (d) Ethane

56. X is heated with soda lime and gives ethane, X is ...... **[AFMC 2005]**
   (a) ethanoic acid   (b) methanoic acid   (c) propanoic acid   (d) either (a) or (c)

57. Which of the following gas has the highest heat of combustion? **[Haryana PMT 2005]**
   (a) Methane   (b) Ethane   (c) Ethene   (d) Ethyne

58. When a mixture of methane and oxygen is passed through heated molybdenum oxide, the main product formed is ...... **[KCET 2004]**
   (a) Methanoic acid   (b) Ethanol   (c) Methanol   (d) Methanal

59. A is predominantly

$$\begin{array}{c} CH_3 \\ | \\ CH_3-CH-CH=CH_2 \xrightarrow{HBr} A \end{array}$$

[CBSE AIPMT 2009]

(a) $\begin{array}{l} CH_3-CH-CH_2-CH_2Br \\ \quad\quad\;\; | \\ \quad\quad CH_3 \end{array}$

(b) $\begin{array}{l} \quad\quad\quad Br \\ \quad\quad\quad\; | \\ CH_3-C-CH_2-CH_3 \\ \quad\quad\quad\; | \\ \quad\quad\; CH_3 \end{array}$

(c) $\begin{array}{l} \quad\quad\quad\quad\quad Br \\ \quad\quad\quad\quad\quad\; | \\ CH_3-CH-CH-CH_3 \\ \quad\quad\;\; | \\ \quad\quad CH_3 \end{array}$

(d) $\begin{array}{l} \quad\quad\;\; Br \\ \quad\quad\;\;\; | \\ CH_3-CH-CH-CH_3 \\ \quad\quad\quad\quad\quad\; | \\ \quad\quad\quad\quad\; CH_3 \end{array}$

60. An alkene on vigorous oxidation with $KMnO_4$ gives only acetic acid. The alkene is ......

[Manipal 2008]

(a) $CH_3CH_2CH = CH_2$ (b) $CH_3CH = CHCH_3$ (c) $(CH_3)_2C = CH_2$ (d) $CH_3CH = CH_2$

61. Predict the product C obtained in the following reaction of butyne-1 with HCl followed by HI **[CBSE AIPMT 2007]**

$$CH_3CH_2-C\equiv CH + HCl \rightarrow B \rightarrow C$$

(a) $\begin{array}{l} H_3C-CH-CH_2CH_2I \\ \quad\quad\;\; | \\ \quad\quad\; Cl \end{array}$

(b) $\begin{array}{l} \quad\quad\quad\quad\quad\; I \\ \quad\quad\quad\quad\quad\; | \\ CH_3CH_2-C-CH_3 \\ \quad\quad\quad\quad\quad\; | \\ \quad\quad\quad\quad\quad Cl \end{array}$

(c) $\begin{array}{l} \quad\quad\quad\quad\;\; I \\ \quad\quad\quad\quad\;\; | \\ CH_3CH_2CH-CH_2Cl \end{array}$

(d) $\begin{array}{l} \quad\quad\quad\quad\quad\quad\; I \\ \quad\quad\quad\quad\quad\quad\; | \\ CH_3CH_2CH_2C-H \\ \quad\quad\quad\quad\quad\quad\; | \\ \quad\quad\quad\quad\quad\quad Cl \end{array}$

62. Oxidation of an alkene X gives a diol; further oxidation gives a diketone. Which one of the following could be ...... **[Kerala CEE 2007]**

(a) $(CH_3)_2C = C(CH_3)_2$
(b) $CH_3CH = C(CH_3)_2$
(c) $(CH_3)_2CHCH = CH_2$
(d) $C_6H_5CH = CHC_6H_5$
(e) $(C_6H_5)_2C = CHCH_3$

63. For the synthesis of 1-butene, CH_3MgI should be treated with ...... **[MHT CET 2007]**

(a) propene (b) 2-chloropropene (c) allyl chloride (d) ethyl chloride

64. The reaction of HBr with propene in the presence of peroxide gives ...... **[Manipal 07]**

(a) isopropyl bromide (b) 3-bromo propane (c) allyl bromide (d) n-propyl bromide

65. **Assertion :** Addition of HBr on 2-butene gives two isomeric products.

Reason : Addition of HBr on 2-butene follows Markownikoff's rule **[AIIMS 2006]**

(a) Both Assertion and Reason are true and Reason is the correct explanation of Assertion.
(b) Both Assertion and Reason are true but Reason is not the correct explanation of Assertion.
(c) Assertion is true but Reason is false.
(d) Both Assertion and Reason are false.

66. $C_6H_9Br \xrightarrow[-(CH_3)_3COH]{(CH_3)_3CO^-K^+}$ X $\xrightarrow{CH_2 = CH - COCH_3}$ B

Conversion of X to B is ......   **[DUMET 2006]**

(a) Claisen reaction   (b) Perkin reaction

(c) Diels-Alder reaction   (d) Mannich reaction

67. 3-phenylpropene on reaction with HBr gives (as a major product) ......   **[AIIMS 2005]**

(a) $C_6H_5CH_2CH(Br)CH_3$ (b) $C_6H_5CH(Br)CH_2CH_3$

(c) $C_6H_5CH_2CH_2CH_2Br$ (d) $C_6H_5CH(Br)CH = CH_2$

68. $R - CH = CH_2 \rightarrow RCH_2CH_3$ **[Haryana PMT 2005]**

This reaction is called ......

(a) Arndt-Eistert reaction   (b) Birch reduction

(c) Clemmensen reduction   (d) Fisher-Spier reaction

69. Which of the following yield both alkane and alkene?   **[AFMC 2004]**

(a) Kolbe's reaction   (b) Williamson's synthesis

(c) Wurtz reaction   (d) Sandmeyer reaction

70. **Assertion :** 2-bromobutane on reaction with sodium ethoxide in ethanol gives 1-butene as a major product.   **[AIIMS 2004]**

Reason : 1-butene is more stable than 2-butene.

(a) Both Assertion and Reason are true and Reason is the correct explanation of Assertion.

(b) Both Assertion and Reason are true but Reason is not the correct explanation of Assertion.

(c) Assertion is true but Reason is false.

(d) Both Assertion and Reason are false.

71. Which of the following is industrially prepared by passing ethylene into hypochlorous acid?

[BHU 2004]

(a) Ethylene glycol   (b) Ethylene oxide   (c) Ethylene dinitrate   (d) Ethane

72. A reagent used to test for unsaturation of alkene is ......   **[BHU 2004]**

(a) conc. H_2SO_4 (b) ammoniacal Cu_2Cl_2

(c) ammoniacal $AgNO_3$ (d) solution of Br_2 in CCl_4

73. $RCH = CH_2 + CO + H_2 \rightarrow RCH_2CH_2CHO$

The above reaction is ......   **[DUMET 2004]**

(a) Mendius reaction   (b) Oxo process

(c) Sandmeyer reaction   (d) Stephen's reaction

74. What are X and Y in the reaction   **[EAMCET 2004]**

$C_2H_4 + H_2SO_4 \xrightarrow{80°C}$ X $\xrightarrow{H_2O}$ Y

(a) C_2H_6, C_2H_5OH (b) C_2H_2, C_2H_5SH

(c) $C_2H_5OSO_3H, C_2H_5OH$ (d) C_2H_2, CH_3CHO

75. Which one of the following compounds decolourises cold alkaline potassium permanganate solution? **[EAMCET 2004]**

(a) C_2H_6 (b) C_2H_5Cl (c) C_2H_4 (d) $C_2H_5OCH_3$

76. The reaction of H_2 on ethene in the presence of catalyst is called ...... **[RPMT 2004]**

(a) Sabatier-Sanderen's reaction   (b) Darzen reaction

(c) Rosenmund reaction   (d) None of these

77. The compound $CH_3 - \overset{\overset{\displaystyle |}{\underset{\displaystyle CH_3}{}}}{C} = CH - CH - CH_3$ on reaction with $NaIO_4$ in the presence of $KMnO_4$

gives ...... **[CBSE AIPMT 2003]**

(a) $CH_3COCH_3 + CH_3CHO$ (b) $CH_3CHO + CO_2$

(c) CH_3COCH_3 (d) $CH_3COCH_3 + CH_3COOH$

78. **Assertion :** Trans-2 butene on reaction with Br_2 gives meso-2, 2-dibromobutane

Reason : The reaction involves syn-addition o: bromine. **[AIIMS 2004]**

(a) Both Assertion and Reason are true and Reason is the correct explanation of Assertion.

(b) Both Assertion and Reason are true but Reason is not the correct explanation of Assertion.

(c) Assertion is true but Reason is false

(d) Both Assertion and Reason are false.

79. Identify the alkyne in the following sequence of reactions : **[EAMCE 2009]**

$$\text{Alkyne} \xrightarrow[\text{Lindler's catalyst}]{H_2} (A) \xrightarrow{\text{Ozonolysis}} CH_2 = CH_2 \xrightarrow{\text{Wacker's process}} B \text{ only}$$

(a) $CH_3HC = CHCH_3$ (b) $H_3C - CH_2 - CH = CH$

(c) $H_2C = CH - CH = CH_2$ (d) $HC = CH - CH_2 - C \equiv CH$

80. Ethylidene dichloride is obtained by the reaction of excess of CH_3I with **[MHT CET 2009]**

(a) ethylene   (b) acetylene   (c) propene   (d) methane

81. The homologue of ethyne is ...... **[CPMT 2008]**

(a) C_2H_2 (c) C_2H_6 (c) C_3H_8 (d) C_3H_4

82. Propylene on hydrolysis with sulphuric acid forms ...... **[MHT CET 2004]**

(a) n-propyl alcohol   (b) iso-propyl alcohol

(c) ethyl alcohol   (d) butyl alcohol

83. Among the given compounds, one which can be distinguished by $AgNO_3$ is ...**[AFMC 2010]**

(a) ethane   (b) ethylene   (c) acetylene   (d) diethyl ether

84. A dibromo derivative of an alkane react with sodium metal to form an alicyclic hydrocarbon. The derivative is ...... **[KCET 2010]**

(a) 1, 1-dibromopropane   (b) 2, 2-dibromopropane

(c) 1, 2-dibromopropane   (d) 1-dibromopropane

85. Identify the reagent from the following list which can easily distinguish between 1-butyne and 2-butyne ?

(a) Bromine, CCl_4 (b) H_2, Lindlar catalyst

(c) Dilute H_2SO_4, $HgSO_4$ (d) Ammonical Cu_2Cl_2

86. The treatment of benzene with iso-butene in the presence of sulphuric acid gives ......

    (a) iso-butyl benzene   (b) tert-butyl benzene   **[AIIMS 2003]**

    (c) n-butyl benzene   (d) no reaction

87. **Assertion :** Alkyl benzene is not prepared by Friedel-Craft's alkylation of benzene.

    Reason : Alkyl halides are less reactive than acyl halides   **[AIIMS 2003]**

    (a) Both Assertion and Reason are true and Reason is the correct explanation of Assertion.

    (b) Both Assertion and Reason are true but Reason is not the correct explanation of Assertion.

    (c) Assertion is true but Reason is false.

    (d) Both Assertion and Reason are false.

88. Angle strain in cyclopropane is ......   **[KCET 2007]**

    (a) 24° 44'   (b) 9° 44'   (c) 44'   (d) –5° 16'

89. The general formula of a cycloalkane is ......   **[KCET 2007]**

    (a) C_nH_n (b) C_nH_{2n} (c) C_nH_{2n-2} (d) C_nH_{2n+2}

90. Which cycloalkane has the lowest heat of combustion per CH_2 group?   **[KCET 2006]**

    (a) Cyclopropane   (b) Cyclobutane   (c) Cyclopentane   (d) Cyclohexane

91. From which one of the following, both ethylene and acetylene could be prepared in a single step reaction?   **[Kerala CEE 2008]**

    (a) CH_3CH_2OH (b) $Br - CH_2 - CH_2 - Br$

    (c) CH_3CH_2Br (d) $Br - CH_2 - CH_2 - OH$

92. In the following reaction : $C_2H_2 + X \xrightleftharpoons[\text{HgSO}_4/\text{H}_2\text{SO}_4]{\text{H}_2\text{O}} CH_3CHO$, what is X ?   **[BCECE 2008]**

    $HgSO_4/H_2SO_4$

    (a) CH_3CH_2OH (b) $CH_3–CH_2–OH$ (c) CH_3CH_2CHO (d) $CH_2 = CHOH$

93. A hydrocarbon of molecular formula C_6H_{10} reacts with sodamide and the same on ozonolysis followed by hydrogen peroxide on oxidation gives two molecules of carboxylic acids, one being optically active. Then the hydrocarbon may be ......   **[Kerala CEE 2007]**

    (a) 1-hexyne   (b) 2-hexyne

    (c) 3-hexyne   (d) 3-methyl-1-pentyne

    (e) 3, 3-dimethyl-1-butyne

94. In the reactions : $B \xrightarrow[\text{H}_2]{\text{Lindler's catalyst}} RC = CR \xrightarrow{\text{NaNH}_3} A$

    A and B are geometrical isomers. Then ......   **[EAMCET 2007]**

    (a) A is cis and B is trans   (b) A is trans and B is cis

    (c) A and B are cis   (d) A and B are trans

95. The C – C bond distance is the longest in ......   **[Manipal 2006]**

    (a) C_2H_6 (b) C_2H_2 (c) $C_2H_2Br_2$ (d) C_2H_4

96. What is the product formed when acetylene reacts with hypochlorous acid?

[MHT CET 2006]

(a) CH_3COCl (b) $ClCH_2CHO$ (c) Cl_2CHCHO (d) $ClCH_2COOH$

97. Which of the following gives propyne on hydrolysis?   **[AIIMS 2006]**

(a) Al_4C_3 (b) Mg_2C_3 (c) B_4C (d) La_4C_3

98. The percentage s-character of hybrid orbitals in methane, ethane and ethyne are respectively ......   **[Manipal 2006]**

(a) 25, 50, 75   (b) 25, 33, 50   (c) 10, 20, 30   (d) 50, 75, 100

99. Acetylene can be obtained by the reaction ......   **[MHTCET 2006]**

(a) $HCOOK \rightarrow$ (b) $CHI_3 + Ag \rightarrow$ (c) $H_3CCH_2OH \rightarrow$ (d) $Be_2C + H_2O \rightarrow$

100. What will be obtained when acetylene is treated with arsenic chloride?

(a) Lewisite   (b) Mustard gas   (c) Westron   (d) None of these

101. Westrosol is ......   **[RPMT 2004]**

(a) trichloro ethylene

(b) tetrachloro ethane

(c) tetrachloro ethylene

(d) none of these

102. Ethyl benzene cannot be prepared by ......   **[KCET 2011]**

(a) Wurtz reaction

(b) Wurtz-Fittig reaction

(c) Friedel-Craft's reaction

(d) Clemmensen reduction

103. Which one is the most reactive towards electrophilic reagent?   **[CBSE AIPMT 2010]**

(a) 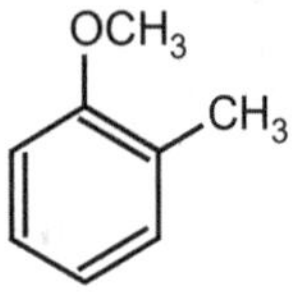   (b) 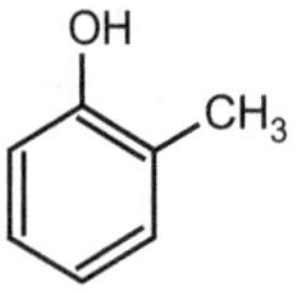   (c) 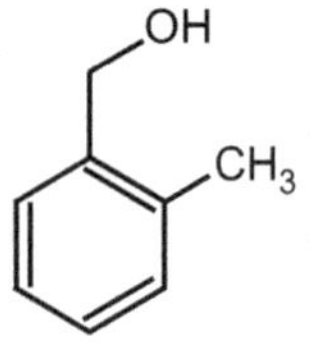   (d)

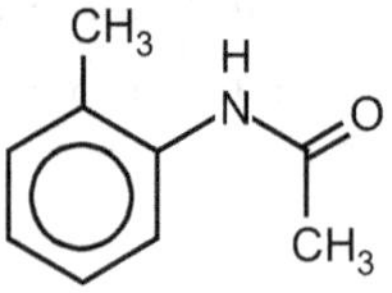

104. In the following reaction, the product 'R' is

$$CaC_2 \xrightarrow{H_2O} P \xrightarrow{\text{Hot iron tube}} Q \xrightarrow{CH_3Cl/AlCl_3} R$$

[AFMC 2010]

(a) benzene   (b) ethylbenzene   (c) toluene   (d) n-propylbenzene

105. Benzene does not undergo addition reactions easily because ......   **[BVP 2010]**

(a) it has a cyclic structure

(b) double bonds in it are very strong

(c) resonance stabilized system is to be preserved

(d) It has six hydrogen atoms

106. Benzene reacts with CH_3Cl in the presence of anhydrous $AlCl_3$ to form ......

[CBSE AIPMT 2009]

(a) toluene   (b) chlorobenzene   (c) benzyl chloride   (d) xylene

107. Oxidation of toluene with CrO_3 in the presence of $(CH_3CO)_2O$ give a product which on treatment with aqueous NaOH produces ......   **[Manipal 2009]**

(a) C_5H_5CHO (b) $(C_6H_5CO)_2O$ (c) C_6H_5COONa (d) 2, 4-diacetyl toluene

108. A catalyst that can be employed for Friedel-Craft's acylation is ...... **[Manipal 2009]**
   (a) anhydrous $CuCl_2$ (b) anhydrous BCl_3 (c) anhydrous $CaCl_2$ (d) hydrated $AlCl_3$

109. Which of the following when treated with superheated steam under pressure gives benzene? **[Manipal 2009]**
   (a) Benzene sulphonic acid
   (b) Benzyl chloride
   (c) Bromobenzene
   (d) Nitrobenzene

110. Assertion : Friedel-Craft's reaction is used to introduce an alkyl or acyl group in benzene nucleus.

   Reason : Benzene is a solvent for Friedel-Craft's alkylation of bromobenzene **[AIIMS 2008]**
   (a) Both Assertion and Reason are true and Reason is the correct explanation of Assertion.
   (b) Both Assertion and Reason are true but Reason is not the correct explanation of Assertion.
   (c) Assertion is true but Reason is false.
   (d) Both Assertion and Reason are false.

111. Identify B in the following reaction : **[DUMET 2008]**

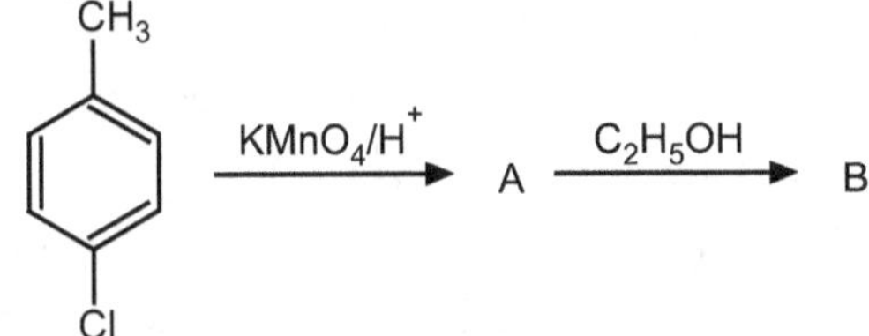

(a) 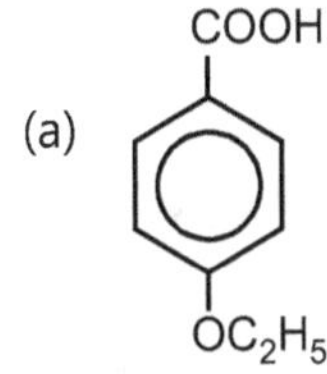   (b)   (c) 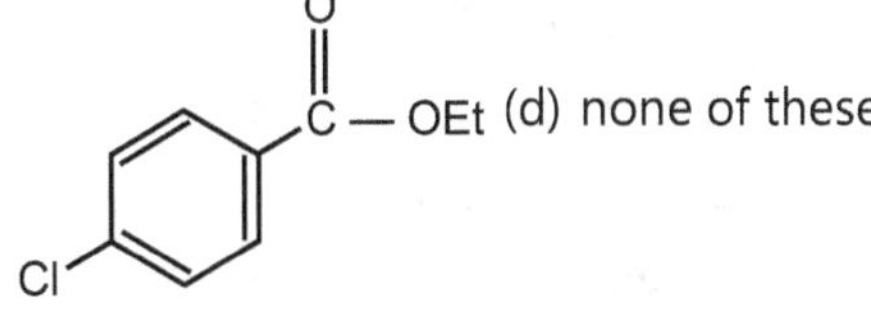 (d) none of these

112. An aromatic compound 'X' with molecular formula C_8H_{10} produces on nitration one mononitro derivative and three dinitro derivatives. Compound would be ... **[Manipal 2008]**
   (a) ethyl benzene   (b) m-xylene   (c) o-xylene   (d) p-xylene

113. The hydrocarbon which does not decolourise alkaline $KMnO_4$ solution and also does not give any precipitate with ammoniacal silver nitrate is ...... **[AIIMS 2007]**
   (a) benzene   (b) acetylene   (c) propyne   (d) butyne-1

114. The compound X in the reaction **[AIIMS 2007]**

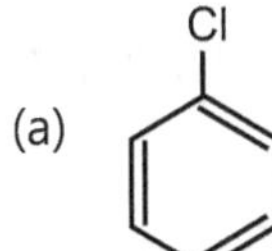

(a)   (b)   (c)   (d)

115. Using anhydrous $AlCl_3$ as a catalyst, which one of the following reactions produce ethyl benzene? **[Manipal 2007]**

(a) $CH_3CH_2OH + C_6H_6$

(b) $CH_3 - CH = CH_2 + C_6H_6$

(c) $CH_2 = CH_2 + C_6H_6$

(d) $CH_3 - CH_3 + C_6H_6$

116. Which of the following sequence of reactions (reagents) can be used for the conversion of $C_6H_5CH_2CH_3$ into $C_6H_5CH = CH_2$? **[AIIMS 2006]**

(a) $SOCl_2, H_2O$ (b) SO_2Cl_2; alc KOH (c) $(Cl_2)/hv; H_2O$ (d) $SOCl_2$; alc KOH

117. What is obtained when chlorine is passed in boiling toluene and product is hydrolysed? **[AMU 2006]**

(a) o-cresol

(b) p-cresol

(c) 2, 4-dihydroxytoluene

(d) benzyl alcohol

118. The compound 'C' in the following reaction is

$$C_7H_8 \xrightarrow{3Cl_2/heat} A \xrightarrow{Br_2/Fe} B \xrightarrow{Zn/HCl} C$$

(a) o-bromotoluene

(b) m-bromotoluene

(c) p-bromotoluene

(d) 3-bromo - 2,4,6- trichlorotoluene

119. Assertion : Rates of nitration of benzene and hexadeuterobenzene are different.

Reason : C – H bond is stronger than C – D bond. **[AIIMS 2005]**

(a) Both Assertion and Reason are true and Reason is the correct explanation of Assertion.

(b) Both Assertion and Reason are true but Reason is not the correct explanation of Assertion.

(c) Assertion is true but Reason is false.

(d) Both Assertion and Reason are false.

120. Assertion : Styrene on reaction with HBr gives 1-bromo-1-phenylethane.

Reason : Benzyl radical is more stable than alkyl **[AIIMS 2004]**

(a) Both Assertion and Reason are true and Reason is the correct explanation of Assertion.

(b) Both Assertion and Reason are true but Reason is not the correct explanation of Assertion.

(c) Assertion is true but Reason is false.

(d) Both Assertion and Reason are false.

121. $CH_3 - CH = CH_2 + HI \rightarrow X$. Here X is ...... **[CET Karnataka 2000]**

(a) $CH_3 - CH_2 - CH_2I$ (b) $CH_3 - CHI - CH_3$ (c) CH_3CH_2CH (d) None of these

122. Which of the following compounds exhibits stereoisomerism ? **[AFMC 2000]**

(a) 2-Methylbutene-1

(b) 3-Methylbutyne-2

(c) 3-Methylbutanoic acid

(d) 2-Methylbutanoic acid

123. Gammexane is ...... **[JKCMEE 2000]**

(a) DDT

(b) Benzene hexachloride

(c) Chloral

(d) Hexachloro ethane

124. Touelne on oxidation with dilute HNO_3 gives ......   **[JIPMER 2000]**

(a) Benzaldehyde   (b) Phenol   (c) Nitrotoulene   (d) Benzoic acid

125. Chloroprene is used in making ......   **[DPMT 2001]**

(a) Synthetic rubber   (b) Plastic   (c) Petrol   (d) All of these

126. Reactions of alkanes with halogens is explosive in case of ......   **[CBSE 2005]**

(a) F_2 (b) Cl_2 (c) Br_2 (d) I

127. On heating C_2H_2 to red heat, the compound formed is ......   **[J.I.P.M.E.R. 2000]**

(a) Ethylene   (b) Benzene   (c) Ethane   (d) Methane

128. An alkane C_7H_{16} is produced by the reaction of Lithium di (3-pentyl) cuperate with ethyl bromide. The structural formula of product is ......   **[Kerala M.E.E. 2000]**

(a) 3-Methylhexane   (b) 2-Ethylpentane   (c) 3-Ethylpentane (d) n-Heptane

(e) 2-Dimethylhexane

129. When 2-butyne is treated with dil. $H_2SO_4/HgSO_4$, the product formed is

[Haryana C.E.E.T. 2000]

(a) Butanol-1   (b) Butanone   (c) 2-Butanol   (d) Butanoic acid

130. The conversion of $ClCH = CH-Cl$ to $Cl_2CH-CHCl_2$ can be carried out with ...   **[D.C.E. 2000]**

(a) Cl_2 (b) Cl_2/hv (c) $Cl_2/AlCl_3$ (d) $Cl_2/aq.$ NaOH

131. One mole of 1, 2-dibromopropane on treatment with X moles of $NaNH_2$ followed by treatment with ethyl bromide gave a pentyne. The value of X is ...   **[D.C.E. 2000]**

(a) One   (b) Two   (c) Three   (d) Four

132. The order of activity of various o- and p- director is   **[D.C.E. 2000]**

(a) $-O^- > -OH > -OCOCH_3 > -COCH_3$ (b) $-OH > -O^- > -OCOCH_3 > -COCH_3$

(c) $-OH > -O^- > -COCH_3 > -OCOCH_3$ (d) $-O^- > -COCH_3 > -OCOCH_3 > -OH$

133. The conversion of 2, 3-dibromobutane to 2-butene with Zn is ...   **[D.C.E. 2000]**

(a) Redox reaction   (b) α-Elimination

(c) β-Elimination   (d) Both α-elimination and redox reaction

134. The addition of HBr is easiest with ......   **[M.P.P.M.T. 2000]**

(a) $CH_2 = CHCl$ (b) $ClCH = CHCl$

(c) $CH_3 - CH = CH_2$ (d) $(CH_3)_2C = CH_2$

135. 1, 3-Butadiene when treated with Br_2 gives   **[D.P.M.T. 2000]**

(a) 1, 4-Dibromo-2-butene   (b) 1, 3-Dibromo-2-butene

(c) 3, 4-Dibromo-1-butene   (d) 2, 3-Dibromo-2-butene

136. When ethyl alcohol is heated with conc. H_2SO_4 at 443 K, ethylene is formed by ......

[Tamil Nadu C.E.T. 2001]

(a) Intramolecular hydration   (b) Intermolecular hydration

(c) Intermolecular dehydration   (d) Intramolecular dehydration

137. Which of the following possesses the highest melting point ?   **[Manipal 2001]**

(a) Chlorobenzene   (b) o-Dichlorobenzene

(c) m-Dichlorobenzene   (d) p-Dichlorobenzene

138. When 2-pentyne is treated with dil. H_2SO_4 and $HgSO_4$, the product formed is ......

[J.I.P.M.E.R. 2001]

(a) 1-pentanol　　　(b) 2-pentanol　　　(c) 2-pentanone　　　(d) 3-pentanone

139. A salt producing hydrocarbon among these compounds is ......　　**[Karnataka C.E.T. 2002]**

(a) Ethyne　　　(b) Ethene　　　(c) Methane　　　(d) Ethane

140. The compound　　　　　　　　　　　　　　　　　　**[C.B.S.E. 2003]**

$$CH_3$$
$$|$$
CH_3—C $=$ CH—CH_3 on reaction with $NaIO_4$ in the presence of $KMnO_4$ gives ......

(a) $CH_3CHO + CO_2$

(b) CH_3COCH_3

(c) $CH_3COCH_3 + CH_3COOH$

(d) $CH_3COCH_3 + CH_3CHO$

141. The reaction of HBr with propene in the presence of peroxide gives ......　　**[C.B.S.E. 2004]**

(a) Isopropyl bromide

(b) 3-bromo propane

(c) Allyl bromide

(d) n-propyl bromide

142. Using anhydrous $AlCl_3$ as a catalyst, which one of the following reactions produces ethylbenzene (PhEt) ?　　**[C.B.S.E. 2004]**

(a) $H_3C - CH_2OH + C_6H_6$

(b) $CH_3 - CH = CH_2 + C_6H_6$

(c) $H_2C = CH_2 + C_6H_6$

(d) $H_3C - CH_3 + C_6H_6$

143. Which one of the following has the minimum boiling point ?　　**[A.I.E.E.E. 2004]**

(a) n-Butane　　　(b) Isobutane　　　(c) 1-Butene　　　(d) 1-Butyne

144. Among the following compounds which can be dehydrated very easily is　　**[A.I.E.E.E. 2004]**

(a) $CH_3CH_2CH_2CH_2CH_2OH$

(b) $CH_3CH_2CHCH_2CH_2OH$
　　　　　　　$|$
　　　　　　　CH_3

(c)
$$CH_3$$
$$|$$
$CH_3CH_2CCH_2CH_3$
$$|$$
$$OH$$

(d)
$$OH$$
$$|$$
$CH_3CH_2CH_2CHCH_3$

145. Which of the following requires radical intermediates?　　**[Orissa J.E.E. 2004]**

(a) $CH_3 - CH = CH_2 + HBr \rightarrow CH_3 - CH - CH_3$
　　　　　　　　　　　　　　　　　　　　$|$
　　　　　　　　　　　　　　　　　　　Br

(b) $CH_3 - CHO + HCN \rightarrow CH_3 - CH_3 - CH{\overset{CN}{\underset{OH}{<}}}$

(c) $CH_3 - CH = CH_2 + HBr \rightarrow CH_3 - CH_2 - CH_2 - Br$

(d) $CH_3CHO + NH_2OH \xrightarrow{H^+} CH_3 - CH = N - OH$

146. Which does not follow Markownikov rule ?　　**[Orissa J.E.E. 2004]**

(a) $CH_3 - CH = CH_2$

(b) $CF_3 - CH = CH_2$

(c) $CH_3 - CH - CH = CH_2$
　　　$|$
　　CH_3

(d) $CH_3 - CH_2 - CH = CH_2$

147. Gasoline has composition　　　　　　　　　**[A.F.M.C. 2004]**

(a) $C_8 - C_{12}$　　　(b) $C_2 - C_5$　　　(c) $C_7 - C_9$　　　(d) None of these

148. Which of the following cannot be used in Friedel-Craft's reactions ?　　　**[A.F.M.C. 2004]**

(a) $FeCl_3$　　　(b) BF_3　　　(c) $AlCl_3$　　　(d) $NaCl$

149. Benzene can be obtained by heating either benzoic acid with X or phenol with Y. X and Y are respectively ......　　　　　　　　　**[Karnataka, 2004]**

(a) Zinc dust and soda lime　　　　　　(b) Soda lime and zinc dust

(c) Zinc dust and sodium hydroxide　　　(d) Soda lime and copper

150. On treating a mixture of two alkyl halides with sodium metal in dry ether, 2-methyl propane was obtained. The alkyl halides are ......　　　　　**[Karnataka, 2004]**

(a) 2-chloropropane and chloromethane　　(b) 2-chloropropane and chloroethane

(c) Chloromethane and chloroethane　　　(d) Chloromethane and 1-chloropropane

151. The chemicals and the reaction conditions required for the preparation of ethane are ......

[E.A.M.C.E.T. 2005]

(a) C_2H_5I, Zn-Cu, C_2H_5OH　　　　(b) CH_3Cl, Na, H_2O

(c) $KOOC - CH = CH - COOK$, electrolysis　　(d) CH_3CO_2Na, NaOH, CaO, Δ.

152. Which of the following gives propyne on hydrolysis ?　　　**[A.I.I.M.S. 2005]**

(a) Al_4C_3　　　(b) Mg_2C_3　　　(c) B_4C　　　(d) La_4C_3

153. 2-Methylbutene on reaction with bromine in the presence of sunlight gives mainly ......

[A.I.E.E.E. 2005]

(a) 1-bromo-2-methylbutane　　　　　(b) 2-bromo-2-methylbutane

(c) 2-bromo-3-methylbutane　　　　　(d) 1-bromo-3-methylbutane

154. Propyne and propene can be distinguished by ......

(a) Conc. H_2SO_4　　　(b) Br_2 in CCl_4　　　(c) Dil. H_2SO_4　　　(d) $AgNO_3$ in ammonia

155. In the presence of peroxide, hydrogen chloride and hydrogen iodide do not give anti Markownikoff's addition to alkenes because ......

(a) Both are highly ionic

(b) One is oxidizing, the other is reducing

(c) One of the step is endothermic in both the cases

(d) All the steps are endothermic in both the cases

156. The reaction of propene with HOCl proceeds via the addition of ......

(a) H^+ in the first step　　　　　　(b) Cl^+ in the first step

(c) OH^- in the first step　　　　　　(d) Cl^+ and OH^- in a single step

ANSWER KEY

1. (b)	2. (a)	3. (b)	4. (a)	5. (b)	6. (d)	7. (b)	8. (b)
9. (d)	10. (a)	11. (c)	12. (a)	13. (c)	14. (c)	15. (b)	16. (d)
17. (d)	18. (b)	19. (b)	20. (a)	21. (c)	22. (c)	23. (b)	24. (b)
25. (a)	26. (a)	27. (b)	28. (d)	29. (b)	30. (a)	31. (a)	32. (c)
33. (a)	34. (b)	35. (a)	36. (c)	37. (b)	38. (a)	39. (c)	40. (a)
41. (d)	42. (b)	43. (a)	44. (b)	45. (c)	46. (d)	47. (b)	48. (d)

49. (c)	50. (d)	51. (b)	52. (a)	53. (c)	54. (b)	55. (a)	56. (b)
57. (b)	58. (c)	59. (c)	60. (c)	61. (c)	62. (a)	63. (c)	64. (b)
65. (c)	66. (b)	67. (b)	68. (c)	69. (b)	70. (b)	71. (a)	72. (b)
73. (c)	74. (b)	75. (d)	76. (b)	77. (a)	78. (d)	79. (b)	80. (a)
81. (c)	82. (a)	83. (c)	84. (a)	85. (d)	86. (b)	87. (c)	88. (c)
89. (a)	90. (a)	91. (c)	92. (c)	93. (b)	94. (b)	95. (b)	96. (d)
97. (d)	98. (c)	99. (b)	100. (c)	101. (d)	102. (b)	103. (d)	104. (d)
105. (c)	106. (b)	107. (c)	108. (c)	109. (c)	110. (a)	111. (b)	112. (a)
113. (d)	114. (b)	115. (c)	116. (d)	117. (c)	118. (b)	119. (c)	120. (a)
121. (c)	122. (d)	123. (c)	124. (c)	125. (c)	126. (c)	127. (d)	128. (a)
129. (d)	130. (a)	131. (a)	132. (c)	133. (b)	134. (d)	135. (b)	136. (c)
137. (a)	138. (c)	139. (c)	140. (d)	141. (d)	142. (d)	143. (b)	144. (b)
145. (a)	146. (a)	147. (c)	148. (c)	149. (a)	150. (a)	151. (b)	152. (b)
153. (c)	154. (d)	155. (a)	156. (c)	157. (d)	158. (c)	159. (a)	160. (b)
161. (c)	162. (d)	163. (b)	164. (a)	165. (d)	166. (c)	167. (c)	168. (b)
169. (d)	170. (d)	171. (d)	172. (a)	173. (c)	174. (a)	175. (b)	176. (a)
177. (c)	178. (b)	179. (c)	180. (d)	181. (b)	182. (a)	183. (c)	184. (b)

Previous Years Questions

1. (a)	2. (a)	3. (d)	4. (c)	5. (d)	6. (c)	7. (a)	8. (d)
9. (a)	10. (a)	11. (b)	12. (c)	13. (d)	14. (a)	15. (b)	16. (b)
17. (d)	18. (a)	19. (c)	20. (d)	21. (d)	22. (a)	23. (c)	24. (d)
25. (a)	26. (a)	27. (a)	28. (d)	29. (d)	30. (a)	31. (d)	32. (a)
33. (d)	34. (d)	35. (d)	36. (a)	37. (c)	38. (a)	39. (b)	40. (c)
41. (d)	42. (c)	43. (c)	44. (b)	45. (a)	46. (c)	47. (b)	48. (a)
49. (c)	50. (b)	51. (b)	52. (b)	53. (d)	54. (c)	55. (c)	56. (c)
57. (b)	58. (d)	59. (b)	60. (b)	61. (b)	62. (a)	63. (c)	64. (d)
65. (b)	66. (c)	67. (a)	68. (b)	69. (a)	70. (d)	71. (a)	72. (d)
73. (b)	74. (c)	75. (c)	76. (a)	77. (d)	78. (c)	79. (b)	80. (b)
81. (d)	82. (b)	83. (c)	84. (d)	85. (d)	86. (b)	87. (b)	88. (a)
89. (b)	90. (d)	91. (b)	92. (d)	93. (d)	94. (b)	95. (a)	96. (c)
97. (b)	98. (b)	99. (b)	100. (a)	101. (a)	102. (a)	103. (b)	104. (c)
105. (c)	106. (a)	107. (d)	108. (b)	109. (a)	110. (c)	111. (c)	112. (d)
113. (a)	114. (b)	115. (c)	116. (b)	117. (d)	118. (b)	119. (d)	120. (b)
121. (b)	122. (d)	123. (b)	124. (d)	125. (a)	126. (b)	127. (b)	128. (c)
129. (b)	130. (a)	131. (c)	132. (d)	133. (b)	134. (b)	135. (b)	136. (c)
137. (c)	138. (b)	139. (a)	140. (c)	141. (d)	142. (c)	143. (b)	144. (c)
145. (c)	146. (b)	147. (c)	148. (d)	149. (b)	150. (a)	151. (a)	152. (b)
153. (b)	154. (d)	155. (c)	156. (b)				

❑❑❑

ENVIRONMENTAL CHEMISTRY

1. What level of the atmosphere occurs at the highest altitude?
   (a) Ozone   (b) Mesosphere   (c) Stratosphere   (d) Troposphere

2. Which is not a pure substance?
   (a) Helium   (b) Copper wire   (c) Air   (d) Sucrose

3. A natural phenomenon that becomes harmful due to pollution is ......
   (a) Global warming   (b) Ecological balance
   (c) Greenhouse effect   (d) Desertification

4. Which environmental problem could lead to rise in sea level?
   (a) Acid rain   (b) Cutting down the trees in rain forests
   (c) Damage to the ozone layer   (d) Global warming

5. Which of the following gases is not a green house gas?
   (a) CO   (b) O_3 (c) CH_4 (d) H_2O vapour

6. The Intergovernmental Panel on Climate Change (IPCC) issued a report in 2001 which attached probabilities to the predictions and statements made. Which prediction/statement was considered "very unlikely" ?
   (a) The temperatures in the northern hemisphere during the 20th century have been the highest for past 1,000 years.
   (b) The observed warming over the past 100 years is solely because of climatic variability.
   (c) Carbon dioxide contributes to higher global temperatures.
   (d) Increased carbon dioxide levels are a consequence of human activity.

7. Photochemical smog occurs in warm, dry and sunny climate. One of the following is not amongst the components of photochemical smog, identify it.
   (a) NO_2 (b) O_3
   (c) SO_2 (d) Unsaturated hydrocarbon

8. Which of the following statements is not true about classical smog?
   (a) Its main components are produced by the action of sunlight on emissions of automobiles and factories
   (b) Produced in cold and humid climate
   (c) It contains compounds of reducing nature
   (d) It contains smoke, fog and sulphur dioxide

9. Biochemical Oxygen Demand (BOD) is a measure of organic material present in water. BOD value less than 5 ppm indicates a water sample to be ......
   (a) Rich in dissolved oxygen   (b) Poor in dissolved oxygen
   (c) Highly polluted   (d) Not suitable for aquatic life

10. Name the substance whose accumulation in pelicans of Lake Michigan led to the formation of thin shells of their eggs ......
    (a) CFC   (b) PAN   (c) DDT   (d) PAC

11. Name the process in which a harmful chemical enters the food chain and gets concentrated at each level in the food chain ......

    (a) Concentration (b) Biomagnification (c) Expansion (d) Pollution

12. Which environmental problem could cause an increase in number of people with skin cancers?

    (a) Acid rain (b) Cutting down the trees in rain forests
    (c) Damage to the ozone layer (d) Global warming

13. Chlorofluorocarbons rise to the stratosphere and ......

    (a) React directly with stratospheric ozone to destroy it

    (b) After interacting with UV energy become free radicals, which destroy ozone

    (c) Become free radicals that react with oxygen to create ozone

    (d) React with free radicals to remove carbon dioxide

14. During the Antarctic spring, ozone is destroyed at a greater rate than it is formed

    (a) On the surface of atmospheric ice crystals (b) In a process that is catalytic

    (c) In polar stratospheric clouds (d) All of these are correct

15. Scientists believe they know the average global temperature over the last 160,000 years. Which property of the ice core samples from Antarctica provides this information?

    (a) Thickness (b) Carbon dioxide concentration
    (c) 1H/2H ratio (d) Temperature

16. Which of the following conditions shows the polluted environment ?

    (a) pH of rain water is 5.6

    (b) Amount of carbon dioxide in the atmosphere is 0.03%

    (c) Biological oxygen demand 4 ppm

    (d) Eutrophication

17. Which environmental problem could lead to death of fish in a lake?

    (a) Acid rain (b) Cutting down the trees in rain forests
    (c) Damage to the ozone layer (d) Global warming

18. A farmer tested the soil in a field and found that it had a pH of 6. This shows that the soil was ......

    (a) Slightly acidic, so gypsum needs to be added

    (b) Slightly acidic, so lime needs to be added

    (c) Slightly alkaline, so gypsum needs to be added

    (d) Strongly acidic, so lime needs to be added

19. Phosphate containing fertilizers cause water pollution. Addition of such compounds in water bodies causes ......

    (a) Less growth of algae

    (b) Decrease in amount of dissolved oxygen in water

    (c) Deposition of calcium phosphate

    (d) Increase in fish population

20. Acid rain will not attack buildings made from ......

(a) Chalk　　　　(b) Granite　　　　(c) Limestone　　　　(d) Marble

21. The acids present in acid rain are ......

(a) Peroxyacetyl nitrate　(b) H_2CO_3　　　　(c) HCl　　　　(d) H_2SO_4

22. Acidity in a lake can be reduced by adding ......

(a) Basic salt　　　　(b) Granite　　　　(c) Gravel　　　　(d) Limestone

23. The main reason that water supplies are chlorinated is ......

(a) To filter out solids from the water

(b) To kill bacteria in the water

(c) To make the water softer

(d) To remove lead salts from the water as insoluble lead chloride

24. Which of the following statements is wrong?

(a) Ozone is not responsible for green house effect

(b) Ozone can oxidize sulphur dioxide present in the atmosphere to sulphur trioxide

(c) Ozone hole is thinning of ozone layer present in stratosphere

(d) Ozone is produced in upper stratosphere by the action of UV rays on oxygen

25. Sewage containing organic waste should not be disposed in water bodies, because it causes major water pollution. Fishes in such a polluted water die because of ......

(a) Large number of mosquitoes

(b) Increase in the amount of dissolved oxygen

(c) Decrease in the amount of dissolved oxygen in water

(d) Clogging of gills by mud

26. The combustion process for an effective fossil fuel must have an activation energy of 25. Both Clinton and Bush (the younger) administrations had been unwilling to sign the Kyoto Protocol. What has been their primary objection to the treaty?

(a) The target emission levels are not sufficiently low to affect the greenhouse effect

(b) The treaty does not include a provision for trading emission allowances

(c) Developing countries are not required to control greenhouse gas emissions

(d) Enforcement of the treaty will be impossible

27. Which substances are regulated by the Kyoto Protocol?

(I) Argon　　　　　　　　　　(II) Carbon dioxide

(III) Nitrogen　　　　(IV) Nitrous oxide　　　(V) Sulphur hexafluoride

(a) I, II and III only　　(b) I and III only　　(c) II and V only　　(d) II, IV and V only

28. Argon which comprises almost 1% of the atmosphere, is approximately 27 times more abundant than CO_2, but does not contribute to global warming. Which explanation accounts for this fact?

(a) Single atoms do not vibrate

(b) Argon's vibrational energy is not excited by infrared radiation

(c) The mass of Argon does not allow it to reach sufficiently high in the atmosphere to interact with the earth's radiant energy

(d) Argon is transparent to UV radiation

29. One of the best solutions to get rid of non-biodegradable wastes is ......

(a) Burning   (b) Dumping   (c) Burying   (d) Recycling

30. Name one non-biodegradable waste which may pollute the earth to dangerous levels of toxicity, if not handled properly ......

(a) DDT   (b) CFC

(c) Radioactive substances   (d) PAN

31. Dinitrogen and dioxygen are main constituents of air but these do not react with each other to form oxides of nitrogen because ......

(a) The reaction is endothermic and requires very high temperature

(b) The reaction can be initiated only in the presence of a catalyst

(c) Oxides of nitrogen are unstable

(d) N_2 and O_2 are unreactive

32. The pollutants which are introduced directly in air from sources are called primary pollutants. Primary pollutants are sometimes converted into secondary pollutants. Which of the following belongs to secondary air pollutants?

(a) Carbon monoxide   (b) Hydrocarbon

(c) Peroxyacetyl nitrate   (d) Nitrogen monoxide

33. Which of the following statements is correct?

(a) Ozone hole is a hole formed in stratosphere from which ozone oozes out

(b) Ozone hole is a hole formed in the troposphere from which ozone oozes out

(c) Ozone hole is thinning of ozone layer of stratosphere at some places

(d) Ozone hole means vanishing of ozone layer around the earth completely

34. Which of the following practices will not come under green chemistry?

(a) If possible, making use of soap made of vegetable oils instead of using synthetic detergents

(b) Using H_2O_2 for bleaching purpose instead of using chlorine based bleaching agents

(c) Using bicycle for travelling small distances instead of using petrol/diesel based vehicles

(d) Using plastic cans for storing substances

35. The pollutant responsible for ozone holes is ......

(a) CO_2 (b) SO_2 (c) CO   (d) CFC

36. Which of the following statements about photochemical smog is wrong?

(a) It has high concentration of oxidizing agents

(b) It has low concentration of oxidizing agents

(c) It can be controlled by controlling the release of NO_2, hydrocarbons, ozone etc.

(d) Plantation of some plants like Pinus helps in controlling photochemical smog

37. The gaseous envelope around the earth is known as atmosphere. The lowest layer of this is extended upto 10 km from sea level, this layer is ......

(a) Stratosphere   (b) Troposphere   (c) Mesosphere   (d) Hydrosphere

38. Thermal pollution is possible at water sources near ......

(a) Coal-burning plants.
(b) Nuclear plants.
(c) Both coal-burning and nuclear plants.
(d) Neither coal-burning nor nuclear plants.

39. Animal dung is ...... waste.

(a) Biodegradable
(b) Non-biodegradable
(c) Hazardous
(d) Toxic

40. Which of the following is biodegradable?

(a) Iron nails   (b) Plastic mugs   (c) Leather belts   (d) Silver foil

41. Which of the following is non-biodegradable?

(a) Animal bones   (b) Nylon   (c) Tea leaves   (d) Wool

42. In a lake polluted with pesticides, which one of the following will contain the maximum amount of pesticides?

(a) Small fish   (b) Microscopic animals   (c) Big fish   (d) Water birds

43. Name the process in which a harmful chemical enters the food chain and gets concentrated at each level in the food chain ......

(a) Concentration   (b) Biomagnification   (c) Expansion   (d) Pollution

44. The consequences of global warming may be ......

(a) Increase in average temperature of the earth
(b) Melting of Himalayan glaciers
(c) Increased biochemical oxygen demand
(d) Eutrophication

45. Primary pollutants can be ......

(a) SO_2, CO
(b) PAN, O_3
(c) Both (a) and (b)
(d) None of these

46. Secondary pollutants can be ....

(a) PAN   (b) O_3 (c) Cl   (d) All of these

47. Bhopal gas tragedy is due to leakage of ....

(a) Ammonia
(b) Methyl isocyanide
(c) Methyl isocyanate
(d) Carbonate

48. Synergism relates to phenomenon due to ....

(a) Single pollutant
(b) Two or more pollutants having much effect than the total of individual pollutants
(c) Atmospheric gases
(d) Water pollutant

49. Which of the following combines with haemoglobin in blood ?

(a) Carbon dioxide
(b) Carbon monoxide
(c) Methyl isocyanide
(d) Methyl cyanide

50. In the following equilibrium,

$$HbO_2 + CO \rightleftharpoons HbCO + O_2 \quad \Delta G < 0$$

(a) Oxygen carrying capacity is reduced (b) Oxygen carrying capacity is increased

(c) Addition of H_2O makes ΔG more negative (d) Temperature has no effect

51. Higher incidence of heart diseases in smokers is related to high content of ....

(a) CO_2 (b) CO (c) CN^- (d) H_2O

52. Cl_2 and SO_2 are pollutants but used in bleaching of textiles bleaching action of Cl_2 and SO_2 is due to ......

(a) Oxidation of both Cl_2 and SO_2 (b) Reduction of both Cl_2 and SO_2

(c) Reduction of Cl_2 and oxidation of SO_2 (d) Reduction of SO_2 and oxidation of Cl_2

53. Which city is not a part of Taj trapezium ?

(a) Agra (b) Firozabad (c) Mathura (d) Faridabad

54. Acid rain is specified when pH is ....

(a) below 7 (b) below 5.6 (c) above 7 (d) above 9

55. Acid rain can be reduced by use of ....

(a) LPG (b) CNG (c) both of these (d) none of these

56. Which is not a part of acid rain ?

(a) $CO_2 + H_2O \longrightarrow H_2CO_3$ (b) $SO_3 + H_2O \longrightarrow H_2SO_4$

(c) $NO_2 + O_2 + H_2O \longrightarrow HNO_3$ (d) $ClONO_2 + H_2O \longrightarrow HOCl + HNO_3$

57. Ozone depletion is initiated by ....

(a) $Cl^\bullet$ (b) $\overset{\bullet}{C}H_3$ (c) $ClO^\bullet$ (d) $CF_2Cl^\bullet$

58. Select correct statements

(a) CFCs are transporting agents for continuously generating $Cl^\bullet$ into stratosphere and damaging ozone layer.

(b) The upper stratosphere consists of considerable amount of ozone.

(c) Ozone in the stratosphere is a product of UV radiations acting on O_2 molecules.

(d) All of the above are correct statements.

59. Nobel prize in Green Chemistry is not associated with ......

(a) R. Williamson (b) Yues Chauvin

(c) Robert H. Grubbs (d) Richard S. Schrock

60. Eye irritation is caused by ......

(a) HCHO (b) $CH_2 = CHCHO$ (c) PAN (d) All of these

61. Which is not the constituent of photochemical smog?

(a) RCHO (b) RCOR (c) PAN (d) CF_2Cl_2

62. Smog can be controlled by ......

(a) Use of catalytic converters in automobiles

(b) Setting the air-fuel ratio in engine in such a way to produce some CO and unburned hydrocarbons

(c) Both of the above

(d) None of the above

63. NO_x in the atmosphere is due to ......

(a) Lightening

(b) Incomplete combustion of fuel

(c) Thermal plant

(d) Radioactive decay

64. Which disinfectant cannot be used in drinking water?

(a) Potassium permanganate

(b) Bleaching powder

(c) Phenol

(d) Chlorine

65. Particulate pollutant is ....

(a) hydrocarbons

(b) dust

(c) hydrogen sulphide

(d) ozone

66. CFCs are stable in .... part of atmosphere ......

(a) lower　　　　(b) middle　　　　(c) upper　　　　(d) none of these

67. Toxic materials that are not broken down by natural biological or chemical processes are known as ....

(a) partial poison　　　(b) true poison　　　(c) filled poison　　　(d) incomplete poison

68. The lack of oxygen leads to ......

(a) killing all aquatic life

(b) killing all plant life

(c) killing all aquatic and plant life

(d) none of the above

69. To control smog, automobiles are now provided with ......

(a) oxidation catalysis

(b) reduction catalysis

(c) catalytic converter

(d) shortwave radiations

70. Clean water contains BOD ......

(a) < 5 ppm　　　(b) > 5 ppm　　　(c) < 2.5 ppm　　　(d) > 2.5 ppm

71. Ozone layer acts as ....

(a) protective layer　　(b) oxidation layer　　(c) reduction layer　　(d) hazardous layer

72. The process in which nutrient enriched water bodies support a dense plant population which kills animal life by depriving it of oxygen and results in subsequent loss of biodiversity is known as ....

(a) detrophication　　(b) eutrophication　　(c) desalination　　(d) salination

73. In the formation of acid rain .... gases combine with oxygen and water to form acid.

(a) NO_3　　　(b) SO_2　　　(c) SO_3　　　(d) SO_4

74. .... is lowest layer of atmosphere.

(a) Troposphere　　(b) Mesosphere　　(c) Stratosphere　　(d) Thermosphere

75. Highly polluted water has BOD ....

(a) less than 10 ppm　　(b) 17 ppm　　(c) 17 ppm or more　　(d) 5 ppm

76. Inorganic oxygen consuming materials found in aquatic environments are ....

(a) NH_4, H_2, SO_3　　(b) NH_3, H_2S, SO_2　　(c) NO_2, SO_2, CO_2　　(d) NO_2, CH_3, CO

77. In .... region, ozone is produced continuously.

(a) mesosphere　　(b) troposphere　　(c) stratosphere　　(d) ionosphere

78. Supersonic aircraft fly in the lower region of ....

(a) stratosphere　　(b) mesosphere　　(c) troposphere　　(d) none of these

79. The first 80 km of the atmosphere is a region known as ....

(a) homosphere　　(b) heterosphere　　(c) stratosphere　　(d) ionosphere

80. CO enters the respiratory system along with O_2 and combines with haemoglobin in the blood stream to form ....

(a) oxy haemoglobin

(b) deoxy haemoglobin

(c) carboxy haemoglobin

(d) nitro haemoglobin

81. Sea levels are rising due to ....

(a) increased CO_2 content

(b) melting of ice

(c) absorption of CO_2 gas

(d) none of these

82. Lead damages .... of the body.

(a) heart　　(b) kidney　　(c) lungs　　(d) throat

83. The increase of .... gas leads to global warming.

(a) CO　　(b) NO_2　　(c) CO_2　　(d) SO_3

84. Mists are ....

(a) solid aerosols　　(b) liquid aerosols　　(c) gaseous aerosols　　(d) none of these

85. SO_2 gas accounts for about .... rain.

(a) 40%　　(b) 50%　　(c) 60%　　(d) 70%

86. Match the following :

	A		B
(i)	DDT	(a)	Photochemical smog
(ii)	$NaClO_3$	(b)	Disinfectant
(iii)	Cl_2	(c)	Herbicides
(iv)	PAN	(d)	Pesticides

(a) (i) – (d); (ii) – (c); (iii) – (b); (iv) – a

(b) (i) – (d); (ii) – (b); (iii) – (c); (iv) – (a)

(c) (i) – (d); (ii) – (d); (iii) – (a); (iv) – (c)

(d) (i) – (a); (ii) – (c); (iii) – (d); (iv) – (b)

87. Photochemical smog is mainly ....

(a) O_3, PAN, O_2　　(b) O_3, SO_2, NO_X　　(c) O_3, PAN, NO_X　　(d) SO_2, CO_2, O_3

ANSWER KEY

1. (c)	2. (c)	3. (c)	4. (d)	5. (a)	6. (b)	7. (c)	8. (a)
9. (a)	10. (c)	11. (b)	12. (c)	13. (b)	14. (d)	15. (c)	16. (d)
17. (a)	18. (b)	19. (b)	20. (b)	21. (b)	22.(d)	23. (b)	24. (a)
25. (c)	26. (c)	27. (d)	28. (a)	29. (d)	30. (c)	31. (a)	32. (c)
33. (c)	34. (d)	35. (d)	36. (b)	37. (b)	38. (c)	39. (a)	40. (c)
41. (b)	42. (d)	43. (b)	44. (a)	45. (a)	46. (d)	47. (c)	48. (b)
49. (b)	50. (a)	51. (b)	52. (d)	53. (d)	54. (b)	55. (c)	56. (d)
57. (a)	58. (d)	59. (a)	60. (d)	61. (d)	62. (c)	63. (a)	64. (a)
65. (b)	66. (a)	67. (b)	68. (a)	69. (c)	70. (a)	71. (a)	72. (b)
73. (b)	74. (a)	75. (c)	76. (b)	77. (c)	78. (a)	79. (a)	80. (c)
81. (b)	82. (b)	83. (b)	84. (b)	85. (c)	86. (a)	87. (c)	

❑❑❑

SOLID STATE

1. In solids, the particles may be ......
   - (a) Atoms
   - (b) Molecules
   - (c) Ions
   - (d) All of these

2. Crystalline solids are ......
   - (a) Anisotropic
   - (b) Isotropic
   - (c) Anisotropic supercooled liquids
   - (d) Anisotropic superheated liquids

3. In solids, the constituent particles are arranged in ......
   - (a) Definite pattern in one direction
   - (b) Random arrangement
   - (c) Definite pattern in three dimensions
   - (d) Definite pattern in two directions

4. Amorphous solids may be classified as ......
   - (a) Isotropic
   - (b) Anisotropic and supercooled liquids
   - (c) Isotropic and superheated liquids
   - (d) Isotropic and supercooled liquids

5. Which of the following show anisotropy ?
   - (a) Gas
   - (b) Wood
   - (c) Paper
   - (d) Sugar

6. Isotropic solids have ......
   - (a) Similar electrical and different mechanical properties
   - (b) Dissimilar electrical and mechanical properties
   - (c) Similar electrical and mechanical properties in all directions
   - (d) Similar mechanical and different electrical properties

7. Glass is an example of ......
   - (a) True solid
   - (b) Pseudo solid
   - (c) Polar solid
   - (d) Non-polar solid

8. Which types of forces are present in dry ice ?
   - (a) Ionic
   - (b) van der Waal
   - (c) Hydrogen bond
   - (d) Covalent bond

9. S_8 and P_4 are examples of ......
   - (a) Ionic solid
   - (b) Covalent solid
   - (c) Molecular solid
   - (d) van der Waal solid

10. Quartz is an example of ......
    - (a) Metallic solid
    - (b) Covalent solid
    - (c) Molecular solid
    - (d) Ionic solid

11. NaCl is an example of ......
    - (a) Molecular solid
    - (b) Metallic solid
    - (c) Ionic solid
    - (d) Covalent solid

12. Diamond is an ......
    - (a) Ionic crystal
    - (b) Covalent crystal
    - (c) Molecular crystal
    - (d) Metallic crystal

13. The binding forces in molecular crystal are ......
    - (a) Covalent bond
    - (b) Ionic bond
    - (c) van der Waal forces
    - (d) Metallic bond

14. Amorphous silicon is used in ......

(a) Electrolytic cell

(b) Electrochemical cell

(c) Photovoltaic cell

(d) In all these cells

15. Plastic is an example of ......

(a) Crystalline solids

(b) Amorphous solids

(c) Pseudo solids

(d) Anisotropic solids

16. Examples of electrical insulators are ......

(a) Iodine, diamond   (b) Dry ice and alloy   (c) Wax, NaCl   (d) P_4 and S_8

17. Particles in solids have fixed positions and exhibit ......

(a) Vibratory motion

(b) Oscillations about their mean position

(c) No oscillations about their mean positon

(d) Have rotatory motion

18. Solids have ......

(a) Short intermolecular distance and weak intermolecular forces

(b) Short intermolecular distance and strong intermolecular forces

(c) Long intermolecular distance and weak intermolecular forces

(d) Long intermolecular distance and strong intermolecular forces

19. Quartz has ......

(a) Metallic bonding

(b) Covalent bonding

(c) Ionic bonding

(d) Hydrogen bonding

20. The total number of crystal systems and the number of Bravais lattices are respectively ......

(a) 14, 28   (b) 14, 7   (c) 7, 14   (d) 14, 14

21. A unit cell is characterized by how many parameters?

(a) 3   (b) 6   (c) 4   (d) 8

22. When a unit cell has constituent particles only on the corner of a unit cell, it is termed as ......

(a) Centered unit cell   (b) Primitive unit cell

(c) Body centered   (d) Face centered

23. A unit cell having constituent particles at corner and at any two opposite faces is ......

(a) Body centered   (b) Face centered   (c) End centered   (d) Edge centered

24. The unit cell with crystallographic dimensions $a = b \neq c$, $\alpha = \beta = \gamma = 90°$ is ......

(a) Cubic   (b) Tetragonal   (c) Hexagonal   (d) Rhombohedral

25. The unit cell with dimensions $a = b = c$, $\alpha = \beta = \gamma = 90°$ is ......

(a) Monoclinic   (b) Triclinic   (c) Cubic   (d) Rhombic

26. Rhombic sulphur, KNO_3, $BaSO_4$ are examples of ...... crystal system.

(a) Rhombohedral   (b) Orthorhombic   (c) Hexagonal   (d) Trigonal

27. Graphite and ZnO are examples of ......

(a) Triclinic   (b) Monoclinic   (c) Tetragonal   (d) Hexagonal

28. Monoclinic crystal system has dimensions ......
(a) $a \neq b \neq c,\ \alpha \neq b \neq \gamma \neq 90°$
(b) $a \neq b \neq c,\ \alpha = \beta = \gamma = 90°$
(c) $a = b \neq c,\ \alpha = \beta = 90°,\ \gamma = 120°$
(d) $a \neq b \neq c,\ \alpha = \gamma = 90°,\ \beta \neq 120°$

29. In fcc, the number of atoms per unit cell is ......
(a) 2　　　(b) 1　　　(c) 8　　　(d) 4

30. The number of NaCl formula units per unit cell is ......
(a) 2　　　(b) 4　　　(c) 6　　　(d) 8

31. The number of zinc sulphide units per unit cell is ......
(a) 8　　　(b) 6　　　(c) 4　　　(d) 2

32. The density of the crystal is given by ......
(a) $\dfrac{a^3 M}{Z \cdot N_A}$
(b) $\dfrac{a^3 NA}{ZM}$
(c) $\dfrac{a^3 Z}{MN_A}$
(d) $\dfrac{ZM}{a^3 N_A}$

33. To get n-type doped semiconductor, impurities to be added to silicon should have the following number of valence electrons ......
(a) 2　　　(b) 5　　　(c) 3　　　(d) 1

34. If molten zinc is cooled to solid state, it assumes hcp structure. What will be the number of nearest neighbours of zinc atom ?
(a) 4　　　(b) 6　　　(c) 8　　　(d) 12

35. The interionic distance in calcium chloride crystal would be ......
(a) a
(b) $a\sqrt{2}$
(c) $\dfrac{a\sqrt{3}}{2}$
(d) $\dfrac{2a}{\sqrt{3}}$

36. Which among the following is antiferromagnetic?
(a) MnO_2　　　(b) TiO_2　　　(c) VO_2　　　(d) CrO_2

37. How many unit cells are present in cube shaped ideal crystals of NaCl of mass 1.00 g?
(a) 2.57×10^{21} unit cells
(b) 5.14×10^{21} unit cells
(c) 1.28×10^{21} unit cells
(d) 1.71×10^{21} unit cells

38. The pycnometer density of NaCl crystal is 2.165×10^3 kg m^{-3}, while its X-ray density is 2.178×10^3 kg m^{-3}, what is the fraction of unoccupied sites in sodium chloride crystal?
(a) 5.96×10^{-3}
(b) 5.96
(c) 5.96×10^{-2}
(d) 5.96×10^{-1}

39. What is the co-ordination number of sodium in Na_2O?
(a) 6　　　(b) 4　　　(c) 8　　　(d) 2

40. The crystal system of a compound with unit cell dimensions a = 0.387; b = 0.387; c = 0.504 nm and $\alpha = \beta = 90°$; d = 120° is ......
(a) Cubic　　　(b) Hexagonal　　　(c) Orthorhombic　　(d) Rhombohedral

41. In face centered cubic lattice, a unit cell is shared equally by how many unit cells ?
(a) 2　　　(b) 4　　　(c) 6　　　(d) 8

42. If the distance between Na^+ and Cl^- ions in sodium chloride crystal is X pm, the length of the edge of unit cell is ......

(a) 4X pm (b) $\dfrac{X}{4}$ pm (c) $\dfrac{X}{2}$ pm (d) 2X pm

43. If Z is the number of atoms in the unit cell that represents the closed packing sequence ABC–ABC–, the number of tetrahedral voids in the unit cell is equal to ......

(a) Z (b) 2Z (c) $\dfrac{Z}{2}$ (d) $\dfrac{Z}{4}$

44. The material possessing superconducting properties is ......

(a) $Yb\ Ba\ Cu_2\ O_8$ (b) $Hg\ Be_2\ Ca_2\ Cu_2\ O_8$

(c) $YBa_2\ Cu_3\ O_7$ (d) $YB\ Cu_3\ O_7$

45. The appearance of colour in solid alkali metal halides is generally due to ......

(a) Schottky defect (b) Frenkel defect

(c) Interstitial position (d) F-centre

46. For CsBr crystallized in bcc the unit cell length is 436.6 pm. (Atomic mass of Cs and Br = 133 and 80 amu respectively). The density of CsBr is ......

(a) $0.425\ gm\ cm^{-3}$ (b) $8.25\ gm\ cm^{-3}$ (c) $4.25\ gm\ cm^{-3}$ (d) $42.5\ gm\ cm^{-3}$

47. Total volume of atoms present in a face centered cubic unit cell of a metal is ......

(a) $\dfrac{16}{3}\pi r^3$ (b) $\dfrac{20}{3}\pi r^3$ (c) $\dfrac{24}{3}\pi r^3$ (d) $\dfrac{12}{3}\pi r^3$

48. The energy gaps between valence band and conduction band for diamond, silicon and germanium are in the order ......

(a) Diamond > Si > Ge (b) Diamond < Si < Ge

(c) Diamond = Si = Ge (d) Diamond > Ge > Si

49. The Ca^{2+} and F^- are located in CaF_2 crystal respectively at face centered cubic. Lattice point is ......

(a) Tetrahedral voids (b) Half of tetrahedral voids

(c) Octahedral voids (d) Half of octahedral voids

50. For a cubic crystal structure, which one of the following relations indicating the cell characteristic is correct ?

(a) $a = b = c$ and $\alpha = \beta = \gamma = 90°$ (b) $a \neq b \neq c$ and $\alpha \neq \beta \neq \gamma = 90°$

(c) $a \neq b \neq c$ and $\alpha = \beta = \gamma = 90°$ (d) $a = b = c$ and $\alpha \neq \beta \neq \gamma = 90°$

51. The fraction of the total volume occupied by atoms present in a simple cube is ......

(a) $\dfrac{\pi}{4}$ (b) $\dfrac{\pi}{6}$ (c) $\dfrac{\pi}{3\sqrt{2}}$ (d) $\dfrac{\pi}{4\sqrt{2}}$

52. A metal crystallizes in a bcc lattice. Its unit cell edge length is about 300 pm and its molar mass is about 50 gm mol^{-1}. What would be the density of the metal in gm cm^{-3} ?

(a) 3.1 (b) 6.15 (c) 9.3 (d) 12.4

53. The basic unit in orthosilicates and pyrosilicates are respectively ......
(a) SiO_4^{4-} and $Si_2O_7^{6-}$
(b) SiO_4^{4-} and $(SiO_3)^{2n}$
(c) $(Si_3O_5)^{2n-}$ and $Si_2O_7^{6-}$
(d) $(Si_2O_5)^{2n-}$ and $(SiO_3)_n^{2n-}$

54. In fcc, the radius of atom in terms of the edge length of the unit cell is ......
(a) $\dfrac{a}{2}$
(b) $\dfrac{a}{\sqrt{2}}$
(c) $\dfrac{a}{2\sqrt{2}}$
(d) $\dfrac{\sqrt{3}}{4}a$

55. In a solid lattice, the cation has left a lattice site and is located at an interstitial position. The lattice defect is ......
(a) Interstitial defect   (b) Vacancy defect   (c) Frenkel defect   (d) Schottky defect

56. Lithium metal crystallises in bcc crystal. If the edge length is 351 pm the atomic radius of lithium will be ......
(a) 300.5 pm   (b) 240.8 pm   (c) 151.8 pm   (d) 75.5 pm

57. Metals have conductivities of the order ......
(a) 10^4 ohm^{-1} m^{-1} (b) 10^7 ohm^{-1} m^{-1} (c) 10^{-7} ohm^{-1} m^{-1} (d) 10^{-20} ohm^{-1} m^{-1}

58. Doping produces ......
(a) Electronic defect   (b) Frenkel defect   (c) Interstitial defect   (d) Schottky defect

59. When silicon and germanium are doped with P or As, the semiconductor is ......
(a) n-type   (b) p-type   (c) Both   (d) None of these

60. The conductivity in n-type semiconductor is due to movement of ......
(a) Positive holes
(b) Negatively charged electrons
(c) Ions
(d) Positively charged protons

61. Electron trapped in anion vacancy is called as ......
(a) Schottky defect
(b) Frenkel defect
(c) Metal excess non-stoichiometric defect
(d) F-centre

62. Schottky defect is due to the missing of ......
(a) Cations
(b) Anions
(c) Unequal number of cations and anions
(d) Equal number of cations and anions

63. The density of crystal decreases due to ......
(a) Frenkel defect   (b) Schottky defect   (c) Vacancy defect   (d) Line defect

64. The density of a crystal remains the same due to ......
(a) F-centre   (b) Schottky defect   (c) Frenkel defect   (d) Dislocation

65. Doping is ......
(a) Removal of impurities
(b) Addition of impurities
(c) Removal of anions
(d) Removal of cations

66. Frenkel defect is caused due to ......
(a) The presence of extra positive ion in the interstitial site
(b) The presence of extra negative ion in the interstitial site
(c) Shifting of positive ion from normal lattice site to interstitial site
(d) A cation missing from the lattice site creating a vacancy

67. Yellow colour of white salt of zinc carbonate salt on heating is due to ......
    (a) F-centre
    (b) Extra cations at interstitial site
    (c) The presence of zinc cation and electrons in the neighbouring interstitial site
    (d) Metal deficiency

68. Which of the following oxides is ferromagnetic ?
    (a) Fe_3O_4 (b) CrO_2 (c) Fe_2O_3 (d) MnO

69. Which of the following is paramagnetic ?
    (a) Benzene   (b) NaCl   (c) TiO_2 (d) O_2

70. Which of the following is diamagnetic ?
    (a) NaCl   (b) CrO_2 (c) MnO   (d) Fe_3O_4

71. Fe_3O_4 is ......
    (a) Ferromagnetic   (b) Antiferromagnetic
    (c) Ferrimagnetic   (d) Paramagnetic

72. Polar crystals on heating produce ......
    (a) Piezoelectricity   (b) Ferroelectricity   (c) Pyroelectricity   (d) Antiferroelectricity

73. Pickup in record player is an example of ......
    (a) Pyroelectricity   (b) Piezoelectricity   (c) Antiferroelectricity   (d) Ferroelectricity

74. Ferroelectric crystal is ......
    (a) Rochelle salt   (b) Quartz   (c) Lead chromate   (d) Barium titanate

75. Potassium has bcc structure with nearest neighbour distance of 4.42 Å (Atomic mass of potassium = 39), its density is ......
    (a) 454 kg m^{-3} (b) 804 kg m^{-3} (c) 852 kg m^{-3} (d) 900 kg m^{-3}

76. 8 : 8 type of packing is present in ......
    (a) NaCl   (b) CsCl   (c) KCl   (d) $MgCO_2$

77. Which of the following is hcp crystal structure?
    (a) NaCl   (b) CsCl   (c) ZnS   (d) RbCl

78. A pure crystalline substance on being heated gradually, first forms a turbid liquid at constant temperature and at higher temperature, the turbidity completely disappears. This behaviour is characteristic of ......
    (a) Allotropic crystal   (b) Liquid crystal   (c) Isomeric crystal   (d) Isomorphous crystal

79. NaCl is an example of ......
    (a) Ionic solid   (b) Covalent solid   (c) Metallic solid   (d) Molecular solid

80. Doping of Ge metal with a little of Indium produces ......
    (a) p-type conductor   (b) n-type   (c) Insulator   (d) Rectifier

81. The existence of a substance in more than one solid modification is known as ......
    (a) Isomorphism   (b) Polymorphism   (c) Allotropy   (d) Desmotropism

82. The number of atoms in 100 g of fcc crystal with density 10 gm^{-3} and edge length 200 pm is equal to

(a) 3×10^{25} (b) 5×10^{24} (c) 1×10^{25} (d) 2×10^{25}

83. BCC lattice has a coordination number of ......

(a) 8   (b) 12   (c) 6   (d) 4

84. Ionic solids with Schottky defect contain in their structure ......

(a) Equal number of cation and anion vacancies

(b) Interstitial anions and anion vacancy

(c) Cation vacancies only

(d) Cation vacancies and cation interstitials

85. Which of the following is hexagonal closed packed arrangement of spheres?

(a) AB–AB   (b) ABC–ABC   (c) ABB–ABB   (d) ABC-ABA

86. A given sample of an element having bcc structure has 12.08×10^{23} unit cells. The number of atoms in the sample is ......

(a) 12.8×10^{23} (b) 24.16×10^{23} (c) 48.33×10^{23} (d) 12.8×10^{22}

87. Bragg's law is given by ......

(a) $n\lambda = 2\phi \sin d$ (b) $n\lambda = 2d \sin \theta$ (c) $2n\lambda = d \sin \theta$ (d) $n\lambda = \dfrac{d \sin \theta}{Z}$

88. An element (at. mass = 100) having bcc structure has unit cell edge 400 pm, the density of the element is ......

(a) 10.376 gm cm^{-3} (b) 5.188 gm cm^{-3} (c) 1.289 g cm^{-3} (d) 2.144 g cm^{-3}

89. fcc arrangement of atoms contain number of atoms in each unit cell equal to ......

(a) 4   (b) 6   (c) 3   (d) 8

90. If we mix pentavalent impurity in a crystal lattice of germanium, the type of semiconductor formed is ......

(a) n-type   (b) p-type

(c) Both n-type and p-type   (d) None of these

91. A solid has a structure in which W atoms are located at the corners of the cube, O atoms are at the centre of the edges and Na atoms are at the centre of the cube. The formula of the compound is ......

(a) $NaWO_2$ (b) $NaWO_3$ (c) $NaWO_4$ (d) Na_2WO_3

92. The intermetallic compound LiAg crystallises in cubic lattice in which both lithium and silver have coordination number 8. The crystal is ......

(a) Simple cube   (b) Body centered cube

(c) Face centered cube   (d) End centered cube

93. Which of the following is a ferroelectric compound?

(a) $BaTiO_3$ (b) $K_4[Fe(CN)_6]$ (c) Pb_2O_3 (d) None of these

94. In the crystal of which of the following ionic compounds would you expect maximum distance between the centres of cations and anions?

(a) LiF　　　　　　(b) CsF　　　　　　(c) CsI　　　　　　(d) LiI

95. The number of NaCl formula per unit cell is ......

(a) 2　　　　　　(b) 4　　　　　　(c) 6　　　　　　(d) 8

96. Which of the following has Frenkel defect

(a) NaCl　　　　　　(b) Graphite　　　　　　(c) Silver bromide (d) Diamond

97. The appearance of colour in solid alkali metal halides is generally due to ......

(a) interstitials　　　(b) F-centres　　　(c) Schottky defects　(d) Frenkel defects

98. The fraction of total volume occupied by the atoms in a simple cube is ......

(a) $\dfrac{\pi}{4}$　　　　　(b) $\dfrac{\pi}{6}$　　　　　(c) $\dfrac{\pi}{3\sqrt{2}}$　　　　　(d) $\dfrac{\pi}{4\sqrt{2}}$

99. Which type of crystal defect is indicated in the diagram below ?

Na^+	Cl^-	Na^+	Cl^-	Na^+	Cl^-
Cl^-	□	Cl^-	Na^+	□	Na^+
Na^+	Cl^-	□	Cl^-	Na^+	Cl^-
Cl^-	Na^+	Cl^-	Na^+	□	Na^+

(a) Frenkel defect　　　　　　　　(b) Frenkel and Schottky defects

(c) Interstitial defect　　　　　　(d) Schottky defect

100. The number of atoms present in FCC unit cell is .....

(a) 4　　　　　　(b) 3　　　　　　(c) 2　　　　　　(d) 1

101. To get n-type semiconductor, impurity to be added to silicon should have the following number of valence electrons ......

(a) 2　　　　　　(b) 3　　　　　　(c) 1　　　　　　(d) 5

102. Among the following type of voids, which is the largest ?

(a) cubic　　　　　(b) triangular　　　　　(c) tetrahedral　　　(d) octahedral

103. Potassium crystallizes with a ......

(a) face centered cubic lattice　　　　　　(b) body centered cubic lattice

(c) simple cubic lattice　　　　　　　　(d) orthorhombic lattice

104. Which of the following is a ferromagnetic compound?

(a) $BaTiO_3$　　　(b) $K_4[Fe(CN)_6]$　　　(c) Pb_2O_3　　　(d) CrO_2

105. Schottky defect in crystals is observed when ......

(a) Unequal number of cations and anions are missing from the lattice

(b) Equal number of cations and anions are missing from the lattice

(c) An ion leaves its normal site and occupies an interstitial site

(d) Density of crystals is increased

106. How many kinds of space lattices are possible in a crystal ?

(a) 23   (b) 7   (c) 230   (d) 14

107. The material used in solar cells contains ......

(a) Cs   (b) Si   (c) Sn   (d) Ti

108. Na_3PO_4 and Na_3AsO_4 show ......

(a) Isomorphism   (b) Polymorphism   (c) Amorphism   (d) Allotropy

109. Which of the following is a diamagnetic compound ?

(a) MnO_2 (b) V_2O_5 (c) TiO   (d) Fe_2O_3

110. Which of the following is a ferromagnetic compound?

(a) Fe_2O_3 (b) Fe_3O_4 (c) Cr_2O_3 (d) CrO_2

111. Which of the following is an amorphous solid ?

(a) NaCl   (b) CaF_2 (c) Glass   (d) CsCl

112. An ionic compound has a unit cell consisting of A ions at the corners of the cube and B ions on the centre of faces of cube. The empirical formula of the compound is ......

(a) A_3B (b) AB_3 (c) A_2B (d) AB

113. The electrical conductivity of metals is in the order of ....

(a) 10^{12} ohm^{-1} cm^{-1} (b) 10^8 ohm^{-1} cm^{-1} (c) 10^2 ohm^{-1} cm^{-1} (d) 10^{-6} ohm^{-1} cm^{-1}

114. Which of the following is an example of paramagnetic solid ?

(a) NaCl   (b) KF   (c) TiO_2 (d) CuO

115. Solid A^+B^- has rock salt structure and radius of A^+ is 75 pm. What would be the minimum size of B^- be fitted in the void ?

(a) 181.5 pm   (b) 102.5 pm   (c) 205 pm   (d) 90.5 pm

116. The number of atoms in a body centered cubic unit cell of a monoatomic elementary substance is equal to

(a) One   (b) Two   (c) Three   (d) Four

117. In a metal M having BCC arrangement, edge length of the unit cell is 400 pm. The atomic radius of 'M' is

(a) 200 pm   (b) 100 pm   (c) 173 pm   (d) 141 pm

118. An atom at the edge centre of a unit cell makes .... contribution to a particular unit cell.

(a) $\dfrac{1}{2}$ (b) $\dfrac{1}{4}$ (c) 1   (d) $\dfrac{1}{8}$

119. The percentage of the available space occupied in a hexagonal close packing of spheres in three dimensions is ....

(a) 26%   (b) 76%   (c) 52.4%   (d) 74%

120. Tetragonal crystal system has the following unit cell dimensions

(a) $a = b = c$ and $\alpha = \beta = \gamma = 90°$

(b) $a \neq b \neq c$ and $\alpha = \beta = \gamma = 90°$

(c) $a = b \neq c$ and $\alpha = \beta = \gamma = 90°$

(d) $a = b \neq c$ and $\alpha \neq \beta = 90°$ and $\gamma = 120°$

121. Can a cation of radius 82 pm be slipped in octahedral void of A^+B^-, if the radius of anion is 195 pm ?

(a) yes   (b) no   (c) not sure   (d) none of these

122. ABABA ...... represents an arrangement of layers called ......

(a) hcp   (b) ccp   (c) bcc   (d) trigonal packing

123. In hcp arrangement, the number of nearest neighbours are ....

(a) 10   (b) 7   (c) 2   (d) 12

124. Mark the incorrect statement

(a) In hcp and ccp the sphere is in contact with 6 spheres of its own layer.

(b) In both hcp and ccp the sphere has 3 spheres above it and 3 below it.

(c) In both hcp and ccp the coordination number is 12.

(d) In inverse spinel (e.g. magnetite, Fe_3O_4) only

125. For an ionic crystal of the general formula AX and coordination number 6, the value of radius ratio will be ......

(a) In between 0.732 and 0.414   (b) In between 0.414 and 0.225

(c) Less than 0.225   (d) Greater than 0.732

126. Dipositive ions occupy octahedral voids while tripositive ions occupy tetrahedral voids. Pick out the incorrect statement.

(a) NaCl structure transform to CsCl structure on heating

(b) In CaF_2 structure each F^- ion is coordinated by $4Ca^{++}$ ions and each Ca^{++} ion is coordinated by $8F^-$ ions.

(c) NaCl has 6 : 6 coordination, while CsCl is with 8 : 8 coordination

(d) In Na_2O each oxide ion is coordinated by $8Na^+$ ions and each Na^+ ion by 44 oxide ions

127. A NaCl crystal is found to have CsCl structure because it might have been subjected to:

(a) High temperature   (b) Low temperature   (c) High pressure   (d) Low pressure

128. If the pressure on a NaCl structure is increased, then its coordination number will

(a) Increase   (b) Decrease

(c) Either (a) or (b)   (d) Remain the same

129. In diamond the coordination number of carbon is ......

(a) 4 and its unit cell has 8 carbon atoms   (b) 4 and its unit cell has 6 carbon atoms

(c) 6 with 4 carbon atoms in unit cell   (d) 4 with 4 carbon atoms in unit cell

130. Which of the following crystals shows 4:2 coordination?

(a) CaF_2 (b) SiO_2 (c) PbO_2 (d) None of these

131. The fluorite structure shows 8 : 4 coordination, which of the following lattices have fluorite like structure ?

(a) $SrCl_2$ (b) BaF_2 (c) ThO_2 (d) All of these

132. What is the co-ordination number of cations and anions in the calcium fluoride structure ?

(a) 4 and 4   (b) 4 and 8   (c) 8 and 4   (d) 6 and 6

133. A_2B structure is closely related to that of fluorite, it is actually reverse of fluorite structure, hence called ANTIFLUORITE structure. In such a structure ......

(a) Smaller cations occupy the position of fluoride ion and larger anions that of Ca^{++} ions.

(b) Larger cations occupy the position of F^- ions and smaller anions that of Ca^{++} ions.

(c) Each F^- is surrounded by $4Ca^{++}$ in a tetrahedral arrangement

(d) F^- ions occupy all the 8 octahedral voids.

134. In an NaCl structure, all the ......

(a) Octahedral voids are unoccupied

(b) Tetrahedral voids are unoccupied

(c) Octahedral as well as tetrahedral voids are occupied

(d) Octahedral as well as tetrahedral voids are unoccupied

135. A solid has 3 types of atoms namely x, y and z, x forms a fcc lattice with y atoms occupying all the tetrahedral voids and z atoms occupying half the octahedral voids. The formula of the solid is –

(a) X_2Y_4Z (b) XY_2Z_2 (c) X_4Y_2Z (d) X_4YZ_2

136. The number of molecules per unit cell which crystalizes in the form of end face centred (monoclinic) lattice with a molecule at each lattice site is ......

(a) 1   (b) 2   (c) 4   (d) 6

137. How many octahedral voids are there per sphere in a ccp structure ?

(a) 4   (b) 2   (c) 1   (d) 6

138. The coordination number of fcc structure for metals is 12, since ......

(a) Each atom touches 6 others in same layer, 3 in layer above and 3 in layer below.

(b) Each atom touches 4 others in same layer, 4 in layer above and 4 in layer below.

(c) Each atom touches 6 others in same layer, 6 in layer above and 6 in layer below.

(d) Each atom touches 3 atoms in the same layer, 6 in layer above and 6 in layer below.

139. The incorrect statement for sphalerite is ......

(a) Its structure is similar to diamond except that alternate atoms are Zn and S.

(b) Because the S^- is larger than the Zn ion, only 6 rather than 4 or 8 sulfide ions can be packed around a Zn ion.

(c) As S^- is larger than Zn^{++} only 4 rather than 6 or 8 S^- can be packed around Zn^{++}

(d) ZnS is a polar covalent compound

140. The packing efficiency in simple cubic unit cell is ......

(a) 52.4%   (b) 68%   (c) 74%   (d) 80%

141. The space occupied by b.c.c. arrangement is ......

(a) 50%   (b) 68%   (c) 74%   (d) 56%

142. For FCC unit cell, volume of cube is ......

(a) $64/2\sqrt{2}\ r^3$ (b) $64r^3/3\sqrt{3}$ (c) $25r^3/3\sqrt{3}$ (d) $64/3r^3$

143. Packing efficiency in hexagonal close packing is given by ......

(a) Packing efficiency $= \dfrac{4 \times (4/3)\pi r^3 \times 100}{(2\sqrt{2}r)^3}$ %

(b) Packing efficiency $= \dfrac{6 \times 4/3\pi r^3 \times 100}{6 \times \sqrt{3/4}\,(2r)^2 \times 4r\sqrt{2/3}}$ %

(c) Packing efficiency $= \dfrac{2 \times (4/3)\,\pi r^3 \times 100}{[(4/\sqrt{3})\,r]^3}$ %

(d) Packing efficiency $= \dfrac{1 \times (4/3)\,\pi r^3 \times 100}{8r^3}$ %

144. F^- centres are ......

(a) The electrons trapped in anionic vacancies

(b) The electrons trapped in cation vacancies

(c) Non-equivalent sites of stoichiometric compounds

(d) All of these

145. Total volume of atoms present in a face-centred cubic unit cell of a metal is ......

(a) $\dfrac{20}{3}\pi r^3$ (b) $\dfrac{24}{3}\pi r^3$ (c) $\dfrac{12}{3}\pi r^3$ (d) $\dfrac{16}{3}\pi r^3$

146. First three nearest neighbour distances for primitive cubic lattice are respectively ......

(a) $a, \sqrt{2}a, \sqrt{3}a$ (b) $\sqrt{3}a, \sqrt{2}a, a$ (c) $a, \sqrt{2}a, 2a$ (d) $a, \sqrt{3}a, 2a$

147. The distance between an octahedral and tetrahedral void in fcc lattice would be ......

(a) $\sqrt{3}a$ (b) $\dfrac{\sqrt{3a}}{2}$ (c) $\dfrac{\sqrt{3a}}{3}$ (d) $\dfrac{\sqrt{3a}}{4}$

148. The ratio of edge length of the unit cell of KCl to NaCl is (given $\dfrac{r_{Na^+}}{r_{Cl^-}} = 0.55$ and $\dfrac{r_{K^+}}{r_{Cl^-}} = 0.74$) ......

(a) 1.123   (b) 1.224   (c) 1.414   (d) 1.732

149. Iron atom of atomic radius 1.42 A° has rock salt structure, the density will be (A_R of iron is 56 amu)

(a) 5.7 kg m^{-1} (b) 5.7 g cm^{-1} (c) 3.0 kg m^{-1} (d) 3.0 g cm^{-1}

150. The solid AB has rock salt structure. If the radius of the cation A is 100 pm, the radius of the anion B will be ......

(a) 40 pm   (b) 140 pm   (c) 340 pm   (d) 241 pm

151. AB compound crystallises in ccp. What will be the co-ordination number of A^+, if A^+ and B^- have radii 88 and 200 pm respectively ?

(a) 6   (b) 4   (c) 2   (d) 8

152. Calculate the interionic distance in CsCl if it has bcc arrangement and its unit cell edge length is 400 pm.

(a) 346 pm   (b) 346.4 pm   (c) 346.8 pm   (d) 345 pm

153. Li metal has a bcc structure. Its density is 0.53 g per cm^3 and its atomic mass is 6.94 gm per mol. Calculate the edge length of a unit cell of Li metal.

(a) 153.6 pm   (b) 351.6 pm   (c) 527.4 pm   (d) 263.7 pm

154. A metal crystallizes in 2 cubic phases i.e., fcc and bcc whose unit cell lengths are 3.5 A° and 3.0 A° respectively. The ratio of their densities is ......

(a) 3.12　　　　(b) 2.04　　　　(c) 1.46　　　　(d) 1.259

155. In the X-ray diffraction of a set of crystal planes having d equal to 0.18 nm, a first order reflection is found to be at an angle of 22°. The wavelength of X-ray is ......

(Given sin 22° = 0.208)

(a) 0.0749 nm　　　(b) 0.0374 nm　　　(c) 0.749 nm　　　(d) None of these

156. NaCl is doped with 2×10^{-3} mole % of $SrCl_2$. The concentration of cation vacancies is ......

(a) 6.02×10^{8} per mol　　　　　　(b) 12.04×10^{18} per mol

(c) 3.01×10^{18} per mol　　　　　　(d) 12.04×10^{20} per mol

157. The radius of Na^+ is 95 pm and that of Cl^- is 181 pm. The coordination number of Na^+ is ...

(a) 8　　　　(b) 6　　　　(c) 4　　　　(d) 3

158. Sodium metal crystallizes as a bcc with the cell edge 4.29 A°. What is the radius of sodium atom?

(a) 1.857×10^{-8} cm　　(b) 2.371×10^{-7} cm　　(c) 3.817×10^{-8} cm　　(d) 9.312×10^{-7} cm

159. The edge length of a fcc unit cell is 620 pm. The radius of the atom is ......

(a) 221 pm　　　(b) 219 pm　　　(c) 223 pm　　　(d) 230 pm

160. Copper metal has fcc structure with edge length 0.37 nm. The radius of copper atom is......

(a) 0.130 nm　　　(b) 130 nm　　　(c) 0.32 nm　　　(d) 0.42 nm

161. An element of atomic mass 6.94 g/mol and density 0.53 g/cm^3 is a cube of edge length 3.5 A°. The structure of crystal lattice is ......

(a) fcc　　　(b) bcc　　　(c) hcp　　　(d) none of these

162. KF having density 2.48 g/cm^3 and molar mass 58 amu has NaCl structure. The distance between K^+ and F^- is ......

(a) 538 pm　　　(b) 269 pm　　　(c) 133 pm　　　(d) 600 pm

163. The edge length of bcc unit cell is 390 pm and the radius of the cation is 150 pm. The radius of the anion is ......

(a) 666 pm　　　(b) 188 pm　　　(c) 200 pm　　　(d) 516 pm

164. Nickel oxide has formula $Ni_{0.98} O_{1.00}$. The fraction of Ni^{3+} is ......

(a) 96%　　　(b) 4%　　　(c) 98%　　　(d) 2%

165. Xenon crystallises in fcc and has edge length 620 pm. The radius of xenon atom is ......

(a) 438 pm　　　(b) 537 pm　　　(c) 220 pm　　　(d) 268 pm

PREVIOUS YEAR'S QUESTIONS

1. If a is the length of the side of a cube, then the distance between the body centered atom and one corner atom in the cube will be ......　　　**[AIPMT 2014]**

(a) $\dfrac{\sqrt{3}}{4} a$　　　(b) $\dfrac{\sqrt{3}}{2} a$　　　(c) $\dfrac{2}{\sqrt{3}} a$　　　(d) $\dfrac{3}{\sqrt{3}} a$

2. A metal has fcc lattice. The edge length of the unit cell is 404 pm. The density of the metal is 2.72 $g\,cm^{-3}$. The molar mass of the metal is ......　　　**[NEET 2013]**

(a) 30 gm mol^{-1}　　　(b) 27 gm mol^{-1}　　　(c) 20 gm mol^{-1}　　　(d) 40 gm mol^{-1}

3. The number of carbon atoms per unit cell of diamond unit cell is ......   **[NEET 2013]**

(a) 8   (b) 6   (c) 1   (d) 4

4. Structure of a mixed oxide is cubic close packed (ccp). The cubic unit cell of mixed oxide is composed of oxide ions. One fourth of the tetrahedral voids are occupied by divalent metal a and the octahedral voids are occupied by a monovalent metal. The formula of the oxide is

[NEET 2013]

(a) $A_2B_3O_4$ (b) AB_2O_2 (c) ABO_2 (d) A_2BO_2

5. The number of octahedral void(s) per atom present in a cubic close-packed structure is ...

[CBSE Prelim 2012]

(a) 2   (b) 4   (c) 1   (d) 3

6. A metal crystallizes with a face-centered cubic lattice. The edge of the unit cell is 408 pm. The diameter of the metal atom is ......   **[CBSE Prelim 2010]**

(a) 144 pm   (b) 204 pm   (c) 288 pm   (d) 408 pm

7. AB crystallises in a body centered cubic lattice with edge 'a' equal to 307 pm. The distance between two oppositely charged ions in the lattice is ......   **[CBSE AIPMT 2010]**

(a) 300 pm   (b) 335 pm   (c) 250 pm   (d) 200 pm

8. Radius of copper atom in pm is ......   **[CBSE AIPMT]**

(a) 128   (b) 157   (c) 181   (d) 108

9. Sodium crystallizes in bcc arrangement with the interfacial separation between the atoms and edge 53 pm. The density of the solid is ......   **[AIIMS 2005]**

(a) 1.23 g/cc   (b) 485 g/cc   (c) 4.85 g/cc   (d) 123 g/cc

10. Which of the following statements is not correct?   **[CBSE AIPMT 2008]**

(a) The fraction of the total volume occupied by the atoms in primitive cell is 0.48

(b) Molecular solids are generally volatile

(c) The number of carbon atoms in unit cell of diamond is 4

(d) The number of Bravais lattices in which a crystal can be categorized is 14

11. If 'a' stands for the edge length of the cubic systems: simple cubic, body centred cubic and face centered cubic, then the ratio of radii of the spheres in these systems will be respectively ......   **[CBSE AIPMT 2008]**

(a) $\dfrac{1}{2}a : \dfrac{\sqrt{3}}{4}a; \dfrac{1}{2\sqrt{2}}a$ (b) $\dfrac{1}{2}a : \sqrt{3}a; \dfrac{1}{\sqrt{2}}a$ (c) $\dfrac{1}{2}a : \dfrac{\sqrt{3}}{2}a; \dfrac{\sqrt{3}}{2}a$ (d) $1a : \sqrt{3}a : \sqrt{2}a$

12. Percentage of free space in body centred cubic unit cell is ......   **[CBSE AIPMT 2008]**

(a) 30%   (b) 32%   (c) 34%   (d) 28%

13. With which one of the following elements silicon should be doped so as to give p-type of semiconductor?   **[CBSE AIPMT 2008]**

(a) Germanium   (b) Arsenic   (c) Selenium   (d) Boron

14. Edge length of a cube is 400 pm, its body diagonal would be ......   **[AFMC 2008]**

(a) 566 pm   (b) 600 pm   (c) 500 pm   (d) 693 pm

15. If NaCl is doped with 10^{-4} mol % of $SrCl_2$ the concentration of cation vacancies will be ($N_A = 6.02 \times 10^{23}$ mol^{-1})   **[CBSE AIPMT 2007]**
(a) 6.02×10^{15} mol^{-1} (b) 6.02×10^{16} mol^{-1} (c) 6.02×10^{17} mol^{-1} (d) 6.02×10^{14} mol^{-1}

16. A fcc unit cell of aluminium contains the equivalent of how many atoms?   **[AFMC 2007]**
(a) 1   (b) 2   (c) 3   (d) 4

17. If AgI crystallizes in zinc blende structure with 1^- ions at lattice points, what fraction of tetrahedral voids is occupied by Ag^+ ions?   **[AIIMS 2007]**
(a) 25%   (b) 50%   (c) 100%   (d) 75%

18. CsBr crystallizes in a body centred cubic lattice. The unit cell length is 436.6 pm. Given that the atomic mass of Cs = 133 u and that of Br = 80 u and Avogadro number being 6.02×10^{23} mol^{-1}, the density of CsBr is ......   **[CBSE AIPMT 2006]**
(a) 42 g/cm^3 (b) 0.425 g/cm^3 (c) 8.25 g/cm^3 (d) 4.25 g/cm^3

19. The Ca^{2+} and F^- are located in CaF_2 crystal, respectively at body centred cubic lattice points and in ......   **[AIIMS 2006]**
(a) tetrahedral voids   (b) half of tetrahedral voids
(c) octahedral voids   (d) half of octahedral voids

20. **Assertion :** Graphite is an example of Tetragonal crystal system.   **[AIIMS 2006]**
Reason : For a tetragonal system, a = b $\neq$ c, $\alpha = \beta = 90°$, $\gamma = 120°$
(a) Both Assertion and Reason are true and Reason is correct explanation of Assertion.
(b) Both Assertion and Reason are true and Reason is not the correct explanation of Assertion.
(c) Assertion is true but Reason is false
(d) Both Assertion and Reason are false.

21. In a face-centred cubic lattice, a unit cell is shared equally by how many unit cells?
                    [CBSE AIPMT 2005]
(a) 8   (b) 4   (c) 2   (d) 6

22. If Z is the number of atoms in the unit cell that represent the closest packing sequence... ABC..., the number of tetrahedral voids in the unit cells is equal to......   **[AIIMS 2005]**
(a) Z   (b) 2Z   (c) Z/2   (d) Z/4

23. A solid AB has NaCl structure. If the radius of cation A^+ is 170 pm, calculate the maximum possible radius of the anion B^{-} ......   **[CBSE AIPMT 2004]**
(a) 410.6 pm   (b) 397.4 pm   (c) 210.9 pm   (d) 347.9 pm

24. Naphthalene is a/an ......   **[AFMC 2004]**
(a) ionic solid   (b) covalent solid   (c) metallic solid   (d) molecular solid.

25. The crystal system of a compound with unit cell dimenstions a = 0.387, b = 0.387 and c = 0.504 nm and $\alpha = \beta = 120°$ is ......   **[AIIMS 2004]**
(a) cubic   (b) hexagonal   (c) orthorhombic   (d) rhomobohedral

26. The pyknometric density of sodium chloride crystal is 2.165×10^3 kg m^3 while its X-rays density is 2.178×10^3 kg m^3. The fraction of unoccupied sites in sodium chloride crystal is
                    [CBSE AIPMT 2003]
(a) 5.96×10^{-3} (b) 5.96   (c) 5.96×10^{-2} (d) 5.96×10^{-1}

27. What is the coordination number for sodium in Na_2O ?　　**[ALLMS 2003]**

(a) 6　　　　　(b) 4　　　　　(c) 8　　　　　(d) 2

28. A given metal crystallizes out with a cubic structure having edge length of 361 pm. If there are four metal atoms in one unit cell, what is the radius of one atom?　　**[AIPMT 2015]**

(a) 127 pm　　　　(b) 80 pm　　　　(c) 108 pm　　　　(d) 40 pm

29. The vacant space in bcc lattice unit cell is ......　　**[AIPMT 2015]**

(a) 23%　　　　(b) 32%　　　　(c) 26%　　　　(d) 48%

30. The correct statement regarding defects in crystalline solids is:　　**[AIPMT 2015]**

(a) Frenkel defect is a dislocation defect.

(b) Frenkel defect is found in halides of alkaline metals.

(c) Schottky defects have no effect on the density of crystalline solids.

(d) Frenkel defects have no effect on the density of crystalline solids.

31. Which of the following is Bragg's equation ?　　**[M.P.P.M.T. 2002]**

(a) $n\lambda = 2\theta \sin \theta$　　　　　　　(b) $n\lambda = 2d \sin \theta$

(c) $2n\lambda = d \sin \theta$　　　　　　　(d) $n \cdot \theta/2 = d/2 \sin \theta$

32. The edge length of fcc unit cell is 508 pm. If the radius of cation is 110 pm, the radius of anion is ......　　**[BHU 2000]**

(a) 110 pm　　　　(b) 144 pm　　　　(c) 618 pm　　　　(d) 398 pm

33. In a metal M having bcc arrangement, edge length of the unit cell is 400 pm. The atomic radius of M is ...　　**[CBSE 2000]**

(a) 100 pm　　　　(b) 141 pm　　　　(c) 172 pm　　　　(d) 200 pm

34. The second order Bragg diffraction of X-rays with I if 1 A° from a set of parallel planes in a metal occurs at an angle of 60°. The distance between the scattering planes in the crystal is [$\sin 60° = 0.866$] ......　　**[MPPMT 2001]**

(a) 2.00 A°　　　　(b) 1.15 A°　　　　(c) 1.00 A°　　　　(d) 2.575 A°

35. How many Cd^{2+} ions surround each fluoride ion in cadmium fluoride crystal which adopts fluoride type structure ?　　**[CBSE 2001]**

(a) 8　　　　　(b) 4　　　　　(c) 12　　　　　(d) 6

36. A compound formed by elements A and B crystallizes in the cubic structure where A atoms are at the corners of a cube and B atoms are at the face centres. The formula of the compound is ......　　**[AIIMS 2001]**

(a) AB_2　　　　(b) AB_3　　　　(c) A_3B　　　　(d) A_2B_3

37. The number of unit cells in 58.5 g of NaCl is nearly ......　　**[Uttranchal PMT 2002]**

(a) 6×10^{20}　　　(b) 3×10^{22}　　　(c) 1.5×10^{23}　　　(d) 0.5×10^{24}

38. The number of octahedral sites per sphere in fcc structure is ......　　**[KCET 2009]**

(a) 8　　　　　(b) 4　　　　　(c) 2　　　　　(d) 1

39. The packing fraction for a body centered cubic is ......　　**[CBSE 2006]**

(a) 0.42　　　　(b) 0.53　　　　(c) 0.68　　　　(d) 0.82

40. In a hexagonal close packed (hcp) structure of sphere, the fraction of the volume occupied by the sphere is A. In a cubic close packed structure, the fraction is B. The relation for A and B is ......   **[Kerala M.E.E. 2000]**
(a) A = B
(b) A < B
(c) A > B
(d) A is equal to the fraction in a simple cubic lattice
(e) A = B = the fraction of a body centred cubic lattice

41. The total number of lattice arrangements in different crystal systems is ......   **[C.E.T. Karnataka 2001]**
(a) 7.0
(b) 3.0
(c) 8.0
(d) 14

42. Body centred cubic lattice has a coordination number ......   **[M.P.P.M.T. 2002]**
(a) 8
(b) 12
(c) 6
(d) 4

43. Which of the following crystals does not exhibit Frenkel defect ?   **[M.P.C.E.T. 2002]**
(a) AgBr
(b) AgCl
(c) KBr
(d) ZnS

44. A semiconductor of Ge can be made p-type by adding ......   **[M.P.C.E.T. 2002]**
(a) Trivalent impurity
(b) Tetravalent impurity
(c) Pentavalent impurity
(d) Divalent impurity

45. Superconductors are derived from compounds of ......   **[Kerala P.M.T. 2002]**
(a) p-block elements
(b) Lanthanides
(c) Actinides
(d) Transition elements
(e) Scandium

46. The major binding force of diamond, silicon and quartz is ......   **[Kerala P.M.T. 2002]**
(a) Electrostatic force
(b) Electrical attraction
(c) Covalent bond force
(d) Non-covalent bond force

47. An AB_2 type of structure is present in ......   **[A.I.I.M.S. 2002]**
(a) NaCl
(b) N_2O
(c) Al_2O_3
(d) CaF_2

48. An element (atomic mass = 100 g/mol) having bcc structure has unit cell edge 400 pm. The density of the element is ......   **[C.B.S.E. P.M.T. 1986, A.I.I.M.S. 2002]**
(a) $2.144 \, g \, cm^{-3}$
(b) $5.188 \, g \, cm^{-3}$
(c) $7.289 \, g \, cm^{-3}$
(d) $10.376 \, g \, cm^{-3}$

49. How many unit cells are present in a cube-shaped ideal crystal of NaCl of mass 1.00 g ?
(a) 2.57×10^{21} unit cells
(b) 5.14×10^{21} unit cells
(c) 1.28×10^{21} unit cells
(d) 1.71×10^{21} unit cells

50. The ratio of the cationic radius to anionic radius in an ionic crystal is greater than 0.732. Its co-ordination number is ......   **[Karnataka C.E.T. 2003]**
(a) 1
(b) 4
(c) 6
(d) 8

51. What is the coordination number of sodium in Na_2O ?   **[A.I.I.M.S. 2003]**
(a) 6
(b) 4
(c) 8
(d) 2

52. Density of a crystal remains unchanged as a result of ......   **[Kerala C.E.T. 2004]**
(a) Ionic defect
(b) Schottky defect
(c) Frenkel defect
(d) Crystal defect
(e) Point defect

53. What type of crystal defect is indicated in the diagram below ?   **[A.I.E.E.E. 2004]**

Na^+	Cl^-	Na^+	Cl^-	Na^+	Cl^-
Cl^-	□	Cl^-	Na^+	□	Na^+
Na^+	Cl^-	□	Cl^-	Na^+	Cl^-
Cl^-	Na^+	Cl^-	Na^+	□	Na^+

(a) Frenkel defect
(b) Frenkel and Schottky defect
(c) Interstitial defect
(d) Schottky defect

54. Which of the following statements about amorphous solids is incorrect ?
   (a) They melt over a range of temperature   **[Karnataka C.E.T. 2004]**
   (b) They are anisotropic
   (c) There is no orderly arrangement of particles
   (d) They are rigid and incompressible

55. Coordination number of Zn in ZnS (Zine blende) is ......   **[Orissa J.E.T. 2004]**
   (a) 4   (b) 6   (c) 2   (d) None of these

56. In a face centred cubic lattice, a unit cell is shared equally by how many unit cells ?
   (a) 4   (b) 2   (c) 6   (d) 8 **[A.I.P.M.T. 2005]**

57. A metal crystallises in a bcc lattice. Its unit cell edge length is about 300 pm and its molar mass is about 50 g mol^{-1}. What would be the density of the metal (in g cm^{-3}) ?
                                                                  [Kerala Med. 2005]
   (a) 3.1   (b) 6.2   (c) 9.3   (d) 12.4   (e) 15.5

58. A crystalline solid has a cubic structure in which tungsten (W) atoms are located at the cubic corners of the unit cell, oxygen atoms at the cube edges and sodium atom at the cube centre. The molecular formula of the compound is ......   **[Kerala Med. 2005]**
   (a) Na_2WO_3 (b) $NaWO_4$ (c) $NaWO_3$ (d) Na_2WO_4
   (e) $NaWO_2$

59. The compound which possesses the antifluorite structure is ......   **[H.P. P.M.T. 2005]**
   (a) Rb_2S (b) PbF_2
   (c) Amorphous sphalerite   (d) $BaCl_2$

60. Which has no rotation of symmetry ?   **[Orissa J.E.E. 2004]**
   (a) Hexagonal   (b) Orthorhombic   (c) Cubic   (d) Triclinic

61. Metallic luster is explained by ......   **[D.C.E. 2005]**
   (a) Diffusion of metal ions   (b) Oscillation of loose electrons
   (c) Excitation of free protons   (d) Existence of bcc lattice

62. The radii of Na^+ and Cl^- ions are 95 pm and 181 pm respectively. The edge length of NaCl unit cell is ......   **[Karnataka C.E.T. 2006]**
   (a) 276 pm   (b) 138 pm   (c) 552 pm   (d) 45 pm

63. In AgBr, there can occur ......   **[H.P. P.M.T. 2006]**
   (a) Only Schottky defect   (b) Only Frenkel defect
   (c) Both (a) and (b)   (d) None of these

64. An element (atomic mass = 250 u) crystallises in a simple cubic. If the density of the unit cell is 7.2 g cm^{-3}, what is the radius of the element ?   **[Orissa J.E.E. 2006]**
   (a) 1.93×10^{-3} cm   (b) 1.93×10^{-8} cm   (c) 1.93×10^{-8}Å   (d) 1.93×10^{-8} m

65. Which of the following is not ferromagnetic ?   **[Karnataka C.E.T. 2007]**
   (a) Cobalt   (b) Iron   (c) Manganese   (d) Nickel

66. A metallic crystal has the bcc type stacking pattern. What percentage of volume of this lattice is empty space ?   **[Gujarat C.E.T. 2007]**
   (a) 68%   (b) 32%   (c) 26%   (d) 74%

67. KCl crystallises in the same type of lattice as does NaCl. Given that r_{Na^+}/r_{Cl^-} = 0.55 and r_{K^+}/r_{Cl^-} = 0.74. Calculate the ratio of the side of the unit cell of KCl to that of NaCl.
                                                                  [Kerala P.E.T. 2008]
   (a) 1.123   (b) 0.891   (c) 1.414   (d) 0.414   (e) 1.732

68. A compound is formed by elements A and B. This crystallizes in the cubic structure where A atoms are at the corners of the cube and B atoms are at the body centres. The simplest formula of the compound is ...... **[Karnataka C.E.T. 2008]**

(a) A_8B_4 (b) AB_6 (c) AB   (d) A_6B

69. An ionic compound is expected to have tetrahedral structure if r^+/r^- lies in the range of ... **[Karnataka C.E.T. 2008]**

(a) 0.155 to 0.225   (b) 0.731 to 1   (c) 0.414 to 0.732   (d) 0.225 to 0.414

70. Total volume of atoms present in a face centred cubic unit cell of a metal is (r = atomic radius) ...... **[Bihar C.E.C.E. Engg. 2008]**

(a) $\dfrac{20}{3}\pi r^3$ (b) $\dfrac{24}{3}\pi r^3$ (c) $\dfrac{12}{3}\pi r^3$ (d) $\dfrac{16}{3}\pi r^3$

71. The cubic unit cell of a metal (molar mass = 63.55 g mol^{-1}) has an edge length of 362 pm. Its density is 8.92 g cm^3. The type of cell is ...... **[E.A.M. C.E.T. Engg. 2009]**

(a) fcc   (b) bcc   (c) Simple cubic   (d) None of these

72. A substance $A_x B_y$ crystallises in a face centred cubic (FCC) lattice in which atoms 'A' occupy each corner of the cube and atoms 'B' occupy the centres of each face of the cube. Identify the correct composition of the substance $A_x B_y$. **[I.I.T. Screening 2002]**

(a) AB_3 (b) A_4B_3 (c) A_2B

(d) Composition cannot be specified

73. CsBr crystallizes in a body centred cubic lattice. The unit cell length is 436.6 pm. Given that the atomic mass of Cs = 133 and that of Br = 80 amu and Avogadro's number being 6.02×10^{23} mol^{-1}, the density of CsBr is ...... **[A.I.P.M.T. 2006]**

(a) 8.25 g/cm^3 (b) 4.25 g/cm^3 (c) 0.425 g/cm^3 (d) 42.5 g/cm^3

74. The fraction of the total volume occupied by the atoms present in a simple cube is ......

[A.I.P.M.T. 2007]

(a) π/r (b) $\pi/6$ (c) $\dfrac{\pi}{3\sqrt{2}}$ (d) $\dfrac{\pi}{4\sqrt{2}}$

75. A metallic crystal has the bcc type stacking pattern. What percentage of volume of this lattice is empty space ? **[A.I.P.M.T. 2008]**

(a) 68%   (b) 32%   (c) 26%   (d) 74%

76. Which of the following statements is not correct ? **[A.I.P.M.T. 2008]**

(a) The fraction of the total volume occupied by the atoms in a primitive cell is 0.48.

(b) Molecular solids are generally volatile.

(c) The number of carbon atoms in a unit cell of diamond is 4.

(d) The number of Bravais lattices in which a crystal cell of diamond is 14.

77. With which one of the following elements silicon should be doped so as to give p-type of semiconductor ? **[A.I.P.M.T. 2008]**

(a) Germanium   (b) Arsenic   (c) Selenium   (d) Boron

78. The edge length of a face centred cubic cell of an ionic substance is 508 pm. If the radius of the cation is 110 pm, the radius of the anion is ...... **[A.I.E.E.E. 2010]**

(a) 144 pm   (b) 288 pm   (c) 398 pm   (d) 618 pm

ANSWER KEY

1. (d)	2. (a)	3. (c)	4. (a)	5. (d)	6. (c)	7. (b)	8. (c)
9. (c)	10. (b)	11. (c)	12. (b)	13. (b)	14. (c)	15. (b)	16. (a)
17. (a)	18. (b)	19. (c)	20. (b)	21. (b)	22. (b)	23. (c)	24. (b)
25. (c)	26. (b)	27. (d)	28. (d)	29. (d)	30. (b)	31. (c)	32. (d)
33. (b)	34. (d)	35. (b)	36. (a)	37. (a)	38. (a)	39. (b)	40. (b)
41. (c)	42. (d)	43. (b)	44. (c)	45. (d)	46. (c)	47. (a)	48. (a)
49. (a)	50. (a)	51. (b)	52. (b)	53. (a)	54. (c)	55. (c)	56. (b)
57. (b)	58. (a)	59. (b)	60. (b)	61. (d)	62. (d)	63. (b)	64. (c)
65. (b)	66. (c)	67. (c)	68. (b)	69. (d)	70. (a)	71. (c)	72. (c)
73. (b)	74. (a)	75. (d)	76. (b)	77. (c)	78. (b)	79. (a)	80. (b)
81. (b)	82. (b)	83. (a)	84. (a)	85. (a)	86. (b)	87. (b)	88. (b)
89. (a)	90. (a)	91. (b)	92. (b)	93. (a)	94. (c)	95. (b)	96. (c)
97. (b)	98. (b)	99. (d)	100. (a)	101. (d)	102. (a)	103. (b)	104. (d)
105. (b)	106. (d)	107. (b)	108. (a)	109. (b)	110. (d)	111. (c)	112. (b)
113. (b)	114. (d)	115. (a)	116. (b)	117. (c)	118. (b)	119. (a)	120. (c)
121. (a)	122. (a)	123. (d)	124. (d)	125. (b)	126. (a)	127. (c)	128. (a)
129. (a)	130. (d)	131. (b)	132. (c)	133. (b)	134. (a)	135. (a)	136. (b)
137. (a)	138. (a)	139. (d)	140. (a)	141. (b)	142. (a)	143. (b)	144. (a)
145. (d)	146. (a)	147. (d)	148. (a)	149. (b)	150. (d)	151. (a)	152. (b)
153. (b)	154. (d)	155. (a)	156. (c)	157. (b)	158. (a)	159. (b)	160. (a)
161. (b)	162. (b)	163. (b)	164. (b)	165. (c)			

Previous Year's Questions

1. (b)	2. (b)	3. (a)	4. (a)	5. (c)	6. (c)	7. (b)	8. (a)
9. (a)	10. (a)	11. (a)	12. (b)	13. (d)	14. (d)	15. (c)	16. (d)
17. (b)	18. (d)	19. (a)	20. (d)	21. (d)	22. (b)	23. (a)	24. (d)
25. (b)	26. (b)	27. (b)	28. (a)	29. (b)	30. (a)	31. (b)	32. (b)
33. (c)	34. (b)	35. (a)	36. (b)	37. (c)	38. (b)	39. (c)	40. (a)
41. (a)	42. (a)	43. (c)	44. (a)	45. (a)	46. (c)	47. (d)	48. (b)
49. (a)	50. (d)	51. (b)	52. (b)	53. (d)	54. (b)	55. (a)	56. (c)
57. (b)	58. (c)	59. (a)	60. (d)	61. (b)	62. (c)	63. (c)	64. (b)
65. (c)	66. (b)	67. (a)	68. (c)	69. (d)	70. (d)	71. (a)	72. (a)
73. (b)	74. (b)	75. (b)	76. (a)	77. (d)	78. (a)		

❑❑❑

UNIT 15

SOLUTIONS

1. The number of moles of a solute per kilogram of a solvent is called as ......

    (a) Molarity   (b) Molality   (c) Normality   (d) Formality

2. Alloys are ......

    (a) substitutional solution
    (b) interstitial solution
    (c) colloidal solution
    (d) suspension

3. Cast iron is ......

    (a) interstitial solution
    (b) colloidal solution
    (c) suspension
    (d) substitutional solution

4. Which statement is wrong ?

    (a) Mole fraction is independent of temperature
    (b) Mole fraction is number of moles of solute to total number of moles in solution
    (c) Sum of the mole fraction is always greater than one
    (d) Sum of the mole fraction is equal to one.

5. Molarity is the ...

    (a) number of moles of solvent per decimeter cube of the solution
    (b) number of moles of solute per kg of the solution
    (c) number of moles of solute per decimeter cube of the solution
    (d) number of moles of solute per litre of the solvent

6. Molality is ......

    (a) the number of moles of a solute per litre of the solution.
    (b) the number of moles of a solute per 1000 gm of the solution
    (c) the number of moles of solute per litre of the solvent.
    (d) the number of moles of solute per 1000 gm of the solvent.

7. 4L of 0.02 M aqueous solution of NaCl was diluted by adding one litre of water. The molality of the resultant solution is ....

    (a) 0.004   (b) 0.008   (c) 0.012   (d) 0.016

8. With increase in temperature, molarity ......

    (a) increases
    (b) decreases
    (c) remains same
    (d) temperature independent

9. Formality for electrolytic solutions is same as ......

    (a) normality   (b) molality   (c) mole fraction   (d) molarity

10. Normality is the number of ......

    (a) moles per 1000 cm^3 of the solution
    (b) gram equivalents of solute in 1000 cm^3 of the solution
    (c) gram equivalents of solute per litre of the solvent
    (d) moles per 1000 gm of the solution

15.1

11. Normality of 2M $KMnO_4$ solution is ......

(a) same   (b) 10 N   (c) 5 N   (d) 4 M

12. 5.8 ppm pollutants in sea water means ......

(a) 5.8 gm per 10^3 gm of sea water

(b) 5.8 gm of pollutants per 10^6 gm of sea water

(c) 5.8 cm^3 of pollutants per litre of sea water

(d) 5.8 cm^3 of pollutants per 10^6 gm of solution

13. Iodine vapours in air is ......

(a) gas in solid   (b) gas in gas   (c) solid in gas   (d) liquid in gas

14. What is the mole fraction of methanol in 5.2 molal solution?

(a) 0.100   (b) 0.050   (c) 0.190   (d) 0.086

15. Which of the following is useful in relating concentration of solution with its vapour pressure?

(a) mole fraction   (b) parts per million

(c) mass percentage   (d) molality

16. Maximum amount of a solid solute that can be dissolved in a specified amount of a given liquid solvent does not depend upon __________.

(a) Temperature   (b) Nature of solute   (c) Pressure   (d) Nature of solvent

17. Low concentration of oxygen in the blood and tissues of people living at high altitude is due to __________.

(a) low temperature

(b) low atmospheric pressure

(c) high atmospheric pressure

(d) both low temperature and high atmospheric pressure

18. The value of Henry's constant K_H ....

(a) increases with increase in temperature   (b) decreases with increase in temperature

(c) remains constant   (d) first increases then decreases

19. Bend in deep sea diver is due to ......

(a) low solubility of nitrogen   (b) low partial pressure

(c) high solubility of nitrogen   (d) low solubility of oxygen

20. People living at higher altitude or climbers suffer from anoxia due to ......

(a) high partial pressure of oxygen gas

(b) high concentration of oxygen in the blood and tissues

(c) low partial pressure of oxygen and less concentration of oxygen in blood and tissues.

(d) high partial pressure of oxygen and high concentration of oxygen in blood and tissues.

21. The value of Henry's constant K_H is ......

(a) greater for gases with higher solubility   (b) greater for gases with lower solubility

(c) constant for all gases   (d) not related to the solubility of gases

22. On the basis of information given, which is the correct option ?

(i) In ethyl bromide and ethyl chloride mixture, intermolecular interactions of A–A and B–B type are nearly same as A–B type interactions.

(ii) In ethanol and acetone mixture, A–A or B–B type intermolecular interactions are stronger than A–B type interactions.

(iii) In chloroform and acetone mixture, A–A or B–B type intermolecular interactions are weaker than A–B type interactions.

(a) Solutions (ii) and (iii) will follow Raoult's law.

(b) Solution (i) will follow Raoult's law.

(c) Solution (ii) will show negative deviation from Raoult's law.

(d) Solution (iii) will show positive deviation from Raoult's law.

23. Which of the following statement is correct about the vapour pressure of pure water (A) and that of NaCl solution (B) at the same temperature ?

(a) vapour pressure in container (A) is more than that in container (B).

(b) vapour pressure in container (A) is less than that in container (B).

(c) vapour pressure is equal in both the containers.

(d) vapour pressure in container (B) is twice the vapour pressure in container (A).

24. In minimum boiling azeotropic mixture ......

(a) A–B interactions are weaker than those between A–A or B–B.

(b) vapour pressure of solution increases because more number of molecules of liquids A and B can escape from the solution.

(c) vapour pressure of solution decreases because less number of molecules of only one of the liquids escape from the solution.

(d) A–B interactions are stronger than those between A–A or B–B.

25. In acetone and methanol mixture ......

(a) At specific composition, methanol-acetone mixture will form minimum boiling azeotrope and will show positive deviation from Raoult's law.

(b) At specific composition, methanol-acetone mixture forms maximum boiling azeotrope and will show positive deviation from Raoult's law.

(c) At specific composition, methanol-acetone mixture will form minimum boiling azeotrope and will show negative deviation from Raoult's law.

(d) At specific composition, methanol-acetone mixture will form maximum boiling azeotrope and will show negative deviation from Raoult's law

26. Arrange these gases in the order of their increasing solubility. (K_H value for Ar(g), CO_2(g), HCHO (g) and CH_4(g) are 40.39, 1.67, 1.83×10^{-5} and 0.413 respectively.)

(a) HCHO < CH_4 < CO_2 < Ar   (b) HCHO < CO_2 < CH_4 < Ar

(c) Ar < CO_2 < CH_4 < HCHO   (d) Ar < CH_4 < CO_2 < HCHO

27. What is the formality of 1.2 gm of CH_3COOH in benzene when its solution is one litre ?

    (a) 0.01 F   (b) 0.02 F   (c) 0.1 F   (d) 0.2 F

28. The relationship between molarity, molality and density is ......

    (a) Molality = molarity/density – $\dfrac{\text{molarity} \times \text{mol. wt. of solute}}{1000}$

    (b) Molarity = molality/density – molarity × mol. wt.

    (c) Molality = molarity – density/mol. wt.

    (d) Molality = density/density – molarity × mol. wt.

29. Which is not affected by temperature ?

    (a) Normality   (b) Formality   (c) Molarity   (d) Molality

30. Azeotropic mixture of HCl and H_2O has ......

    (a) 48% HCl   (b) 22.2% HCl   (c) 36% HCl   (d) 20.2 HCl

31. A 5% solution of cane sugar (MR – 342) is isotonic with 1% solution of a subtance X. The molecular unit of X is ......

    (a) 34.2   (b) 171.2   (c) 68.4   (d) 136.8

32. The vapour pressure of a solvent is decreased, when a non-volatile solute was added in the solvent. The mole fraction of the solute in the solution is 0.2. What should be the mole fraction of the solvent if the decrease in the vapour pressure is to be 20 mm of Hg ?

    (a) 0.8   (b) 0.6   (c) 0.4   (d) 0.2

33. How many millilitres of 6.0 M HCl should be used to prepare 150 ml of a solution which is 0.30 M in hydrogen ion ?

    (a) 3.0   (b) 7.5   (c) 9.3   (d) 30

34. A solution was obtained by mixing methanol and ethanol. If the partial vapour pressure of methanol and ethanol are 2.619 kPa and 4.556 kPa respectively, the composition of the vapour in millilitres of mole fraction will be ......

    (a) 0.635 CH_3OH, 0.365 C_2H_5OH (b) 0.365 CH_3OH, 0.635 C_2H_5OH

    (c) 0.574 CH_3OH, 0.326 C_2H_5OH (d) 0.173 CH_3OH, 0.827 C_2H_5OH

35. The rise in the boiling point of a solution containing 1.8 gram of glucose in 100 g of a solvent is 0.1°C. The molal elevation contact of the liquid is ......

    (a) 0.01 k/m   (b) 0.1 k/m   (c) 1 k/m   (d) 10 k/m

36. The osmotic pressure of 1 M solution at 27°C is ......

    (a) 2.46 atm   (b) 24.6 atm   (c) 1.21 atm   (d) 12.1 atm

37. The vapour pressure of pure benzene is 639.7 mm at 25°C and at the same temperature, the vapour pressure of the solute in the solution of benzene is 631.9 mm. The molality of the solution will be ......

    (a) 0.1563   (b) 0.1472   (c) 0.1378   (d) 0.1275

38. Which of the following solutions will have highest boiling point ?

    (a) 0.1 M $FeCl_3$ (b) 0.1 M NaCl   (c) 0.1 M $BaCl_2$ (d) 0.1 M urea

39. Which of the following solutions have lowest freezing point ?

(a) 0.1 M $NaNO_3$ (b) 0.01 M glucose   (c) 0.01 M BCl_3 (d) 9.2 M Na_2SO_4

40. Which of the following is not a colligative property?

(a) Osmotic pressure   (b) Elevation in boiling point

(c) Depression in freezing point   (d) Modification of refractive index

41. Partial pressure of a solution component is directly proportional to its mole fraction and this statement is known as

(a) Raoult's law   (b) Henry's law

(c) Ostwald's dilution law   (d) Distribution law

42. An aqueous solution of 6.3 g oxalic acid dihydrate is made upto 250 ml. The volume of 0.1 N NaOH required to completely neutralize 10 ml of this solution is ......

(a) 40 ml   (b) 20 ml   (c) 10 ml   (d) 4 ml

43. 2.5 litre of 1 M NaOH solution is mixed with 3 litres of 0.5 M NaOH solution. What is the molarity of this solution?

(a) 0.80 M   (b) 1.0 M   (c) 0.73 M   (d) 0.50 M

44. A solution contains non-volatile solute of molecular mass M_2, which of the following can be used to calculate the molecular mass of solute in terms of osmotic pressure?

(a) $M_2 = \left(\dfrac{m_2}{\pi} VRT\right)$ (b) $M_2 = \left(\dfrac{m_2}{V}\right)\dfrac{RT}{\pi}$ (c) $M_2 = \left(\dfrac{m_2}{V}\right)\pi RT$ (d) $M_2 = \left(\dfrac{m_2}{V}\right)\dfrac{\pi}{RT}$

45. Freezing point of an aqueous solution is $-0.186°C$. Elevation in boiling point of the same solution is ($K_f = 1.86°$ and $K_b = 0.512°C$)

(a) 0.180°C   (b) 0.0512°C   (c) 0.092°C   (d) 0.2372°C

46. A 0.004 M solution of Na_2SO_4 is isotonic with a 0.010 M solution of glucose at the same temperature. The apparent degree of dissociation of Na_2SO_4 is ......

(a) 25%   (b) 50%   (c) 75%   (d) 85%

47. 6.02×10^{20} molecules of urea are present in 100 ml of solution. The concentration of urea solution is

(a) 0.001 M   (b) 0.1 M   (c) 0.02 M   (d) 0.01 M

48. To neutralise completely 20 ml of 0.1 M aqueous solution of phosphorus acid (H_3PO_3), the volume of 0.1 M aqueous KOH solution required is ......

(a) 10 ml   (b) 60 ml   (c) 40 ml   (d) 20 ml

49. Which of the following liquid pairs show a positive deviation for Raoult's law ?

(a) Water - hydrochloric acid   (b) Acetone - chloroform

(c) Water - nitric acid   (d) Benzene - methanol

50. Which will show a positive deviation from Raoult's law?

(a) Methanol and acetone   (b) Chloroform and acetone

(c) Nitric acid and water   (d) Phenol and aniline

51. Colligative properties depend on ......

    (a) the nature of the solute particles dissolved in solution.

    (b) the number of solute particles in solution.

    (c) the physical properties of the solute particles dissolved in solution.

    (d) the nature of solvent particles.

52. Which of the following aqueous solutions will show highest boiling point?

    (a) 1.0 M NaOH   (b) 1.0 M Na_2SO_4 (c) 1.0 M NH_4NO_3 (d) 1.0 M KNO_3

53. The unit of ebullioscopic constant is ......

    (a) $K\ kg\ mol^{-1}$ (b) $mol\ kg\ K^{-1}$ (c) $kg\ mol^{-1}\ K^{-1}$ (d) $K\ mol\ kg^{-1}$

54. In comparison to a 0.01 M solution of glucose, the depression in freezing point of a 0.01 M $MgCl_2$ solution is ......

    (a) the same   (b) about twice

    (c) about three times   (d) about six times

55. Which of the following statements is false?

    (a) Units of atmospheric pressure and osmotic pressure are the same.

    (b) In reverse osmosis, solvent molecules move through a semipermeable membrane from a region of lower concentration of solute to a region of higher concentration.

    (c) The value of molal depression constant depends on the nature of solvent.

    (d) Relative lowering of vapour pressure, is a dimensionless quantity.

56. The vapour pressure of two liquids 'P' and 'Q' are 80 and 60 torr respectively. The total vapour pressure of solution obtained by mixing 3 mole of P and 2 mole of Cl would be ......

    (a) 68 torr   (b) 140 torr   (c) 72 torr   (d) 20 torr

57. A solution of urea (molecular mass 56 g mol^{-1}) boils at 100.18°C at the atmosphere pressure. If K_f and K_b for water are 1.86 and 0.512 K kg mol^{-1} respectively, the above solution will freeze at ......

    (a) – 6.54°C   (b) – 0.654°C   (c) 654°C   (d) 0.654°C

58. Which one of the following statements is false?

    (a) Raoult's law states that the vapour pressure of a component over solution is proportional to the mole fraction.

    (b) Two sucrose solutions of same molality prepared in different solvents will have the freezing point depression

    (c) The correct criteria of osmotic pressure for 0.01 M aqueous solution of each compound is $BaCl_2$ > KCl > CH_3COOH > NHOH

    (d) The osmotic pressure (p) of a solution is given by equation π = MRT, where M is the molarity.

59. The elevation in boiling point of a solution of 13.44 g of $CuCl_2$ in 1 kg of water using the following information will be (Molecular weight of $CuCl_2$ = 134.4 and K_b = 0.52 K)

    (a) 0.16   (b) 0.05   (c) 0.1   (d) 0.2

60. Three aqueous solutions of NaCl labelled as 'A', 'B' and 'C' with concentrations 0.1 M, 0.01 M and 0.001 M, respectively. The value of van't Hoff factor (i) for these solutions will be in the order ......

    (a) $i_A < i_B < i_C$ (b) $i_A > i_B > i_C$ (c) $i_A = i_B = i_C$ (d) $i_A < i_B > i_C$

61. To prepare a solution of concentration 0.03 g/mol of $AgNO_3$, what amount of $AgNO_3$ should be added in 60 ml of solution ?

    (a) 1.8   (b) 0.8   (c) 0.18   (d) 18

62. A 5 molar solution of H_2SO_4 is diluted from 1 litre to 10 litres. What is the normality of the solution ?

    (a) 0.25 N   (b) 1 N   (c) 2 N   (d) 7 N

63. 1.00 g of non-electrolyte solute of molecular mass 250 g mol^{-1} was dissolved in 51.2 g of benzene. If K_f for benzene is 5.12 K kg mol^{-1}, the freezing point of benzene is lowered by ......

    (a) 0.3 K   (b) 0.5 K   (c) 0.2 K   (d) 0.4 K

64. The density of a 2.05 M solution of acetic acid in water is 1.02 g/ml. The molality of solution is

    (a) 0.44 mol kg^{-1} (b) 1.14 mol kg^{-1} (c) 3.28 mol kg^{-1} (d) 2.28 mol kg^{-1}

65. 139.18 g of glucose is added to 178.2 g of water. The vapour pressure of water for this aqueous solution at 100°C is ......

    (a) 752.40 torr   (b) 759.00 torr   (c) 7.60 torr   (d) 76.00 torr

66. A 5% solution by mass of cane sugar in water has freezing point of 271 K and freezing point of pure water is 273.15 K. The freezing point of a 5% solution of glucose in water is ......

    (a) 271 K   (b) 273.15 K   (c) 269 K   (d) 277.23 K

67. 72.5 g of phenol is dissolved in 1 kg of a solvent (K_f K kg mol^{-1}) which leads to dimerization of phenol and freezing point is lowered by 7 Kelvin. What percent of total phenol is present in dimeric form ?

    (a) 3.5   (b) 35   (c) 0.35   (d) 0.70

68. Concentrated sulphuric acid is 98% mass and has a density 1.80 g ml^{-1}. Volume of the acid required to make one litre of 0.1 M H_2SO_4 solution is ......

    (a) 5.55 ml   (b) 11.10 ml   (c) 16.65 ml   (d) 22.20 ml

69. 0.01 M solution of KCl and $BaCl_2$ are prepared in water. The freezing point of KCl is found to be –2°C. What is the freezing point $BaCl_2$ to be ionised?

    (a) –30°C   (b) –3°C   (c) –2°C   (d) –4°C

70. A 0.002 molar aqueous solution of an ionic compound $[Co(NH_3)S(NO_2)]Cl$ freezes at – 0.00732°C . Number of moles of ions with 1 mole of ionic compound produces on being dissolved in water will be (K_f – 1.86°C)

    (a) 1   (b) 2   (c) 3   (d) 4

71. Pure benzene freezes at 5.3°C. A solution of 0.223 g of phenyl acetic acid $C_6H_5CH_2COOH$ in 4.4 g of benzene

(K_f = 5.12 K kg mol^{-1}) freezes at 4.47°C. From this observation one can conclude that

(a) Phenyl acetic acid exists as solution benzene

(b) Phenyl acetic acid undergoes particle ionization in benzene

(c) Phenyl acetic acid undergoes complete ionization in benzene

(d) Phenyl acetic acid dimerizes in benzene

72. Which one of the following is an example of colligative property ?

(a) Boiling point   (b) Osmosis   (c) Freezing point   (d) Osmotic pressure

73. Osmotic pressure of a solution increases by ......

(a) Decreasing the temperature

(b) Increasing the volume

(c) Increasing the number of molecules of the solute

(d) None of these

74. A solution containing 6.8 g of non-ionic solute in 100 g of water was found to freeze at -0.93°C. If K_f for water is 1.86, the molecular mass of solute is ......

(a) 13.6   (b) 34   (c) 68   (d) 136

75. Equal volumes of 0.1 M $AgNO_3$ and 0.2 M NaCl are mixed. The concentration of ions in the mixture will be

(a) 0.1 M   (b) 0.05 M   (c) 0.2 M   (d) 0.15 M

76. At 25°C, the highest osmotic pressure is exhibited by 0.1 M solution of

(a) $CaCl_2$ (b) KCl   (c) Glucose   (d) Urea

77. Which one of the following salt will have the same value of vant Hoff's factor as that of $K_4[Fe(CN)_6]$?

(a) $Al_2(SO_4)_3$ (b) NaCl   (c) $Al_2(NO_3)_3$ (d) Na_2SO_4

78. vant Hoff factor of $Ca(NO_3)_2$ is ......

(a) 1   (b) 2   (c) 3   (d) 4

79. 120 g of urea is present in 5 L of solution, what is active mass of urea ?

(a) 0.2   (b) 0.86   (c) 0.4   (d) 0.88

80. The osmotic pressure of 5% (mass-volume) solution of cane sugar at 150°C (molecular mass of sugar 342) is ......

(a) 4 atm   (b) 5.07 atm   (c) 3.55 atm   (d) 2.45 atm

81. 4.0 g of caustic soda is dissolved in 100 cc of solution. The normality of solution is

(a) 1   (b) 0.1   (c) 0.5   (d) 4.0

82. Isotonic solutions have same ......

(a) Molar concentration   (b) Molality

(c) Normality   (d) None of these

83. Which of the following method is used for measuring the osmotic pressure of the solution?

    (a) Ostwald method　　　　　　　(b) Berkeley–Hartley method

    (c) Solvay method　　　　　　　　(d) Haber's method

84. The normal boiling point of water is 373 K (at 760 mm). Vapour pressure of water at 298 K is 23 mm. If enthalpy of vaporization is 40.656 kJ mol^{-1}, the boiling point of water at 23 mm atmospheric pressure will be ......

    (a) 250 K　　　　(b) 298 K　　　　(c) 51.6 K　　　　(d) 12.5 K

85. The volume of 0.1 M H_2SO_4 required to neutralise completely 40 mL of 0.2 M NaOH solution is

    (a) 10 ml　　　　(b) 40 ml　　　　(c) 20 ml　　　　(d) 80 ml

86. What is the molarity of H_2SO_4 solution that has a density of 1.84 g/cc at 35°C and contains 98% by weight ?

    (a) 4.18 M　　　　(b) 8.14 M　　　　(c) 18.14 M　　　　(d) 18 M

87. Which of the following 0.10 M aqueous solution will have the lowest freezing point?

    (a) $Al_2(SO_4)_3$　　　(b) $C_6H_{12}O_6$　　　(c) $C_{12}H_{22}O_{11}$　　　(d) KI

88. 0.15 g of a substance dissolved in 15 g of a solvent boiled at a temperature higher by 0.216°C than that of the pure solvent. Find out the molecular weight of the substance (K_b for solvent is 2.16°C)

    (a) 1.01　　　　(b) 10.1　　　　(c) 100　　　　(d) 10

89. An aqueous solution freezes at −0.186°C (K_f = 1.86°, K_b = 0.512°). What is the elevation in boiling point?

    (a) 0.186　　　　(b) 0.512　　　　(c) $\dfrac{0.512}{1.86}$　　　　(d) 0.0512

90. The freezing point of a solution prepared from 1.25 g of non-electrolyte and 20 g of water is 271.9 K. If molar depression constant is 1.86 Km^{-1} then molar mass of the solute will be ......

    (a) 105.7　　　　(b) 106.7　　　　(c) 115.3　　　　(d) 93.9

91. Molal depression constant for water is 1.86°C. The freezing point of a 0.05 molal solution of a non-electrolyte in water is ......

    (a) −186°C　　　　(b) −0.93°C　　　　(c) −0.093°C　　　　(d) 0.93°C

92. The vapour pressure of a solvent is decreased by 10 mm of Hg when a non-volatile solute was added to the solvent. The mole fraction of solute in solution is 0.2. What would be the mole fraction of solvent if decrease in vapour pressure is 20 mm of Hg?

    (a) 0.8　　　　(b) 0.6　　　　(c) 0.4　　　　(d) 0.2

93. If 100 mL of 1 N sulphuric acid were mixed with 100 mL of 1 M sodium hydroxide, the solution will be ......

    (a) Acidic　　　　(b) Basic　　　　(c) Neutral　　　　(d) Slightly acidic

94. The vapour pressure of benzene at a certain temperature is 640 mm of Hg. A non-volatile and non-electrolyte solid weighing 2.175 g is added to 39.08 g of benzene. If the vapour pressure of the solution is 600 mm of Hg, what is the molecular weight of solid substance?

(a) 49.50   (b) 59.60   (c) 69.60   (d) 79.82

95. For a 1 molar solution of NaCl in water at 25°C and 1 atm. pressure ......

(a) Molality = normality   (b) Molarity = normality

(c) Molality = mole fraction   (d) Molarity = mole fraction

96. 1.8 g of fructose ($C_6H_{12}O_6$) is added to 2 kg of water. The freezing point of the solution is ...

(a) $-1.86°C$ (b) $0.86°C$ (c) $-0.0186°C$ (d) $0.0093°C$

97. Molarity of $HCl_{(aq)}$ if its density is 1.17 g/cc is ......

(a) 36.5   (b) 36.5   (c) 36.05   (d) 42.10

98. The vapour pressure of a solution (P) and the vapour pressure of the solvent (P°) are related to each other as (x_1 is the mole fraction of solvent)

(a) $P = P°x_2$ (b) $P = P°x_2$ (c) $P° = Px_1$ (d) $P° = Px_2$

99. In a mixture A and B compounds show negative deviation as ......

(a) $\Delta V_{mix} > 0$ (b) $\Delta H_{mix} > 0$

(c) A-B interaction is weaker than A-A and B-B interactions

(d) None of the above reason is correct

100. The density (in g ml^{-1}) of 3.60 M H_2SO_4 acid solution that is 29% H_2SO_4 by mass will be ....

(a) 1.22   (b) 1.45   (c) 1.64   (d) 1.88

101. In a 0.2 molal aqueous solution of a weak acid HX, the degree of ionization is 0.3. Taking K_f for water is 1.85, the freezing point of the solution will be nearest to ......

(a) $-0.480°C$ (b) $-0.360°C$ (c) $-0.260°C$ (d) $+0.480°C$

102. If liquids A and B form an ideal solution

(a) The enthalpy of mixing is zero

(b) The entropy of mixing is zero

(c) The free energy of mixing is zero

(d) The free energy as well as the entropy of mixing are both zero

103. How much $K_2Cr_2O_7$ (M.W. = 294.19) is required to prepare one litre of 0.1 N solution?

(a) 0.8063 g   (b) 7.3548 g   (c) 3.6774 g   (d) 4.903 g

104. 3.65 grams of HCl is dissolved in 16.2 g of water. The mole fraction of HCl in the resulting solution is ......

(a) 0.4   (b) 0.3   (c) 0.2   (d) 0.1

105. Which of the following aqueous solutions will exhibit highest boiling point?

(a) 0.01 M Na_2SO_4 (b) 0.015 M glucose   (c) 0.015 M urea   (d) 0.01 M KNO_3

106. Consider the following aqueous solutions and assume 100% of ionisation of electrolytes :

  (I) 0.1 M urea   (II) 0.04 M $Al_2(SO_4)_3$ (III) 0.05 M $CaCl_2$ (IV) 0.005 M NaCl

  Pick up correct statements.

  (a) Freezing point will be lowest for solution I

  (b) Freezing point will be highest for solution IV

  (c) Vapour pressure is highest for solution (II)

  (d) Osmotic pressure is highest for solution (III)

107. 100 cc of 0.6 N H_2SO_4 and 200 cc of 0.3 N HCl were mixed together. The normality of the solution will be ......

  (a) 0.2 N   (b) 0.4 N   (c) 0.8 N   (d) 0.6 N

108. Maximum freezing point falls in ......

  (a) Camphor   (b) Naphthalene   (c) Benzene   (d) Water

109. A solution contains 1.2046×10^{24} hydrochloric acid molecules in one dm^3 of the solution. The strength of the solution is ......

  (a) 6 N   (b) 2 N   (c) 4 N   (d) 8 N

110. The average osmotic pressure of human blood is 7.8 bar at 37°C. What is the concentration of an aqueous NaCl solution that could be used in the blood stream?

  (a) 0.16 mol/L   (b) 0.32 mol/L   (c) 0.60 mol/L   (d) 0.45 mol/L

111. Camphor is often used in molecular mass determination because ......

  (a) It serves as solvent for organic substances (b) It is readily available

  (c) It has a very high cryoscopic constant   (d) It is volatile

112. If a is the degree of dissociation of Na_2SO_4, then van't Hoff's factor (i) used for calculating the molecular mass is ......

  (a) $1 + \alpha$ (b) $1 - \alpha$ (c) $1 + 2\alpha$ (d) $1 - 2\alpha$

113. Benzene and toluene form nearly ideal solutions. At 20°C, the vapour pressure of benzene is 75 torr and that of toluene is 22 torr. The partial vapour pressure of benzene at 20°C for a solution containing 87g of benzene and 46 g of toluene in torr is

  (a) 50   (b) 25   (c) 375   (d) 535

114. Two solutions of a substance (non-electrolyte) are mixed in the following manner. 480 mL of 15 M first solution + 520 mL of 12 M second solution. What is the molarity of the final mixture ?

  (a) 1.20 M   (b) 1.50 M   (c) 1.344 M   (d) 2.70 M

115. 0.5 M of H_2SO_4 is diluted from 1 litre to 10 litre, then normality of resulting solution is ......

  (a) 1 N   (b) 0.1 N   (c) 10 N   (d) 11 N

116. A molal solution is that which contains one mole of a solute in ......

  (a) 1000 gm of solvent   (b) one litre of solvent

  (c) one litre of solution   (d) one kg of solution

117. Osmotic pressure of a solution is 0.0821 atm at a temperature of 300 K. The concentration in mole/litre will be ......

    (a) 3.3   (b) 0.066   (c) 0.3×10^{-2} (d) 3

118. Increasing the temperature of an aqueous solution will cause

    (a) Decrease in molality   (b) Decrease in molarity

    (c) Decrease in mole fraction   (d) Decrease in % (w/w)

119. How many moles of Fe^{2+} ions are formed when excess iron is treated with 500 ml of 0.4 N HCl under inert atmosphere ? Assume no change in volume.

    (a) 0.4   (b) 0.1   (c) 0.2   (d) 0.8

120. The solubility of a gas at a given temperature is directly proportional to pressure at which it is dissolved. This is called as ....

    (a) Henry's law   (b) Ostwald's law   (c) Raoult's law   (d) Avogadro's law

121. For ideal solutions ......

    (a) $\Delta H_{mix} = 0$ (b) $\Delta H_{mix} > 0$ (c) $\Delta H_{mix} < 0$ (d) None of these

122. Shrivelling of raw mangoes in pickle is an example of ......

    (a) Vapour pressure   (b) Osmosis   (c) Reverse osmosis   (d) Freezing point

123. Equimolar solutions of electrolytes in the same solvent have ......

    (a) Same boiling point but different freezing point

    (b) Same freezing point but different boiling points

    (c) Same boiling and freezing points

    (d) Different boiling and freezing points

124. Two solutions of a substance (non-electrolyte) are mixed in the following manner : 480 ml of 1.5 M first solution to 520 ml of 1.2 M second solution. What is the molarity of final mixture ?

    (a) 1.20 M   (b) 1.50 M   (c) 1.344 M   (d) 2.70 M

125. If two substances A and B have $P_A^0 : P_B^0 = 1 : 2$ and also $x_A : x_B$ solution as 1 : 2, then mole fraction of A in vapours is ......

    (a) 0.33   (b) 0.25   (c) 0.52   (d) 0.2

126. Solution A contains 7 g/L $MgCl_2$ and solution B contains 7 g/L of NaCl. At room temperature, the osmotic pressure of ....

    (a) Solution A is greater than B   (b) Both have same osmotic pressure

    (c) Solution B is greater than A   (d) Cannot determine

127. Among the following mixtures, dipole-dipole as major interactions is present in

    (a) KCl and water   (b) Benzene and CCl_4

    (c) Benzene and ethanol   (d) Acetonitrile and acetone

128. Density of 2.05 M solution of acetic acid in water is 1.00 g/ml. The molality of solution is ....

    (a) 2.28 ml kg^{-1} (b) 0.44 mol kg^{-1} (c) 1.14 mol kg^{-1} (d) 3.28 mol kg^{-1}

129. Vapour pressure of solution containing 18 gms of glucose ($C_6H_{12}O_6$) and 178.2 g of water at 100°C is ......

    (a) 76.0 torr   (b) 752.40 torr   (c) 759.0 torr   (d) 7.60 torr

130. 1.0 g of non-electrolyte (molar mass = 250 g mol^{-1}) was dissolved in 51.2 g of benzene. If K_f of benzene is 5.12 K kg mol^{-1} then freezing point of benzene will be lowered by ....

(a) 0.2 (b) 0.4 (c) 0.3 (d) 0.25

131. During osmosis flow of water through semipermeable membrane is from ....

(a) Solution having lower concentration only

(b) Both sides and semipermeable membrane with equal flow rates

(c) Solutions having higher concentration

(d) Both sides of semipermeable membrane with unequal flow rates

132. 0.5 molal aqueous solution of weak acid HX is 20% ionised, if K_f for water is 1.86 kg mol^{-1}, the lowering in freezing point of solution is

(a) – 0.56 K (b) – 1.12 K (c) 0.56 K (d) + 1.12 K

133. Concentrated aqueous sulphuric acid is 98% H_2SO_4 by mass and has a density of 1.80 g mol^{-1}. The volume of acid required to make one litre of 0.1 M H_2SO_4 solution is

(a) 5.56 ml (b) 11.10 ml (c) 16.65 ml (d) 22.20 ml

134. A mixture of ethyl alcohol and methyl alcohol has a vapour pressure of 290 mm at 300°K. The vapour pressure of propyl alcohol is 200 mm. If the mole fraction of ethyl alcohol is 0.6, its vapour pressure (in mm) at same temperature is ....

(a) 700 (b) 360 (c) 350 (d) 300

135. A 5.25% solution of substance is isotonic with 1.5% solution of urea (mol. wt. 60 g mol^{-1}) in the same solvent. If the densities of both the solutions are assumed to be equal to 1.0 g cm^{-3}, molar mass of substance will be ....

(a) 105.0 g mol^{-1} (b) 210.0 g mol^{-1} (c) 90.0 g mol^{-1} (d) 115.0 g mol^{-1}

136. RBC placed in a 0.9% salt solution will ......

(a) swell due to osmosis (b) will shrink due to plasmolysis

(c) will burst due to haemolysis (d) will remain same

137. At a given temperature, osmotic pressure of a concentrated solution of a substance

(a) is higher than that at a dilute solution.

(b) is lower than that of a dilute solution.

(c) is same as that of a dilute solution.

(d) cannot be compared with osmotic pressure of dilute solution.

138. Which of the following statements is false?

(a) Two different solutions of sucrose of same molality prepared in different solvents will have the same depression in freezing point.

(b) The osmotic pressure of a solution is given by the equation π = CRT (where C is the molarity of the solution).

(c) Decreasing order of osmotic pressure for 0.01 M aqueous solutions of barium chloride, potassium chloride, acetic acid and sucrose is $BaCl_2$ > KCl > CH_3COOH > sucrose.

(d) According to Raoult's law, the vapour pressure exerted by a volatile component of a solution is directly proportional to its mole fraction in the solution.

139. The values of van't Hoff factors for KCl, $K_4[Fe(CN)_6]$ and K_2SO_4, respectively, are

(a) 2, 2 and 2   (b) 2, 5 and 3   (c) 2, 2 and 3   (d) 1, 1 and 1

140. The van't Hoff factor for a solute that associates in solution is ......

(a) Zero   (b) 1   (c) Less than 1   (d) More than 1

141. Blood cells do not shrink in blood because blood is ......

(a) Hypotonic   (b) Isotonic   (c) Equimolar   (d) Hypertonic

142. Phenol dimerises in benzene having van't Hoff factor 0.54. What is the degree of association?

(a) 0.40   (b) 0.54   (c) 0.27   (d) 0.92

143. Two liquids X and Y form an ideal solution. The mixture has a vapour pressure of 400 mm at 300 K when mixed in the molar ratio 1 : 1. But when mixed in the molar ratio of 1 : 2 at the same temperature, the vapour pressure of the mixture is 350 mm. The vapour pressure of the two pure liquids X and Y respectively are ......

(a) 250 mm, 550 mm   (b) 350 mm, 450 mm

(c) 350 mm, 700 mm   (d) 550 mm, 250 mm

144. The freezing point of water is depressed by 0.37°C in a 0.01 molar NaCl solution. The freezing point of 0.02 molar solutions is depressed by ......

(a) 0.37°C   (b) 0.74°C   (c) 0.185°C   (d) 0°C

145. The increase in boiling point of a solution containing 0.6 g urea in 200 gram water is 0.50°C. Find the molal elevation constant.

(a) 10 K gram mol^{-1} (b) 1.0 K kg mol^{-1} (c) 10 kg mol^{-1} (d) 10 K kg mol^{-1}

146. Which of the following aqueous solutions has the highest boiling point?

(a) 0.1 M KNO_3 (b) 0.1 M Na_3PO_4 (c) 0.1 M $BaCl_2$ (d) 01 M K_2SO_4

147. What is the osmotic pressure of a 0.0020 mole dm^{-3} sucrose $(C_{12}H_{22}O_{11})$ solutions at 20°C? (Molar gas constant, $R = 8.314$ J $K^{-1}mol^{-1}$, 1 $dm^3 = 0.001$ m^3)

(a) 4870 Pa   (b) 487 Pa   (c) 0.00487 Pa   (d) 0.33 Pa

148. Arrange the following aqueous solutions in order of decreasing freezing point.

0.1 m urea, 0.1 m NaCl, 0.05 m $CaCl_2$ and 0.05 m HF

(a) urea = HF > NaCl > $CaCl_2$ (b) HF > urea > $CaCl_2$ > NaCl

(c) HF > $CaCl_2$ > urea > NaCl   (d) NaCl > urea > $CaCl_2$ > HF

(e) NaCl > $CaCl_2$ > urea > HF

149. Arrange the following aqueous solutions in decreasing order of boiling points.

(i) 10^{-3} NaCl   (ii) 10^{-3} urea   (iii) 10^{-3} $MgCl_2$ (iv) 10^{-2} NaCl

(a) (ii) > (i) = (iii) < (iv)   (b) (i) > (ii) > (iii) > (iv)

(c) (ii) > (i) > (iii) > (iv)   (d) (iv) > (iii) > (ii) > (i)

150. During osmosis, flow of water through a semipermeable membrane is ......

(a) From both sides of semipermeable membrane with unequal flow rates

(b) From solution having lower concentration only

(c) From solution having higher concentration only

(d) From both sides of semipermeable membrane with equal flow rates

151. A 5% solution (by mass) of cane sugar in water has freezing point of 271 °K and freezing point of pure water is 273.15 °K. The freezing point of a 5% solution (by mass) of glucose in water is

(a) 271 °K   (b) 273.15 °K   (c) 269.07 °K   (d) 277.23 °K

152. 0.5 molar aqueous solution of a weak acid (HX) is 20% ionised. If K_f for water is 1.86 K kg mol^{-1}, the lowering in freezing point of the solution is

(a) −0.56 K   (b) −1.12 K   (c) 0.56 K   (d) + 1.12 K

153. When 20 g of naphthonic acid ($C_{11}H_8O_2$) is dissolved in 50 g of benzene (K_f = 1.72 K kg mol^{-1}) a freezing point depression of 2 K is observed. The van't Hoff factor (i) is

(a) 0.5   (b) 1   (c) 2   (d) 3

154. The vapour pressure of water at 20°C is 17.5 mm Hg. If 18 g glucose ($C_6H_{12}O_6$) is added to 178.2 g of water at 20°C the vapour pressure of the resulting solution will be ......

(a) 16.500 mm Hg   (b) 17.325 mm Hg   (c) 17.675 mm Hg   (d) 15.750 mm Hg

155. A binary liquid solution is prepared by mixing n-heptane and ethanol. Which one of the following statements is correct regarding the behavior of the solution ?

(a) The solution formed is non-ideal

(b) The solution is non-ideal, showing positive deviations from Raoult's law

(c) The solution is non-ideal showing negative deviations from Raoult's law

(d) n-heptane shows positive while ethanol shows negative deviations from Raoult's law

156. 50 mL of 10 N H_2SO_4, 25 mL of 12 N HCl and 40 mL of 5N HNO_3 are mixed and the volume of the mixture is made 1000 mL by adding water. The normality of the resulting solution will be ......

(a) 1 N   (b) 2 N   (c) 3 N   (d) 4 N

157. To neutralise completely 20 mL of 0.1 M aqueous solution of phosphorus acid (H_3PO_3) the volume of 0.1 M aqueous KOH solution required is ......

(a) 10 mL   (b) 20 mL   (c) 40 mL   (d) 60 mL

158. Mole fraction of solute in benzene is 0.2, then the molality of the solution is

(a) 3.2   (b) 2   (c) 4   (d) S_8

159. If two substances A and B have $p_A^o : p_B^o$ = 1 : 2 and have mole fraction in solution as 1 : 2 then mole fraction of A in vapour phase is ......

(a) 0.33   (b) 0.25   (c) 0.52   (d) 0.2

160. At same temperature, which pair of the following solutions are isotonic solutions?

(a) 0.2 M $BaCl_2$ and 0.2 urea   (b) 0.1 M urea and 0.1 M NaCl

(c) 0.1 M NaCl and 0.1 M K_2SO_4 (d) 0.1 M $Ba(NO_3)_2$ and 0.1 M Na_2SO_4

161. 5 litres of a solution contains 25 mg of $CaCO_3$. What is its concentration in ppm? (mol. wt. of $CaCO_3$ is 100)

(a) 25   (b) 1   (c) 5   (d) 250

162. The vapour pressure of a dilute aqueous solution of glucose is 740 mm of mercury at 373 K. The mole fraction of the solute is ......

(a) $\dfrac{1}{20}$ (b) $\dfrac{1}{38}$ (c) $\dfrac{1}{76}$ (d) $\dfrac{1}{760}$

163. The vapour pressure of a pure liquid is 0.80 atm. When a non-volatile solute is added to this liquid, its vapour pressure drops to 0.60 atm. The mole fraction of the solute in the solution is ......

(a) 0.75　　　　　(b) 0.20　　　　　(c) 0.25　　　　　(d) 0.85

164. For getting accurate value of molar mass of a solute by osmotic pressure measurement.

(a) The solute must be volatile　　　　　(b) The solution concentration must be high

(c) The solute should undergo dissociation　　(d) The solute must be non-volatile

165. For dilute solutions, Raoult's law state that ......

(a) Lowering of vapour pressure is equal to the mole fraction of the solute

(b) Relative lowering of vapour pressure is equal to mole fraction of the solvent

(c) Relative lowering of vapour pressure of the solvent is equal to the mole fraction of the solute

(d) Vapour pressure of the solution is equal to the mole fraction of the solute

166. During depression of freezing point in a solution the following are in equilibrium

(a) Liquid solvent, solid solvent　　　　　(b) Liquid solvent, solid solute

(c) Liquid solute, solid solute　　　　　　(d) Liquid solute, solid solvent

167. A 0.004 M solution of Na_2SO_4 is isotonic with a 0.010 M solution of glucose at same temperature. The apparent degree of dissociation of Na_2SO_4 is ......

(a) 25%　　　　　(b) 50%　　　　　(c) 75%　　　　　(d) 85%

168. The elevation boiling point for 13.44 g of $CuCl_2$ dissolved in 1 kg of water as solvent will be (K_b = 0.52 Km^{-1}, molar mass of $CuCl_2$ = 134.4 g mol^{-1})

(a) 0.05　　　　　(b) 0.10　　　　　(c) 0.16　　　　　(d) 0.20

169. 18 g of glucose ($C_6H_{12}O_6$) is added to 178.2 g of water. The vapour pressure of water for this aqueous solution at 100°C is ......

(a) 76.00 Torr　　(b) 752.40 Torr　　(c) 759.00 Torr　　(d) 7.60 Torr

170. A solution of acetone in ethanol ......

(a) Behaves like a near ideal solution

(b) Obeys Raoult's law

(c) Shows a negative deviation from Raoult's law

(d) Shows a positive deviation from Raoult's law

171. Concentrated aqueous sulphuric acid is 98% H_2SO_4 by mass and has a density of 1.80 ml^{-1}. Volume of the acid required to make one litre of 0.1 M H_2SO_4 solution is

(a) 5.55 ml　　　　(b) 11.10 ml　　　　(c) 16.65 ml　　　　(d) 22.20 ml

172. The density (in g mL^{-1}) of a 3.60 M sulphuric acid solution that is 29% H_2SO_4 (Molar mass = 98 g mol^{-1}) by mass will be

(a) 1.45　　　　　(b) 1.04　　　　　(c) 1.88　　　　　(d) 1.22

173. At 80°C, the vapour pressure of pure liquid 'A' is 520 mm Hg and that of pure liquid 'B' is 1000 mm Hg. If a mixture solution of A and B boil at 80°C and 1 atm pressure, then amount of A in the mixture is (1 atm = 760 mm Hg) ......

(a) 48 mol percent　　(b) 50 mol percent　　(c) 52 mol percent　(d) 34 mol percent

174. 0.002 M aqueous solution of an ionic compound $Co(NH_3)_5(NO_2)Cl$ freezes at $-0.00732°C$. Number of moles of ions which 1 mole of ionic compound produces in water will be ($K_f = 1.86°C/m$)

(a) 1   (b) 2   (c) 3   (d) 4

175. An aqueous solution is 1.00 molal in KI. Which change will cause the vapour pressure of the solution to increase ?

(a) Addition of Na_2SO_4 (b) Addition of 1.00 molal KI

(c) Addition of water   (d) Addition of NaCl

176. The degree of dissociation (α) of a weak electrolyte A_xB_y is related to van't Hoff factor by …

(a) $\alpha = \dfrac{i-1}{x+y+1}$ (b) $\alpha = \dfrac{x+y-1}{i-1}$ (c) $\alpha = \dfrac{x+y+1}{i-1}$ (d) $\alpha = \dfrac{i-1}{x+y-1}$

177. Ethylene glycol is used as an antifreeze in a cold climate. Mass of ethylene glycol which should be added to 4 kg of water to prevent it from freezing at $-6°C$ will be (K_f for water $= 1.86$ K kg mol^{-1}, and molar mass of ethylene glycol $= 62$ g mol^{-1})

(a) 204.30 g   (b) 400.08 g   (c) 304.60 g   (d) 804.32 g

178. The freezing point depression constant for water is $1.86°C$ m^{-1}. If 5.00 g Na_2SO_4 is dissolved in 45.0 g H_2O, the freezing point is changed by $3.82°C$. Calculate the van't Hoff factor for Na_2SO_4.

(a) 3.11   (b) 0.381   (c) 2.05   (d) 2.63

179. Dissolving 120 g of urea (mol. wt. = 60) in 1000 g of water gave a solution of density 1.15 g/mL. The molarity of the solution is ……

(a) 1.78 M   (b) 2.00 M   (c) 2.05 M   (d) 2.22 M

PREVIOUS YEAR'S QUESTIONS

1. The freezing point of 1% solution of lead nitrate in water will be …… **[Manipal 2006]**

(a) 2°C   (b) 1°C   (c) 0°C   (d) below 0°C

2. A solution of urea (mol. 56 g mol^{-1}) boils at $100.18°C$ at the atmospheric pressure. If K_f and K_b for water are 1.86 and 0.512 K kg mol^{-1} respectively, the above solution will freeze at …

[CBSE AIPMT 2005]

(a) $-6.54°C$ (b) 6.54°C   (c) 0.54°C   (d) $-0.654°C$

3. The average osmotic pressure of human blood is 7.8 bar at 37°C. What is the concentration of an aqueous NaCl solution that could be used in the blood stream? **[AIIMS 2004]**

(a) 0.16 mol/L   (b) 0.31 mol/L   (c) 0.60 mol/L   (d) 0.45 mol/L

4. Which one of the statement given below concerning properties of solution, describes a colligative effect? **[AIIMS 2003]**

(a) Boiling point of pure water decreases by the addition of ethanol.

(b) Vapour pressure of pure water decreases by the addition of nitric acid.

(c) Vapour pressure of pure benzene decreases by the addition of naphthalene

(d) Boiling point of pure benzene increases by the addition of toluene

5. Camphor is often used in molecular mass determination because …… **[Manipal 2007]**

(a) it is readily available   (b) it has a very high cryoscopic constant

(c) it is volatile   (d) it is solvent for organic substances.

6. If α is the degree of dissociation of Na_2SO_4 then van't Hoff factor (i) used for calculating the molecular mass is ...... **[Manipla 2007]**
(a) $1 + 2\alpha$ (b) $1 - 2\alpha$ (c) $1 - \alpha$ (d) $1 + \alpha$

7. A solution containing 10 g per dm^3 of urea (molecular mass = 60 g mol^{-1}) is isotonic with a 5% solution of a non-volatile solute. The molecular mass of this non-volatile solute is ......
[CBSE AIPMT 2006]
(a) 250 g mol^{-1} (b) 300 g mol^{-1} (c) 350 g mol^{-1} (d) 200 g mol^{-1}

8. A 5% solution (by mass) of cane sugar in water has freezing point of 271 K and freezing point of pure water is 273.15 K. The freezing point of a 5% solution (by mass) of glucose in water is ...... **[AIIMS 2006]**
(a) 271 K   (b) 273.15 K   (c) 269.07 K   (d) 277.23 K

9. Which of following aqueous solutions has the highest boiling point? **[DUMET 2009]**
(a) 0.1 M KNO_2 (b) 0.1 M Na_3PO_4 (c) 0.1 M $BaCl_2$ (d) 0.1 M K_2SO_4

10. 0.01 m solution of KCl and $BaCl_2$ are prepared in water. The freezing point of KCl is found to be $-2°C$. What is the freezing point of $BaCl_2$ to be completely ionized? **[AIIMS 2008]**
(a) $-3°C$ (b) $+3°C$ (c) $-2°C$ (d) $-4°C$

11. Which of the following can be measured by Ostwald-Walker dynamic method?
[AIIMS 2008]
(a) Relative lowering of vapour pressure   (b) Lowering of vapour pressure
(c) Vapour pressure of the solvent   (d) All of the above

12. Solutions A, B, C and D are respectively 0.1 M glucose, 0.05 M $BaCl_2$ and 0.1 M $AlCl_3$. Which one of the following pairs is isotonic? **[Manipal 2008]**
(a) A & B   (b) B & C   (c) A & D   (d) A & C

13. The vapour pressure of benzene of a certain temperature is 640 mm of Hg. A non-volatile and non-electrolyte solid weighing 2.175 g is added to 39.08 g of benzene. If the vapour pressure of the solution is 600 mm of Hg, what is the molecular weight of solid substance?
[MHT CET 2008]
(a) 49.50 (b) 59.60 (c) 69.60 (d) 79.89

14. If the elevation in boiling point of a solution of 10 g of solute (mol. wt. = 100) in 100 g of water is ΔT_b, the ebullioscopic constant of water is ...... **[Manipal 2010]**
(a) 10 (b) $100\ T_b$ (c) ΔT_b (d) $\dfrac{\Delta T_b}{10}$

15. A 0.0020 m aqueous solution of an ionic compound $[Co(NH_3)_5(NO_2)]Cl$ freezes at $-0.00732°C$. Number of moles of ions which one of mole of ionic compound produces on being dissolved in water will be $\left(K_f = \dfrac{1.86°C}{m}\right)$ ...... **[CBSE AIPMT 2009]**
(a) 2 (b) 3 (c) 4 (d) 1

16. The concentration (in mol/L) of the solution having osmotic pressure 0.0821 atm at 30 K will be ...... **[AFMC 2009]**
(a) 0.33 (b) 0.066 (c) 0.3×10^{-2} (d) 3

17. The order of boiling points of four equimolar aqueous solutions is C < B < A < D. The correct order of their freezing points is ...... **[AIIMS 2009]**
(a) $D > D < B < A$ (b) $D > C < B < A$ (c) $D < B > A < C$ (d) $D > A > B > C$

18. A solution of sucrose (molar mass = 342 g mol^{-1}) has been prepared by dissolving 68.5 g of sucrose in 1000 g of water. The freezing point of the solution obtained will be (K_f for water = 1.86 K kg mol^{-1}) **[CBSE AIPMT 2010]**

(a) −0.570°C   (b) −0.372°C   (c) −0.520°C   (d) +0.372°C

19. Pure benzene freezes at 5.3°C. A solution of 0.223 g of phenylacetic acid ($C_6H_5CH_2COOH$) in 4.4 g of benzene (K_f = 5.12 kg mol^{-1}) freezes at 4.47°C. From the observation, one can conclude that ...... **[AFMC 2010]**

(a) phenyl acetic acid exists as such in benzene

(b) phenyl acetic acid undergoes partial ionization in benzene

(c) phenyl acetic acid undergoes complete ionization in benzene

(d) phenyl acetic acid dimerises in bensene

20. Which has the least freezing point? **[CPMT 2010]**

(a) 1% sucrose   (b) 1% NCl   (c) 1% $CaCl_2$ (d) 1% glucose

21. Dissolution of 1.5 g of a non-volatile solute (mol. wt. = 60) in 250 g of a solvent reduces its freezing point by 0.01°C. Find the molal depression constant of the solvent. **[MHT CET 2010]**

(a) 0.01   (b) 0.001   (c) 0.0001   (d) 0.1

22. Lowering of vapour pressure of an aqueous solution of a non-volatile, non-electrolye 1 m aqueous solution of 100°C is **[Manipal 2009]**

(a) 14.12 Torr   (b) 312 Torr   (c) 13.45 Torr   (d) 352 Torr

23. If two substances A and B have $P_A^o : P_B^o = 1 : 2$ and have mole fraction in solution 1:2 then molefraction of A in vapours is ...... **[DUMET 2005]**

(a) 0.33   (b) 0.25   (c) 0.52   (d) 0.2

24. The freezing point depression constant for water is −1.86°C cm^{-1}. If 5.00 g Na_2SO_4 is dissolved in 45.0 g H_2O, the freezing point is changed by −0.82°C. Calculate the van't Hoff factor for Na_2SO_4. **[CBSE AIPMT 2011]**

(a) 0.381   (b) 2.05   (c) 2.63   (d) 3.11

25. The van't Hoff factor i for a compound which undergoes dissociation in one solvent and association in other solvent is respectively ...... **[CBSE AIPMT 2011]**

(a) greater than one and greater than one   (b) less than one and greater than one

(c) less than one and less than one   (d) greater than one and less than one

26. An aqueous solution is 1.00 molal in KI. Which change will cause the vapour pressure of the solution to increase? **[CBSE AIPMT 2010]**

(a) Addition of water   (b) Addition of NaCl

(c) Addition of Na_2SO_4 (d) Addition of 1.00 molal KI

27. Among the following, the azeotropic mixture ...... **[CPMT 2010]**

(a) CCl_4 + $CHCl_3$ (b) C_6H_{14} + C_7H_{16}

(c) C_2H_5Br + C_2H_5Cl (d) chlorobenzene + bromobenzene

28. The ratio of loss in mass of solvent to gain in $CaCl_2$ tube is ...... **[MHT CET 2010]**

(a) $\dfrac{P^o}{P}$ (b) $\dfrac{P}{P^o}$ (c) $\dfrac{P^o - P}{P^o}$ (d) $\dfrac{P - P^o}{P^o}$

29. Which of the following azeotropic solutions has the boiling point less than boiling point of the constituents A and B? **[AIIMS 2009]**
(a) CHI_3 and CH_3COCH_3
(b) CS_2 and CH_3COCH_3
(c) CH_3CH_2 and CH_3COCH_3
(d) CH_3CHO and CS_2

30. Assertion : One molal aqueous solution of glucose contains 180 g of glucose in 1 kg water.
Reason : Solution containing one mole of solute in 1000 g of solvent is called one molal solution. **[AIIMS 2008]**
(a) both assertion and reason are true and reason is the correct option
(b) both assertion and reason are true but reason is not correct
(c) assertion is true but reason is false
(d) assertion and reason both are false

31. Which of the following concentration factor affected by change in temperature?
(a) Molarity
(b) Molality
(c) Mole fraction
(d) Weight fraction

32. Concentrated aqueous sulphuric acid is 98% H_2SO_4 by mass and has a density of 1.80 gmL^{-1}. Volume of acid required to make 1 L of 0.1 M H_2SO_4 solution is ......
[CBSE AIPMT 2007]
(a) 400 cm^3
(b) 450 cm^3
(c) 500 cm^3
(d) 100 cm^3

33. An aqueous solution of glucose is 10% in strength. The volume in which 1 g mole of it is dissolved will be ...... **[AFMC 2007]**
(a) 18 L
(b) 9 L
(c) 0.9 L
(d) 1.8 L

34. To prepare a solution of concentration 0.03 g/ml of $AgNO_3$, what amount of $AgNO_3$ should be added in 60 mL of solution ? **[AFMC 2005]**
(a) 1.8 g
(b) 0.8 g
(c) 0.18 g
(d) None of these

35. 40 g of NaOH is dissolved in 100 mL solution. The normality of the solution is ......
(a) 0.1 N
(b) 0.5 N
(c) 4.0 N
(d) 1.0 N **[Manipal 10]**

36. The molarity of a solution containing 5.0 g of NaOH in 250 mL solution is ......
(a) 0.1 N
(b) 0.5 N
(c) 1.0 N
(d) 2.0 N

37. Assertion 1.575 g $H_2C_2O_4 \cdot H_2O$ in 250 mL solution makes it 0.1 N. **[AIIMS 09]**
Reason $H_2C_2O_4 \cdot 2H_2O$ is dehydrate organic acid.

38. 0.126 g of an acid is titrated with 0.1 N 20 mL of an base. The equivalent weight of the acid is ...... **[CPMT 2009]**
(a) 63
(b) 50
(c) 53
(d) 23

39. 60 mL of $\dfrac{N}{5}$ H_2SO_4, 10 mL of $\dfrac{N}{2}$ HNO_3 and 30 mL of $\dfrac{N}{10}$ HCl are mixed together. The strength of the resulting mixture is **[CPMT 2009]**
(a) 0.10 N
(b) 0.2 N
(c) 0.3 N
(d) 0.4 N

40. The percentage (by weight) of sodium hydroxide in a 1.25 molal NaOH solution is ......
(a) 4.76%
(b) 1.25%
(c) 5%
(d) 40%

41. The vapour pressure lowering caused by the addition of 100 g of sucrose (molecular mass = 342) to 1000 g of water, if the vapour pressure of pure water at 25°C is 23.8 mm Hg is **[AFMC 2012]**
(a) 0.12 mmHg
(b) 0.125 mmHg
(c) 1.15 mmHg
(d) 1.25 mmHg

42. 138 g of ethyl alcohol is mixed with 72 g of water. The ratio of mole fraction of alcohol to water is ...... **[Manipal 2012]**
(a) 3:4
(b) 1:2
(c) 1:4
(d) 1:1

43. In which case Raoult's law is not applicable?   **[AIIMS 2012]**
    (a) 1 M NaCl   (b) 1 M urea   (c) 1 M glucose   (d) 1 M sucrose

44. The freezing point of one molal NaCl solution assuming NaCl to be 100% dissociated in water is (molar depression constant is 1.86) ......   **[Manipal 12]**
    (a) $-2.72°C$ (b) $-3.72°C$ (c) $2.72°C$ (d) $3.72°C$

45. Mole fraction of the solute in a 1.00 molal aqueous solution is ......   **[CBSE AIPMT 2011]**
    (a) 1.7700   (b) 0.1770   (c) 0.0177   (d) 0.0344

46. 25.3 g of sodium carbonate, Na_2CO_3 is dissolved in enough water to make 250 mL of solution. If sodium carbonate dissociates completely, molar concentration of sodium ion, Na^+ and carbonate ions CO_3^{2-} are respectively (Molar mass of Na_2CO_3 = 16 g mol^{-1})

    [CBSE AIPMT 2010]
    (a) 0.477 M and 0.477 M   (b) 0.955 M and 1.910 M
    (c) 1.910 M and 0.955 M   (d) 1.90 M and 1.910 M

47. 450 mg of glucose is dissolved in 100 g of solvent. What is the molality of the solution?
    [MHT CET 2010]
    (a) 0.0025 m   (b) 0.025 m   (c) 0.25 m   (d) 2.5 m

48. 2.5 cm^2 of 0.2 M H_2SO_4 solution is diluted to 0.5 dm^3. Find normality of the diluted solution.
    [MHT CET 2010]
    (a) 0.2 N   (b) 0.02 N   (c) 0.002 N   (d) 0.04 N

49. What is the mole fraction of the solute in a 1.00 m aqueous solution?   **[AIPMT 2015]**
    (a) 0.0354   (b) 0.0177   (c) 0.177   (d) 1.770

50. Which one of the following electrolytes has the same value of van't Hoff's factor (i) as that of $Al_2(SO_4)_3$ (if all are 100% ionised) ?   **[AIPMT 2015]**
    (a) $K_3[Fe(CN)_6]$ (b) $Al(NO_3)_3$ (c) $K_4[Fe(CN)_6]$ (d) K_2SO_4

51. The boiling point of 0.2 mol kg solution of X in water is greater than equimolal solution of Y in water. Which one of the following statements is true in this case?
    (a) Molecular mass of X is greater than the molecular mass of Y.
    (b) Molecular mass of X is less than the molecular mass of Y.
    (c) Y is undergoing dissociation in water while X undergoes no change.
    (d) X is undergoing dissociation in water.

52. Of the following 0.10 m aqueous solutions, which one will exhibit the largest freezing point depression?   **[AIPMT 2014]**
    (a) $Al_2(SO_4)_3$ (b) K_2SO_4 (c) KCl   (d) $C_6H_{12}O_6$

53. How many grams of concentrated nitric acid solution should be used to prepare 250 mL of 2.0 M HNO_3 ? The concentrated acid is 70% HNO_3 ?   **[CBSE NEET 2013]**
    (a) 54.0 conc. HNO_3 (b) 45.0 g conc. HNO_3
    (c) 90.0 g conc. HNO_3 (d) 70.0 g conc. HNO_3

54. An excess of $AgNO_3$ is added to 100 mL of a 0.01 M solution of dichlorotetraaquachromium (III) chloride. The number of moles of AgCl precipitated would be ......   **[CBSE NEET 2013]**
    (a) 0.01   (b) 0.001   (c) 0.002   (d) 0.003

55. 6.02×10^{20} molecules of urea are present in 100 mL of its solution. The concentration of solution is ......   **[CBSE NEET 2013]**
    (a) 0.1 M   (b) 0.02 M   (c) 0.01 M   (d) 0.001 M

56. p_A and p_B are the vapour pressure of pure liquid components, A and B, respectively of an ideal binary solution. If X_A represents the mole fraction of component A, the total pressure of the solution will be ...... **[CBSE AIPMT 2012]**

(a) $p_A + X_A (p_A - p_A)$

(b) $p_A + X_A (p_A - p_B)$

(c) $p_B + X_A (p_B - p_A)$

(d) $p_B + X_A (p_A - p_B)$

57. Vapour pressure of chloroform ($CHCl_3$) and dichloromethane (CH_2Cl_2) at 25°C are 200 mmgHg and 41.5 mmgHg respectively. Vapour pressure of the solution obtained by mixing 25.5 g of $CHCl_3$ and 40 g of CH_2Cl_2 at the same temperature will be ...... **[CBSE AIPMT 2012]**

(Molecular mass of $CHCl_3$ = 119.5 u and molecular mass of CH_2Cl_2 = 85 u)

(a) 173.9 mmHg　　(b) 615.0 mmHg　　(c) 347.9 mmHg　　(d) 90.63 mmHg

ANSWER KEY

1. (b)	2. (a)	3. (a)	4. (c)	5. (c)	6. (d)	7. (d)	8. (b)
9. (d)	10. (b)	11. (b)	12. (b)	13. (b)	14. (d)	15. (a)	16. (c)
17. (b)	18. (a)	19. (c)	20. (c)	21. (b)	22. (b)	23. (a)	24. (a)
25. (a)	26. (c)	27. (b)	28. (a)	29. (d)	30. (d)	31. (c)	32. (b)
33. (b)	34. (b)	35. (b)	36. (b)	37. (c)	38. (a)	39. (b)	40. (d)
41. (a)	42. (a)	43. (c)	44. (b)	45. (b)	46. (c)	47. (d)	48. (c)
49. (d)	50. (a)	51. (b)	52. (b)	53. (a)	54. (c)	55. (b)	56. (c)
57. (b)	58. (b)	59. (a)	60. (a)	61. (a)	62. (a)	63. (d)	64. (d)
65. (a)	66. (c)	67. (b)	68. (a)	69. (b)	70. (b)	71. (d)	72. (d)
73. (b)	74. (d)	75. (b)	76. (a)	77. (a)	78. (c)	79. (c)	80. (b)
81. (a)	82. (a)	83. (b)	84. (b)	85. (b)	86. (c)	87. (a)	88. (c)
89. (d)	90. (a)	91. (c)	92. (c)	93. (c)	94. (c)	95. (b)	96. (c)
97. (c)	98. (b)	99. (b)	100. (a)	101. (a)	102. (a)	103. (d)	104. (d)
105. (a)	106. (b)	107. (b)	108. (a)	109. (b)	110. (a)	111. (c)	112. (c)
113. (a)	114. (c)	115. (b)	116. (a)	117. (c)	118. (b)	119. (b)	120. (a)
121. (a)	122. (b)	123. (d)	124. (c)	125. (d)	126. (a)	127. (d)	128. (a)
129. (b)	130. (b)	131. (c)	132. (d)	133. (a)	134. (c)	135. (b)	136. (d)
137. (a)	138. (c)	139. (b)	140. (c)	141. (b)	142. (d)	143. (d)	144. (a)
145. (c)	146. (b)	147. (a)	148. (a)	149. (c)	150. (b)	151. (d)	152. (b)
153. (a)	154. (b)	155. (b)	156. (a)	157. (c)	158. (a)	159. (d)	160. (d)
161. (c)	162. (b)	163. (c)	164. (d)	165. (c)	166. (a)	167. (c)	168. (c)
169. (b)	170. (d)	171. (a)	172. (d)	173. (b)	174. (b)	175. (c)	176. (d)
177. (d)	178. (d)	179. (c)					

Previous Year's Questions

1. (d)	2. (d)	3. (b)	4. (c)	5. (c)	6. (a)	7. (b)	8. (c)
9. (b)	10. (a)	11. (d)	12. (a)	13. (c)	14. (c)	15. (a)	16. (c)
17. (c)	18. (b)	19. (d)	20. (c)	21. (d)	22. (c)	23. (d)	24. (c)
25. (d)	26. (a)	27. (a)	28. (c)	29. (c)	30. (a)	31. (a)	32. (d)
33. (d)	34. (a)	35. (d)	36. (b)	37. (a)	38. (d)	39. (b)	40. (a)
41. (b)	42. (a)	43. (a)	44. (b)	45. (c)	46. (c)	47. (b)	48. (c)
49. (a)	50. (c)	51. (d)	52. (a)	53. (b)	54. (b)	55.(c)	56. (d)
57. (d)							

ELECTROCHEMISTRY

1. For a galvanic cell, which of the following statements is never true?
   (a) The potential of the cathode is higher than that of the anode.
   (b) The electricity flows in the external circuit from the anode to the cathode.
   (c) Reduction takes place at the cathode.
   (d) Oxidation takes place at the anode

2. Reduction potential is ......
   (a) an intensive property
   (b) always positive
   (c) measured in amperes
   (d) an extensive property

3. If the electrode potentials of both the electrodes become equal in magnitude but opposite in sign then ......
   (a) an electrochemical cell stops working
   (b) an electrochemical cell starts working
   (c) an electrochemical cell is reversed
   (d) none of these

4. Which one of the following is a false statement?
   (a) Salt bridge maintains electrical neutrality
   (b) When salt bridge is removed then the potential of the cell drops to zero.
   (c) Salt bridge increases the emf of the cell.
   (d) Salt bridge connects two half cells.

5. If $E_{EXTERNAL}$ voltage is greater than E_{CELL} in an electrochemical cell then flow of electron will be from ......
   (a) anode to cathode
   (b) cathode to anode
   (c) salt bridge to anode
   (d) salt bridge to cathode

6. Which of the following statement is correct?
   (a) E_{Cell} and ΔG of cell reaction both are extensive properties.
   (b) E_{Cell} and ΔG of cell reaction both are intensive properties.
   (c) E_{Cell} is an intensive property while ΔG of cell reaction is an extensive property.
   (d) E_{Cell} is an extensive property while ΔG of cell reaction is an intensive property.

7. The difference between the electrode potentials of two electrodes when no current is drawn through the cell is called as ......
   (a) Cell potential
   (b) Cell emf
   (c) Potential difference
   (d) Cell voltage

8. Which of the following statement is not correct about an inert electrode in a cell?
   (a) It does not participate in the cell reaction.
   (b) It provides surface either for oxidation or for reduction reaction.
   (c) It provides surface for conduction of electrons.
   (d) It provides surface for redox reaction.

9. An electrochemical cell can behave like an electrolytic cell when ......

(a) $E_{cell} = 0$ (b) $E_{cell} > E_{ext}$ (c) $E_{ext} > E_{cell}$ (d) $E_{cell} = E_{ext}$

10. Which of the statements about solutions of electrolytes is not correct?

(a) Conductivity of solution depends upon size of ions.

(b) Conductivity depends upon viscosiy of solution.

(c) Conductivity does not depend upon solvation of ions.

(d) Conductivity of solution increases with temperature.

11. Which is the strongest reducing agent ?

$E_{Cr_2O_7^{2-}/Cr^{3+}} = 1.33$ V, $E_{Cl_2/Cl^-} = 1.36$ V, $E_{MnO_4^-/Mn^{2+}} = 1.51$ V, $E_{Cr^{3+}/Cr} = -0.74$ V

(a) Cl^- (b) Cr (c) Cr^{3+} (d) Mn^{2+}

12. The standard cell potential for the Daniell cell ......

$Zn_{(s)} + Cu^{2+}_{(aq)} \rightarrow Zn^{2+}_{(aq)} + Cu_{(s)}$ is +1.102 V at 298 K and +1.095 V at 363 K.

The standard reaction entropy is ......

(a) $+20.8$ J K^{-1} mol^{-1} (b) -20.8 J K^{-1} mol^{-1}

(c) $+10.4$ J K^{-1} mol^{-1} (d) -10.4 J K^{-1} mol^{-1}

13. The cell which directly convert free energy of a chemical reaction into electricity is ......

(a) Lead storage battery   (b) Fuel cell

(c) Leclanche cell   (d) Concentration cell

14. Four alkali metals A, B, C and D are having standard electrode potentials as −4.05, −2.66, −0.50 and 0.70 V respectively. Which one of the following is most reducing?

(a) D   (b) C   (c) B   (d) A

15. The ΔG° for the following reaction is is −793 kJ mol^{-1}, therefore, E°_{cell} is ......

$$Cr_2O_7^{2-} + 2Fe + 14H^+ \rightarrow 2Cr^{3+} + 2Fe^{3+}\ 7H_2O$$

(a) $+1.37$ V   (b) $+4.11$ V   (c) $+2.74$ V   (d) $+2.05$ V

16. The oxidation potential of Mg and Al are +2.37 and +1.66 volt respectively. The Mg in chemical reaction ......

(a) will not replace Al at all   (b) will replace Al

(c) will be replaced by Al   (d) none of these

17. The equilibrium constant for the reaction is

$S_2O_8^{2-}{}_{(aq)} + 2Fe^{2+}{}_{(aq)} \rightleftharpoons 2Fe^{3+}{}_{(aq)} + 2SO_4^{2-}{}_{(aq)}$ at 25.0°C, given that the standard cell potentials for the two half reactions at this temperature are

$$S_2O_8^{2-}{}_{(aq)} + 2e \rightleftharpoons 2SO_4^{2-}{}_{(aq)},\ E = +2.08\ V$$

$$Fe^{3+}{}_{(aq)} + e^- \rightleftharpoons Fe^{2+}{}_{(aq)},\ E = +0.77\ V$$

(a) 10^2 (b) 2×10^{96} (c) 2×10^{44} (d) 2×10^{48}

18. The standard cell potential for the reaction is +0.240 V. Calculate the standard reaction Gibbs energy.

$$2NO + \frac{1}{2}O_2 + H_2O \rightarrow 2HNO_2$$

(a) -11.6 kJ mol^{-1}　　(b) -23.2 kJ mol^{-1}　　(c) -46.3 kJ mol^{-1}　　(d) -96.5 kJ mol^{-1}

19. The EMF of the following cell is 0.20 V at 298 K at what molar concentration of Cd^{2+} ions in the solution?

$$Cd \mid Cd^{2+} \parallel Ni^{2+} \text{ (2.0 M)} \parallel Ni$$

(a) 0.05 M　　　　(b) 0.004 M　　　　(c) 0.040 M　　　　(d) 0.03 M

20. A mole of electrons has a charge of 96,487 coulombs which is known as ......

(a) 1 ampere　　　　(b) 1 joule　　　　(c) 1 volt　　　　(d) 1 faraday

21. A gas X at 1 atm is bubbled through a solution containing a mixture of 1 M Y$^-$ and 1 M Z$^-$ at 25ºC. If the reduction potential of Z > Y > X then ......

(a) Y will reduce both X and Z　　　　　　(b) Y will oxidise Z and not X

(c) Y will oxidise X and not Z　　　　　　(d) Y will oxidise both X and Z

22. Certain gram equivalents of an ion is reduced to the element when it absorbs 6×10^{20} electrons. The number of equivalents of the ion is ......

(a) 0.001　　　　(b) 0.01　　　　(c) 0.10　　　　(d) 0.001

23. The standard reduction potential values of three metallic cations X, Y, Z are 0.52, -3.03 and 1.18 V respectively. The order of reducing power of corresponding metals is ......

(a) X > Y > Z　　　　(b) Y > Z > X　　　　(c) Z > X > Y　　　　(d) Z > Y > Z

24. The standard reduction potential at 298 °K for the following half reactions are given against each

$$Zn^{2+}_{(aq)} + 2e^- \rightarrow Zn_{(s)}; -0.762 \text{ V} \qquad ; \qquad Cr^{+}_{(aq)} + 3e^- \rightarrow Cr_{(s)}; -0.740 \text{ V}$$

$$2H^{+}_{(aq)} + 2e^- \rightarrow H_{2(g)}; 0.00 \text{ V} \qquad ; \qquad Fe^{3+}_{(aq)} + e^- \rightarrow Fe^{2+}; 0.770 \text{ V}$$

Which is the strongest reducing agent ?

(a) $Fe^{2+}_{(aq)}$　　　　(b) $H_{2(g)}$　　　　(c) $Cr_{(s)}$　　　　(d) $Zn_{(s)}$

25. A standard hydrogen electrode has zero electrode potential because ......

(a) Hydrogen atom has only one electron

(b) Hydrogen is the lighest element

(c) This electrode potential is assumed to be zero

(d) Easier to oxidise

26. The standard reduction potentials of Cu^{2+}/Cu and Cu^{2+}/Cu^+ are 0.337 and 0.153 V respectively. The standard electrode potential of Cu^{2+}/Cu half cell is ......

(a) 0.521 V　　　　(b) 0.184 V　　　　(c) 0.490 V　　　　(d) 0.827 V

27. The e.m.f. of the cell Zn | Zn^{2+} (0.01 M) || Fe^{2+} (0.001 M) | Fe at 298 °K is 0.295 V Then the value of equilibrium constant for the cell reaction is ......

(a) $10^{\frac{0.32}{0.591}}$　　　　(b) $10^{\frac{0.32}{0.0295}}$　　　　(c) $10^{\frac{0.32}{0.0295}}$　　　　(d) $10^{\frac{0.26}{0.0295}}$

28. The standard e.m.f. of a Galvanic cell involving 3 moles of electrons in a redox reaction is 0.59 V. The equilibrium constant for the reaction of the cell is ......

(a) 10^{25}　　　　(b) 10^{20}　　　　(c) 10^{15}　　　　(d) 10^{30}

29. Standard electrode potential values are used for predicting the suitable oxidant for a redox titration.

$$MnO_4^-{}_{(aq)} + 8H^+_{(aq)} + 5e^- \rightarrow Mn^{2+}_{(aq)} + 4H_2O_{(l)}, \quad E^\circ = 1.51 \ V$$

$$Cr_2O_7^{2-}{}_{(aq)} + 14H^+_{(aq)} + 6e^- \rightarrow 2Cr^{3+}_{(aq)} + 7H_2O_{(l)}, \quad E^\circ = 1.38 \ V$$

$$Fe^{3+}_{(aq)} + e^- \rightarrow Fe^{2+}_{(aq)}; \quad E^\circ = 0.77$$

$$Cl_{2\ (aq)} + 2e^- \rightarrow 2Cl^-_{(aq)}; \quad E^\circ = 1.40 \ V$$

On the basis of above information given identify the only incorrect statement for the quantitative estimation of aqueous $Fe(NO_3)_2$

(a) $Cr_2O_7^{2-}$ can be used in aqueous HCl

(b) $Cr_2O_7^{2-}$ can be used in aqueous H_2SO_4

(c) MnO_4^- can be used in aqueous HCl

(d) MnO_4^- can be used in aqueous H_2SO_4

30. The reaction $\dfrac{1}{2} H_{2(aq)} + AgCl_{(s)} \rightarrow H^+_{(aq)} + Cl^-_{(aq)} + Ag_{(s)}$ occurs in which of the Galvanic cell ?

(a) $Ag/AgCl_{(s)}/KCl$ (solution)/$AgNO_3$(solution)/Ag

(b) $Pt/H_{2(aq)}/HCl$ (solution)/$AgCl_{(s)}$/Ag

(c) $Pt/H_{2(aq)}/HCl$ (solution)/$AgNO_3$ (solution)/Ag

(d) None of these

31. Electrode potential for Mg electrode varies according to the following equation

$$E_{Mg^{2+}/Mg} = E^\circ{}_{Mg^{2+}/Mg} - \frac{0.0591}{2} \log\left[\frac{1}{Mg^{2+}}\right]$$

The graph of $E_{Mg^{2+}|Mg}$ versus $\log [Mg^{2+}]$ is ......

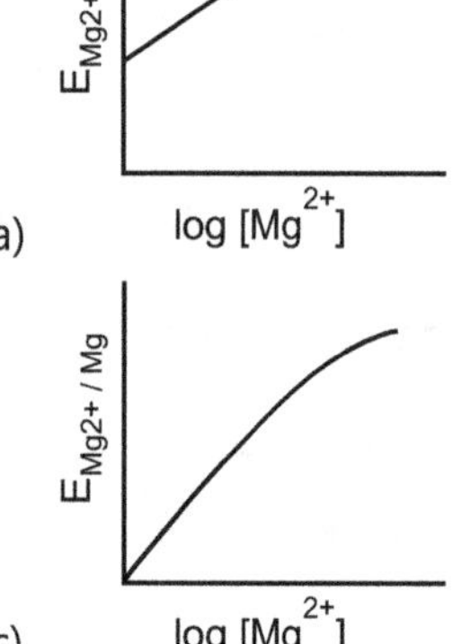

(a) $\log [Mg^{2+}]$ (c) $\log [Mg^{2+}]$

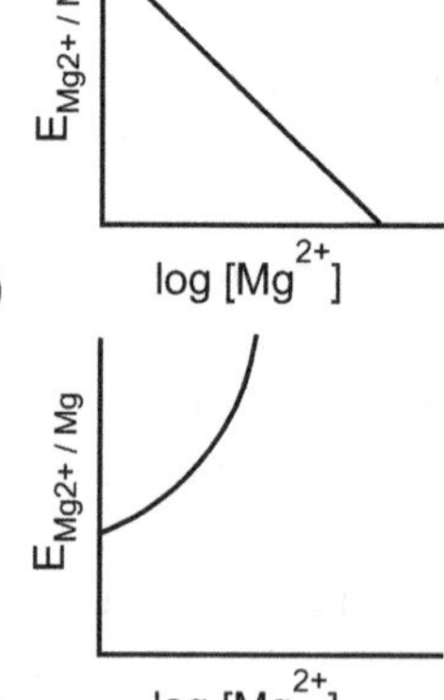

(b) $\log [Mg^{2+}]$ (d) $\log [Mg^{2+}]$

32. The standard reduction potential for Cu is +0.34 V. Calculate the reduction potential if the pH is 14. K_{sp} of $Cu(OH)_2$ is 1.0×10^{19}.

(a) +0.22 V   (b) −0.22 V   (c) +0.57 V   (d) −0.57 V

33. Which cell will measure standard electrode potential of copper electrode?

(a) $Pt(s)\ H_2\ (g,\ 0.1\ bar)\ H^+\ (aq.,1\ M) \| Cu^{2+}(aq.,\ 1M)\ Cu$

(b) $Pt(s)\ H_2\ (g,\ 1\ bar)\ H^+\ (aq.,1\ M) \| Cu^{2+}\ (aq.,\ 2M)\ Cu$

(c) $Pt(s)\ H_2\ (g,\ 1\ bar)\ H^+\ (aq.,1\ M) \| Cu^{2+}\ (aq.,\ 1M)\ Cu$

(d) $Pt(s)\ H_2\ (g,\ 1\ bar)\ H^+\ (aq.,0.1\ M) \| Cu^{2+}\ (aq.,\ 1M)\ Cu.$

34. The half cell reactions for corrosion are

$$2H^+ + 1/2\ O_2 + 2e^- \rightarrow H_2O;\ E^\circ = 1.23\ V$$

$$Fe^{2+} + 2e^- \rightarrow Fe_{(s)};\ E^\circ = -0.44\ V$$

Find ΔG° (in kJ) for the overall reaction.

(a) -322 (b) -152 (c) -161 (d) -76

35. A solution containing one mole per litre of each $Cu(NO_3)_2$; $AgNO_3$; $Hg_2(NO_3)_2$; $Mg(NO_3)_2$ is being electrolysed by using inert electrodes. The values of standard electrode potential in volts are

$$Ag^+/Ag = +0.80\ V;\ /Hg_2^{2-}\ /\ Hg = +0.79\ V;$$

$$Cu^{2+}/Cu = +0.34\ V\ and\ Mg^{2+}/Mg = -2.37\ V$$

With increasing voltage, the sequence of deposition of metals on the cathode will be ......

(a) Cu, Hg, Ag   (b) Ag, Hg, Cu, Mg   (c) Ag, Hg, Cu   (d) Mg, Cu, Hg, Ag

36. The standard reduction potential for

$Fe^{2+}/\ Fe$ and $Sn^{2+}/\ Sn$ electrodes are -0.44 and -0.14 volt respectively. For the cell reaction $Fe^{2+} + Sn \rightarrow Fe + Sn^{2+}$ the standard emf is ......

(a) $-0.58\ V$ (b) $+0.58\ V$ (c) $+0.30\ V$ (d) $-0.30\ V$

37. The standard oxidation potential E° for the half reactions are as follows.

$$Zn \rightarrow Zn^{2+} + 2e^-;\ E^\circ = 0.75\ V$$

$$Fe \rightarrow Fe^{2+} + 2e^-;\ E^\circ = +0.41\ V$$

The emf for the cell reaction

$Fe^{2+} + Zn \rightarrow Zn^{2+} + Fe$ is ......

(a) $+0.35\ V$ (b) $0.117\ V$ (c) $-0.35\ V$ (d) $+1.17\ V$

38. Given standard electrode potentials

$$Fe^{2+} + 2e^- \rightarrow Fe;\ \ E^\circ = -0.44\ V$$

$$Fe^{3+} + 3e^- \rightarrow Fe;\ \ E^\circ = -0.036\ V$$

The standard electrode potential (E°) for

$Fe^{3+} + e^- \rightarrow Fe^{2+}$ is ......

(a) $-0.404\ V$ (b) $+0.772\ V$ (c) $-0.476\ V$ (d) $+0.404\ V$

39. The value of $E_{H_2O/H_2\ (1\ atm)/Pt}$ at 298 K would be ......

(a) $-0.207\ V$ (b) $+0.414\ V$ (c) $-0.414\ V$ (d) $+0.207\ V$

40. The cell reaction is spontaneous when ......

(a) E^o_{Red} is negative　　　(b) E^o_{Red} is positive　　　(c) ΔG^o is positive　(d) ΔG^o is negative

41. The standard electrode potential (E^o) for OCl^- / Cl^- and Cl^- / $\frac{1}{2}Cl_2$ respectively are 0.94 V

and -1.36 V. The E^o value for $OCl^-/\frac{1}{2}Cl_2$ will be ......

(a) -0.42 V　　　　　(b) 1.04 V　　　　　(c) -2.20 V　　　　　(d) 0.52 V

42. The reduction potential of hydrogen half cell will be negative if ......

(a) $P(H_2) = 1$ atm and $[H^+] = 1M$　　　　　(b) $P(H_2) = 2$ atm and $[H^+] = 2M$

(c) $P(H_2) = 2$ atm and $[H^+] = 1M$　　　　　(d) $P(H_2) = 1$ atm and $[H^+] = 2M$

43. An electrochemical cell is set up as follows

$Pt\ (H_{2,\ 1\ atm})$ | 0.1 M HCl || 0.1 M Acetic acid | $(H_{2,\ 1\ atm})$ Pt. E.M.F. of this cell will not be zero because ......

(a) The pH of 0.1 M HCl and 0.1 M acetic acid is not the same

(b) E.M.F. of a cell depends on the molarities of acids used

(c) Acids used in the two compartments are different

(d) The temperature is constant

44. What is the potential of a cell containing hydrogen electrodes, the negative one in contact with 10^{-10} M H^+ and positive one in contact with 0.25 M H^+ ?

(a) 0.48 V　　　　　(b) 0.32 V　　　　　(c) 0.18 V　　　　　(d) 0.38 V

45. A cell constituted by two electrodes ($E^o_{A|A^+} = 0.35V$) and B ($E^o_{B|B} = -0.42$ V) has value of

E^o cell equal to ......

(a) 0.07 V　　　　　(b) 0.77 V　　　　　(c) -0.77 V　　　　　(d) -0.07 V

46. Which of the following statements is true for the electrochemical Daniell cell ?

(a) Cations move towards zinc electrode

(b) Cations move towards copper electrode

(c) Current flows from zinc electrode to zinc electrode

(d) Electrons flow from copper electrode to zinc electrode

47. $E^o_{(Cu)} = 0.34$ V, $E^o_{(Zn)} = -0.76$ V. A Daniell cell contains 0.1 M $ZnSO_4$ solution and 0.01 M $CuSO_4$ solution at its electrodes. E.M.F. of the cell is ......

(a) 1.04 V　　　　　(b) 1.00 V　　　　　(c) 1.16 V　　　　　(d) 1.07 V

48. What is the standard cell potential for the cell

Zn^{2+} (1 M) || Cu^+ (1 M) | Cu　　(E° for $Zn^{2+}/Zn = -0.76$ V; E° for $Cu^{2+}/Cu = +0.34$ V)

(a) $-0.76 - (+0.34) = -1.10$ V　　　　　(b) $-0.76 + (-0.34) = -0.42$ V

(c) $0.34 - (-0.76) = +1.10$ V　　　　　(d) $-0.34 + 0.76 = +0.42$ V

49. Compute the standard free energy change (ΔG^o) for the process

$Zn^{2+}_{(aq)} + 2e^- \rightarrow Zn_{(s)}$　　($E^o_{Zn^{2+}} = -0.76$ V)

(a) 1100 kJ　　　　　(b) 73.34 kJ　　　　　(c) 146.68 kJ　　　　　(d) 220.2 kJ

50. One Faraday of electricity is passed through molten Al_2O_3, aqueous solution of $CuSO_4$ and molten NaCl taken in three different electrolytic cells connected in series. The mole ratio of Al, Cu, Na deposited at the respective cathode is ......

(a) $2:3:6$　　　　　(b) $6:2:3$

(c) $6:3:2$　　　　　(d) $1:2:3$　　　(e) $3:6:2$

51. In the cell reaction

$$Cu_{(s)} + 2Ag^{+}_{(aq)} \rightarrow Cu^{2+}_{(aq)} + 2Ag_{(s)}$$

E^{o}_{cell} = 0.46 V. By doubling the concentration of Cu^{2+}, E_{cell} will be ......

(a) Unchanged   (b) Doubled

(c) Decrease by small fraction   (d) Halved

52. Aluminium displaces hydrogen from acids, but copper does not. A galvanic cell prepared by combining Cu/Cu^{2+} and Al/Al^{+3} has an emf of 2.0 V at 298 K. If the potential of copper electrode is +0.34 V, that of aluminium electrode is ......

(a) 1.66 V   (b) –2.3 V   (c) + 2.34 V   (d) – 1.66 V

53. The standard reduction potential for two reactions are given below

$$AgCl_{(s)} + e^{-} \rightarrow Ag_{(s)} + Cl^{-}_{(aq)} \quad (E^{o} = 0.22 \text{ V})$$

$$Ag^{+}_{(aq)} + e^{-} \rightarrow Ag_{(s)} \quad (E^{o} = 0.80 \text{ V})$$

The solubility product of AgCl under standard conditions of temperature is given by ......

(a) 1.5×10^{-10} (b) 3.2×10^{-10} (c) 1.5×10^{-8} (d) 1.6×10^{-5}

54. In a hydrogen-oxygen fuel cell, combustion of hydrogen occurs to ......

(a) Produce high purity water

(b) Create potential difference between two electrodes

(c) Generate heat

(d) Remove absorbed oxygen from electrode surface

55. Consider the following E^{o} values

$$E^{o}_{Fe^{3+}/Fe^{2+}} = 0.77 \text{ V}, \ E^{o}_{Sn^{3+}/Sn} = -0.14 \text{ V}$$

Under standard condition, the potential for the reaction

$$Sn_{(s)} + 2Fe^{3}_{(aq)} \rightarrow 2Fe^{2+}_{(aq)} + Sn^{2+}_{(aq)} \text{ is ......}$$

(a) 1.68 V   (b) 0.63 V   (c) 0.91 V   (d) 1.40 V

56. The standard emf of a cell involving one electron change is found to be 0.591 V at 25°C. The equilibrium constant of the reaction is ......

(F = 96500 C mol^{-1}; R = 8.314 $JK^{-1} mol^{-1}$)

(a) 1.0×10^{10} (b) 1.0×10^{5} (c) 1.0×10^{30} (d) 1.0×10^{1}

57. If half cell reaction A + e $\rightarrow$ A⁻ has a large negative reduction potential, it follows that ......

(a) A is readily reduced   (b) A is readily oxidized

(c) A⁻ is readily reduced   (d) A⁻ is readily oxidized

58. Out of Cu, Ag, Fe and Zn, the metal which can displace all others from their salt solutions is ......

(a) Ag   (b) Cu   (c) Zn   (d) Fe

59. In a Galvanic cell ......

(a) Chemical energy is converted into electricity

(b) Chemical energy is converted into heat

(c) Electrical energy is converted into heat

(d) Electrical energy is converted into chemical energy

60. Which of the following is correct?

(a) Ag^+ can be reduced by H_2 (b) Ag can oxidise H_2 into H^+

(c) Zn^{2+} can be reduced by H_2 (d) Ag can reduce Zn^{2+} ion

61. The standard reduction potential of Li^+/Li, Ba^{2+}/Ba, Na^+/Na and Mg^{2+}/Mg are $- 3.05$, -2.73, -2.71 and -2.37 volts respectively. Which one of the following is the strongest oxidising agent ?

(a) Na^+ (b) Li^+ (c) Ba^{2+} (d) Mg^{2+}

62. The standard emf of a cell, involving one electron change is found to be 0.591 V at 25°C. The equilibrium constant for the reaction is ....

(a) 1.0×10^1 (b) 1.0×10^5 (c) 1.0×10^{10} (d) 1.0×10^{30}

63. The chemical reaction,

$2AgCl_{(s)} + H_{2(g)} \longrightarrow 2HCl_{(aq)} + 2Ag_{(s)}$

taking place in a Galvanic cell is represented by the following notation ......

(a) $Pt, H_2 (1 \text{ bar}) \mid 1 \text{ M } KCl_{(aq)} \parallel AgCl_{(s)} \mid Ag_{(s)}$ (b) $Pt, H_2 (1 \text{ bar}) \mid 1 \text{ M } HCl_{(aq)} \parallel Ag^+_{(aq)} \mid Ag_{(s)}$

(c) $Pt, H_2 (1 \text{ bar}) \mid 1 \text{ M } HCl_{(aq)} \parallel AgCl_{(s)} \mid Ag_{(s)}$ (d) $Pt, H_2 (1 \text{ bar}) \mid 1 \text{ M } HCl_{(aq)} \parallel Ag_{(s)} \mid AgCl_{(s)}$

64. For the electrochemical Daniell cell, which statement is true ?

(a) Electrons flow from copper to zinc   (b) Current flows from zinc to copper

(c) Cations move towards copper electrode   (d) Cations move towards zinc electrode

65. If hydrogen electrode is dipped in two solutions of pH = 3 and pH = 6 are connected through the salt bridge then the emf of the resulting cell is ......

(a) 0.177 V   (b) 0.3 V   (c) 0.052 V   (d) 0.104 V

66. For the cell reaction,

$Cu^{2+}_{(C_1(aq))} + Zn_{(s)} \rightarrow Zn^{2+} + C_{2 (aq)} + Cu_{(s)}$

of an electrochemical cell, the change in free energy ΔG at a given temperature is a function of ......

(a) $\ln (C_1)$ (b) $\ln (C_2/C_1)$ (c) $\ln (C_1 + C_2)$ (d) $\ln (C_2)$

67. The half cell reactions, with its standard reduction potentials are

(i) $Pb^{2+} + 2e^- \longrightarrow Pb$ (E° $- 0.13$ V)   (ii) $Ag^+ + e^- \longrightarrow Ag$ (E° $= +0.80$ V)

Which of the following reactions will occur ?

(a) $Pb^{2+} + 2Ag \longrightarrow 2Ag^+ + Pb$ (b) $Pb^{2+} + H_2 \longrightarrow 2H^+ + Pb$

(c) $2H^+ + 2Ag \longrightarrow 2Ag^+ + H_2$ (d) $2Ag^+ + Pb \longrightarrow Pb^{2+} + 2Ag$

68. For the cell

    $Zn_{(s)} \mid Zn^{2+}_{(aq)} \parallel Cu^{2+}_{(aq)} \mid Cu_{(s)}$ is 1.1 V at 25°C. The equilibrium constant for the cell reaction is about ......
    (a) 10^{-37}　　　(b) 10^{37}　　　(c) 10^{-73}　　　(d) 10^{37}

69. In a Galvanic cell, the electrons flow from ......
    (a) Anode to cathode through the solution
    (b) Cathode to anode through the solution
    (c) Anode to cathode through the external circuit
    (d) Cathode to anode through the external circuit.

70. In a hydrogen-oxygen fuel cell, combustion of hydrogen occurs to ......
    (a) Generate heat
    (b) Remove absorbed oxygen from electrode surfaces
    (c) Produce high purity water
    (d) Create potential difference between two electrodes

71. For the electrolysis of alkaline water, a total of 1 mole of gas is evolved. The amount of water decomposed is ......
    (a) 2/3 moles　　　(b) 1/3 moles　　　(c) 2 moles　　　(d) 1 mole

72. The correct order of equivalent conductance at infinite dilution of LiCl, NaCl and KCl is ......
    (a) NaCl > KCl > LiCl　　　　　　(b) LiCl > KCl > NaCl
    (c) KCl > NaCl > LiCl　　　　　　(d) LiCl > NaCl > KCl

73. Faraday's laws of electrolysis are related to the ......
    (a) Atomic number of anion　　　　(b) Equivalent mass of products
    (c) Atomic number of cation　　　　(d) Speed of cations

74. The electric charge for electrode deposition of one gram equivalent of a substance is
    (a) 96500 coulombs per second　　　(b) One ampere for one hour
    (c) One ampere per second　　　　　(d) Charge on the electrons

75. A dilute aqueous solution of Na_2SO_4 is electrolysed using platinum electrodes. The products at the anode and cathode are ......
    (a) $S_2O_8^{2-}$　　　(b) O_2, H_2　　　(c) $S_2O_8^{2-}, Na$　　　(d) O_2, Na

76. In the electrolytic cell, flow of electrons is from ......
    (a) Cathode to anode through internal supply
    (b) Cathode to anode through external supply
    (c) Cathode to anode in solution
    (d) Anode to cathode through internal supply

77. When a lead storage battery is discharged ......
    (a) SO_2 is evolved　　　　　　　(b) Sulphuric acid is consumed
    (c) Lead sulphate is consumed　　　(d) Lead is formed

78. On electrolysis, which of the following does not give out hydrogen ?

(a) Dilute H_2SO_4 using Pt electrodes

(b) Dilute H_2SO_4 using Cu electrodes

(c) Acidic water using Pt electrodes

(d) Fused NaOH using Pt electrodes

79. The specific conductances of four electrolytes in $ohm^{-1}\ cm^{-1}$ are given below, which one offers higher resistance to the passage of electric current?

(a) 4.0×10^{-9} (b) 9.2×10^{-10} (c) 7.0×10^{-6} (d) 6.0×10^{-8}

80. The electroplating with chromium is undertaken because ......

(a) Electrolysis of chromium is easier

(b) Chromium can form alloys with other metals

(c) Chromium gives a protective and decorative coating to the base metal

(d) Of high reactivity of chromium metal

81. The resistance of 1N solution of acetic acid is 250 ohm, when measured in a cell of cell constant $1.15\ cm^{-1}$. The equivalent conductance (in $ohm^{-1}\ C^2\ equivalent^{-1}$) of 1N acetic acid is ......

(a) 4.6   (b) 9.2   (c) 18.4   (d) 0.023

82. Time required to deposit one millimole of aluminium metal by the passage of 9.65 amperes through molten electrolyte containing aluminium ion is ......

(a) 10,000 s   (b) 30 s   (c) 10 s   (d) 30,000 s

83. Which of the following reactions is used to make a fuel cell ?

(a) $Pb_{(s)} + PbO_{2(s)} + 2H_2SO_{4(aq)} \rightarrow PbSO_{4(s)} + 2H_2O_{(l)}$

(b) $2Fe_{(s)} + O_{2(g)} + 4H^+_{(aq)} \rightarrow 2Fe^{2+}_{(aq)} + 2H_2O_{(l)}$

(c) $2H_{2(g)} + O_{2(g)} \rightarrow 2H_2O_{(l)}$

(d) $Cd_{(s)} + 2Ni(OH)_{3(s)} \rightarrow Cu_{(s)} + 2Ni(OH)_{2(s)} + H_2O_{(l)}$

84. If three Faraday of electricity is passed through the solutions of $AgNO_3$, $CuSO_4$ and $AuCl_3$, the molar ratio of the cations deposited at the cathodes will be ......

(a) $6:3:2$ (b) $2:3:1$ (c) $1:1:1$ (d) $1:2:3$

85. Specific conductance of 0.1 M nitric acid is $6.3 \times 10^{-2}\ ohm^{-1}\ cm^{-1}$. The molar conductance of the solution is ......

(a) $100\ ohm^{-1}\ cm^2\ mol^{-1}$

(b) $315\ ohm^{-1}\ cm^2\ mol^{-1}$

(c) $630\ ohm^{-1}\ cm^2\ mol^{-1}$

(d) $6.300\ ohm^{-1}\ cm^2\ mol^{-1}$

86. The specific conductance of 0.1 M NaCl solution is $1.06 \times 10^{-2}\ ohm^{-1}\ cm^{-1}$. Its molar conductance in $ohm^{-1}\ cm^2\ mol^{-1}$ is ......

(a) 1.06×10^2 (b) 1.06×10^4 (c) 1.06×10^3 (d) 53×10^2

87. The conductivity of a saturated solution of Na_2SO_4 is $3.06 \times 10^{-6}\ ohm^{-1}$. The K_{sp} for Na_2SO_4 will be (equivalent conductance = $1.53\ ohm^{-1}\ equiv^{-1}$)

(a) 3.5×10^{-9} (b) 2.5×10^{-14} (c) 5×10^{-15} (d) 4×10^{-6}

88. The molar conductance of NaCl, HCl and C_2H_5COONa at infinite dilution are 126.45, 426.16 and 9.1 ohm^{-1} cm^2 respectively. The molar conductance of C_2H_5COOH is ......
(a) 698.28 ohm cm^2
(b) 390.71 ohm cm^2
(c) 201.28 ohm cm^2
(d) 540.48 ohm cm^2

89. In the electrolysis of H_2SO_4 using platinum electrode ......
(a) Cl_2 is obtained at cathode
(b) O_2 is produced at cathode
(c) H_2 is liberated at cathode
(d) NH_3 is produced at anode

90. Faraday's laws of electrolysis are related to the ......
(a) atomic number of the cation
(b) atomic number of the anion
(c) equivalent weight of the electrolyte
(d) speed of the cation

91. The electric charge for electrode deposition of one equivalent of the substance is ......
(a) one ampere per second
(b) 96,500 coulombs per second
(c) one ampere per hour
(d) charge on 1 mole of electrons

92. Electrolysis of dilute aqueous NaCl solution was carried out by passing 10 milliampere current. The time required to liberate 0.01 mol of H_2 gas at the cathode is ......
(a) 9.65×10^4 s
(b) 28.95×10^4 s
(c) 19.3×10^4 s
(d) 38.6×10^4 s

93. A 4.0 molar aqueous solution of NaCl is prepared and 500 mL of this solution is electrolyzed. The total number of moles of chlorine gas evolved is ......
(a) 3.0
(b) 2.0
(c) 0.5
(d) 1.0

94. Which of the substances Na, Hg, S, Pt and graphite can be used as electrodes in electrolytic cell having aqueous solutions?
(a) Pt and graphite only
(b) Na, Pt and graphite
(c) Na and S only
(d) Na and Hg

95. A current of 0.65 ampere flowing for 10 minutes deposits 3.0 g of the metal which is monovalent. The atomic mass of the metal is ......
(a) 96.5
(b) 50
(c) 10
(d) 30

96. The conductivity of strong electrolyte ......
(a) Increases on dilution slightly
(b) Decreases on dilution
(c) Does not change on dilution
(d) Depends on density of electrolyte itself

97. The amount of electricity that can deposit 108 g of silver from silver nitrate solution is
(a) 2 amperes
(b) 1 ampere
(c) 1 coulomb
(d) 1 Faraday

98. Which of the following is not a strong electrolyte ?
(a) KNO_3
(b) Na_2SO_4
(c) $Al_2(SO_4)_3$
(d) $BaCl_2$

99. For which of the following electrolyte the value of $\wedge_m$ and $\wedge_{eq}$ are same ?
(a) KCl
(b) Na_2SO_4
(c) $Al_2(SO_4)_3$
(d) $BaCl_2$

100. Which expressions can be used to calculate degree of ionisation of weak electrolyte of type $A^+ + B^-$?
(a) $\sqrt{K/C}$
(b) $\wedge_m/\wedge_m^\infty$
(c) Both (a) and (b)
(d) Neither (a) nor (b)

101. On passing 3 amperes of electricity for 50 minutes, 1.8 g of metal deposits. The equivalent mass of metal is ......

(a) 25.8　　　　(b) 19.3　　　　(c) 30.7　　　　(d) 20.5

102. The charge in coulombs on 1 g ion of N^{3-} is ......

(a) 6×10^{23}　　　(b) 96500　　　(c) 1.45×10^{6}　　　(d) 2.89×10^{6}

103. A solution of sodium sulphate was electrolysed using some inert electrodes. The product at the electrodes are ......

(a) O_2, H_2　　　(b) O_2, S_2O　　　(c) O_2, Na　　　(d) O_2, SO_2

104. The substance having highest conductivity at room temperature among the following is ...

(a) 0.1 N NaCl　　(b) Graphite　　(c) 0.1 N HCl　　(d) Glass

105. The quantity of electricity required to liberate 112 cm^3 of hydrogen at STP from acidified water is ......

(a) 1 Faraday　　(b) 965 C　　(c) 96500 C　　(d) 0.1 F

106. Calculate the amount of charge flowing in 2 minutes in a wire of resistance 10 W when a potential difference of 20 V is applied.

(a) 240 C　　(b) 120 C　　(c) 20 C　　(d) 80 C

107. For the reaction

$C + O_2 \rightarrow CO_2$　　　($\Delta H = -393$ kJ)

$2Zn + O_2 \rightarrow 2ZnO$　　($\Delta H = -412$ kJ)

(a) Carbon can oxidise zinc　　　　(b) Oxidation of carbon is not possible

(c) Oxidation of zinc is not possible　　(d) Zinc can oxidise carbon

108. A smuggler could not carry gold by chemically depositing iron on the gold surface because ......

(a) Gold is dense　　　　　　　　　(b) Iron rusts

(c) Gold has higher reduction potential than iron

(d) Gold has lower reduction potential than iron

109. Several blocks of magnesium are fixed to the bottoms of a ship to ......

(a) Keep away the sharks　　　　　(b) Prevent action of water and salt

(c) Make the ship lighter　　　　　(d) Prevent puncturing by sea rocks

110. The limiting molar conductivities $\wedge^\circ$ for NaBr are 126, 152 and 150 S cm^2 respectively. The $\wedge^\circ$ for NaBr is ......

(a) 302 S cm^2 mol^{-1}　　(b) 128 S cm^2 mol^{-1}　　(c) 176 S cm^2 mol^{-1}　　(d) 278 S cm^2 mol^{-1}

111. In a cell that utilises the reaction

$Zn_{(s)} + 2H^{+}_{(aq)} \rightarrow Zn^{2+}_{(aq)} + H_2$

Addition of H_2SO_4 to cathode compartment will ......

(a) Lower E and shift equilibrium to the right

(b) Lower E and shift equilibrium to the left

(c) Increase E and shift equilibrium to the right

(d) Increase E and shift equilibrium to the left

112. The highest electrical conductivity among the following aqueous solution is of ......

  (a) 0.1 M difluoroacetic acid   (b) 0.1 M fluoroacetic acid

  (c) 0.1 M acetic acid   (d) 0.1 M chloroacetic acid

113. The molar conductances of HCl, NaCl and CH_3COONa are 426, 126 and 91 Ω^{-1} cm^2 mol^{-1} respectively. The molar conductance for CH_3COOH is ......

  (a) 612 Ω^{-1} cm^2 mol^{-1} (b) 391 Ω^{-1} cm^2 mol^{-1}

  (c) 561 Ω^{-1} cm^2 mol^{-1} (d) 261 Ω^{-1} cm^2 mol^{-1}

114. The number of coulombs required to deposit 5.4 g of Al when the electrode reaction is $Al^{3+} + 3e^- \rightarrow Al$ is ......

  (a) 5.86×10^5 C   (b) 1.83×10^5 C   (c) 57900 C   (d) None of these

115. A certain current liberates 0.5 g of hydrogen in 2 hours. How many grams of copper can be liberated by the same current flowing for the same time in a copper sulphate solution ?

  (a) 63.5 gm   (b) 31.8 gm   (c) 15.9 gm   (d) 12.7 gm

116. What will be the weight of deposited silver on passing 965 coulombs of electricity in solution of $AgNO_3$?

  (a) 1.08 g   (b) 0.27 g   (c) 0.54 g   (d) 2.16 g

117. The standard EMF of Daniell cell is 1.10 volt. The maximum electrical work obtained from the Daniell cell is ......

  (a) 106.15 kJ   (b) 175.4 kJ   (c) 212.3 kJ   (d) 53.07 kJ

118. A cell constant is generally found by measuring the conductivity of aqueous solution of ...

  (a) $BaCl_2$ (b) KCl   (c) NaCl   (d) $MgCl_2$

119. An unknown metal M displaces nickel from nickel (II) sulphate solution but does not displace manganese from manganese sulphate solution. Which order represents the correct order of reducing power?

  (a) Mn > Ni > M   (b) Ni > Mn > M   (c) Mn > M > Ni   (d) M > Ni > Mn

120. The art of electroplating was given by ......

  (a) Faraday   (b) Edison

  (c) Thomas Graham   (d) Brugan

121. A depolarizer used in dry cell is ......

  (a) Ammonium chloride   (b) Sodium carbonate

  (c) Lead sulphate   (d) Manganese dioxide

122. The unit of molar conductivity is ......

  (a) Ohm^{-1} cm   (b) Ohm^{-1} cm^2 mol^{-1}

  (c) Ohm cm^2 mol   (d) S cm^{-2}

123. The volume of H_2 gas at STP obtained by passing 4 amperes through acidified water for 30 minutes is ......

  (a) 0.0836 L   (b) 0.0432 L   (c) 0.1672 L   (d) 0.836 L

124. The efficiency of fuel cell is given by ......

    (a) $\Delta S/\Delta G$ (b) $\Delta H/\Delta G$ (c) $\Delta G/\Delta S$ (d) $\Delta G/\Delta H$

125. The charge required for reduction of 1 mol of MnO_4^- to MnO_2 is ....
    (a) 1 F (b) 3 F (c) 5 F (d) 6 F

126. The products formed when aqueous solution of NaBr is electrolysed in an electrolytic cell having inert electrodes are ......
    (a) Na and Br (b) Na and O_2
    (c) H_2, Br_2 and NaOH (d) H_2 and O_2

127. On passing 0.1 Faraday of electricity through fused sodium chloride, the amount of chlorine liberated is (Atomic mass of Cl = 35.45) ......
    (a) 35.45 g (b) 70.9 g (c) 3.454 g (d) 17.77 g

128. When the samples of copper with zinc impurity are to be purified by electrolysis, the appropriate electrodes are ......

    Cathode   **Anode**
    (a) Pure zinc   Pure copper
    (b) Impure sample   Pure copper
    (c) Impure zinc   Impure sample
    (d) Pure copper   Impure sample

129. The equivalent conductivity of 0.1 M weak acid is 100 times less than that at infinite dilution. The degree of dissociation is ......
    (a) 100 (b) 10 (c) 0.01 (d) 0.001

130. The standard EMF of Daniell cell is 1.10 volt. The maximum electrical work obtained from the Daniell cell is ......
    (a) 212.3 kJ (b) 175.4 kJ (c) 106.15 kJ (d) 53.07 kJ

131. Same amount of electric current is passed through solutions of $AgNO_3$ and HCl. If 1.08 g of silver is obtained in the first case, the amount of hydrogen liberated at S.T.P. in the second case is ......
    (a) 112 cm^3 (b) 22400 cm^3 (c) 224 cm^3 (d) 1.008 g

132. Ionic mobility of Ag^+ at infinite dilution is ($\lambda^o_{Ag^+} = 5 \times 10^{-4}$ $\text{ohm}^{-1} \text{ m}^2 \text{ eq}^{-1}$)
    (a) 5.2×10^{-8} (b) 2.4×10^{-8} (c) 1.52×10^{-8} (d) 8.25×10^{-8}

133. An electric current is passed through silver voltmeter connected to a water voltmeter. The cathode of the silver voltmeter is 0.108 g more at the end of electrolysis. The volume of oxygen at STP is ......
    (a) 56 cm^3 (b) 550 cm^3 (c) 5.6 cm^3 (d) 11.2 cm^3 (e) 22.4 cm^3

134. The limiting molar conductivities $\wedge_o$ for NaCl, KBr and KCl are 126, 152 and 150 S cm^2 respectively. The $\wedge_o$ for NaBr is ......
    (a) $128 \text{ S cm}^2 \text{ mol}^{-1}$ (b) $302 \text{ S cm}^2 \text{ mol}^{-1}$
    (c) $278 \text{ S cm}^2 \text{ mol}^{-1}$ (d) $176 \text{ S cm}^2 \text{ mol}^{-1}$

135. What is the quantity of electricity (in coulombs) required to deposit all the silver from 250 mL of 1 M $AgNO_3$ solution ? (Ag = 108)
    (a) 2412.5 (b) 24125 (c) 4825.0 (d) 28250

136. The highest electrical conductivity of the following aqueous solutions is of ......
(a) 0.1 M fluoroacetic acid
(b) 0.1 M difluoroacetic acid
(c) 0.1 M acetic acid
(d) 0.1 M chloroacetic acid

137. The volume of H_2 gas at NTP obtained by passing 4 amperes through acidified water for 30 minutes is ......
(a) 0.836 L
(b) 0.0432 L
(c) 0.1672 L
(d) 5.6 L

138. When a quantity of electricity is passed through $CuSO_4$ solution, 0.16 g of copper gets deposited. If the same quantity of electricity is passed through acidulated water, then the volume of H_2 gas liberated at S.T.P. will be (Given atomic weight of Cu = 64)
(a) $40 \ cm^3$
(b) $56 \ cm^3$
(c) $604 \ cm^3$
(d) $80 \ cm^3$

139. The equivalent conductance at infinite dilution of HCl and NaCl are 426.15 and 126.15 ohm cm^2 g equ^{-1} respectively. It can be said that the mobility of ......
(a) H^+ ions is much more than that of Cl^- ions
(b) Cl^- ions is much more than that of H^+ ions
(c) H^+ ions is much more than that of Na^+ ions
(d) Na^+ ions is much more than that of H^+ ions

140. When a strip of copper is dipped in a solution of ferrous sulphate ......
(a) Iron is deposited on the copper strip
(b) Copper is precipitated
(c) Copper dissolves
(d) No reaction occurs

141. For a spontaneous reaction G, equilibrium constant, K and E^o_{cell} will be respectively ......
(a) –ve, > 1, + ve
(b) + ve, > 1, + eV
(c) –ve, < 1, –ve
(d) –ve, > 1, –ve

142. The amount of substance deposited by the passage of 1 amp current for 1 second is equal to ......
(a) Equivalent mass
(b) Molecular mass
(c) Electrochemical equivalent
(d) Specific equivalent

143. Given the limiting molar conductivities

λ^o_m (HCl) = 425.9 Ω^{-1} cm^2 mol^{-1}

λ^o_m (NaCl) = 126.4 Ω^{-1} cm^2 mol^{-1}

λ^o_m (CH_3COONa) = 91 Ω^{-1} mol^{-1}

The molar conductivity of acetic acid at infinite dilution (in Ω^{-1} cm^2 mol) will be ......
(a) 481.5
(b) 390.5
(c) 299.5
(d) 561.9

PREVIOUS YEAR'S QUESTIONS

1. The weight of silver (atomic weight = 108) displaced by a quantity of electricity which displaces 5600 ml is ......
(a) 54 g
(b) 108 g
(c) 5.4 g
(d) 10.8 g

2. Weight of O_2 at STP will be ......   **[AIPMT 2014]**
(a) 54.0 g
(b) 108.0 g
(c) 5.4 g
(d) 10.8 g

3. A hydrogen gas electrode is made by dipping platinum wire in a solution of HCl of pH = 10 and by passing hydrogen gas around the platinum wire at one atm pressure. The oxidation potential of electrode would be ......   **[NEET 2013]**
(a) 0.059 V
(b) 0.59 V
(c) 0.118 V
(d) 1.18 V

4. At 25°C, molar conductance of 0.1 molar aqueous solution of ammonium hydroxide is 9.54 ohm^{-1} cm^2 mol^{-1} and at infinite dilution its molar conductance is 238 ohm^{-1} cm^2 mol^{-1}. The degree of ionisation of ammonium hydroxide at the same concentration and temperature is ...... **[NEET 2013]**

(a) 2.080%   (b) 20.800%   (c) 4.008%   (d) 40.800%

5. A button cell used in watches functions as follows: **[NEET 2013]**

$$Zn_{(s)} + Ag_2O_{(s)} + H_2O_{(l)} \rightleftharpoons 2Ag_{(s)} + Zn^{2+}_{(aq)} + 2OH^-_{(aq)}$$

If half cell potentials are

$$Zn^{2+}_{(aq)} + 2e \rightarrow Zn_{(s)};\ E° = -0.76\ V$$

$$Ag_2O_{(s)} + H_2O_{(l)} + 2e^- \rightarrow 2Ag_{(s)} + 2OH^-_{(aq)};\ E° = 0.34\ V$$

The cell potential will be ......

(a) 1.10 V   (b) 0.42 V   (c) 0.84 V   (d) 1.34 V

6. Molar conductivities (λ_m) at infinite dilution of NaCl, HCl and CH$_3$COONa are 126.4, 425.9 and 91.0 S cm^2 mol^{-1} respectively. λ_m for CH$_3$COOH will be ...... **[AIPMT 2012]**

(a) 290.8 S cm^2 mol^{-1} (b) 390.5 S cm^2 mol^{-1}

(c) 425.5 S cm^2 mol^{-1} (d) 180.5 S cm^2 mol^{-1}

7. A solution contains Fe^{2+}, Fe^{3+} and I$^-$ ions. This solution was treated with iodine at 35°C, E° for Fe^{3+}/Fe^{2+} is +0.77 V and E° for I$_2$/2I$^-$ is 0.536 V. The favourable reaction is ......

[AIPMT Mains]

(a) I$_2$ will be reduced to I$^-$ (b) There will be no redox reaction

(c) I$^-$ will be oxidised to I$_2$ (d) Fe^{3+} will be oxidised to Fe^{2+}

8. One gram of silver gets distributed between 10 cm^3 of molten zinc and 100 cm^3 of molten lead at 800°C. The percentage of silver still left in the lead layer is approximately ......

(a) 2   (b) 5   (c) 3   (d) 1   **[KCET 2011]**

9. An increase in equivalent conductance of a strong electrolyte with dilution is mainly due to ...... **[CBSE AIPMT 2010]**

(a) increase in number of ions.

(b) increase in ionic mobility of ions.

(c) 100% ionisation of electrolyte at normal dilution.

(d) increase in both i.e., number of ions and ionic mobility of ions.

10. At 18°C, the conductance of H$^+$ and CH$_3$COO$^-$ at infinite dilution are 315 and 35 mho cm^2 eq^{-1} respectively. The equivalent conductivity of CH$_3$COOH at infinite dilution is.... mho cm^2 eq^{-1}

[AFMC 2010]

(a) 350   (b) 280   (c) 30   (d) 315

11. 1 C electricity deposits **[MHT CET 2010]**

(a) 10.8 g of Ag

(b) 96500 g of Ag

(c) electrochemical equivalent of Ag

(d) half of electrochemical equivalent of Ag

12. In electrolysis of dil. H_2SO_4 using platinum electrodes ...... **[BVP 2010]**
(a) H_2 is evolved at cathode
(b) SO_2 is produced at anode
(c) O_2 is obtained at cathode
(d) SO_2 is produced at cathode

13. Al_2O_3 is reduced by electrolysis at low potentials and high current. If 4.0×10^4 amperes of current is passed through molten Al_2O_3 for 6 h, what mass of aluminium is produced? (Assume 100% current efficiency, atomic weight of Al = 27). **[CBSE AIPMT 2009]**
(a) 9.0×10^3 g
(b) 8×10^4 g
(c) 2.4×10^3 g
(d) 1.3×10^4 g

14. Assertion : On dilution, the equivalent as well as conductivity of solution increases.
Reasons : With dilution, the number of current carrying particles per cm^3 increase.
(a) Both Assertion and Reason are true and Reason is the correct explanation of Assertion.
(b) Both Assertion and Reason are true but Reason is not the correct explanation of Assertion.
(c) Assertion is true but Reason is false.
(d) Both Assertion and Reason are false

15. An aqueous solution containing 6.5 g of NaCl of 90% purity was subjected to electrolysis. After complete electrolysis, the solution was evaporated to get solid NaOH. The volume of 1 M acetic acid required to neutralize NaOH obtained above is ...... **[KCET 2009]**
(a) $2000 \ cm^3$
(b) $100 \ cm^3$
(c) $200 \ cm^2$
(d) $1000 \ cm^3$

16. At 25°C, the molar conductances at infinite dilution for the strong electrolytes NaOH, NaCl and $BaCl_2$ are 248×10^{-4}, 126×10^{-4} and $280 \times 10^{-4} \ Sm^2 \ mol^{-1}$ respectively. **[EAMCET 2009]**
(a) 52.4×10^{-4}
(b) 524×10^{-4}
(c) 402×10^{-4}
(d) 262×10^{-4}

17. Copper is a divalent metal. The value of its electrochemical equivalent is 3.29×10^{-4} gm.
(a) 31.74 g
(b) 63.5 g
(c) 126.9 g
(d) 15.87 g

18. 4.5 g of aluminium (atomic mass 27 u) is deposited at cathode from a molten electrolyte containing Al^3 ions by a certain quantity of electric charge. The volume of hydrogen produced at STP from H^+ ions in a solution by the same quantity of electric charge will be ...... **[Manipal 2009]**
(a) 44.8 L
(b) 11.2 L
(c) 22.4 L
(d) 5.6 L

19. How many coulombs of electricity are required for the reduction of 1 mol of MnO_4 to Mn^{2+} ? **[Manipal 2009]**
(a) 96500 C
(b) 9.65×10^6 C
(c) 4.83×10^5 C
(d) 1.93×10^5 C

20. Kohlrausch's law states that at ...... **[BSSE AIPMT 2008]**
(a) finite dilution, each ion makes definite contribution to the equivalent conductance of an electrolyte, whatever may be the nature of the other ion of the electrolyte.
(b) infinite dilution, each ion makes definite contribution to equivalent conductance of an electrolyte depending on the nature of the other ion of the electrolyte.
(c) infinite dilution, each ion makes definite contribution to conductance of an electrolyte whatever be the nature of the other ion of the electrolyte.
(d) infinite dilution, each ion makes definite contribution to equivalent conductance of an electrolyte, whatever be the nature of the other ion of the electrolyte.

21. What is the time (in sec) required for depositing all the silver present in 125 mL of 1 M $AgNO_3$ solution by passing a current of 241.25 A ? (1 F = 96500 C)   **[AFMC 2008]**

    (a) 10   (b) 50   (c) 1000   (d) 100

22. Which one of the following reaction occurs at the cathode?   **[MHT CET 2008]**

    (a) $20H^- \rightarrow H_2O + \dfrac{1}{2}O_2 + 2e^-$ (b) $Ag \rightarrow Ag^+ + e^-$

    (c) $Fe^{2+} \rightarrow Fe^{3+} + e^-$ (d) $Cu^{2+} + 2e^- \rightarrow Cu$

23. A current of 96.5 A is passed for 18 min between nickel electrodes in 500 mL solution 2 M $NI(NO_3)_2$. The molarity of solution after electrolysis would be ......   **[AIIMS 2007]**

    (a) 0.46 M   (b) 0.92 M   (c) 0.625 M   (d) 1.25 M

24. **Assertion :** According to Kohlrausch's law the molar conductivity of a strong electrolyte at infinite dilution is sum of molar conductivities of its ions.

    Reasons : The current carried by cation and anion is always at equilibrium.   **[AIIMS 2007]**

    (a) Both Assertion and Reason are true and Reason is the correct explanation of Assertion.

    (b) Both Assertion and Reason are true but Reason is not the correct explanation of Assertion.

    (c) Assertion is true but Reason is false.

    (d) Both Assertion and Reason are false

25. **Assertion :** In the electrolysis of equeous NaCl, Na is preferentially discharged at mercury cathode forming sodium amalgam.

    Reason : It is due to the fact that hydrogen has a high over voltage at mercury cathode.

    [AIIMS 2007]

    (a) Both Assertion and Reason are true and Reason is the correct explanation of Assertion.

    (b) Both Assertion and Reason are true but Reason is not the correct explanation of Assertion.

    (c) Assertion is true but Reason is false.

    (d) Both Assertion and Reason are false

26. If the E^o_{cell} for a given reaction has a negative value, then which of the following gives the correct relationships for the value of ΔG° and K_{eq} ?   **[CBSE AIPMT 2011]**

    (a) $\Delta G^\circ > 0; K_{eq} < 1$ (b) $\Delta G^\circ > 0; K_{eq} > 1$ (c) $\Delta G^\circ < 0; K_{eq} > 1$ (d) $\Delta G^\circ < 0; K_{eq} < 1$

27. The electrode potentials for $Cu^{2+}_{(aq)} + e \rightarrow Cu^+_{(aq)}$ and $Cu^{2+}_{(aq)} + e^- \rightarrow Cu_{(s)}$ are + 0.15 V and + 0.50 V respectively. The value of $E^o_{Cu^{+2}/Cu}$ will be ......   **[CBSE AIPMT 2011]**

    (a) 0.150 V   (b) 0.500 V   (c) 0.325 V   (d) 0.650 V

28. Standard electrode potential of three metals X, Y and Z are –1.2 V, +0.5 V and –3.0 V respectively. The reducing power of these metals will be ......   **[CBSE AIPMT 2011]**

    (a) X > Y > Z   (b) Y > Z > X   (c) Y > X > Z   (d) Z > X > Y

29. Standard electrode potential for Sn^{4+}/Sn^{2+} couple is +0.15 V and that for Cr^{3+}/Cr couple is –0.74 V. These two couples in their standard state are connected to make a cell. The cell potentials will be ......   **[CBSE AIPMT 2011]**

    (a) +1.83 V   (b) +1.19 V   (c) +0.89 V   (d) +0.18 V

30. Given the following reactions involving A, B, C and D **[DPMT 2011]**

(i) $C + B^+ \rightarrow C^+ + B$

(ii) $A^- + D \rightarrow$ No reaction

(iii) $C + A \rightarrow$ No reaction

(iv) $D + B^+ \rightarrow D^+ + B$

The correct arrangement of A, B, C, D in the order of their decreasing ability as reducing agent

(a) $D > B > C > A$ (b) $A > C > D > B$ (c) $C > A > B > D$ (d) $C > A > D > A$

31. For the reduction of silver ions with copper metal, the standard cell potential was found to be +0.46 V at 25°C. The value of standard Gibbs energy, ΔG° will be (F = 96500 C mol^{-1})

[CBSE AIPMT 2010]

(a) −98.0 kJ   (b) −89.0 kJ   (c) −89.0 J   (d) −44.5 kJ

32. For Sn^{4+}/Sn^{2+}, standard reduction potential is 0.15 V and for Au/Au, standard reduction potential is 1.5 V. For the reaction $3Sn^{2+} + 2Au^{3+} \rightarrow 3Sn^{4+} + 2Au$, the value of E^o_{cell} is ......

[MHT CET 2010]

(a) +1.35   (b) +2.55   (c) −1.35   (d) −2.55

33. Given : **[CBSE AIPMT, AMU 2009]**

(i) $Cu^{2+} + 2e^- \rightarrow Cu$

(ii) $E^\circ = 0.337$ V

(iii) $Cu^{2+} + 2e^- \rightarrow Cu^+$

(iv) $E^\circ = 0.153$ V

Electrode potential E° for the reaction $Cu^+ + e^- \rightarrow Cu$, will be ......

(a) 0.52 V   (b) 0.90 V   (c) 0.30 V   (d) 0.38 V

34. Given, $Pb^{2+}/Pb = -0.126$ V; $Zn^{2+}/Zn = -0.763$ V. Find the emf of the following cell

$Zn|Zn^{2+}$ (0.1 M) $||$ Pb^{2+} (1 M) $|$ Pb. **[AFMC 2009]**

(a) −0.537   (b) +0.637   (c) > 0.637   (d) +0.889

35. The reduction potential at pH = 14 for the Cu^{2+}/Cu couple is ......

[Given : $E^o_{Cu^{2+}/Cu} = 0.34$ V; K_{sp} [Cu(OH)$_2$] = 1×10^{-19}]

(a) 0.34 V   (b) −0.34 V   (c) 0.22 V   (d) −0.22

36. E° for $Mg^{2+}/Mg = -237$ V, $Zn^{2+}/Zn = 0.76$ V and $Fe^{2+}/Fe = -0.44$ V. Which statement is correct? **[CPMT 2009]**

(a) Zn reduces Fe^{2+} (b) Zn reduces Mg^{2+} (c) Mg oxidises Fe   (d) Zn oxidises Fe

37. On the basis of the following E° values, the strongest oxidising agent is ......

[CBSE AIPMT 2008]

$[Fe(CN)_6]^{4-} \rightarrow [Fe(CN)_6]^{2-} + e^-;\ E^\circ = -0.35$ V

$Fe^{2+} \rightarrow Fe^{3+} + e^-;\ E^\circ = -0.77$ V

(a) $[Fe(CN)_6]^{4-}$ (b) Fe^{2+} (c) Fe^{3+} (d) $[Fe(CN)_6]^{3-}$

38. $Cu^+_{(aq)}$ is unstable in solution and undergoes simultaneous oxidation and reduction, according to the reaction $2Cu^+_{(aq)} \rightarrow Cu^{2+}_{(aq)} + Cu_{(s)}$, choose the correct E° for the above reaction if **[MHTCET 2008]**

$E^o_{Cu^{2+}|Cu} = 0.34$ V and $E^o_{Cu^{2+}|Cu^+} = 0.15$ V

(a) −0.38 V   (b) +0.49 V   (c) +0.38 V   (d) −0.19 V

39. EMF of hydrogen electrode in terms of pH is (at 1 tm pressure) ...... **[MHTCET 207]**

(a) $E_{H_2} = \dfrac{RT}{F} \, pH$

(b) $E_{H_2} = \dfrac{RT}{F} \dfrac{1}{pH}$

(c) $E_{H_2} = \dfrac{2.303 \, RT}{F} \, pH$

(d) $E_{H_2} = -0.0592 \, pH$

40. A hypothetical electrochemical cell in the reaction is ...... **[CBSE AIFMT 2006]**

$A|A^+ (xM) \| B^+ (yM)|B$

The emf measured is +0.20 V. The cell reaction is ......

(a) $A^+ + B \rightarrow A + B^+$

(b) $A^+ + e^- \rightarrow A; \, B^+ + e^- \rightarrow B$

(c) the cell reaction cannot be predicted

(d) $A + B^+ \rightarrow A^+ + B$

41. **Assertion :** Copper metal gets readily corroded in an acidic aqueous solution.

Reason : Free energy change for this process is positive **[AIIMS 2004]**

(a) Both Assertion and Reason are true and Reason is the correct explanation of Assertion.

(b) Both Assertion and Reason are true but Reason is not the correct explanation of Assertion.

(c) Assertion is true but Reason is false.

(d) Both Assertion and Reason are false

42. For the following cell with hydrogen electrode at two different pressures p_1 and p_2

[MHT CET 2004]

(a) $\dfrac{RT}{F} \log_e \dfrac{p_1}{p_2}$

(b) $\dfrac{RT}{2F} \log_e \dfrac{p_1}{p_2}$

(c) $\dfrac{RT}{F} \log_e \dfrac{p_2}{p_1}$

(d) $\dfrac{RT}{2F} \log_e \dfrac{p_2}{p_1}$

43. On the basis of information available from the reaction

$\dfrac{4}{3} Al + O_2 \rightarrow \dfrac{2}{3} Al_2O_3$, $\Delta G = -827$ kJ mol^{-1} of O_2, the minimum emf required to carry out an electrolysis of Al_2O_3 is (F = 96500 C mol^{-1}) ...... **[CBSE AIPMT 2003]**

(a) 6.42 V　　　(b) 8.56 V　　　(c) 2.14 V　　　(d) 4.28 V

44. Which of the following statement is true for the electrochemical Daniell cell?

(a) Electrons flow from copper electrode to zinc electrode.

(b) Current flows from copper electrode to copper electrode.

(c) Cations move towards copper electrode

(d) Cations move towards zinc electrode **[Manipal 2010]**

45. Standard free energies of formation (in kJ/mol) at K are − 237.2, −394.4 and −8.2 for $H_2O(l)$, $CO_2(g)$ and pentane (g) respectively. The value of E^o_{cell} for the pentane-oxygen fuel cell is ...... **[CBSE AIPMT 2008]**

(a) 1.968 V　　　(b) 2.0968 V　　　(c) 1.0968 V　　　(d) 0.0968 V

46. **Assertion :** The cell potential of mercury cell is 1.35 V, which remains constant.

Reasons : In mercury cell, the electrolyte is a paste of KOH and ZnO.

(a) Both Assertion and Reason are true and Reason is the correct explanation of Assertion.

(b) Both Assertion and Reason are true but Reason is not the correct explanation of Assertion.

(c) Assertion is true but Reason is false.

(d) Both Assertion and Reason are false **[AIIMS 2008]**

47. The efficiency of a fuel cell is given by ...... **[CBSE AIPMT 2007]**

(a) $\dfrac{\Delta H}{\Delta G}$ (b) $\dfrac{\Delta G}{\Delta S}$ (c) $\dfrac{\Delta G}{\Delta H}$ (d) $\dfrac{\Delta S}{\Delta G}$

48. When lead storage battery is charged ...... **[AFMC 2005]**
(a) lead dioxide dissolves
(b) sulphuric acid is regenerated
(c) the lead electrode becomes coated with lead sulphate
(d) the amount of sulphuric acid decreases.

49. When an acid cell is charged then ...... **[AFMC 2005]**
(a) voltage of cell increases (b) electrolyte of cell dilutes
(c) resistance of cell increases (d) none of these

50. The chemical reaction, $2AgCl_2 + H_{2(g)} \rightarrow 2HCl_{(aq)} + 2Ag_{(s)}$ taking place in a Galvanic cell is represented by the notation ...... **[AIIMS 2005]**
(a) $Pt(s) \mid H_2(g), 1 \text{ bar} \parallel 1 \text{ M KCl (aq)} \parallel AgCl(s) \mid Ag(s)$
(b) $Pt(s) \mid H_2(g), 1 \text{ bar} \parallel 2 \text{ M KCl (aq)} \parallel 1 \text{ M Ag}^+ \text{ (aq)} \mid Ag(s)$
(c) $Pt(s) \mid H_2(g), 1 \text{ bar} \parallel 1 \text{ M KCl (aq)} \parallel AgCl \text{ (s)} \mid Ag(s)$
(d) $Pt(s) \mid H_2(g), 1 \text{ bar} \parallel 1 \text{ M KCl (aq)} \parallel Ag(s) \mid AgCl(s)$

51. Assertion : Galvansied iron does not rust. **[AIIMS 2005]**
Reason : Zinc has a more negative electrode potential than iron.
(a) Both Assertion and Reason are true and Reason is the correct explanation of Assertion.
(b) Both Assertion and Reason are true but Reason is not the correct explanation of Assertion.
(c) Assertion is true but Reason is false.
(d) Both Assertion and Reason are false

52. Which of the following reaction is used to make a fuel cell? **[AIIMS 2003]**
(a) $Cd(s) + 2Ni(OH)_3(s) \rightarrow CdO(s) + 2Ni(OH)_2(s) + H_2O(l)$
(b) $Pb(s) + PbO_2(s) + 2H_2SO_4(aq) \rightarrow 2PbSO_4(s) + 2H_2O(l)$
(c) $2H_2(g) + O_2(g) \rightarrow 2H_2O(l)$
(d) $2Fe(s) + O_2(g) + 4H^+(aq) \rightarrow 2Fe^{2+}(aq) + 2H_2O(l)$

53. Zinc gives H_2 with H_2SO_4 and HCl but not with HNO_3 because ...... **[C.B.S.E. P.M.T. 2002]**
(a) Zinc acts as oxidising agent when it reacts with HNO_3
(b) HNO_3 is a weaker acid than H_2SO_4 and HCl
(c) In electrochemical series, zinc is above hydrogen
(d) NO_3^- is reduced in preference to hydronium ion

54. During electrolysis of a solution of $AgNO_3$, 96500 coulombs of charge pass through the electroplating bath, the mass of silver deposited on the cathode will be ... **[A.I.P.M.T. 2003]**
(a) 1.08 g (b) 10.8 g (c) 21.6 g (d) 108 g

55. Which of the following reactions is used to make a fuel cell? **[A.I.M.S. 2003]**
(a) $Cd_{(s)} + 2Ni(OH)_{3(s)} \rightarrow CuO_{(s)} + 2Ni(OH)_{2(s)} + H_2O_{(l)}$
(b) $Pb_{(s)} + PbO_{2(s)} + 2H_2SO_{4(aq)} \rightarrow 2PbSO_{4(s)} + 2H_2O_{(l)}$
(c) $2H_{2(g)} + O_{2(g)} \rightarrow 2H_2O_{(l)}$
(d) $2Fe_{(s)} + O_{2(g)} + 4H^+_{(aq)} \rightarrow 2Fe^{2+}_{(aq)} + 2H_2O_{(l)}$

56. Which of the following (1M) conducts more electricity? **[A.F.M.C. 2003]**

    (a) Sulphuric acid   (b) Boric acid   (c) Nitric acid   (d) Phosphorus acid

57. Specific conductivity of a solution ...... **[J & K Med. 2004]**

    (a) Increases with dilution   (b) Decreases with dilution

    (c) Remains unchanged with dilution   (d) Depends on mass of electrolyte

58. How many coulombs of electricity are required for the reduction of 1 mol of MnO_4 to Mn^{2+} ? **[Kerala Med. 2005]**

    (a) 96500 C   (b) 1.93×10^5 C   (c) 4.83×10^5 C   (d) 9.66×10^6 C

    (e) 5.62×10^5 C

59. The electrical resistance of a column of 0.04 M NaOH solution of diameter 1.2 cm and length 50 cm is 5.55×10^3 ohm, The resistivity of the column would be ... **[H.P.P.M.T. 2005]**

    (a) 125.47 ohm cm   (b) 120.47 ohm cm   (c) 102.47 ohm cm   (d) 12.547 ohm cm

60. If Zn^{2+}/Zn electrode is diluted to 100 times, then the change in reduction potential is ......

    [D.P.M.T. 2005]

    (a) Increase of 59 mV   (b) Decrease of 59 mV

    (c) Increase of 25.5 mV   (d) Decrease of 2.95 mV

61. If the molar conductance value of Ca^{2+} and Cl at infinite dilution are respectively 118.88×10^{-4} m^2 ohm mol^{-1} and 77.33×10^{-4} m^2 ohm mol^{-1}, then that of $CaCl_2$ is (in m^2 ohm mol^{-1}) ...... **[Vellore 2007]**

    (a) 118.88×10^{-4} (b) 154.66×10^{-4} (c) 273.54×10^{-4} (d) 196.21×10^{-4}

62. How many moles of Pt may be deposited on the cathode when 0.80 F of electricity is passed through 1.0 M solution of Pt^{4+} ? **[Kerala P.M.T. 2010]**

    (a) 1.0 mol   (b) 0.20 mol   (c) 0.4 mol   (d) 0.80 mol

    (e) 0.60 mol

63. Consider the following four electrodes

    $P = Cu^{2+}$ (0.0001 M)/$Cu_{(s)}$, $Q = Cu^{2+}$ (0.1 M)/$Cu_{(s)}$, $R = Cu^{2+}$ (0.01 M)/$Cu_{(s)}$

    $S = Cu^{2+}$ (0.001 M)/$Cu_{(s)}$

    If the standard electrode potential of Cu^{2+}/Cu is 0.34 V, the reduction potentials in volts of the above electrodes follow the order ...... **[Kerala P.M.T. 2010]**

    (a) P > S > R > Q   (b) S > R > Q > P   (c) R > S > Q > P   (d) Q > R > S > P

64. Best way to prevent rusting of iron is by ...... **[D.P.M.T. 2000]**

    (a) Making iron cathode   (b) Putting it in saline water

    (c) Both of these   (d) None of these

65. At infinite dilution, the aqueous solution of $BaCl_2$, molar conductivity of Ba^{2+} and Cl^- ions are 127.32 S cm^2/mol and 76.34 S cm^2/mol respectively. What is $\wedge_m^\infty$ for $BaCl_2$ at same dilution ? **[C.B.S.E. 2000]**

    (a) 280 S cm^2 mol^{-1} (b) 330.98 S cm^2 mol^{-1}

    (c) 90.98 S cm^2 mol^{-1} (d) 203.6 S cm^2 mol^{-1}

66. Standard electrode potentials are **[C.B.S.E. 2001]**

    Fe^{2+}/Fe (E° = – 0.44), Fe^{3+}/Fe^{2+} (E° = 0.77)

    Fe^{2+}, Fe^{3+} and Fe blocks are kept together, then ......

    (a) Fe^{3+} increases   (b) Fe^{3+} decreases

    (c) Fe^{2+}/Fe^{3+} remains unchanged   (d) Fe^{2+} decreases

67. Molar conductivity of a solution is $1.26 \times 10^2 \; \Omega^{-1} \; cm^2 \; mol^{-1}$. Its molarity is 0.01. Its specific conductivity will be ...... **[Manipal P.M.T. 2002]**

 (a) 1.26×10^{-25} (b) 1.26×10^{-3} (c) 1.26×10^{-4} (d) 0.0063

68. Molar ionic conductivities of a bivalent electrolyte are 57 and 73. The molar conductivity of the solution will be ...... **[D.P.M.T. 2002]**

 (a) $130 \; S \; cm^2 \; mol^{-1}$ (b) $65 \; S \; cm^2 \; mol^{-1}$ (c) $260 \; S \; cm^2 \; mol^{-1}$ (d) $187 \; S \; cm^2 \; mol^{-1}$

ANSWER KEY

1.	2. (a)	3. (a)	4. (c)	5. (b)	6. (c)	7. (b)	8. (c)
9. (c)	10. (c)	11. (b)	12. (b)	13. (a)	14. (d)	15. (a)	16. (b)
17. (c)	18. (c)	19. (c)	20. (d)	21. (b)	22. (c)	23. (b)	24. (d)
25. (c)	26. (a)	27. (b)	28. (d)	29. (c)	30. (b)	31. (b)	32. (b)
33. (c)	34. (a)	35. (c)	36. (d)	37. (a)	38. (b)	39. (c)	40. (d)
41. (a)	42. (c)	43. (a)	44. (b)	45. (b)	46. (b)	47. (d)	48. (c)
49. (c)	50. (a)	51. (c)	52. (d)	53. (a)	54. (b)	55. (c)	56. (a)
57. (c)	58. (c)	59. (a)	60. (a)	61. (d)	62. (a)	63. (c)	64. (d)
65. (a)	66. (b)	67. (d)	68. (b)	69. (c)	70. (d)	71. (a)	72. (c)
73. (b)	74. (d)	75. (b)	76. (c)	77. (b)	78. (b)	79. (b)	80. (a)
81. (a)	82. (b)	83. (c)	84. (a)	85. (c)	86. (a)	87. (d)	88. (b)
89. (c)	90. (c)	91. (b)	92. (c)	93. (b)	94. (a)	95. (b)	96. (a)
97. (d)	98. (b)	99. (a)	100. (c)	101. (b)	102. (d)	103. (a)	104. (b)
105. (b)	106. (a)	107. (a)	108. (c)	109. (b)	110. (b)	111. (c)	112. (a)
113. (b)	114. (c)	115. (d)	116. (a)	117. (c)	118. (b)	119. (c)	120. (a)
121. (d)	122. (d)	123. (d)	124. (d)	125. (b)	126. (c)	127. (c)	128. (d)
129. (b)	130. (a)	131. (c)	132. (a)	133. (c)	134. (a)	135. (b)	136. (b)
137. (a)	138. (b)	139. (c)	140. (d)	141. (a)	142. (c)	143. (b)	

Previous Year's Questions

1. (b)	2. (b)	3. (b)	4. (c)	5. (a)	6. (b)	7. (c)	8. (c)
9. (b)	10. (a)	11. (c)	12. (a)	13. (b)	14. (c)	15. (b)	16. (b)
17. (b)	18. (d)	19. (c)	20. (d)	21. (b)	22. (d)	23. (b)	24. (c)
25. (a)	26. (a)	27. (c)	28. (d)	29. (c)	30. (d)	31. (b)	32. (a)
33. (a)	34. (c)	35. (d)	36. (a)	37. (c)	38. (c)	39. (d)	40. (d)
41. (d)	42. (b)	43. (c)	44. (c)	45. (c)	46. (b)	47. (c)	48. (b)
49. (a)	50. (b)	51. (a)	52. (c)	53. d)	54. (b)	55. (c)	56. (a)
57. (b)	58. (c)	59. (a)	60. (b)	61. (c)	62. (b)	63. (d)	64. (a)
65. (a)	66. (b)	67. (b)	68. (a)				

CHEMICAL KINETICS

1. The speed of a chemical reaction ......
   (a) Is constant no matter what the temperature is
   (b) Is independent of the amount of contact surface of a solid involved
   (c) Between gases should in all cases be extremely rapid because the average kinetic energy of the molecules is great
   (d) Between ions in aqueous solution is extremely rapid because there are no bonds that need to be broken

2. Rate constants usually ......
   (a) Decrease with time
   (b) Increase with time
   (c) Decrease with temperature
   (d) Increase with temperature

3. Of the following, all units are valid for a reaction rate except _________.
   (a) Mol/L
   (b) M/s
   (c) Mol/hr
   (d) g.s

4. The overall kinetics of a reaction is governed by ......
   (a) The main reaction
   (b) Slowest step in the reaction scheme
   (c) Fastest step in the reaction scheme
   (d) The step involving the maximum number of reacting species.

5. Collision theory states that ......
   (a) All collisions lead to chemical reactions
   (b) Most collisions lead to chemical reactions
   (c) Very few reactions involve particle collisions
   (d) Effective collisions lead to chemical reactions

6. The rate of reaction increases with temperature according to the collision theory due to ...
   (a) Greater number of collisions
   (b) Greater velocity of reacting molecules
   (c) Greater number of molecules having activation energy
   (d) None of these

7. The number of collisions depend upon ......
   (a) Pressure
   (b) Concentration
   (c) Temperature
   (d) All of these

8. According to collision theory, not all collisions between molecules lead to reaction. Which of the following statements provide reasons why this is so?
   (1) The total energy of the two colliding molecules is less than some minimum amount of energy
   (2) Molecules cannot react with each other unless a catalyst is present
   (3) Molecules that are improperly oriented during collision will not react
   (4) Molecules in different states of matter cannot react with each other
   (a) 1 and 3
   (b) 2 and 3
   (c) 1 and 4
   (d) 3 and 4

9. In the collision theory of reaction rates, which of the following accounts most for the observed temperature dependence?

    (a) As temperature increases the rate of collisions between reacting molecules decreases

    (b) In order for reaction to result from a collision, there is some minimum energy the colliding molecules must possess

    (c) There are many collisions in which the molecules are not properly oriented to result in the reaction

    (d) The electrons in the reacting molecules are moving faster at higher temperatures

10. When the concentration of reactant molecules is increased, the rate of reaction increases. The best explanation is: As the reactant concentration increases ......

    (a) The average kinetic energy of molecules increases

    (b) The frequency of molecular collisions increases

    (c) The rate constant increases

    (d) The activation energy increases

11. Which of the following statements is correct?

    (a) The rate of a reaction decreases with passage of time as the concentration of reactants decreases

    (b) The rate of a reaction is same at any time during the reaction

    (c) The rate of a reaction is independent of temperature change

    (d) The rate of a reaction decreases with increase in concentration of reactant(s)

12. The rate of disappearance of HBr in the gas phase reaction

$$2HBr_{(g)} \rightarrow H_{2(g)} + Br_{2(g)}$$

    is 0.301 Ms^{-1} at $150°C$. The rate of appearance of Br_2 is _________ Ms^{-1}.

    (a) 1.66　　　　(b) 0.151　　　　(c) 0.0906　　　　(d) 0.602

13. Which of the statements concerning relative rates of reaction is correct for the decomposition of dinitrogen pentoxide?

$$2N_2O_{5(g)} \rightarrow 4\,NO_{2(g)} + O_{2(g)}$$

    (a) The rate of disappearance of N_2O_5 is 1/2 the rate of appearance of O_2

    (b) The rate of appearance of NO_2 is 1/4 the rate of appearance of O_2

    (c) The rate of disappearance of N_2O_5 is 1/2 the rate of appearance of NO_2

    (d) The rate of appearance of NO_2 equals the rate of appearance of O_2 i.e. the rate of disappearance of N_2O_5 equals the rate of appearance of NO_2

14. The half lives of two samples are 0.1 and 0.4 seconds. The initial concentrations are 200 ml and 50 ml respectively. What is the order of the reaction ?

    (a) 4　　　　(b) 0　　　　(c) 1　　　　(d) 2

15. Half-life period of a first order reaction is 10 min. Starting with 10 M, rate after 20 minutes is ......

    (a) 0.693×5.5 M min^{-1}　　　　(b) 0.00693×2.5 M min^{-1}

    (c) 0.0693×2.5 M min^{-1}　　　　(d) 0.693×5 M min^{-1}

16. The combustion of ethane (C_2H_6) is represented by the equation:

$$2C_2H_{6(g)} + 7O_{2(g)} \rightarrow 4CO_{2(g)} + 6H_2O_{(l)}$$

In this reaction :

(a) The rate of consumption of ethane is seven times faster than the rate of consumption of oxygen

(b) The rate of formation of CO_2 equals the rate of formation of water

(c) Water is formed at a rate equal to two-thirds the rate of formation of CO_2

(d) CO_2 is formed twice as fast as ethane is consumed

17. If $3A \rightarrow 2B$ then the rate of reaction of $+\dfrac{d(B)}{dt}$ is equal to ......

(a) $+2\dfrac{d(A)}{dt}$ 　　(b) $-\dfrac{1}{3}\dfrac{d(A)}{dt}$ 　　(c) $-\dfrac{2}{3}\dfrac{d(A)}{dt}$ 　　(d) $-\dfrac{3}{2}\dfrac{d(A)}{dt}$

18. The differential rate law for the reaction $H_2 + I_2 \rightarrow 2HI$ is ......

(a) $-\dfrac{d[H_2]}{dt} = -\dfrac{d[I_2]}{dt} = +\dfrac{1}{2}\dfrac{d[HI]}{dt}$ 　　(b) $\dfrac{d[H_2]}{dt} = \dfrac{d[HI]}{dt} = \dfrac{1}{2}\dfrac{d[HI]}{dt}$

(c) $\dfrac{1}{2}\dfrac{d[H_2]}{dt} = \dfrac{1}{2}\dfrac{d[I_2]}{dt} = -\dfrac{d[HI]}{dt}$ 　　(d) $-2\dfrac{d[H_2]}{dt} = -2\dfrac{d[I_2]}{dt} = +\dfrac{d[HI]}{dt}$

19. Which of the following expressions correctly describes the relationship between the rates at which NO_2 and Cl_2 are consumed in the reaction below?

$$2NO_{2(g)} + Cl_{2(g)} \rightarrow 2\,NO_2Cl_{(g)}$$

(a) $\dfrac{-\Delta(NO_2)}{\Delta t} = -\dfrac{1}{2}\left[\dfrac{\Delta(Cl_2)}{\Delta t}\right]$ 　　(b) $\dfrac{-\Delta(NO_2)}{\Delta t} = 2\left[\dfrac{\Delta(Cl_2)}{\Delta t}\right]$

(c) $\dfrac{-\Delta(NO_2)}{\Delta t} = \dfrac{1}{2}\left[\dfrac{\Delta(Cl_2)}{\Delta t}\right]$ 　　(d) $\dfrac{-\Delta(NO_2)}{\Delta t} = \left[\dfrac{-\Delta(Cl_2)}{\Delta t}\right]$

20. Consider the reaction : $3A + B + 2C \rightarrow D + 2E$

The rate law for this reaction is $k[A][B]^2$

Doubling the concentration of A increases the rate of the reaction by a factor of ......

(a) 2 　　　　(b) 3 　　　　(c) 4 　　　　(d) 9

21. A reaction has a rate constant of 0.01 mol L^{-1} min^{-1}.

(a) The reaction is second order 　　　　(b) The reaction is first order

(c) The reaction is zero order 　　　　(d) None of these

22. A large increase in the rate of a reaction for a rise in temperature is due to ......

(a) The decrease in number of collisions

(b) The increase in number of activated molecules

(c) The shortening of mean free path

(d) The lowering of the activation energy

23. What is the order of a reaction which has a rate expression, rate $= k[A]^{3/2}[B]^{-1}$?

(a) 3/2 　　　　(b) 1/2 　　　　(c) 0 　　　　(d) None of these

24. What is the overall order of the reaction

$$CO_{(g)} + NO_{2(g)} \rightarrow CO_{2(g)} + NO_{(g)}$$

if it proceeds via the following rate expression?

$$R = k[CO]\,[NO_2]$$

(a) Zero-order 　　(b) First-order 　　(c) Second-order 　　(d) Third-order

25. For a reaction $2NO_{(g)} + Cl_{2(g)} \rightarrow 2NOCl_{(g)}$. When concentration is doubled, the rate of reaction becomes two times of the original. When the concentration of NO is doubled the rate becomes four times. What is the order of the reaction?
    (a) 1　　　　　　　(b) 2　　　　　　　(c) 3　　　　　　　(d) 4

26. Nitric oxide reacts with hydrogen at a measurable rate at 1000 °K according to the equation below.
$$2NO_{(g)} + 2H_{2(g)} \rightarrow N_{2(g)} + 2H_2O_{(g)}$$
    What is the overall order of the reaction?
    (a) First-order
    (b) Second-order
    (c) Third-order
    (d) Not enough information given to solve

27. Which of the following graphs is correct for a first order reaction?

(a) 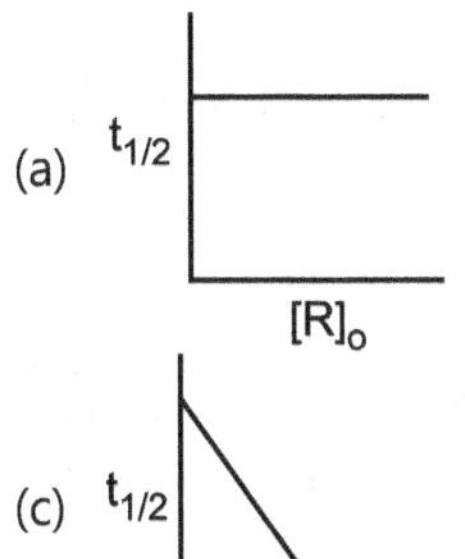

(b) 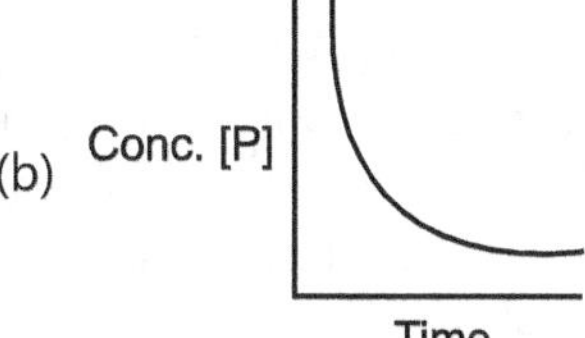

(c) 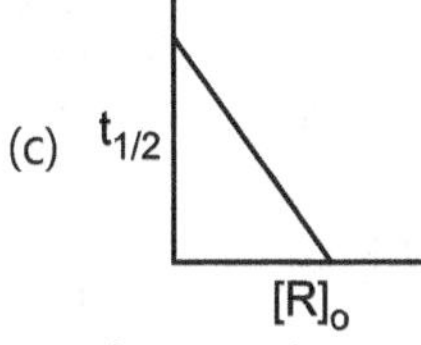

(d) 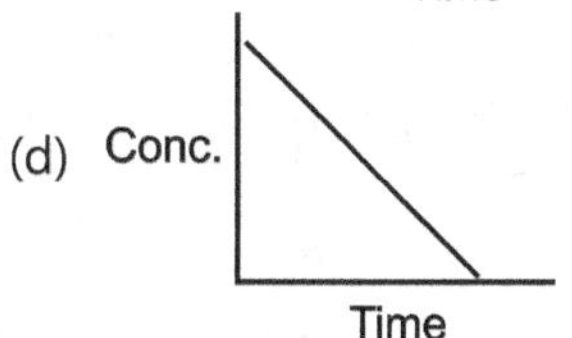

28. For the reaction $A + B \rightarrow C$, the rate law is ......
$$Rate = k[A][B]$$
    What are the units of rate constant where time is measured in seconds?
    (a) Ms^{-1}　　　　(b) M^2s^{-1}　　　　(c) Ms　　　　(d) $M^{-1}s^{-1}$

29. For the reaction $A \rightarrow B$, the rate law is
$$Rate = k[A]$$
    What are the units of rate constant where time is measured in minutes?
    (a) $mol/litre\ min^{-1}$
    (b) min^{-1}
    (c) $mol^{-1}/litre\ min^{-1}$
    (d) $mol\ litre^{-1}\ min$

30. A substance 'A' decomposes by a first order reaction starting initially with [A] = 2.00 m and after 200 min, [A] = 0.15 m. For this reaction, what is the value of k?
    (a) $1.29 \times 10^{-2}\ min^{-1}$
    (b) $2.29 \times 10^{-2}\ min^{-1}$
    (c) $3.29 \times 10^{-2}\ min^{-1}$
    (d) $4.40 \times 10^{-2}\ min^{-1}$

31. Consider a first order gas phase decomposition reaction given below :
$$A_{(g)} \rightarrow B_{(g)} + C_{(g)}$$
    The initial pressure of the system before decomposition of A was P_i. After a lapse of time 't', total pressure of the system increased by x units and became 'P_t'. The rate constant k for the reaction is given as ......

(a) $k = \dfrac{2.303}{t} \log \dfrac{P_1}{P_1 - x}$

(b) $k = \dfrac{2.303}{t} \log \dfrac{P_1}{2P_1 - P_t}$

(c) $k = \dfrac{2.303}{t} \log \dfrac{P_1}{2P_1 + P_t}$

(d) $k = \dfrac{2.303}{t} \log \dfrac{P_1}{P_1 + x}$

32. Given the initial rate data for the decomposition reaction, $A \rightarrow 2B$

Determine the rate expression for the reaction.

[A], m	$\Delta[A]/\Delta t$ m/s
0.125	5.14×10^2
0.175	1.01×10^3
0.250	2.06×10^3

    (a) Rate $= 4.11 \times 10^3$ [A]   (b) Rate $= 4.11 \times 10^3$ $[A]^2$

    (c) Rate $= 3.29 \times 10^4$ $[A]^2$ (d) Rate $= 5.14 \times 10^2$

33. Which of the following statements is not correct about order of a reaction?

    (a) The order of a reaction can be a fractional number

    (b) Order of a reaction is experimentally determined quantity

    (c) The order of a reaction is always equal to the sum of the stoichiometric coefficients of reactants in the balanced chemical equation for a reaction

    (d) The order of a reaction is the sum of the powers of molar concentration of reactants in the rate law expression

34. For the reaction products, doubling the concentration of A the rate of the reaction is doubled, but on doubling the concentration of B, rate remains unaltered. The overall order of the reaction is ......

    (a) 1   (b) 0   (c) 2   (d) 3

35. The value of rate constant of a pseudo first order reaction ......

    (a) depends on the concentration of reactants present in small amount.

    (b) depends on the concentration of reactants present in excess.

    (c) is independent of the concentration of reactants.

    (d) depends only on temperature.

36. The rate law of the reaction $A + 2B \rightarrow$ Product is given by $\dfrac{d[dB]}{dt} = k[B]^2$. If A is taken in excess, the order of the reaction will be ......

    (a) 1   (b) 2   (c) 3   (d) 0

37. Which of the following rate laws is consistent with the reaction mechanism shown below ?

$$NO_{(g)} + Cl_{2(g)} \rightarrow NOCl_{2(g)} \text{ (fast equilibrium)}$$
$$NO_{(g)} + NOCl_{2(g)} \rightarrow 2NOCl_{(g)} \text{ (slow)}$$

    (a) Rate $= k[NO][Cl_2]$ (b) Rate $= k[NO]_2$

    (c) Rate $= k[NO][NOCl_2]$ (d) Rate $= k[NO]_2[Cl]$

38. The rate law for the reaction

$2A + B \rightarrow$ products is Rate $= k[A]^2$. What effect would adding additional B have? (Assume no change in temperature or volume)

    (a) Both the value of k and the reaction rate would decrease

    (b) Neither the value of k nor the reaction rate would change

    (c) The value of k would remain constant, but the rate would decrease

    (d) The value of k would remain constant, but the rate would increase

39. If a reaction $2A + 3B \rightarrow$ products, is first order for A and second order for B, the rate law for the overall reaction will be written as Rate = ...
    (a) $k[A][B]$
    (b) $k[A][B]^2$
    (c) $k[A]^2[B]^2$
    (d) $k[A]^2[B]^3$

40. The rate law for the reaction $A + 2B \rightarrow C$ is found to be Rate = $k[A][B]$
    Concentration of reactant 'B' is doubled, keeping the concentration of 'A' constant, the value of rate constant will be_____.
    (a) The same
    (b) Doubled
    (c) Quadrupled
    (d) Halved

41. The rate law for the reaction $2A + B \rightarrow C$ was found to be Rate = $k[A][B]^2$. If the concentration of B is tripled, what will happen to the rate of the reaction?
    (a) It will stay the same
    (b) It will increase by nine times
    (c) It will increase by three times
    (d) It will increase by six times

42. Which among the following is a false statement ?
    (a) Half life of a third order reaction is inversely proportional to the square of initial concentration of the reactant
    (b) Molecularity of a reaction may be zero or fractional
    (c) For a first order reaction, $t_{1/2} = \dfrac{0.693}{2k}$
    (d) Rate of zero order reaction is independent of initial concentration of reactant

43. A first order reaction is 50% completed in 1.26×10^{14} s. How much time would it take for 100% completion?
    (a) 1.26×10^{15} s
    (b) 2.52×10^{14} s
    (c) 2.52×10^{28} s
    (d) Infinite

44. For a second-order decomposition reaction, $2A \rightarrow B$, Rate = $k[A]^2$
    Which of the following can be plotted versus time to give a straight line?
    (a) $[A]$
    (b) $ln\,[A]$
    (c) $ln\,\dfrac{1}{[A]}$
    (d) $\dfrac{1}{[A]}$

45. The rate law for a reaction between the substances A and B is given by, rate = $k[A]^n[B]^m$. On doubling the concentration of A and halving the concentration of B, the ratio of the new rate to the earlier rate of the reaction will be as ......
    (a) $\dfrac{1}{2^{(m+n)}}$
    (b) $(m + n)$
    (c) $(n - m)$
    (d) $2(n - m)$

46. Certain bimolecular reactions which follow the first order kinetics are called ......
    (a) First order reactions
    (b) Unimolecular reactions
    (c) Bimolecular reactions
    (d) Pseudounimolecular reactions

47. What are the units of k for the rate law:
    Rate = $k[A][B]^2$, when the concentration unit is mol/L?
    (a) s^{-1}
    (b) s
    (c) $L\,mol^{-1}\,s^{-1}$
    (d) $L^2\,mol^{-2}\,s^{-1}$

48. Nitrogen dioxide decomposes according to the following reaction : $2NO_2 \rightarrow 2NO_{(g)} + O_{2(g)}$

Experiment	Initial $[NO_2]$m	Initial Reaction Rate ms^{-1}
1.	0.010	7.1×10^{-5}
2.	0.020	28×10^{-5}ms

    For the initial rate data given above, what is the value of k in the rate law?
    (a) 0.010 m
    (b) $7.1 \times 10^{-3}\,s^{-1}$
    (c) $3.5 \times 10^{-3}\,s^{-1}$
    (d) $0.71\,m^{-1}s^{-1}$

49. For the reaction $H_2 + Cl_2 \xrightarrow{\text{Sunlight}} 2HCl$ taking place on water, the order of reaction is ...

(a) 1　　　(b) 2　　　(c) 3　　　(d) 0

50. The rate constant of a first order reaction is 3×10^6 second. If the initial concentration is 0.10 M, the initial rate of reaction is ......

(a) 3×10^{-5} ms^{-1}　　(b) 3×10^{-6} ms^{-1}　　(c) 3×10^{-8} ms^{-1}　　(d) 3×10^{-7} ms^{-1}

51. For a first-order reaction, it takes 48 minutes for a reactant to decrease to 25% of its initial value. What is the rate constant (in inverse seconds) for the reaction?

(a) 1.92×10^{-5} s　　(b) 2.41×10^{-4} s　　(c) 4.81×10^{-4} s　　(d) 2.90×10^{-2} s

52. For a reaction aG + bH→ Products

When concentration of both the reactants G and H are doubled, the rate increases by eight times. However, when concentration of G is doubled keeping the concentration of H fixed, the rate is doubled, hence the order of the reaction is ......

(a) 0　　　(b) 1　　　(c) 2　　　(d) 3

53. The rate constant for a second order reaction is 8×10^{-5} m^{-1} min^{-1}. How long will it take for 1 M solution to be reduced to 0.5 M?

(a) 8×10^{-5} min.　　　　　　　(b) 8.665×10^3 min.

(c) 4×10^{-5} min.　　　　　　　(d) 1.25×10^4 min.

54. Hydrogen peroxide decomposes as below

$2H_2O_{2(l)} \rightarrow 2H_2O_{(l)} + O_{2(g)}$, which is first order for H_2O_2 and has a half-life 18.0 minutes. If H_2O_2 solution that was initially 0.80 M is allowed to decompose for 72 minutes, what will be the concentration at that time?

(a) 0.80 M　　　(b) 0.40 M　　　(c) 0.20 M　　　(d) 0.05 M

55. For a reaction 2A + B → 2C, with the rate equation : Rate = $k[A]^2[B]$

(a) The order with respect to A is 1 and the order overall is 1

(b) The order with respect to A is 2 and the order overall is 2

(c) The order with respect to A is 2 and the order overall is 3

(d) The order with respect to B is 2 and the order overall is 2

56. For a reaction $2NO_{(g)} + Cl_{2(g)} \rightarrow 2NOCl_{(g)}$, when concentration of Cl_2 is doubled, the rate of reaction becomes two times of the original. When the concentration of NO is doubled, the rate becomes four times. What is the order of the reaction?

(a) 1　　　(b) 2　　　(c) 3　　　(d) 4

57. If the reaction is zeroth (0th) order with respect to [X], which of the following quantities when plotted versus t should be a straight line ?

(a) ln [X]　　　(b) 1/[X]　　　(c) [X]　　　(d) $[X]^2$

58. For A + 3B → 2C + D the reaction is first order with respect to reactant A and second order with respect to reactant B. If the concentration of A is doubled and the concentration of B is halved, the rate of the reaction would ____ by a factor of ____.

(a) Increase, 2　　(b) Decrease, 2　　(c) Increase, 4　　(d) Decrease, 4

59. Which of the following expressions is correct for first order reaction? If [CO] refers to initial concentration of reactant ?

(a) $t_{1/2} \propto CO$　　(b) $t_{1/2} \propto CO^{-1}$　　(c) $t_{1/2} \propto CO^{-2}$　　(d) $t_{1/2} \propto CO^0$

60. Consider a reaction A $\rightarrow$ products, with a rate equation: Rate of disappearance of A = $k[A]^n$. Three of the following units correspond to those for zero, first and second order rate constants. Which unit does not refer to one of these cases?

(a) $1\,s^{-1}$ (b) $mol\ dm^{-3}\,s^{-1}$ (c) $mol^2\ dm^6\,s^{-1}$ (d) $mol^{-1}\ dm^3\,s^1$

61. Half life of a reaction is found to be inversely proportional to the cube of its initial concentration. The order of the reaction is ......

(a) 2   (b) 5   (c) 3   (d) 4

62. For a reaction : A + B $\rightarrow$ C the rate equation is:

Rate of reaction = $k[A]$

Which statement is incorrect?

(a) The rate is independent of the concentration of B

(b) The units of the rate constant are s^{-1}

(c) A plot of [A] against time is linear

(d) The rate depends on the concentration of A

63. The rate constant k, for the reaction $N_2O_{5(g)} \rightarrow 2NO_{2(g)} + \dfrac{1}{2}O_{2(g)}$. Which equation given below describes the change of $[N_2O_5]$ with time?

(a) $[N_2O_5]_t/[N_2O_5]_0 = kt$ (b) $[N_2O_5]_0/[N_2O_5]_t = e^{kt}$

(c) $\log_{10}[N_2O_5]_t/\log_{10}[N_2O_5]_0 = kt$ (d) $\ln\dfrac{[N_2O_5]_0}{[N_2O_5]_t} = kt$

64. The decomposition of carbon disulphide CS_2 to carbon monosulphide CS, and sulphur is first order with k = $2.8 \times 10^{-7}\,s^{-1}$ at 1000°C.

$$CS_2 \rightarrow CS + S$$

What is the half-life of this reaction at 1000°C?

(a) $5.0 \times 10^7\,s$ (b) $4.7 \times 10^{-6}\,s$ (c) $3.8 \times 10^5\,s$ (d) $6.1 \times 10^4\,s$

65. The rate of a first order reaction is $0.6932 \times 10^{-2}\ mol^{-1}\ min^{-1}$ and the initial concentration of the reactants is 1M, $t_{1/2}$ is equal to ......

(a) 6.932 min   (b) 100 min

(c) 0.6932×10^{-3} min   (d) 0.6932×10^{-2} min

66. A radionuclide has a half-life of 62 min. What is the rate constant for the decay of the nuclide?

(a) 89 s   (b) $0.011\ min^{-1}$ (c) $0.011\ s^{-1}$ (d) 89 min

67. For a given reaction, $t_{1/2} = 1/k[A]_0$, the order of the reaction is ......

(a) 1   (b) 0   (c) 3   (d) 2

68. The decomposition of an ether at 770 °K is first order with a half-life of 1570 seconds. What fraction of an initial amount of ether remains after 4710 seconds?

(a) 1/3   (b) 1/6   (c) 1/8   (d) 1/16

69. The integrated rate equation is $R_t = \log C_0 - \log C_t$. The straight line graph is obtained by plotting ......

(a) time v/s $\log C_t$ (b) $\dfrac{1}{time}$ v/s C_t (c) time v/s C_t (d) $\dfrac{1}{time}$ v/s $\dfrac{1}{C_t}$

70. A reaction involving two different reactants can never be ......

(a) Unimolecular reaction
(b) First order reaction
(c) Second order reaction
(d) Bimolecular reaction

71. The rate constant of a reaction is 0.69×10^{-2} min^{-1} and the initial concentration is 0.2 mol lit^{-1}. The half-life period is ......

(a) 400 sec
(b) 600 sec
(c) 800 sec
(d) 1200 sec

72. The reaction of peroxy disulphate with iodide ions is: $[S_2O_8^{2-}] + 3I^- \rightarrow 2SO_4^{2-} + I_3^-$

Expt. No.	$[S_2O_8^{2-}]$ (mol L^{-1})	$[I^-]$ (mol L^{-1})	Initial rate of reaction (mol L^{-1} s^{-1})
1.	0.200	0.200	2.2×10^{-3}
2.	0.400	0.200	4.4×10^{-3}
3.	0.400	0.400	8.8×10^{-3}

The rate law of reaction is ......

(a) Rate = $k[S_2O_8^{2-}]^2[I^-]$
(b) Rate = $k[S_2O_8^{2-}][I^-]$
(c) Rate = $k[S_2O_8^{2-}][I^-]^2$
(d) Rate = $k[S_2O_8^{2-}]^2[I^-]^2$

73. 75% of a first order reaction is completed in 30 minutes. What is the time required for 93.75% of the reaction (in minutes)?

(a) 45
(b) 120
(c) 90
(d) 60

74. The half-life for a first-order reaction is 32 s. What was the original concentration if after 2.0 minutes, the reactant concentration is 0.062 M?

(a) 0.069 M
(b) 0.84 M
(c) 0.091 M
(d) 0.075 M

75. A first order reaction is half completed in 45 minutes. How long does it need 99.9% of the reaction to be completed?

(a) 5 hours
(b) 7.5 hours
(c) 10 hours
(d) 20 hours

76. Given the following data for this reaction:

$$NH_{4(aq)}^+ + NO_{2(aq)}^- \rightarrow N_{2(g)} + 2H_2O_{(l)}$$

Expt. No.	$[NH_4^+]$	$[NO_2^-]$	Rate
1.	0.010 M	0.020 M	0.020 m/s
2.	0.015 M	0.020 M	0.030 m/s
3.	0.010 M	0.010 M	0.005 m/s

The rate law for the reaction is ......

(a) Rate = $k[NH_4^+][NO_2^-]$
(b) Rate = $k[NH_4^+]^2[NO_2^-]^2$
(c) Rate = $k[NH_4^+]^2[NO_2^-]$
(d) Rate = $k[NH_4^+][NO_2^-]^2$

77. The rate at which CO_2 is produced in the following reaction:

$$2C_6H_{6(g)} + 15O_{2(g)} \rightarrow 12CO_{2(g)} + 6H_2O_{(l)}$$

is 2.2×10^{-2} mol L^{-1} s^{-1}. What is the rate at which O_2 is consumed?

(a) 2.2×10^{-2} mol L^{-1} s^{-1}
(b) 1.3×10^{-1} mol L^{-1} s^{-1}
(c) 2.8×10^{-2} mol L^{-1} s^{-1}
(d) 1.8×10^{-3} mol L^{-1} s^{-1}

78. The rate of the chemical reaction between substances A and B is found to follow the rate law, rate = $k[A]^2[B]$ where k is the rate constant. The concentration of A is reduced to half its original value. To make the reaction proceed at 50% of its original rate, the concentration of B should be ......

(a) Decreased by 1/4　　(b) Halved　　　　　　　(c) Kept constant　　(d) Doubled

79. For a certain decomposition reaction, the rate is 0.50 mole/litre^{-1} sec when the concentration of the reactant is 0.10 M. If the reaction is second order, what will be the new rate when the concentration of the reactant is increased to 0.40 M?

(a) 0.50 mole/litre sec　　　　　　　　　　(b) 1.0 mole/litre sec

(c) 8.0 mole/litre sec　　　　　　　　　　(d) 16 mole/litre sec

80. The conversion of A to B follows second order kinetics. Doubling the concentration of A will increase the rate of formation of B by a factor ......

(a) 4　　　　　　　　(b) 2　　　　　　　　(c) 1/4　　　　　　　　(d) 1/2

81. In a reversible reaction between A and B, k_1 is the rate constant for the formation of B from A, and k^{-1} is the rate constant for the formation of A from B. What is the rate equation if both the reactions are first order with respect to the reactant?

(a) Rate of disappearance of A = k^{-1} [A] k_1[B]

(b) Rate of disappearance of A = k^1 [A] + k^{-1}[B]

(c) Rate of disappearance of A = k^{-1} [A] + k^1[B]

(d) Rate of disappearance of A = k^1 [A] k^{-1}[B]

82. The reaction $2X + Y \rightarrow 3Z$ was studied and the following data were obtained:

Experiment No.	X	Y	Rate (mole / litre-sec)
1	3.0	1.5	1.8
2	1.5	3.0	0.45
3	1.5	1.5	0.45

What is the proper rate expression?

(a) rate = $k[X][Y]$　　　(b) rate = $k[Y]^2$　　　(c) rate = $k[X]^2$　　　(d) rate = $k[X]^2[Y]$

83. After how many seconds will the concentration of the reactants in a first order reaction be halved, if the decay constant is 1.155×10^{-3} sec^{-1}

(a) 100 sec　　　　　(b) 200 sec　　　　　(c) 400 sec　　　　　(d) 600 sec

84. For the reaction $A + B \rightarrow C + D$ the reaction rate halves when the concentration of A halves (B is in excess), and when A is in excess, the reaction rate is unaffected by changes in the concentration of B. Which equation is consistent with these observations?

(a) Rate of reaction = k [A][B]　　　　　　(b) Rate of reaction = k [A]

(c) Rate of reaction = k [A]^2　　　　　　(d) Rate of reaction = k [A]^2[B]

85. For a first order reaction, the plot of $\log_{10} k$ against $1/T$ is a straight line. The slope of the line is equal to ......

(a) $\dfrac{E_a}{R}$　　　　　　(b) $\dfrac{2.303}{E_a \times R}$　　　　　　(c) $\dfrac{E_a}{2.303}$　　　　　　(d) $\dfrac{-E_a}{2.303\,R}$

86. The half life for the acid-catalyzed hydrolysis of sucrose to form glucose and fructose, which is first order overall is 3.20 h at 25°C. The rate constant for the reaction at this temperature is ......
    (a) $6.02 \times 10^{-5}\ s^{-1}$ (b) $8.68 \times 10^{-5}\ s^{-1}$ (c) $0.217\ s^{-1}$ (d) $2.61 \times 10^{-5}\ s^{-1}$

87. The rate constant of a first order reaction is 3×10^{-6} per second. If the initial concentration is 0.10 M, the initial rate of the reaction is ......
    (a) $3 \times 10^{-5}\ ms^{-1}$ (b) $3 \times 10^{-6}\ ms^{-1}$ (c) $3 \times 10^{-8}\ m\ s^{-1}$ (d) $3 \times 10^{-7}\ ms^{-1}$

88. Suppose the reaction : $A + 2B \rightarrow AB_2$ occurs by the following mechanism :
    Step 1 $A + B \rightarrow AB$ (slow)
    Step 2 $AB + B \rightarrow AB_2$ (fast)
    Overall $A + 2B \rightarrow AB_2$
    The rate law expression must be Rate = ...
    (a) k[A]   (b) k[B]   (c) k[A][B]   (d) $k[B]^2$

89. A possible mechanism for the reaction,
    $$2A + B \rightarrow C + D, \text{ is}$$
    (1) $A + A \rightarrow A_2$ fast, equilibrium
    (2) $A_2 + A \rightarrow A_3$ slow
    (3) $A_3 + B \rightarrow A + C + D$ fast
    According to the mechanism, the rate law will be ......
    (a) Rate = $k[A]^2$ (b) Rate = k[A][B]   (c) Rate = $k[A]^2[B]$ (d) Rate = $k[A]^3$

90. At 300 K, the decomposition of NOCl follows the rate law: Rate = $k[NOCl]^2$
    $$2NOCl \rightarrow 2NO + Cl_2$$
    Following mechanisms are proposed. Predict the possibly correct ones.

    Mechanism-1: $NOCl \rightarrow NO + Cl$ slow
                            $Cl + NOCl \rightarrow NOCl_2$ fast
                            $NOCl_2 + NO \rightarrow 2NO + Cl_2$ fast
                            Overall : $2NOCl \rightarrow 2NO + Cl_2$

    Mechanism-2: $2NOCl \rightarrow NOCl_2 + NO$ slow
                            $NOCl_2 \rightarrow NO + Cl_2$ fast
                            Overall : $2NOCl \rightarrow 2NO + Cl_2$

    Mechanism-3: $NOCl \rightleftharpoons NO + Cl$ fast, equilibrium
                            $NOCl + Cl \rightarrow NO + Cl_2$ slow
                            Overall : $2NOCl \rightarrow 2NO + Cl_2$

    (a) 2, 3   (b) 3   (c) 1   (d) 2

91. For the reaction:
    $$(CH_3)_3CBr_{(aq)} + OH^-_{(aq)} \rightarrow (CH_3)_3COH_{(aq)} + Br^-_{(aq)}$$
    by halving the concentration of $(CH_3)_3CBr$ causes the reaction rate to be halved but halving the concentration of OH^- has no effect on the rate, what is the rate law?
    (a) Rate = $k[(CH_3)_3CBr]^{1/2}[OH^-]$ (b) Rate = $k[(CH_3)_3CBr]^2[OH^-]$
    (c) Rate = $k[(CH_3)_3CBr]^{1/2}$ (d) Rate = $k[(CH_3)_3CBr]$

92. Which is constant for different reactant concentrations in a first-order reaction?
  (a) The time required for the concentration of reactants to drop below 0.001 M
  (b) The time required for one-half of reactant to disappear.
  (c) The rate of disappearance of reactants in $mol \cdot L^{-1} \cdot time^{-1}$
  (d) The rate of formation of products in $mol \cdot L^{-1} \cdot time^{-1}$

93. The activation energy is represented by the following graph

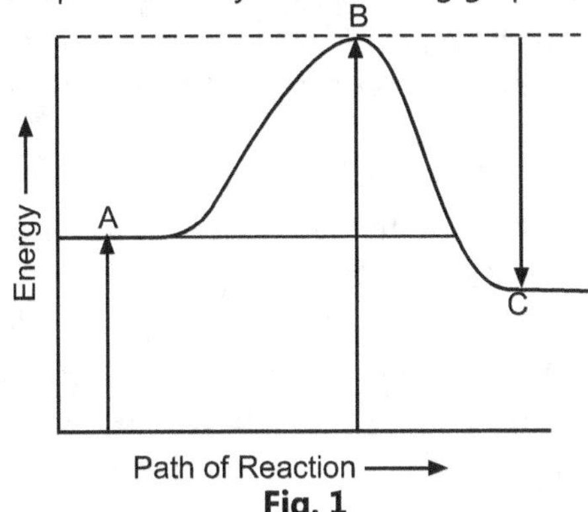

Fig. 1

  (a) A   (b) B   (c) C   (d) BA

94. Given that a reaction absorbs energy and has an activation energy of 50 kJ/mol, which of the following statements are correct?
  (1) The reverse reaction has an activation energy equal to 50 kJ/mol.
  (2) The reverse reaction has an activation energy less than 50 kJ/mol.
  (3) The reverse reaction has an activation energy greater than 50 kJ/mol.
  (4) The change in internal energy is less than zero.
  (5) The change in internal energy is greater than zero.
  (a) (1) and (4)   (b) (2) and (4)   (c) (3) and (4)   (d) (2) and (5)

95. If reaction A has an activation energy of 250 kJ and reaction B has an activation energy of 100 kJ, which of the following statements must be correct?
  (a) If reaction A is exothermic and reaction B is endothermic then reaction A is favoured kinetically.
  (b) At the same temperature, the rate of reaction B is greater than the rate of reaction A.
  (c) The energy of reaction A must be greater than the energy of reaction B.
  (d) The energy of reaction B must be greater than the energy of reaction A.

96. A reaction has an activation energy of 40 kJ and an overall energy change of reaction of −100 kJ. In each of the following potential energy diagrams, the horizontal axis is the reaction co-ordinate and the vertical axis is potential energy in kJ. Which potential energy diagram best describes this reaction?

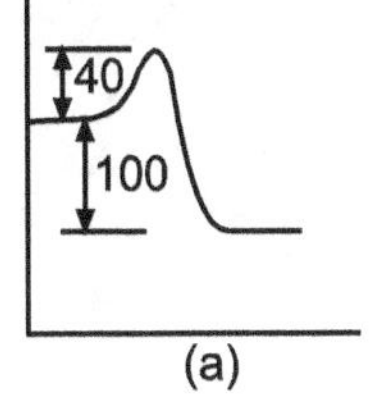

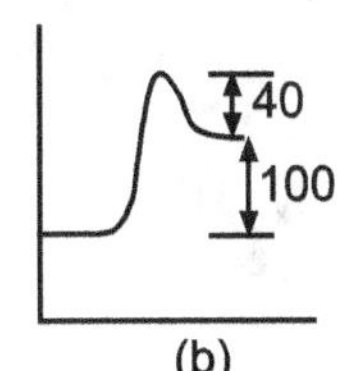

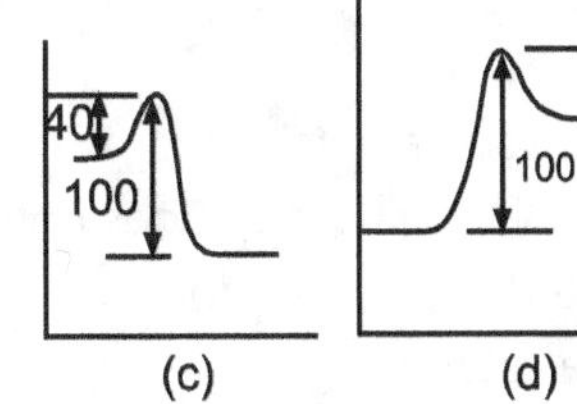

97. Which of the following statements concerning graphical methods for determining reaction order is false?

(a) For a first-order reaction, the plot of ln [A] vs. time gives a straight line.

(b) For a first-order reaction, the slope of the straight-line graph equals – ak.

(c) For a second-order reaction, the plot of $[A]^2$ vs. time gives a straight line.

(d) For a zero-order reaction, the plot of [A] vs. time gives a straight line.

98. If the activation energy in the forward direction of an elementary step is 52 kJ and the activation energy in the reverse direction is 74 kJ, what is the energy of reaction ΔE for this step?

(a) 22 kJ (b) –22 kJ (c) 52 kJ (d) –52 kJ

99. A student determined the value of the rate constant, k, for a chemical reaction at several different temperatures. Which of the following graphs of the student's data would give a straight line?

(a) k versus T (b) k versus (1/T) (c) ln k versus (1/T) (d) ln k versus T

100. What is the order of reaction for which the units of k are $L \cdot mol^{-1} \cdot s^{-1}$?

(a) Zero order (b) First order (c) Second order (d) Some other order

101. Which does NOT change with time for a first order reaction?

(a) The amount of reactant that disappears in each half life

(b) The concentration of the reactant

(c) The length of each half life

(d) The rate of the reaction

102. A reaction follows the rate law: Rate $= k[A]^2$.

Which of the following plots will give a straight line?

(a) 1/[A] versus 1/time (b) $[A]^2$ versus time

(c) 1/[A] versus time (d) ln [A] versus time

103. For the following reaction:

$NO_{2(g)} + CO_{(g)} \rightarrow NO_{(g)} + CO_{2(g)}$

the rate law is: Rate $= k[NO_2]^2$

If a small amount of gaseous carbon monoxide (CO) is added to a reaction mixture that was 0.10 molar in NO_2 and 0.20 molar in CO, which of the following statements is true?

(a) Both k and the reaction rate remain the same

(b) Both k and the reaction rate increase

(c) Both k and the reaction rate decrease

(d) Only k increases, the reaction rate remains the same

104. When the concentration of $H_{(aq)}$ is doubled for the reaction

$H_2O_{2(aq)} + Fe^{2+}_{(aq)} + 2H^+_{(aq)} \rightarrow 2Fe^{3+}_{(aq)} + 2H_2O_{2(g)}$, there is no change in the reaction rate. This indicates ......

(a) The H^+ is a spectator ion

(b) The rate-determining step does not involve H^+

(c) The reaction mechanism does not involve H^+

(d) The H^+ is a catalyst

105. What is the activation energy for the formation of ozone?
  (a) 14 kJ   (b) 392 kJ   (c) 406 kJ   (d) None of these

106. The rate constant for the substitution reaction
$$C_4H_9Cl + H_2O \rightarrow C_4H_9OH + HCl$$
increases by a factor of 10.6 when the temperature is increased from 298 °K to 308 °K. Calculate the activation energy of the reaction.
  (a) 180 kJ mol^{-1} (b) 78.2 kJ mol^{-1} (c) 809 kJ mol^{-1} (d) 2.14 kJ mol^{-1}

107. Which items correctly complete the following statement?
  A catalyst can act in a chemical reaction to ......
  (I)   Increase the equilibrium constant.   (II) Lower the activation energy.
  (III) Provide a new path for the reaction.
  (a) Only I and II   (b) Only II and III   (c) Only III and I   (d) Only III

108. A catalyst ......
  (a) Actually does not participate in the reaction
  (b) Changes the equilibrium concentration of products
  (c) Does not affect the reaction energy path
  (d) Always decreases the rate of a reaction

109. Which statement is false?
  (a) If a reaction is thermodynamically spontaneous, it may occur rapidly
  (b) If a reaction is thermodynamically spontaneous, it must have a low activation energy
  (c) If a reaction is thermodynamically spontaneous, it may occur slowly
  (d) If a reaction is thermodynamically non-spontaneous, it will not occur spontaneously

110. Which of the following statements are true?
  (1) Reactions with more negative values of G_o are spontaneous and proceed at a higher rate than those with less negative values of G_o
  (2) The activation energy, E_a, is usually about the same as E for a reaction
  (3) The activation energy for a reaction does not change significantly as temperature changes
  (4) Reactions usually occur at faster rates at higher temperatures
  (a) 1, 2, 4   (b) 3, 4   (c) 1, 2, 3   (d) 2, 3, 4

111. When the concentration of reactant molecules is increased, the rate of reaction increases. The best explanation is: As the reactant concentration increases ......
  (a) The average kinetic energy of molecules increases
  (b) The frequency of molecular collisions increases
  (c) The rate constant increases
  (d) The activation energy increases

112. For the reaction $2H_2S_{(g)} + O_{2(g)} \rightarrow 2S_{(s)} + 2H_2O_{(l)}$, which one of the following statements is absolutely true?
  (a) The reaction is first order with respect to H_2S and second order with respect to O_2.
  (b) The reaction is fourth order overall.
  (c) The rate law is: rate $= k[H_2S]^2[O_2]$.
  (d) The rate law cannot be determined from the information given.

113. Which of the following statements about the kinetics of the reaction

$H_{2(g)} + Br_{2(g)} \rightarrow 2HBr_{(g)}$ is definitely true?

(a) The reaction is first order with respect to bromine Br_2.

(b) The reaction is second order overall.

(c) The presence of hydrogen bromide, HBr, inhibits the rate of the reaction.

(d) It is not possible to determine anything about the kinetics of the reaction from the stoichiometry.

114. Which of the following would be correct units for the rate constant of a reaction that is second order overall?

(a) s^{-1}
(b) $mol^{-1} dm^3 s^{-1}$
(c) $mol\ cm^{-3} s^{-1}$
(d) $mol^{-2} dm^6 s^{-1}$

115. The rate constant for the reaction $H_2 + OH \rightarrow H + H_2O$

which is an important step in the hydrogen-oxygen reaction mechanism, has the value $k = 3.52 \times 10^6\ mol^{-1} dm^3 s^{-1}$. What is the equivalence value expressed in units of $molecule^{-1} cm^3 s^{-1}$?

(a) $2.12 \times 10^{27}\ molecule^{-1} cm^3 s^{-1}$
(b) $5.85 \times 10^{-15}\ molecule^{-1} cm^3 s^{-1}$

(c) $5.85 \times 10^{-21}\ molecule^{-1} cm^3 s^{-1}$
(d) $2.12 \times 10^{-15}\ molecule^{-1} cm^3 s^{-1}$

116. The rate constant for the second order reaction between iodomethane, CH_3I, and ethoxy anions, $C_2H_5O^-$, in ethanol solution is $9.86 \times 10^{-5}\ mol\ dm^{-3} s^{-1}$ at 298 °K and $6.17 \times 10^{-3}\ mol\ dm^{-3} s^{-1}$ at 338 °K. Calculate the activation energy.

(a) $300\ kJ\ mol^{-1}$
(b) $116\ kJ\ mol^{-1}$
(c) $10.4\ kJ\ mol^{-1}$
(d) $86.6\ kJ\ mol^{-1}$

117. What is the activation energy (in kJ) of a reaction whose rate constant increases by a factor of 100 upon increasing the temperature from 300 °K to 360 K?

(a) 27
(b) 35
(c) 69
(d) 53

118. A plot of ln k against 1/T (T measured in K) for a reaction is linear with a gradient of -1.20×10^4 °K. The activation energy, E_a, for the reaction is therefore ......

(a) $1.44\ kJ\ mol^{-1}$
(b) $693\ J\ mol^{-1}$
(c) $99.8\ J\ mol^{-1}$
(d) $99.8\ kJ\ mol^{-1}$

119. For a zero order reaction $A \longrightarrow P$, $t_{1/2}$ is (k is rate constant) ......

(a) $\dfrac{[A]_0}{2k}$
(b) $\dfrac{\ln 2}{2k}$
(c) $\dfrac{1}{k[A]_0}$
(d) $\dfrac{\ln 2}{[A]_0 k}$

120. Select the law that corresponds to data shown for the following reaction

$$A + B \longrightarrow Products$$

Exp.	[A]	[B]	initial rate
1	0.012	0.035	0.1
2	0.024	0.070	0.8
3	0.024	0.035	0.1
4	0.012	0.070	0.8

(a) rate = k $[B]^3$
(b) rate = k $[B]^4$
(c) rate = k $[A]\ [B]^3$
(d) rate = k $[A]^2[B]^2$

121. The rate of reaction, $A + B \rightarrow$ Product is given by the equation $r = k\,[A]\,[B]$. If B is taken in large excess, the order of the reaction would be ......

(a) 2 (b) 1 (c) 0 (d) unpredictable

122. The first order rate constant for the decomposition of N_2O_5 is 6.2×10^{-4} $\sec^{-1}$. The $t_{1/2}$ of decomposition is ......

(a) 1117.2 (b) 111.7 (c) 223.4 (d) 160.9

123. Which of the following statement about the catalyst is/are true?

(a) A catalyst accelerates the rate of reaction by bringing down the energy of activation

(b) A catalyst does not participate in reaction mechanism

(c) A catalyst makes the reaction more feasible by making ΔG more negative

(d) A catalyst makes equilibrium constant more favourable for forward reaction

124. Half-life period of second order reaction is ......

(a) Proportional to initial concentration of reactants

(b) Independent of initial concentration of reactants

(c) Inversely proportional to initial concentration of reactants

(d) Inversely proportional to square of initial concentration of reactants

125. The hydrolysis of ester in alkaline medium is a ......

(a) 1st order reaction with molecularity 1 (b) 2nd order reaction with molecularity 2

(c) 1st order reaction with molecularity 2 (d) 2nd order reaction with molecularity 1

126. Diazonium salt decomposes as ......

$C_6H_5N_2^+Cl^- \longrightarrow C_6H_5Cl + N_2$

At 0°C, the evolution of N_2 becomes two times faster when initial concentration of the salt is doubled. Thus, it is ......

(a) A first order reaction

(b) A second order reaction

(c) Independent of initial concentration of reactant

(d) A zero order reaction

127. The reaction

N_2O_5 (in CCl_4) $\longrightarrow 2NO_2 + 1/2O_{2(g)}$

What is the value of rate constant 6.2×10^{-4} s^{-1} ? What is the value of rate of reaction when $[N_2O_5] = 1.25$ mol L^{-1}?

(a) 7.75×10^{-4} mol $L^{-1}\,s^{-1}$ (b) 6.35×10^{-3} mol $L^{-1}\,s^{-1}$

(c) 5.15×10^{-5} mol $L^{-1}\,s^{-1}$ (d) 3.85×10^{-4} mol $L^{-1}\,s^{-1}$

128. The reaction $2H_2O_2 \longrightarrow 2H_2O + O_2$ is ......

$r = k[H_2O_2]$

(a) Zero order reaction (b) First order reaction

(c) Second order reaction (d) Third order reaction

129. If initial concentration of reactants in certain reaction is doubled, the half-life period of the reaction doubles, the order of a reaction is ......

(a) Zero (b) First (c) Second (d) Third

130. For a first order reaction, the half-life period is independent of ......

(a) Initial concentration

(b) Cube root of initial concentration

(c) First power of final concentration

(d) Square root of final concentration.

131. A substance 'A' decomposes in solution following the first order kinetics. Flask I contains 1 L of 1 M solution of A and flask II contains 100 mL of 0.6 M solution. After 8 hr the concentration of A in flask I becomes 0.25 M. What will be the time for concentration of A in flask II to become 0.3 M?

(a) 0.4 hr (b) 2.4 hr (c) 4.0 hr

(d) Unpredictable as rate constant is not given

132. A first order reaction is 75% complete after 32 minutes. When was 50% of the reaction completed?

(a) 16 minutes (b) 8 minutes (c) 4 minutes (d) 32 minutes

133. The rate of disappearance of HBr in the gas phase reaction $2HBr_{(g)} \rightarrow H_{2_{(g)}} + Br_{2_{(g)}}$ is $0.130\ Ms^{-1}$ at 150°C. The rate of reaction is .... Ms^{-1}.

(a) 3.85 (b) 0.0650 (c) 0.0169 (d) 0.260

134. If the activation energy for the forward reaction is $150\ kJ\ mol^{-1}$ and that of the reverse reaction is $260\ kJ\ mol^{-1}$, what is the enthalpy change for the reaction ?

(a) $410\ kJ\ mol^{-1}$ (b) $-110\ kJ\ mol^{-1}$ (c) $110\ kJ\ mol^{-1}$ (d) $-410\ kJ\ mol^{-1}$

135. The decomposition of dimethylether at 504 °C is first order with a half-life of 1570 seconds. What fraction of an initial amount of dimethylether remains after 4710 seconds?

(a) 1/3 (b) 1/6 (c) 1/8 (d) 1/16

136. The following homogeneous gaseous reactions were experimentally found to be second order overall ......

(i) $2NO_2 \longrightarrow N_2 + O_2$

(ii) $3O_2 \longrightarrow 2O_3$

(iii) $N_2O_3 \longrightarrow NO + NO_2$

(iv) $H_2 + I_2 \longrightarrow 2HI$

Which of these are most likely to be elementary reactions that occur in one step?

(a) (iii) only (b) (i) and (iii) (c) (i) and (iv) (d) (iii) and (iv)

137. Which is correct about zero order reaction?

(a) Rate of reaction depends on decay constant.

(b) Rate of reaction is independent of concentration.

(c) Unit of rate constant is $conc^{-1}$

(d) Unit of rate constant is $conc^{-1}\ time^{-1}$

138. In Arrhenius plot, intercept is equal to ......

(a) $-E_a/R$ (b) ln A (c) ln k (d) $log_{10}\ a$

139. For a first order reaction, to obtain a positive slope, we need to plot [A] in the concentration of reactant AB.

(a) log_{10} [A] vs t

(b) $-log_e$ [A] vs t

(c) $-log_{10}$ [A] vs log t

(d) [A] vs t

140. For a reaction of type, it is observed that doubling concentration of A causes the reaction rate to be four times as great, but doubling the amount of B does not affect the rate. The rate equation is ......

(a) Rate = k [A] [B]

(b) Rate = $\dfrac{k}{4}$ [A]^2

(c) Rate = k [A]^2 [B]^0

(d) Rate = k [A]^2[B]^2

141. The fraction of molecules having energy equal to or greater than activation energy is given by ......

(a) X = $-E_a$ / 2.303 RT

(b) log X = $-E_a$ /2.303 R

(c) X = antilog ($-E_a$ /2.303 RT)

(d) X = antilog E_a/2.303 RT

142. The decomposition of hexane follows k = $(4 \times 10^{11}$ s$^{-1})$ e$^{-20000\ K/T}$, the activation energy is ...

(a) 170 kJ/mol   (b) 166.28 kJ/mol   (c) 166.3 kJ/mol   (d) 166 kJ/mol

143. The amount of radioactive element left in 10 years old baby if the bones of newly born absorbed 1 mirogram radioactive element. (Decay constant of radioactive element is 2×10^{-1} year)

(a) log (a – x) = 0.8694

(b) log (a – x) = – 0.0460

(c) log (a – x) = –0.8694

(d) log (a – x) = 0.0460

144. Calculate the energy of activation for the decomposition of a compound which follows the equation log k = 12 – 2 × 10^4 K/T

(a) 383 kJ/mol   (b) 383 J/mole   (c) 483 kJ/mole   (d) 283 kJ/mol

145. The order w.r.t oxygen during the decomposition of ozone which follows the mechanism

$O_3 \rightarrow O_2 + O$ (fast, equilibrium)

$O_3 + O \rightarrow 2O_2$ (slow)

(a) –1   (b) +1   (c) zero   (d) –2

146. The decomposition of compound A follows two parallel first order reactions and gives B and C. What will be the percentage of B and C if k_b = 4 and k_c = 2 ?

(a) 75% B, 25%C

(b) 25% B, 75% C

(c) 66.7% B, 33.3% C

(d) 33.3% B, 66.7% C

147. The rate of reaction for decomposition of nitrogen pentaoxide can be expressed in following ways ......

$2N_2O_5 \rightarrow 4NO_2 + O_2$

$-\Delta[N_2O_5]/\Delta t = k[N_2O_5]$

$+ \Delta[NO_2]/\Delta t = k'\ [N_2O_5]$

$+ \Delta[O_2]/\Delta t = k''[N_2O_5]$

The relationship between k, k' and k" is ......

(a) k' = 2k; k" = k   (b) k' = k; k" = k   (c) k' = 2k; k" = 2k   (d) k' = 2k; k" = k/2

148. The inversion of cane sugar is ......

$$C_{12}H_{22}O_{11} + H_2O \rightarrow 6CO_2 + 12H_2O$$

(a) first order, bimolecular
(b) second order, bimolecular
(c) first order, pseudounimolecular
(d) first order, unimolecular

149. The rate of the reaction : $BrO_3^- (aq) + 5Br^- (aq) + 6H^+ (aq) \rightarrow 3Br_2 (aq) + 3H_2O$

was studied and the following information was obtained:

$[BrO_3^-]$	$[Br^-]$	$[H^+]$	I. Rate (m/sec)
0.10	0.10	0.10	8.0×10^{-4}
0.20	0.20	0.10	3.2×10^{-3}
0.20	0.10	0.10	1.6×10^{-3}
0.10	0.10	0.20	3.2×10^{-3}

The rate law for this reaction is:

(a) Rate = $k[BrO_3^-][Br^-]^5[H^+]^2$
(b) Rate = $k[BrO_3^-][Br^-]^5[H^+]^6$
(c) Rate = $k[BrO_3^-]^2[Br^-][H^+]^2$
(d) Rate = $k[BrO_3^-][Br^-][H^+]^2$
(e) Rate = $k[BrO_3^-][Br^-]^2[H^+]$

150. The rate of constant of a chemical reaction has unit L mol^{-1} s^{-1}. Order of the reaction will be ......

(a) 0 order
(b) 1st order
(c) 2nd order
(d) 3rd order

151. In a first order reaction, the concentration of the reactant decreases from 0.8 M to 0.4 M in 15 minutes. The time taken for the concentration to change from 0.1 M to 0.025 M is ......

(a) 30 minutes
(b) 60 minutes
(c) 7.5 minutes
(d) 15 minutes

152. Temperature coefficient of a reaction is 2. When temperature is increased from 30°C to 100°C, rate of the reaction increases by ......

(a) 500 times
(b) 250 times
(c) 128 times
(d) 100 times

153. For a first order reaction, half life is 14 sec. The time required for the initial concentration to reduce to 1/8 of its value is ......

(a) $(14)^3$
(b) 28 sec
(c) 42 sec
(d) $(14)^2$ sec

154. The time taken for 10% completion of a first order reaction is 20 minutes. Then for 19% completion, the reaction will take ......

(a) 40 min
(b) 60 min
(c) 30 min
(d) 50 min

155. For a chemical reaction A $\rightarrow$ B the rate of the reaction is 2×10^{-3} mol dm^3 s^{-1}, when the initial concentration is 0.05 mol dm^{-3}. The rate of the same reaction is 1.6×10^{-2} mol dm^{-3} s^{-1} when the initial concentration is 0.1 mol dm^{-3}. The order of the reaction is ......

(a) 2
(b) 0
(c) 3
(d) 1

156. For the reaction $2A + B \rightarrow C + D$, measurement of rates of reaction at varying concentration are given below.

Trial No.	[A]	[B]	Rate $(mmol\ L^{-1}s^{-1})$
1	0.010	0.010	2.5
2	0.010	0.020	5.0
3	0.030	0.020	45.0

The rate law is therefore ......

(a) rate = $k\,[A]^2\,[B]$　　　(b) rate = $k\,[A]\,[B]^2$　　(c) rate = $k\,[A]\,[B]$　　(d) rate = $k\,[A]^2\,[B]^2$

(e) rate = $k\,[A]^3$

157. A reaction $P \rightarrow Q$ is completed 25% in 25 min, 50% completed in 25 min, if [P] is halved, 25% completed in 50 min. If [P] is doubled, the order of the reaction is ......

(a) 1　　　　　　　(b) 2　　　　　　　(c) 0　　　　　　　(d) 3

158. The rate law for a reaction between the substances A and B is given by

$$rate = k[A]^n\,[B]^m$$

On doubling the concentration of A and halving the concentration of B, the ratio of the new rate to the earlier rate of the reaction will be ......

(a) $\dfrac{1}{2^{m+n}}$　　　　　(b) $(m + n)$　　　　　(c) $(n\ to\ m)$　　　　(d) $2(n - m)$

PREVIOUS YEAR'S QUESTIONS

1. For a reaction $2N_2O_5 \longrightarrow 4NO_2 + O_2$ rate and rate constant are $1.02 \times 10^{-4}\,mol\ L^{-1}\ s^{-1}$ and $3.4 \times 10^{-5}\,sec^{-1}$. The concentration of N_2O_5 at that time will be ......　　**[C.B.S.E. 2001]**

(a) $1.732\ mol\ L^{-1}$　　　　　　　　　(b) $3\ mol\ L^{-1}$

(c) $1.02 \times 10^{-4}\,mol\ L^{-1}$　　　　　　(d) $3.2 \times 10^5\,mol\ L^{-1}$

2. The rate constant of a reaction at temperature 200°K is 10 times less than the rate constant at 400 °K. What is the activation energy (E_a) of the reaction? (R = gas constant)

[E.A.M.C.E.T. 2003]

(a) 1842.4 R　　　　　(b) 921.2 R　　　　　(c) 460.6 R　　　　　(d) 230.3 R

3. An endothermic reaction with high activation energy for the forward reaction is given by the diagram　　**[A.I.I.M.S. 2005]**

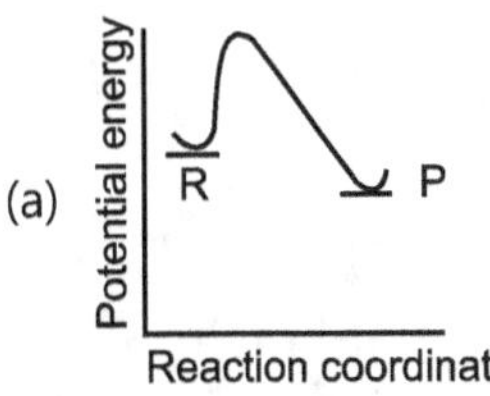

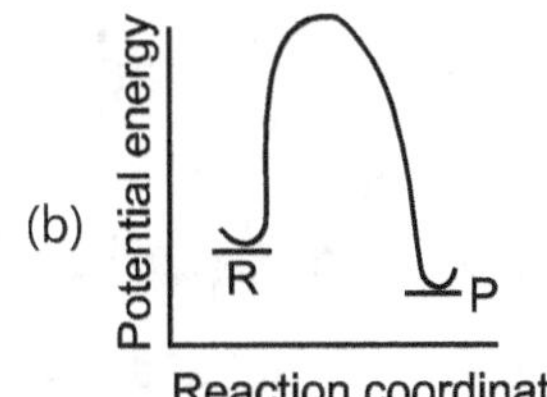

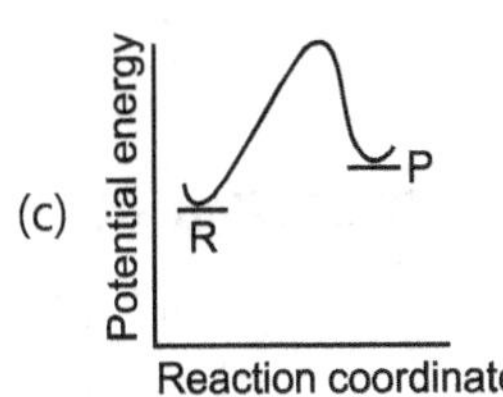

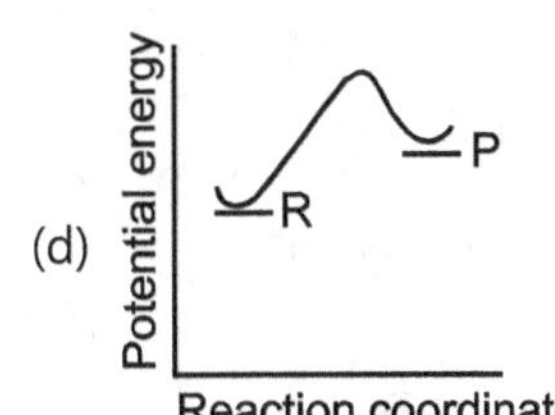

4. An exothermic chemical reaction proceeds by two stages　　　　**[Kerala P.M.T. 2006]**

reactants $\xrightarrow{\text{Stage I}}$ intermediate $\xrightarrow{\text{Stage II}}$ products.

The activation energy of stage I is 50 kJ mol^{-1}. The overall enthalpy change of the reaction is -100 kJ mol^{-1}. Which diagram could represent the energy level diagram for the reaction?

(a) 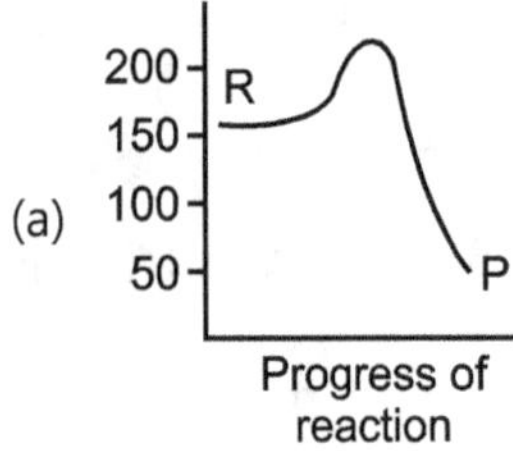

Progress of reaction

(b) 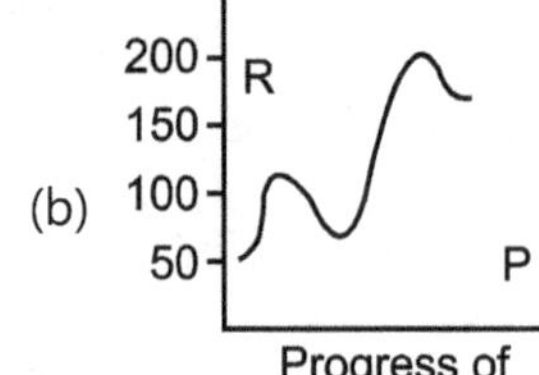

Progress of reaction

(c) 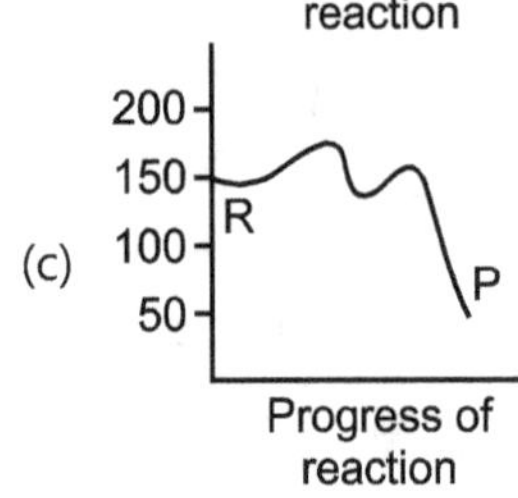

Progress of reaction

(d) 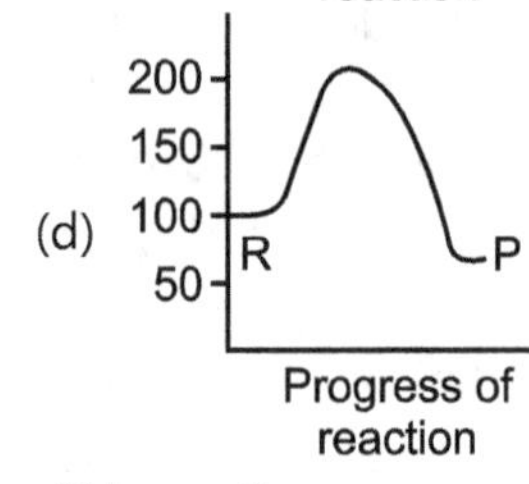

Progress of reaction

(e) 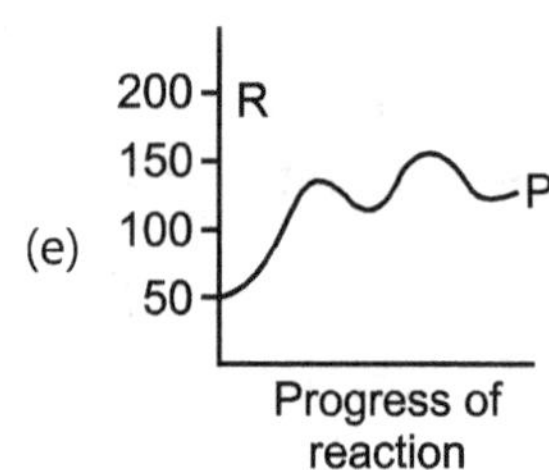

Progress of reaction

5. The first order reaction $2N_2O_{(g)} \longrightarrow 2N_{2(g)} + O_{2(g)}$　　　　**[D.P.M.T. 2010]**

has a rate constant of 1.3×10^{-11} s^{-1} at 270°C and 4.5×10^{-10} s^{-1} at 350°C. What is the activation energy for this reaction?

(a)　15 kJ　　　　(b)　30 kJ　　　　(c)　68 kJ　　　　(d)　120 kJ

6. Consider the decomposition of N_2O_5 as

$N_2O_5 \longrightarrow 2NO_2 + 1/2O_2$　　　　**[A.M.U. Medical 2010]**

The rate of reaction is given by,

$$\frac{d[N_2O_5]}{dt} = \frac{1}{2}\frac{[NO]}{dt} = 2\frac{d[O_2]}{dt}$$

$$= k_1 [N_2O_5]$$

$$\frac{+d[NO_2]}{dt} = 2k_1 [N_2O_5] = k_1' [N_2O_5]$$

$$\frac{+d[NO_2]}{dt} = \frac{1}{2} k_1 [N_2O_5] = k_1'' [N_2O_5]$$

Choose the correct option

(a)　$k_1 = k_1' = k_1''$　　　(b)　$k_1 = k_1' = k_1''$　　　(c)　$2k_1 = k_1' = k_1''$　　　(d)　$4k_1 = 2 k_1' = k_1''$

7. If the rate of reaction is equal to the rate constant, then the order of the reaction is

[C.B.S.E. P.M.T. 2003]

(a)　3　　　　(b)　0　　　　(c)　1　　　　(d)　2

8. $RCOOR' + H_2O \xrightarrow{\text{HCl}} RCOOH + R'OH$

What type of reaction is this?　　　　**[C.E.T. Karnataka 2001]**

(a) Second order　　　　　　　(b)　Unimolecular

(c) Pseudo unimolecular　　　　(d)　Third order

9. The rate of a first order reaction is 1.5×10^{-2} mol L^{-1} min^{-1} at 0.5 M concentration of the reactant. The half life of the reaction is ...... **[C.B.S.E. P.M.T. 2003]**

(a) 7.53 min   (b) 0.383 min   (c) 23.1 min   (d) 8.73 min

10. For a first order reaction, the rate constant is 6.909 min^{-1}. The time taken for 75% conversion in minutes is ...... **[Kerala C.E.T (Med.) 2009]**

(a) 3/2 log 2   (b) 2/3 log 3   (c) 2/3 log 2   (d) 3/2 log 3/4

(e) 2/3 log 4/3

11. For the reaction R $\rightarrow$ P, a graph of [R] against time is found to be a straight line with a negative slope. What is the order of reaction? **[J & K C.E.T. 2010]**

(a) Second order   (b) Third order   (c) First order   (d) Zero order

12. The rate constant of a second order reaction,

$$2A \longrightarrow \text{Products}$$

is 10^{-4} lit mole^{-1} min^{-1}. The initial concentration of the reactant is 10^{-2} mol lit^{-1}. What is the half life (in min)? **[J & K C.E.T. 2006]**

(a) 10   (b) 1000   (c) 100   (d) 10^{6}

13. The experimental rate law for a reaction

$$2A + 2B \longrightarrow \text{Products, is}$$

Rate $\propto C_A \, C_B^{1/2}$. If the concentration of both A and B are doubled, the rate of reaction increases by a factor of ...... **[Kerala Med. 2005]**

(a) $\sqrt{2}$ (b) 2   (c) $2\sqrt{2}$ (d) 4

(e) $4\sqrt{2}$

14. For a zero order reaction, the plot of concentration of a reactant vs time is (intercept refers to concentration axis) ...... **[Kerala P.E.T. 2008]**

(a) Linear with positive slope and zero intercept

(b) Linear with negative slope and zero intercept

(c) Linear with negative slope and non-zero intercept

(d) Linear with positive slope and non-zero intercept

15. For the reaction $H_2 + Cl_2 \xrightarrow{\text{Sunlight}} 2HCl$ **[A.I.I.M.S. 2002]**

taking place on water, the order of reaction is ......

(a) 0   (b) 1   (c) 2   (d) 3

16. The decomposition of a substance follows first order kinetics. If its concentration is reduced to $1/8^{th}$ of its initial value in 24 minutes, the rate constant of decomposition process is **[Kerala M.E.E. 2001]**

(a) 1/24 min^{-1} (b) 0.692/24 min^{-1}

(c) 2.303/24 log (1/8) min^{-1} (d) $\dfrac{2.303}{24}$ log (8/1) min^{-1}

17. The activation energy for a reaction at temperature T K was found to be 2.303 RT J mol^{-1}. The ratio of rate constant to Arrhenius factor is ......

[Kerala P.M.T. 2006, Karnataka C.E.T. 2010]

(a) 10^{-1} (b) 10^{-2} (c) 2×10^{-3} (d) 10^{-4}

18. Predict the rate law of the following reaction based on the data given below :

$$2A + B \longrightarrow C + 3D$$

[Kerala P.M.T. 2007]

[A] M	[B] M	Magnitude of initial rate, Ms^{-1}
1	1	x
2	1	2x
1	2	4x
2	2	8x

(a) Rate = $k[A][B]^2$
(b) Rate = $k[A]^2[B]$
(c) Rate = $k[A][B]$
(d) Rate = $k[A]^2$

19. The rate of a gaseous reaction triples when temperature is increased by 10°C from 25°C. The energy of activation of the reaction in $kJ\ mol^{-1}$ will be ...... **[M.P.P.M.T. 2009]**

(a) 410
(b) 735
(c) 514
(d) 205

20. The first order reaction was started with a decimolar solution of the reactant 8 minutes and 20 seconds later its concentration was found to be M/100. So the rate constant of the reaction is ...... **[Kerala P.M.T. 2004]**

(a) $2.303 \times 10^{-5}\ sec^{-1}$
(b) $2.303 \times 10^{-4}\ sec^{-1}$
(c) $4.606 \times 10^{-3}\ sec^{-1}$
(d) $2.606 \times 10^{-5}\ sec^{-1}$
(e) $2.606 \times 10^{-4}\ sec^{-1}$

21. The potential energy diagram for a reaction $R \rightarrow P$ is given by **[A.I.I.M.S. 2003]**

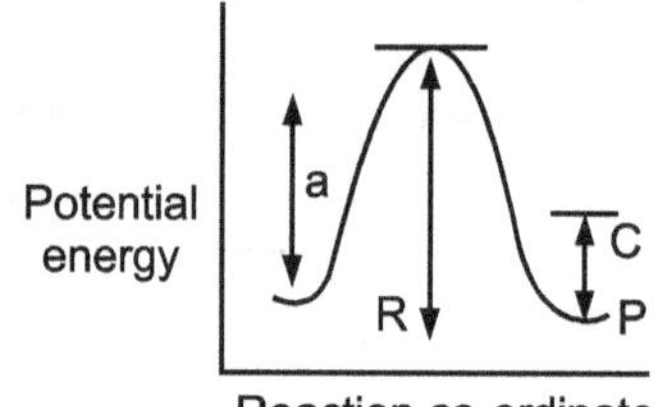

Fig. 2

$\Delta H°$ of the reaction corresponds to the energy ......

(a) a
(b) b
(c) c
(d) a + b

22. Which of the following is correct for a first order reaction? **[D.P.M.T. 2002]**

(a) $t_{1/2} \propto a$
(b) $t_{1/2} \propto a$
(c) $t_{1/2} \propto a^0$
(d) $t_{1/2} \propto \dfrac{1}{\alpha^2}$

23. What is the time required for a first order reaction to be 99% complete, compared to the time taken for the reaction to be 90% complete? **[Kerala Med. 2005]**

(a) There is no change
(b) Time taken is double
(c) Time taken is triple
(d) The time required is half the initial value
(e) The reaction is instantaneous

24. The substance with initial concentration of 'a' mole dm^{-3} proceeds according to zero order kinetics. The time it takes for the completion of the reaction is k = ... rate constants. **[Kerala Med. 2005]**

(a) k/a
(b) a/2k
(c) a/k
(d) 2k/a
(e) ka.

25. In Arrhenius equation, for activation energy, $k = Ae^{-E_a/RT}$, A represents the following ......

(1) Pre-exponential factor   (2) Frequency factor

(3) Arrhenius factor   (4) Collision factor and frequency

The correct answer is :   **[Kerala Med. 2005]**

(a) 1 and 3   (b) 1 and 2   (c) 2, 3 and 4   (d) 1, 2 and 3

26. When initial concentration of a reactant is doubled in a reaction, its half-life period is not affected. The order of the reaction is ......   **[AIPMT 2015]**

(a) First   (b) Second

(c) More than zero but less than first   (d) Zero

27. The rate constant of a reaction (k) is 175 litre^2 mol^2 sec^{-1}. What is the order of reaction?

       [Gujrat C.E.T. 2006]

(a) First   (b) Second   (c) Third   (d) Zero

28. The rate law equation for a reaction A $\longrightarrow$ is; ...... r = k [A°].

If the initial concentration is 'a' mol dm^{-3}, then the half life of the reaction is ......

       [Karnataka C.E.T. 2009, Gujarat C.E.T. 2009]

(a) $\dfrac{2k}{\alpha}$ (b) $\dfrac{0.693}{k}$ (c) $\dfrac{k}{a}$ (d) $\dfrac{\alpha}{2k}$

29. Hydrolysis of DDT is a first order reaction, its half life is 10 years. Time to hydrolyse 10 g DDT to half is ......   **[BVP 2004]**

(a) 100 years   (b) 20 years   (c) 5 years   (d) 10 years

30. In a first order reaction, the concentration of the reactant, decreases from 0.8 m to 0.4 m in 15 minutes. The time taken for the concentration to change from 0.1 m to 0.225 m is ......

       [AIEEE 2004]

(a) 7.5 minutes   (b) 15 minutes   (c) 30 minutes   (d) 60 minutes

31. In the first order reaction, the concentration of the reactant is reduced to 20% in one hour. The half-life period of the reaction is ......   **[DCE 2004]**

(a) 2 hr   (b) 4 hr   (c) 1/2 hr   (d) 1/4 hr

32. The rate of first order reaction is 1.5×10^2 mol L^{-1} sec^{-1} at 0.5 M concentration of the reactant. The half life of the reaction is ......   **[CBSE PMT 2004]**

(a) 8.73 min   (b) 7.53 min   (c) 0.383 min   (d) 23.1 min

33. In respect of the equation $k = Ae^{-E_a/RT}$ in chemical kinetics, which one of the following statement is correct ?   **[AIEEE 2003]**

(a) k is equilibrium constant   (b) A is adsorption factor

(c) E_a is energy of activation   (d) R is Rydberg's constant

34. The temperature dependence of rate constant (k) of a chemical reaction is written in terms of Arrhenius equation, $k = A \cdot e^{-E^*/RT}$. Activation energy (E*) of the reaction can be calculated by plotting ......   **[CBSE PMT 2003]**

(a) $\log k$ vs $\dfrac{1}{\log T}$ (b) k vs T (c) k vs $\dfrac{1}{\log T}$ (d) $\log k$ vs $\dfrac{1}{T}$

35. The reaction A → B follows first order kinetics. The time taken for 0.8 mole of A to produce 0.6 mole is 1h. What the time taken for conversion of 0.9 mole to produce 0.675 mole of B?

[CBSE AIIPMT 2003]

(a) 0.25 h   (b) 2 h   (c) 1 h   (d) 0.5 h

36. The potential energy for a reaction R → P is given below.   **[AIIMS 2003]**

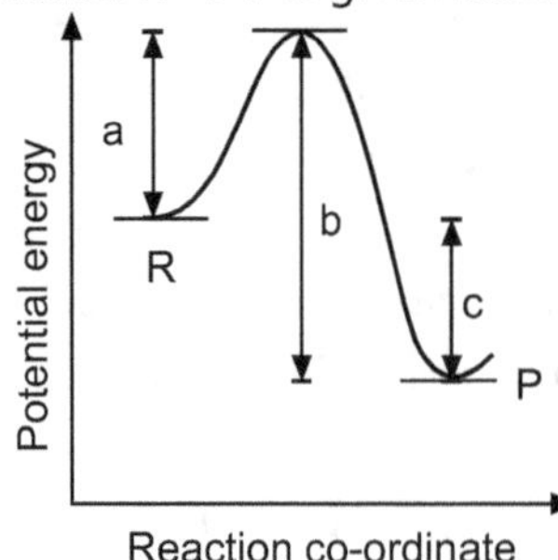

Fig. 3

ΔH° of the reaction corresponds to the energy

(a) a   (b) b   (c) c   (d) a + b

37. For the reaction system $2NO_{(g)} + O_{2(g)} \rightarrow 2NO_{2(g)}$ volume is suddenly produced to half its value by increasing the pressure in it. If the reaction is of first order with respect to O_2 and second order with respect to NO, then the reaction will ......   **[AIEE 2003]**

(a) diminish to one fourth of its initial value   (b) diminish to one eighth of its initial value

(c) increase to eight times of its initial value   (d) increase to four times of its initial value

38. If the rate of reaction is equal to the rate constant, then the order of the reaction is ......

(a) 3   (b) 0   (c) 1   (d) 2 **[CBSE PMT 2003]**

39. The reaction A → B follows first order kinetics. The time taken for 0.8 mole of A to produce 0.6 mole of B is 1 hour. What is the time taken for conversion of 0.9 mole of A to produce 0.675 mole of B ?   **[CBSE PMT 2003]**

(a) 2 hours   (b) 1 hour   (c) 0.5 hour   (d) 0.25 hour

40. A graph plotted between log k vs 1/T for calculating activation energy is shown by

[MP PET 2002]

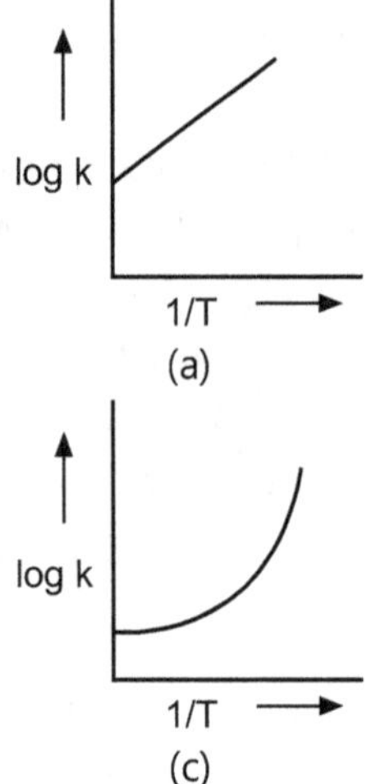

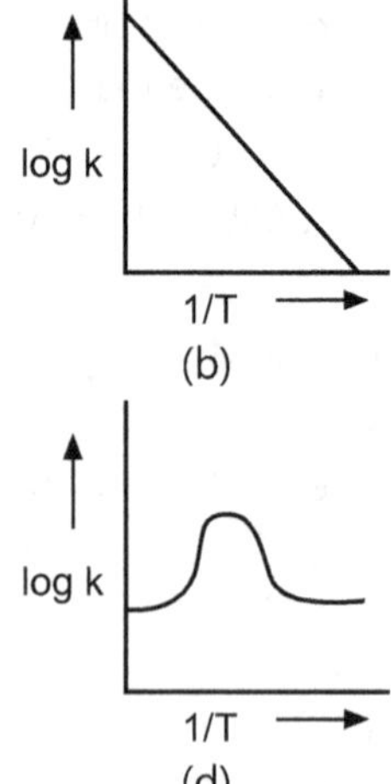

41. For the reaction $H_2 + Cl_2 \rightarrow 2HCl$ taking place on water, the order of the reaction is ......

[KCET 1998; AIIMS 2002; Pb.PMT 2002]

(a) 1 (b) 2 (c) 3 (d) 0

42. The rate of a first order reaction is 0.6932×10^{-2} mol/litre^{-1} and the initial concentration of the reactants is 1 M, $t_{1/2}$ is equal to ...... **[JIPMER (Med) 2001]**

(a) 6.932 min (b) 100 min

(c) 0.6932×10^{-3} min (d) 0.6932×10^{-2} min

43. A first order reaction is half completed in 45 minutes. How long does it need 99.9% of the reaction to be completed ? **[AIIMS 2001]**

(a) 5 hours (b) 7.5 hours (c) 10 hours (d) 20 hours

44. Substance 'A' decomposes by a first order reaction starting initially with [A] = 2.00 m and after 200 min, [A] = 0.12 m. For this reaction, what is the value of k ? **[AIIMS 2001]**

(a) 1.29×10^{-2} min^{-1} (b) 2.29×10^{-2} min^{-1}

(c) 3.29×10^{-2} min^{-2} (d) 24.40×10^{-2} min^{-1}

45. The rate of a chemical reaction depends upon ...... **[AFMC 2002]**

(a) Time (b) Pressure (c) Concentration (d) All of these

46. The rate of disappearance of SO_2 in the reaction $2SO_3 + O_2 \rightarrow 2SO_3$ is 1.28×10^{-3} g/sec then the rate of formation of SO_3 is ...... **[JIPMER 2002]**

(a) 0.64×10^{-3} g/sec (b) 0.80×10^{-3} g/sec

(c) 1.28×10^{-3} g/sec (d) 1.60×10^{-3} g/sec

47. The rate constant for a second order reaction is 8×10^{-5} M^{-1} min^{-1}. How long will it take for 1 M solution to be reduced to 0.5 M ? **[MHT CET 2001]**

(a) 8×10^{-5} min (b) 8.665×10^{3} min (c) 4×10^{-5} min (d) 1.25×10^{4} min

48. The rate constant k for the reaction $N_2O_{5(g)} \rightarrow 2NO_{2(g)} + \frac{1}{2}O_{2(g)}$ is 2.3×10^{-2} s^{-1}. Which equation given below describe the change of $[N_2O_5]$ with time? $[N_2O_5]_t$ corresponds to concentration of N_2O_5 initially and at time, t. **[AIIMS 2004]**

(a) $[N_2O_5]_t = [N_2O_5]_0 + kt$ (b) $[N_2O_5]_0 = [N_2O_5]_t \, e^{kt}$

(c) $\log_{10}[N_2O_5]_t = \log_{10}[N_2O_5]_0 - kt$ (d) $\ln \dfrac{[N_2O_5]_0}{[N_2O_5]_t} = kt$

49. For a reaction, $aA \rightarrow xP$, when [A] = 2.2 Mm, the rate was found to be 2.4 Mms^{-1}. On reducing the concentration of A to half, the rate changes to 0.6 Mms^{-1}. The order of reaction with respect to A is ...... **[AIIMS 2004]**

(a) 1.5 (b) 2.0 (c) 2.5 (d) 3.0

50. Which of the following graphs represent relation between initial concentration of reactants and half-life for third order reaction? **[AIIMS 2004]**

(a) $t_{1/2}$ vs Conc. (b) $t_{1/2}$ vs Conc. (c) $t_{1/2}$ vs $1/a$ (d) $t_{1/2}$ vs $1/a^2$

51. $A + 2B \rightarrow C + D$. If $-\dfrac{d[A]}{dt} = 5 \times 10^{-4}$ mol litre^{-1} s^{-1}, then $-\dfrac{d[B]}{dt}$ is ...... **[DPMT 2005]**

(a) 2.5×10^{-4} mol litre^{-1} s^{-1} (b) 5.0×10^{-4} mol litre^{-1} s^{-1}

(c) 2.5×10^{3} mol litre^{-1} s^{-1} (d) 1.0×10^{-3} mol litre^{-1} s^{-1}

52. The rate constant of the reaction $A \rightarrow B$ is 0.6×10^{-3} mole per second. If the concentration of A is 5 M, then concentration of B after 20 minutes is ...... **[AIPMT 2015]**

(a) 0.36 M (b) 0.72 M (c) 1.08 M (d) 3.60 M

53. For a first order reaction $A \rightarrow B$ the reaction rate at reactant concentration of 0.01 M is found to be 2.0×10^{-5} mol litre^{-1} s^{-1}. The half-life period of the reaction is ......

[CBSE PMT 2005]

(a) 20 s (b) 30 s (c) 300 s (d) 347 s

54. The rate of reaction between two reactants A and B decreases by a factor of 4. If the concentration of reactant B is doubled, the order of this reaction with respect to reactant B is ...... **[CBSE PMT 2005]**

(a) –1 (b) –2 (c) 1 (d) 2

55. If a substance with half life of 3 days is taken at other place in 12 days, what amount of substance is left now ? **[AFMC 2005]**

(a) 1/4 (b) 1/8 (c) 1/16 (d) 1/32

56. Which of the following reactions end in finite time ? **[DPMT 2005]**

(a) 0 order (b) 1st order (c) 2nd order (d) 3rd order

57. An endothermic reaction with high activation energy for the forward reaction is given by the diagram : **[AIIMS 2005]**

(a)

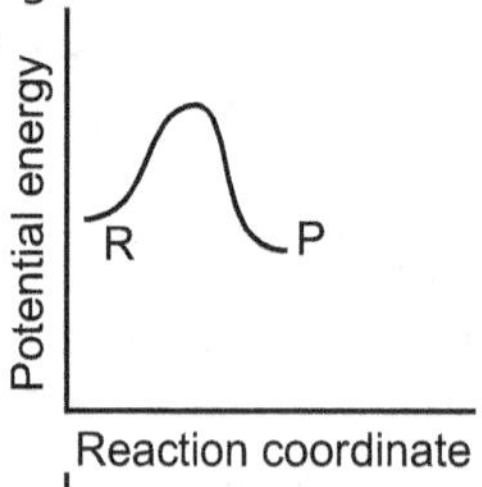

(b)

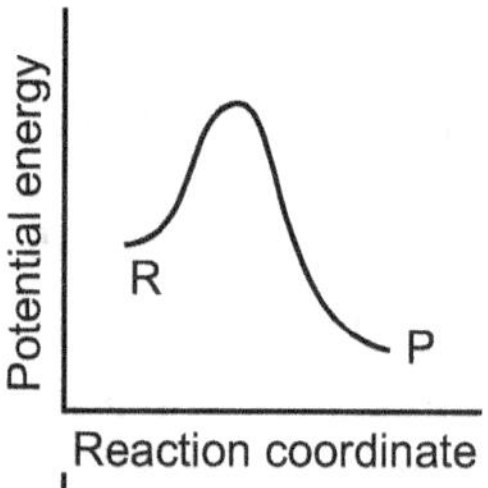

(c)

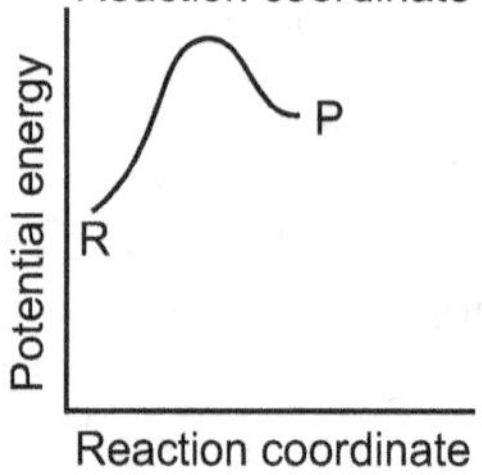

(d)

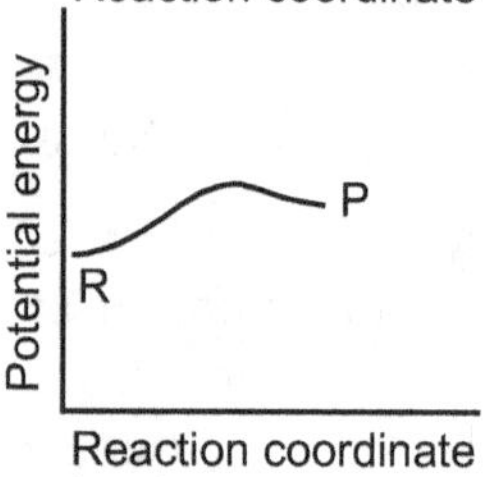

58. According to law of mass action, rate of a chemical reaction is proportional to ......

[AFMC 2005]

(a) concentration of reactants (b) molar concentration of reactants

(c) concentration of products (d) molar concentration of products

59. In a first order reaction $A \rightarrow B$, if k is rate constant and initial concentration of the reactant A is 0.5 M then the half-life is ...... **[CBSE AIPMT 2007]**

(a) $\dfrac{0.693}{0.5\,k}$ (b) $\dfrac{\log 2}{k}$ (c) $\dfrac{\log 2}{k\sqrt{0.5}}$ (d) $\dfrac{ln\,2}{k}$

60. **Assertion :** The hydrolysis of methyl acetate by dil HCl is a pseudo first order reaction.
    Reason : HCl acts as a catalyst for the hydrolysis.　　　　　　　**[AIIMS 2007]**
    (a) Both Assertion and Reason are true and Reason is the correct explanation of Assertion.
    (b) Both Assertion and Reason are true and Reason is not the correct explanation of Assertion.
    (c) Assertion is true but Reason is false
    (d) Both Assertion and Reason are false

61. The temperature dependence of rate constant (k) of a chemical reaction is written in terms of Arrhenius equation $k = Ae^{-E_a/RT}$. Activation energy (E_a) of the reaction can be calculated by plotting ......　　　　　　　**[AIIMS 2007]**
    (a) $\log k$ vs T　　　　(b) $\log k$ vs $\dfrac{1}{T}$　　　　(c) k vs T　　　　(d) k vs $\dfrac{1}{\log T}$

62. For a first order reaction, to obtain a positive slope, we need to plot (where "A" is the concentration of reaction A) ......　　　　　　　**[AIIMS 2008]**
    (a) $-\log_{10} [A]$ vs t　　　　　　　　　(b) $-\log_e [A]$ vs t
    (c) $\log_{10} [A]$ vs $\log t$　　　　　　　　(d) $[A]$ vs t

63. **Assertion :** The order of a reaction can have fraction value.　　　**[AIIMS 2008]**
    Reason : The order of a reaction cannot be written from balanced equation of a reaction.
    (a) Both Assertion and Reason are true and Reason is the correct explanation of Assertion.
    (b) Both Assertion and Reason are true and Reason is not the correct explanation of Assertion.
    (c) Assertion is true but Reason is false　　　　(d) Both Assertion and Reason are false

64. Consider the following statements　　　　　　　**[Manipal 2008]**
    The rate for the acid catalysed hydrolysis of an ester being given as
    Rate $= k[H^+]$ [ester] $= k'$[ester]. If the acid concentration is doubled at constant ester concentration
    (i) The second order rate constant, k is doubled.
    (ii) The pseudo first order rate constant, k is doubled
    (iii) The rate of the reaction is doubled.
    Which of the above statements are correct?
    (a) (i) and (ii)　　　　(b) (ii) and (iii)　　　　(c) (i) and (iii)　　　　(d) (i), (ii) and (iii)

65. The rate constants k_1 and k_2 for two different reactions are $10^{16} \cdot e^{-2000/T}$ and $10^{15} \cdot e^{-1000/T}$, respectively. The temperature at which $k_1 = k_2$ is ......　　　　　**[CBSE AIPMT 2008]**
    (a) 1000 k　　　　(b) $\dfrac{2000}{2.303}$ k　　　　(c) 2000 k　　　　(d) $\dfrac{1000}{2.303}$ k

66. The rate constant of a first order reaction at 27°C is 10^{-3} min^{-1}. The temperature coefficient of this reaction is 2. What is the rate constant (in min^{-1}) at 17°C for this reaction?
    　　　　　　　[AFMC 2008]
    (a) 10^{-3}　　　　(b) 5×10^{-4}　　　　(c) 2×10^{-3}　　　　(d) 10^{-2}

67. For the reaction, $N_2 + 3H_2 \rightarrow 2NH_3$, if $\dfrac{d[NH_3]}{dt} = 2 \times 10^{-4}$ mol L^{-1} s^{-1}, the value of $-\dfrac{d[H_2]}{dt}$ would be ......　　　　　　　**[CBSE AIPMT 2009]**
    (a) 3×10^{-4} mol L^{-1} s^{-1}　　　　　　　(b) 4×10^{-4} mol L^{-1} s^{-1}
    (c) 6×10^{-4} mol L^{-1} s^{-1}　　　　　　　(d) 1×10^{-4} mol L^{-1} s^{-1}

68. In the reaction BrO_3^- (aq) + $5Br^-$ (aq) + $6H^+ \rightarrow 3Br_2$ (l) + $3H_2O$ (l) **[AIIMS 2009]**
the rate of appearance of bromine (Br_2) is related to rate of disappearance of the bromide ions as following ......

(a) $\dfrac{d[Br_2]}{dt} = -\dfrac{3}{5}\dfrac{d[Br^{-1}]}{dt}$
(b) $\dfrac{d[Br_2]}{dt} = \dfrac{5}{3}\dfrac{d[Br^-]}{dt}$
(c) $\dfrac{d[Br_2]}{dt} = -\dfrac{5}{3}\dfrac{d[Br^-]}{dt}$
(d) $\dfrac{d[Br_2]}{dt} = \dfrac{3}{5}\dfrac{d[Br^-]}{dt}$

69. The half-life period of a first order reaction is 1386s. The specific rate constant of the reaction is ...... **[CBSE AIPMT 2009]**
(a) $5.0 \times 10^{-3}\ s^{-1}$
(b) $0.5 \times 10^{-2}\ s^{-1}$
(c) $0.5 \times 10^{-3}\ s^{-1}$
(d) $5.0 \times 10^{-2}\ s^{-1}$

70. For the reaction A + B $\rightarrow$ products, it is observed that ...... **[CBSE AIPMT 2009]**
(a) On doubling the initial concentration of A only, the rate of reaction is also doubled.
(b) On doubling the initial concentration of both A and B, there is a change by a factor of 8 in the rate of reaction.
The rate of this reaction is given by
(a) rate = $k[A]^2 [B]$
(b) rate = $k[A] [B]^2$
(c) rate = $k[A]^2 [B]^2$
(d) rate = $k[A] [B]$

71. For a reaction, the dimensions of rate constant are same as that of rate, hence order of the reaction is ...... **[AFMC 2009]**
(a) 0
(b) 1
(c) 2
(d) 3

72. In the presence of a catalyst, activation energy of reaction is lowered by 2 kcal at 27°C. Hence, rate will be ...... **[AFMC 2009]**
(a) 20 times
(b) 28 times
(c) 14 times
(d) remains the same

73. For the reaction $N_2O_{5(g)} \rightarrow 2NO_{2(g)} + \dfrac{1}{2} O_{2(g)}$ the value of the rate of disappearance of N_2O_5 is given as 6.25×10^{-13} mol $L^{-1} s^{-1}$. The rate of formation of NO_2 and O_2 is given respectively as **[CBSE AIPMT 2010]**
(a) 1.25×10^{-2} mol $L^{-1} s^{-1}$ and 6.25×10^{-3} mol $L^{-1} s^{-1}$
(b) 6.25×10^{-3} mol $L^{-1} s^{-1}$ and 6.25×10^{-3} mol $L^{-1} s^{-1}$
(c) 1.25×10^{-2} mol $L^{-1} s^{-1}$ and 3.125×10^{-3} mol $L^{-1} s^{-1}$
(d) 6.25×10^{-3} mol $L^{-1} s^{-1}$ and 3.125×10^{-3} mol $L^{-1} s^{-1}$

74. During the kinetic study of the reaction 2A + B $\rightarrow$ C + D, following results were obtained. **[CBSE AIPMT 2010]**

Run	[A]/mol L^{-1}	[B]/mol L^{-1}	Initial rate of formation of D/mol L^{-1} min^{-1}
I	0.1	0.1	6.0×10^{-3}
II	0.3	0.2	7.2×10^{-2}
III	0.3	0.4	2.88×10^{-1}
IV	0.4	0.1	2.40×10^{-2}

Based on the above data which one of the following is correct?
(a) rate = $k[A] [B]^2$
(b) rate = $k[A]^2 [B]$
(c) rate = $k[A] [B]$
(d) rate = $k[A]^2 [B]^2$

75. Which one of the following statements for the order of a reaction is incorrect?
(a) Order of reaction is always whole number **[CBSE AIPMT 2011]**
(b) Order can be determined only experimentally
(c) Order is not influenced by stoichiometric coefficient of reactants
(d) Order of reaction is sum of power to the concentration terms of reactants to express the rate of reaction.

76. Activation energy (E_a) and rate constants (k_1 and k_2) of a chemical reaction at two different temperatures T_1 and T_2 are related by ...... **[AIPMT 2012]**

(a) $\ln \dfrac{k_2}{k_1} = -\dfrac{E_a}{R}\left(\dfrac{1}{T_2} + \dfrac{1}{T_1}\right)$

(b) $\ln \dfrac{k_2}{k_1} = \dfrac{E_a}{R}\left(\dfrac{1}{T_1} + \dfrac{1}{T_2}\right)$

(c) $\ln \dfrac{k_2}{k_1} = \dfrac{E_a}{R}\left(\dfrac{1}{T_1} + \dfrac{1}{T_2}\right)$

(d) $\ln \dfrac{k_2}{k_1} = +\dfrac{E_a}{R}\left(\dfrac{1}{T_2} - \dfrac{1}{T_1}\right)$

77. What is the activation energy for a reaction if its rate doubles when the temperature is raised from 20°C to 35°C ? ($R = 8.314$ J mol^{-1} K^{-1}) **[NEET 2013]**

(a) 15.1 kJ mol^{-1}　　(b) 342 kJ mol^{-1}　　(c) 269 kJ mol^{-1}　　(d) 34.7 kJ mol^{-1}

ANSWER KEY

1. (d)	2. (d)	3. (a)	4. (b)	5. (d)	6. (c)	7. (d)	8. (d)
9. (b)	10. (b)	11. (a)	12. (d)	13. (c)	14. (d)	15. (c)	16. (d)
17. (c)	18. (a)	19. (b)	20. (a)	21. (a)	22. (b)	23. (b)	24. (c)
25. (c)	26. (d)	27. (a)	28. (d)	29. (b)	30. (a)	31. (b)	32. (c)
33. (c)	34. (a)	35. (b)	36. (b)	37. (b)	38. (b)	39. (b)	40. (b)
41. (b)	42. (b)	43. (d)	44. (d)	45. (d)	46. (d)	47. (d)	48. (d)
49. (d)	50. (d)	51. (c)	52. (d)	53. (d)	54. (d)	55. (c)	56. (c)
57. (c)	58. (b)	59. (d)	60. (c)	61. (d)	62. (c)	63. (d)	64. (d)
65. (c)	66. (b)	67. (d)	68. (c)	69. (a)	70. (a)	71. (b)	72. (b)
73. (d)	74. (b)	75. (b)	76. (d)	77. (c)	78. (d)	79. (c)	80. (a)
81. (d)	82. (c)	83. (d)	84. (b)	85. (d)	86. (a)	87. (d)	88. (c)
89. (d)	90. (d)	91. (d)	92. (b)	93. (d)	94. (d)	95. (b)	96. (a)
97. (c)	98. (b)	99. (c)	100. (c)	101. (c)	102. (c)	103. (a)	104. (c)
105. (c)	106. (a)	107. (b)	108. (a)	109. (b)	110. (b)	111. (a)	112. (d)
113.(d)	114. (b)	115. (a)	116. (d)	117. (c)	118. (c)	119. (c)	120. (a)
121. (b)	122. (a)	123. (a)	124. (c)	125. (b)	126. (a)	127. (a)	128. (b)
129. (a)	130. (a)	131. (c)	132. (a)	133. (d)	134. (b)	135. (c)	136. (c)
137. (d)	138. (b)	139. (b)	140. (c)	141. (c)	142. (b)	143. (c)	144. (a)
145. (a)	146. (c)	147. (c)	148. (c)	149. (d)	150. (c)	151. (a)	152. (c)
153. (c)	154. (a)	155. (c)	156. (a)	157. (c)	158. (d)		

Previous Year's Questions

1. (b)	2. (b)	3. (c)	4. (c)	5. (d)	6. (c)	7. (b)	8. (c)
9. (a)	10. (c)	11. (d)	12. (d)	13. (c)	14. (c)	15. (a)	16. (c)
17. (a)	18. (a)	19. (c)	20. (c)	21. (c)	22. (c)	23. (b)	24. (c)
25. (d)	26. (a)	27. (c)	28. (b)	29. (d)	30. (c)	31. (c)	32. (d)
33. (c)	34. (d)	35. (c)	36. (c)	37. (c)	38. (b)	39. (b)	40. (b)
41. (d)	42. (b)	43. (b)	44. (a)	45. (d)	46. (c)	47. (d)	48. (d)
49. (a)	50. (d)	51. (a)	52. (b)	53. (d)	54. (b)	55. (c)	56. (a)
57. (c)	58. (b)	59. (d)	60. (b)	61. (b)	62. (b)	63. (b)	64. (b)
65. (d)	66. (b)	67. (a)	68. (a)	69. (c)	70. (b)	71. (a)	72. (b)
73. (c)	74. (a)	75. (a)	76. (b)	77. (b)			

UNIT 18

SURFACE CHEMISTRY

1. The adsorption normally results in decrease in residual forces thereby ......
   (a) Decreasing the surface energy
   (b) Decreasing the activation energy
   (c) Increasing the surface energy
   (d) Increasing the activation energy

2. The amount of heat evolved when 1 mole of any gas is adsorbed on a solid adsorbent surface is called as ......
   (a) Entropy
   (b) Enthalpy
   (c) Heat of reaction
   (d) Enthalpy of adsorption

3. A substance which concentrates at the surface is called as ......
   (a) Adsorbate
   (b) Adsorbent
   (c) Absorbent
   (d) Sorbent

4. At the equilibrium position in the process of adsorption, enthalpy change is ......
   (a) $\Delta H > 0$
   (b) $\Delta H = T\Delta S$
   (c) $\Delta H < T\Delta S$
   (d) $\Delta H > T\Delta S$

5. For the process of adsorption, ΔH is ......
   (a) Positive
   (b) Negative
   (c) Zero
   (d) May be positive or negative

6. The term 'sorption' is applicable to ......
   (a) Absorption
   (b) Adsorption
   (c) Both absorption and adsorption
   (d) Desorption

7. If the substance is uniformly distributed throughout the body of a solid or a liquid, then it is called as ......
   (a) Adsorption
   (b) Chemisorption
   (c) Physisorption
   (d) Absorption

8. The absorption due to gas molecules being held to the solid surface by van der Waal's attractive forces is called as ......
   (a) Chemical adsorption
   (b) Physical adsorption
   (c) Chemisorption
   (d) Absorption

9. In adsorption of marsh gas on activated charcoal, charcoal is ......
   (a) Absorbent
   (b) Adsorbent
   (c) Adsorbate
   (d) Absorbate

10. Adsorption of gases on metal surface is called as
    (a) Diffusion
    (b) Occlusion
    (c) Partition
    (d) Dissolution

11. Which of the following is an example of absorption?
    (a) Water on silica gel
    (b) Water on calcium chloride
    (c) Hydrogen on finely divided nickel
    (d) Oxygen on metal surface

12. The mathematical expression for adsorption given by Freundlich is ......
    (a) $x/m = kP$
    (b) $x/n = kP$
    (c) $x/m = kP^{1/n}$
    (d) $x/m = kP^{n}$

18.1

13. Finely divided metals and porous substances provide ......
(a) Large surface area
(b) Small surface area
(c) No surface area
(d) Moderate surface area

14. The phenomenon of concentration of molecule of a gas, liquid or solid at a solid surface is called as ......
(a) Chemisorption
(b) Physisorption
(c) Adsorption
(d) Absorption

15. During the adsorption of Krypton on activated charcoal at low temperature, ...
(a) $\Delta H < 0$ and $\Delta S < 0$
(b) $\Delta H > 0$ and $\Delta S < 0$
(c) $\Delta H > 0$ and $\Delta S > 0$
(d) $\Delta H < 0$ and $\Delta S > 0$

16. The heats of adsorption in physisorption lie in the range (in kJ mol^{-1}) ......
(a) $1 - 10$
(b) $10 - 40$
(c) $40 - 100$
(d) $40 - 400$

17. Extent (x/m) of physisorption of a gas increases with ......
(a) Increase in temperature
(b) Decrease in strength of van der Waal's forces
(c) Decrease in temperature
(d) Decrease in surface area of adsorbent

18. Extent of adsorption of adsorbate from solution phase increases with ......
(a) Decrease in surface area of adsorbent
(b) Increase in temperature of solution
(c) Decrease in amount of adsorbate in solution
(d) Increase in amount of adsorbate in solution

19. Which one of the following is not applicable to the phenomenon of adsorption?
(a) $\Delta H > 0$
(b) $\Delta G < 0$
(c) $\Delta S < 0$
(d) $\Delta H < 0$

20. Physical adsorption decreases with ......
(a) High pressure
(b) Negative ΔH
(c) Higher critical temperature of adsorbate
(d) High temperature

21. The extent of adsorption of a gas on a solid depends on ......
(a) Temperature of the gas
(b) Pressure of the gas
(c) Nature of the gas
(d) All are correct

22. Which of the following characteristics is not correct for physical adsorption?
(a) Adsorption on solid is reversible
(b) Adsorption is spontaneous
(c) Adsorption increases with increase in temperature
(d) Both enthalpy and entropy of adsorption are negative

23. In physisorption, adsorbent is not specific for any particular gas because ......
(a) Gases involved behave like ideal gases
(b) Involved van der Waal's forces are universal
(c) Enthalpy of adsorption is low
(d) It is a reversible process

24. The plot of x/m versus temperature at constant pressure is called as ......

(a) Adsorption isotherm

(b) Adsorption isobar

(c) Adsorption isochore

(d) Freundlich isotherm

25. Freundlich adsorption isotherm gives a straight line on plotting ......

(a) (x/m) vs P

(b) log (x/m) vs P

(c) log (x/m) vs log P

(d) (x/m) vs (1/P)

26. For adsorption of gas on a solid, the plot of log x/m versus log P is linear with slope equal to (n being whole number) ......

(a) 1/n

(b) log k

(c) n

(d) log k

27. Which of the following curves is in accordance with Freundlich adsorption isotherm?

(a) 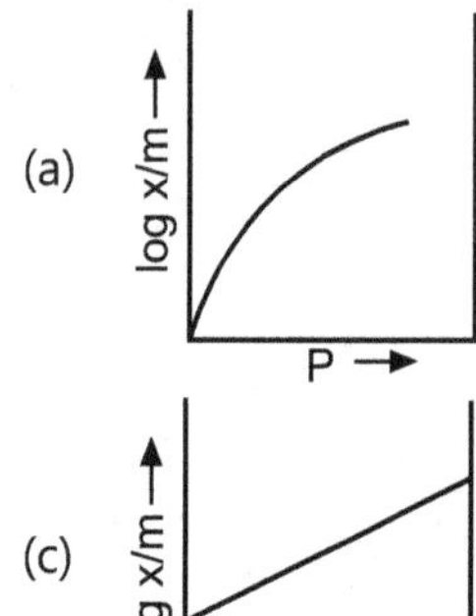

(b) 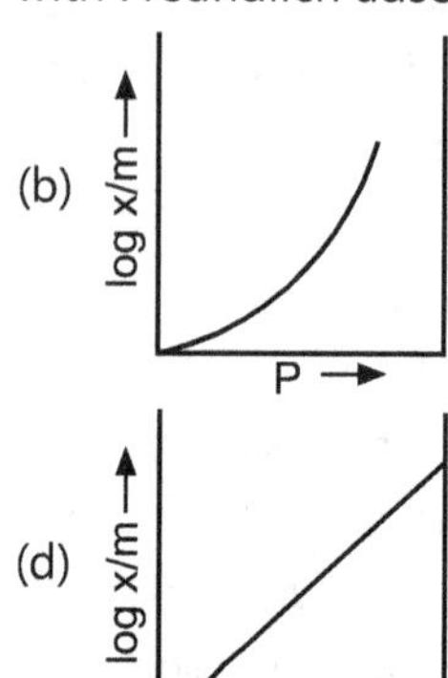

(c)

(d)

28. Freundlich adsorption isotherm is given by the expression $\dfrac{x}{m} = kP^{1/n}$. Which of the following conclusions can be drawn from this expression ?

(a) When 1/n = 0, the adsorption is independent of pressure

(b) When 1/n = 0, the adsorption is directly proportional to pressure

(c) When 1/n = 1, the adsorption is directly proportional to pressure

(d) When n = 0, plot of x/m versus P is a curve

29. In Langmuir's method of adsorption of a gas on a solid surface ......

(a) The rate of dissociation of adsorbed molecules from the surface does not depend on the surface covered

(b) The adsorption at a single site on the surface may involve multiple molecules at the same time

(c) The mass of gas striking a given area of surface is proportional to the pressure of the gas

(d) The mass of gas striking a given area of surface is independent of the pressure of the gas

30. 50 ml of 1 M oxalic acid is shaken with 0.5 g wood charcoal. The final concentration of the solution after adsorption is 0.5 M. The amount of oxalic acid absorbed per gm of carbon is ......

(a) 3.15 g   (b) 3.45 g   (c) 6.30 g   (d) 1.50 g

31. Physical adsorption of a gaseous species may change to chemical adsorption with ......

(a) Decrease in temperature   (b) Increase in temperature

(c) Increase in surface area of adsorbent   (d) Decrease in surface area of adsorbent

32. Which of the following statements are true with respect to adsorption of gas on a solid?

(i) The extent of adsorption is equal to kP^n according to Freundlich isotherm

(ii) The extent of adsorption is equal to $kP^{1/n}$ according to Freundlich isotherm

(iii) The extent of adsorption is equal to $(1 + bP) / aP$ according to Langmuir isotherm.

(iv) At low pressure, x/m is directly proportional to pressure.

(a) (i) and (iii)   (b) (i) and (iv)   (c) (ii) and (iii)   (d) (ii) and (iv)

33. A process in which substances are separated through differences in the rates at which the components migrate is called as ......

(a) Filtration   (b) Chromatography (c) Elution   (d) Titration

34. Chromatography is used to ......

(a) Separate two or more compounds based on their polarities.

(b) Separate two or more compounds based on their differential adsorption

(c) Separate two or more compounds based on how strongly they interact with other compounds

(d) More than one of the above

35. Which of the following process does not occur at the interface of phases?

(a) Crystallization   (b) Heterogeneous catalysis

(c) Homogeneous catalysis   (d) Corrosion

36. In which of the following reactions, heterogeneous catalysis is involved?

(a) $2SO_{2(g)} + O_{2(g)} \xrightarrow{NO_{(g)}} 2SO_{3(g)}$ (b) $2SO_{2(g)} \xrightarrow{Pt_{(s)}} 2SO_{3(g)}$

(c) $N_{2(g)} + 3H_{2(g)} \xrightarrow{Fe_{(s)}} 2NH_{3(g)}$

(d) $CH_3COOCH_{3(l)} + H_2O_{(l)} \xrightarrow{HCl_{(l)}} CH_3COOH_{(aq)} + CH_3OH_{(aq)}$

(a) b, c   (b) b, c, d   (c) a, b, c   (d) d

37. $SO_{2(g)} + \dfrac{1}{2} O_{2(g)} \underset{}{\overset{V_2O_{5(s)}}{\rightleftharpoons}} SO_{2(g)}$ is an example of ......

(a) Irreversible reaction   (b) Heterogeneous catalysis

(c) Homogeneous catalysis   (d) Neutralization reaction

38. According to adsorption theory of catalysis, the speed of the reaction increases because ...

   (a) Adsorption produces heat which increases the speed of the reaction

   (b) In the process of adsorption, the activation energy of the molecules becomes large

   (c) The concentration of the reactant molecules at the active centres of the catalyst becomes high due to adsorption

   (d) Adsorption lowers the activation energy of the reaction

39. Identify the correct statement regarding enzymes ......

   (a) Enzymes are specific biological catalysts that cannot be poisoned.

   (b) Enzymes are normally heterogeneous catalysts that are very specific in action

   (c) Enzymes are specific biological catalysts that can normally function at very high temperature (1000 K).

   (d) Enzymes are specific biological catalysts that possess well defined active sites.

40. The depth of the colour of the solution of methylene blue when treated with finely divided charcoal appreciably ......

   (a) Increases

   (b) Does not change

   (c) Decreases

   (d) May increase or may not increase

41. In the manufacture of cane sugar, the coloured solution is clarified by the treatment with ...

   (a) Semipermeable membrane

   (b) Animal charcoal

   (c) Coke

   (d) Coal

42. Which factor distinguishes a suspension from a colloid?

   (a) Light reflects off the particles of suspension

   (b) The particles of suspension will sink out if left over time to rest

   (c) Suspensions are clear

   (d) Suspensions cannot be filtered

43. An example of an emulsifying agent would be ......

   (a) Oil

   (b) Soap

   (c) Water

   (d) Salt

44. An example of a homogeneous mixture is ......

   (a) Sand and water

   (b) Flour and water

   (c) Salt dissolved in water

   (d) Oil and water

45. Size of colloidal particles is between ......

   (a) 1 nm to 100 nm

   (b) 10 nm to 1000 nm

   (c) 1 nm to 1000 nm

   (d) 100 nm to 1000 nm

46. Volume of a colloidal particle, V_c as compared to the volume of a solute particle in a true solution, V_s could be ......

   (a) $\dfrac{V_c}{V_s} \approx 1$

   (b) $\dfrac{V_c}{V_s} \approx 10^{-3}$

   (c) $\dfrac{V_c}{V_s} \approx 10^{3}$

   (d) $\dfrac{V_c}{V_s} \approx 10^{23}$

47. The colour of sky is due to ......

   (a) Absorption of light by atmospheric gases

   (b) Wavelength of scattered light

   (c) Transmission of light

   (d) All of these

48. Hydrophilic sols are stable due to ......

(a) Small size of the particles

(b) Large size of the particles

(c) Charge on the particles

(d) Attractive interaction between colloidal particles and dispersion medium

49. Which statement is true about Brownian motion ?

(a) Brownian motion is caused by collisions with molecules of the surrounding medium

(b) Brownian motion is the random movement of colloidal particles

(c) Brownian motion may be used to distinguish between solutions and colloids

(d) All of the above

50. Medically used emulsions for oral administration are usually .... type.

(a) o/w (b) w/o (c) w/o/w (d) o/w/o

51. An emulsifier is a substance which ......

(a) Coagulates the emulsion

(b) Homogenises the emulsion

(c) Stabilises the emulsion

(d) Accelerates the dispersion of liquid in liquid

52. At high concentration of soap in water, soap behaves as __________.

(a) Molecular colloid (b) Associated colloid

(c) Macromolecular colloid (d) Lyophilic colloid

53. When a sulphur sol is evaporated, sulphur is obtained. On mixing with water, sulphur sol is not formed. The sol is ......

(a) Reversible (b) Hydrophobic (c) Hydrophilic (d) Lyophilic

54. W/O emulsion is ......

(a) Cold cream (b) Vanishing cream (c) Milk (d) Cheese

55. Calcium palmitate, cholesterol and wool fat are emulsifiers used in the preparation of ......

(a) w/o (b) o/w (c) w/o/w (d) o/w/o

56. Colloidal dispersions are distinguished from the solutions and coarse dispersions on the basis of ......

(a) Viscosity (b) Density (c) Particle size (d) None of these

57. The main difference between a suspension and a colloid is that ......

(a) In suspensions the particles eventually settle at the bottom

(b) In colloids the particles eventually settle at the bottom

(c) In colloids, the solute is permanently dissolved in the solvent

(d) None of these

58. A biological colloid is prevented from coagulating by ......

(a) Steric (polymeric) stabilizers only

(b) Electrostatic stabilizers only

(c) Charged species bound to the surface only

(d) Both steric (polymeric) and electrostatic stabilizers

59. Which of the following is not an example of a colloid?

(a) Milk　　　　　(b) Paint　　　　　(c) Blood　　　　　(d) An isotonic solution

60. In a colloidal solution ......

(a) The size of a colloidal particle lies roughly between 0.1 nm to 1 nm

(b) The particles have a tendency to settle when the solution is left standing

(c) The particles pass through ultrafilter papers and animal and vegetable membranes

(d) The dispersed phase is uniformly distributed in the dispersion medium

61. A colloidal solution of a solid as dispersed phase and liquid as dispersion medium is known as ......

(a) Gel　　　　　(b) Sol　　　　　(c) Solid foam　　　(d) Emulsion

62. Tyndall effect depends upon the ......

(a) Charge on the colloidal particles

(b) Difference between the refractive indices of dispersed phase and dispersion medium

(c) Size of the colloidal particles

(d) Magnitude of the charge

63. Tyndall effect can be observed in ......

(a) Colloidal solution　(b) Solvent　　　(c) Solute　　　　(d) Precipitate

64. Which of the following will show Tyndall effect?

(a) Aqueous solution of soap below critical micelle concentration

(b) Aqueous solution of soap above critical micelle concentration

(c) Aqueous solution of sodium chloride

(d) Aqueous solution of sugar

65. When a beam of light is passed through colloidal solution, it is ......

(a) Scattered　　　(b) Reflected　　　(c) Deviated　　　(d) Adsorbed

66. What phenomenon clearly distinguishes a colloid from a solution?

(a) Adsorption　　　　　　　　　(b) Tyndall effect

(c) Brownian motion　　　　　　　(d) Electrical charge effect

67. As you enter the building, you observe a beautiful beam of light from the glass roof. What best explains this phenomenon?

(a) Adsorption　　　　　　　　　(b) Tyndall effect

(c) Brownian motion　　　　　　　(d) Electrical charge effect

68. Brownian movement is found in ......

(a) Unsaturated solution

(b) Saturated solution

(c) Colloidal solution

(d) Suspension solution

69. The random or zigzag motion of colloidal particles in the dispersion medium is referred as ......

(a) Tyndall effect

(b) Brownian movement

(c) Electrophoresis

(d) Electro-osmosis

70. Which of the following solutions will be transparent to bright source of light?

(a) Boiled starch solution

(b) Sugar solution

(c) Egg white solution

(d) Flour solution

71. The migration of colloidal particles under the influence of electric field is known as ......

(a) Electrophoresis

(b) Tyndall effect

(c) Dialysis

(d) Brownian movement

72. Colloidal solution can be purified by method of ......

(a) Dialysis

(b) Peptization

(c) Oxidation

(d) Mechanical dispersion

73. The process of separation of crystalloids by using the semipermeable membrane is referred to as ......

(a) Ultrafiltration   (b) Dialysis   (c) Filtration   (d) Electrophoresis

74. Which one of the following impurities present in colloidal solution cannot be removed by electrodialysis ?

(a) Sodium chloride

(b) Potassium sulphate

(c) Urea

(d) Calcium chloride

75. Which of the following involves adsorption?

(a) Plating of copper on a steel object

(b) Brown colour of eyes of Filipinos

(c) Adherence of paint to wood surfaces

(d) Removal of odour inside a refrigerator using charcoal

76. A colloidal system having a liquid substance as a dispersed phase and a solid as a dispersion medium is classified as ......

(a) Solid sol   (b) Gel   (c) Emulsion   (d) Sol

77. Which of the following size of the solute particles represent a suspension?

(a) 10 nm   (b) Less than 10 nm   (c) 100 nm   (d) 1100 nm

78. Which of the following materials can produce a true solution?

(a) Common salt   (b) Garden soil   (c) Boiled starch   (d) Corn flour

79. Which of the following is correct for lyophilic sols?

(a) They are irreversible

(b) They are formed by inorganic substances

(c) They are readily coagulated by addition of electrolytes

(d) They are self stabilized

80. Which of the following is a positively charged colloid?

    (a) Haemoglobin   (b) As_2S_3 sol   (c) CdS sol   (d) Sb_2S_3 sol

81. Which of the following process is not responsible for the presence of electric charge on sol particles?

    (a) Electron capture by sol particles

    (b) Absorption of ionic species from solution

    (c) Adsorption of ionic species from solution

    (d) Formation of Helmholtz electrical double layer

82. Fog is a colloidal dispersion of ......

    (a) Solid in a gas   (b) Liquid in a liquid   (c) Gas in a gas   (d) Liquid in a gas

83. Milk is an example of

    (a) Sol   (b) Gel   (c) Emulsion   (d) Foam

84. The dispersion of solid phase in a gas dispersion medium is called as ......

    (a) Sol   (b) Aerosol   (c) Gel   (d) Foam

85. The following is an example of gel

    (a) Milk   (b) Fog   (c) Soap   (d) Cheese

86. The process of precipitation of the colloidal sol is called as ......

    (a) Peptization   (b) Electrophoresis   (c) Coagulation   (d) Filtration

87. The dispersed phase, dispersion medium and nature of colloidal solution (lyophobic or lyophilic) of gold sol respectively are ......

    (a) Solid, solid, lyophobic   (b) Liquid, liquid, lyophobic

    (c) Solid, liquid, lyophobic   (d) Solid, liquid, lyophilic

88. Which one of the following set represents same type of solution?

    (a) Milk, Emulsion, Sugar   (b) Fog, Milk, Salt

    (c) Gel, Cheese, Chalk Powder   (d) Boot Polish, Butter, Cheese

89. When egg yolk is added to oil and water with vinegar to make mayonnaise, the egg yolk serves as ......

    (a) Solvent   (b) Coagulant   (c) Surfactant   (d) Emulsifying agent

90. Which of the following is an example of micelle system ?

    (a) Soap + water   (b) Protein + water

    (c) As_2O_3 + $Fe(OH)_3$ (d) Colloidal solution

91. The clustering of colloidal phase particles reasonably at high concentrations to form thermodynamically stable, bigger particles of colloidal dimensions in washing machines to ......

    (a) Associate colloids   (b) Lyophilic colloids

    (c) Lyophobic colloids   (d) Electrophilic colloids

92. Among the following, the surfactant that will form micelle in aqueous solution at the lowest molar concentration at ambient conditions is ......

    (a) $CH_3(CH_2)_{15}N^+(CH_3)_3Br^-$

    (b) $CH_3(CH_2)_{11}OSO_3^- Na^+$

    (c) $CH_3(CH_2)_6COO^-Na^+$

    (d) $CH_3(CH_2)_{11}N^+(CH_3)_3Br^-$

93. Emulsion is a colloidal dispersion of ......

    (a) Gas in liquid　　(b) Gas in gas　　(c) Solid in liquid　　(d) Liquid in liquid

94. The coagulation power of an electrolyte for As_2S_3 decreases in the order ......

    (a) Na^+, Al^{3+}, Ba^{2+}　　(b) $Cl^-, SO_4^{2-}, PO_4^{3-}$　　(c) Al^{3+}, Ba^{2+}, Na^+　　(d) Cl^-

95. The coagulating power of ions Na^+, Mg^{2+} and Al^{3+} on As_2S_3 sol is in the order ......

    (a) $Al^{3+} > Mg^{2+} > Na^+$

    (b) $Na^+ > Mg^{2+} > Al^{3+}$

    (c) $Mg^{2+} > Al^{3+} > Na^+$

    (d) $Na^+ > Al^{3+} > Mg^{2+}$

96. Which of the following electrolytes is least effective in causing flocculation of ferric hydroxide sol ?

    (a) $K_3[Fe(CN)_6]$　　(b) K_2CrO_4　　(c) KBr　　(d) K_2SO_4

97. The method by which lyophobic sol can be protected is ......

    (a) By addition of oppositely charged sol

    (b) By addition of an electrolyte

    (c) By addition of lyophilic sol

    (d) By boiling

98. Which of the following can bring about the coagulation of $Fe(OH)_3$ sol quickest and in the least concentration ?

    (a) KCl　　(b) Na_2SO_4　　(c) $AlPO_4$　　(d) $K_4Fe(CN)_6$

99. The coagulation of 100 ml of colloidal sol of gold is completely prevented from coagulation by the addition of 0.25 g of a substance 'X' to it, before adding 1% NaCl solution. The gold number of 'X' is ......

    (a) 0.25　　(b) 25　　(c) 250　　(d) 2.5

100. Which of the following electrolytes will have maximum coagulating value for AgI/Ag^+ sol?

    (a) Na_2S　　(b) Na_2SO_4　　(c) $NaCl$　　(d) Na_3PO_4

101. Which of the following electrolytes will have maximum flocculation value of $Fe(OH)_3$ sol?

    (a) $NaCl$　　(b) Na_2S　　(c) $(NH_4)_3PO_4$　　(d) K_2SO_4

102. Which of the following will have the most coagulating power for arsenious sulphide sol ?

    (a) Na^+　　(b) Mg^{2+}　　(c) Al^{3+}　　(d) Ca^{2+}

103. Gold number is a measure of ......

    (a) Electrical charge on colloidal particles

    (b) Size of the colloidal particles

    (c) Coagulating power of lyophilic colloid

    (d) Protective power of lyophilic colloid

104. The protective action of different colloids is expressed in terms of ......

    (a) Avogadro number

    (b) Gold number

    (c) Oxidation number

    (d) Atomic number

105. Which of the following has the maximum protective action ?

(a) Gelatin　　　　(b) Gum-arabic　　(c) Starch　　　　(d) Egg albumin

106. What happens when a lyophilic sol is added to a lyophobic sol?

(a) Colloidal mixture is formed

(b) Lyophilic sol is protected

(c) Film of lyophilic sol is formed over lyophobic sol

(d) Film of lyophobic sol is formed over lyophilic sol

107. Which of the following can act as a protective colloid ?

(a) Hydrophilic　　(b) Hydrophobic　(c) Gold sol　　(d) Both (a) and (b)

108. Alum helps in purifying water by ......

(a) Coagulating the mud particles

(b) Sulphate part which combines with dirt and removes it

(c) Forming Si complex with clay particles

(d) Making mud water soluble

109. Which of the following process is responsible for the formation of delta at a place where rivers meet the sea?

(a) Emulsification　　(b) Colloid formation　(c) Coagulation　(d) Peptization

110. Silver nano particles are used in housing appliances such as refrigerator or washing machines to ......

(a) Give shine to cloth　(b) Cleaning　　(c) Kill bacteria　(d) Air cooling

111. The basic principle of Cottrell's precipitator is ......

(a) Le-Chatelier's principle

(b) Peptization

(c) Neutralisation of charge on colloidal particles

(d) Scattering of light

112. A liquid is found to scatter a beam of light but leaves no residue when passed through the filter paper. The liquid can be described as ......

(a) A suspension　　(b) Oil　　　(c) A colloidal sol　(d) True solution

113. As_2S_3 sol is ......

(a) Positive colloid　(b) Negative colloid　(c) Neutral colloid　(d) None of these

114. A colloidal solution is subjected to an electrical field. The particles move towards anode. The coagulation of same sol is studied using NaCl, $BaCl_2$ and $AlCl_3$ solutions. Their coagulating power should be ......

(a) $NaCl > BaCl_2 > AlCl_3$　　　　　(b) $BaCl_2 > AlCl_3 > NaCl$

(c) $AlCl_3 > BaCl_2 > NaCl$　　　　　(d) $BaCl_2 > NaCl > AlCl_3$

115. For adsorption of a gas on a solid, the plot of log x/m versus log P is linear with slope equal to (n being whole number) ......

(a) k　　　　(b) log k　　　(c) n　　　　(d) 1/n

116. Which of the following constitute irreversible colloidal system in water as dispersion medium ?

    (a) Clay   (b) Platinum   (c) $Fe(OH)_3$ (d) All of these

117. The stability of lyophilic colloid is due to which of the following ?

    (a) Charge on their particles   (b) Large size of their particles

    (c) Small size of their particles   (d) A layer of dispersion medium

118. Catalyst only ......

    (a) Decreases activation energy   (b) Increases activation energy

    (c) Brings about equilibrium   (d) None of these

119. The cause of Brownian movement is ......

    (a) Heat changes in liquid state

    (b) Conventional currents

    (c) The impact of molecules of the dispersion medium on the colloidal particles

    (d) Attractive forces between the colloidal particles and molecules of dispersion medium

120. Random motion of colloidal particles is known as ......

    (a) Dialysis   (b) Brownian movement

    (c) Electro-osmosis   (d) Tyndall effect

121. Milk can be preserved by adding a few drops of ......

    (a) Formic acid solution   (b) Formaldehyde solution

    (c) Acetic acid solution   (d) Acetaldehyde solution

122. Which of the following is a lyophilic colloid ?

    (a) Milk   (b) Gum   (c) Fog   (d) Blood

123. Point out the false statement :

    (a) Brownian movement and Tyndall effect are shown by colloidal systems

    (b) Gold number is a measure of the protective power of lyophilic colloid

    (c) The colloidal solution of a liquid in liquid is called gel

    (d) Hardy-Schulz's rule is related with coagulation

124. In Zeigler-Natta polymerization of ethylene the active species is ......

    (a) $AlCl_3$ (b) Et_3Al (c) CH_2CH_2 (d) Ti^{3+}

125. Alum helps in purifying water by ......

    (a) Forming Si complex with clay particles

    (b) Sulphate part which combines with dirt and removes it

    (c) Aluminium which coagulates the mud particle

    (d) Making mud water soluble

126. Identify the gas which is readily adsorbed by activated charcoal ......

    (a) N_2 (b) SO_2 (c) H_2 (d) O_2

127. Which is the equation form of Langmuir isotherm under high pressure ?

    (a) $\dfrac{x}{m} = \dfrac{a}{b}$ (b) $\dfrac{x}{m} = aP$ (c) $\dfrac{x}{m} = \dfrac{1}{aP}$ (d) $\dfrac{x}{m} = \dfrac{b}{a}$

128. If (x/m) is the mass of the adsorbate adsorbed per unit mass of adsorbent, P is pressure of the adsorbate gas and a and b are constants, which of the following represents Langmuir adsorption isotherm ?

(a) $\log \dfrac{x}{m} = \log\left(\dfrac{a}{b}\right) + \dfrac{1}{a}\log P$

(b) $\dfrac{x}{m} = \dfrac{b}{a} + \dfrac{1}{aP}$

(c) $\dfrac{x}{m} = \dfrac{1 + bP}{aP}$

(d) $\dfrac{1}{x/m} = \dfrac{a}{b} + \dfrac{P}{a}$

(e) $\dfrac{1}{(x/m)} = \dfrac{b}{a} + \dfrac{1}{aP}$

129. The gold numbers of some colloids are given below ......

COLLOID	GOLD NUMBER
A	0.01
B	2.5
C	20

The protective nature of these colloids follows the following order ......

(a) $C > B > A$　　(b) $A > B > C$　　(c) $A = B = C$　　(d) $B > A > C$

130. The physical states of dispersed phase and dispersion medium in colloid like pesticide spray respectively are ......

(a) Solid, gas　　(b) Gas, liquid　　(c) Liquid, gas　　(d) Liquid, solid

131. In Langmuir's method of adsorption of a gas on a solid surface ......

(a) The mass of gas striking a given area of surface is proportional to the pressure of the gas

(b) The mass of gas striking a given area of surface is independent of the pressure of the gas

(c) The rate of dissociation of adsorbed molecules, from the surface does not depend on the surface covered

(d) The adsorption at a single site on the surface covered

132. Due to adsorption ......

(a) surface energy increases　　　　(b) surface energy becomes zero

(c) surface energy decreases　　　　(d) no change occurs in surface energy

133. On the basis of critical temperature for the gases carbon dioxide, sulphur dioxide, methane and hydrogen, predict which of gases show least adsorption on a definite amount of charcoal?

Gas	CO_2	SO_2	CH_4	H_2
Critical temp./K	304	630	190	33

(a) CO_2　　　　(b) SO_2　　　　(c) CH_4　　　　(d) H_2

134. Which of the following statement is not true ?

(a) The value of adsorption enthalpy of physical adsorption is less than chemical adsorption.

(b) Physical adsorption occurs due to van der Waals' forces

(c) Chemical adsorption decreases at high temperacture and low pressure.

(d) Physical adsorption is reversible

135. Which one of the following characteristics is not correct for physical adsorption ?

  (a) Adsorption on solids is reversible.

  (b) Adsorption increases with increase in temperature

  (c) Adsorption is spontaneous

  (d) Both enthalpy and entropy of adsorption are negative

136. At which temperature, chemical adsorption occurs ?

  (a) At high temperature　　　　　　　　(b) At very low temperature

  (c) At low temperature　　　　　　　　　(d) Temperature does not affect.

137. Which of the following statements is incorrect regarding physisorption ?

  (a) It occurs because of van der Waal's forces

  (b) More easily liquefiable gas is absorbed readily

  (c) Under high pressure it results into multimolecular layers on adsorbent surface

  (d) Enthalpy of adsorption (ΔH adsorption) is low and positive

138. Gas having high enthalpy of adsorption is ......

  (a) H_2　　　　　　(b) N_2　　　　　　(c) H_2O　　　　　　(d) He

139. The value of slope in the graph of log P versus x/m in Freundlich adsorption isotherm represents ......

  (a) 1/P　　　　　　(b) 1/n　　　　　　(c) 1/a　　　　　　(d) –k

140. The intercept in a graph of Freundlich adsorption isotherm is ......

  (a) k　　　　　　(b) log k　　　　　　(c) 1/a　　　　　　(d) 1/n

141. If the value of 1/n becomes zero in Freundlich adsorption isotherm then adsorption is independent of ......

  (a) pressure　　　　(b) temperature　　　(c) quantity　　　(d) a and b

142. The correct statement(s) pertaining to adsorption of a gas on a solid surface is (are) ......　　　　　　**[I.I.T. 2011]**

  (a) Adsorption is always exothermic

  (b) Physisorption may transform into chemisorption at high temperature

  (c) Physisorption increases with increasing temperature but chemisorption decreases with increasing temperature

  (d) Chemisorption is more exothermic than physisorption, however it is very slow due to higher energy of activation

143. Adsorption of gases on solid surface is generally exothermic because ......

  (a) Enthalpy is positive　　　　　　　　(b) Entropy decreases

  (c) Entropy increases　　　　　　　　　(d) Free energy increases

144. If the value of 1/n is 1 in Freundlich adsorption isotherm then x/m = ---

  (a) k/P　　　　　　(b) kP　　　　　　(c) k　　　　　　(d) none of these

145. The volume of gases H_2, CH_4, CO_2 and NH_3 absorbed by 1 gm of activated charcoal at 298 °K are in the order ......

  (a) $H_2 > CH_4 > CO_2 > NH_3$　　　　　　(b) $CH_4 > CO_2 > NH_3 > H_2$

  (c) $CO_2 > NH_3 > H_2 > CH_4$　　　　　　(d) $NH_3 > CO_2 > CH_4 > H_2$

  (e) $CO_2 > NH_3 > CH_4 > H_2$

146. 0.25 g of starch sol is required to prevent coagulation of 10 ml gold sol when 1 ml of 10% NaCl solution is present. What is gold number of starch sol ?

    (a) 0.25   (b) 2.5   (c) 250   (d) 0.025

147. For the preparation of which substances, reversible micelle is used ?

    (a) Medicines   (b) Nano products
    (c) Rubber plating   (d) All of these

148. Which of the following substance is used as a stabilizer in emulsion ?

    (a) Protein   (b) Gum   (c) Agar   (d) All the given

149. Tyndall effect is associated with which property of colloid ?

    (a) Mechanical   (b) Colligative   (c) Optical   (d) Electrical

150. Which method is used for demulsification ?

    (a) Sublimation   (b) Distillation   (c) Filtration   (d) Centrifugation

151. At CMC the surfactant molecule ......

    (a) Decomposes   (b) Becomes completely soluble
    (c) Associates   (d) Dissociates

152. Which of the following substances contain negative charge in their colloidal solution ?

    (a) Arsenious sulphide (b) Platinum   (c) Gold-Silver   (d) All of these

153. Which peptizing agent is used to obtain sol of $Fe(OH)_3$?

    (a) HCl   (b) $FeCl_2$ (c) KCl   (d) $FeCl_3$

154. Which of the following is correct order of coagulations for the coagulation of As_2S_3?

    (a) $Fe^{3+} > Ba^{2+} > Na^+$ (b) $Na^+ > Ba^{2+} > Fe^{3+}$
    (c) $Fe^{3+} > Na^+ > Ba^{2+}$ (d) $Ba^{2+} > Na^+ > Fe^{3+}$

155. Which of the following is correct order of coagulation ions for the coagulation of $Fe(OH)_3$?

    (a) $Cl^- > SO_4^{2-} > PO_4^{3-}$ (b) $PO_4^{3-} > SO_4^{2-} > Cl^-$
    (c) $SO_4^{2-} > Cl^- > PO_4^{3-}$ (d) $SO_4^{2-} > PO_4^{3-} > Cl^-$

156. Which method is used to obtain sol of gold and silver ?

    (a) Electric dispersion   (b) Peptization
    (c) Excessive cooling   (d) Mechanical dispersion

157. What is the approximate value of CMC for soap ?

    (a) 10^{-9} M to 10^4 M   (b) 10^{-3} M to 10^{-4} M
    (c) 10^{-9} M to 10^{-14} M   (d) 10^3 M to 10^5 M

158. Which of the following is physical method for the preparation of colloidal sol ?

    (a) coagulation   (b) peptization
    (c) fusion   (d) excessive cooling

159. On addition of one ml solution of 10% NaCl to 10 ml gold solution in the presence of 0.025 g of starch, the coagulation is prevented because starch has the following gold numbers.

    (a) 25   (b) 0.02   (c) 0.25   (d) 2.5

160. The dispersed phase in colloidal iron (II) hydroxide and colloidal gold is positively and negatively charged respectively. Which of the following statements is not correct ?
(a) Mixing the sols has no effect
(b) Coagulation in both sols can be brought about by electrophoresis
(c) Magnesium chloride solution coagulates the gold sol more readily than the iron (III) hydroxide sol.
(d) Sodium sulphate solution causes coagulation in both sols.

161. Which sol is formed due to hydrolysis of $FeCl_3$?
(a) $FeCl_2$　　　　(b) $Fe(OH)_2$　　　　(c) Fe_2O_3　　　　(d) $Fe(OH)_3$

162. Which of the following is double decomposition ?
(a) $SO_2 + 2H_2S \rightarrow 3S + 2H_2O$　　　　(b) $FeCl_3 + 2H_2O \rightarrow Fe(OH)_2 + 3HCl$
(c) $As_2O_3 + 3H_2S \rightarrow As_2S_3 + 3H_2O$　　　　(d) All the given

163. Which of the following ions can cause coagulation of proteins ?
(a) Ag^+　　　　(b) Na^+　　　　(c) Mg^{2+}　　　　(d) Ca^{2+}

164. By which method, As_2S_3 sol can be obtained by the reaction between As_2O_3 and H_2S ?
(a) Reduction　　　　(b) Oxidation
(c) Hydrolysis　　　　(d) Double decomposition

165 In which of the following method, condensation and dispersion are associated ?
(a) Excessive cooling　　(b) Hydrolysis　　(c) Bredig's arc　　(d) Peptization

166. What is called to that temperature at which the formation of micelle takes place ?
(a) Zero temperature　　　　(b) Kraft temperature
(c) Kelvin temperature　　　　(d) Absolute temperature

167. Solid in solid dispersion medium is called as ......
(a) Gel　　　　(b) Emulsion　　　　(c) Sol　　　　(d) Aerosol

168. Gas in liquid dispersion medium is called as ......
(a) Gel　　　　(b) Aerosol　　　　(c) Emulsion　　　　(d) Sol

PREVIOUS YEAR'S QUESTIONS

1. Which one of the following characteristics is associated with absorption? **[NEET-UG 2016]**
(a) ΔG and ΔS are negative but ΔH is positive
(b) ΔG is negative but ΔH and ΔS are positive
(c) ΔG, ΔH and ΔS all are negative
(d) ΔG and ΔH are negative but ΔS is positive

2. Fog is a colloidal solution of ......　　　　　　**[NEET-UG 2016]**
(a) Gas in gas　　　　(b) Liquid in gas　　　　(c) Gas in liquid　　　　(d) Solid in gas

3. Which of the following statements is correct for the spontaneous adsorption of gas?
　　　　　　　　　　　　　　　　　　　[AIPMT 2014]
(a) ΔS is positive and therefore, ΔS should be negative.
(b) ΔS is positive and therefore, ΔH should also be highly positive.
(c) ΔS is negative and therefore, ΔH should be highly positive.
(d) ΔS is negative and therefore, ΔH should be highly negative.

4.	Which property of colloidal solution is independent of charge on the colloidal particles?

[AIPMT 2015]

(a) Electrophoresis		(b) Electro-osmosis		(c) Tyndall effect		(d) Coagulation

5.	Which property of colloids is not dependent on the charge of colloidal particles?

[AIPMT 2014]

(a) Electro-osmosis		(b) Tyndall effect		(c) Coagulaiton		(d) Electrophoresis

6.	In Freundlich adsorption isotherm, the value of $1/n$ is		**[CBES Prelim 2012]**

(a) 1 in case of physical adsorption			(b) 1 in case of chemisorptions

(c) Between 0 and 1 in all cases			(d) Between 2 and 4 in all cases

7.	In x is the amount of adsorbate and m is the amount of adsorbent, which of the following relations is not related to adsorption process?		**[CBSE AIPMT 2011]**

(a) $\dfrac{x}{m} = p \times T$

(b) $\dfrac{x}{m} = f(p)$ at constant T

(c) $\dfrac{x}{m} = f(T)$ at constant p

(d) $p = f(T)$ at constant $\left(\dfrac{x}{m}\right)$

8.	"The greater the charge on an ion, the greater its coagulating power" is a statement of ...

[BHU 2006]

(a) Tyndall		(b) Faraday's law		(c) Mosley's law		(d) Hardy-Schulze law

9.	Sulphur colloid is prepared by		**[MHT CET 2005]**

(a) mechanical dispersion			(b) oxidation

(c) electrical dispersion			(d) reduction

10.	**Assertion :** Aqueous gold colloidal solution is red in colour.		**[AIIMS 2004]**

Reason : The colour arises due to scattering of light by colloidal gold particles.

(a) Both Assertion and Reason are true and Reason is the correct explanation of Assertion.

(b) Both Assertion and Reason are true but Reason is not correct explanation of Assertion.

(c) Assertion is true but Reason is false.

(d) Both Assertion and Reason are false.

11.	An example of intrinsic colloid is		**[AFMC 2007]**

(a) glue		(b) sulphur		(c) Fe		(d) As_2S_3

12.	**Assertion :** The conversion of fresh precipitate to colloidal state is called peptization

Reason : It is caused by addition of common ions		**[ALLMS 2007]**

(a) Both Assertion and Reason are true and Reason is the correct explanation of Assertion.

(b) Both Assertion and Reason are true but Reason is not the correct explanation of Assertion

(c) Assertion is true but Reason is false

(d) Both Assertion and Reason are false.

13.	When a sulphur sol is evaporated, sulphur is obtained. On mixing with water, sulphur sol is not formed. The sol is		**[KCET 2007]**

(a) lyophilic		(b) reversible		(c) hydrophobic		(d) hydrophilic

14.	Which of the following forms cationic micelles above certain concentration?**[Manipal 2007]**

(a) Sodium ethyl sulphate			(b) Sodium acetate

(c) Urea			(d) Cetyl trimethyl ammonium bromide

15. Peptization denotes ......   **[MHTCET 2007]**
(a) Digestion of food
(b) Hydrolysis of proteins
(c) Breaking of solid from colloidal dispersion
(d) Precipitation of solid from colloidal dispersion

16. Blue colour of water in sea is due to ......   **[MHTCET 2007]**
(a) Refraction of blue light by impurities   (b) Refraction of blue sky by water
(c) Scattering of light by water   (d) None of these

17. **Assertion :** Fe^{3+} can be used for coagulation of As_2S_3 sol.   **[AIIMS 2006]**
Reason : Fe^{3+} reacts with As_2S_3 to give Fe_2S_3.
(a) Both Assertion and Reason are true but Reason is the correct explanation of Assertion.
(b) Both Assertion and Reason are true but Reason is not the correct explanation of Assertion
(c) Assertion is true but Reason is false
(d) Both Assertion and Reason are false.

18. The process of separation of colloids by passing through semipermeable membrane is called as ......   **[Manipal 2009]**
(a) filtration   (b) electrophoresis   (c) dialysis   (d) ultrafiltration

19. Which of the following metal sols cannot be prepared by Bredig's arc method?
                                                                                [Manipal 2009]
(a) Copper   (b) Potassium   (c) Gold   (d) Platinum

20. If x is the amount of adsorbate and m is the amount of adsorbent, which of the following relations is not related to adsorption process ?   **[A.I.P.M.T. 2011]**
(a) $p = f(T)$ at constant (x/m) (b) $x/m = p \times T$
(c) $x/m = f(p)$ at constant T   (d) $x/m = f(T)$ at constant P

21. Which of the following electrolyes will have maximum flocculation value for $Fe(OH_3)$ sol?
                                                                                [AFMC 2008]
(a) NaCl   (b) Na_2S (c) $(NH_4)_3PO_4$ (d) K_2SO_4

22. Which of the following is incorrect match?   **[BHU 2008]**

	Name of colloidal solution	Examples	Dispersed phase	Dispersion medium
(a)	Foam	Soap, leather, soda water	Gas	Liquid
(b)	Solid foam	Rubber, bread, mist, fog, cloud	Gas Liquid	Solid Solid
(c)	Emulsion	Milk, cod liver oil	Liquid	Liquid

23. The protection power of lyophilic colloidal sol is expressed in terms of ......
                                                                                [CBSE Prelim 2012]
(a) Critical micelle concentration   (b) Oxidation number
(c) Coagulation value   (d) Gold number

24. Which substance is not used for preparing lyophilic sols?　　　　**[Manipal 2010]**

(a) Starch　　　　(b) Gum　　　　(c) Gelatin　　　　(d) Metal sulphide

25. Gold number of protective colloids A, B, C and D are 0.50, 0.01, 0.10 and 0.005 respectively. The correct order of their protective power is ......　　**[Haryana PMT 2010]**

(a) D < A < C < B　　　　(b) C < B < D < A　　　　(c) A < C < B < D　　　(d) B < D < A < C

26. Gold number is associated with ......　　　　**[VMMC 2010]**

(a) electrophoresis

(b) purple of cassius

(c) protective colloid

(d) amount of pure gold

27. Freundlich adsorption isotherm is ......　　　　**[MHT CET 2007]**

(a) $\dfrac{x}{m} = kP^{1/n}$　　　　(b) $x = mkP^{1/n}$　　　　(c) $\dfrac{m}{m} = kP^{-n}$　　　　(d) All of these

28. A plot of $\log \dfrac{x}{m}$ versus $\log P$ for the adsorption of a gas on a solid gives a straight line with slope equal to ......　　　　**[CBSE AIMT 2006]**

(a) $- \log k$　　　　(b) n　　　　(c) $\dfrac{1}{n}$　　　　(d) $\log k$

29. 0.2 g of fine animal charcoal is mixed with half litre of acetic acid solution and shaken for 30 min ......　　　　**[DUMET 2004]**

(a) concentration remains same

(b) concentration increases

(c) concentration decreases

(d) none of these

30. The Langmuir adsorption isotherm is deduced using the assumption　　**[CBSE AIPMT 2007]**

(a) the adsorption takes place in multilayer

(b) the adsorption sites are equivalent in their ability to absorb the particles.

(c) the heat of adsorption varies with coverage.

(d) the adsorbed molecules interact with each other.

31. According to the adsorption theory of catalysis, the speed of reaction increases because

(a) adsorption produces heat which increases the speed of the reaction.　　**[AIIMS 2007]**

(b) adsorption lowers the activation energy of the reaction.

(c) the concentration of reactant molecules at the active centres of the catalyst becomes high due to adsorption.

(d) in the process of adsorption, the activation energy of the molecules becomes large.

32. At high pressure, Langmuir adsorption isotherm takes the form ......　　**[AIIMS 2007]**

(a) $\dfrac{x}{m} = \dfrac{ap}{1 + bp}$　　　　(b) $\dfrac{x}{m} = \dfrac{a}{b}$　　　　(c) $\dfrac{x}{m} = ap$　　　　(d) $\dfrac{m}{x} = \dfrac{b}{a} + \dfrac{1}{ap}$

33. Select the incorrect statement.　　　　**[AIIMS 2009]**

(a) Physical adsorption is reversible while chemical adsorption is irreversible

(b) High pressure favors physical adsorption while low pressure favours chemical adsorption.

(c) Physical adsorption is not specific while chemical adsorption is highly specific.

(d) High activation energy is involved in chemical adsorption.

34. Which characteristic is not associated with chemical adsorption? **[AU 2009]**
    (a) Is irreversible   (b) Forms monolayer
    (c) Not very specific   (d) Heat of adsorption > 50 kJ mol^{-1}

35. Which one of the following statement is incorrect about enzyme catalysis?
[CBSE Prelim 2012]
    (a) Enzymes are denudated by ultraviolet rays and at high temperature
    (b) Enzymes are least reactive at optimum temperature
    (c) Enzymes are mostly proteinous in nature
    (d) Enzyme action is specific

36. Following reaction is catalysed by I^- (aq).   **[CPMT 2009]**
$$2H_2O_{2(aq)} \rightarrow 2H_2O_{(l)} + O_{2(g)}$$
This is an example of ......
    (a) Homogeneous catalysis   (b) Heterogeneous catalysis
    (c) Autocatalysis   (d) Enzyme catalysis

37. Given below, catalyst and corresponding process/reaction are matched. The mismatch is
[AIIMS 2006]
    (a) $[RhCl(PPH_3)_2]$: Hydrogenation   (b) $[TiCl_4 + Al(C_2H_5)_3]$: Polymerisation
    (c) V_2O_5 : Haber Bosch process   (d) Nickel : Hydrogenation

38. A biological catalyst is ......   **[Manipal 2006]**
    (a) the N_2 molecule   (b) an enzyme   (c) an amino acid   (d) a carbohydrate

39. Adsorption due to strong chemical forces is called as ......   **[Manipal P.M.T. 2001]**
    (a) Chemisorption   (b) Physisorption
    (c) Reversible adsorption   (d) Both (b) and (c)

40. Adsorbed acetic acid on activated charcoal is ......   **[M.P.P.M.T. 2002]**
    (a) Adsorber   (b) Absorber   (c) Adsorbent   (d) Adsorbate

41. Milk is colloid in which a ......   **[M.P. P.M.T. 2002]**
    (a) Liquid is dispersed in a liquid   (b) Solid is dispersed in a liquid
    (c) Gas is dispersed in a liquid   (d) Sugar is dispersed in a liquid

42. In the case of autocatalysis ......
    (a) Reactant catalyses   (b) Heat produced in the reaction catalyses
    (c) Product catalyses   (d) Solvent catalyses

43. Langmuir adsorption isotherm is deduced using the assumption.   **[A.I.P.M.T. 2007]**
    (a) The adsorbed molecules interact with each other
    (b) The adsorption takes place in multilayers
    (c) The adsorption sites are equivalent in their ability to adsorb the particles
    (d) The heat of adsorption varies with the coverage

44. The formation of a colloid from suspension is ......   **[Manipal P.M.T. 2002]**
    (a) Peptization   (b) Condensation   (c) Sedimentation   (d) Fragmentation

45. Arsenic sulphide is a negative sol. The reagent with least precipitating power is ......
[Manipal P.M.T. 2002]
    (a) $AlCl_3$ (b) NaCl   (c) CaF_2 (d) Glucose

46. According to adsorption theory of catalysis, the speed of the reaction increases because ...

   (a) Adsorption lowers the activation energy of the reaction   **[C.B.S.E. 2003]**

   (b) The concentration of reactant molecules at the active centres of the catalyst becomes high due to adsorption

   (c) In the process of adsorption, the activation energy of the molecules becomes large

   (d) Adsorption produces heat which increases the speed of the reaction

47. Which one of the following is not a surfactant ?   **[CPMT 2003]**

   (a) $CH_3 - (CH_2)_{15} - \overset{\overset{\displaystyle CH_3}{|}}{\underset{\underset{\displaystyle CH_3}{|}}{N^+}} - CH_3 Br^-$ (b) $CH_3(CH_2)_{14}CH_2NH_2$

   (c) $CH_3(CH_2)_{16}CH_2OSO_2\,Na^+$ (d) $OHC(CH_2)_{14}CH_2COO^-\,Na^+$

48. Colloidal solutions of gold prepared by different methods are of different colours because of ......   **[E.A.M.C.E.T. Med. 2003]**

   (a) Variable valency of gold

   (b) Different concentrations of gold particles

   (c) Impurities produced by different methods

   (d) Different diameters of colloidal gold particles

49. Which of the following is an example for heterogeneous catalysis reaction ?   **[E.A.M.C.E.T. 2005]**

   (a) $2SO_{2(g)} + O_{2(g)} \xrightarrow{\ NO_{(g)}\ } 2SO_{3(g)}$

   (b) Hydrolysis of aqueous sucrose solution in the presence of aqueous mineral acid

   (c) $2H_2O_{2(l)} + Pt\tfrac{3}{4} \rightarrow 2H_2O_{(l)} + O_{2(g)}$

   (d) Hydrolysis of liquid ester in the presence of aqueous mineral acid

50. Which does not cause coagulation of colloidal solution?   **[Wardha 2003]**

   (a) Filtration   (b) Non-electrolyte   (c) Electrolyte   (d) All of these

51. Bredig's arc method cannot be used to prepare colloidal solution of which of the following ?   **[A.F.M.C. 2004]**

   (a) Pt   (b) Fe   (c) Ag   (d) Au

52. Milk is ......   **[J & K Med. 2004]**

   (a) Fat dispersed in water   (b) Fat dispersed in milk

   (c) Fat dispersed in fat   (d) Water dispersed in milk

53. Which of the following forms cationic micelles above certain concentration ?   **[C.B.S.E. Med. 2004]**

   (a) Cetyl trimethyl ammonium bromide   (b) Sodium dodecyl sulphate

   (c) Sodium acetate   (d) Urea

54. Which of the following is used to produce smoke screens ?   **[A.F.M.C. 2005]**

   (a) Calcium phosphide   (b) Zinc sulphide

   (c) Sodium carbonate   (d) Zinc phosphide

55. 10^{-4} g of gelatin is required to be added to 100 cm^3 of a standard gold sol to just prevent its coagulation by the addition of 1 cm^3 of 10% NaCl solution to it. Hence, the gold number of gelatin is ......   **[Kerala Med. 2005]**

(a) 10   (b) 1.0   (c) 0.1   (d) 0.01

(e) 0.001

56. The coagulation of 200 ml of a positive colloid took place when 0.073 g HCl was added to it without changing the volume much. The flocculation value of HCl for the colloid is ......

[Kerala P.M.T. 2008]

(a) 0.365   (b) 36.5   (c) 100   (d) 150   (e) 200

57. Although nitrogen does not adsorb on the surface at the room temperature, it absorbs on the same surface at 83 K. Which one of the following statement is correct ?

[H.P. P.M.T. 2006]

(a) At 83 K, there is formation of monomolecular layer

(b) At 83 K, there is formation of multimolecular layer

(c) At 83 K, nitrogen molecules are held by chemical bonds

(d) At 83 K, nitrogen is absorbed as atoms

58. Which one of the following act as the best coagulation agent for ferric hydroxide sol ?

[Kerala P.M.T. 2007]

(a) Magnesium chloride   (b) Hydrochloric acid

(c) Aluminium chloride   (d) Potassium ferricyanide

59. An emulsion is a colloidal solution of one of the following dispersed in another liquid.

[M.P. P.M.T. 2009]

(a) Solid   (b) Liquid   (c) Gas   (d) Medium

60. Colloidian is a 4% of which one of the following alcohol-ether mixture ?

[Kerala P.M.T. 2010]

(a) Nitroglycerine   (b) Cellulose acetate (c) Glycol dinitrite (d) Nitrocellulose

61. The formation of micelles takes place only above ......   **[Kerala P.E.T. 2010]**

(a) Inversion temperature   (b) Boyle temperature

(c) Critical temperature   (d) Kraft temperature

62. A plot of x/m versus log P for the adsorption of a gas on a solid gives a straight line with slope equal to   **[A.I.P.M.T. 2006]**

(a) 1/n   (b) log k   (c) – log k   (d) n

ANSWER KEY

1. (a)	2. (d)	3. (a)	4. (b)	5. (a)	6. (c)	7. (d)	8. (b)
9. (c)	10. (b)	11. (b)	12. (c)	13. (a)	14. (c)	15. (a)	16. (b)
17. (c)	18. (d)	19. (a)	20. (b)	21. (d)	22. (c)	23. (b)	24. (b)
25. (b)	26. (a)	27. (c)	28. (a)	29. (c)	30. (d)	31. (b)	32. (d)

33. (b)	34. (b)	35. (c)	36. (a)	37. (b)	38. (c)	39. (d)	40. (c)
41. (b)	42. (b)	43. (b)	44. (c)	45. (c)	46. (c)	47. (b)	48. (d)
49. (b)	50. (a)	51. (c)	52. (b)	53. (b)	54. (a)	55.	56. (a)
57. (c)	58. (d)	59. (d)	60. (d)	61. (b)	62. (b)	63. (a)	64. (b)
65. (a)	66. (b)	67. (b)	68. (c)	69. (b)	70. (b)	71. (a)	72. (a)
73. (b)	74. (c)	75. (d)	76. (b)	77. (d)	78. (a)	79. (d)	80. (a)
81. (b)	82. (d)	83. (c)	84. (b)	85. (d)	86. (b)	87. (c)	88. (d)
89. (d)	90. (a)	91. (a)	92. (a)	93. (d)	94. (c)	95. (a)	96. (c)
97. (c)	98. (d)	99. (c)	100. (d)	101. (a)	102. (c)	103. (d)	104. (b)
105. (a)	106. (d)	107. (a)	108. (a)	109. (c)	110. (c)	111. (c)	112. (c)
113.(b)	114. (c)	115. (c)	116. (d)	117. (d)	118. (a)	119. (c)	120. (b)
121. (b)	122. (b)	123. (c)	124. (b)	125. (c)	126. (b)	127. (a)	128. (e)
129. (b)	130. (c)	131. (a)	132. (c)	133. (d)	134. (c)	135. (b)	136. (a)
137. (d)	138. (c)	139. (b)	140. (b)	141. (a)	142. (a)	143. (b)	144. (b)
145. (d)	146. (b)	147. (b)	148. (d)	149. (c)	150. (d)	151. (c)	152. (a)
153. (d)	154. (a)	155. (b)	156. (a)	157. (d)	158. (b)	159. (a)	160. (c)
161. (d)	162. (c)	163. (a)	164. (d)	165. (c)	166. (b)	167. (c)	168. (b)

Previous Year's Questions

1. (c)	2. (b)	3. (d)	4. (c)	5. (b)	6. (c)	7. (a)	8. (d)
9. (b)	10. (a)	11. (a)	12. (b)	13. (c)	14. (b)	15. (c)	16. (c)
17. (b)	18. (c)	19. (b)	20. (b)	21. (a)	22. (c)	23. (d)	24. (d)
25. (c)	26. (c)	27. (a)	28. (d)	29. (c)	30. (a)	31. (b)	32. (b)
33. (b)	34. (c)	35. (b)	36. (a)	37. (c)	38. (b)	39. (a)	40. (d)
41. (a)	42. (c)	43. (c)	44. (a)	45. (d)	46. (a)	47. (b)	48. (d)
49. (c)	50. (b)	51. (b)	52. (a)	53. (a)	54. (a)	55. (d)	56. (c)
57. (b)	58. (d)	59. (b)	60. (d)	61. (d)	62. (a)		

GENERAL PRINCIPLES AND PROCESSES OF ISOLATION OF ELEMENTS

1. Froth floatation process is used for the concentration of ......
   - (a) Oxide ores
   - (b) Sulphide ores
   - (c) Chloride ores
   - (d) Amalgams

2. The oil used in the floatation method for the purification of ores is ......
   - (a) Coconut oil
   - (b) Olive oil
   - (c) Pine oil
   - (d) Mustard oil

3. Electrolytic reduction method is used in the extraction of ......
   - (a) Highly electronegative elements
   - (b) Highly electropositive elements
   - (c) Transition metals
   - (d) Noble gases

4. An ore of tin containing $FeCrO_4$ is concentrated by ......
   - (a) Magnetic separation
   - (b) Froth floatation
   - (c) Electrostatic method
   - (d) Gravity separation

5. Zone refining process is used for the ......
   - (a) Concentration of an ore
   - (b) Reduction of a metal oxide
   - (c) Purification of metal
   - (d) Purification of an ore

6. The purpose of smelting an ore is ......
   - (a) To oxidise it
   - (b) To reduce it
   - (c) To separate volatile impurities
   - (d) To obtain an alloy

7. Cupellation process is used in the metallurgy of ......
   - (a) Cu
   - (b) Ag
   - (c) Zn
   - (d) Al

8. Which one of the following beneficiation process is used for the mineral $Al_2O_3 \cdot 2H_2O$?
   - (a) Froth floatation
   - (b) Leaching
   - (c) Liquation
   - (d) Magnetic separation

9. Galvanizing of iron sheets is done by ......
   - (a) Cu plating
   - (b) Zn plating
   - (c) Ag plating
   - (d) Tin plating

10. The natural materials from which an element can be extracted economically are called as ......
    - (a) Ores
    - (b) Minerals
    - (c) Gangue
    - (d) None of these

11. Purification of silicon element used in semi-conductors is done by ......
    - (a) Zone refining
    - (b) Heating
    - (c) Froth floatation
    - (d) Heating in vacuum

12. When a metal is to be extracted from its ore and if the gangue associated with the ore is silica, then ......
    - (a) An acidic flux is needed
    - (b) A basic flux is needed
    - (c) Both acidic and basic fluxes are needed
    - (d) Neither of them is needed

13. Which is the strongest reducing agent?

(a) Rb (b) Na (c) K (d) Mg

14. The chief source of iodine, in which it is present as sodium iodate is ......

(a) Carnallite (b) Sea weeds (c) Caliche (d) Rocks

(e) Iodine never exists as sodium iodate

15. A basic lining is given to a furnace by using ......

(a) Calcined dolomite (b) Limestone (c) Haematite (d) Silicate

16. The metal extracted by cyanide process is ......

(a) Silver (b) Copper (c) Iron (d) Sodium/Aluminium

17. Malachite is an ore of ......

(a) Iron (b) Zinc (c) Copper (d) Mercury

18. Which of the following metals is obtained by electrolytic reduction process?

(a) Fe (b) Cu (c) Ag (d) Al

19. Cassiterite is an ore of ......

(a) Mn (b) Ni (c) Sb (d) Sn

20. Which of the following element is extracted commercially by the electrolysis of an aqueous solution of its compound?

(a) Chlorine (b) Bromine (c) Sodium (d) Aluminium

21. Galena is an ore of ......

(a) Pb (b) Hg (c) Sn (d) Zn

22. Cryolite is ......

(a) Na_3AlF_6 and is used in the electrolysis of alumina for decreasing electrical conductivity

(b) Na_3AlF_6 and is used in the electrolysis of alumina for lowering the melting point of alumina

(c) Na_3AlF_6 and is used in the electrolytic purification of alumina

(d) Na_3AlF_6 and is used in the electrolysis of alumina

23. In the extraction of iron, slag is produced. Slag is ......

(a) CO (b) $FeSiO_3$ (c) $MgSiO_3$ (d) $CaSiO_3$

24. Heating pyrites to remove sulphur is called as ......

(a) Smelting (b) Calcination (c) Liquation (d) Roasting

25. Nickel is purified by thermal decomposition of its ......

(a) Hydride (b) Chloride (c) Azide (d) Carbonyl

26. The most electropositive metals are isolated from their ores by ......

(a) High temperature reduction with carbon (b) Self reduction

(c) Thermal decomposition (d) Electrolysis of fused ionic salts

(e) Displacement method

27. The process of converting hydrated alumina into anhydrous alumina is called as

(a) Roasting (b) Smelting (c) Dressing (d) Calcination

28. The metal always found in the free state is ......

(a) Au (b) Ag (c) Cu (d) Na

29. Which of the following metals are extracted by the electrometallurgical method?

    (a) Cu   (b) Fe   (c) Na   (d) Ag

30. The common method of extraction of metals from oxide ores is ......

    (a) Reduction with carbon   (b) Reduction with hydrogen

    (c) Reduction with aluminium   (d) Electrolytic method

31. Which one of the following ores is not concentrated by froth floatation process ?

    (a) Copper pyrites   (b) Pentlandite   (c) Pyrolusite   (d) Zinc blende

32. The metal which cannot be obtained by electrolysis of aqueous solution of its salts is ......

    (a) Ag   (b) Zn   (c) Cu   (d) Al

33. Refractory metals are used in the construction of furnaces because ......

    (a) They can withstand high temperature   (b) They are chemically inert

    (c) Their melting point is high   (d) None of these

34. Which of the following is an ore of aluminum?

    (a) Dolomite   (b) Azurite   (c) Bauxite   (d) Malachite

35. The method of zone refining of metals is based on the principle of ......

    (a) Greater solubility of the impurities in the molten state than in the solid

    (b) Greater solubility of pure metal than that of the impurity

    (c) Higher melting point of the impurity than that of the pure metal

    (d) Greater noble character of the solid metal than that of the impurity

36. The reduction of FeO to Fe by CO occurs around ......

    (a) 873 K   (b) 1031 K   (c) 1123 K   (d) 1213 K

37. During reduction of CuO, impurity of FeO can be removed by adding ......

    (a) An acidic flux, SiO_2 (b) A basic flux, limestone

    (c) A basic flux, SiO_2 (d) An acidic flux, CaF

38. In electrorefining of metals, pure metal is made anode and a strip of pure metal is the cathode during the electrolysis of an aqueous solution of complex metal salt. The method cannot be used for refining of ......

    (a) Al   (b) Cu   (c) Au   (d) Ag

39. Which of the following methods is used for obtaining aluminium metal ?

    (a) By heating alumina in Muffle furnace

    (b) By a process called pyrometallurgy

    (c) Electrolysing fused purified alumina and cryolite

    (d) By heating alumina with carbon

40. Extraction of zinc from zinc blende is achieved by ......

    (a) Roasting followed by reduction with carbon

    (b) Roasting followed by reduction with other metal

    (c) Roasting followed by self-reduction

    (d) Electrolytic reduction

41. Heating mixture of Cu_2O and Cu_2S will give ......
(a) $CuS + CO$ (b) $Cu + SO_3$ (c) $CuO + SO_2$ (d) $Cu + SO_2$

42. In extraction of iron, limestone is used for
(a) Formation of slag   (b) Reduction of Fe ore
(c) Purification of Fe formed   (d) Oxidation of Fe ore

43. During roasting of copper pyrites, the major reaction observed is ......
(a) $2FeS + 3O_2 \rightarrow 2FeO + 2SO_2$ (b) $CuFeS_2 + 3O_2 \rightarrow FeO + CuO + 2SO_2$
(c) $CuFeS_2 + O_2 \rightarrow Cu_2S + 2FeS + SO_2$ (d) $2CuS + 3O_2 \rightarrow 2CuO + 2SO_2$

44. Which of the following is an oxide ore?
(a) Galena   (b) Zinc blende   (c) Bauxite   (d) Malachite

45. In froth floatation method ......
(a) The ore is washed with a stream of water
(b) The ore is treated with water and pine oil
(c) There is pouring off the ore over a conveyor belt rolling over magnetic roller
(d) None of these

46. During smelting, silica is added to roasted copper ore for removal of ......
(a) Ferrous sulphide   (b) Ferrous oxide
(c) Cuprous sulphide   (d) Cuprous oxide

47. In purification of ore by froth floatation method, the particles float because ......
(a) They are light
(b) They are insoluble
(c) They bear electrostatic charge
(d) Their surface is not easily wetted by water

48. An ore containing both iron and copper is ......
(a) Chalcocite   (b) Chalcopyrite   (c) Azurite   (d) Malachite

49. The calcination and roasting are ......
(a) Used in purification of metals   (b) Different names of the same operation
(c) Usually carried in reverberatory furnace   (d) Employed for concentration of ores

50. Among the following, ores concentrated by froth floatation method are ......
(a) Oxides   (b) Phosphates   (c) Sulphides   (d) Carbonates

51. In a metallurgical process, an acid flux is used for the removal of ......
(a) Basic gangue   (b) Basic flux   (c) Acidic gangue   (d) Slag

52. The zone refining method is used to obtain the ultrapure sample of ......
(a) Sodium   (b) Zinc   (c) Copper   (d) Germanium

53. In a blast furnace, the reduction of iron oxide occurs by ......
(a) Carbon   (b) Silica
(c) Carbon monoxide   (d) Limestone

54. The process of removal of impurities from crude metal is called as ......
(a) Calcination   (b) Roasting   (c) Concentration   (d) Refining

55. Which of the following metals is obtained by auto-reduction method?

(a) Ag   (b) Cu   (c) Fe   (d) Mg

56. The metal obtained by leaching its ore with dilute cyanide solution is

(a) Zn   (b) V   (c) Ti   (d) silver

57. Which of the following form contains higher percentage of carbon?

(a) Pig iron   (b) Mild iron

(c) Wrought iron   (d) Stainless steel

58. Among the following, the correct statement is

(a) All minerals are ores   (b) All ores are minerals

(c) An ore cannot be a mineral   (d) A mineral cannot be an ore

59. A mineral that does not contain aluminium is ......

(a) Feldspar   (b) Mica   (c) Cryolite   (d) Fluorspar

60. Identify the metal that cannot be obtained by the electrolysis of aqueous solution of its salt

(a) Mg   (b) Cu   (c) Cr   (d) Ag

61. Which one of the following is used as an acid flux in metallurgy?

(a) SiO_2 (b) CaO   (c) SO_2 (d) Na_2CO_3

62. The ore that is concentrated by froth floatation process is ......

(a) Malachite   (b) Magnetite   (c) Galena   (d) Fluorite

63. Which of the following process is used in extractive metallurgy of magnesium?

(a) Aqueous solution electrolysis   (b) Fused salt electrolysis

(c) Self reduction   (d) Thermite reduction

64. Which of the following represents horn silver?

(a) Ag   (b) $AgNO_3$ (c) AgCl   (d) Ag_2S

65. Impure copper containing 1% impurity obtained from Bessemerisation of molten matte is called as

(a) Blister copper   (b) Bronze   (c) Brass   (d) None of these

66. Heating pyrites in air to remove sulphur is known as ......

(a) Calcination   (b) Fluxing   (c) Smelting   (d) Roasting

67. The salt which is least likely to be found in minerals is ......

(a) Chloride   (b) Sulphides   (c) Sulphates   (d) Nitrates

68. The component having low melting point can be separated in an impure metal by ......

(a) Washing with water   (b) Froth floatation

(c) Liquation   (d) Magnetic separation

69. .... and .... are ores of aluminium ......

(a) Bauxite and Malachite   (b) Cuprite and Calamine

(c) Bauxite and Kaolinite   (d) Cuprite and Kaolinite

70. Discharge potential relates to the potential at which ......

(a) The metal is discharged at the anode   (b) The metal is discharged at the cathode

(c) The metal ion is discharged   (d) The metal is reduced

71. Van Arkel method of purification of metals involves converting the metal to a ......
    (a) Volatile compound
    (b) Volatile unstable compound
    (c) Non-volatile stable compound
    (d) Non-volatile unstable compound

72. The reason for floating of ore particles in the concentration by froth flotation process is ...
    (a) Being hydrophobic
    (b) Being charged
    (c) Being light
    (d) Being insoluble

73. Which of the following is gangue ?
    (a) Waste material left after concentration
    (b) Waste material left after purification of metal
    (c) Waste material after electrolysis
    (d) Waste material present in ore to be removed during concentration

74. The ore having two different metal atoms is ......
    (a) Copper pyrites
    (b) Haematite
    (c) Magnetite
    (d) Calamine

75. The chief ore of zinc is ......
    (a) Cryolite
    (b) Calcite
    (c) Calamine
    (d) Cuprite

76. The principal reaction in the zone of fusion of blast furnace employed in the metallurgy of iron is ......
    (a) $C + O_2 \rightarrow CO_2$
    (b) $2C + O_2 \rightarrow 2CO$
    (c) $CO_2 + C \rightarrow CO$
    (d) $Fe_2O_3 + 3CO \rightarrow 2Fe + 3CO_2$

77. Purification of a substance can be done by sublimation under the condition such that ......
    (a) Substance to be purified must have relatively high vapour pressure
    (b) Impurities must have vapour pressure lower than the distance to be purified
    (c) Both (a) and (b)
    (c) None of these

78. When the difference in boiling points of two liquids is not too much, then separation can be carried out by using .....
    (a) Steam distillation
    (b) Fractional distillation
    (c) Vacuum distillation
    (d) Simple distillation

79. In adsorption chromatography, absorbent and absorbate are respectively .....
    (a) Solid, liquid
    (b) Liquid, solid
    (c) Solid, solid
    (d) Liquid, liquid

80. Colourless spots can be made visible by ......
    (a) U.V light in case of aromatic compounds
    (b) Ninhydrin in case of amino acids
    (c) Both (a) and (b)
    (d) None of these

81. Which of the following metal is obtained by the reduction of metal oxide with hydrogen gas?
    (a) Cu
    (b) Al
    (c) Mg
    (d) Fe

82. The impurities associated with ore after mining are called ....
    (a) Flux
    (b) Slag
    (c) Minerals
    (d) Gangue

83. An ore after levigation is found to have acidic impurities. Which of the following can be used as a flux during smelting operation ?

(a) H_2SO_4 (b) $CaCO_3$ (c) SiO_2 (d) both (b) and (c)

84. The process in which metal oxide is reduced to metal by Al is called ....

(a) Smelting   (b) Alumino therapy (c) Hydrothermy   (d) None of these

85. Extraction of silver from Ag_2S by the use of sodium cyanide is an example of ....

(a) Roasting   (b) Hydrometallurgy

(c) Electrometallurgy   (d) Smelting

86. Which of the following metals can be extracted by smelting ?

(a) Aluminium   (b) Magnesium   (c) Iron   (d) None of these

87. The most abundant element in earth's crust is ....

(a) Nitrogen   (b) Oxygen   (c) Iron   (d) Magnesium

88. Which of the following barium salts is soluble in water?

(a) Barium sulphate   (b) Barium carbonate

(c) Barium nitrate   (d) Barium phosphate

89. Alkali metals do not exist in free state in nature because these are ......

(a) Very reactive   (b) Very volatile

(c) Metallic in nature   (d) Highly electronegative elements

90. Heating an ore in the absence of air below its melting point is called as ......

(a) Leaching   (b) Roasting   (c) Smelting   (d) Calcination

91. Cassiterite is concentrated by ....

(a) Levigation   (b) Electromagnetic separation

(c) Floatation   (d) Liquefication

92. When an aqueous solution of sodium chloride is electrolysed using platinum electrodes, the ions discharged at the electrodes are ......

(a) Sodium and hydrogen   (b) Sodium and chloride

(c) Hydrogen and chloride   (d) Hydroxyl and chloride

93. For which ore of the metal, froth-floatation method is used for concentration ?

(a) Horn silver   (b) Bauxite   (c) Cinnabar   (d) Haematite

94. Which of the following metal is extracted by the electrometallurgical method ?

(a) Cu   (b) Fe   (c) Na   (d) Ag

95. Electromagnetic separation is used in the concentration of ....

(a) copper pyrites   (b) bauxite   (c) cassiterite   (d) cinnabar

96. In the extraction of copper from its sulphide ore the metal is formed by reduction of Cu_2O with ....

(a) FeS   (b) CO   (c) Cu_2S (d) SO_2

97. Which one of the following ores is best concentrated by froth-floatation method ?

(a) Magnetic   (b) Malachite   (c) Galena   (d) Cassiterite

98. During the process of electrolytic refining of copper, some metals present as impurity settle as 'anode mud'. These are ....

(a) Fe and Ni   (b) Ag and Au   (c) Pb and Zn   (d) Sn and Ag

99. Which of the following is not an ore of magnesium ?

    (a) Carnallite   (b) Dolomite   (c) Calamine   (d) Sea water

100. Which of the following metal can be obtained by the electrolysis of the aqueous solution of their salts ?

    (a) Cu   (b) Na   (c) Mg   (d) K

101. Which of the following statements, about the advantage of roasting of sulphide are before reduction is not true ?

    (a) Roasting of the sulphide to the oxide is thermodynamically feasible

    (b) Carbon and hydrogen are suitable reducing agents for metal sulphides

    (c) The $\Delta_f G^\ominus$ of the sulphide is greater than those for CS_2 and H_2S

    (d) The $\Delta_f G^\ominus$ is negative for roasting of sulphide ore to oxide.

102. Sulphide ores of metals are usually concentrated by froth floatation process. Which one of the following sulphide ores offer an exception and is concentrated by chemical leaching ?

    (a) Sphalerite   (b) Argentite   (c) Galena   (d) Copper pyrite

103. Extraction of zinc from zinc blende is achieved by .....

    (a) Electrolytic reduction

    (b) Roasting followed by reduction with carbon

    (c) Roasting followed by reduction with another metal

    (d) Roasting followed by self reduction

104. A metal which can be purified by vapour phase refining is ....

    (a) Cu   (b) Al   (c) Fe   (d) Zr

105. What is the role of graphite rod in the electrometallurgy of aluminium ?

    (a) Graphite rod acts as anode and facilitates reduction of Al_2O_3 to Al by electrolysis.

    (b) Graphite rod acts as cathode and facilitates reduction of Al_2O_3 to Al by electrolysis.

    (c) Carbon rod acts as anode and facilitates oxidation of Al_2O_3.

    (d) Carbon rod acts as cathode and facilitates reduction of Al_2O_3.

106. .... is a pure iron.

    (a) Cast iron   (b) Wrought iron   (c) Spongy iron   (d) Hard iron

107. If a steel part is heated to redness and then suddenly cooled in water is known as ....

    (a) Annealing   (b) Tempering   (c) Quenching   (d) Reduction

108. The process in which the molten mass is stirred with long poles of green wood. This process is known as ......

    (a) Poling   (b) Smelting   (c) Refining   (d) Electrolysis

109. Brass has Cu 60% and Zn ....

    (a) 20%   (b) 30%   (c) 40%   (d) 50%

110. Zinc is extracted by ......

    (a) The carbon reduction of ZnO   (b) The carbon monoxide reduction of ZnO

    (c) The hydrogen reduction of ZnO   (d) The copper reduction of ZnO

111. Which of the following is magnetite ?

    (a) Fe_2CO_3 (b) Fe_2O_3 (c) Fe_3O_4 (d) $Fe_2O_3.3H_2O$

112. The formula of azurite is ......
(a) $CuCO_3 \cdot Cu(OH)_2$ (b) $2CuCO_3 \cdot Cu(OH)_2$ (c) $CuCO_2 \cdot Cu(OH)_2$ (d) $CuSO_4 \cdot Cu(OH)_2$

113. Which of the following materials is the best conductor of electricity ?
(a) Platinum   (b) Gold   (c) Silicon   (d) Copper

114. Fe_2O_3 is converted to FeO in the presence of CO at ......
(a) 473-573 °K   (b) 573-673 °K   (c) 673-773 °K   (d) 773-873 °K

115. Froth floatation process is used for the metallurgy of ......
(a) Chloride ores   (b) Amalgams   (c) Oxide ores   (d) Sulphide ores

116. Flux is used to ......
(a) Remove all impurities from ores
(b) Reduce metal oxide
(c) Remove silica
(d) Remove silica and undesirable metal oxide

117. Which one of the following elements does not exist in the native form ?
(a) Au   (b) Pt   (c) Fe   (d) S
(e) He

118. Which of the following statement is true ?
(a) The process of obtaining aluminium by electrolysis of a mixture of aluminium oxide and cryolite is called Haber's process
(b) Cryolite is added during metallurgy of aluminium to reduce alumina
(c) Bauxite is purified by leaching with a hot concentrated solution of NaOH
(d) Bauxite is purified by zone refining

119. The purification of aluminium metal is done by ......
(a) Mac Arthur process   (b) Hall's process
(c) Serpeck's process   (d) Baeyer's process

120. Aluminium in thermite process acts as ......
(a) An oxidising agent   (b) A flux
(c) Soldering agent   (d) A reducing agent

121. Which of the following reaction represents aluminothermy?
(a) $2Al + N_2 \rightarrow 2AlN$ (b) $2Al + 3Cl_2 \rightarrow 2AlCl_3$
(c) $2Al + 6HCl \rightarrow 2AlCl_3 + 3H_2$ (d) $2Al + Fe_2O_3 \rightarrow Al_2O_3 + 2Fe$

122. The role of fluorspar during the electrolytic reduction of alumina dissolved in fused cryolite is ......
(a) As a catalyst
(b) to lower the temperature of the melt and to make fused mixture very conducting
(c) to decrease the rate of oxidation of carbon at the anode
(d) to make the electrolyte conducting

123. Copper obtained after auto oxidation reduction is ......
(a) pure copper   (b) copper alloy   (c) blister copper   (d) impure copper

124. In the electrolytic refining of copper, Ag and Au are found ......
(a) On anode   (b) In electrolyte solution
(c) In anode mud   (d) In cathode mud

125. Silver can be separated from lead by
    (a) Fractional crystallization
    (b) Amalgamation
    (c) Cupellation
    (d) Addition of zinc

126. Percentage of silver in the alloy german silver is ......
    (a) 2.5%
    (b) 1.5%
    (c) 10 %
    (d) 0%

127. Cinnabar is the sulphide ore of ......
    (a) Zn
    (b) Cd
    (c) Hg
    (d) Ag

128. Heamatite ore is concentrated by ......
    (a) Gravity separation method
    (b) Froth floatation
    (c) Amalgamation
    (d) Leaching

129. The charge added during the smelting of oxide ore of iron in a blast furnace contains ......
    (a) Coke and silica
    (b) Coke and limestone
    (c) Limestone and silica
    (d) Coke, limestone and silica

130. For which one of the metal, froth floatation method is used for concentration?
    (a) Horn silver
    (b) Bauxite
    (c) Cinnabar
    (d) Haematite

131. Calcination is used in metallurgy for removal of ......
    (a) Water and sulphide
    (b) Water and CO_2
    (c) CO_2 and H_2S
    (d) H_2O and H_2S

132. Match list I with list II and select the correct answer using the codes given below the lists.

List I	List II
I. Cyanide process	A. Ultrapure Ge
II. Floatation process	B. Pine oil
III. Electrolytic reduction	C. Extraction of Al
IV. Zone refining	D. Extraction of Au

    (a) I-C, II-A, III-D, IV-B
    (b) I-D, II-B, III-C, IV-A
    (c) I-C, II-B, III-D, IV-A
    (d) I-D, II-A, III-C, IV-B

133. Among the following statements, the incorrect one is ......
    (a) Calamine and siderite are carbonates
    (b) Argentite and cuprite are oxides
    (c) Zinc blende and iron pyrites are sulphides
    (d) Malachite and azurite are ores of copper.

134. In the extraction of chlorine by electrolysis of brine __________.
    (a) oxidation of Cl^- ion to chlorine gas occurs.
    (b) reduction of Cl^- ion to chlorine gas occurs.
    (c) For overall reaction ΔG_V has negative value.
    (d) a displacement reaction takes place.

135. Brine is electrolysed by using inert electrodes. The reaction at anode is ______.
    (a) $Cl^-_{(aq)} \rightarrow 2Cl_{2\,(g)} + e^-$; Cell E_V = 1.36 V
    (b) $2H_2O_{(l)} \rightarrow O_{2\,(g)} + 4H^+ + e^-$; Cell E_V = 1.23 V
    (c) $Na^+_{(aq)} + e^- \rightarrow Na_{(s)}$; Cell E_V = 2.71 V
    (d) $H^+_{(aq)} + e^- \rightarrow 2H_{2\,(g)}$; Cell E_V = 0.00 V

136. Electrolytic refining is used to purify which of the following metals?

(a) Cu and Zn   (b) Ge and Si   (c) Zr and Ti   (d) Zn and Hg

137. Titanium and zirconium are refined by ......

(a) Cupellation   (b) Van Arkel   (c) Poling   (d) Zone refining

138. Zinc metal is refined by ......

(a) Distillation   (b) Van Arkel   (c) Poling   (d) Zone refining

139. Zone refining is based on the principle that __________.

(a) impurities of low boiling metals can be separated by distillation.

(b) impurities are more soluble in molten metal than in solid metal.

(c) different components of a mixture are differently adsorbed on an adsorbent.

(d) vapours of volatile compound can be decomposed in pure metal.

140. The three curves intersect at 710°C, which statement is correct

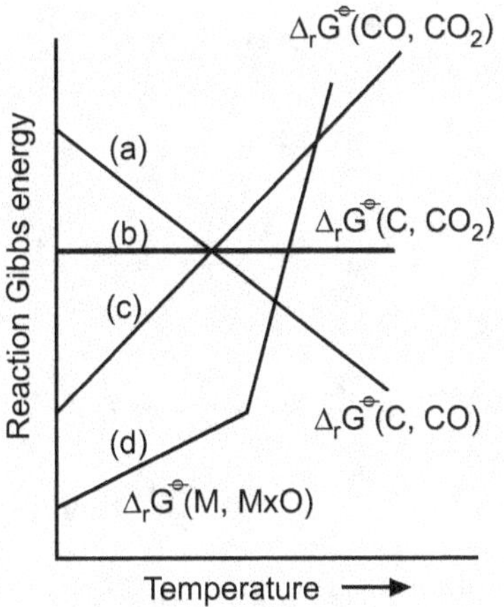

Fig. 1

(a) Below 710°C, CO is better reducing agent and above 710°C, carbon is better reducing agent

(b) Above 710°C, CO is better reducing agent and below 710°C, carbon is better reducing agent

(c) above 710°C, CO_2 is better reducing agent and below 710°C, carbon is better reducing agent

(d) Below 710°C, CO_2 is better reducing agent and above 710°C, carbon is better reducing agent

141. At any given temperature, any element will reduce the oxide of other metals which lie

(a) below it in Ellingham diagram because net free Gibbs energy is negative

(b) above it in Ellingham diagram because net free Gibbs energy is negative

(c) below it in Ellingham diagram because free Gibbs energy is negative

(d) above it in Ellingham diagram because Gibbs energy is negative

142. $\Delta G°$ Vs T plot in the Ellingham's diagram slopes downwards for the reaction ......

(a) $Mg + O_2 \rightarrow MgO$

(b) $2Ag + O_2 \rightarrow Ag_2O$

(c) $C + O_2 \rightarrow CO$

(d) $CO + O_2 \rightarrow CO_2$

PREVIOUS YEAR'S QUESTIONS

1. Match items of Column I with the items of Column II and assign the correct code.

[NEET - UG 2016]

Column I	Column II
(a) Cyanide process	(i) Ultrapure Ge
(b) Froth floatation process	(ii) Dressing of ZnS
(c) Electrolytic reduction	(iii) Extraction of A
(d) Zone refining	(iv) Extraction of A
	(v) Purification of

Code

	(a)	(b)	(c)	(d)
(a)	(iii)	(iv)	(v)	(i)
(b)	(iv)	(ii)	(iii)	(i)
(c)	(ii)	(iii)	(i)	(v)
(d)	(i)	(ii)	(iii)	(iv)

2. In the extraction of copper from its sulphide ore, the metal is finally obtained by the reduction of cuprous oxide with ......   **[RE AIPMT 2015]**

(a) copper (I) sulphide

(b) sulphur dioxide

(c) iron (II) sulphide

(d) carbon monoxide

3. "Metals are usually not found as nitrate in their ores".   **[AIPMT 2015]**

Out of the following two (a and b) reasons which is/are true for the above observation?

(1) Metal nitrates are highly unstable

(2) Metal nitrates are highly soluble in water.

(a) (1) and (2) are flase

(b) (1) is false but (2) is true

(c) (1) but (2) is false

(d) (1) and (2) are ture

4. Aluminium is extracted from alumina (Al_2O_3) by electrolysis of a molten mixture of

[CBSE AIPMT 2012]

(a) $Al_2O_3 + HF + NaAlF_4$

(b) $Al_2O_3 + CaF_2 + NaAlF_4$

(c) $Al_2O_3 + Na_3AlF_5 + CaF_2$

(d) $Al_2O_3 + KF + Na = 3AlF_6$

5. Which of the following is an oxide ore?   **[OJEE 2012]**

(a) Malachite   (b) Haematite   (c) Copper glance   (d) Zinc blende

6. Auto reduction process is used in the extraction of   **[AFMC 2012]**

(a) Cu and Hg   (b) Zn and Hg   (c) Cu and Al   (d) Fe and Pb

7. Identify the ore not containing iron ......   **[UP CPMT 2012]**

(a) limonite   (b) siderite   (c) camalite   (d) chalcopyrites

8. During the process of electrolytic refining of copper, some metals present as impurity settle as "anode mud". These are ......   **[Manipal 2012]**
(a) Fe and Ni   (b) Ag and Au   (c) Pb and Zn   (d) Se and Ag

9. NaCN is sometimes added in the froth floatation process as a depressant when ZnS and PbS minerals are extracted because ......   **[AIIMS 2012]**
(a) ZnS forms soluble complex $Na_2[Zn(CN)_4]$ while PbS forms froth
(b) $Pb(CN)_2$ is precipitated while no effect on ZnS
(c) PbS forms soluble complex $Na_2[Pb(CN)_4]$ while ZnS forms froth.
(d) NaCN is never added in froth floatation process

10. Which one of the following does not occur as sulphide ore ?   **[Kerala CEE 2011]**
(a) Zn   (b) Cr   (c) Ag   (d) Fe
(e) Hg

11. Which of the following pairs of metals is purified by Van Arkel method **[CBSE, AIPMT 2011]**
(a) Ni and Fe   (b) Ga and In   (c) Zr and Ti   (d) Ag and Au

12. Carbon can be formed from iron because ......
(a) free energy change for the formation of CO is more negative than that of Fe_2O_3
(b) CO is thermodynamically more stable than Fe_2O_3
(c) carbon has higher affinity towards oxygen than iron
(d) iron has higher affinity towards oxygen than carbon

13. Which one of the following statement is false?   **[KCET 2011]**
(a) During roasting, moisture is removed from the ore
(b) The ore is freed from almost all non-metallic impurities
(c) Calcination of ore is carried out in the absence of any blast of air
(d) The concentrated zinc blende is subjected to calcinations during its extraction by pyrometallurgy

14. Solder is an alloy of ......   **[CMC Ludhiana 2010]**
(a) Pb + Sn   (b) Pb + Sn + Zn   (c) Pb + Zn   (d) Sn + Zn

15. A major constituent of Portland cement (except lime) is ......   **[BVP 2010]**
(a) silica   (b) alumina   (c) iron oxide   (d) magnesia

16. Calcium ammonium nitrate is known as ......   **[VMMC - 2010]**
(a) Nangal fertilizer   (b) Chile salt petre   (c) Thomas slag   (d) Sindri

17. German silver is an alloy of   **[CPMT 2009]**
(a) Cu and Zn   (b) Cu and Ag   (c) Cu and Sn   (d) Cu, Zn and Ni

18. Willemite is ......   **[MHT CET 2009]**
(a) Zn_2SiO_4 (b) H_2PtCl_6 (c) ZnO   (d) $ZnO \cdot Fe_2O_3$

19. Cassiterite is an ore of ......   **[Manipal 2009]**
(a) Na   (b) Cu   (c) Pb   (d) Fe

20. Invar is an alloy of ......
(a) Mg and Zn   (b) Fe and Ni   (c) Ni and Zn   (d) Al and Zn

21. Calamine is ......   **[MHT CET 2008]**
(a) $CaCO_3$ (b) $MgCO_3$ (c) $ZnCO_3$ (d) $CaCO_3 + CaO$

22. Which of the following does not contain silicon?   **[MHT CET 2007]**
(a) Kaoline   (b) Agate   (c) Ruby   (d) Quartz

23. Which of the following ore is not an ore of Al?   **[Guj. CET 2007]**
    (a) Mica   (b) Anglesite   (c) Orthoclase   (d) Beryl

24. Cinnabar is ......   **[BHU 2006]**
    (a) HgS (b) PbS (c) SnO_2 (d) $PbCO_3$

25. Apatite is an ore of ......   **[MHT CET 2006]**
    (a) fluorine   (b) chlorine   (c) bromine   (d) iodine

26. Which of the following ores is an ore of copper?   **[J & K CET 2006]**
    (a) Argentite   (b) Haematite   (c) Malachite   (d) Calamine

27. Carbon cannot reduce Fe_2O_3 to Fe at a temperature below 983 K because ...... **[KCET 2006]**
    (a) free energy change for the formation of CO is more negative than that of Fe_2O_3
    (b) CO is thermodynamically more stable than Fe_2O_3
    (c) carbon has higher affinity towards oxygen than iron
    (d) iron has higher affinity towards oxygen than carbon

28. Which one of the following statements is false?   **[KCET 2006]**
    (a) During roasting, moisture is removed from the ore
    (b) The ore is freed from almost all non-metallic impurities
    (c) Calcination of ore is carried out in the laboratory
    (d) The concentration of zinc blende is subjected to calcination during its extraction by pyrometallurgy

29. In the equation   **[AFMC 2010]**
$$4M + 8CN^- + 2H_2O + O_2 \rightarrow 4[M(CN)_2]^- + 4OH^-$$
    identify the metal M.
    (a) copper   (b) iron   (c) gold   (d) zinc

30. Gravity separation process is used for the concentration of ......   **[AFMC 2009]**
    (a) calamine   (b) haemetite   (c) chalcopyrite   (d) bauxite

31. In zone refining method, the molten zone ......   **[AIIMS 2009]**
    (a) contains impurities
    (b) contains purified metal only
    (c) contains more impurity than the original metal
    (d) moves to either side

32. The process of converting hydrated alumina into anhydrous alumina is called as ......
                                                                          [CPMT 2009]
    (a) roasting   (b) smelting   (c) dressing   (d) calcinations

33. The incorrect statement among the following is ......   **[J & K CET 2009]**
    (a) Hydrogen is used to reduce NiO
    (b) Zirconium is refined by Van Arkel method
    (c) The sulphite ore galena is concentrated by froth floatation
    (d) In the metallurgy of iron, the flux used is SiO_2

34. $(Ag + Pb)_{alloy} \rightarrow (Ag + Pb + Zn)_{melt} \rightarrow$ **[AIIMS 2008]**
    Select the correct statement based on above scheme.
    (a) Layer X contains Zn and Ag
    (b) Layer Y contains Pb and Ag but amount of silver in this layer is smaller than in layer X
    (c) X and Y are immiscible layers
    (d) All of the above are correct

35. Steel is heated to below red heat and then cooled slowly. The process refers to ......

[CPMT, MP, PMT, RPMT 2008]

    (a) hardening   (b) annealing   (c) tempering   (d) nitriding

36. Impurities of Cu and Ag from gold are removed by ......   **[Manipal 2008]**

    (a) boiling impure gold with dil. H_2SO_4 (b) boiling impure gold with conc. H_2SO_4

    (c) electrolytically   (d) both (b) and (c)

37. Silica is a/an ......   **[Manipal 2008]**

    (a) acidic flux only   (b) gangue only

    (c) basic flux only   (d) both gangue and acidic

38. Sulphide ores of metals are usually concentrated by froth floatation process. Which one of the following sulphide ores offers an exception and is concentrated by chemical leaching?

[CBSE AIPMT 2007]

    (a) Argentite   (b) Galena   (c) Copper pyrite   (d) Sphalerite

39. Which of the following ores does not represent the ore of iron ?   **[AIIMS 2002]**

    (a) Heamatite   (b) Magnetite   (c) Cassiterite   (d) Limonite

40. An ore of potassium is ......   **[JIPMER - 2001]**

    (a) Bauxite   (b) Dolomite   (c) Carnalite   (d) Cryolite

41. Formula of felspar is ......   **[MHCET 2004]**

    (a) $K_2O \cdot Al_2O_3 \cdot 6SiO_2$ (b) $K_2O_3 \cdot Al_2O_3 \cdot 6Si_2 \cdot O_2 \cdot 2H_2O$

    (c) $Al_2O_3 \cdot 2SiO_2 \cdot 2H_2O$ (d) $3MgO \cdot 4SiO_2 \cdot H_2O$

42. The substance which is mixed with the ore for removal of impurities is termed as ......

[JIPMER 2002]

    (a) Slag   (b) Gangue   (c) Flux   (d) Catalyst

43. During extraction of Fe; slag obtained is   **[CPMT 2000]**

    (a) FeO   (b) $FeSiO_3$ (c) $MgSiO_3$ (d) $CaSiO_3$

44. The final step for the extraction of copper from copper pyrite in Bessemere converter involves the reaction ......   **[CPMT 2000]**

    (a) $4Cu_2O + FeS \rightarrow 8Cu + FeSO_4$ (b) $Cu_2S + 2Cu_2O \rightarrow 6Cu + SO_2$

    (c) $2Cu_2O + FeS \rightarrow 4Cu + Fe + SO_2$ (d) $Cu_2S + 2FeO \rightarrow 2Cu + 2FeCO + SO_2$

45. Gold is extracted by hydrometallurgical process based on its property ......   **[KCET 2005]**

    (a) Of being electropositive

    (b) Of being less reactive

    (c) To form complexes which are water soluble

    (d) To form salts which are water soluble

46. Identify the process when an ore is heated in limited supply of air ......   **[BVP 2010]**

    (a) Smelting   (b) Roasting   (c) Calcination   (d) Liquation

47. When the impurities are removed from an ore, the metal becomes liable to ......

[CBSE-AIPMT 2009]

    (a) Calcination   (b) Oxidation

    (c) Magnetic concentration   (d) Reduction

48. A mineral is known as an ore if the metal ......   **[Pb PMT 2001]**

    (a) Cannot be produced from it   (b) Can be produced from it

    (c) Can be produced from it profitably   (d) Is very costly

49. Aluminium is ...... **[AIIMS 2005]**
(a) Third abundant element in earth's crust
(b) Second abundant element in earth's crust
(c) Fourth abundant element in earth's crust
(d) Twenty fourth abundant element in earth's crust

50. Rutile is separated from chlorapatite by ...... **[BHU 2005]**
(a) Froth floatation method (b)   Levigation
(c) Electromagnetic separation method   (d) Electrostatic separation method

51. The main function of roasting is ...... **[BVP 2007]**
(a) Concentration   (b) Reduction   (b) Oxidation   (d) Isolation

52. Commercial zinc is refined by ...... **[AIIMS 2006]**
(a) Liquation   (b) Poling   (c) Electrolysis   (d) Amalgamation

53. Consider the following reaction at 1000°C

$$Zn_{(s)} + \frac{1}{2} Cr_{3(s)} \rightarrow ZnO_{(s)} \quad \Delta G° = -360 \text{ kJ mol}^{-1}$$

$$C_{(graphite)} + \frac{1}{2} O_{2\,(g)} \rightarrow CO_{(g)}; \Delta G° = -460 \text{ kJ mol}^{-1}$$

Choose the correct statement at 1000°C.
(a) zinc can be oxidized by CO   (b) zinc oxide can be reduced by graphite
(c) both (a) and (b) are true   (d) both (a) and (b) are false

54. Which of the following is the impurest form of iron ? **[Haryana PMT 2008]**
(a) Bessemer iron   (b) Steel
(c) Pig iron   (d) Wrought iron

55. Which of the following has highest melting point ? **[CBSE-AIPMT 2004]**
(a) Pig iron   (b) Cast iron   (c) Steel   (d) Wrought iron

56. Which form of iron is least ductile ? **[J & K 2003]**
(a) Hard steel   (b) Cast iron   (c) Mild steel   (d) Wrought iron

57. The most abundant ore of iron is ...... **[BHU 2001]**
(a) Haematite   (b) Limonite   (c) Magnetite   (d) Siderite

58. Which of the following is used as a depressant in froth-floatation process ? **[Pb PMT 2009]**
(a) Amyl xanthate   (b) Pine oil
(c) Copper sulphate   (d) Potassium cyanide

59. Constantan is an alloy of ...... **[Kerala PMT 2003]**
(a) Cu and Ni   (b) Fe and Ni   (c) Cu and Sn   (d) Cu and Zn

60. Which of the following is constituent of lithophone ? **[BVP 2005]**
(a) $ZnSO_4$ (b) ZnS (c) $ZnCl_2$ (d) ZnO

61. The impurities associated with mineral used in metallurgy are collectively called ......
(a) Slag   (b) Gangue   (c) Flux   (d) Froth **[CPMT 2008]**

62. The trace metal present in insulin is **[RPMT 2002]**
(a) Fe   (b) Co   (c) Zn   (d) Mn

63. In smelting process, the impurities of an ore is removed by ...... **[BHU 2000]**
(a) Addition of flux   (b) Levigation   (c) Addition of slag (d) Liquation

64. Formula of Magnetite is ...... **[DPMT 2002]**
(a) Fe_2O_5 (b) FeO (c) Fe_3O_4 (d) Fe_2O_3

65. Which of the following is carbonate ore ?   **[AMU 2010]**
    (a) Siderite   (b) Cuprite   (c) Calamine   (d) Both (a) and (c)

66. Zinc is extracted by ......
    (a) The carbon reduction of ZnO (b) The carbon monoxide reduction of ZnO
    (c) The hydrogen reduction of ZnO (d) The copper reduction of ZnO

67. The temperature of 3000°C is obtained ......   **[BVP 2000]**
    (a) In an open hearth   (b) By electric arc
    (c) In blast furnace   (d) In muffle furnace

68. In metallurgy of iron, hot air is blown in blast furnace through ......   **[AMU 2010]**
    (a) An inlet   (b) A tapping hole   (c) Tuyeres   (d) An outlet

69. The most abundant element in earth's crust (by weight) is ......   **[Kerala P.M.T. 2000]**
    (a) Si   (b) Al   (c) O   (d) Fe
    (e) Na

70. Pyrolusite is a/an ......   **[D.P.M.T. 2002]**
    (a) Oxide ore   (b) Sulphide ore   (c) Carbide ore   (d) Not an ore

ANSWER KEY

1. (b)	2. (c)	3. (b)	4. (a)	5. (c)	6. (b)	7. (b)	8. (b)
9. (b)	10. (a)	11. (a)	12. (b)	13. (b)	14. (c)	15. (a)	16. (a)
17. (c)	18. (d)	19. (d)	20. (b)	21. (d)	22. (b)	23. (d)	24. (d)
25. (d)	26. (d)	27. (d)	28. (a)	29. (c)	30. (a)	31. (c)	32. (d)
33. (a)	34. (c)	35. (a)	36. (c)	37. (a)	38. (b)	39. (c)	40. (a)
41. (d)	42. (a)	43. (c)	44. (c)	45. (b)	46. (b)	47. (d)	48. (b)
49. (c)	50. (c)	51. (a)	52. (d)	53. (c)	54. (d)	55. (b)	56. (d)
57. (a)	58. (b)	59. (d)	60. (a)	61. (a)	62. (c)	63. (b)	64. (c)
65. (a)	66. (d)	67. (d)	68. (c)	69. (c)	70. (b)	71. (b)	72. (a)
73. (d)	74. (a)	75. (c)	76. (a)	77. (c)	78. (b)	79. (a)	80. (c)
81. (a)	82. (d)	83. (b)	84. (b)	85. (b)	86. (c)	87. (b)	88. (c)
89. (a)	90. (d)	91. (a)	92. (a)	93. (c)	94. (c)	95. (c)	96. (c)
97. (c)	98. (b)	99. (c)	100. (a)	101. (b)	102. (b)	103. (b)	104. (d)
105. (a)	106. (b)	107. (c)	108. (a)	109. (c)	110. (a)	111. (c)	112. (b)
113.(d)	114. (d)	115. (d)	116. (d)	117. (c)	118. (c)	119. (b)	120. (d)
121. (d)	122. (d)	123. (c)	124. (c)	125. (c)	126. (d)	127. (c)	128. (a)
129. (b)	130. (c)	131. (b)	132. (b)	133. (b)	134 (c)	135. (a)	136. (a)
137. (b)	138. (a)	139. (b)	140. (a)	141. (b)	142. (c)		

Previous Years Questions

1. (b)	2. (d)	3. (d)	4. (c)	5. (b)	6. (a)	7. (c)	8. (b)
9. (a)	10. (b)	11. (c)	12. (a)	13. (a)	14. (a)	15. (a)	16. (a)
17. (d)	18. (a)	19. (c)	20. (b)	21. (c)	22. (c)	23. (b)	24. (a)
25. (a)	26. (c)	27. (d)	28. (d)	29. (c)	30. (b)	31. (c)	32. (d)
33. (d)	34. (d)	35. (b)	36. (d)	37. (d)	38. (d)	39. (c)	40. (c)
41. (a)	42. (c)	43. (d)	44. (b)	45. (c)	46. (c)	47. (a)	48. (c)
49. (a)	50. (c)	51. (b)	52. (b)	53. (b)	54. (c)	55. (d)	56. (b)
57. (a)	58. (d)	59. (a)	60. (b)	61. (b)	62. (c)	63. (a)	64. (c)
65. (a)	66. (a)	67. (d)	68. (c)	69. (c)	70. (a)		

p-BLOCK ELEMENTS (GROUP 13-18)

1. Boron with the highest purity (~99.9%) is obtained by ......
   (a) Reduction of BCl_3 with H_2 at 1270 K
   (b) Reduction of B_2O_3 by Mg
   (c) Thermal decomposition of boranes at 1175 K
   (d) None of these

2. Boron is non-metallic because of ......
   (a) Large size and higher nuclear charge
   (b) Small size and higher nuclear charge
   (c) Small size and smaller nuclear charge
   (d) None of these

3. The element which exists in liquid state for a wide range of temperature and can be used for measuring high temperature is ......
   (a) B
   (b) Al
   (c) Ga
   (d) In

4. Radius of Ga is less than Al because of ......
   (a) Lanthanoid contraction
   (b) Inert pair effect
   (c) Increased screening effect
   (d) None of these

5. Ionisation enthalpy ($Ä_i H_1$ kJ mol^{-1}) for the elements of Group 13 follows the order ......
   (a) B > Al > Ga > In > Tl
   (b) B < Al < Ga < In < Tl
   (c) B < Al > Ga < In > Tl
   (d) B > Al < Ga > In < Tl

6. Which of the following elements does not form MF_6^{-3} ?
   (a) B
   (b) Al
   (c) Ga
   (d) In

7. Which of the following elements form strongest acidic oxide?
   (a) B
   (b) Al
   (c) Ga
   (d) In

8. The geometry and the hybridisation in BF_3 is ......
   (a) Linear, sp
   (b) Pyramidal, sp^3
   (c) Tetrahedral, sp^3
   (d) Trigonal planar, sp^2

9. Identify the statement that is not correct as far as the structure of diborane is concerned
   (a) There are two bridging hydrogen atoms and four terminal hydrogen atoms in diborane
   (b) Each boron atom forms four bonds in diborane
   (c) The hydrogen atoms are not in the same plane in diborane
   (d) All B-H bonds in diborane are similar

10. The type of hybridisation of boron in diborane is ......
   (a) sp
   (b) sp^2
   (c) sp^3
   (d) sp^3d^2

11. In a molecule of diborane ......
   (a) 4-bridged hydrogens and two terminal hydrogens are present
   (b) 2-bridged hydrogens and four terminal hydrogens are present
   (c) 3-bridged and three terminal hydrogens are present
   (d) None of these

12. The tendency of BF_3, BCl_3 and BBr_3 to behave as Lewis acid decreases in the sequence ......

(a) $BCl_3 > BF_3 > BBr_3$

(b) $BF_3 > BCl_3 > BBr_3$

(c) $BBr_3 > BF_3 > BCl_3$

(d) $BBr_3 > BCl_3 > BF_3$

13. When BCl_3 is treated with water, the following compound is formed ......

(a) $H_3BO_3 + HCl$ (b) $B_2H_6 + HCl$ (c) $B_2O_3 + HCl$ (d) None of these

14. H_3BO_3 is ......

(a) Monobasic and strong Lewis acid

(b) Monobasic and weak Lewis acid

(c) Monobasic and weak Bronsted acid

(d) Tribasic and weak Bronsted acid

15. Borax is not used ......

(a) As a styptic to stop bleeding

(b) In making enamel and pottery glazes

(c) As a flux in soldering

(d) In making optical glasses

16. Which of the following oxides is acidic in nature?

(a) B_2O_3 (b) Al_2O_3 (c) Ga_2O_3 (d) In_2O_3

17. Inorganic benzene is ......

(a) $B_3N_3H_6$ (b) B_3N_3 (c) SiC (d) P_4S_3

18. A compound X of boron reacts with NH_3 on heating to give another compound Y which is called inorganic benzene. The compound X can be prepared by treating BF_3 with lithium aluminium hydride. The compounds X and Y are represented by the formulas ......

(a) B_2H_6, $B_3N_3H_6$ (b) B_2O_3, $B_3N_3H_6$ (c) BF_3, $B_3N_3H_6$ (d) $B_3N_3H_6$, B_2H_6

19. Borax occurs as natural deposit called tincal in the dried up lakes of ......

(a) Tibet

(b) California

(c) Tibet and California

(d) Virginia

20. The best stiffening and glazing agent for silk is ......

(a) Boric acid   (b) Na_2CO_3 (c) Borax   (d) Sodium perborate

21. Borazole is obtained by reacting B_2H_6 with ......

(a) NH_3 in the ratio 1 : 2

(b) NH_3 in the ratio 2 : 1

(c) NH_3 in the ratio 1 : 4

(d) Cannot be formed

22. Borax on heating with ethyl alcohol and conc. H_2SO_4 yields ......

(a) Meta borate   (b) Triethyl borate   (c) Dimethyl borate   (d) No reaction

23. Formula of borax is ......

(a) $Na_2B_4O_7 . 4H_2O$

(b) $Na_2B_4O_7 . 8H_2O$

(c) $Na_2[B_4O_5(OH)_4] . 8H_2O$

(d) $Na_2[B_4O_5(OH)_4] . 10H_2O$

24. Which metaborate is blue ?

(a) $Ni(BO_2)_2$ (b) $Co(BO_2)_2$ (c) $Cr(BO_2)_2$ (d) $NaBO_2$

25. Diborane on hydrolysis gives ......

(a) Metaboric acid   (b) Boric anhydride   (c) Orthoboric acid (d) Boron oxide

26. The bonds present in borazole or inorganic benzene are ......

(a) $9\sigma, 6\pi$ (b) $16\sigma, 3\pi$ (c) $6\sigma, 9\pi$ (d) 15σ only

27. The acidic strength of boron trihalides is ......

(a) $BF_3 < BCl_3 < BBr_3 < BI_3$

(b) $BI_3 < BBr_3 < BCl_3 < BF_3$

(c) $BCl_3 < BBr_3 < BI_3 < BF_3$

(d) $BF_3 < BI_3 < BCl_3 < BBr_3$

28. The structure of diborane (B_2H_6) contains ......

(a) Two 2c–2e bonds and two 3c–3e bonds

(b) Four 2c–2e bonds and two 3c–2e bonds

(c) Four 2c–2e bonds and four 3c–2e bonds

(d) Two 2c–2e bonds and four 3c–2e bonds

29. In diborane the two H–B–H angles are nearly ......

(a) 60°, 120°　　　(b) 120°, 180°　　　(c) 97°, 120°　　　(d) 95°, 150°

30. On moderate heating, the compound which gives off oxygen is ......

(a) Aluminium oxide　　(b) Cupric oxide　　(c) Mercuric oxide　(d) Zinc oxide

31. Which imparts green colour to the burner flame?

(a) $Sn(OH)_2$　　　(b) $B(OMe)_3$　　　(c) $Al(OBr_2)_3$　　　(d) $Na(OMe)$

32. Which of the following boron compounds is optically active ?

(a) Boron anhydride

(b) Boron salicylic acid

(c) Boron trifluoride

(d) Sodium tetraborate

33. In the structure of diborane ......

(a) All hydrogen atoms lie in one plane and boron atoms lie in a plane perpendicular to this plane.

(b) 2 boron atoms and 4 terminal hydrogen atoms lie in the same plane and two bridging hydrogen atoms lie in the perpendicular plane.

(c) 4 bridging hydrogen atoms and boron atoms lie in one plane and two terminal hydrogem atoms lie in a plane perpendicular to this plane.

(d) All the atoms are in the same plane.

34. Boric acid is an acid because its molecule ......

(a) Contains replaceable H^+ ion

(b) Gives up a proton

(c) Accepts OH^- from water releasing proton

(d) Combines with proton from water molecule

35. Crystalline boron is ______ in colour.

(a) Red　　　　　(b) Black　　　　　(c) Brown　　　　　(d) Green

36. $B_2H_6 + NH_3 \rightarrow$ Addition $\xrightarrow{\text{450°K}}$ Y + Z (g)

　　　　　　　compound (X)

In the above sequence, Y and Z are respectively ......

(a) Boron, H_2

(b) Borazine, H_2

(c) Boron, hydrazine

(d) Boron nitride, H_2

37. When borax is heated strongly, it gives ......

(a) $NaBO_2$　　　(b) $NaBO_2 + B_2O_3$　　(c) B_2O_3　　　(d) $Na_2B_4O_7$

38. In borax bead test, the coloured ions give characteristic coloured beads due to the formation of ......

(a) Metal metaborates

(b) Metal borates

(c) Metal tetraborates

(d) Metal phosphates

39. B_2H_6 reacts with sodium hydride to form ......

(a) Interstitial hydride

(b) Complex hydride

(c) Simple hydride

(d) Saline hydride

40. In B_2H_6 ......

(a) There is direct bonding between Boron - Boron

(b) All the B–H bonds are of equal distance

(c) Boranes are easily hydrolysed

(d) Boron atoms are linked through hydrogen bridges

41. Boron nitride has the structure of the type ......

(a) Both diamond and graphite

(b) Diamond

(c) Graphite

(d) NaCl

42. The allotropic form of carbon soluble in toluene is ......

(a) Fullerenes   (b) Graphite   (c) Diamond   (d) None of these

43. Fullerenes contain ......

(a) Six membered rings

(b) Five membered rings

(c) Both (a) and (b)

(d) None of these

44. Carbon atoms in diamond are bonded together by which forces ?

(a) Covalent   (b) Dipolar   (c) Van der Waals   (d) Ionic

45. Which one of the following is not the characteristic property of carbon ?

(a) It exhibits catenation

(b) It forms compounds with multiple bonds

(c) Its melting point and boiling point are exceptionally high

(d) It shows semi-metallic character

46. The ability of a substance to assume two or more crystalline structures is called ......

(a) Isomerism   (b) Polymorphism   (c) Isomorphism   (d) Amorphism

47. The tendency of catenation in Group 14 elements follows the order ......

(a) C > Si > Ge > Sn

(b) C >> Si > Ge $\equiv$ Sn

(c) Si > C > Sn > Ge

(d) Ge > Sn > Si > C

48. The shape of carbon dioxide molecule is ......

(a) Octahedral   (b) Linear   (c) Tetrahedral   (d) Square planar

49. Tungsten carbide is an example of ......

(a) Substitutional solid solution

(b) Interstitial solid solution

(c) Passive solid solution

(d) Sandwich solid solution

50. Carborundum is obtained when silica is heated at high temperature with ......

(a) Carbon
(b) Calcium carbonate
(c) Carbon dioxide
(d) Carbon monoxide

51. Moderate electrical conductivity is shown by ......

(a) Silica (b) Diamond (c) Graphite (d) Carborundum

52. Assertion (a) : Silicons are water repelling in nature.

Reason (R) : Silicons are organosilicon polymers, which have ($-R_2SiO-$) as repeating unit.

(a) A and R both are correct and R is the correct explanation of A.

(b) Both A and R are correct but R is not the correct explanation of A.

(c) A and R both are not true.

(d) A is not true but R is true.

53. Cement, the important building material is a mixture of oxides of several elements. Besides calcium, iron and sulphur, oxides of elements of which of the group(s) are present in the mixture?

(a) Group 2
(b) Groups 2, 13 and 14
(c) Groups 2 and 13
(d) Groups 2 and 14

54. Dry ice is ......

(a) Solid NH_3 (b) Solid SO_2 (c) Solid CO_2 (d) Solid N_2

55. CO forms a volatile compound with ......

(a) Ni (b) Cu (c) Al (d) Si

56. CO is a poisonous gas. Antidote for CO poisoning is ......

(a) Carborundum (b) Carbogen (c) Carbonic acid (d) Pure oxygen

57. Reducing agent in the Blast Furnace is ......

(a) O_2 (b) CaCO (c) SiO_2 (d) CO

58. Which one of the following is carborundum?

(a) Al_2O_3 (b) SiC (c) $ZnSO_4$ (d) Fe_2O_3

59. Identify the correct statement with respect to carbon monoxide.

(a) It combines with water to form carbonic acid

(b) It reacts with haemoglobin in red blood cells

(c) It is a powerful oxidising agent

(d) It is used to prepare aerated drinks

60. The oxide of carbon which polymerises to coloured solids is ......

(a) CO (b) CO_2 (c) C_3O_2 (d) None of these

61. Colloidal solution of graphite in water is called ......

(a) Oil day (b) Aqua dag (c) Lamp black (d) Anthracite

62. What is the colour of C_{60} in toluene ?

(a) Pinkish (b) Bluish (c) Reddish (d) Greenish

63. Which among the following is known as pyrene ?

(a) CCl_4　　　　(b) CS_2　　　　(c) S_2Cl_2　　　　(d) Solid CO_2

64. Graphite on oxidation with conc. HNO_3 gives ......

(a) CO　　　　(b) Graphitic acid　　　　(c) C_3O_2　　　　(d) None of these

65. Carbogen is ......

(a) Pure form of carbon　　　　(b) $COCl_2$

(c) Mixture of CO and CO_2　　　　(d) Mixture of O_2 and CO_2

66. Silicon has a strong tendency to form polymers like silicons. The chain length of silicon polymer can be controlled by adding ......

(a) $MeSiCl_3$　　　　(b) Me_2SiCl_2　　　　(c) Me_3SiCl　　　　(d) Me_4Si

67. Quartz is extensively used as a piezoelectric material, it contains __________

(a) Pb　　　　(b) Si　　　　(c) Ti　　　　(d) Sn

68. The most commonly used reducing agent is ......

(a) $AlCl_3$　　　　(b) $PbCl_2$　　　　(c) $SnCl_4$　　　　(d) $SnCl_2$

69. Among the following substituted silanes, the one which will give rise to cross-linked silicone polymer on hydrolysis is ......

(a) R_4Si　　　　(b) $RSiCl_3$　　　　(c) R_2SiCl_2　　　　(d) R_3SiCl

70. The major constituent of cement is ......

(a) Silica　　　　(b) Magnesium oxide

(c) Calcium carbonate　　　　(d) Iron oxide

71. Graphite is an allotropic form of________

(a) Tin　　　　(b) Diamond　　　　(c) Coal　　　　(d) Carbon

72. The triple bond between N atoms of nitrogen molecule consists of ......

(a) Three s-bonds　　　　(b) Two s-bonds and one p-bond

(c) One s-bond and two p-bonds　　　　(d) Three p-bonds

73. In the reaction

$$4HNO_3 + P_4O_{10} \longrightarrow 4HPO_3 + X, \text{ the product X is ......}$$

(a) N_2O_5　　　　(b) N_2O_3　　　　(c) NO_2　　　　(d) H_2O

74. The brown ring test for nitrates depends on ......

(a) Reduction of ferrous sulphate to iron

(b) Oxidation of nitric oxide to nitrogen dioxide

(c) The reduction of nitrate to nitric oxide

(d) Oxidising action of sulphuric acid

75. Which of the following does not give NO_2 on heating ?

(a) $AgNO_3$　　　　(b) KNO_3　　　　(c) $Pb(NO_3)_2$　　　　(d) $Cu(NO_3)_2$

76. Three reactions involving H_2PO_4 are given below ......

(i) $H_3PO_4 + H_2O \rightarrow H_3O^+ + H_2PO_4$

(ii) $H_2PO_4 + H_2O \rightarrow HPO_4^- + H_3O^+$

(iii) $H_2PO_4 + OH^- \rightarrow H_3PO_4 + O^{2-}$

In which of the above does H_2PO_4 act as an acid?

(a) (i) only   (b) (ii) only   (c) (iii) only   (d) (i) and (ii)

77. Nitric acid on standing develops brownish colour which may be attributed to the presence of ......

(a) NO_2^- (b) NO_2 (c) NO (d) HNO_2

78. Which oxide does not act as a reducing agent?

(a) NO (b) NO_2 (c) N_2O (d) N_2O_5

79. When NH_3 is passed over heated CuO, it is oxidised to ......

(a) N_2 (b) NO_2 (c) N_2O (d) HNO_2

80. The bonds present in N_2O_5 are ......

(a) Covalent and co-ordinate   (b) Only ionic

(c) Only covalent   (d) Covalent ionic

81. Nitrogen shows different oxidation states in the range of ......

(a) −3 to +5   (b) −5 to +3   (c) 0 to 5   (d) +3 to +5

82. Which among the following oxides of nitrogen is a coloured gas ?

(a) NO_2 (b) N_2O (c) NO (d) N_2O_4

83. Which trihalide of nitrogen is least basic ?

(a) NF_3 (b) NI_3 (c) NCl_3 (d) NBr_3

84. The lightning bolts in the atmosphere cause the formation of ......

(a) NH_3 (b) NO (c) NH_2OH (d) NH_4OH

85. Ammonia is dried over ......

(a) Calcium chloride   (b) Slaked lime

(c) Phosphorus pentoxide   (d) Quick lime

86. Iodine reacts with concentrated HNO_3 to form ......

(a) $HOIO_3$ (b) HOI (c) $HOIO_2$ (d) HI

87. Nitrogen is liberated by the thermal decomposition of ......

(a) NH_3NO_2 (b) NaN_3 (c) $(NH_4)_2Cr_2O_7$ (d) All of these

88. CN^- ion and N_2 are isoelectronic but in contrast to CN^-, N_2 is chemically inert because of ...

(a) Absence of bond polarity

(b) Unsymmetrical electron distribution

(c) Presence of more number of electrons in bonding orbitals

(d) Low bond energy

89. Among the following species, identify the isostructural pairs NF_3, NO_3^-, BF_3, H_3O^+, HN_3

 (a) $[NF_3, H_3O^+]$ and $[NO, BF_3]$ (b) $[NF_3, NO]$ and $[BF_3, H_2O^+]$

 (c) $[NF_3, HNO_3]$ and $[NO, BF_3]$ (d) $[NF_3, H_3O^+]$ and $[HN_3, BF_3]$

90. Liquid ammonia is used for refrigeration because ......

 (a) It has a high dipole moment (b) It has a high heat of vaporization

 (c) It is a basic compound (d) It is a stable compound

91. Ammonium dichromate is used in some fire works. The green coloured powder blown in the air is ......

 (a) Cr_2O_3 (b) Cr (c) CrO_3 (d) $CrO(O_2)$

92. Sodium nitrate decomposes above 800°C to give ......

 (a) Na_2O (b) O_2 (c) N_2 (d) NO_2

93. On heating ammonium dichromate, the gas evolved is ......

 (a) Nitrous oxide (b) Nitrogen (c) Ammonia (d) Oxygen

94. Cane sugar reacts with conc. HNO_3 to give ......

 (a) Carbonic acid (b) CO_2 and H_2O (c) CO and H_2O (d) Oxalic acid

95. The hybridization of atomic orbitals of nitrogen in NO_2^+, NO_3^- and NH_4^+ are ......

 (a) sp^2, sp and sp^3 respectively (b) sp, sp^3 and sp^2 respectively

 (c) sp, sp^2 and sp^3 respectively (d) sp^2, sp^3 and sp respectively

96. Specify the coordination geometry and hybridization of N and B atoms in a 1 : 1 complex of BF_3 and NH_3.

 (a) N : pyramidal, sp^3; B : plane, sp^3 (b) N : pyramidal, sp^3; B : tetrahedral, sp^3

 (c) N : tetrahedral, sp^3; B : tetrahedral, sp^3 (d) N : pyramidal, sp^3; B : pyramidal, sp^3

97. $(NH_4)_2Cr_2O_7$ on heating liberates a gas. The same gas will be obtained by ......

 (a) Heating NH_4NO_3 (b) Heating NH_4NO_2

 (c) Treating H_2O_2 with $NaNO_2$ (d) Treating Mg_3N_2 with H_2O

98. In which of the following compounds, nitrogen exhibits highest oxidation state?

 (a) N_3H (b) NH_2OH (c) N_2H_4 (d) NH_3

99. Which of the following contains P – O – P bond?

 (a) Hypophosphorous acid (b) Phosphorous acid

 (c) Pyrophosphoric acid (d) Orthophosphoric acid

100. P_4O_{10} is the anhydride of ......

 (a) H_3PO_2 (b) H_3PO_3 (c) H_3PO_4 (d) $H_4P_2O_7$

101. Which of the following is a monobasic reducing agent ?

 (a) HPO_3 (b) H_3PO_3 (c) H_3PO_2 (d) $H_4P_2O_7$

102. The number of atoms of hydrogen attached to phosphorus atom in hypophosphorus acid is ......

 (a) Zero (b) Two (c) One (d) Three

103. The number of P–O–P bonds in cyclic metaphosphoric acid is ......

    (a) Zero   (b) Two   (c) Three   (d) Four

104. Which is the most thermodynamically stable allotropic form of phosphorous ?

    (a) Red   (b) White   (c) Black   (d) Yellow

105. Which blue liquid is obtained on reacting equimolar amounts of two gases at $-30°C$?

    (a) N_2O (b) N_2O_3 (c) N_2O_4 (d) N_2O_5

106. Which of the following oxides of nitrogen is neutral?

    (a) N_2O_5 (b) N_2O_3 (c) N_2O_4 (d) N_2O

107. Nitrogen (I) oxide is produced by ......

    (a) Thermal decomposition of ammonium nitrate

    (b) Disproportionation of N_2O_4

    (c) Thermal decomposition of ammonium nitrite

    (d) None of these

108. The correct order of decreasing acidic strength is ......

    (a) $HNO_3 > H_3SbO_4 > H_2AsO_4 > H_3PO_4$ (b) $H_3PO_4 > H_2AsO_4 > H_3SbO_4 > HNO_3$

    (c) $HNO_3 > H_3PO_4 > H_2AsO_4 > H_3SbO_4$ (d) $HNO_3 > H_2AsO_4 > H_3PO_4 > H_3SbO_4$

109. Skin tunes yellow in contact with concentrated HNO_3 because ......

    (a) Proteins are converted into xantho proteins

    (b) Decomposes into two oxides of nitrogen

    (c) Reacts with water to form nitric acid

    (d) Reacts with water to form two acids

110. The correct order of increasing bond angles in the following species is ......

    (a) $Cl_2O < ClO_2 < ClO_2^-$ (b) $ClO_2^- < Cl_2O < ClO_2$

    (c) $Cl_2O < ClO_2^- < ClO_2$ (d) $ClO_2 < Cl_2O < ClO_2$

111. Man dies, when nitrous oxide is inhaled in large quantities because it ......

    (a) Is poisonous   (b) Cause laughing hysteria

    (c) Decomposes haemoglobin   (d) React with organic tissues

112. Fixation of nitrogen means ......

    (a) Reaction of nitrogen with oxygen

    (b) Conversion of free atmospheric nitrogen into nitrogen compound

    (c) Decomposition of nitrogenous compounds to yield free nitrogen

    (d) The action of denitrifying bacteria on nitrogen compound

113. Fertilizer having the highest nitrogen percentage is ......

    (a) Calcium cynamide   (b) Urea

    (c) Ammonium nitrite   (d) Ammonium sulphate

114. Anomalous behavior of nitrogen is due to ......

    (a) Small size and high electronegativity

    (b) Non-availability of d-orbital in valency shell

    (c) Ease of multiple bond formation

    (d) All are correct

115. The starting material in Ostwald's process for the manufacture of HNO_3 is ......

(a) NH_3 (b) NO_2 (c) Air   (d) Chile saltpetre

116. When white phosphorus reacts with caustic soda to give PH_3 and NaH_2PO_2 and the reaction is ......

(a) Oxidation   (b) Reduction

(c) Neutralization   (d) Oxidation and reduction

117. PH_3 produces smoky rings when it comes in contact with air because of ......

(a) its inflammability   (b) its reaction with water vapour

(c) its reaction with oxygen   (d) its impurity of P_2H_4

118. Calcium phosphide reacts with excess of water to give ......

(a) phosphine   (b) phosphoric acid

(c) phosphorus pentaoxide   (d) phosphorus

119. Which is the incorrect statement about white phosphorous ......

(a) Six P – P single bonds are present   (b) Four P – P single bonds are present

(c) Four lone pair of electrons are present   (d) P – P – P bond angle is $60°$

120. Nitric acid (conc.) oxidizes phosphorus to ......

(a) H_3PO_4 (b) P_2O_3 (c) H_3PO_3 (d) $H_4P_2O_7$

121. Phosphorus is manufactured by heating ......

(a) Bone-ash, sodium chloride and coke   (b) Bond-ash, silica and coke

(c) Bone-ash, silica and lime   (d) Bone-ash, coke and lime stone

122. Red phosphorus is chemically unreative due to ......

(a) absence of P – P bonds   (b) absence of tetrahedral P_4 molecules

(c) presence of triple bond   (d) it has a polymeric structure

123. Phosphine is prepared by action of water on ......

(a) $CaCl_2$ (b) HPO_3 (c) Ca_3P_2 (d) P_4O_7

124. What is the geometry of molecule of bromine penta fluoride ?

(a) square planar   (b) trigonal bipyramidal

(c) square pyramidal   (d) octahedral

125. For the properties mentioned, the correct trend for different species is in ......

(a) strength as Lewis acid – $BCl_3 > AlCl_3 > GaCl_3$

(b) inert pair effect – Al > Ga > In

(c) oxidising property – $Al^{+3} > In^{+3} > Tl^{+3}$

(d) first ionization enthalpy – B > Al > Tl

126. The basic character of hydride of V group elements decrease in the order ......

(a) $NH_3 > PH_3 > AsH_3 > SbH_3$ (b) $SbH_3 > AsH_3 > PH_3 > NH_3$

(c) $NH_3 > SbH_3 > PH_3 > AsH_3$ (d) $SbH_3 > PH_3 > AsH_3 > NH_3$

127. The decreasing order of bond angle in group 15 hydrides is ......

(a) $NH_3 > PH_3 > AsH_3 > SbH_3$ (b) $NH_3 > AsH_3 > PH_3 > SbH_3$

(c) $SbH_3 > AsH_3 > PH_3 > NH_3$ (d) $PH_3 > NH_3 > AsH_3 > SbH_3$

128. Which of the following is paramagnetic ?

(a) N_2O (b) NO (c) N_2O_3 (d) N_2O_5

129. Which of the following are peroxoacids of sulphur ?

(a) $H_2SO_5, H_2S_2O_8$ (b) $H_2SO_5, H_2S_2O_7$

(c) $H_2S_2O_7, H_2S_2O_8$ (d) $H_2S_2O_6, H_2S_2O_7$

130. A gas liberated when PbO_2 reacts with HNO_3 is ......

(a) N_2O (b) NO_2 (c) O_2 (d) N_2

131. Phosphorous pentaoxide reacts with nitric acid and forms ......

(a) H_3PO_4 and N_2O_5 (b) H_3PO_4 and $NO_2 + O_2$

(c) HPO_3, NO_2 and O_2 (d) HPO_3 and N_2O_5

(e) A highly inert medium for carrying out various reactions

132. The orange colour solid used in volcano experiment is ......

(a) Fe_2O_3 (b) $K_2Cr_2O_7$ (c) $(NH_4)_2Cr_2O_7$ (d) K_2CrO_4

133. Which one of the following nitrogen oxides is the anhydride of nitrous acid ?

(a) N_2O_4 (b) NO (c) N_2O (d) N_2O_3

134. The gas formed when lightning flash is produced through air is ......

(a) Nitrous oxide   (b) Nitrous acid   (c) Nitric acid   (d) Nitric oxide

135. Laughing gas is ......

(a) Nitric oxide   (b) Nitrous oxide

(c) Nitrogen pentoxide   (d) Nitrogen trioxide

136. Nitrous oxide is formed by heating ......

(a) NH_4NO_2 (b) HNO_3 (c) $AgNO_3$ (d) NH_4NO_3

137. Nitrogen is used to fill eletric bulbs because it ......

(a) Is inert   (b) Is lighter than air

(c) Is non-toxic   (d) Makes the bulb give more light

138. Of the following compounds, the most acidic is ......

(a) As_2O_3 (b) P_2O_5 (c) Sb_2O_3 (d) Bi_2O_3

139. Which of the following statements is not valid for oxoacids of phosphorus?

(a) All oxoacids contain tetrahedral four coordinated phosphorus

(b) All oxoacids contain at least one $P = O$ unit and one $P - OH$ group

(c) Orthophosphoric acid is used in the manufacture of triple superphosphate

(d) Hypophosphorous acid is a diprotic acid

140. Magnesium nitride on reaction with an excess of water gives ......

(a) ammonia   (b) nitric acid   (c) nitrous oxide   (d) nitrous acid

141. Phosphine is prepared by the action of ......

(a) P and H_2SO_4 (b) P and NaOH   (c) P and H_2S (d) P and HNO_3

142. Orthophosphoric acid is ......

(a) Monobasic   (b) Dibasic   (c) Tribasic   (d) Tetrabasic

143. Excess of PCl_5 reacts with conc. H_2SO_4 giving ......

    (a) chlorosulphonic acid   (b) thionyl chloride

    (c) sulphuryl chloride   (d) sulphurous acid

144. Ammonia is manufactured by ......

    (a) Contact process   (b) Haber's process

    (c) Ostwald's process   (d) Newland Arc process

145. Elements of group 16 are called as ......

    (a) pniicogens   (b) chalcogens   (c) carbogens   (d) halogens

146. The most abundant element on earth is ......

    (a) O   (b) S   (c) Se   (d) Te

147. In the upper layers of atmosphere, ozone is formed ......

    (a) By action of electric discharge on oxygen molecule

    (b) By action of ultraviolet rays on oxygen molecule

    (c) By action of infrared rays on oxygen molecule

    (d) Due to sudden drops of pressure

148. Sulphur trioxide is an anhydride of ......

    (a) Sulphurous acid   (b) Sulphuric acid

    (c) Hyposulphuric acid   (d) Hydrosulphuric acid

149. Which statement is not correct for ozone?

    (a) It is obtained by silent electric discharge on oxygen

    (b) It is an endothermic compound

    (c) It can be obtained by the action of ultraviolet rays on oxygen

    (d) It cannot be regarded as an allotrope of oxygen

150. Oxygen gas can be prepared from solid $KMnO_4$ by ......

    (a) Dissolving the solid in dil. HCl   (b) Dissolving the solid in conc. H_2SO_4

    (c) Treating the solid with H_2 gases   (d) Strongly heating the solid.

151. Starch paper moistened with KI solution turns blue in ozone because of ......

    (a) Iodine liberation   (b) Oxygen liberation

    (c) Alkali formation   (d) Ozone reacts with litmus paper

152. Ozone reacts with dry iodine to give ......

    (a) IO_2 (b) I_2O_3 (c) I_2O_4 (d) I_4O_9

153. When copper turnings are added to sulphuric acid, the gas evolved which turns paper soaked in potassium dichromate green is ......

    (a) CO_2 (b) SO_2 (c) H_2S (d) H_2

154. When SO_2 gas is passed through an acidified solution of $K_2Cr_2O_7$ ......

    (a) The solution becomes blue   (b) The solution becomes colourless

    (c) SO_2 is reduced   (d) Green $Cr_2(SO_4)_3$ is formed

155. The anhydride of sulphuric acid is ......

    (a) SO_2 (b) SO_3 (c) HSO_3^- (d) SO_3^{-2}

156. The compund of sulphur used in transformer as insulator is ......

(a) SO_2　　　　(b) H_2S　　　　(c) SO_3　　　　(d) SF_6

157. Peroxy linkage is present in ......

(a) Caro's acid　　　　　　　　(b) Pyrosulphuric acid

(c) Sulphurous acid　　　　　　(d) Dithionic acid

158. When conc. H_2SO_4 comes in contact with sugar, it becomes black due to ......

(a) Hydrolysis　　　(b) Hydration　　　(c) Decolourisation　(d) Dehydration

159. When oxalic acid is dehydrated by conc. H_2SO_4, then it forms ......

(a) $C + CO_2$　　　(b) CO　　　(c) CO_2　　　(d) $CO + CO_2$

160. Which of the following behaves as both oxidising and reducing agents ?

(a) H_2SO_4　　　(b) SO_2　　　(c) H_2S　　　(d) HNO_3

161. The molecular shapes of SF_4, CF_4 and XeF_4 are ......

(a) The same with 2, 0 and 1 lone pairs of electrons on the central atoms respectively.

(b) The same with 1, 1 and 1 lone pair of electrons on the central atoms respectively.

(c) Different with 0, 1 and 2 lone pairs of electrons on the central atoms respectively.

(d) Different with 1, 0 and 2 lone pairs of electrons on the central atoms respectively.

162. What is the hybridisation of S in SF_4 ?

(a) $sp^3 d^2$　　　(b) $sp^3 d$　　　(c) $sp^3 d^3$　　　(d) sp^3

163. Atomicity of sulphur in rhombic sulphur is ......

(a) 1　　　(b) 2　　　(c) 4　　　(d) 8

164. There is S–S bond in ......

(a) $H_2S_2O_7$　　　(b) $H_2S_2O_8$　　　(c) $H_2S_2O_6$　　　(d) $H_2S_2O_3$

165. Which of the following causes damage to the building containing calcium and responsible for cough and choking in human ?

(a) Sulphur　　　　　　　　(b) Carbon

(c) Nitrogen dioxide　　　　(d) Sulphur dioxide

166. Oleum is chemically known as ......

(a) H_2O　　　(b) H_2S　　　(c) $H_2S_2O_7$　　　(d) $H_2S_2O_8$

167. Ozone on reaction with KI solution produces ......

(a) Cl_2　　　(b) I_2　　　(c) HI　　　(d) IO_3^-

168. O_2F_2 molecule resembles H_2O_2 in ......

(a) Bond angle　　　(b) Geometry　　　(c) Acidic strength　(d) Polarity

169. Greenish white chemiluminescence is produced when atomic oxygen reacts at room temperature with ......

(a) NO　　　(b) CO　　　(c) H_2　　　(d) CH_4

170. In the preparation of oxygen from potassium chlorate, MnO_2 act as a/an ......

(a) Catalyst　　　　　　　(b) Autocatalyst

(c) Activator　　　　　　　(d) Dehydrating agent

171. The function of $Fe(OH)_3$ in the contact process is ......

(a) To detect colloidal impurity

(b) To remove moisture

(c) To remove dust particles

(d) To remove arsenic impurity

172. In which of the following arrangements, the sequence is not strictly according to the property written against it?

(a) $CO_2 < SiO_2 < SnO_2 < PbO_2$: Increasing oxidising power

(b) $HF < HCl < HBr < HI$: Increasing acid strength

(c) $NH_3 < PH_3 < AsH_3 < SbH_3$: Increasing basic strength

(d) $B < C < O < N$: Increasing first ionisation enthalpy

173. reduction potntials of XO_4^- are $E^o_{CrO_4^-} = 1.19$ V, $E^o_{BrO_4^-} = 1.74$ V, $E^o_{IO_4^-} = 1.65$ V

Arrnage these in increasing order of oxidising power as

(a) $CrO_4^- > IO_4^- > BrO_4^-$

(b) $IO_4^- > BrO_4^- > CrO_4^-$

(c) $BrO_4^- > IO_4^- > CrO_4^-$

(d) $BrO_4^- > CrO_4^- > IO_4^-$

174. P_4O_{10} is the anhydride of ......

(a) H_3PO_2　　　　(b) H_3PO_3　　　　(c) H_3PO_4　　　　(d) $H_4P_2O_7$

175. Which of the following statements regarding sulphur is incorrect?

(a) The oxidation state of sulphur is never less than +4 in its compounds

(b) S_2 molecule is paramagnetic

(c) The vapour at 200°C consists mostly of S_8 rings

(d) At 600°C the gas mainly consists of S_2 molecules

176. Fluorine react with water to give ......

(a) Hydrogen fluoride and oxygen

(b) Hydrogen fluoride and ozone

(c) Hydrogen fluoride and oxygen fluoride

(d) Hydrogen fluoride, oxygen and ozone

177. Which of the following statement is not correct when conc. H_2SO_4 is added to a mixture of $NaCl$ and $K_2Cr_2O_7$?

(a) A deep red vapour is evolved.

(b) The vapour when passed into NaOH solution gives a yellow solution of Na_2CrO_4

(c) Chlorine gas is evolved

(d) Chromyl chloride is formed

178. The increasing order of oxidising power of halogens is ......

(a) $Cl_2 < Br_2 < I_2 < F_2$

(b) $Cl_2 < I_2 < Br_2 < F_2$

(c) $I_2 < F_2 < Cl_2 < Br_2$

(d) $I_2 < Br_2 < Cl_2 < F_2$

179. The solubility of iodine in water is greatly increased by ......

(a) Adding an acid

(b) Boiling the solution

(c) Cooling the solution

(d) Adding potassium iodide

180. When Cl_2 gas reacts with hot and concentrated sodium hydroxide solution, the oxidation number of chlorine changes from ......

(a) Zero to – 1 and zero to +3

(b) Zero to + 1 and zero to –3

(c) Zero to + 1 and zero to –5

(d) Zero to – 1 and zero to +5

181. When Cl_2 water is added to aqueous solution of KI containing some CCl_4 ......

(a) Upper layer becomes violet

(b) Lower layer becomes violet

(c) Homogeneous violet layer is formed

(d) None of these

182. Which of the following is not the characteristic of interhalogen compounds ?

(a) They are more reactive than halogens

(b) They are quite unstable but none of them is explosive

(c) They are covalent in nature

(d) They have low boiling points and are highly volatile

183. Among the following, which is the strongest oxidising agent?

(a) Br_2 (b) I_2 (c) Cl_2 (d) F_2

184. Which nitrogen compound of carbon is called pseudohalogen ?

(a) Cyanogen   (b) CaNCN   (c) HCN   (d) None of these

185. Which gives Cl_2 at room temperature?

(a) conc. HCl + $KMnO_4$

(b) NaCl + conc. H_2SO_4

(c) NaCl + MnO_2

(d) NaCl + conc. HNO_3

186. The decreasing order of bond energy among halogens is ......

(a) F-F > Cl – Cl > Br–Br < I – I

(b) I – I > Cl – Cl > Br – Br > F-F

(c) Br – Br > Cl – Cl > I – I >F-F

(d) Cl –Cl > Br – Br > F-F > I-I

187. Which of the following halogens does not form oxyacid ?

(a) Fluorine   (b) Chlorine   (c) Bromine   (d) Iodine

188. When chlorine gas is passed through caustic soda solution in cold, which products are obtained?

(a) Cl_2 + NaOH

(b) NaOH + HCl

(c) NaCl + NaClO + H_2O

(d) NaCl + Cl_2 + H_2O

189. Chlorine gas is prepared by ......

(a) Kraft's process   (b) Deacon's process (c) Ostwald's process   (d) Haber's process

190. Aqua regia is ......

(a) 1 part nitric acid and 3 parts hydrochloric acid

(b) 3 parts nitric acid and 1 part hydrochloric acid

(c) 1 part nitric acid and 3 parts sulphuric acid

(d) 3 parts nitric acid and 1 part sulphuric acid

191. When chlorine gas is passed over hot concentrated sodium hyroxide solution ......

(a) sodium chloride and sodium hypochlorite is formed

(b) sodium chloride and sodium perchlorate is formed

(c) sodium chloride and sodium chlorate is formed

(d) sodium chloride and sodium chlorite is formed

192. When chlorine gas is passed over slaked lime ......

(a) CCl_4 is formed

(b) $CaCl_2$ is formed

(c) HCl gas is formed

(d) $Ca(OCl)_2$ and calcium chloride is formed

193. Which is the weakest acid out of HF, HCl, HBr and HI ?

(a) HF   (b) HCl   (c) HBr   (d) HI

194. A greenish yellow gas reacts with an alkali metal hydroxide to form a halide which can be used in fire works and safety matches. The gas and halide respectively are ......

(a) Br_2, $KBrO_3$ (b) Cl_2, $KClO_3$ (c) I_2, $NaIO_3$ (d) Cl_2, $NaClO_3$

195. The reaction of $KMnO_4$ and HCl results in ......

(a) Oxidation of Mn in $KMnO_4$ and production of Cl_2

(b) Reduction of Mn in $KMnO_4$ and production of H_2

(c) Oxidation of Mn in $KMnO_4$ and production of H_2

(d) Reduction of Mn in $KMnO_4$ and production of Cl_2

196. When I_2 is passed through KCl, KF and KBr solutions ......

(a) Cl_2 and Br_2 are evolved

(b) Cl_2 is evolved

(c) Cl_2, Br_2 and F_2 are evolved

(d) None of these

197. Which one of the following halogen liberates oxygen, when passed through hot concentrated KOH solution?

(a) I_2 (b) Cl_2 (c) Br_2 (d) F_2

198. "Fluorosis" disease is caused due to the reaction of ...... with excess of fluoride in the body.

(a) Ca   (b) Mg   (c) Fe   (d) K

199. Which one of the following oxyacids of chlorine is least oxidising in nature ?

(a) HOCl   (b) $HClO_2$ (c) $HClO_3$ (d) $HClO_4$

200. 1.0 M solution of which of the following salts is most basic ?

(a) NaClO   (b) $NaClO_4$ (c) $NaClO_2$ (d) $NaClO_3$

201. Oxidation of thiosulphate with iodine gives ......

(a) Sulphate ion

(b) Sulphite ion

(c) Tetrathionate ion

(d) Sulphide ion

202. Which of the following represents calcium chlorite?

(a) $CaClO_2$ (b) $Ca(ClO_4)_2$ (c) $Ca(ClO_3)_2$ (d) $Ca(ClO_2)_2$

203. Which is the anhydride of $HClO_4$?

(a) Cl_2O (b) ClO_2 (c) Cl_2O_6 (d) Cl_2O_7

204. Which one of the following is the true covalent oxide of iodine ?

(a) I_2O_4 (b) I_2O_5 (c) I_2O_7 (d) I_2O_9

205. Fluorine is a stronger oxidising agent than chlorine in aqueous solution. This is attributed to many factors except ......

(a) Heat of dissociation

(b) Electron affinity

(c) Ionisation potential

(d) Heat of hydration

206. Which of the following halogens has metallic character?

(a) F_2　　　　(b) Cl_2　　　　(c) Br_2　　　　(d) I_2

207. Which statement is wrong?

(a) Feldspars are not aluminosilicates

(b) Beryl is an example of cyclic silicate

(c) Mg_2SiO_4 is orthosilicate

(d) Basic structural unit in silicates is the SiO_4 tetrahedron

208. Fluorine is a better oxidising agent than Br_2. It is due to ......

(a) Small size of the fluorine　　　　(b) More electron repulsion in fluorine

(c) More electronegativity of fluorine　　　　(d) Non-metallic nature of fluorine

209. Charge distribution in iodine monochloride is best represented as ......

(a) $I^+ Cl^-$　　　　(b) $I^{2+} Cl^{2-}$　　　　(c) $I^- Cl^+$　　　　(d) $I^{2+} Cl^{2+}$

210. Which of the following pairs is not correctly matched?

(a) A halogen which is liquid at room temperature-Bromine

(b) The most electronegative element - Fluorine

(c) The most reactive halogen - Fluorine

(d) The strongest oxidising halogen – Iodine

211. What products are expected from the disproportionation reaction of hypochlorous acid?

(a) $HClO_3$ and Cl_2O　　　　(b) $HClO_2$ and $HClO_4$

(c) HCl and Cl_2O　　　　(d) HCl and $HClO_3$

212. Which one of the following orders correctly represent the increasing acid strengths of the given acids?

(a) $HOClO_2 < HOClO_3 < HOClO < HOCl$　　　　(b) $HOClO < HOCl < HOClO_3 < HOClO_2$

(c) $HOClO_3 < HOClO_2 < HOClO < HOCl$　　　　(d) $HOCl < HOClO < HOClO_2 < HOClO_3$

213. Which one of the following arrangement does not give the correct picture of the trends indicated against it?

(a) $F_2 < Cl_2 > Br_2 > I_2$: Electron gain enthalpy

(b) $F_2 > Cl_2 > Br_2 > I_2$: Bond dissociation energy

(c) $F_2 > Cl_2 > Br_2 > I_2$: Electronegativity

(d) $F_2 > Cl_2 > Br_2 > I_2$: Oxidising power

214. Which noble gas is most abundant in atmosphere?

(a) He　　　　(b) Ne　　　　(c) Ar　　　　(d) Kr

215. The noble gas mixture is cooled in a coconut bulb at 173 K. The gases that are not adsorbed are ......

(a) He and Ne　　　　(b) Ar and Kr　　　　(c) He and Xe　　　　(d) Ne and Xe

216. In the Dewar's method of separation of noble gases, the mixture of noble gases is kept in contact with coconut charcoal at 173 K. Which one of the following gaseous mixtures is not absorbed on to the charcoal?

(a) Ar, Kr　　　　(b) Xe, Kr　　　　(c) He, Ne　　　　(d) Xe, Ar

217. Which of the following noble gas is not present in atmosphere?

(a) He   (b) Ne   (c) Ar   (d) Rn

218. The number of lone pair of electrons present on Xe in XeF_2 is ......

(a) 3   (b) 4   (c) 2   (d) 1

219. The number of lone pairs of electrons on Xe atoms in XeF_2, XeF_4 and XeF_6 molecules are respectively ......

(a) 3, 2 and 1   (b) 4, 3 and 2   (c) 2, 3 and 1   (d) 3, 2 and 0

220. Which one of the following is a correct pair with respect to molecular formula of xenon compound and hybridisation state of xenon in it ?

(a) XeF_4, sp^3 (b) XeF_2, sp   (c) XeF_2, sp^3d (d) XeF_4, sp^2

221. Which noble gas is most soluble in water ?

(a) He   (b) Ar   (c) Ne   (d) Xe

222. Which of the following gas mixture is used by the divers inside the sea ?

(a) O_2 + He   (b) O_2 + Xe   (c) O_2 + Ar   (d) O_2 + N_2

223. Noble gases can be separated by ......

(a) Passing them through some solution

(b) Electrolysis of their compounds

(c) Adsorption and desorption on coconut charcoal

(d) Fractional distillation

224. Which is most easily liquefiable rare gas?

(a) Xe   (b) Ne   (c) Ar   (d) Kr

225. The solubility of noble gases in water follows the order ......

(a) He > Ar > Kr > Ne > Xe   (b) He > Ne > Ar > Kr > Xe

(c) Xe > Kr > Ar > Ne > He   (d) None of these

226. The decreasing order of ease of liquefaction of noble gases follows ......

(a) He > Ar > Kr > Xe   (b) Xe > Ar > Ne > He

(c) Kr > Xe > He > Ar > Ne   (d) Ar > Kr > Xe > He > Ne

227. Among the following which has the lowest boiling point ?

(a) Ar   (b) He   (c) Ne   (d) Xe

228. Which statement is false?

(a) Radon is obtained from the decay of radium

(b) Helium is an inert gas

(c) The most abundant noble gas in the atmosphere is He

(d) Xe is the most reactive among the noble gases

229. What gave idea to Neil Bartlett for the compounds of xenon ?

(a) High bond energy of Xe-F

(b) Low bond energy of F – F in F_2

(c) Ionization energy of oxygen and xenon were almost similar

(d) None of these

230. XeF_6 on complete hydrolysis gives ......

(a) Xe (b) XeO_2 (c) XeO_3 (d) XeO_4

231. Which of the following reactions of xenon compounds is not feasible?

(a) $XeO_3 + 6HF \rightarrow XeF_6 + 3H_2O$

(b) $3XeF_4 + 6H_2O \rightarrow 2Xe + XeO_3 + 12HF + 1.5O_2$

(c) $2XeF_2 + 2H_2O \rightarrow 2Xe + 4HF + O_2$

(d) $XeF_6 + RbF \rightarrow Rb\,[XeF_7]$

232. Helium is used in balloons in place of hydrogen because it is ......

(a) Incombustible   (b) More abundant than hydrogen

(c) Radioactive   (d) Lighter than hydrogen

233. Match the compounds of xenon with hybridization and shape

XeF_4	1	Pyramidal, sp^3
XeF_6	2	Trigonal bipyramidal, sp^3d
XeO_3	3	Distorted octahedral, sp^3d^3
XeO_4	4	Square planar, sp^3d^2

(a) 1 2 1 2   (b) 1 2 3 4   (c) 2 1 3 4   (d) 4 1 3 2

234. Helium is added to oxygen cylinder used by deep sea divers due to its ......

(a) less solubility in blood than nitrogen under high pressure

(b) less density than nitrogen

(c) readily miscibility with oxygen

(d) less poisonous nature than nitrogen

235. Argon is used ......

(a) to obtain low temperature   (b) in high temperature welding

(c) in radio therapy for treatment of cancer   (d) in filling airships

236. Among the following substituted silanes, the one which will give rise to cross-linked silicone polymer on hydrolysis is ......

(a) R_4Si (b) $RSiCl_3$ (c) R_2SiCl_2 (d) R_3SiCl

237. Which one of the following arrangements represents the correct order of least negative to most negative electron gain enthalpy for C, Ca, Al, F and O?

(a) $Ca < Al < C < O < F$ (b) $Al < Ca < O < C < F$

(c) $Al < O < C < Ca < F$ (d) $C < F < O < Al < Ca$

238. In Ramsay and Rayleigh's isolation of noble gases from air, the nitrogen of the air is finally converted into ......

(a) NO and NO_2 (b) $NaNO_2$ only

(c) $NaNO_2$ and $NaNO_3$ (d) $NaNO_3$ only

239. Which of the following has $- O - O -$ linkage ?

(a) $H_2S_2O_6$ (b) $H_2S_2O_8$ (c) $H_2S_2O_3$ (d) $H_2S_4O_6$

240. Which of the following is not oxidized by O_3?

 (a) KI   (b) $FeSO_4$ (c) $KMnO_4$ (d) K_2MnO_4

241. Which one of the following is the correct statement?

 (a) Boric acid is a protonic acid

 (b) Beryllium exhibits coordination number of six

 (c) Chlorides of both beryllium and aluminium have bridged chloride structures in solid phase

 (d) $B_2H_6 \cdot 2NH_3$ is known as 'inorganic benzene'

242. XeF_2 is isostructural with ......

 (a) ICl_2^- (b) $SbCl_3$ (c) $BaCl_2$ (d) TeF_2

243. Which one of the following is an amphoteric oxide?

 (a) ZnO (b) Na_2O (c) SO_2 (d) B_2O_3

244. Which blue liquid is obtained on reacting equimolar amounts of two gases at $-30°C$?

 (a) N_2O (b) N_2O_3 (c) N_2O_4 (d) N_2O_5

245. Which of the following is arranged in the increasing order of enthalpy of vaporisation?

 (a) NH_3, AsH_3, PH_3 (b) AsH_3, PH_3, NH_3 (c) NH_3, PH_3, AsH_3 (d) PH_3, AsH_3, NH_3

246. Which of the following statements is true?

 (a) H_3PO_3 is a stronger acid than H_2SO_3

 (b) In aqueous medium, HF is a stronger acid than HCl

 (c) $HClO_4$ is a weaker acid than $HClO_3$

 (d) HNO_3 is a stronger acid than HNO_2

247. The decreasing values of bond angles from NH_3 (106°) to SbH_3 (101°) down group-15 of the periodic table is due to ......

 (a) increasing bp-bp repulsion   (b) increasing p-orbital character in sp^3

 (c) decreasing lp-bp repulsion   (d) decreasing electronegativity

248. Which of the following molecules has trigonal planar geometry ?

 (a) NH_3 (b) BF_3 (c) PCl_3 (d) IF_3

249. Which is the most thermodynamically stable allotropic form of phosphorus?

 (a) red   (b) white   (c) black   (d) yellow

250. Roasting of sulphides gives the gas X as a byproduct. This is a colourless gas with choking smell of burnt sulphur and causes great damage to respiratory organs as a result of acid rain. Its aqueous solution is acidic and acts as a reducing agent and its acid has never been isolated. The gas X is ......

 (a) SO_2 (b) CO_2 (c) SO_3 (d) H_2S

Assertion and Reasons

 Direction : In the following question, a statement of Assertion (A) is given followed by a corresponding statement of Reason (R) just below it. Of the statements, mark the correct answer as

 (a) If both A and R are true and R is correct explanation of A

 (b) If both A and R are true but R is not the correct explanation of A

 (c) If A is true but reason is false.

 (d) If A is false but reason is true.

 (e) If both A and R are false.

251. Assertion : B_2H_6 contains 2-3 centre electron pair bonds.
Reason : B_2H_6 is electron deficient molecule.

252. Assertion : Anhydrous $AlCl_3$ is covalent but hydrated $AlCl_3$ is ionic.
Reason : In water, Al_2Cl_6 dissociates into hydrated Al^{3+} and Cl^- ions due to high heat of hydration of these ions.

253. Assertion : Al forms $[AlF_6]^{3-}$ but B does not form $[BF_6]^{3-}$.
Reason : B does not react with F_2.

254. Assertion : $Al(OH)_3$ is amphoteric in nature.
Reason : Al – O and O–H bonds can be broken with equal ease in $Al(OH)_3$.

255. Assertion : Between $SiCl_4$ and CCl_4 only $SiCl_4$ reacts with water.
Reason : $SiCl_4$ is ionic and CCl_4 is covalent.

256. Assertion : Nitrogen has higher ionisation energy than that of oxygen.
Reason : Nitrogen has smaller atomic size than that of oxygen.

257. Assertion : HNO_3 is a stronger acid than HNO_2.
Reason : In HNO_3 there are two nitrogen-oxygen bonds while in HNO_2 there is only one.

258. Assertion : PCl_5 is covalent in gaseous and liquid states but ionic in solid state.
Reason : PCl_5 in solid state consists of tetrahedral PCl_4^+ cation and octahedral PCl_6^- anion.

259. Assertion : NO_3^- is planar while NH_3 is pyramidal.
Reason : N in NO_3^- is sp^2 hybridised but in NH_3 it is sp^3 hybridised.

260. Assertion : Oxidising acids such as HNO_3 convert boron to H_3BO_3.
Reason : Boron reacts with all types of acids.

261. Assertion : Phosphoric acid has no reducing properties.
Reason : Phosphoric acid does not contain P-H bonds.

262. Assertion : Among chalcogens, tendency of catenation is maximum for sulphur.
Reason : S-S bond dissociation energy is higher than O-O bond dissociation energy.

263. Assertion : Sulphuric acid is more viscous than water.
Reason : Concentrated sulphuric acid has a great affinity for water.

264. Assertion : Concentrated H_2SO_4 reacts with KCl to give Cl_2 gas.
Reason : HCl cannot be oxidised by concentrated H_2SO_4.

265. Assertion : Caro's acid has S atom in +6 oxidation state.
Reason : Caro's acid contains one peroxo (O_2^{2-}) group.

266. Assertion : OF_2 is named as oxygen difluoride.
Reason : In OF_2, oxygen is less electronegative than fluorine.

267. Assertion : F atom has less negative electron affinity than Cl atom.
Reason : Additional electrons are repelled more effectively by 3p-electrons in Cl than by 2p- electron in F atom.

268. Assertion　　　　　:　Cl_2 gas bleaches the articles permanently.

　　　　Reason　　　　　　:　Cl_2 is a strong reducing agent.

269. Assertion　　　　　:　Oxidising power of perhalates are in the order :

　　　　　　　　　　　　　　　$BrO_4^- > IO_4^- > ClO_4^-$

　　　　Reason　　　　　　:　The standard reduction potential for BrO_4^- is more positive and

　　　　　　　　　　　　　　　decreases in the order : $BrO_4^- > IO_4^- > ClO_4^-$

270. Assertion　　　　　:　Xenon forms fluoride.

　　　　Reason　　　　　　:　Because 5d-orbitals are available for valence shell expansion.

PREVIOUS YEAR'S QUESTIONS

1. When copper is heated with conc. HNO_3, it produces ......　　　　**[NEET-UG 2016]**

(a) $Cu[NO_3]_2$ and N_2O　　　　　　　　　(b) $Cu[NO_3]_2$ and NO_2

(c) $Cu[NO_3]_2$ and NO　　　　　　　　　(d) $Cu[NO_3]_2$, NO and NO_2

2. Which is the correct statement for the given acids?　　　　**[NEET-UG 2016]**

(a) Phosphinic acid is a diprotic while phosphonic acid is a monoprotic acid

(b) Phosphinic acid is a monoprotic acid while phosphonic acid is a diprotic acid

(c) Both are diprotic acids

(d) Both are triprotic acids

3. Among the following, the correct order of acidity is ......　　　　**[NEET-UP 2016]**

(a) $HClO_4 < HClO_2 < HClO < HClO_3$　　　　(b) $HClO_3 < HClO_4 < HClO_2 < HClO$

(c) $HClO < HClO_2 < HClO_3 < HClO_4$　　　　(d) $HClO_2 < HClO < HClO_3 < HClO_4$

4. Which one of the following orders is correct for the bond dissociation enthalpy of halogen molecules?　　　　**[NEET–UG 2016]**

(a) $F_2 > Cl_2 > Br_2 > I_2$　　　　　　　　　(b) $I_2 > Br_2 > Cl_2 > F_2$

(c) $Cl_2 > Br_2 > F_2 > I_2$　　　　　　　　　(d) $Br_2 > I_2 > F_2 > Cl_2$

5. Nitrogen dioxide and sulphur dioxide have some properties in common. Which property is shown by one of these compounds, but not by the other?　　　　**[AIPMT 2015]**

(a) is a reducing agent　　　　　　　　　(b) is soluble in water

(c) is used as a food preservative　　　　　(d) form 'acid-rain'

6. Strong reducing behavior of H_3PO_2 is due to ......　　　　**[RE AIPMT 2015]**

(a) High oxidation state of phosphorus

(b) Presence of two –OH groups and one P-H bond

(c) High electron gain enthalpy of phosphorus

(d) High electron gain enthalpy of phosphorus

7. The stability of +1 oxidation state among Al, Ga, In and Ti increases in the sequence ......

(a) $Tl < In < Ga < Al$　　　　　　　　　(b) $In < Ti < Ga < Al$　　　**[RE AIPMT 2015]**

(c) $Ga < In < Al$　　　　　　　　　　　(d) $Al < Ga < In < Tl$

8. Magnetic moment 2.83 BM is given by which of the following ions?

　　(At. Nos. Ti = 22, Cr = 24, Mn = 25, Ni = 28)　　　　**[AIPMT 2014]**

(a) Cr^{3+}　　　　　(b) Mn^{2+}　　　　　(c) Ti^{3+}　　　　　(d) Ni^{2+}

9. Acidity of diprotic acids in aqueous solution increases in the order ...... **[AIPMT 2014]**
   (a) $H_2Te < H_2S < H_2Se$
   (b) $H_2Se < H_2Te < H_2S$
   (c) $H_2S < H_2Se < H_2Te$
   (d) $H_2Se < H_2S < H_2Te$

10. The pair of compounds that can exist together is ...... **[AIPMT 2014]**
    (a) $FeCl_2 \cdot SnCl_2$
    (b) $FCl_3 \cdot KI$
    (c) $FeCl_3 \cdot SnCl_2$
    (d) $HgCl_2 \cdot SnCl_2$

11. The reaction of aqueous $KMnO_4$ with H_2O_2 in acidic conditions gives...... **[AIPMT 2014]**
    (a) Mn^{2+} and O_3
    (b) Mn^{4+} and O_2
    (c) Mn^{4+} and O_2
    (d) Mn^{2+} and O_2

12. In acidic medium, H_2O_2 changes $Cr_2O_7^{-2}$ to CrO_5 which has two (--O—O--) bonds. Oxidation state of Cr in CrP_5 is ...... **[AIPMT 2014]**
    (a) $+6$
    (b) -10
    (c) $+5$
    (d) $+3$

13. Which of the following is electron deficient? **[NEET 2013]**
    (a) PH_3
    (b) $(CH_2)_2$
    (c) $(AlH_3)_2$
    (d) $(BH_3)_2$

14. XeF_2 is isostructural with ......
    (a) $BaCl_2$
    (b) TeF_2
    (c) ICl_2^-
    (d) $SbCl_3$

15. The basic structural unit of silicates is ......
    (a) SiO_4^{2-}
    (b) SiO^-
    (c) SiO_4^{4-}
    (d) SiO_3^{2-}

16. Which of the following unit of silicates is ...... **[NEET 2013]**
    (a) B_2H_6
    (b) BN
    (c) B
    (d) B_4C

17. Which of these in not a monomer for a high molecular mass silicone polymer? **[NEET 2013]**
    (a) $PhSiCl_5$
    (b) $MeSiCl_3$
    (c) Me_2SiCl_2
    (d) Me_3SiCl

18. A magnetic moment of 1.73 BM will be shown by among the following...... **[NEET 2013]**
    (a) $[CoCl_6]^{4-}$
    (b) $[Cu(NH_3)_4]^{2+}$
    (c) $[Ni(CN)_4]^{2-}$
    (d) $TiCl_4$

19. $KMnO_4$ can be prepared from K_2MnO_4 as per the reaction: **[NEET 2013]**

$$3MnO_4^{2} + 2H_2O \rightleftharpoons 2MnO_4^- + MnO_2 + 4OH^-$$

The reaction can go to completion by removing OH^- ions by adding ......
    (a) SO_2
    (b) HCl
    (c) KOH
    (d) CO_2

20. Which of the following does not give oxygen on heating? **[NEET 2013]**
    (a) $(NH_4)_2Cr_2O_7$
    (b) $KClO_3$
    (c) $Zn(ClO_3)_2$
    (d) $K_2Cr_2O_7$

21. Which of the following is a polar molecule? **[NEET 2013]**
    (a) XeF_4
    (b) BF_3
    (c) SF_4
    (d) SiF_4

22. Which is the strongest acid in the following ? **[NEET 2013]**
    (a) H_2SO_3
    (b) H_2SO_4
    (c) $HClO_3$
    (d) $HClO_4$

23. Which of the following species contains three bond pairs and one lone pair around the contral atom? **[CBSE AIPMT 2012]**
    (a) NH_2^-
    (b) PCl_3
    (c) H_2O
    (d) BF_3

24. Which of the following statements is not valid for oxoacids of phosphorus?
    (a) All oxoacids contain tetrahedral four coordinated phosphorus **[CBSE AIPMT 2012]**
    (b) All oxoacids contain atleast one P=O units and one P –OH group
    (c) Orthophosphoric acid is used in the manufacture of triple superphosphate
    (d) Hypophosphorous acid is a diprotic acid.

25. When Cl_2 gas reacts with hot and concentrated sodium hydroxide solution, the oxidation number of chlorine changes from ......   **[CBSE AIPMT]**

(a) Zero to –1 and Zero to +3   (b) Zero to +1 and Zero to –3

(c) Zero to +1 and Zero to –5   (d) Zero to –1 and Zero to +5

26. A hydride of nitrogen which is acidic is ......   **[AIIMS 2012]**

(a) NH_3 (b) N_3H (c) N_3H_2 (d) N_2H_4

27. When a colourless gas is passed through bromine water, only decolorisation takes place. The gas is ......   **[AFMC 2012]**

(a) SO_2 (b) HBr (c) HCl (d) H_2S

28. Which of the following is a not peroxy acid?   **[Manipal 2012]**

(a) Perphosphoric acid   (b) Pernitric acid

(c) Perdisulphuric acid   (d) Perchloric acid

29. Which one of the following compounds is peroxide?   **[CBSE AIPMT 2010]**

(a) NO_2 (b) KO_2 (c) BaO_2 (d) MnO_2

30. Ammonia on reaction with excess of chlorine gives ......   **[AFMC 2010]**

(a) NCl_3 and HCl (b) N_4 and NH_4Cl (c) NCl_3 and NH_3Cl (d) N_2 and HCl

31. If the supply of oxygen is limited, H_2S reacts with O_2 to form ......   **[AFMC 2010]**

(a) $H_2O + SO_3$ (b) $H_2O + S$ (c) $H_2SO_4 + S$ (d) $H_2O + SO_2$

32. Bromine water reacts with SO_2 to form ......   **[AFMC 2010]**

(a) HBr and S (b) H_2O and HBr (c) S and H_2O (d) H_2SO_4 and HBr

33. O_2 and O_3 are ......   **[CPMT 2010]**

(a) allotropes   (b) isotopes   (c) isomorphs   (d) polymorphs

34. The number of P-O bonds in P_4O_{10} is ......   **[CPMT 2010]**

(a) 16   (b) 12   (c) 8   (d) 4

35. Sulphuric acid reacts with PCl_5 to give ......   **[Manipal 2010]**

(a) thionyl chloride   (b) sulphur monochloride

(c) sulphuryl chloride   (d) sulphur tetrachloride

36. Given are H_3PO_2, H_3PO_3, HPO_4 and $H_4P_2O_7$.   **[Guj. CET 2010]**

Which of the above oxoacids result into two series of salts?

(a) H_3PO_2 (b) H_3PO_3 (c) H_2PO_4 (d) $H_4P_2O_7$

37. Caro's acid is ......   **[VNN 2010]**

(a) $H_2S_2O_3$ (b) H_2SO_5 (c) $H_2S_2O_8$ (d) $H_2S_2O_7$

38. By which of the following processes, pure nitrogen gas is prepared?   **[AFMC 2009]**

(a) $(NH_4)_2Cr_2O_7 \rightarrow$ (b) $NH_4Cl + NaNO_2 \rightarrow$

(c) $NH_3 + NaNO_2 \rightarrow$ (d) $N_2O + Cu \rightarrow$

39. Thermodynamically, most stable form of phosphorus is ......

                    [AFMC, CG PMT, Haryana PMT 2009]

(a) red   (b) black   (c) white   (d) yellow

40. When nitric acid reacts with nitric oxide, a gas is released, which converts H_2S into ......

(a) SO_4^{2-} (b) S^{2-} (c) S (d) S_2O^{2-} **[AIIMS 2009]**

41. Peroxide bond is absent in ......   **[CPMT 2009]**

(a) $(S_2O_7)^{2-}$ (b) $(S_2O_8)^{2-}$ (c) CrO_5 (d) BaO_2

42. Perdisulphuric acid has the following bond ......   **[AIIMS 2009]**

(a) $O \leftarrow O = O$ (b) $\leftarrow O = O \rightarrow$ (c) $> O \rightarrow O <$ (d) $- O - O -$

43. S^{2-} and S_3^{2-} can be distinguished by using   **[AIIMS 2008]**

(a) $CH_3COO)_2Pb$ (b) $Na[Fe(en)_5NO]$ (c) Both (a) and (b)   (d) None of these

44. Which of the following salt would give SO_2 with hot and dil. H_2SO_4 and also decolourises Br_2 water?   **[Manipal 2008]**

(a) Na_2SO_3 (b) $NaHSO_4$ (c) Na_2SO_4 (d) Na_2S

45. Which of the following metal oxides is most basic?   **[J&K CET 2008]**

(a) ZnO (b) Al_2O_3 (c) As_2O_3 (d) K_2O

46. H_2S is not a/an ......   **[CPMT 2007]**

(a) Reducing agent   (b) Acid   (c) Oxidising agent   (d) None of these

47. Sodium pyrophosphate is represented by which of the following formula?   **[Manipal 2007]**

(a) $Na_2P_2O_4$ (b) $Na_4O_2O_5$ (c) $Na_4P_2O_7$ (d) $Na_2P_2O_5$

48. The sides of safety matches contain ......   **[BCECE 2007]**

(a) red phosphorus + sand powder   (b) P_4S_3

(c) $Ca_3(PO_4)$ + glass pieces   (d) $KClO_3$, KNO_3, sulphur + antimony

49. BaO_2 and ozone react to produce ......   **[AFMC 2006]**

(a) Ba (b) Ba_2O_3 (c) BaO (d) $Ba(OH)_3$

50. The incorrect statement among the following is ......   **[AIIMS 2006]**

(a) C_{60} is an allotropic form of carbon.

(b) O_3 is an allotropic form of oxygen.

(c) S_8 is only allotropic form of sulphur.

(d) red phosphorus is more stable in air than white phosphorus.

51. Which of the following acts as a pickling agent?   **[CPMT 2006]**

(a) HNO_3 (b) NCl (c) H_2SO_4 (d) HNO_2

52. The acidity of hydrides of O, S, Se, Te varies in the order ......   **[Punjab PMER 2006]**

(a) $H_2O > H_2S > H_2Se > H_2Te$ (b) $H_2O < H_2S < H_2Se < H_2Te$

(c) $H_2S > H_2O > H_2Se > H_2Te$ (d) $H_2Se > H_2S > H_2O > H_2Te$

53. Pnicogens are the elements of group ......   **[MHT CET 2006]**

(a) 15   (b) 13   (c) VIII   (d) Zero

54. If an allotropic form changes slowly to stable form, it is called ......   **[MHT CET 2006]**

(a) enantiotropy   (b) dynamic   (c) monotropy   (d) none of these

55. Which of the following form vortex ring?   **[MHT CET 2006]**

(a) P_2O_3 (b) PH_3 (c) NH_3 (d) P_4O_{10}

56. As the number of $-OH$ groups increases in hypophosphorous acid, phosphorous acid and phosphoric acid, the acidic strength ......   **[MHT CET 2006]**

(a) increases   (b) decreases

(c) remains nearly same   (d) remains appropriately same

57. What is the correct relationship between the pHs of isomolar solutions of sodium oxide (pH_1), sodium sulphide (pH_2), sodium selenide (pH_3) and sodium telluride (pH_4) ?

[CBSE AIPMT 2005]

(a) $pH_1 > pH_2 \approx pH_3 > pH_4$

(b) $pH_1 < pH_2 < pH_3 < pH_4$

(c) $pH_1 < pH_2 < pH_3 \approx pH_4$

(d) $pH_1 > pH_2 > pH_3 > pH_4$

58. A colourless gas with the smell of rotten fish is ...... **[AFMC 2005]**

(a) H_2S (b) PH_3 (c) SO_2 (d) None of these

59. Which of the following oxides of nitrogen is solid? **[AFMC 2004]**

(a) NO_2 (b) N_2O (c) N_2O_3 (d) N_2O_5

60. The statement true for N_3^- is ...... **[AIIMS 2004]**

(a) it has non-linear structure

(b) it is called pseudohalogen

(c) the formal oxidation state of nitrogen in this anion is +1

(d) it is isoelectronic with N_2O

61. The maximum concentration of nitrogen is present in ...... **[AFMC 2003]**

(a) nitrolim

(b) calcium ammonium nitrate

(c) ammonium sulphate

(d) urea

62. The true statement for the acids of phosphorus H_3PO_2, H_3PO_3 and H_3PO_4 is ... **[AIIMS 2003]**

(a) the order of their acidity is $H_3PO_4 > H_3PO_2 > H_3PO_3$

(b) all of them are reducing in nature

(c) all of them are tribasic acids

(d) the geometry of phosphorus is tetrahedral in all the three

63. Which of the following is not correct? **[AFMC 2003]**

(a) $3O_2 \rightleftharpoons 2O_3$; $\Delta H = - 284.5$ kJ

(b) Ozone undergoes addition reaction with unsaturated carbon compounds

(c) Sodium thiosulphate reacts with I_2 to form sodium tetrathionate and sodium iodide

(d) Ozone oxidizes lead sulphide to lead sulphate ......

64. The correct order of increasing hydration energy of the following conjugate bases of oxyacids of chlorine is ...... **[AMU 2010]**

(a) $ClO^- < ClO_2^- < ClO_3^- < ClO_4^-$

(b) $ClO_4^- < ClO_3^- < ClO_2^- < ClO^-$

(c) $ClO_4^- < ClO_3^- < ClO^- < ClO_2^-$

(d) $ClO_3^- < ClO_4^- < ClO_2^- < ClO^-$

65. The least volatile hydrogen halide is ...... **[CPMT 2010]**

(a) HF   (b) HCl   (c) HI   (d) HBr

66. To make a painting over glass, we use ...... **[CPMT 2010]**

(a) fluorine   (b) chlorine   (c) bromine   (d) hydrogen chloride

67. Which of the following is a germicidal? **[CPMT 2010]**

(a) KCl   (b) KBr   (c) KI   (d) NaCl

68. Argon possesses ...... **[MHT CET 2010]**

(a) translational motion only

(b) translational + rotational motion

(c) translational + vibrational motion

(d) translational + rotational + vibrational motion

69. The noble gas was first time discovered by ......   **[Manipal 2010]**
    (a) Cavendish   (b) William Ramsay   (c) Rayleigh   (d) Frankland
70. Fluorine is not prepared by general methods because ......   **[BVP 2010]**
    (a) HF can be easily oxidized   (b) HF cannot be easily oxidized
    (c) HF is highly poisonous   (d) HF is a good conductor of electricity
71. Fluorine reacts with water to give ......   **[BVP 2010]**
    (a) HF and O_2 (b) HF and OF_2 (c) HF and O_3 (d) HF, O_2 and O_3
72. The forces acting between noble gas atoms are ......   **[Manipal 2010]**
    (a) van der Waals' forces   (b) ion-dipole forces
    (c) London dispersion forces   (d) magnetic forces
73. Anhydrous ferric chloride is prepared by ......   **[CG PMT 2009]**
    (a) heating $FeCl_3$ at high temperature in stream of air
    (b) heating iron in stream of dry chlorine
    (c) heating ferric oxide with hydrochloric acid
    (d) reacting iron with hydrochloric acid.
74. What is the correct order of occurrence (% by weight) in air of Ne, Ar and Kr ? **[AFMC 2008]**
    (a) Ne > Ar> Kr   (b) Ar > Ne > Kr   (c) Ar > Kr > Ne   (d) Ne > Kr > Ar
75. Which of the following dissolves in water but does not give any oxyacid solution?
                                        [CPMT 2008]
    (a) SO_2 (b) OF_2 (c) SCl_4 (d) SO_3
76. Which one below is a pseudohalide?   **[AFMC 2007]**
    (a) CN^- (b) ICl   (c) IF_5 (d) I_3
77. Which of the following gas mixture is used by the divers inside the sea?   **[AFMC 2007]**
    (a) O_2 + He   (b) O_2 + Xe   (c) O_2 + Ar   (d) $O_2 + N_2$
78. Which one of the following is the true covalent oxide of iodine?   **[AIIMS 2007]**
    (a) I_2O_4 (b) I_2O_5 (c) I_2O_7 (d) I_2O_9
79. Which two of the salts are used to prepare iodized salt ?
    (i) KIO_3 (ii) KI   (iii) I_2 (iv) HI   **[AIIMS 2006)**
    (a) (i) and (ii)   (b) (i) and (iii)   (c) (ii) and (iv)   (d) (iii) and (iv)
80. Oxygen molecule is ......   **(C.P.M.T. 2000)**
    (a) Diamagnetic with no unpaired electrons
    (b) Diamagnetic with two unpaired electrons
    (c) Paramagnetic with two unpaired electrons
    (d) Paramagnetic with no unpaired electrons
81. Oxidation state of oxygen is zero in ......   **(M.P.P.M.T. 2001)**
    (a) CO   (b) O_3 (c) SO_2 (d) H_2O_2
82. Which one of the following is an oxyacid ?   **(E.A.M.C.E.T. (Med.) 2001)**
    (a) $Ba(OH)_2$ (b) $Mg(OH)_2$ (c) H_3PO_3 (d) HCl
83. Which of the following is incorrect ?   **(D.P.M.T. 2002)**
    (a) O_2 is weaker oxidant than O_3 (b) O_2 has larger bond length than O_3
    (c) Both O_2 and O_3 are paramagnetic   (d) O_2 is linear and O_3 is angular in shape

84. Which of the following show the highest boiling point?   **(M.P.C.E.T. 2002)**

(a) H_2O (b) H_2S (c) H_2Se (d) H_2Te

85. White phosphorus is ......   **(C.P.M.T. 2000)**

(a) A monoatomic gas   (b) P_4, a tetrahedral solid

(c) P_6, a crown   (d) A linear diatomic molecule

86. The oxidation state of nitrogen is highest in ......   **(M.P.P.M.T. 2001)**

(a) N_3H (b) NH_2OH (c) N_2H_4 (d) NH_3

87. The substance used in smoke screen is ......   **(Kerala P.M.T. 2003)**

(a) Sodium chloride   (b) Zinc phosphate   (c) Calcium phosphide   (d) Calcium fluoride

(e) Calcium phosphate

88. Nitrogen shows different oxidation states in the range ......   **(Kerala P.M.T. 2003)**

(a) 0 to + 5   (b) −3 to + 5   (c) −5 to + 3   (d) −3 to + 3

(e) + 5 to + 5

89. Which of the following is arranged in the increasing order of enthalpy of vaporisation ?

(A.I.I.M.S. 2004)

(a) NH_3, PH_3, AsH_3 (b) AsH_3, PH_3, NH_3 (c) NH_3, AsH_3, PH_3 (d) PH_3, AsH_3, NH_3

90. Boron compounds behave as Lewis acids because of their ......   **(CBSE AIPMT 2012)**

(a) Acidic nature   (b) Covalent nature

(c) Electron deficient character   (d) Ionisation property

91. Oxygen will directly react with each of the following elements except ...**(CBSE AIPMT 2012)**

(a) P   (b) Cl   (c) Na   (d) S

92. Laughing gas is ......   **(CBSE AIPMT 2008)**

(a) Nitrous oxide   (b) Nitric oxide

(c) Nitrogen trioxide   (d) Nitrogen pentoxide

93. Which of the following is acidic?   **(CBSE AIPMT 2008)**

(a) SO_3 (b) N_2O (c) BeO (d) HgO

94. Nitrogen is an essential constituent of all ......   **(CBSE AIPMT 2012)**

(a) Proteins   (b) Fats

(c) Proteins and fats   (d) None of these

95. Which of the nitrates on strong heating leaves the metal as the residue? **(CBSE AIPMT 2007)**

(a) $AgNO_3$ (b) $Pb(NO_3)_2$ (c) $Cu(NO_3)_2$ (d) $Al(NO_3)_3$

96. Pure N_2 gas is obtained from ......   **(Delhi PMT 2010)**

(a) $NH_3 + NaNO_2$ (b) $NH_4Cl + NaNO_2$ (c) $N_2O + Cu$ (d) $(NH_4)_2Cr_2O_7$

97. Aqueous solution of ammonia consists of ......   **(CBSE AIPMT 2012)**

(a) H^+ (b) OH^- (c) NH_4^+ (d) NH_4^+ and OH^-

98. Which is the weakest out of HF, HCl, HBr and HI ?   **(M.P. P.M.T. 1995, C.P.M.T. 2001)**

(a) HF   (b) HCl

(c) HBr   (d) HI

99. A greenish yellow gas reacts with an alkali metal hydroxide to form a halite which can be used in fire works and safety matches. The gas and halite respectively are ......
(a) Br_2, $KBrO_3$ (b) Cl_2, $KClO_3$ (c) I_2, $NaIO_3$ (d) Cl_2, $NaClO_3$

100. The reaction of $KMnO_4$ and HCl results in ...... **(C.P.M.T. 2000)**
(a) Oxidation of Mn in $KMnO_4$ and production of Cl_2
(b) Reduction of Mn in $KMnO_4$ and production of H_2
(c) Oxidation of Mn in $KMnO_4$ and production of H_2
(d) Reduction of Mn in $KMnO_4$ and production of H_2

101. When I_2 is passed through KCl, KF and KBr solutions ......
(a) Cl_2 and Br_2 are evolved   (b) Cl_2 is evolved
(c) Cl_2, Br_2 and F_2 are evolved   (d) None of these

102. Which one of the following elements show different oxidation states ? **(E.A.M. C.E.T. 2001)**
(a) Sodium   (b) Fluorine   (c) Chlorine   (d) Potassium

103. Which of the following elements exhibits the most basic properties ? **(M.P. P.M.T. 2001)**
(a) F   (b) Cl   (c) Br   (d) I

104. Which noble gas is most soluble in water ? **(U.P.C. P.M.T. 2002)**
(a) He   (b) Ar   (c) Ne   (d) Xe

105. Which of the following gas mixture is used by the diverse inside the sea ? **(A.F.M.C. 2004)**
(a) O_2 + He   (b) O_2 + Xe   (c) O_2 + Ar   (d) O_2 + N_2

106. Which of the following is an inert gas ? **(A.F.M.C. 2005)**
(a) H_2 (b) O_2 (c) N_2 (d) Argon

107. There is S–S bond in ...... **(J.I.P.M.E.R. 2001)**
(a) $H_2S_2O_7$ (b) $H_2S_2O_8$ (c) $H_2S_2O_6$ (d) $H_2S_2O_3$

108. Which of the following causes damage to the building containing calcium and responsible for cough and choking in human ? **(Manipal P.M.T. 2001)**
(a) Sulphur   (b) Carbon
(c) Nitrogen dioxide   (d) Sulphur dioxide

109. Which of the following has $p\pi - d\pi$ bonding ? **(C.B.S.E. P.M.T. 2002)**
(a) NO_3^- (b) SO_3^{2-} (c) BO_3^{3-} (d) CO_3^{2-}

110. Which of the following is a monobasic, reducing agent ? **(J.I.P.M.E.R. 2002)**
(a) HPO_3 (b) H_3PO_3 (c) H_3PO_2 (d) $H_4P_2O_7$

111. Which of the following compound is tribasic acid ? **(A.I.I.M.S. 2002)**
(a) H_3PO_2 (b) H_3PO_3 (c) H_3PO_4 (d) $H_4P_2O_7$

112. An example of a neutral oxide is ...... **(Kerala P.M.T. 2003)**
(a) NO   (b) CO_2 (c) CaO   (d) ZnO

113. H_3PO_3, phosphorus acid is ...... **(Kerala P.M.T. 2003)**
(a) a diprotic acid   (b) a triprotic acid
(c) a monoprotic acid   (d) not acidic
(e) not soluble in water

114. Which of the following does not give oxygen on heating? **[NEET 2013]**
(a) $Zn(ClO_3)_2$ (b) $K_2Cr_2O_7$ (c) $(NH_4)_2Cr_2O_7$ (d) $KClO_3$

115. The pair of species that has the same bond order in the following is ...... **[NEET 2013]**
(a) O_2, B_2 (b) CO, NO^+ (c) NO^-, CN^- (d) O_2, N_2

ANSWER KEY

1. (a)	2. (b)	3. (c)	4. (c)	5. (d)	6. (a)	7. (a)	8. (d)
9. (d)	10. (c)	11. (b)	12. (d)	13. (a)	14. (a)	15. (a)	16. (a)
17. (a)	18. (a)	19. (c)	20. (c)	21. (a)	22. (b)	23. (c)	24. (b)
25. (c)	26. (a)	27. (a)	28. (b)	29. (c)	30. (c)	31. (b)	32. (b)
33. (b)	34. (c)	35. (b)	36. (b)	37. (b)	38. (a)	39. (b)	40. (d)
41. (c)	42. (a)	43. (c)	44. (a)	45. (d)	46. (b)	47. (b)	48. (b)
49. (b)	50. (a)	51. (c)	52. (b)	53. (b)	54. (c)	55. (a)	56. (b)
57. (d)	58. (b)	59. (b)	60. (c)	61. (b)	62. (a)	63. (a)	64. (b)
65. (d)	66. (c)	67. (b)	68. (d)	69. (c)	70. (a)	71. (d)	72. (c)
73. (a)	74. (c)	75. (b)	76. (b)	77. (b)	78. (d)	79. (a)	80. (a)
81. (a)	82. (a)	83. (b)	84. (b)	85. (a)	86. (c)	87. (b)	88. (c)
89. (a)	90. (b)	91. (a)	92. (c)	93. (b)	94. (d)	95. (c)	96. (c)
97. (b)	98. (a)	99. (c)	100. (c)	101. (c)	102. (c)	103. (c)	104. (c)
105. (b)	106. (d)	107. (a)	108. (b)	109. (a)	110. (a)	111. (b)	112. (d)
113. (b)	114. (d)	115. (a)	116. (d)	117. (d)	118. (a)	119. (d)	120. (a)
121. (d)	122. (d)	123. (c)	124. (b)	125. (d)	126. (a)	127. (a)	128. (b)
129. (a)	130. (c)	131. (d)	132. (c)	133. (d)	134. (d)	135. (b)	136. (d)
137. (a)	138. (b)	139. (d)	140. (a)	141. (b)	142. (c)	143. (c)	144. (b)
145. (b)	146. (a)	147. (b)	148. (b)	149. (d)	150. (d)	151. (a)	152. (d)
153. (b)	154. (d)	155. (b)	156. (d)	157. (a)	158. (d)	159. (d)	160. (b)
161. (d)	162. (b)	163. (d)	164. (c)	165. (d)	166. (c)	167. (b)	168. (a)
169. (c)	170. (a)	171. (d)	172. (c)	173. (c)	174. (c)	175. (a)	176. (a)
177. (c)	178. (d)	179. (d)	180. (d)	181. (b)	182. (d)	183. (d)	184. (a)
185. (a)	186. (d)	187. (a)	188. (c)	189. (b)	190. (a)	191. (c)	192. (d)
193. (a)	194. (b)	195. (d)	196. (d)	197. (d)	198. (a)	199. (d)	200. (a)
201. (c)	202. (d)	203. (d)	204. (b)	205. (d)	206. (d)	207. (a)	208. (b)
209. (a)	210. (d)	211. (d)	212. (d)	213. (b)	214. (c)	215. (a)	216. (c)
217. (d)	218. (a)	219. (a)	220. (c)	221. (d)	222. (a)	223. (c)	224. (d)
225. (c)	226. (b)	227. (b)	228. (c)	229. (c)	230. (c)	231. (a)	232. (a)
233. (c)	234. (a)	235. (b)	236. (c)	237. (a)	238. (b)	239. (b)	240. (c)
241. (c)	242. (a)	243. (a)	244. (b)	245. (a)	246. (d)	247. (d)	248. (b)
249. (c)	250. (a)	251. (a)	252. (a)	253. (c)	254. (a)	255. (c)	256. (c)
257. (c)	258. (b)	259. (a)	260. (c)	261. (a)	262. (b)	263. (b)	264. (d)
265. (a)	266. (a)	267. (c)	268. (c)	269. (a)	270. (a)		

Previous Years Questions							
1. (b)	2. (b)	3. (c)	4. (c)	5. (a)	6. (b)	7. (d)	8. (d)
9. (c)	10. (a)	11. (d)	12. (a)	13. (d)	14. (c)	15. (c)	16. (b)
17. (a)	18. (b)	19. (d)	20. (a)	21. (c)	22. (d)	23. (b)	24. (d)
25. (d)	26. (b)	27. (a)	28. (d)	29. (c)	30. (a)	31. (b)	32. (d)
33. (a)	34. (a)	35. (c)	36. (b)	37. (b)	38. (b)	39. (b)	40. (c)
41. (a)	42. (d)	43. (c)	44. (a)	45. (d)	46. (c)	47. (c)	48. (a)
49. (c)	50. (c)	51. (a)	52. (b)	53. (a)	54. (c)	55. (b)	56. (c)
57. (d)	58. (b)	59. (c)	60. (d)	61. (d)	62. (d)	63. (a)	64. (a)
65. (a)	66. (a)	67. (c)	68. (a)	69. (b)	70. (d)	71. (b)	72. (a)
73. (b)	74. (b)	75. (b)	76. (a)	77. (a)	78. (b)	79. (a)	80. (c)
81. (b)	82. (c)	83. (c)	84. (a)	85. (b)	86. (a)	87. (c)	88. (b)
89. (d)	90. (c)	91. (b)	92. (a)	93. (a)	94. (a)	95. (a)	96. (b)
97. (d)	98. (a)	99. (b)	100. (a)	101. (d)	102. (c)	103. (d)	104. (d)
105. (a)	106. (d)	107. (c)	108. (d)	109. (b)	110. (d)	111. (c)	112. (a)
113. (a)	114. (c)	115. (b)					

❑❑❑

d AND f BLOCK ELEMENTS

1. Electronic configuration of a transition element X in +3 oxidation state is $[Ar]3d^5$. What is its atomic number?

   (a) 25   (b) 26   (c) 27   (d) 24

2. In the first transition series, the element with highest melting point is ......

   (a) Mn   (b) Fe   (c) Cr   (d) Cu

3. Which metal has the highest melting point?

   (a) Platinum   (b) Gold   (c) Osmium   (d) Tungsten

4. The correct order of ionic radii of Y^{3+}, La^{3+}, Eu^{3+} and Li^{+3} is ......

   (a) $La^{3+} < Eu^{3+} < Lu^{3+} < Y^{3+}$ (b) $Y^{3+} < La^{3+} < Eu^{3+} < Lu^{3+}$

   (c) $Lu^{3+} < Y^{3+} < Eu^{3+} < La^{3+}$ (d) $Lu^{3+} < Eu^{3+} < La^{3+} < Y^{3+}$

5. Metallic radii of some transition elements are given below. Which of these elements will have highest density?

   Elements Fe, Co, Ni, Cu. Metallic radii/pm : 126, 125, 125, 128

   (a) Fe   (b) Ni   (c) Co   (d) Cu

6. Which of the following metal does not show variable valence ?

   (a) Fe   (b) Hg   (c) Zn   (d) Cu

7. The atomic radii from Cr to Cu is almost identical because of ......

   (a) Increasing nuclear charge from Cr to Cu

   (b) Repulsion among increased electrons

   (c) Increased screening effect to nullify increased nuclear charge

   (d) All of these

8. Which of the following is a condition for complex salt formation?

   (a) Small size   (b) Higher nuclear charge

   (c) Availability of vacant d-orbitals   (d) All of these

9. In which compound, chromium has +6 oxidation state?

   (a) $K_2Cr_2O_7$ (b) $CrCl_3$ (c) $Cr_2(SO_4)_3$ (d) None of these

10. Which transition metal has the lowest density?

    (a) Os   (b) Zn   (c) Sc   (d) La

11. Which of the following pair of transition elements exhibit highest and lowest density?

    (a) Os and Sc   (b) Os and Pt   (c) Hg and Sc   (d) Os and Ir

12. Which metal among following has strongest tendency to undergo oxidation ?

    (a) Zn   (b) Cu   (c) Mg   (d) Al

13. Which transition metal is known as Wonder metal?

    (a) Tungsten   (b) Platinum   (c) Iron   (d) Titanium

14. Which of the following is ferromagnetic ?

(a) Cr (b) Mn (c) W (d) Co

15. The most stable oxidation state of Mn is ......

(a) +2 (b) +4 (c) +5 (d) +7

16. The number of unpaired electrons in Mn^{3+} is ......

(a) 3 (b) 1 (c) 2 (d) 4

17. Which of the following has highest paramagnetic character ?

(a) Mn(II) (b) Fe(II) (c) Co(II) (d) Ni(II)

18. Which of the following metals will not react with solution of $CuSO_4$?

(a) Fe (b) Zn (c) Mg (d) Ag

19. Colour of transition metal compounds is attributed to ......

(a) small size metal ions (b) absorption of light in UV region

(c) complete (ns) subshell (d) incomplete $(n-1)$ d subshell

20. Identify the statement which is not correct regarding $CuSO_4$ ......

(a) it reacts with KI to give iodine

(b) it reacts with KCl to give Cu_2Cl_2

(c) it reacts with NaOH and glucose to give Cu_2O

(d) it reacts with CuO on strong heating in air

21. Actinides ......

(a) are all synthetic elements (b) include element 104

(c) have only short lived isotopes (d) have variable valency

22. Acidified potassium dichromate is treated with H_2S. In this reaction, the oxidation number of chromium ......

(a) increases from +3 to +6 (b) decreases from +6 to +3

(c) remains unchanged (d) decreases from +6 to +2

23. When $KMnO_4$ reacts with acidified $FeSO_4$ ......

(a) only $FeSO_4$ is oxidised (b) only $KMnO_4$ is oxidised

(c) $FeSO_4$ is oxidised and $KMnO_4$ is reduced (d) none of these

24. The number of moles of $KMnO_4$ that will be needed to react with one mole of sulphite ion in acidic solution is ......

(a) 2/5 (b) 3.5 (c) 4/5 (d) 1

25. Which of the following compounds is coloured ?

(a) Ag_2SO_4 (b) CuF_2 (c) MgF_2 (d) CuCl

26. Which of the following reactions are disproportionation reactions?

(a) $Cu^+ \rightarrow Cu^{2+} + Cu$

(b) $3MnO_4^- + 4H^+ \rightarrow 2MnO_4^- + MnO_2 + 2H_2O$

(c) $2KMnO_4^- \rightarrow K_2MnO_4 + MnO_2 + O_2$

(d) $2MnO_4^- + 3Mn^{2+} + 2H_2O \rightarrow 5MnO_2 + 4H^+$

(a) a, b (b) a, b, c (c) b, c, d (d) a, d

27. CrO_3 dissolves in aqueous NaOH to give ......
    (a) CrO_4^{2-}　　　(b) $Cr(OH)_3$　　　(c) CrO_7^{2-}　　　(d) $Cr(OH)_2$

28. The electronic configuration of Gadolinium (At. No. 64) is ......
    (a) $[Xe]\ 4f^8, 5d^9, 6s^2$　　(b) $[Xe]\ 4f^7, 5d^1, 6s^2$　　(c) $[Xe]\ 4f^3, 5d^5, 6s^2$　　(d) $[Xe]\ 4f^6, 5d^2, 6s^2$

29. The metal present in vitamin B_{12} is ......
    (a) Copper　　　(b) Iron　　　(c) Cobalt　　　(d) Zinc

30. Which of the following oxide is amphoteric in nature?
    (a) FeO　　　(b) NiO　　　(c) CoO　　　(d) ZnO

31. Number of moles of $K_2Cr_2O_7$ reduced by one mole of iodide ions are ......
    (a) 3　　　(b) 1/3　　　(c) 6　　　(d) 1/6

32. Chromyl chloride dissolved in NaOH solution gives yellow solution. The yellow solution contains ......
    (a) $Cr_2O_7^{2-}$　　　(b) CrO_4^{2-}　　　(c) CrO_5　　　(d) Cr_2O_3

33. Which of the following sulphide is yellow in colour?
    (a) ZnS　　　(b) NiS　　　(c) CdS　　　(d) MgS

34. Transuranic elements begin with ......
    (a) Np　　　(b) Cm　　　(c) Pu　　　(d) U

35. When ammonia is added to cupric salt solution, the deep blue colour observed is due to the formation of ......
    (a) $[Cu(OH)_4]^{2-}$　　　(b) $[Cu(NH_3)_4]^{2+}$　　　(c) $[Cu(OH)_2(NH_3)_2]$　　　(d) $[Cu(H_2O)]^{2+}$

36. Amongst TiF_6^{2+}, CoF_6^{3-}, Cu_2Cl_2 and $NiCl_4^{2-}$ (At. Nos. Ti = 22, Co = 27, Cu = 29, Ni = 28) the colourless species are ......
    (a) TiF_6^{2-} and CuCl　　　(b) Cu_2Cl_2 and $NiCl_4^{2-}$　　　(c) TiF_6^{2-} and CoF_6^{3-}　　　(d) CoF_6^{3-} and $NiCl_4^{2-}$

37. On addition of NH_4OH to a copper sulphate solution ......
    (a) blue precipitate of copper hydroxide is obtained
    (b) black precipitate of copper oxide is obtained
    (c) a deep blue solution is obtained
    (d) no change is observed

38. Copper sulphate solution reacts with KCN to give ......
    (a) $Cu(CN)_2$　　　(b) CuCN　　　(c) $K_2[Cu(CN)_4]$　　　(d) $K_3[Cu(CN)_4]$

39. Among the following ions which one has the highest paramagnetism?
    (a) $[Cr(H_2O)_6]^{3+}$　　　(b) $[Fe(H_2O)_6]^{2+}$　　　(c) $[Cr(H_2O)_6]^{2+}$　　　(d) $[Zn(H_2O)_6]^{2+}$

40. The highest magnetic moment is shown by the transition metal ion with the outer electronic configuration ......
    (a) $3d^2$　　　(b) $3d^5$　　　(c) $3d^7$　　　(d) $3d^9$

41. Transuranic elements begin with ......
    (a) Np　　　(b) Cm　　　(c) Pu　　　(d) U

42. On heating ammonium dichromate, the gas evolved is ......

    (a) Oxygen　　　　(b) Ammonia　　　　(c) Nitrous oxide　　(d) Nitrogen

43. The correct formula of permanganic acid is ......

    (a) $HMnO_4$　　　　(b) $HMnO_5$　　　　(c) H_2MnO_4　　　　(d) H_2MnO_3

44. Which of the following is explosively unstable ?

    (a) Mn_2O_7　　　　(b) MnO_2　　　　(c) $MnSO_4$　　　　(d) Mn_2O_3

45. The chemical process in the production of steel from haematite ore involves ......

    (a) reduction　　　　　　　　　　　　(b) oxidation

    (c) reduction followed by oxidation　　　　(d) oxidation followed by reduction

46. In permanganate ion MnO_4^-, manganese has an oxidation number of +7. Therefore it is ......

    (a) sp^3d^3 hybridised　　　　　　　　(b) sp^3 hybridised

    (c) dsp^2 hybridised　　　　　　　　　(d) d^3sp^3 hybridised

47. Amongst the following, the compound that is both paramagnetic and coloured is ......

    (a) $K_2Cr_2O_7$　　　　(b) $(NH_4)_2[FeCl_6]$　　　(c) $VOSO_4$　　　　(d) $K_3[Cu(CN)_6]$

48. Which of the statements is not true?

    (a) $K_2Cr_2O_7$ solution in acidic medium is orange

    (b) $K_2Cr_2O_7$ solution becomes yellow on increasing the pH beyond 7

    (c) On passing H_2S through acidified $K_2Cr_2O_7$ solution, a milky colour is observed

    (d) $Na_2Cr_2O_7$ is preferred over $K_2Cr_2O_7$ in volumetric analysis

49. Oxidation number of chromium in chromyl chloride is ......

    (a) +3　　　　(b) +6　　　　(c) +2　　　　(d) 0

50. The last element of the third transition series is ......

    (a) Ag　　　　(b) Hg　　　　(c) C　　　　(d) Au

51. Iron is rendered passive by treatment with concentrated ......

    (a) HCl　　　　(b) HNO_3　　　　(c) H_2SO_4　　　　(d) H_3PO_4

52. The equivalent weight of $MnSO_4$ is half of its molecular weight when it is converted to ......

    (a) MnO_2　　　　(b) Mn_2O_3　　　　(c) MnO_4^{2-}　　　　(d) MnO_4^-

53. The ground state electronic configuration of Ar atom (Z = 24) is ......

    (a) [Ar] $3d^5 4s^1$　　　(b) [Ar] $3d^4 4s^2$　　　(c) [Ar] $3d^6 4s^0$　　　(d) [Ar] $4d^5 4s^1$

54. The first man-made element is ......

    (a) Iron　　　　(b) Technetium　　　　(c) Zirconium　　　　(d) Mercury

55. The number of moles of $KMnO_4$ that will be needed to react completely with one mole of ferrous oxalate in acidic solution is ......

    (a) 3/5　　　　(b) 2/5　　　　(c) 4/5　　　　(d) 1

56. When $KMnO_4$ solution is added to oxalic acid solution, the decolourisation is slow in the beginning but becomes instantaneous after some time because ......

    (a) CO_2 is formed as the product　　　　(b) reaction is exothermic

    (c) MnO_4^- catalyses the reaction　　　　(d) Mn^{2+} acts as a autocatalyst

57. $KMnO_4$ acts as an oxidising agent in acidic medium. The number of moles of $KMnO_4$ that will be needed to react with one mole of sulphide ions in acidic solution is ......

(a) 2, 5　　　(b) 3, 5　　　(c) 4, 5　　　(d) 1, 5

58. Which of the following is amphoteric oxide?

Mn_2O_7, CrO_3, Cr_2O_3, CrO, V_2O_5, V_2O_4

(a) V_2O_5, Cr_2O_3　　　(b) Mn_2O_7, CrO_3　　　(c) CrO, V_2O_5　　　(d) V_2O_5, V_2O_4

59. In the dichromate anion ......

(a) 6 Cr–O bonds are equivalent　　　(b) 4 Cr–O bonds are equivalent

(c) All Cr–O bonds are equivalent　　　(d) All Cr–O bonds are non-equivalent

60. Transition elements show magnetic moment due to spin and orbital motion of electrons. Which of the following metallic ions have almost same spin only magnetic moment?

(a) Co^{2+}, Cr^{3+}　　　(b) Cr^{2+}, Mn^{2+}　　　(c) Mn^{2+}, Co^{2+}　　　(d) Cr^{3+}, Co^{2+}

61. Amongst the following, identify the species with an atom in +6 oxidation state ......

(a) MnO_4^-　　　(b) CrO_2Cl_2　　　(c) $Cr(CN)_6^{3-}$　　　(d) NiF_6^{2-}

62. In the standardisation of $Na_2S_2O_3$ using $K_2Cr_2O_7$ by iodometry, the equivalent weight of $K_2Cr_2O_7$ is ......

(a) (Molecular weight)/3　　　(b) (Molecular weight)/2

(c) (Molecular weight)/6　　　(d) Same as molecular weight

63. The 3d element show variable oxidation state. What is the maximum oxidation state shown by the element Mn?

(a) +6　　　(b) +7　　　(c) +4　　　(d) +5

64. When MnO_2 is fused with KOH in the presence of air, the product and the colour of the compound formed is ......

(a) $KMnO_4$, dark green　　(b) Mn_2O_3, brown　　(c) $KMnO_4$, purple　　(d) Mn_3O_4, black

65. The pair of which salt have same colour when freshly prepared?

(a) $CuCl_2$, $FeCl_2$　　　(b) $VOCl_2$, $CuCl_2$　　　(c) $MnCl_2$　　　(d) $FeCl_2$, $VOCl_2$

66. The product of oxidation of I^- and MnO_4^- in alkaline medium is ......

(a) I_2　　　(b) IO_3^-　　　(c) IO_4^-　　　(d) IO^-

67. Dichromate, Cr(VI) is a strong oxidising agent in acidic medium but Mo(VI) in MoO_3 and W(VI) in WO_3 are not because ......

(a) Cr(VI) is more stable than Mo(VI) and W(VI).

(b) Mo(VI) and W(VI) are more stable than Cr(VI).

(c) Higher oxidation states of heavier members of group-6 of transition series are more stable.

(d) Lower oxidation states of heavier members of group-6 of transition series are more stable

68. Ferric sulphate on heating gives ......

(a) SO_3 only　　　(b) SO_2 only　　　(c) S　　　(d) SO_2 and SO_3

69. What is the correct order of spin only magnetic moment (in BM) of Mn^{2+}, Cr^{2+} and V_2^+ ?

    (a) $Mn^{2+} > V^{2+} > Cr^{2+}$

    (b) $V^{2+} > Cr^{2+} > Mn^{2+}$

    (c) $Mn^{2+} > Cr^{2+} > V^{2+}$

    (d) $Cr^{2+} > V^{2+} > Mn^{2+}$

70. What would happen when a solution of potassium chromate is treated with an excess of dilute sulphuric acid?

    (a) Cr^{3+} and $Cr_2O_7^{2-}$

    (b) $Cr_2O_7^{2-}$ and H_2O are formed

    (c) $Cr_2O_4^{2-}$ is reduced to +7 state of Cr

    (d) $Cr_2O_4^{2-}$ is reduced to +3 state of Cr

71. Zn does not show variable valency because of ......

    (a) complete d sub-shell

    (b) inert pair effect

    (c) $4s^2$ sub-shell

    (d) none of these

72. In the metallurgy of iron, when limestone is added to blast furnace, the calcium ion ends up in ......

    (a) Gangue

    (b) Slag

    (c) Calcium carbonate

    (d) Metallic calcium

73. The lowest degree of paramagnetism per mole of the compound at 298 °K is shown by ...

    (a) $FeSO_4 \cdot 6H_2O$ (b) $CuSO_4 \cdot 5H_2O$ (c) $NiSO_4 \cdot 6H_2O$ (d) $MnSO_4 \cdot 4H_2O$

74. Which among the following salts are coloured in their aqueous form ?

    (a) $LiNO_3$ (b) $Co(NO_3)_2$ (c) $Zn(NO_3)_2$ (d) Potash alum

75. Which among the following has maximum number of unpaired electrons ?

    (a) Fe^{2+} (b) Ti^{3+} (c) Mg^{2+} (d) V^{3+}

76. The only cations present in a slightly acidic solution are Fe^{3+}, Zn^{2+} and Cu^{2+}. Name the reagent added in excess to this solution, that identifies and separates Fe^{3+} in one step is ...

    (a) 6M NaOH   (b) 2M HCl   (c) 6M NH_3 (d) H_2S gas

77. Ammonium dichromate is used in some fire works. The green coloured powder blown in air is ......

    (a) Cr   (b) Cr_2O_3 (c) $CrO(O_2)$ (d) CrO_3

78. Which of the following statements is not correct?

    (a) Copper liberates hydrogen from acids.

    (b) In its higher oxidation states, manganese forms stable compounds with oxygen and fluorine.

    (c) Mn^{3+} and Co^{3+} are oxidising agents in aqueous solution.

    (d) Ti^{2+} and Cr^{2+} are reducing agents in aqueous solution.

79. Which of the following metals is used in incandescent lamps ?

    (a) Tungsten   (b) Chromium   (c) Molybdenum   (d) Zirconium

80. Which metal is used as a catalyst in the Haber's process ?

    (a) Iron containing molybdenum

    (b) Chromium

    (c) Molybdenum

    (d) Tungsten

81. Which transition metal shows lowest oxidation state in its compounds with chlorine ?

(a) Cu　　　　　　(b) Fe　　　　　　(c) Ti　　　　　　(d) Zn

82. Highest oxidation state of manganese in fluoride (MnF_4) is +4 but highest oxidation state in oxides (Mn_2O_7) is +7 because ......

(a) fluorine is more electronegative than oxygen

(b) fluorine does not possess d-orbitals

(c) fluorine stabilises lower oxidation state

(d) in covalent compounds fluorine can form single bond only while oxygen forms double bond

83. The first man-made element belongs to ...... transition series.

(a) 3d　　　　　　(b) 5d　　　　　　(c) 4d　　　　　　(d) 6d

84. The oxidation number of manganese is maximum in ......

(a) MnO_2　　　　(b) $MnSO_4$　　　　(c) $KMnO_4$　　　　(d) K_2MnO_4

85. The electronic configuration of Cu(II) is $3d^9$ whereas that of Cu(I) is $3d^{10}$. Which of the following is correct?

(a) Cu(II) is more stable

(b) Cu(II) is less stable

(c) Cu(I) and Cu(II) are equally stable

(d) Stability of Cu(I) and Cu(II) depends on the nature of copper salts

86. The catalyst used in Deacon process for the manufacture of Cl_2 from HCl is ......

(a) CuCl　　　　　(b) $CuCl_2$　　　　(c) Pt　　　　　(d) $FeCl_3$

87. Arrange the following in order of their decreasing thermal conductivities ......

(a) Al, Ag, Cu　　(b) Cu, Ag, Al　　(c) Ag, Cu, Al　　(d) Al, Cu, Ag

88. In the first transition series, the element with lowest melting point belongs to group ......

(a) 3　　　　　　(b) 4　　　　　　(c) 7　　　　　　(d) 10

89. Zr and Hf have almost equal atomic and ionic radii because ......

(a) of diagonal relationship　　　　　(b) both are in the same group

(c) of lanthanide contraction　　　　(d) they have same outermost shell

90. Ag^+ ion is isoelectronic with ......

(a) Cu^+　　　　(b) Cd^{2+}　　　　(c) Zn^{2+}　　　　(d) Pd^{2+}

91. A transition element X has a configuration [Ar] $3d^4$ in its +3 oxidation state. Its atomic number is ......

(a) 25　　　　　　(b) 19　　　　　　(c) 22　　　　　　(d) 26

92. Which of the transition element is synthetic ?

(a) Tc　　　　　　(b) Pm　　　　　　(c) Mo　　　　　　(d) Re

93. Which of the following is diamagnetic ?

(a) Zn^{2+}　　　　(b) Cr^{2+}　　　　(c) Cu^{2+}　　　　(d) Fe^{2+}

94. Which of the following transition element exhibit the oxidation state of +8 ?

(a) Au　　　　(b) Cd　　　　(c) Ru　　　　(d) Tc

95. Cerium shows oxidation state of +4 because ......

(a) it has tendency to attain f^0 configuration

(b) it resembles alkali metals

(c) it has very low I.E.

(d) it has tendency to attain noble gas configuration

96. Which of the two have almost similar size ?

(a) $_{22}Ti$ and $_{40}Zr$　　　　(b) $_{41}Nb$ and $_{73}Ta$　　　(c) $_{39}Y$ and $_{57}La$　　　(d) $_{20}Ca$ and $_{31}Ir$

97. General electronic configuration of actinoids is $(n-2)f^{1-14}$ $(n-1)d^{0-1}$ ns^2. Which of the following actinoids have no electron in 5f orbital?

(a) U (Atomic No. 92)　　　　　　　　(b) Np (Atomic No. 93)

(c) Pu (Atomic No. 94)　　　　　　　　(d) Am (Atomic No. 95)

98. Which of the following is a ferrous alloy ?

(a) German silver　　　(b) Gunmetal　　　(c) Nichrome　　　(d) Devarda's alloy

99. White vitriol is ......

(a) $CuSO_4 . 5H_2O$　　　(b) $FeSO_4 . 7H_2O$　　　(c) $ZnSO_4 . 7H_2O$　　(d) $NiSO_4 . 5H_2O$

100. Which forms interstitial compounds ?

(a) Fe　　　　(b) Co　　　　(c) Ni　　　　(d) All

101. Mohr salt is ......

(a) Double salt　　　(b) Complex salt　　　(c) Acid salt　　　(d) Basic salt

102. In the equation $4M + 8CN^- + 2H_2O + O_2 \rightarrow 4[M(CN)_2]^- + 4OH^-$

identify the metal M. It is ......

(a) Copper　　　(b) Iron　　　(c) Gold　　　(d) Zinc

103. Silver ore dissolves in excess of sodium cyanide solution forming ......

(a) AgCN　　　(b) $Na[Ag(CN)_2]$　　　(c) $Na_2[Ag(CN)_3]$　　(d) $Na_4[Ag(CN)_5]$

104. The total number of inner transition elements in the periodic table is ......

(a) 10　　　　(b) 14　　　　(c) 28　　　　(d) 30

105. In Ziegler-Natta polymerisation of ethylene, the active species is ......

(a) $AlCl_3$　　　(b) Ti(III)　　　(c) Et_3Al　　　(d) $TiCl_4$

106. Which of the following reactions represents "developing" in photography ?

(a) $AgNO_3 + NaBr \rightarrow AgBr + NaNO_3$

(b) $C_6H_4(OH)_2 + 2AgBr^* \rightarrow C_6H_4O_2 + 2HBr^* + 2Ag$

(c) $AgBr + h\upsilon \rightarrow AgBr^*$

(d) $AgBr + 2Na_2S_2O_3 \rightarrow Na_3[Ag(S_2O_3)_2] + NaBr$

107. Which of the following compounds has colour but no unpaired electrons ?

(a) K_2MnO_4　　　(b) $KMnO_4$　　　(c) $MnCl_2$　　　(d) $MnSO_4$

108. Interstitial compounds are formed when small atoms are trapped inside the crystal lattice of metals. Which of the following is not the characteristic property of interstitial compounds?

(a) they have high melting points in comparison to pure metals

(b) they are very hard

(c) they retain metallic conductivity

(d) they are chemically very reactive

109. Which one of the following ionic species will impart colour to an aqueous solution ?

(a) Tl^{4+} (b) Cu^+ (c) Zn^{2+} (d) Cr^{3+}

110. Which of the following is most stable ?

(a) Sn^{2+} (b) Ni^{2+} (c) Cd^{2+} (d) Mn^{2+}

111. Which is not the property of transition elements?

(a) coloured salts   (b) variable valency

(c) fixed valency   (d) coordinate complex formation

112. Which one of the following characteristics of transition metals is associated with their catalytic activity ?

(a) Variable oxidation states   (b) High enthalpy of atomisation

(c) Paramagnetic behaviour   (d) Colour of hydrated ions

113. When acidified $K_2Cr_2O_7$ solution is added to Sn^{2+} salts then it changes to ......

(a) Sn (b) Sn^{3+} (c) Sn^{4+} (d) Sn^+

114. Why HCl is not used to make the medium acidic in oxidation reactions of $KMnO_4$ in acidic medium?

(a) both HCl and $KMnO_4$ act as oxidising agents.

(b) $KMnO_4$ oxidises HCl into Cl_2 which is also an oxidising agent.

(c) $KMnO_4$ is a weaker oxidising agent than HCl.

(d) $KMnO_4$ acts as a reducing agent in the presence of HCl.

115. Percentage of silver in German silver is ......

(a) 0%   (b) 1%   (c) 5%   (d) none of these

116. Which of the following transition metal ions will have definite value of magnetic moment?

(a) Sc^{3+} (b) Ti^{3+} (c) Cu^+ (d) Zn^{2+}

117. Which of the following metal exhibits more than one oxidation state?

(a) Na   (b) Mg   (c) Fe   (d) Al

118. Which of the following compounds is formed when a mixture of $K_2Cr_2O_7$ and NaCl is heated with concentrated H_2SO_4 ?

(a) CrO_2Cl_2 (b) $CrCl_2$ (c) $Cr_2(SO_4)_3$ (d) Na_2CrO_4

119. The magnetic moment is associated with its spin angular momentum and orbital angular momentum. Spin only magnetic moment value of Cr^{3+} ion is ......

(a) 2.87 B.M.   (b) 3.87 B.M.   (c) 3.47 B.M.   (d) 3.57 B.M.

120. The reaction $MnO_4^- + e^- \rightleftharpoons MnO_4^{2-}$ takes place in ......

(a) a basic medium   (b) an acidic medium

(c) a neutral medium   (d) both acidic and basic media

121. Pick out the wrong reaction from ......

(a) $2Na_2CrO_4 + H^+ \rightarrow Na_2Cr_2O_7 + 2Na^+ + H_2O$

(b) $2MnO_2 + 4KOH + 5O_2 \rightarrow 4KMnO_4 + 2H_2O$

(c) $MnO_4^- + 8H^+ + 5Fe^{2+} \rightarrow 5Fe^{3+} + Mn^{2+} + 4H_2O$

(d) $2MnO_4^- + 5C_2O_4^{2-} + 16H^+ \rightarrow 2Mn^{2+} + 10CO_2 + 8H_2O$

122. The number of unpaired electrons in ferrous ion ($Z = 26$) is ......

(a) 3 　　　　(b) 2 　　　　(c) 4 　　　　(d) 5

123. Transition metals are often paramagnetic owing to ......

(a) High melting point and boiling point　　　(b) The presence of vacant orbitals

(c) The presence of unpaired electrons　　　(d) Malleability and ductility

124. Both acid and base may react with which of the following oxides?

(a) CaO 　　　　(b) Na_2O_2 　　　　(c) ZnO 　　　　(d) Mn_3O_4

125. Among the following which is used as an electrolyte in electroplating a base metal with gold?

(a) NH_4Cl 　　　　(b) $K[Au(CN)_2]$ 　　　　(c) HgCN 　　　　(d) AgCN

126. Mohr's salt is ......

(a) $FeSO_4.7H_2O$ 　　　　　　　　(b) $Fe(NH_4).SO_4.6H_2O$

(c) $(NH_4)_2SO_2 \cdot FeSO_4 \cdot 6H_2O$ 　　　　(d) $[Fe(NH_4)_2](SO_4)_2.6H_2O$

127. $FeCr_2O_4 + Na_2CO_3 + O_2 \rightarrow$ products

(a) $Na_2CrO_4 + Fe_2O_3 + CO_2$ 　　　　(b) $Na_2Cr_2O_7 + Fe_2O_3 + CO_2$

(c) $Fe_2CrO_4 + Na_2O + CO_2$ 　　　　(d) $Na_2CrO_4 + FeO + CO_2$

128. The number of unpaired electrons in Zn^{2+} is ......

(a) 2 　　　　(b) 3 　　　　(c) 4 　　　　(d) 0

129. German silver is an alloy of copper and ......

(a) Zn and Ni 　　　　(b) Al 　　　　(c) Zn 　　　　(d) Sn

130. Among the lanthanides the one obtained by synthetic method is ......

(a) Lu 　　　　(b) Pm 　　　　(c) Pr 　　　　(d) Gd

131. One of the following is diamagnetic ......

(a) Cu 　　　　(b) Cu^+ 　　　　(c) Cu^{2+} 　　　　(d) All of these

132. The common oxidation states of Ti are ......

(a) $+2, +3$ 　　　　(b) $+3, +4$ 　　　　(c) $-3, -4$ 　　　　(d) $+2, +3, +4$

133. Which of the following types of metals make the most efficient catalysts?

(a) Transition metals 　　　　(b) Alkali metals

(c) Alkaline earth metals 　　　　(d) Coloured metals

134. Which one of the following transition metal ions has the lowest density?

(a) Copper 　　　　(b) Nickel 　　　　(c) Scandium 　　　　(d) Zinc

135. When SO_2 is passed through acidified $K_2Cr_2O_7$ solution ......

(a) the solution turns blue   (b) the solution is decolourised

(c) SO_2 is reduced   (d) green $Cr_2(SO_4)_2$ is formed

136. Which do not decolourise $KMnO_4$ aqueous solution ?

(a) $C_2O_4^{2-}$ (b) HSO_3^- (c) CO_3^{2-} (d) SO_3^{2-}

137. Which of the following arrangements does not represent the correct order of the property stated against it?

(a) $V^{2+} < Cr^{2+} < Mn^{2+} < Fe^{2+}$ (paramagnetic behaviour)

(b) $Ni^{2+} < Co^{2+} < Fe^{2+} < Mn^{2+}$ (ionic size)

(c) $Co^{3+} < Fe^{3+} < Cr^{3+} < Sc^{3+}$ (stability in aqueous solution)

(d) $Sc < Ti < Cr < Mn$ (number of oxidation states)

138. $(NH_4)_2Cr_2O_7$ on heating gives a gas which is also given by ......

(a) heating NH_4NO_2 (b) heating NH_4NO_3

(c) $Mg_3N_2 + H_2O$ (d) Na (comp.) $+ H_2O_2$

139. Lanthanide contraction is caused due to ......

(a) the appreciable shielding on outer electrons by 4f electrons from the nuclear charge

(b) the appreciable shielding on outer electrons by 5d electrons from the nuclear charge

(c) the same effective nuclear charge from Ce to Lu

(d) the imperfect shielding on outer electrons by 4f electrons from the nuclear charge

140. Arrange Ce^{3+}, La^{3+}, Pm^{3+} and Yb^{3+} in increasing order of their ionic radii ......

(a) $Yb^{3+} < Pm^{3+} < Ce^{3+} < La^{3+}$ (b) $Ce^{3+} < Yb^{3+} < Pm^{3+} < La^{3+}$

(c) $Yb^{3+} < Pm^{3+} < La^{3+} < Ce^{3+}$ (d) $Pm^{3+} < La^{3+} < Ce^{3+} < Yb^{3+}$

141. $[X] + H_2SO_4 \rightarrow [Y]$ a colourless gas with irritating smell. $[Y] + K_2Cr_2O_7 + H_2SO_4 \rightarrow$ green solution. $[X]$ and $[Y]$ are ......

(a) SO_3^{2-}, SO_2 (b) Cl^-, HCl (c) Cl_2^-, H_2S (d) CO_3^{2-}, CO_2

142. Among the following pairs of ions, the lower oxidation state in aqueous solution is more stable than the other in ......

(a) Tl^+, Tl^{3+} (b) Cu^+, Cu^{2+} (c) Cr^{3+}, Cr^{2+} (d) V^{2+}, Vo^{2+}

143. The atomic number of V, Cr, Mn and Fe are respectively 23, 24, 25 and 26. Which one of these may be expected to have the second highest ionisation enthalpy ?

(a) V   (b) Cr   (c) Mn   (d) Fe

144. The radius of La^{3+} (At. No. 57) is 1.06 Å. Which one of the following given values will be closest to the radius of Lu^{3+} (At. No. 71) ?

(a) 1.60 Å   (b) 1.40 Å   (c) 1.06 Å   (d) 0.85 Å

145. How many electrons are involved in the oxidation by $KMnO_4$ in basic medium ?

(a) 1   (b) 2   (c) 5   (d) 3

146. Which of the following metal is found in gun metal, monel metal and constantan alloys ?

(a) Zn　　　　　(b) Hg　　　　　(c) Fe　　　　　(d) Cu

147. Excess of KI reacts with $CuSO_4$ solution and then $Na_2S_2O_3$ solution is added to it. The correct statements for this reaction are ......

(a) Cu_2I_2 is formed

(b) CuI_2 is formed

(c) $Na_2S_2O_3$ is oxidised

(d) Evolved I_2 is oxidised

148. Colourless solutions of the following four salts are placed separately in four different test tubes and a strip of copper is dipped in each one of these. Which solution will turn blue ?

(a) KNO_3　　　(b) $AgNO_3$　　　(c) $Zn(NO_3)_2$　　　(d) $ZnSO_4$

149. Invar, an alloy of Fe and Ni is used in watches and meter scales. Its characteristic property is ......

(a) small coefficient of expansion

(b) resistance to corrosion

(c) hardness and elasticity

(d) resistance to water

(e) magnetic nature

150. Number of electrons transferred in each case when $KMnO_4$ acts as an oxidising agent to give MnO_2, Mn^{2+}, $Mn(OH)_3$ and MnO_4^{2-} are respectively ......

(a) 3, 5, 4 and 1　　(b) 4, 3, 1 and 5　　(c) 1, 3, 4 and 5　　(d) 5, 4, 3 and 1

151. In an alkaline condition, $KMnO_4$ reacts as follows :

$$2KMnO_4 + 2KOH \longrightarrow 2K_2MnO_4 + H_2O + [O]$$

Its equivalent weight is ......

(a) 31.6　　　(b) 52.7　　　(c) 49　　　(d) 158

152. Amongst the following, identify the species with an atom in +6 oxidation state.

(a) MnO_4^-　　　(b) $Cr(CN)_6^{3-}$　　　(c) NiF_6^{2-}　　　(d) CrO_2Cl_2

153. In the standardisation of $Na_2S_2O_3$ using $K_2Cr_2O_7$ by iodometry, the equivalent weight of $K_2Cr_2O_7$ is ......

(a) (Molecular weight)/2

(b) (Molecular weight)/6

(c) (Molecular weight)/3

(d) Same as molecular weight

154. Anhydrous ferric chloride is prepared by ......

(a) heating hydrated ferric chloride at a high temperature in a stream of air

(b) heating metallic iron in a stream of dry chlorine gas

(c) reaction of ferric oxide with hydrochloric acid

(d) reaction of metallic iron with hydrochloric acid

155. When MnO_2 is fused with KOH in the presence of air, a coloured compound is formed, the product and its colour is ......

(a) K_2MnO_4, dark green　(b) $KMnO_4$, purple　(c) Mn_2O_3, brown　(d) Mn_3O_4, black

156. Which of the following lanthanoids show +2 oxidation state besides the characteristic oxidation state +3 of lanthanoids?

(a) Ce　　　(b) Tb　　　(c) Yb　　　(d) Ho

157. Which of the following ions show higher spin only magnetic moment value?

(a) Ti^{3+}　　　(b) Mn^{2+}　　　(c) Fe^{2+}　　　(d) Co^{3+}

Assertion and Reasons

Direction : In the following question, a statement of Assertion (A) is given followed by a corresponding statement of Reason (R) just below it. Of the statements, mark the correct answer as

(a) If both A and R are true and R is the correct explanation of A

(b) If both are correct and R is not the correct explanation of A

(c) If A is true but R is false.

(d) If A is false but reason is true.

(e) If both A and R are false.

158. Assertion　　　　:　Mn^{2+} is more stable than Mn^{3+}.

　　　Reason　　　　:　Mn^{2+} has half filled configuration.

159. Assertion　　　　:　Fe^{2+} is paramagnetic.

　　　Reason　　　　:　Fe^{2+} contains four unpaired electrons.

160. Assertion　　　　:　Transition metals form substitutional alloys.

　　　Reason　　　　:　Alloys have useful properties which are absent in the constituent elements.

161. Assertion　　　　:　Copper dissolves in dilute nitric acid but not in dilute HCl.

　　　Reason　　　　:　Its standard reduction potential is above hydrogen.

162. Assertion　　　　:　Fe^{3+} is more stable than Fe^{2+}.

　　　Reason　　　　:　Fe^{2+} ions are easily oxidised to Fe^{3+} ions.

163. Assertion　　　　:　Aqueous solution of $FeCl_3$ is acidic.

　　　Reason　　　　:　The hydrated form of $FeCl_3$ consists of six water molecules ($FeCl_3 \cdot 6H_2O$).

164. Assertion　　　　:　A solution of ferric chloride on standing gives a brown precipitate.

　　　Reason　　　　:　$FeCl_3$ possesses covalent bonds and chlorine bridge structure.

165. Assertion　　　　:　$Na_2Cr_2O_7$ is not a primary standard in volumetric analysis.

　　　Reason　　　　:　$Na_2Cr_2O_7$ is hygroscopic.

166. Assertion　　　　:　$La(OH)_3$ is more basic than $Lu(OH)_3$.

　　　Reason　　　　:　Size of Lu^{3+} increases and shows more covalent character.

167. Assertion　　　　:　Ce^{4+} is used as an oxidising agent in volumetric analysis.

　　　Reason　　　　:　Ce^{4+} has the tendency of attaining +3 oxidation state.

168. Assertion　　　　:　Promethium is man made element.

　　　Reason　　　　:　It is radioactive and has been prepared by artificial means.

169. Assertion　　　　:　Most of the trivalent lanthanide ions are coloured both in the solid state and in aqueous solutions.

　　　Reason　　　　:　The elements with xf electrons have a similar colour to those of $(14 - x)f$ electrons.

170. Assertion   :   Europium(II) is more stable than cerium(II).

Reason   :   Cerium salts are used as a catalyst in petroleum cracking.

171. Assertion   : $La(OH)_3$ is more basic than $Lu(OH)_3$.

Reason   :   The basic character of oxides and hydroxides decrease from $La(OH)_3$ to $Lu(OH)_3$.

172. Assertion   :   The degree of complex formation in actinides decreases in the order $M^{4+} > Mo_2^{2+} > M^{3+} > Mo_2^{+}$.

Reason   :   Actinides form complexes with π-bonding ligands such as alkyl phosphines and thioethers.

QUESTIONS FROM VARIOUS COMPETITIVE EXAMINATIONS

1. Which one of the following statements is correct when SO_2 is passed through acidified $K_2Cr_2O_7$ solution?   **[NEET UG 2016]**

(a) Green $Cr_2(SO_4)_3$ is formed.

(b) The solution turns blue

(c) The solution is decolourized

(d) SO_2 is reduced

2. The electronic configurations of Eu (Atomic No. 63), Gd (Atomic No. 64) and To (Atomic No. 65) are ......   **[NEET-UG 2016]**

(a) $[Xe]\ 4f^7\ 6s^2$, $[Xe]\ 4f^7\ 5d^1$ and $[Xe]\ 4f^9\ 6s^2$

(b) $[Xe]\ 4f^7\ 6s^2$, $[Xe]\ 4f^7\ 6s^2$, $[Xe]\ 4f^3\ 6d^1\ 6s^2$ and $[Xe]\ 4f^8\ 5d^1\ 6s^2$

(c) $[Xe]\ 4f^6\ 5d^1\ 6s^2$, $[Xe]\ 4f^7\ 5d^1\ 6s^2$ and $[Xe]\ 4f^9\ 6s^2$

(d) $[Xe]\ 4f^6\ 5d^1\ 6s^2$, $[Xe]\ 4f^7\ 5d^1\ 6s^2$ and $[Xe]\ 4f^9\ 5d^1\ 6s^2$

3. Magnetic moment 2.84 B.M. is given by ......   **[AIPMT 2015]**

(a) Ti^{2+} (b) Cr^{2+} (c) Co^{2+} (d) Ni^{2+}

4. Cobalt(III) chloride forms several octahedral complexes with ammonia. Which of the following will not give test of chloride ions with silver nitrate at 20°C?   **[AIPMT 2015]**

(a) $CoCl_3 \cdot 4NH_3$ (b) $CoCl_3 \cdot 5NH_3$ (c) $CoCl_3 \cdot 6\ NH_3$ (d) $CoCl_3 \cdot 3NH_3$

5. Because of lanthanoid contraction, which of the flowing pairs of elements have nearly same radii? (Number in the parenthesis are atomic numbers).   **[AIPMT 2015]**

(a) Zr (40) and Nb (41)

(b) Zr (40) and Hf (72)

(c) Zr (40) and Ta (73)

(d) Ti (22) and Zr (40)

6. Gadolinium belongs to 4f series. Its atomic number is 64. Which of the following is the correct electronic configuration of Gadolinium?   **[RE AIPMT 2015]**

(a) $[Xe]\ 4f^7\ 5d^1\ 6s^2$ (b) $[Xe]\ 4f^6\ 5d^2\ 6s^2$ (c) $[Xe]\ 4f^9\ 5d^2$ (d) $[Xe]\ 4f^0\ 5s^1$

7. Magnetic moment 2.83 B.M. is given by which of the following ions?

[At. Nos. Ti = 22, Cr = 24, Mn = 25, Ni = 28)   **[AIPMT 2014]**

(a) Cr^{3+} (b) Mn^{2+} (c) Ti^{3+} (d) Ni^{2+}

8. The reaction of aqueous $KMnO_4$ with H_2O_2 in acidic conditions gives ......   **[AIPMT 2014]**

(a) Mn^{2+} and O_3 (b) Mn^{4+} and MnO_2 (c) Mn^{4+} and O_2 (d) Mn^{2+} and O_2

9. In acidic medium, H_2O_2 changes from $Cr_2O_7^{-2}$ to CrO_5 which has two (--O—O--) bonds. Oxidation state of Cr in CrO_5 is ......   **[AIPMT 2014]**

(a) +6   (b) −10   (c) +5   (d) +3

10. Which of the following statements about interstitial compounds is correct?

    (a) they have higher melting points than the pure metal   **[NEET 2013]**

    (b) they retain metallic conductivity

    (c) they are chemically reactive

    (d) they are much harder than the pure metal

11. Which of the following lanthanoid is diamagnetic ?

    (a) Yb^{2+} (b) Ce^{2+} (c) Sm^{2+} (d) Eu^{2+} **[NEET 2013]**

12. Which of the following is not true?   **[CBSE AIPMT 2012]**

    (a) On passing H_2S through acidified $K_2Cr_2O_7$ solution, a milky colour is observed

    (b) $Na_2Cr_2O_7$ is preferred over $K_2Cr_2O_7$ in volumetric analysis

    (c) $K_2Cr_2O_7$ solution in acidic medium is orange

    (d) $K_2Cr_2O_7$ solution becomes yellow on increasing the pH beyond 7

13. Which one of the following does not correctly represent the correct order of the property indicated against it?   **[CBSE AIPMT 2012]**

    (a) Ti < V < Cr < Mn : increasing number of oxidation states

    (b) $Ti^{3+} < V^{3+} < Cr^{3+} < Mn^{3+}$: increasing magnetic moment

    (c) Ti < V < Cr < Mn : increasing melting points

    (d) Ti < V < Mn < Cr : increasing second ionization enthalpy

14. Four successive members of the first series of the transition metals are listed below. For which one of them, the standard potential $(E^{o}_{M^{2+}/M})$ value has a positive sign ?

    [CBSE AIPMT 2012]

    (a) Co (Z = 27)   (b) Ni (Z = 28)   (c) Cu (Z = 29)   (d) Fe (Z = 26)

15. When H_2O_2 is shaken with an acidified solution of $K_2Cr_2O_7$ in presence of ether, the ethereal layer turns blue due to the formation of ......

    (a) Cr_2O_3 (b) CrO_4^{2-} (c) $Cr(SO_3)_3$ (d) CrO_5

16. Which one of the following has a magnetic moment of 1.75 BM?   **[KCET 2012]**

    (a) V^{3+} (b) Cr^{3+} (c) Fe^{3+} (d) Ti^{3+}

17. Across the lanthanide series, the basicity of lanthanide hydroxides ...   **[UP CPMT 2012]**

    (a) increases   (b) decreases

    (c) first increases and then decreases   (d) first decreases and then increases

18. The oxidation state of chromium in the final product formed by the reaction between KI and acidified potassium dichromate solution is ......   **[AIIMS 2012]**

    (a) +3   (b) +2   (c) +6   (d) +4

19. For the successive transition elements (Cr, Mn, Fe and Co), the stability of +2 oxidation state will be there in which of the following order?

    (At. No. Cr = 24, Mn = 25, Fe = 26, Co = 27)   **[CBSE AIPMT 2011]**

    (a) Cr > Mn > Co > Fe   (b) Mn > Fe > Cr > Co

    (c) Fe > Mn > Co > Cr   (d) Co > Mn > Fe > Cr

20. Acidified $K_2Cr_2O_7$ solution turns green when Na_2SO_3 is added to it. This is due to the formation of ...... **[CBSE AIPMT 2011]**

(a) $CrSO_4$ (b) $Cr(SO_4)_3$ (c) CrO_4^{2-} (d) $Cr_2(SO_3)_3$

21. Which is the correct statement about Cr_2O^{2-} structure? **[DUMET 2011]**

(a) it has neither Cr–Cr bonds nor O–O bonds.

(b) it has one Cr–Cr bond and six O–O bonds.

(c) it has no Cr–Cr bond and has six O–O bonds.

(d) it has one Cr–Cr bond and seven Cr–O bonds.

22. The acidic, basic or amphoteric nature of Mn_2O_7, V_2O_5 and CrO respectively are ......

[Kerala CEE 2011]

(a) acidic, acidic and basic   (b) basic, amphoteric and acidic

(c) acidic, amphoteric and basic   (d) acidic, basic and amphoteric

(e) acidic, basic and basic

23. The titanium (atomic number 22) compound that does not exist is ...... **[Kerala CEE 2011]**

(a) TiO   (b) TiO_2 (c) K_2TiF_6 (d) K_2TiO_4

24. Which of the following pairs has the same size ? **[CBSE AIPMT 2010]**

(a) Zn^{2+} (Z = 21)   (b) Fe^{2+}, Ni^{2+} (c) Zr^{4+}, Ti^{4+} (d) Zr^{4+}, Hf^{4+}

25. Which of the following ions will exhibit colour in aqueous solutions? **[CBSE AIPMT 2010]**

(a) Sc^{3+} (Z = 21)   (b) La^{3+} (Z = 57)   (c) Ti^{3+} (Z = 22)   (d) Lu^{3+} (Z = 71)

26. Which of the following transition metal ions is not coloured? **[AFMC 2010]**

(a) Cu^+ (b) V^{3+} (c) Co^{2+} (d) Ni^{2+}

27. The maximum number of unpaired electrons are present in ...... **[CPMT 2010]**

(a) Fe^{2+} (b) Mn^{2+} (c) Cu^+ (d) Cr^{2+}

28. Which of the following species is/are paramagnetic? Fe^{2+}, Zn^0, Hg^{2+}, Ti^{4+} **[Kerala CEE 2010]**

(a) Fe^{2+} and Zn   (b) Zn^0 and Tl^{4+} (c) Fe^{2+} and Hg^{2+} (d) Zn^0 and Hg^{2+}

29. Which of the ions is colourless inspite of the presence of unpaired electrons?

[MHT CET 2010]

(a) La^{3+} (b) Eu^{3+} (c) Gd^{3+} (d) Lu^{3+}

30. Ce^{4+} is stable. This is because of ...... **[MHT CET 2010]**

(a) half-filled d-orbitals   (b) all paired electrons in d-orbitals

(c) empty orbitals   (d) fully filled d-orbitals

31. The more number of oxidation states are exhibited by actinoids than by lanthanoids. The main reason for this is ...... **[VMMC 2010]**

(a) lesser energy difference between 5f and 6d orbitals than between 4f and 5d orbitals

(b) greater metallic character of lanthanoids than that of corresponding actinoids

(c) more active nature of actinoids

(d) more energy difference between 5f and 6d orbitals than that between rf and 5d orbitals

32. Which of the following statements concerning transition elements is false?

    (a) they are all metals   **[Manipal, JCECE 2010]**

    (b) they easily form complex coordination compounds

    (c) they form compounds containing unpaired electrons and their ions are mostly coloured

    (d) they show multiple oxidation states always differing by units of two

33. Choose the correct reaction to prepare mercurous chloride (calomel).   **(Guj. CET 2010)**

    (a) $HgCl_2 + Hg \rightarrow$ (b) $Hg + Cl_2$

    (c) $HgCl_2 + SnCl_2 \rightarrow$ (d) both options (a) and (c)

34. When Zn is treated with excess of NaOH, the product obtained is ......   **[BVP 2010]**

    (a) $Zn(OH)_2$ (b) $ZnOH$ (c) Na_2ZnO_2 (d) none of these

35. Which of the following is magnetite?   **[VMM 2010]**

    (a) Fe_2CO_3 (b) Fe_2O_3 (c) Fe_3O_4 (d) $Fe_2O_3 \cdot 3H_2O$

36. Out of TiF_6^{2-}, CoF_6^{3-}, Cu_2Cl_2 and $NiCl_4^{2-}$ (Z of Ti = 22, Co = 27, Cu = 29, Ni = 28), the colourless species are ......   **[CBSE AIPMT, AMU 2009]**

    (a) TiF_6^{2-} and CoF_6^{3-} (b) Cu_2Cl_2 and $NiCl^{2-}$

    (c) TiF_6^{2-} and Cu_2Cl_2 (d) CoF_6^{2-} and $NiCl^{2-}$

37. Transition metals show paramagnetic behavior. This is because of their ...... **[AFMC 2009]**

    (a) high lattice energy   (b) variable oxidation state

    (c) characteristic configuration   (d) unpaired electrons

38. For which of the following pairs, magnetic moment is same?   **[AIIMS 2009]**

    (a) $MnCl_2$, $CuSO_4$ (b) $CuCl_2$, $TiCl_3$ (c) TiO_2, $CuSO_4$ (d) $TiCl_3$, $NiCl_2$

39. Which compound is expected to be coloured?   **[CPMT 2009]**

    (a) $CuCl$ (b) CuF_2 (c) Ag_2SO_4 (d) MgF_2

40. The magnetic moment of transition metal ion is $\sqrt{15}$ BM. Therefore, the number of unpaired electrons present in it is ......   **[KCET 2009]**

    (a) 4   (b) 1   (c) 2   (d) 3

41. Which of the following is a man-made element?   **[AFMC 2009]**

    (a) Ra   (b) U   (c) Np   (d) C

42. The maximum oxidation state shown by Mn in its compounds is ......   **[Kerala CEE 2009]**

    (a) +4   (b) +5   (c) +6   (d) +7

43. Which one of the following sets correctly represent the increase in the paramagnetic property of the ions?   **[EAMCET 2009]**

    (a) $Cu^{2+} < V^{2+} < Cr^{2+} < Mn^{2+}$ (b) $Cu^{2+} < Cr^{2+} > V^{2+} > Mn^{2+}$

    (c) $Cu^{2+} < V^{2+} > Cr^{2+} > Mn^{2+}$ (d) $V^2 < Cu^{2+} < Cr^{2+} < Mn^{2+}$

44. The maximum number of unpaired electrons is present in ......   **[MHT CET 2009]**

    (a) Fe   (b) Cu   (c) Co   (d) Ni

45. The ion of least magnetic moment among the following is ......   **[J & K CET 2009]**
    (a) Ti^{2+} (b) Ni^{2+} (c) Co^{2+} (d) Mn^{2+}

46. Out of Cu^{2+}, Ni^{2+}, Co^{2+} and Mn^{2+} those dissolve in dil. HCl only but gives a precipitate when H_2S is passed. Identify the corresponding one.   **[OJEE 2009]**
    (a) Ni^{2+} (b) Cu^{2+} (c) Co^{2+} (d) Mn^{2+}

47. The number of unpaired electrons in Mn^{2+} is ......   **[OJEE 2009]**
    (a) 2   (b) 3   (c) 4   (d) 5

48. What is correct order of spin only magnetic moment (in BM) of Mn^{2+}, Cr^{2+} and Ti^{2+} ?
    [AFMC 2008]

    (a) $Mn^{2+} > Tl^{2+} > Cr^{2+}$ (b) $Ti^{2+} > Cr^{2+} > Mn^{2+}$
    (c) $Mn^{2+} > Cr^{2+} > Ti^{2+}$ (d) $Cr^{2+} > Ti^{2+} > Mn^{2+}$

49. Which of the following compounds is coloured?   **[AIIMS 2008]**
    (a) $TiCl_3$ (b) $FeCl_3$ (c) $CoCl_2$ (d) All of these

50. The pair that is referred as chemical twins is ......   **[MHT CET 2009]**
    (a) Ac, Cf   (b) Hf, Ta   (c) Tc, Re   (d) La, Ac

51. The most basic hydroxide among the following is ......   **[MHT CET 2009]**
    (a) $Lu(OH)_3$ (b) $Eu(OH)_3$ (c) $Yb(OH)_3$ (d) $Ce(OH)_3$

52. Which of the following is not an actinide?   **[AMU 2008]**
    (a) Curium   (b) Californium   (c) Uranium   (d) Terbium

53. Identify the incorrect statement among the following.   **[BHU 2008]**
    (a) d-block elements show irregular and erratic chemical properties among themselves.
    (b) La and Ku have partially filled d-orbitals and no other partially filled orbital.
    (c) The chemistry of various lanthanoids is very similar.
    (d) 4f and 5f orbitals are equally shielded.

54. Which of the following pairs of transition metal ions are stronger oxidizing agents in aqueous solutions?   **[Kerala CEE 2008]**
    (a) V^{2+} and Cr^{2+} (b) Ti^{2+} and Cr^{2+} (c) Mn^{3+} and Co^{3+} (d) V^{2+} and Fe^{2+}
    (e) Ni^{2+} and Fe^{2+}

55. Which of the following group of transition metals is celled coinage metals?   **[RPMT 2008]**
    (a) Cu, Ag, Au   (b) Ru, Rh, Pd   (c) Fe, Co, Ni   (d) Os, Ir, Pt

56. Mercury is a liquid metal because ......   **[KCET 2008]**
    (a) it has a completely filled s-orbital
    (b) it has a small atomic size
    (c) it has a completely filled j-orbital that prevents d-d overlapping of orbitals
    (d) it has a completely filled j-orbital that causes d-d overlapping

57. Potassium dichromate is used ......   **[Guj. CET 2008]**
    (a) in electroplating.
    (b) as a reducing agent.
    (c) oxidise ferrous ions into ferric ions in acidic media as an oxidizing agent.
    (d) as an insecticide.

58. Which one of the following statements is not true with regard to transition elements?

[J & K 2008]

(a) they readily form complex compounds   (b) they show variable oxidation states

(c) all their ions are colourless

(d) the ions contain partially filled d-electrons

59. The point of dissimilarity between lanthanides and actinides is ......   **[MHT CET 2008]**

(a) three outermost shells are partially filled.

(b) they show oxidation state of +3 (common).

(c) they are called inner-transition elements.

(d) they are radioactive in nature.

60. The most common oxidation states of Ce (cerium) are......   **[MHT CET 2008]**

(a) +3, +4   (b) +2, +3   (c) +2, +4   (d) +3, +5

61. The correct order of ionic radii of Y^{3+}, La^{3+}, Eu^{3+} and Lu^{3+} is ......   **[Kerala CEE 2007]**

(a) $Y^{3+} < La^{3+} < Eu^{3+} < Lu^{3+}$ (b) $Lu^{3+} < Eu^{3+} < La^{3+} < Y^{3+}$

(c) $Eu^{3+} < Eu^{3+} < Eu^{3+} < Y^{3+}$ (d) $Y^{3+} < Lu^{3+} < Eu^{3+} < La^{3+}$

62. Among the following series of transition metal ions, the one in which all metal ions have $3d^2$, $3p^6$ electronic configuration is (At. No. Ti = 22, V = 23, Cr = 24, Mn = 25) ......

[Manipal 2007]

(a) Ti^{3+}, V^{2+}, Cr^{3+}, Mn^{4+} (b) Ti^{+}, V^{4+}, Cr^{6+}, Mn^{7+}

(c) Ti^{4+}, V^{2+}, Cr^{3+}, Mn^{3+} (d) Ti^{2+}, V^{2+}, Cr^{4+}, Mn^{5+}

63. Among K, Ca, Fe and Zn, the element which can form more than one binary compound with chlorine is ......   **[Manipal 2007]**

(a) Fe   (b) Zn   (c) K   (d) Ca

64. Which one of the following ions is most stable in aqueous solution? (At. No. of Ti = 22, V = 23, Cr = 24, Mn = 25)   **[CBSE AIPMT 2007]**

(a) Cr^{3+} (b) V^{3+} (c) Ti^{3+} (d) Mn^{3+}

65. Acidified potassium permanganate solution is decolourised by ......   **[AFMC 2007]**

(a) bleaching powder   (b) white vitriol   (c) Mohr's salt   (d) microcosmic salt

66. **Assertion :** Mercury vapour is shining silvery in appearance.   **[AIIMS 2007]**

Reason : Mercury is a metal with shining silvery appearance.

(a) Both Assertion and Reason are true and Reason is the correct explanation of Assertion.

(b) Both Assertion and Reason are true but Reason is not the correct explanation of Assertion.

(c) Assertion is true but Reason is false

(d) Both Assertion and Reason are false.

67. Four successive members of the first row of transition elements are listed below with their atomic numbers. Which one of them is expected to have the highest third ionization enthalpy?   **[CBSE AIPMT 2005]**

(a) Vanadium (Z = 23)   (b) Chromium (Z = 24)   (c) Iron (Z = 26)   (d) Manganese (Z = 25)

68. **Assertion :** Solution of Na_2CrO_4 in water is intensely coloured.

    Reason : Oxidation state of Cr in Na_2CrO_4 is + VI.   **[AIIMS 2003]**

    (a) Both Assertion and Reason are true and Reason is the correct explanation of Assertion.

    (b) Both Assertion and Reason are true and Reason is not the correct explanation of Assertion.

    (c) Assertion is true but Reason is false.

    (d) Both Assertion and Reason are false

69. Which of the following is more soluble in ammonia?   **[MHT CET 2003]**

    (a) AgCl   (b) AgBr   (c) Agl   (d) None of these

70. The basic character of transition metal monoxides follows the order ......

    (At. No. Ti = 22, V = 23, Cr = 24, Fe = 26)   **[CBSE AIPMT 2003]**

    (a) TiO > FeO > VO > CrO   (b) TiO > VO > CrO > FeO

    (c) VO > CrO > TiO > FeO   (d) CrO > VO > FeO > TiO

71. The colourless species is ......   **[AIIMS 2003]**

    (a) VCl_3 (b) $VOSO_4$ (c) Na_3VO_4 (d) $[V(H_2O)_6]SO_4H_2O$

72. Lanthanides are ......   **[Manipal 2007]**

    (a) 14 elements in the sixth period (At. No. = 90 to 103) that are filling 4f sub-level.

    (b) 14 elements in the seventh period (At. No. = 90 to 103) that are filling 5f sub-level

    (c) 14 elements in the sixth period (At. No. =58 to 71) that are filling 4f sub-level.

    (d) 14 elements in the seventh period (At. No. = 58 to 71) that are filling 4f sub-level.

73. Which of the following is not an actinoid?

    (a) Am   (b) Cm   (c) Fm   (d) Tm

74. The lanthanoid contraction is responsible for the fact that ......   **[Guj.CET 2006]**

    (a) Zr and Y have about the same radius.   (b) Zr and Nb have similar oxidation state.

    (c) Zr and Hf have about the same radius.   (d) Zr and Zn have the same oxidation sate.

75. Europium is ......   **[DUMET 2005]**

    (a) s-block element   (b) p-block element

    (c) d-block element   (d) f-block element

76. Lanthanides and actinides resemble in ......   **[AFMC 2004]**

    (a) electronic configuration   (b) oxidation state

    (c) ionization energy   (d) formation of complexes

77. Which of the following lanthanides is commonly used in the manufacture of alloys?

                    [Manipal 2004]

    (a) Lanthanum   (b) Nobelium   (c) Thorium   (d) Cerium

78. The atomic size of cerium and promethium are quite close because ......   **[JCECE 2004]**

    (a) they are in same period of the periodic table

    (b) their electronic configuration is same

    (c) f-electrons have poor shielding effect

    (d) nuclear charge is higher on cerium than promethium

79. Lanthanide for which +2 and +3 oxidation states are common is ......　　**[AIIMS 2003]**

(a) La　　　　　(b) Nd　　　　　(c) Ce　　　　　(d) Eu

80. $KMnO_4$ react with ferrous sulphate according to the equation　　**[MHTCET 2001]**

$$MnO_4^- + 5Fe^{2+} + 8H^+ \rightarrow Mn^{2+} + 5Fe^{3+} + 4H_2O$$

Here 10 ml of 0.1 $KMnO_4$ is equivalent to ......

(a) 20 ml of 0.1 M $FeSO_4$　　　　　　　(b) 30 ml of 0.1 M $FeSO_4$

(c) 40 ml of 0.1 M $FeSO_4$　　　　　　　(d) 50 ml of 0.1 M $FeSO_4$

81. General electronic configuration of lanthanides is ......　　**[MHTCET 2001]**

(a) $(n-2) f^{1-14} (n-1) d^{0-1} ns^2$　　　　　(b) $(n-2) f^{10-11} (n-1) d^{0-1} ns^2$

(c) $(n-2) f^{0-14} (n-1) d^{10} ns^2$　　　　　(d) $(n-2) f^{0-1} (n-1) f^{1-14} ns^2$

82. Among the following, the coloured compound is ......　　**[CBSE PMT 2004, 05]**

(a) CuCl　　　(b) $K_3[Cu(CN)_4]$　　　(c) CuF_2　　　(d) $[Cu(CH_3CN)_4] BF_4$

83. In the extraction of silver, Ag_2S is dissolved in ......　　**(A.F.M.C. 2001)**

(a) HCl　　　(b) HNO_3　　　(c) KCN　　　(d) H_2SO_4

84. Zn gives H_2 gas with H_2SO_4 and HCl but not with HNO_3 because ...　　**[C.B.S.E. P.M.T. 2002]**

(a) Zn acts as an oxidising agent when react with HNO_3

(b) HNO_3 is weaker acid than H_2SO_4 and HCl

(c) In electrochemical series, Zn is above hydrogen

(d) NO_3^- ion is reduced in preference to hydronium ion

85. Copper is extracted from copper pyrites ore by heating in a blast furnace. The method is based on the principle that ......　　**[Manipal P.M.T. 2002, A.F.M.C. 2002]**

(a) Copper has more affinity for oxygen than sulphur at high temperature

(b) Iron has less affinity for oxygen than sulphur at high temperature

(c) Sulphur has less affinity for oxygen at high temperature

(d) Copper has less affinity for oxygen than sulphur at high temperature

86. An atom has electronic configuration $1s^2 2s^2 2p^6 3s^2 3p^6 3d^3 4s^2$. In which group would it be placed ?　　**[C.B.S.E. P.M.T. 2002]**

(a) Fifth　　　　　(b) Fifteenth　　　　　(c) Second　　　　　(d) Third

87. In acidic medium, $KMnO_4$ oxidises $FeSO_4$ solution. Which of the following statements is correct ?　　**[D.P.M.T. 2002]**

(a) 10 ml of 1 N $KMnO_4$ solution oxidises 10 ml of 5 N $FeSO_4$ solution

(b) 10 ml of 1 M $KMnO_4$ solution oxidises 10 ml of 5 M $FeSO_4$ solution

(c) 10 ml of 1 M $KMnO_4$ solution oxidises 10 ml of 1 M $FeSO_4$ solution

(d) 10 ml of 1 N $KMnO_4$ solution oxidises 10 ml of 0.1 M $FeSO_4$ solution

88. Which of the following is highly corrosive salt ?

(a) $FeCl_2$　　　(b) $PbCl_2$　　　(c) Hg_2Cl_2　　　(d) $HgCl_2$

89. Non-lanthanide atom is ......　　**[J and K 2002]**

(a) La　　　　　(b) Lu　　　　　(c) Pr　　　　　(d) Pm

90. Nessler's reagent is ......　　　　　　　　　　**[U.P.C.P.M.T. 2002]**
  (a) Potassium iodide in mercuric iodide　　　(b) $TiCl_4$
  (c) Anhydrous $AlCl_3$　　　　　　　　　　　(d) Al_2O_3/Cr_2O_3

91. Green vitriol is ......　　　　　　　　　　　　**[J.I.P.M.E.R. 2002]**
  (a) $FeSO_4.7H_2O$　　(b) $ZnSO_4.7H_2O$　　(c) $CaSO_4.2H_2O$　　(d) $CuSO_4.5H_2O$

92. The amount of $K_2Cr_2O_7$ (eq. wt. 49.04) required to prepare 100 ml of its 0.05 N solution is ...
　　　　　　　　　　　　　　　　　　　　　　[J.I.P.M.E.R. 2002]
  (a) 2.9424 g　　(b) 0.4904 g　　(c) 1.4712 g　　(d) 0.2452 g

93. Which of the following does not have valence electron in 3d-subshell ?　　**[A.I.I.M.S. 2002]**
  (a) Fe(III)　　(b) Mn(II)　　(c) Cr(I)　　(d) P(0)

94. Which of the following compounds has colour but no unpaired electrons ?　　**[J & K 2002]**
  (a) $KMnO_4$　　(b) K_2MnO_4　　(c) $MnSO_4$　　(d) $MnCl_2$

95. In which of the following lanthanides, oxidation state +2 is most stable ?　　**(J & K 2002)**
  (a) Ce　　(b) Eu　　(c) Tb　　(d) Dy

96. The basic character of the transition metal monoxides follows the order ......
　　　　　　　　　　　　　　　　　　　　　　[C.B.S.E. P.M.T. 2003]
  (a) VO > CrO > TiO > FeO　　　　　(b) CrO > VO > FeO > TiO
  (c) TiO > FeO > VO > CrO　　　　　(d) TiO > VO > CrO > FeO

97. Among the following series of transition metal ions, the one where all metal ions have $3d^2$ electronic configuration is ......　　**[C.B.S.E. P.M.T. 2004]**
  (a) $Ti^{3+}, V^{2+}, Cr^{3+}, Mn^{4+}$　　　　(b) $Ti^+, V^{4+}, Cr^{6+}, Mn^{7+}$
  (c) $Ti^{4+}, V^{3+}, Cr^{2+}, Mn^{3+}$　　　　(d) $Ti^{2+}, V^{3+}, Cr^{4+}, Mn^{5+}$
  (At. Nos. of Ti = 22, V = 23, Cr = 24, Mn = 25)

98. Which one of the following forms with an excess of CN^- (cyanide), a complex having coordination number two ?　　　　　　　　　　**[A.I.I.M.S. 2004]**
  (a) Cu^+　　(b) Ag^+　　(c) Ni^{2+}　　(d) Fe^{2+}

99. Misch metal is ......　　　　　　　　　　　**[H.P. P.M.T. 2005]**
  (a) an alloy of aluminium
  (b) a mixture of chromium and lead chromate
  (c) an alloy of lanthanoid metals
  (d) an alloy of copper

100. $KMnO_4$ can be prepared from K_2MnO_4 as per the reaction:
$$3MnO_4^{2-} + 2H_2O \rightarrow 2MnO_4^- + MnO_2 + 4OH^-$$
  The reaction can go to completion by removing OH^- ions by adding ......　　**[NEET 2013]**
  (a) KOH　　(b) CO_2　　(c) SO_2　　(d) HCl

101. Which of the following lanthanoid ions is diamagnetic?　　　　**[NEET 2013]**
  (At. No. of Ce = 58, Sm = 62, Eu = 63, Yb = 70)
  (a) Ce^{2+}　　(b) Sm^{2+}　　(c) Eu^{2+}　　(d) Yb^{2+}

ANSWER KEY

1. (c)	2. (c)	3. (d)	4. (c)	5. (d)	6. (c)	7. (c)	8. (d)
9. (a)	10. (c)	11. (a)	12. (c)	13.(d)	14. (d)	15. (a)	16. (d)
17. (a)	18. (d)	19. (b)	20. (d)	21. (d)	22. (b)	23. (c)	24. (a)
25. (b)	26. (a)	27. (a)	28. (b)	29. (c)	30. (d)	31. (d)	32. (b)
33. (c)	34. (a)	35. (b)	36. (a)	37. (c)	38. (b)	39. (b)	40. (b)
41. (a)	42. (d)	43. (a)	44. (a)	45. (c)	46. (b)	47. (c)	48. (c)
49. (b)	50. (b)	51. (b)	52. (a)	53. (a)	54. (b)	55. (b)	56. (d)
57. (a)	58. (a)	59. (a)	60. (a)	61. (b)	62. (c)	63. (b)	64. (a)
65. (b)	66. (b)	67. (c)	68. (d)	69. (c)	70. (b)	7.1 (a)	72. (b)
73. (b)	74. (b)	75. (a)	76. (c)	77. (b)	78. (a)	79. (a)	80. (a)
81. (a)	82. (d)	83. (d)	84. (c)	85. (a)	86. (b)	87. (d)	88. (c)
89. (c)	90. (a)	91. (a)	92. (a)	93. (a)	94. (c)	95. (a)	96. (b)
97. (d)	98. (d)	99. (c)	100. (d)	101. (a)	102. (c)	103. (b)	104. (c)
105. (c)	106. (d)	107. (b)	108. (d)	109. (d)	110. (d)	111. (c)	112. (a)
113. (c)	114. (b)	115. (a)	116. (b)	117. (c)	118. (a)	119. (b)	120. (a)
121. (b)	122. (c)	123. (c)	124. (c)	125. (b)	126. (c)	127. (a)	128. (d)
129. (a)	130. (b)	131. (b)	132. (b)	133. (a)	134. (a)	135. (d)	136. (c)
137. (a)	138. (a)	139. (d)	140. (a)	141. (a)	142. (b)	143. (b)	144. (d)
145. (d)	146. (a)	147. (a)	148. (b)	149. (a)	150. (a)	151. (b)	152. (d)
153. (c)	154. (b)	155. (a)	156. (c)	157. (b)	158. (a)	159. (a)	160. (b)
161. (d)	162. (a)	163. (b)	164. (b)	165. (a)	166. (a)	167. (a)	168. (a)
169. (b)	170. (b)	171. (b)	172. (b)				

Previous Years Questions

1. (a)	2. (a)	3. (d)	4. (d)	5. (b)	6. (a)	7. (d)	8. (d)
9. (a)	10. (c)	11. (a)	12. (b)	13. (c)	14. (c)	15. (d)	16. (d)
17. (b)	18. (a)	19. (b)	20. (b)	21. (a)	22. (c)	23. (d)	24. (d)
25. (c)	26. (a)	27. (b)	28. (c)	29. (d)	30. (c)	31. (a)	32. (d)
33. (d)	34. (c)	35. (c)	36. (c)	37. (d)	38. (b)	39. (b)	40. (d)
41. (c)	42. (d)	43. (a)	44. (a)	45. (a)	46. (b)	47. (d)	48. (c)
49. (d)	50. (c)	51. (d)	52. (d)	53. (d)	54. (c)	55. (a)	56. (c)
57. (c)	58. (c)	59. (d)	60. (c)	61. (d)	62. (d)	63. (a)	64. (d)
65. (c)	66. (d)	67. (d)	68. (b)	69. (a)	70. (b)	71. (c)	72. (c)
73. (d)	74. (c)	75. (d)	76. (b)	77. (d)	78. (c)	79. (d)	80. (d)
81. (a)	82. (c)	83. (c)	84. (d)	85. (a)	86. (a)	87. (b)	88. (d)
89. (a)	90. (a)	91. (a)	92. (d)	93. (d)	94. (a)	95. (b)	96. (d)
97. (d)	98. (b)	99. (c)	100. (b)	101. (d)			

COORDINATION COMPOUNDS

1. Which one of the following is a bidentate ligand with a –2 charge ?

   (a) SCN^- (b) Cl^- (c) Oxalate   (d) Ethylene diamine

2. Which of the following ligands is called chelating ligand?

   (a) Ethane-1, 2-diamine   (b) Oxalate

   (c) Acetate   (d) All are chelating ligands

3. The denticity of dimethyl glyoxime, glycinato, diethylene triamine and EDTA are respectively ......

   (a) 2, 2, 3 and 4   (b) 2, 2, 3 and 6   (c) 2, 2, 2 and 6   (d) 2, 3, 3 and 6

4. Co-ordination number of cobalt in $[Co(en)_2Cl_2]^+$ is ......

   (a) 2   (b) 4   (c) 6   (d) 8

5. What is incorrect about O^-COCOO^- ?

   (a) It is called oxalate   (b) It can produce chelate

   (c) It is symmetrical bidentate ligand   (d) It is tetradentate ligand

6. Co-ordination number of copper in cuprammonium sulphate is ......

   (a) 2   (b) 4   (c) 6   (d) 8

7. What is incorrect about glycenato ion ?

   (a) Its formula is $H_2\overset{..}{N}–CH_2–COO^-$ (b) It is symmetrical bidentate ligand

   (c) It is a chelating ligand   (d) It is unsymmetrical bidentate ligand

8. According to Werner's theory, the secondary valencies of the central metal atom correspond to its ......

   (a) Co-ordination state   (b) Oxidation number

   (c) Any of the two   (d) Neither of the two

9. The formula for the compound tris (ethane-1, 2-diamine) cobalt(III) sulphate is ......

   (a) $[Co(en)_3]SO_4$ (b) $[Co(SO)_4(en)_3]$

   (c) $[Cr(H_2O)_6(NO_3)_3]$ (d) $[Co(en)_3]_2(SO_4)_3$

10. Co-ordination number of Ni in nickel-DMG complex is ......

    (a) 2   (b) 3   (c) 6   (d) 4

11. Which of the following is antidote for lead poisoning?

    (a) $CoCl_3$ (b) Cisplatin   (c) EDTA   (d) Dmg

12. If oxidation state of cobalt in the complex is same as that of iron in $K_3[Fe(CN)_6]$, find the value of X in the given complex.

$$\left[(NH_3)_4Co \overset{\displaystyle OH}{\underset{\displaystyle OH}{<\;\;>}} Co(NH_3) \right] (SO_4)_x$$

   (a) 1   (b) 2   (c) 3   (d) 0

13. Which among the following is most likely structure of $CrCl_3 \cdot 6H_2O$ if $1/3^{rd}$ of total chlorine of the compound is precipitated by adding $AgNO_3$ to its aqueous solution ?

    (a) $[CrCl(H_2O)_5]Cl_2 \cdot H_2O$ (b) $[CrCl_2(H_2O)_4]Cl_2H_2O$

    (c) $[CrCl(H_2O)_3](H_2O)_3$ (d) $[CrCl_3 \cdot 6H_2O]$

14. Which is the most stable complex among the following at 298°K ?

    (a) $[CdCl_4]^{2-}$ (b) $[Cd(Br_4)]^{2-}$ (c) $[CdI_4]^{2-}$ (d) $[Cd(CN)_4]^{2-}$

15. The co-ordination number and charge on the cobalt ion in the complex trans-bis [ethylene diamine chloro-hydroxocobalt(III)] cation are ......

    (a) +1, 6   (b) −1, 6   (c) +3, 4   (d) +2, 6

16. Which among the following complex is Zeisse's salt?

    (a) $[(C_6H_5)_3P]_3RhCl$ (b) $K[PtCl_3(n^2-C_2H_2)]$ (c) $[Co(en)_2Cl_2]^+$ (d) $[Pt(NH_3)_2Cl_2]$

17. Geometrical isomerism is exhibited by ......

    (a) $[Pt(NH_3)_2Cl_2]$ (b) $[Pt(NH_3)_3]$ (c) $[Pt(NH_3)_2Cl]$ (d) $[PtCl(NH_3)_3]$

18. Ionisation isomerism is exhibited by ......

    (a) $[Cr(NH_3)_6]Cl_3$ (b) $[Cr(en)_2]Cl_2$ (c) $[Cr(en)_3]Cl_3$ (d) $[Co(NH_3)_5Br]SO_4$

19. Square planar structure is exhibited by ......

    (a) $[Co(NH_3)_6]^{3+}$ (b) $[NiCl_4]^2$ (c) $[Ni(CN)_4]^2$ (d) All of these

20. Which one of the following complexes is an outer orbital complex?

    (a) $[Fe(CN)_6]^{4-}$ (b) $[Mn(CN)_6]^{4-}$ (c) $[Co(H_2O)_6]^{3+}$ (d) $[Co(NH_3)_6]^{3+}$

21. Which among the following is an example of octahedral complex ?

    (a) $[FeF_6]^{3-}$ (b) $[Zn(NH_3)_4]^{2+}$ (c) $[Ni(CN)_4]^{2-}$ (d) $[Cu(NH_4)_4]^{2+}$

22. Which among the following is a paramagnetic complex ?

    (a) $[Ni(H_2O)_6]^{2+}$ (b) $[Ni(CO)_4]$ (c) $[Zn(NH_3)_4]^{2+}$ (d) $[Co(NH_3)_6]^{3+}$

23. IUPAC name of $Na_3[Co(NO_2)_6]$ is ......

    (a) Sodium cobaltinitrite   (b) Sodium hexanitritocobaltate(III)

    (c) Sodium hexanitrocobalt(III)   (d) Sodium hexanitrocobaltate(III)

24. The catalyst used for the polymerisation of olefin is ......

    (a) Ziegler-Natta catalyst   (b) Wilkinson's catalyst

    (c) Zeolite   (d) Zeise's salt catalyst

25. The EAN of metal atoms in $Fe(CO)_2(NO)_2$ and $Co_2(CO)_8$ respectively are ......

    (a) 34, 35   (b) 34, 36   (c) 36, 36   (d) 36, 35

26. Which isomerism is exhibited by $[Co(en)_2(NCS)_2]Cl$ and $[Co(en)_2(NCS)Cl]NCS$?

    (a) Co-ordination   (b) Ionisation   (c) Linkage   (d) Cis-trans isomerism

27. Which isomerism is exhibited by $[Rh(en)_2Cl_2][Ir(en)Cl_4]$ and $[Ir(en)_3][RhCl_6]$?

    (a) Linkage   (b) Ionisation   (c) Co-ordination (d) Position

28. Which isomerism exhibited by $[PtCl_2(NH_3)_4]Br_2$ and $[PtBr_2(NH_3)_4]Cl_2$ constitute a pair of ......

    (a) Co-ordination   (b) Linkage   (c) Optical   (d) Ionisation

29. Which among the following show both geometrical and optical isomerism ?

   (a) $[Pt(NH_3)_2Cl_2]$ (b) $[Pt(NH_3)Cl_4]$ (c) $[Pt(en)_3]^{4+}$ (d) $[Pt(en)_2Cl_2]$

30. AgCl dissolves in NH_4OH due to the formation of ......

   (a) $[Ag(NH_4)_2Cl]$ (b) $[Ag(NH_4)_3]Cl$ (c) $[Ag(NH_3)_2]Cl$ (d) $[Ag(NH_3)_2OH]$

31. The geometry of $Ni(CO)_4$ and $Ni(PPh_3)_2Cl_2$ are ......

   (a) Both square and planar   (b) Tetrahedral and square planar

   (c) Both tetrahedral   (d) Square planar and tetrahedral

32. Which among the following does not show optical activity?

   (a) $[Pt(Br)(Cl)(I)(NO_2)(C_5H_5N)(NH_3)]^-$ (b) cis - $[Co(en)_2Cl_2]^+$

   (c) $[Co(en)(NH_3)_2Cl_2]^+$ (d) trans - $[Cr(NH_3)_4Cl_2]^+$

33. Which of the following is paramagnetic ?

   (a) $[Co(NH_3)_6]^{3+}$ (b) $[Ni(CO)_4]$ (c) $[Ni(NH_3)_4]^{2+}$ (d) $[Ni(CN)_4]^{2-}$

34. IUPAC name of $[PtCl(NO_2)(NH_3)_4]SO_4$ is ......

   (a) Tetraaminechloronitroplatinum(IV) sulphate

   (b) Chlorotetraamine nitroplatinum(IV) sulphate

   (c) Chloronitrotetraamineplatinum(IV) sulphate

   (d) None of these

35. IUPAC name for $K_2[PtCl_6]$ is ......

   (a) Potassium hexachloroplatinate(II)   (b) Potassium hexachloroiodoplatinate(IV)

   (c) Platinum hexachloroplatinate(I)   (d) None of these

36. Which of the following complexes is more conducting?

   (a) $CoCl_3.\ 3NH_3$ (b) $CoCl_3.\ 6NH_3$ (c) $CoCl_2.\ 4NH_3$ (d) $CoCl_3.\ 5NH_3$

37. The IUPAC name for $(NH_4)_3[Cr(SCN)_6]$ is

   (a) Ammonium hexathiocyanato-chromate(II)

   (b) Ammonium hexathiocyanato-S-chromate(II)

   (c) Ammonium hexathiocyanato-S-chromate(III)

   (d) Ammonium hexathiocyanato-N-chromate(III)

38. The IUPAC name for $H_4[Pt(CN)_6]$ is ......

   (a) Hydrohexacyanoplatinate(II)   (b) Hexacyanotetrahydridoplatinate(IV)

   (c) Hexacyanoplatinic(II) acid   (d) None of the above

39. The IUPAC name for

$$\left[(NH_3)_4Co \overset{\displaystyle O_2N}{\underset{\displaystyle NH}{\diagup \diagdown}} Co(NH_3)_4 \right]^{3+} \text{ is } ...$$

   (a) tetraamine cobalt (II)–μ–imido–u–nitrotetraamine cobalt (II) ion

   (b) bis [tetraamine]–μ–imido–μ–nitrocobalt(II) ion

   (c) bis [tetraamine]–μ–imido–μ–nitrocobalt(III) ion

   (d) tetraamine cobalt(III)–μ–imido–μ–nitrotetraamine cobalt(III) ion

40. Ferrocene is ......

(a) $Fe\,(\eta_5\text{–}C_5H_5)_2$ (b) $Fe\,(\eta_5 - C_5H_5)_4$ (c) $Fe\,(\eta_5 - C_5H_9)_4$ (d) None of these

41. The IUPAC name for

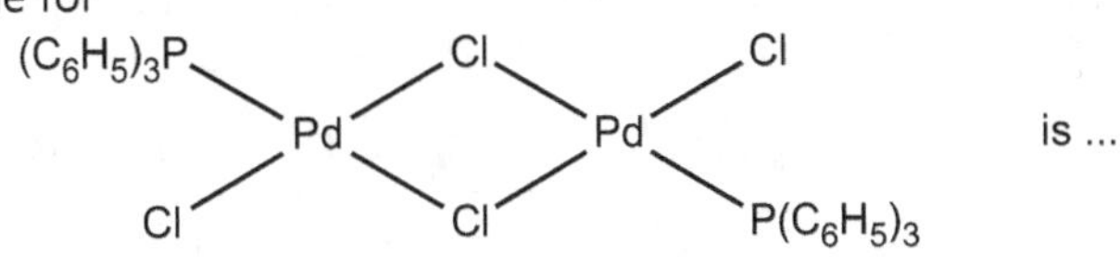

is ...

(a) Chlorotriphenylphosphine palladium(II)–μ-dichloro triphenyl phosphine palladium(II)

(b) Chlorotriphenyl phosphine palladium(III)

  –μ–dichlorochlorotripenyl phosphine palladium(II)

(c) Triphenylphosphine chloropalladium(II)

  –μ–dichlorotriphenyl phosphinechloropalladium(II)

(d) Triphenyl phosphinechloropalladium(III)

  –μ–dichlorotriphenyl phosphine chloropalladium(III)

42. The IUPAC name for $[Co(NH_3)_5(ONO)]SO_4$ is ......

(a) Pentaamine nitro cobalt(II) sulphate (b) Pentaamine nitro cobalt(III) sulphate

(c) Pentaamine nitrito-o-cobalt(II) sulphate (d) Pentaamine nitrito cobalt(III) sulphate

43. 'Cisplatin' used in cancer chemotherapy is ......

(a) cis $[PtCl_2(NH_3)_2]$ (b) trans $[PtCl_2(H_2O)_2]$

(c) cis $[AgCl_2(NH_3)_2]$ (d) trans $[AgCl_2(H_2O_2]$

44. In the brown ring complex $[Fe(H_2O)_5NO]SO_4$, the oxidation state of Fe is ......

(a) 0 (b) +1 (c) +2 (d) +3

45. The complexes $[Co(NH_3)_5(ONO)]Cl_2$ and $[Co(NH_3)_5NO_2]Cl_2$ are examples of ......

(a) Ionisation isomers (b) Co-ordination isomers

(c) Linkage isomers (d) Geometrical isomers

46. The correct order of magnetic moments is ......

(a) $[MnCl_4]^{2-} > [CoCl_4]^{2-} > [Fe(CN)_6]^{4-}$ (b) $MnCl_4]^{2-} > [Fe(CN)_6]^{4-} > [CoCl_4]^{2-}$

(c) $[Fe(CN)_6]^{4-} > [MnCl_4]^{2-} > [CoCl_4]^{2-}$ (d) $[Fe(CN)_6]^{4-} > [CoCl_4]^{2-} > [MnCl_4]^{2-}$

47. Which of the following complex ions is diamagnetic?

(a) $[NiCl_4]^{2-}$ (b) $[CoCl_4]^{2-}$ (c) $[Ni(CN)_4]^{2-}$ (d) $[Cu(NH_3)_4]^{2+}$

48. Which of the following cation does not form an amine complex with excess of ammonia ?

(a) Na^+ (b) Co^{2+} (c) Cu^{2+} (d) AgY

49. Mixture X = 0.02 mol of $[Co(NH_3)_5SO_4]Br$ and 0.02 mol of $[Co(NH_3)_5Br]SO_4$ was prepared in 2 litres of solution

  1 litre of mixture X + excess $AgNO_3 \rightarrow Y$

  1 litre of mixture X + excess $BaCl_2 \rightarrow Z$

Number of moles of Y and Z are ......

(a) 0.01, 0.01 (b) 0.02, 0.01 (c) 0.01, 0.02 (d) 0.02, 0.02

50. Which of the following organometallic compound is σ and π bonded ?

(a) $Fe(CH_3)_3$　　(b) $[Fe(\eta^5–C_5H_5)_2]$　　(c) $[Co(CO)_5NH_3]^{2+}$　(d) $K[PtCl_3(\eta^2–C_2H_4)]$

51. Co-ordination number of Fe in the complexes $[Fe(CN)_6]^{4-}$, $[Fe(CN)_6]^{3-}$ and $[FeCl_4]^-$ would be respectively ......

(a) 2, 3, 3　　　　(b) 6, 6, 4　　　　(c) 6, 3, 3　　　　(d) 6, 4, 6

52. On hydrolysis, $(Me)_2SiCl_2$ will produce ......

(a) $(Me)_2Si(OH)_2$　　　　　　　　(b) $(Me)_2SiO$

(c) $–[–O–(Me)_2Si–O]n$　　　　　　(d) $Me_2SiCl(OH)$

53. $CuSO_4$ reacts with KCN solution and forms ......

(a) $Cu(CN)_2$　　(b) $CuCN$　　　　(c) $K_2[Cu(CN)_4]$　　(d) $K_3[Cu(CN)_4]$

54. In the process of extraction of gold,

Roasted gold ore $+ CN^- + H_2O \xrightarrow{O_2} [X] + OH^-$

$[X] + Zn \rightarrow [Y] + ACl$

Identify the complexes [X] and [Y].

(a) $X = [Au(CN)_2]^-$, $Y = [Zn(CN)_4]^{2-}$　　　　(b) $X = [Au(CN)_4]^{3-}$, $Y = [Zn(CN)_4]^{2-}$

(c) $X = [Au(CN)_2]^-$, $Y = [Zn(CN)_6]^{4-}$　　　　(d) $X = [Au(CN)_4]^-$, $Y = [Zn(CN)_4]^{2-}$

55. A solution of potassium ferrocyanide would contain ________ ions.

(a) 2　　　　　　(b) 3　　　　　　(c) 4　　　　　　(d) 5

56. Which one of the following complexes is an outer orbital complex?

(a) $[Co(NH_3)_6]^{3+}$　　(b) $[Mn(CN)_6]^+$　　(c) $[Fe(CN)_6]^{4-}$　　(d) $[Ni(NH_3)_6]^{2+}$

Atomic Nos. : Mn = 25, Fe = 26, Co = 27, Ni = 28

57. Which one of the following has largest number of isomers?

(a) $[Ir(PP_3)_2H(CO)]^{2+}$　　(b) $[Co(NH_3)_5Cl]^{2+}$　　(c) $[Ru(NH_3)_4Cl_2]^+$　(d) $[Co(en)_2Cl_2]^+$

58. Which kind of isomerism is exhibited by octahedral complex trans-$Co(NH_3)_4Br_2Cl$?

(a) Geometrical and ionisation　　　　(b) Geometrical and optical

(c) Optical and ionisation　　　　　　(d) Geometrical only

59. An aqueous solution of $CoCl_2$ on addition of excess of conc. HCl turns blue due to the formation of ......

(a) $[Co(H_2O)_4Cl_2]$　　(b) $[Co(H_2O)_2Cl_4]^{2-}$　　(c) $[CoCl_4]^{2-}$　　(d) $[Co(H_2O)_2Cl_2]$

60. The correct order for the wavelength of absorption in the visible region is ......

(a) $[Ni(NO_3)_6]^{4-} < [Ni(NH_3)_6]^{2+} < [Ni(H_2O)_6]^{2+}$　　(b) $[Ni(NO_2)_6]^{4-} < [Ni(H_2O)_6]^{2+} < [Ni(NH_3)_6]^{2+}$

(c) $[Ni(NH_3)_6]^{2+} < [Ni(H_2O)_6]^{2+} < [Ni(NO_2)_6]^{4-}$　　(d) $[Ni(H_2O)_6]^{2+} < [Ni(NH_3)_6]^{2+} < [Ni(NO_2)_6]^{4-}$

61. In which of the following pairs of complexes show optical isomerism?

(a) Cis $– [Cr(C_2O_4)_2Cl_2]^{3-}$, Cis $– [Co(NH_3)_4Cl_2]$　　(b) $(Co(en)_3)Cl_3$, Cis $– [Co(en)_2Cl_2]Cl$

(c) $[PtCl(dien)]Cl$, $[NiCl_2Br_2]^{2-}$　　　　　　(d) $[Co(NO_3)_3(NH_3)_3]$, Cis–$[Pt(en)_2Cl_2]$

62. Optical isomerism is exhibited by ......

(a) $[Cu(NH_3)_4]^{2+}$　　(b) $[ZnCl_4]^{2-}$　　　　(c) $[Cr(C_2O_4)_3]^{3-}$　　(d) $[Co(CN)_6]^{3-}$

63. Which among the following is not paramagnetic?

(a) $[Ag(NH_3)_2]Cl$　　　(b) NO_2　　　(c) $[Cu(NH_3)_4]Cl_2$　(d) NO

64. The number of d-electrons in $[Cr(H_2O)_6]^{3+}$ [At. No. of Cr = 24] is ......

(a) 2　　　(b) 5　　　(c) 4　　　(d) 3

65. The number of chloride ions produced by complex tetraminechloroplatinum(IV) chloride in an aqueous solution is ......

(a) Three　　　(b) Two　　　(c) Four　　　(d) One

66. Which among the following is not an organometallic compound ?

(a) Grignard reagent　　(b) Zeise's salt　　(c) Cisplatin　　(d) Ferrocene

67. According to the postulates of Werner for coordination compounds ......

(a) Primary valency is ionisable

(b) Secondary valency is ionisable

(c) Primary and secondary valencies are non-ionisable

(d) Only primary valency is non-ionisable

68. Which one has the highest paramagnetism among the following ions?

(a) $[Cu(H_2O)_6]^{2+}$　　　(b) $[Cr(H_2O)_6]^{3+}$　　　(c) $[Fe(H_2O)_6]^{2+}$　　　(d) $[Zn(H_2O)_6]^{2+}$

69. Which among the following does not involve inner orbital hybridisation?

(a) $[Cr(NH_3)_6]^{3+}$　　　(b) $[Fe(CN)_6]^{3-}$　　　(c) $[Co(NH_3)_6]^{3+}$　　　(d) $[CoF_6]^{3-}$

70. Which among the following is an organometallic compound?

(a) Lithium acetate　　　　　　(b) Methyl lithium

(c) Lithium methoxide　　　　　(d) Lithium dimethylamide

71. The correct order of hybridisation of the central atom in the following species NH_3, $[PtCl_4]^{2-}$, PCl_5 and BCl_3 is : (At. No. of Pt = 78)

(a) dps^2, sp^2, sp^3, dsp^3　　　　　　(b) dps^2, sp^3, sp^2, dsp^3

(c) dps^2, dsp^3, sp^2 and sp^3　　　　　(d) sp^3, dsp^2, dsp^3, sp^2

72. Some salts although containing two different metallic elements give test for only one of them in solution. Such salts are ......

(a) Normal salts　　(b) None of these　　(c) Double salts　　(d) Complex salts

73. In nitroprusside ion, the iron and NO exist as Fe(II) and NO^+ rather than Fe(III) and NO. These forms can be differentiated by ......

(a) Measuring the solid state magnetic moment

(b) Estimating the concentration of iron

(c) Thermally decomposing the compound

(d) Measuring the concentration of CN^-

74. Which among the following has tetrahedral shape ?

(a) $[NiCl_4]^{2-}$　　　(b) $[PdCl_4]^{2-}$　　　(c) $[Ni(CN)_4]^{2-}$　　　(d) $[Pd(CN)_4]^{3-}$

75. The geometry of $Ni(CO_4)$ and $Ni(PPh_3)_2Cl_2$ are ......

(a) Both tetrahedral　　　　　　(b) Both square planar

(c) Tetrahedral and square planar　　　　(d) Square planar and tetrahedral

76. The pair of compounds in which both the metals are in the highest possible oxidation state is ......

    (a) $[Co(CN)_6]^{3-}$, MnO_2 (b) TiO_3, MnO_2

    (c) CrO_2Cl_2 (d) $[Fe(CN)_6]^{3-}$, $[Co(CN)_6]^{3-}$

77. IUPAC name of

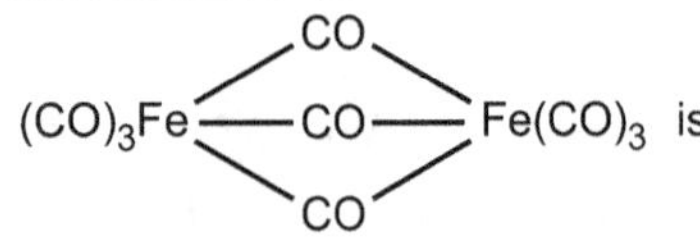

    (a) hexacarbonyl iron(III) μ–tricarbonyl ferrate(0)

    (b) tricarbonyl iron (0) μ–tricarbonyl iron(0) tricarbonyl

    (c) tri–μ–carbonyl bis (tricarbonyl) iron(0)

    (d) noncarbonyl iron

78. Which one of the following statement is incorrect?

    (a) Greater the formation of (K_f) of a complex ion, greater is its stability

    (b) Greater the positive charge on the central metal ion, greater is the stability of the complex

    (c) Greater is the basic character of the ligand, lesser is the stability of the complex.

    (d) Chelate complexes have high stability constants

79. Nitropenta amine chromium (III) chloride exhibits which type of isomerism?

    (a) Linkage   (b) Polymerisation   (c) Optical   (d) Ionisation

80. The co-ordination number of central metal atom in a complex is determined by ......

    (a) The number of ligands around a metal ion bonded by pi-bonds

    (b) The number of ligands around a metal ion bonded by sigma and pi-bonds

    (c) The number of ligands around a metal ion bonded by sigma bonds

    (d) The number of only anionic ligands bonded to the metal ion

81. Which of the following is the correct statement ?

    (a) $[ZnBr_4]^{2-}$ is tetrahedral and diamagnetic

    (b) $[Ni(CN)_6]^{4-}$ is octahedral and Ni has d^2sp^3 hybridization

    (c) $[Cu(CN)_4]^{3-}$ has tetrahedral geometry and dsp^2 hybridization

    (d) $[Cr(NH_3)_6]^{3+}$ has octahedral geometry and sp^3d^2 hybridization

82. Which of the following compounds is not coloured?

    (a) $K_3[Fe(CN)_6]$ (b) $K_4[Fe(CN)_6]$ (c) $Na_2[CdCl_4]$ (d) $Na_2[CuCl_4]$

83. In which of the following coordination entities, the magnitude of Δ_0CFSE in octahedral field will be maximum?

    (a) $[Co(CN)_6]^{3-}$ (b) $[Co(C_2O_4)_3]^{3-}$ (c) $[Co(H_2O)_6]^{3+}$ (d) $[Co(NH_3)_6]^{3+}$

84. The ligand in lithium tetrahydroaluminate compound is ......

    (a) H   (b) H^- (c) A^+ (d) None of these

85. In the complex $K_4[Fe(CN)_6]$, the effective atomic number of Fe is ......

    (a) 24   (b) 36   (c) 18   (d) 12

86. The probable hybrid state of cobalt in hexa fluorocobaltate(III) ion is ......

    (a) sp^3d (b) sp^3d^2 (c) d^2sp^3 (d) sp^3

87. What is the purpose of adding EDTA to prepared foods?

    (a) To keep Ca^{2+} ions in solution

    (b) To complex trace metal ions that catalyze decomposition reaction

    (c) To complex iron (III) to catalyse protein decomposition on cooking

    (d) To aid in browning of the surface during cooking

88. In humans, what percent of absorbed iron is found in blood ?

    (a) 15   (b) 75   (c) 25   (d) 40

89. What purpose would sodium tripolyphosphate serve in a detergent formulation ?

    (a) To remove stains from surface

    (b) To reduce bacterial growth in the detergent upon storage

    (c) To improve the flow characteristics of the detergent in the box

    (d) To complex and hence sequester metal ions in hard water

90. What metal is complexed in chlorophyll ?

    (a) Magnesium   (b) Chromium   (c) Iron   (d) Vanadium

91. What form of haemoglobin is purplish red ?

    (a) Heme   (b) Deoxyhaemoglobin

    (c) Myoglobin   (d) Oxyhaemoglobin

92. Does either or both cis-or-trans-$[Mn(en)_2Br_2]$ have optical isomers ?

    (a) cis only   (b) trans only

    (c) both cis and trans   (d) neither cis nor trans

93. Based on electronic configuration, which is most likely colourless ?

    (a) $[Cu(NH_3)_4]^{2+}$ (b) $[Cd(NH_3)_4]^{2+}$ (c) $[Ni(NH_3)_6]^{2+}$ (d) $[Cr(NH_3)_5Cl]^{2+}$

94. Which complex species has three unpaired d-electrons ?

    (a) $[Cr(CN)_6]^{3-}$ (b) $[Ag(NH_3)_2]^{+}$ (c) $[Zn(NH_3)_4]^{2+}$ (d) $[Cu(NH_3)_4]^{2+}$

95. The attraction of a metal to a neutral ligand is due to _____ bonding.

    (a) Ionic   (b) Covalent   (c) Ion-dipole   (d) Dipole-dipole

96. Chelating ligand among the following is ......

    (a) DMG   (b) Cl^- (c) $H_2\ddot{O}:$ (d) OH^-

97. What is the hybridised state of Co atom in the complex $K_3[CoF_6]$?

    (a) sp^3d^2 (b) sp^3d (c) d^2sp^3 (d) dsp^2

98. Organometallic compound used in the purification of its metals is ......

    (a) $Na_2[Ni(CN)_4]$ (b) $Pb(C_2H_5)_4$ (c) $Ni(CO)_4$ (d) $Li-C_4H_9$

99. The hardness of water is estimated by ......

    (a) EDTA method   (b) Conductivity method

    (c) Distillation method   (d) Titrimetric method

100. The cation that does not form an amine complex with excess of ammonia is ......

    (a) Cd^{2+} (b) Cu^{2+} (c) Al^{3+} (d) Ag^{+}

101. The correct formula of the complex formed in the brown ring test for nitrates is ......

    (a) $[Fe(H_2O)_5NO]^{2+}$ (b) $FeSO_4 \cdot NO$

    (c) $[Fe(H_2O)_4(NO)_2]$ (d) $[Fe(H_2O)_5NO]^{3+}$

102. $[FeF_6]^{3-}$ has ......

    (a) d^2sp^3, 4 unpaired electrons   (b) d^2sp^3, 5 unpaired electrons

    (c) sp^3d^2, 5 unpaired electrons   (d) sp^3d^2, 3 unpaired electrons

103. The colour of $CoCl_3 \cdot 5NH_3 \cdot H_2O$ is ......

    (a) Pink   (b) Violet   (c) Orange   (d) Green

104. Increasing order of carbonyl bond strength is ......

    (a) $[Mn(CO)_6]^+ < [Cr(CO)_6] < [V(CO)_6]^-$ (b) $[V(CO)_6]^- < [Mn(CO)_6]^+ < [Cr(CO)_6]$

    (c) $[V(CO)_6]^- < [Cr(CO)_6] < [Mn(CO)_6]^+$ (d) $[Cr(CO)_6] < [Mn(CO)_6]^+ < [V(CO)_6]^-$

105. In which of the following octahedral complexes of Co (At. No. 27), will be magnitude of Δ_0 be the highest ?

    (a) $[Co(NH_3)_6]^{3+}$ (b) $[Co(CN)_6]^{3+}$ (c) $[Co(C_2H_4)_3]^{3-}$ (d) $[Co(H_2O)_6]^{3+}$

106. Which of the following will give four isomers ?

    (a) $[Co(en)_2(H_2C_2)]Cl_3$ (b) $[Co(en)_3]Cl_3$ (c) $[Co(en)_3]Cl_3$ (d) $[Co(en)_2(NO_2)_2]Cl$

107. The hypothetical complex chlorodiaquatriamine cobalt(III) chloride can be represented as ...

    (a) $[CoCl(NH_3)_3(H_2O)_2]Cl_2$ (b) $[Co(NH_3)_3(H_2O)Cl_3]$

    (c) $[Co(NH_2)_3(H_2O)_2Cl]$ (d) $[Co(NH_3)_3(H_2O)_3]Cl_3$

108. According to IUPAC nomenclature, sodium nitroprusside is named as ......

    (a) Sodium pentacyanonitrosylferrate (III)   (b) Sodium nitroferricyanide

    (c) Sodium nitroferrocyanide   (d) Sodium pentacyanonitrosylferrate (II)

109. One mole of the complex compound $Co(NH_3)_5Cl_3$, give 3 moles of ions on dissolution in water. One mole of the same complex reacts with two moles of $AgNO_3$ solution to yield two moles of AgCl(s). The structure of the complex is ......

    (a) $[Co(NH_3)_5Cl]Cl_2$ (b) $[Co(NH)_3Cl_3] \cdot 2NH_3$

    (c) $[Co(NH_3)_4Cl]Cl_2 \cdot NH_3$ (d) $[Co(NH_3)_4Cl]Cl_2 \cdot NH_3$

110. Which one of the following has a square planar geometry?

    (a) $[CoCl_4]^{2-}$ (b) $[FeCl_4]^{2-}$ (c) $[NiCl_4]^{2-}$ (d) $[PtCl_4]^{2-}$

111. Which of the following is potassium ferricyanide?

    (a) $K_4[Fe(CN)_6]$ (b) $K_3[Fe(CN)_6]$ (c) $K_3[Fe(CN)_3]$ (d) $K_3[Fe(CN)_4]$

112. Nickel (Z = 28) combines with uninegative monodentate ligand X to form a paramagnetic complex $[NiX_4]^{2-}$. The number of unpaired electron(s) in the nickel and geometry of this complex ion are respectively ......

    (a) Two, square planar   (b) One, tetrahedral

    (c) Two, tetrahedral   (d) One, square planar

113. Amongst $Ni(CO)_4$, $[Ni(CN)_4]^{2-}$ and $NiCl_4^{2-}$ ......

(a) $Ni(CO)_4$ and $NiCl_4^{2-}$ are diamagnetic; and $[Ni(CN)_4]^{2-}$ is paramagnetic.

(b) $[Ni(CN)_4]^{2-}$ and $NiCl_4^{2-}$ are diamagnetic; and $Ni(CO)_4$ is paramagnetic.

(c) $Ni(CO)_4$ and $[Ni(CN)_4]^{2-}$ are diamagnetic; and $NiCl_4^{2-}$ is paramagnetic.

(d) $Ni(CO)_4$ is diamagnetic; $[Ni(CN)_4]^{2-}$ and $NiCl_4^{2-}$ are paramagnetic

114. Complexes with general formula Mabcd can have ...... isomers.
 (a) 2 　　　　(b) 3 　　　　(c) 4 　　　　(d) 0

115. The brown ring complex $[Fe(H_2O)_5(NO)]SO_4$ has the magnetic moment of 3.87 B.M. The number of unpaired electrons present are ......
 (a) 3 　　　　(b) 1 　　　　(c) 2 　　　　(d) 5

116. Which of the following statements is incorrect?
 (a) Chlorophyll is a green pigment in plants and contains calcium
 (b) Haemoglobin is the red pigment of blood and contains iron
 (c) Cyanocobalamin is B_{12} and contains cobalt
 (d) Carboxypeptidase A is an enzyme and contains zinc

117. The compound that exhibit geometrical isomerism is ......
 (a) $[Pt(en)Cl_2]$ 　　　(b) $[Pt(en)_2Cl_2]$ 　　　(c) $[Pt(en)_2Cl_2]Cl_2$ 　　(d) $[Pt(NH_3)_4Cl_2]$

118. The complex used as an anticancer agent is ......
 (a) mer-$[Co(NH_3)_3Cl_3]$ 　(b) cis-$[PtCl_2(NH_3)_2]$ 　(c) cis-$K_2[PtCl_2Br_2]$ 　(d) Na_2CoCl_4

119. The compound used for gravimetric estimation of copper(II) is ......
 (a) $Cu_2(SCN)_2$ 　　　(b) Cu_2O 　　　(c) Cu_2I_2 　　　(d) Cu_2CO_3

120. The IUPAC name of the co-ordination compound $K_3[Fe(CN)_6]$ is ......　　**(Orissa JEE 2005)**
 (a) Potassium hexacyanoferrate(II) 　　　　(b) Potassium hexacyanoferrate(III)
 (c) Potassium hexacyanoiron(II) 　　　　(d) Tripotassium hexacyanoiron(II)

121. The correct structure of ethylenediaminetetra-acetic acid (EDTA) is ......

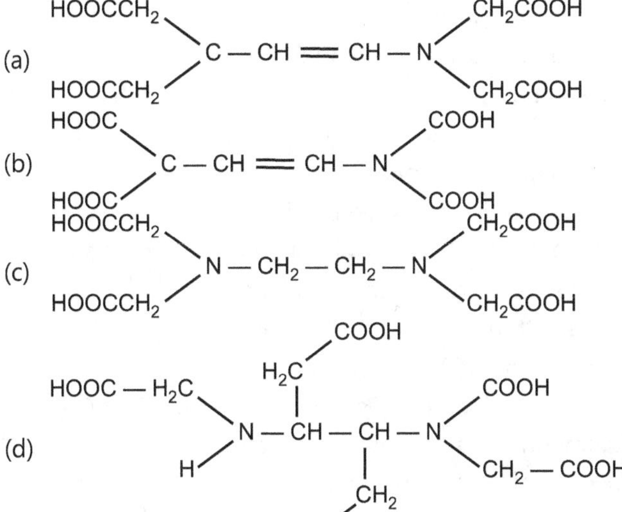

122. Among the following ions, which one has the highest paramagnetism?

(a) $[Cr(H_2O)_6]^{3+}$ (b) $[Fe(H_2O)_6]^{2+}$ (c) $[Cu(H_2O)_6]^{2+}$ (d) $[Zn(H_2O)_6]^{2+}$

123. The total number of possible isomers of the compound $[Cu^{II}(NH_3)_4]\,[Pt^{II}Cl_4]$ are ......

(a) 3   (b) 5   (c) 4   (d) 6

124. In the complex $Fe(CO)_x$, the value of x is ......

(a) 3   (b) 4   (c) 5   (d) 6

125. Violet coloured complex obtained in the detection of sulphur is

(a) $Na_2[Fe(NO)(CN)_5]$ (b) $Na_3[Fe(ONSNa)(CN)_5]$

(c) $Na_4[Fe(CN)_5NOS]$ (d) Both (b) and (c)

126. Which of the following complex will NOT conduct electricity?

(a) $[CrCl(H_2O)_5]Cl_2 \cdot H_2O$ (b) $[Pt(NH_3)_6]Cl_4$

(c) $[CrCl_3(H_2O)_3] \cdot 3H_2O$ (d) $[Cr(NH_3)_4]Cl_2$

127. Which of the following is correct match ?

(a) $[Fe(CN)_6]^{4-}$ and $[Fe(CN)_6]^{3-}$ both are octahedral and diamagnetic

(b) $Ni(CO)_4$ and $[Ni(CN_4)_4]^{2-}$ both are tetrahedral and diamagnetic.

(c) $Ni(CO)_4$ and $[Co(CO)_4]^-$ both are tetrahedral and diamagnetic

(d) $[Fe(H_2O)_6]^{3+}$ and $[Cr(H_2O)_6]^{3+}$ both are paramagnetic and octahedral

128. Ammonia forms the complex ion $[Cu(NH_3)_4]^{2+}$ with copper ions in alkaline solution but not in acidic solution. The probable reason for this is ......

(a) In acidic solution, hydration protects Cu^{2+} ion

(b) In acidic solution, proton co-ordinates with ammonia molecules to form NH_4^+ ions and NH_3 molecules are not available.

(c) In alkaline solutions, insoluble $Cu(OH)_2$ is precipitated which is soluble in excess of any alkali.

(d) Copper hydroxide is amphoteric substance.

129. The colour of light absorbed by an aqueous solution of $CuSO_4$ is ......

(a) orange-red   (b) blue-green   (c) yellow   (d) violet

130. The co-ordination number of a central metal atom in a complex is determined by

(a) The number of ligands around a metal ion bonded by sigma bonds

(b) The number of ligands around a metal ion bonded by pi-bonds

(c) The number of ligands around a metal ion bonded by sigma and pi-bonds

(d) The number of only anionic ligands bonded to the metal ion

131. The complex ion which has no 'd' electrons in the central metal atom is ......

(At. No. of Cr = 24, Mn = 25, Fe = 26, Co = 27)

(a) $[MnO_4]^-$ (b) $[Co(NH_3)_6]^{3+}$ (c) $[Fe(CN)_6]^{3-}$ (d) $[Cr(H_2O)_6]^{3+}$

132. Out of the following d^n configurations, the number of unpaired electrons in octahedral complexes remains same irrespective of the ligand field strength.

(a) d^3 (b) d^4 (c) d^5 (d) d^6

133. EDTA is used to estimate and remove the following ion(s) in the aqueous solution.

(a) Mg^{2+} ion

(b) Ca^{2+} ion

(c) Na^+ ion

(d) both Mg^{2+} and Ca^{2+}

134. The shape of cuprammonium ion is ......

(a) Octahedral   (b) Tetrahedral   (c) Trigonal   (d) Square planar

135. Which of the following species represent the example of dsp^2 hybridisation ?

(a) $[Fe(CN)_6]^{3-}$ (b) $[Ni(CN)_4]^{2-}$ (c) $[Ag(CN)_2]^-$ (d) $[Co(CN)_6]^{3-}$

136. Consider the following complex $[Co(NH_3)_5CO_3]ClO_4$

The co-ordination number, oxidation number, number of d-electrons and number of unpaired d-electrons on the metal are ...... respectively.

(a) 6, 3, 6, 0   (b) 7, 2, 7, 1   (c) 7, 1, 6, 4   (d) 6, 2, 7, 3

137. In $[Cr(C_2O_4)_3]^{3-}$, the isomerism shown is ......

(a) Ligand   (b) Optical   (c) Geometrical   (d) Ionization

138. The optical isomers of $[CrCl_2(en)_2]^+$ are

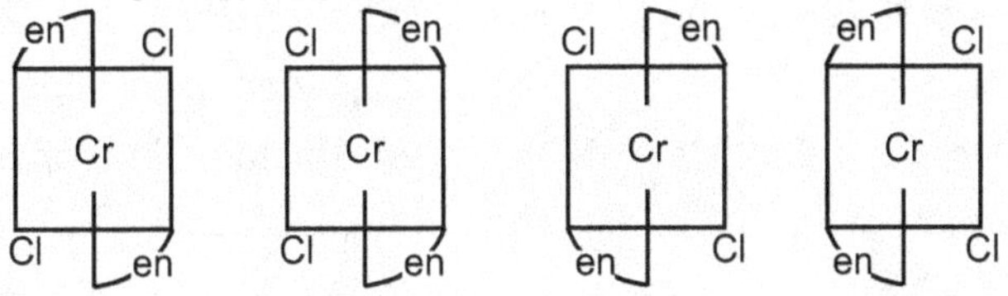

I　　　　　II　　　　　III　　　　　IV

(a) I and II   (b) I and III   (c) II and IV   (d) II and III

139. The species having tetrahedral shape is ......

(a) $[Pd(Cl_4)]^{2-}$ (b) $[Ni(CN)_4]^{2-}$ (c) $[Pd(CN)_4]^{3-}$ (d) $[NiCl_4]^{2-}$

140. In solid $CuSO_4 \cdot 5H_2O$, copper is co-ordinated to ......

(a) Five water molecules

(b) One sulphate anion

(c) Four water molecules

(d) One water molecule

141. According to Werner's theory.

(1) Ligands are connected to metal ions by covalent bonds

(2) Secondary valencies have directional properties

(3) Secondary valencies are non-ionisable. Of these statements

(a) 1, 2 and 3 are correct

(b) 2 and 3 are correct

(c) 1 and 3 are correct

(d) 1 and 2 are correct

142. From the stability constants (hypothetical values), given below, predict which is the strongest ligand ?

(a) $[Cu(NH_3)_4]^{2+}$, $\beta_4 = 4.5 \times 10^{11}$

(b) $[Cu(CN)_4]^{2+}$, $\beta_4 = 2.0 \times 10^2$

(c) $[Cu(CN)_2]^{2+}$, $\beta_4 = 3.0 \times 10^{15}$

(d) $[Cu(H_2O)_4]^{2+}$, $\beta_4 = 9.5 \times 10^8$

143. A square planar complex is formed by hybridisation of which atomic orbitals ?

(a) s, p_x, p_y, d_{yz} (b) $s, p_x, p_y, d_{x^2-y^2}$ (c) s, p_x, p_y, d_{x^2} (d) s, p_x, p_y, d_{xy}

144. Which of the following statements is not true ?

(a) The stability constant of $[Co(NH_3)_6]^{3+}$ is greater than that of $[Co(NH_3)_6]^{2+}$

(b) The cyano complexes are far more stable than those formed by halide ions

(c) The stability of halide complexes follows the order $I < Br < Cl$

(d) The stability constant of $[Cu(NH_3)_4]^{2+}$ is greater than that of $[Cu(en)_2]^{2+}$

145. Which of the following compounds is square planar and does not have any unpaired electron ?

(a) $Ni(CO)_4$ (b) $[Ni(H_2O)_6]^{2+}$ (c) $[NiCl_4]^{2-}$ (d) $[Ni(CN)_4]^{2-}$

146. The unpaired electrons in $Ni(CO)_4$ are ......

(a) 0   (b) 1   (c) 3   (d) 4

147. The complexes $[Co(SO_4)(NH_3)_5]Br$ and $[CoBr(NH_3)_5]SO_4$ can be distinguished by ......

(a) molar conductivity   (b) $BaCl_2$

(c) depression in freezing point   (d) magnetic property

148. The correct name of the compound $[Cu(NH_3)_4](NO_3)_2$ according to IUPAC system is ......

(a) Cuprammonium nitrate   (b) Tetraamminecopper(II) nitrate

(c) Tetraamminecopper(II) nitrate   (d) Tetraammine copper(II) dinitrite

149. The chemical formula of iron [III] hexacyano ferrate(II) is ......

(At. No. of Pt = 78)

(a) $Fe[Fe(CN)_6]$ (b) $Fe_3[Fe(CN)_6]$ (c) $Fe_3[Fe(CN)_6]_4$ (d) $Fe_4[Fe(CN)_6]_3$

150. The shape of $[Cu(NH_3)_4]^{2+}$ is ......

(a) Tetrahedral   (b) Square planar   (c) Pyramidal   (d) Octahedral

151. Which of the following statements is correct?

(a) Geometrical isomerism is not observed in complexes of C.N. 4 having tetrahedral geometry

(b) Square planar complexes generally do now show geometrical isomerism

(c) The square planar complex of general formulae Ma_3b or Mab_3 exhibits cis-trans isomerism

(d) The $[Pt(NH_3)_2Cl_2]$ does not show geometrical isomerism

152. The complex that violates the Sidgwicks's rule is ......

(a) Potassium ferrocyanide   (b) Hexaammine cobalt(III) chloride

(c) Tetraammine copper(II) sulphate

(d) Potassium dichlorodioxalato cobaltate (III)

153. The oxidation state of Cr in $[Cr(NH_3)_4Cl_2]^+$ is ......

(a) +3   (b) +2   (c) +1   (d) 0

154. $CuSO_4$ dissolves in NH_3 due to the formation of ......

(a) $Cu(OH)_2$ (b) $[Cu(NH_3)_4]$

(c) $[Cu(NH_3)_4(OH)_2]$ (d) CuO

Assertion and Reasons

Direction : In the following question, a statement of Assertion (A) is given followed by a corresponding statement of Reason (R) just below it. Of the statements, mark the correct answer as

(a) If both A and R are true and R is the correct explanation of A

(b) If both are correct and R is not the correct explanation of A

(c) If A is true but R is false.

(d) If A is false but reason is true.

(e) If both A and R are false.

155. Assertion	:	Ethylenediamminetetraacetate ion forms an octahedral complex with the metal ion.

Reason	:	It has six donor atoms which coordinate simultaneously to the metal ion.

156. Assertion	:	$[Ni(CN)_4]^{2-}$ is square planar and diamagnetic.

Reason	:	It has no unpaired electrons due to presence of strong field ligand.

157. Assertion	:	The ligands nitro and nitrito are called ambidentate ligands.

Reason	:	These ligands give linkage isomers. Ambidentate ligands are the ligands which have two or more donor atoms but only one donor atom is attached to the metal ion at a time.

158. Assertion	:	$[(en)_2Co\underset{OH}{\overset{NH}{<>}}Co(en)_2]^{3+}$

is named as tetrakis (ethylenediamine) µ-hydroxo-imido dicobalt(III) ion.

Reason	:	In naming polynuclear complexes i.e., containing two or more metal atoms joined by bridging ligands, the word m is added with hyphen before the name of such ligands.

159. Assertion	:	Zeise's salt is a π bonded organo metallic compound.

Reason	:	The oxidation number of platinum in Zeise's salt is + 2.

160. Assertion	:	Square planar complexes do not show optical isomerism.

Reason	:	Optical isomerism is due to the absence of elements of symmetry.

161. Assertion	:	Complex of calcium with EDTA is used to treat lead poisoning.

Reason	:	EDTA is a hexadentate ligand.

162. Assertion	:	$[Al(H_2O)_6]^{3+}$ is a stronger acid than $[Mg(H_2O)_6]^{2+}$.

Reason	:	Size of $[Al(H_2O)_6]^{3+}$ is smaller than $[Mg(H_2O)_6]^{2+}$ and possesses more effective nuclear charge.

163. Assertion	:	$H_2N - NH_2$ is a chelating ligand.

Reason	:	A chelating ligand must possess two or more lone pairs at such a distance that it may form suitable strain free rings at the metal ion.

164. Assertion : $Cu(OH)_2$ is soluble in NH_4OH but not in $NaOH$.

Reason : $Cu(OH)_2$ forms a soluble complex with NH_3.

165. Assertion : Aqueous solution of potassium ferrocyanide does not give the test of iron(II).

Reason : Potassium ferrocyanide is not poisonous like potassium cyanide.

166. Assertion : $[FeF_6]^{3-}$ is a low spin complex.

Reason : Low spin complexes have less number of unpaired electrons.

167. Assertion : F^- ion is a weak ligand and forms outer orbital complex.

Reason : F^- ion cannot force the electrons of $d_{z^2}^2$ and $d_{x^2-y^2}$ orbitals of the inner shell to occupy d_{xy}, d_{yz} and d_{zx} orbitals of the same shell.

168. Assertion : Oxalate ion is a bidentate ligand.

Reason : Oxalate ion has two donor atoms.

169. Assertion : All the octahedral complexes of Ni^{2+} must be outer orbital complexes.

Reason : Outer orbital octahedral complexes are given by weak ligands.

PREVIOUS YEAR'S QUESTIONS FROM VARIOUS COMPETITIVE EXAMINATIONS

1. Which of the following has longest C – O bond length? (Free C – O bond length in CO is 1.128 A°. **[NEET - UG 2016]**

(a) $[Mn(CO)_6]^+$ 　　(b) $[Ni(CO)_4]$ 　　(c) $[Co(CO)_4]^-$ 　　(d) $[Fe(CO)_4]^{2-}$

2. A magnetic moment of 1.73 BM will be shown by one among the following: **[AIPMT 2015]**

(a) $[CoCl_6]^{4-}$ 　　(b) $[Cu(NH_3)_4]^{2+}$ 　　(c) $[Ni(CN)_4]^{2-}$ 　　(d) $TiCl_4$

3. Which of the these statements about $[Co(CN)_6]^{3-}$ is true? **[AIPMT 2015]**

(a) $[Co(CN)_6]^{3-}$ has four unpaired electrons and will be in a low-spin configuration.

(b) $[Co(CN)_6]^{3-}$ has four unpaired electrons and will be in a high-spin configuration.

(c) $[Co(CN)_6]^{3-}$ has no unpaired electrons and will be in a high-spin configuration.

(d) $[Co(CN)_6]^{3-}$ has no unpaired electrons and will be in a low-spin configuration.

4. The name of complex ion $[Fe(CN)_6]^{3-}$ is ...... **[RE AIPMT 2015]**

(a) Tricyanoferrate(III) ion 　　　　(b) Hexacyanidoferrate(III) ion

(c) Hexacyanoiron(III) ion 　　　　(d) Hexacyanitoferrate(III) ion

5. The hybridization involved in complex $[Ni(CN)_4]^{2-}$ is ...... **[RE AIPMT 2015]**

(a) $d^2 sp^2$ 　　(b) $d^2 sp^3$ 　　(c) dsp^2 　　(d) sp^3

6. The sum of coordination number and oxidation number of the metal M in the complex $[M(en)_2(C_2O_4)]Cl$ (where en is ethylenediamine) is ...... **[RE AIPMT 2015]**

(a) 7 　　(b) 8 　　(c) 9 　　(d) 6

7. The number of possible isomers for the complex $[Co(en)_2Cl_2]Cl$ will be .... (en = ethylenediamine) **[RE AIPMT 2015]**

(a) 3 　　(b) 4 　　(c) 2 　　(d) 1

8. Among the following complexes the one which shows zero crystal field stabilization energy (CFSE) is ...... **[AIPMT 2014]**

(a) $[Mn(H_2O)_6]^{3+}$ 　　(b) $[Fe(H_2O)_6]^{3+}$ 　　(c) $[Co(H_2O)_6]^{3+}$ 　　(d) $[Co(H_2O)_6]^{3+}$

9. Magnetic moment 2.83 BM is given by which of the following ions?

(At. nos. Ti = 22, Cr = 24, Mn = 25, Ni = 28)   **[AIPMT 2014]**

(a) Ti^{2+} (b) Ni^{2+} (c) Cr^{3+} (d) Mn^{2+}

10. An excess of $AgNO_3$ is added to 100 mL of a 0.01 M solution of dichlorotetraaquachromium (III) chloride. The number of moles of AgCl precipitated would be ......   **[NEET 2013]**

(a) 0.01   (b) 0.001   (c) 0.002   (d) 0.003

11. Red precipitate is obtained when ethanol solution of dimethylglyoxime is added to ammoniacal Ni(II). Which of the following statements is not true?   **[CBSE AIPMT 2012]**

(a) Red complex has a tetrahedral geometry

(b) Dimethylglyoxime functions as bidentate ligand

(c) Red complex has a square planar geometry

(d) Complex has symmetrical hydrogen-bonding.

12. The d-electron configuration of Cr^{2+}, Mn^{2+}, Fe^{2+} and Co^{2+} are d^4, d^5, d^6 and d^1 respectively. Which one of the following will exhibit minimum paramagnetic behavior?

(At. No Cr = 24, Mn = 25, Fe = 26, Co = 27)   **[CBSE AIPMT 2011]**

(a) $[Cr(H_2O)_6]^{2+}$ (b) $[Mn(H_2O)_6]^{2+}$ (c) $[Fe(H_2O)_6]^{2+}$ (d) $[Co(H_2O)_6]^{2+}$

13. Out of the following complex ions, which is diamagnetic in nature?

(a) $[CoF_6]^{3-}$ (b) $[NiCl_4]^{2-}$ (c) $[Ni(CN)_4]^{2-}$ (d) $[CuCl_2]^{2-}$

14. The complexes $[Co(NH_3)_6][Cr(CN)_6]$ and $[Cr(NH_3)_6][Co(CN)_6]$ are the examples of which type of isomerism?   **[CBSE AIPMT 2011]**

(a) Geometrical isomerism   (b) Linkage isomerism

(c) Ionisation isomerism   (d) Coordination isomerism

15. The complex, $[Pt(Py)(NH_3)BrCl]$ will have how many geometrical isomers?

[CBSE AIPMT 2011]

(a) 2   (b) 3   (c) 4   (d) 0

16. Which can exist both as diastereoisomer and enantiomer?   **[DUMET 2011]**

(a) $[Pt(en)_3]^{4+}$ (b) $[Pt(en)_2ClBr]^{2+}$ (c) $[Ru(NH_3)_4Cl_2]^0$ (d) $[PtCl_2Br_2]^0$

17. Out of four transition metal octahedral complexes (the choice given below) low spin electronic configurations arise only for ......   **[DPMT 2011]**

(a) d^1 to d^3 complexes   (b) d^4 to d^1 complexes

(c) d^1 to d^9 complexes   (d) d^1, d^2 and d^3 complexes

18. Excess of silver nitrate solution is added to 100 mL of 0.01 M pentaaquachlorochromium (III) chloride solution. The mass of silver chloride obtained (in gram) is [Atomic mass of silver is 108] ......   **[KCET 2011]**

(a) 287×10^{-3} (b) 143.5×10^{-3} (c) 147   (d) 287×10^{-2}

19. The crystal field stabilization energy for high spin d^4 octahedral complex is......

[CBSE AIPMT 2010]

(a) $-0.6\,\Delta_0$ (b) $-1.8\,\Delta_0$ (c) $-1.6\Delta_0 + P$ (d) $-1.2\Delta_0$

20. The existence of two different coloured complexes with the composition $[Co(NH_3)_4Cl_2]^+$ is due to ......   **[CBSE AIPMT 2010]**

(a) Ionisation isomerism   (b) Linkage isomerism

(c) Geometrical isomerism   (d) Coordination isomerism

21. Which of the following complex ion is not expected to absorb visible light?

    (a) $[Ni(H_2O)_6]^{2+}$ (b) $[Ni(CN)_4]^{2-}$ (c) $[Cr(NH_3)_6]^{3+}$ (d) $[Fe(H_2O)_6]^{2+}$

22. $AgCl$ is dissolved in excess of each of NH_3, KCN and $Na_2S_2O_3$. The complex ions produced in each case are ...... **[AMU 2010]**

    (a) $[Ag(NH_3)_2]^2$, $[Ag(CN)_2]^+$ and $[Ag(S_2O_3)_2]^{3-}$ (b) $[Ag(NH_3)_2]^+$, $[Ag(CN)_2]^+$ and $[Ag(S_2O_3)_2]^{3-}$
    (c) $[Ag(NH_3)_4]^{2+}$, $[Ag(CN)_2]^{3-}$ and $[Ag(S_2O_3)_2]^{2-}$ (d) $[Ag(NH_3)_2]^+$, $[Ag(CN)_2]^-$ and $[Ag(S_2O_3)_2]^{3-}$

23. The most stable complex among the following is ...... **[AMU 2010]**

    (a) $[Pd(CN)_4]^{4-}$ (b) $[Fe(CO)_5]$ (c) $[Ni(CN)_4]^{4-}$ (d) $[Ni(CN)_4]^{3-}$

24. Choose the correct statement. **[AMU 2010]**

    (a) $[Co(NH_3)_6]^{2+}$ is oxidized to diamagnetic $[Co(NH_3)_6]^{3+}$ by the oxygen in air

    (b) Tetrahedral complexes are more stable than octahedral complexes

    (c) $[Fe(CN)_6]^{3-}$ is stable but $[FeF_6]^{3-}$ is unstable

    (d) The $[Cu(NH_3)_4]^{2+}$ ion has a tetrahedral geometry and is diamagnetic

25. In the complex ion $[Co(NH_3)_6]^{3+}$, the NH_3 molecules are linked to the central metal ion by

    [AFMC 2010]

    (a) ionic bonds   (b) covalent bonds
    (c) coordinate bonds   (d) hydrogen bonds

26. How many ions are produced from $[Co(NH_3)_6]Cl_3$ in solution? **[RPMT 2010]**

    (a) 6   (b) 4   (c) 3   (d) 2

27. The IUPAC name of $K_2[Ni(CN)_4]$ is ...... **[KCET 2010]**

    (a) potassium tetracyanidonickelate(II)   (b) potassium tetracyanatonickelate(III)
    (c) potassium tetradcyanatonickel(II)   (d) potassium tetracyanonickel(III)

28. Which of the following is wrongly matched?
    (a) $[Cu(NH_3)_4]^{2+}$ - Square planar   (b) $[Ni(CO)_4]$ – Neutral ligand
    (c) $[Fe(CN)_6]^{3-}$ - sp^3 d^2 (d) $[Co(en)_3]^{3+}$ - Follows EAN rule

29. The correct order of magnetic moments (spin only values in BM) among the following is ...
    (Atomic number : Mn = 25, Fe = 26, Co = 27) **(KCET 2010)**
    (a) $[MnCl_4]^{2-} > [CoCl_4]^{2-} > [Fe(CN)_6]^{4-}$ (b) $[MnCl_4]^{2-} > [Fe(CN)_6]^{4-} > [CoCl_4]^{2-}$
    (c) $[Fe(CN)_6]^{4-} > [MnCl_4]^{2-} > [CoCl_4]^{2-}$ (d) $[Fe(CN)_6]^{4-} > [CoCl_4]^{2-} > [MnCl_4]^{2-}$

30. $[Co(NH_3)_4Cl_2]NO_2$ and $[Co(NH_3)_4ClNO_2]Cl$ exhibit which type of isomerism? **[Manipal 2010]**
    (a) Geometrical   (b) Optical   (c) Linkage   (d) Ionisation

31. The name of the complex $[Pt(NH_3)_6]Cl_4$ is ...... **[Manipal 2010]**
    (a) hexaammineplatinum(IV) chloride   (b) hexammineplatinum(II) chloride
    (c) tetrachloro hexaammineplatinum(IV)   (d) tetrachloro hexaammineplatinum(II)

32. The effective atomic number of Cr (atomic no. 24) in $[Cr(NH_3)_6]Cl_3$ is ...... **[Manipal 2010]**
    (a) 35   (b) 27   (c) 33   (d) 36

33. Which of the following complex ion is expected to absorb visible light?
    (a) $[Sc(H_2O)_3(NH_3)_3]^{3+}$ (b) $[Ti(en)_2(NH_3)_2]^{4+}$ (c) $[Cr(NH_3)_6]^{3+}$ (d) $[Zn(NH_3)_6]^{2+}$

34. Which of the following coordination entities should be expected to absorb light of lowest frequency? **[AIIMS 2009]**
(a) $[Cr(en)_3]^{3+}$ (b) $[CrCl_6]^{3-}$ (c) $[Cr(NH_3)_6]^{3+}$ (d) $[Cr(CN)_6]^{3-}$

35. What is (are) number(s) of unpaired electrons in the square planar $[Pt(CN)_4]^{2-}$ ion? **[AIIMS 2009]**
(a) zero (b) 1 (c) 4 (d) 6

36. $[Fe(CN)_6]^{3-}$ ion is …… **[AMU 2009]**
(a) hexacyano ferrate(II) ion
(b) hexacyano ferrate(III) ion
(c) hexacyanido iron(III) ion
(d) iron(III) hexacyanide ion

37. What is the oxidation number of Fe in $Fe(CO)_5$? **[CPMT 2009]**
(a) +3 (b) zero (c) +2 (d) +5

38. The magnitude of crystal field stabilization energy in tetrahedral complexes (CFSE of Δ_1) is considerably less than that in the octahedral field because …… **[DUMET 2009]**
(a) There are only four ligands instead of six so the ligand field is only 2/3 the size hence Δ_t is 2/3
(b) The direction of the orbitals does not coincide with the direction of the ligands. This reduces the crystal field stabilization energy (Δ) by further 2/3.
(c) Both points (1) and (2) are correct.
(d) Both points (1) and (2) are wrong.

39. The crystal field splitting energy for octahedral (Δ_0) complexes is related as
(a) $\Delta_t = -\dfrac{1}{2}\Delta_0$ (b) $\Delta_t = -\dfrac{4}{9}\Delta_0$ (c) $\Delta_t = -\dfrac{3}{5}\Delta_0$ (d) $\Delta_t = -\dfrac{2}{5}\Delta_0$
(f) $\Delta_t = -\dfrac{9}{4}\Delta_0$

40. Facial and meridional isomerism will be exhibited by …… **[Kerala CEE 2009]**
(a) $[Co(NH_3)_3Cl_3]$ (b) $[Co(NH_3)_4Cl_2]Cl$ (c) $[Co(en)_3]Cl_3$ (d) $[Co(NH_3)_5Cl]Cl_2$

41. Aluminium reacts with NaOH and forms compound 'X'. If the coordination number of aluminium in 'X' is 6, the correct formula of X is …… **[EAMCET 2009]**
(a) $Al(H_2O)_4(OH)_2]^+$ (b) $[Al(H_2O)_3(OH)_3]$ (c) $[Al(H_2O)_2(OH)_4]$ (d) $[Al(H_2O)_6(OH)_3]$

42. In solid $CuSO_4 \cdot 5H_2O$, copper is coordinated to number of water molecules equal to …… **[CG PMT, Haryana PMT 2009]**
(a) 5 (b) 4 (c) 1 (d) 2

43. The coordination compound of which one of the following compositions will produce two equivalents of AgCl on reaction with aqueous silver nitrate solution? **[J & K CET 2009]**
(a) $CoCl_3 \cdot 3NH_3$ (b) $CoCl_3 \cdot 6NH_3$ (c) $CoCl_3 \cdot 4NH_3$ (d) $CoCl_3 \cdot 5NH_3$

44. The optically active coordination complex ion among the following is **[J & K CET 2009]**
(a) trans $[Co(en)_2Cl_2]^+$
(b) cis$[Co(en)(NH_3)_2Cl_2]^+$
(c) $[Co(NH_3)_6]^{3+}$
(d) $[Fe(CN)_6]^{3+}$

45. In which of the following coordination entities, the magnitude of Δ_0 (CFSE in octahedral field) will be maximum? (At No. of Co = 27) **[CBSE AIPMT 2008]**
(a) $[Co(H_2O)_6]^{3+}$ (b) $[Co(NH_3)_6]^{3+}$ (c) $[Co(CN)_6]^{3-}$ (d) $[Co(C_2O_4)_3]^{3-}$

46. Assertion : $[CoF_6]^{3-}$ is paramagnetic.

Reason : Co^{3+} has $3d^6$ outer electronic configuration. The unpaired electrons do not pair up because of weak field provided by F^-.   **[BHU 2008]**

47. Which of the following is false tetrahedral complexes?   **[DUMET 2008]**

(a) Low spin   (b) High spin   (d) d-d transition   (d) Coloured

48. In the complex with formula $MCl_3 \cdot 4H_2O$, the coordination number of the metal M is six and there is no molecule of hydration in it. The volume of 0.1 M $AgNO_3$ solution needed to precipitate the free chloride ions in 200 mL of 0.01 M solution of the complex, is

[Kerala CEE 2008]

(a) 40 mL   (b) 20 mL   (c) 60 mL   (d) 80 mL

(e) 10 mL

49. Which of the following coordination compounds would exhibit optical isomerism?

[Manipal 2007]

(a) Pentamminenitrocobalt(III) iodide   (b) Diamminedinitroplatinum(II)

(c) Dicyanobis (ethylenediamine)   (d) Tris-(ethylenediamine) cabalt(III) bromide

50. Among $[NiCO]_4$, $[Ni(CN)_4]^{2-}$, $[NiCl_4]^{2-}$ species, the hybridization states of the Ni atom are, respectively (At. no. of Ni = 28) ......   **[Manipal 2007]**

(a) sp^3, dsp^2, dsp^2 (b) sp^3, dsp^2, sp^3 (c) sp^3, sp^3, dsp^2 (d) dsp^2, sp^3, sp

51. The geometry of $Ni(CO)_4$ and $Ni(PPh_3)_2Cl_2$ are ......   **[Manipal 2007]**

(a) both square planar   (b) tetrahedral and square planar respectively

(c) both tetrahedral   (d) square planar and tetrahedral respectively

52. $[Cr(H_2O)_6]Cl_3$ (At No. of Cr = 24) has a magnetic moment of 3.83 MB, the correct distribution of 3d-electrons in the chromium of the complex is ......   **[CBSE AIPMT 2006]**

(a) $3d_{x^2-y^2}^1, 3d_{z^2}^1, 3d_{xz}^1$ (b) $3d_{xy}^1, 3d_{x^2-y^2}^1, 3d_{yz}^1$

(c) $3d_{xy}^1, 3d_{zy}^1, 3d_{zx}^1$ (d) $3d_{xy}^1, 3d_{yz}^1, 3d_{z^2}^1$

53. The correct order for the wavelength of absorption in the visible region is ... **[AIIMS 2005]**

(a) $[Ni(NO_2)_6]^{4-} < [Ni(NH_3)_6]^{2+} < [Ni(H_2O)_6]^{2+}$

(b) $[Ni(NO_2)_6]^{4-} < [Ni(H_2O)_6]^{2+} < [Ni(NH_3)_6]^{2+}$

(c) $[Ni(H_2O)_6]^{2+} < [Ni(NH_3)_6]^{2+} < [Ni(NO_2)_6]^{2+}$

(d) $[Ni(NH_3)_6]^{2+} < [Ni(H_2O)_6]^{2+} < [Ni(NO_2)_6]^{2+}$

54. Co-ordination compounds have great importance in biological systems. In this context which of the following statements is incorrect ?   **[MP PMT 2003]**

(a) Chlorophylls are green pigments in plants and contain calcium

(b) Carboxypeptidase-A is an enzyme and contains zinc

(c) Cyanocobalamin is B_{12} and contains cobalt

(d) Haemoglobin is the red pigment of blood and contains iron

55. Which of the following does not show optical isomerism?   **[JIPMER 2001]**

(a) $[Co(en)_3]^{3+}$ (b) $[Co(en)_2Cl_2]^+$ (c) $[Co(NH_3)_3Cl_3]^0$ (d) $[Co(en)Cl_2(NH_3)_2]^+$

(en = ethylenediamine)

56. In which of the following pairs, both the complexes show optical isomerism?

[Kerala PMT 2007]

(a) cis-$[Cr(C_2O_4)_2Cl_2]^{3-}$, cis-$[Co(NH_3)_4Cl_2]$
(b) $[CoCl(en)_3]Cl_3$, cis-$[Co(en)_2Cl_2]Cl$
(c) $[PtCl(diem) Cl_1[NiCl_2Br_2]^{2-}$
(d) $[Co(NO_3)_3(NH_3)_3]$, cis-$[Pt(en)_2Cl_2]$

57. According to Lewis, the ligands are ......   **[M.P. P.M.T. 2002]**

(a) Acidic in nautre
(b) Basic in nature
(c) Neither acidic nor basic
(d) Some are acidic and others are basic

58. The most stable complex among the following is   **[M.P. P.M.T. 2002]**

(a) $K_3[Al(C_2O_4)_3]$
(b) $[Pt(en)_2]Cl_2$
(c) $[Ag(NH_3)_2]Cl$
(d) $K_2[Ni(EDTA)]$

59. CN^- is a strong field ligand. This is due to the fact that ......   **(C.B.S.E. P.M.T. 2004)**

(a) It carries negative charge
(b) It is a pseudo-halide
(c) It can accept electrons from metal species
(d) It forms high spin complexes with metal species.

60. Considering H_2O as a weak field ligand, the number of unpaired electrons in $[Mn(H_2O)_6]^{2+}$ will be (atomic number of Mn = 25) ......   **(C.B.S.E. P.M.T. 2004)**

(a) Three
(b) Five
(c) Two
(d) Four

61. Which of the following is not considered as an organometallic compound ?**(A.I.I.M.S. 2004)**

(a) Cisplatin
(b) Ferrocene
(c) Zeise's salt
(d) Grignard regent

62. Match the lists I and II and pick the correct matching from the codes given below :

(Kerala Med. 2005)

List I	List II
(Complex)	(Structure and magnetic moment)
(1) $[Ag(CN_2)]^-$	1. Square planar and 1.73 B.M.
(2) $[Cu(CN)_6]^{3-}$	2. Linear and zero
(3) $[Cu(CN)_6]^{3-}$	3. Octahedral and zero
(4) $[Cu(NH_3)_4]^{2+}$	4. Tetrahedral and zero
(5) $[Fe(CN)_6]^{4-}$	5. Octahedral and 1.73 B.M.

(a) a - 2, b - 4, c - 5, d - 1, e - 3
(b) a - 5, b - 4, c - 1, d - 3, e - 2
(c) a - 1, b - 3, c - 4, d - 2, e - 5
(d) a - 4, b - 5, c - 2, d - 1, e - 3
(e) a - 4, b - 2, c - 5, d - 3, e - 1

63. Which of the following compounds exhibits linkage isomerism ?   **(M. P. P.M.T. 2001)**

(a) $[Co(en)_3]Cl_3$
(b) $[Co(NH_3)_6] [Cr(en)_3]$
(c) $[Co(en)_2NO_2Cl]Br$
(d) $[Co(NH_3)_5Cl]Br_2$

64. Which one of the following will not show geometrical isomerism ?   **(M.P. P.M.T. 2002)**

(a) $[Cr(NH_3)_4Cl_2]Cl$
(b) $[Co(en)_2Cl_2]Cl$
(c) $[Co(NH_3)_5NO_2]Cl_2$
(d) $[Pt(NH_3)_2Cl_2]$

65. Which one of the following octahedral complexes will not show geometrical isomerism ?

(C.B.S.E. P.M.T. 2003)

(a) $M[A_2B_2]$
(b) $M[A_3B_3]$
(c) $[MA_4B_2]$
(d) $[MA_5B]$

66. In the co-ordination compound $K_4[Ni(CN)_4]$, the oxidation state of nickel is ......

    (a) -1 (b) 0   (c) $+1$ (d) $+2$

67. Which of the following does not have optical isomer? **(A.I.I.M.S. 2004)**

    (a) $[Co(NH_3)_3Cl_3]$ (b) $[Co(en)_2Cl_3]$

    (c) $[Co(en)_2Cl_2]Cl$ (d) $[Co(en)(NH_3)_2Cl_2]Cl$

ANSWER KEY

1. (c)	2. (d)	3. (b)	4. (c)	5. (d)	6. (b)	7. (d)	8. (a)
9. (d)	10. (d)	11. (c)	12. (b)	13. (a)	14. (d)	15. (a)	16. (b)
17. (a)	18. (d)	19. (c)	20. (c)	21. (a)	22. (a)	23. (b)	24. (a)
25. (a)	26. (c)	27. (c)	28. (d)	29. (b)	30. (c)	31. (c)	32. (c)
33. (c)	34. (a)	35. (b)	36. (b)	37. (c)	38. (a)	39. (d)	40. (a)
41. (a)	42. (c)	43. (a)	44. (b)	45. (c)	46. (a)	47. (c)	48. (a)
49. (a)	50. (d)	51. (b)	52. (c)	53. (d)	54. (a)	55. (d)	56. (d)
57. (c)	58. (a)	59. (c)	60. (a)	61. (a)	62. (c)	63. (a)	64. (d)
65. (a)	66. (c)	67. (a)	68. (c)	69. (d)	70. (b)	71. (d)	72. (d)
73. (a)	74. (a)	75. (c)	76. (d)	77. (b)	78. (c)	79. (d)	80. (c)
81. (a)	82. (b)	83. (a)	84. (b)	85. (b)	86. (b)	87. (b)	88. (b)
89. (d)	90. (a)	91. (a)	92. (a)	93. (b)	94. (a)	95. (b)	96. (a)
97. (a)	98. (c)	99. (a)	100. (c)	101. (a)	102. (c)	103. (a)	104. (b)
105. (b)	106. (d)	107. (a)	108. (d)	109. (a)	110. (d)	111. (b)	112. (d)
113. (c)	114. (b)	115. (a)	116. (a)	117. (b)	118. (b)	119. (a)	120. (b)
121. (c)	122. (b)	123.	124. (a)	125. (c)	126. (c)	127. (c)	128. (b)
129. (a)	130. (a)	131. (a)	132. (c)	133. (d)	134. (d)	135. (b)	136. (a)
137. (b)	138. (c)	139. (d)	140. (c)	141. (b)	142. (c)	143. (b)	144. (d)
145. (a)	146. (a)	147. (b)	148. (b)	149. (c)	150. (c)	151. (a)	152. (c)
153. (a)	154. (c)	155. (a)	156. (a)	157. (a)	158. (d)	159. (b)	160. (b)
161. (b)	162. (a)	163. (d)	164. (a)	165. (b)	166. (d)	167. (a)	168. (a)
169. (b)							

Previous Years Questions

1. (a)	2. (b)	3. (d)	4. (b)	5. (c)	6. (c)	7. (c)	8. (b)
9. (b)	10. (b)	11. (a)	12. (d)	13. (c)	14. (d)	15. (b)	16. (b)
17. (b)	18. (a)	19. (a)	20. (c)	21. (b)	22. (d)	23. (b)	24. (a)
25. (c)	26. (b)	27. (a)	28. (c)	29. (a)	30. (d)	31. (a)	32. (c)
33. (c)	34. (b)	35. (a)	36. (b)	37. (b)	38. (c)	39. (b)	40. (a)
41. (c)	42. (b)	43. (d)	44. (b)	45. (c)	46. (a)	47. (a)	48. (b)
49. (d)	50. (b)	51. (c)	52. (c)	53. (a)	54. (a)	55. (c)	56. (a)
57. (b)	58. (a)	59. (a)	60. (b)	61. (d)	62. (a)	63. (c)	64. (c)
65. (d)	66. (b)	67. (a)					

ALKYL HALIDES AND ARYL HALIDES

1. Which of the following is a iso-butyl bromide ?

   (a) $CH_3CH_2CH_2CH_2Br$ (b) $CH_3CH-CH_2CH_3$ (c) $(CH_3)_2CHCH_2Br$ (d) $(CH_3)_3C-Br$

                                                $|$

                                             Br

2. Iso-propyl chloride is a ......

   (a) primary halide   (b) secondary halide   (c) tertiary halide   (d) neo-halide

3. Which of the following halides has all equivalent hydrogens ?

   (a) neo-pentyl chloride   (b) tert-butyl chloride

   (c) sec-butyl chloride   (d) n-butyl chloride

4. Which of the following is an alkyl halide ?

   (a) 4-bromo butene   (b) 1, 4–dibromo benzene

   (c) bromobenzene   (d) 1–bromo 2-phenylethane

5. Which of the following cannot be used for the preparation of iodoform?

   (a) Acetone   (b) Methanol   (c) Ethanal   (d) Acetaldehyde

6. Which of the following is a gem dihalide ?

   (a) 1, 2-dichloropropane   (b) 1, 3-dichloropropane

   (c) 2, 2-dichloropropane   (d) 2, 3-dichloropropane

7. The formula of westron is ......

   (a) $CHCl_3$ (b) CH_3Cl (c) $CHCl_2 \cdot CHCl_2$ (d) $CCl_2 = CHCl$

8. The common name of 1-chloro but-2-ene is

   (a) Cinnamyl chloride   (b) Crotyl chloride

   (c) Caproyl chloride   (d) Adipoyl chloride

9. The IUPAC name $(CH_3)_3C \cdot CH_2Br$ is ......

   (a) 2, 2–dimethyl–1–bromo propane   (b) 1–bromo–2, 2–dimethyl propane

   (c) trimethyl bromo ethane   (d) 2, 2, 2–trimethyl–1–bromo ethane

10. IUPAC name of westrosol $\begin{matrix} Cl & Cl \\ | & | \\ C & =C-H \\ | \\ Cl \end{matrix}$ is ......

    (a) 1, 1, 2, 2 trichloro ethene   (b) gem-dichloro ethylene chloride

    (c) 1, 1, 3–trichloro ethane   (d) trichloro ethane

11. Which one of the following is a gem-dihalide ?

    (a) CH_3CHBr_2 (b) $CH_2Br \cdot CH_2Br$

    (c) $CH_3CHBrCH_2Br$ (d) $CH_3CHBrCH_2CH_2Br$

12. The formula of Tosyl chloride is ......

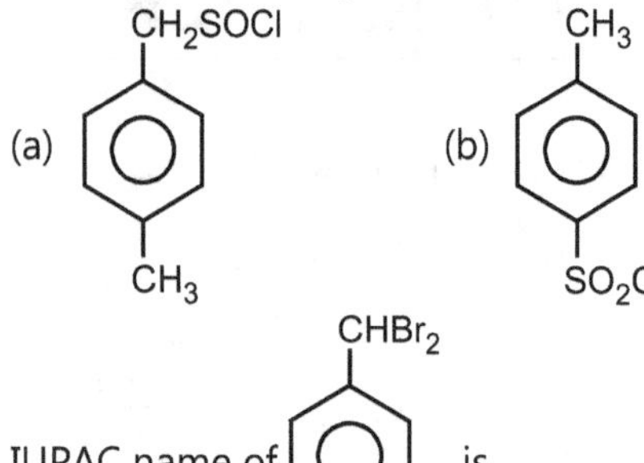

13. IUPAC name of 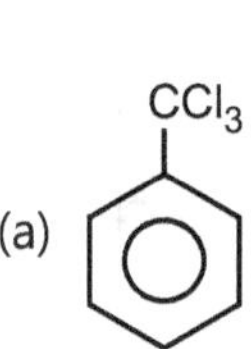 is ......

(a) 4–bromo–1, 1–dibromo–1–phenylmethane

(b) p–bromo dibromo methyl benzene

(c) 1, 1–dibromo–4–(bromophenyl) methane

(d) 4–bromo benzylidine bromide

14. Chloral is ......

(a) $CHCl_2CHO$ (b) CCl_3CHO (c) $CHCl_2CHClO$ (d) $CCl_3C = O$

15. Benzylidene chloride is ......

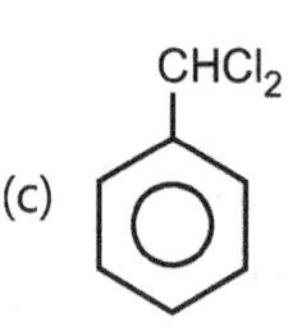

16. How many isomers are exhibited by $C_5H_{11}Br$?

(a) 4   (b) 5   (c) 6   (d) 7

17. How many primary halides are exhibited by $C_5H_{11}Br$?

(a) 1   (b) 2   (c) 3   (d) 4

18. Earlier DDT was widely used to combat malaria

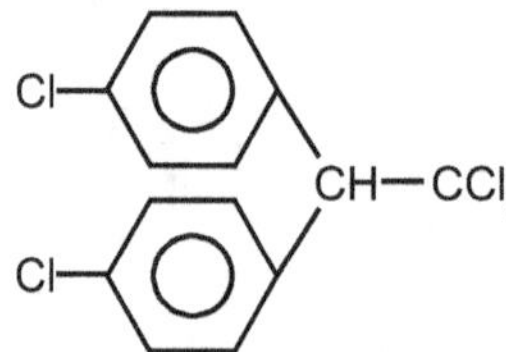

Which of the following statements about DDT is true?

(a) It is soluble in water   (b) It is non polar

(c) It is a polar molecule   (d) None of these

19. How many isomers are possible for $C_2H_2Br_2$?

(a) 5   (b) 4   (c) 3   (d) 2

20. How many isomers are possible for C_7H_7Br ?

(a) 4   (b) 3   (c) 2   (d) 5

21. Optical isomerism will be shown by which of the bromo derivatives of C_4H_9Br ?
    (a) n-butyl bromide
    (b) iso-butyl bromide
    (c) tert-butyl bromide
    (d) sec-butyl bromide

22. What is the general molecular formula of tri halo derivatives ?
    (a) $C_nH_{2n+1}X$
    (b) $C_nH_{2n-1}X_3$
    (c) $C_nH_{2n}X_3$
    (d) $C_nH_{2n+1}X_3$

23. Which of the following can give only two isomeric monochloro derivatives ?
    (a) iso-butane
    (b) n-pentane
    (c) Benzene
    (d) 2, 4-dimethyl propane

24. 1,3-dibromo propane reacts with metallic zinc to form ......
    (a) Propene
    (b) Cyclopropane
    (c) Propane
    (d) Hexane

25. Which of the following compounds is used as a refrigerant?
    (a) $COCl_2$
    (b) CCl_4
    (c) CF_4
    (d) CF_2Cl_2

26. Chloroform is obtained by the chlorination of methane; the mechanism involved is ......
    (a) Electrophilic substitution
    (b) Free radical substitution
    (c) Nucleophilic substitution
    (d) None of these

27. Chlorine was passed over methyl benzene under reflux in the presence of aluminium chloride. The compound formed and the mechanism is ......
    (a) ⬡—CH_2Cl; free radical mechanism
    (b) Cl—⬡—CH_2Cl; nucleophilic substitution
    (c) Cl—⬡—CH_2Cl; electrophilic and free radical substitution
    (d) Cl—⬡—CH_3 ; nucleophilic substitution

28. Tert-butyl bromide can be obtained by the addition of HBr to ......
    (a) But–1–ene
    (b) But–2–ene
    (c) 2–methyl propene
    (d) Propene

29. Name the reagents used during Grove's process for the conversion of propan–2–ol to 2–chloro propane.
    (a) PCl_5
    (b) $SOCl_2$
    (c) HCl | anhydrous $ZnCl_2$
    (d) PCl_3

30. During Finkelstein reaction, alkyl halide prepared is ......
    (a) Alkyl fluoride
    (b) Alkyl chloride
    (c) Alkyl bromide
    (d) Alkyl iodide

31. Hundsdiecker reaction for the preparation of alkyl bromide is the reaction between ......
    (a) Sodium salt of carboxylic acids and bromine
    (b) Silver salt of carboxylic acids and bromine in CCl_4, reflux
    (c) Silver salt of carboxylic acids and HBr
    (d) Diazonium chloride salts and bromine

32. A hydrocarbon of molecular mass 72 gm mol^{-1} gives single monochloro and two dichloro substituted compounds in chlorination in the presence of sunlight. The hydrocarbon is ......

(a) 2, 2–dimethyl propane

(b) 2–methyl butane

(c) Pentane

(d) All of these

33. The name of the following reaction is ......

$2CH_3CH_2Cl + Hg_2F_2 \rightarrow CH_3CH_2F + Hg_2Cl_2$

(a) Finkelstein reaction

(b) Grove's reaction

(c) Swart's reaction

(d) Hundsdiecker reaction

34. Addition of HBr to an alkene in the presence of peroxide is governed by ......

(a) Markownikoff's rule　(b) Kharasch effect　(c) Saytzeff's rule　(d) Hoffmann's rule

35. Identify the product X in the following reaction

$$CH_3—CH_2—CH = CH_2 \xrightarrow{\ HBr\ } X$$

(a) 2–bromo butane

(b) 1–bromo butane

(c) 3–bromo butane

(d) 2–methyl propane

36. The role of $ZnCl_2$ during the preparation of alkyl chloride from alcohol, acts as .... which helps in the ionisation of C–OH ?

(a) Electrophile

(b) Lewis acid

(c) Nucleophile

(d) Lewis base

37. Identify the product 'P' when tert butyl alcohol reacts with $KBr \mid H_2SO_4$.

$$CH_3—\overset{\overset{\displaystyle CH_3}{|}}{\underset{\underset{\displaystyle CH_3}{|}}{C}}—OH \xrightarrow{\ KBr/H_2SO_4\ } \text{'P'}$$

(a) 2–Bromo–2–methyl propane

(b) tert butyl bromide

(c) 2–methyl propene

(d) iso butane

38. The following reaction is called as.........

$2RCOOAg + I_2 \rightarrow RCOOR + CO_2 + 2AgI$

(a) Swart's reaction

(b) Birnbaurn Simonini reaction

(c) Hundsdiecker reaction

(d) Finkelstein reaction

39. Which of the following acts as a fire extinguisher under the name pyrene?

(a) CO_2

(b) CCl_4

(c) $CH_2 = CHCl$

(d) $ClCH = CHCl$

40. Which of the following cannot be obtained by diazonium salt ?

(a) C_6H_5I

(b) C_6H_5F

(c) CH_3Cl

(d) C_6H_5Cl

41. Among the following, which has lowest boiling point?

(a) neopentyl bromide

(b) n–pentyl bromide

(c) isopentyl bromide

(d) sec–pentyl bromide

42. Among the following, which has the highest boiling point ?

(a) RI

(b) RBr

(c) RF

(d) RCl

43. Which isomer of $C_6H_4Cl_2$ has the highest melting point ?

(a) 1, 2-dichlorobenzene

(b) 1, 4-dichlorobenzene

(c) 1, 3-dichlorobenzene

(d) Chlorobenzene

44. Density of alkyl halides is in the order ......

(a) $CH_3I < CH_3Br < CH_3Cl < CH_3F$ (b) $CH_3I > CH_3Br > CH_3Cl > CH_3F$

(c) $CH_3F > CH_3Br > CH_3Cl > CH_3I$ (d) $CH_3I < CH_3F < CH_3Br < CH_3Cl$

45. Which of the following alkyl halides decomposes in the presence of sunlight ?

(a) RF   (b) RBr   (c) RCl   (d) RI

46. Which of the following has maximum density ?

(a) CH_3I (b) C_3H_7I (c) C_4H_9I (d) C_2H_5I

47. Which of the following chloro compounds is not easily hydrolysed by hydroxide ion ?

(a) $C_2H_5Cl \xrightarrow{OH^-} C_2H_5OH$

(b) $CH_2CH_2{-}CH_3 \xrightarrow{OH^-} CH_3{-}CH_2{-}CH_3$, with Cl substituent

(c) $C_6H_5Cl \xrightarrow{OH^-} C_6H_5OH$

(d) $CH_3COCl \xrightarrow{OH^-} CH_3COOH$

48. 1, 2–dibromo–3–chloro propane (DBCP) is used in the control of earthworms in agricultural land. Which of the following would be the best way of synthesis of this compound?

(a) $CH_3CH_2CH_2Cl + 2Br_2 \rightarrow DBCP + 2HBr$ (b) $CH_2 = CHCHBr_2 + HCl \rightarrow DBCP$

(c) $CH_2 = CH{-}CH_2Cl + Br_2 \rightarrow DBCP$ (d) $CH_3CHBrCH_2Br + Cl_2 \rightarrow DBCP + HCl$

49. In which one of the following reactions does the inorganic reagent act as a nucleophile ?

(a) 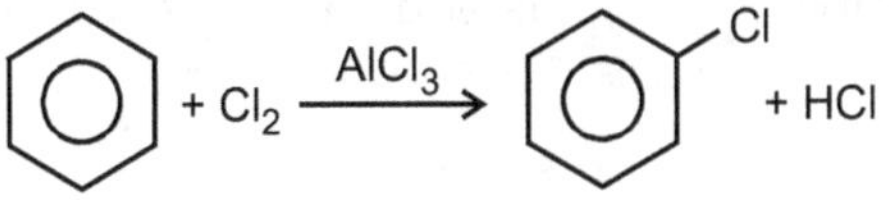 benzene $+ Cl_2 \xrightarrow{AlCl_3}$ chlorobenzene $+ HCl$

(b) $CH_3CH_3 + Cl_2 \xrightarrow{Light} CH_3CH_2Cl + HCl$

(c) $CH_2 = CH_2 + Cl_2 \rightarrow ClCH_2{-}CH_2{-}Cl$

(d) 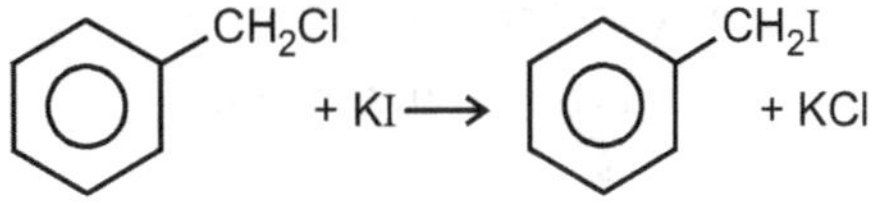 benzyl chloride ($-CH_2Cl$) $+ KI \rightarrow$ benzyl iodide ($-CH_2I$) $+ KCl$

50. A reaction sequence is shown below

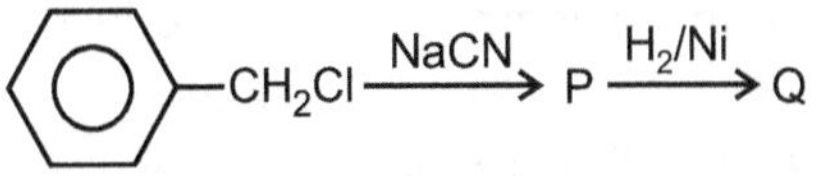

benzene$-CH_2Cl \xrightarrow{NaCN} P \xrightarrow{H_2/Ni} Q$

What would be the product Q ?

(a) 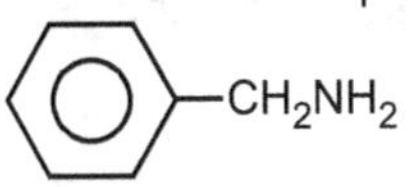 $-CH_2NH_2$ (phenyl)

(b) 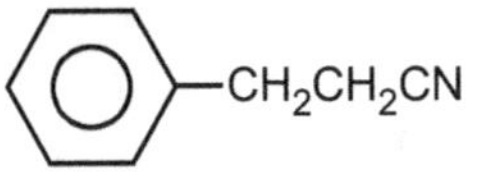 $-CH_2CH_2CN$ (phenyl)

(c) 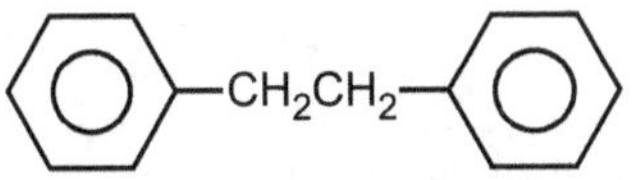 $-CH_2CH_2-$ (diphenyl)

(d) 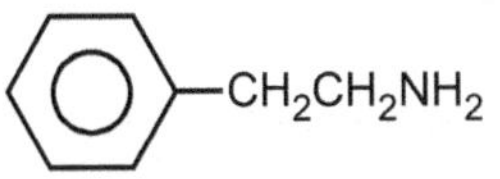 $-CH_2CH_2NH_2$ (phenyl)

51. Which one of the following pairs of reaction types is included in the reaction sequences below ?

$$CH_3CH = CH-CH_3 \xrightarrow[CH_3COOH]{HI\ in} CH_3\underset{\underset{I}{|}}{C}H-CH_3 \xrightarrow{NaOH\ (aq)} CH_3CH_2\underset{\underset{OH}{|}}{C}H-CH_3$$

(a) Electrophilic addition and electrophilic substitution

(b) Electrophilic addition and nucleophilic substitution

(c) Free radical addition and nucleophilic substitution

(d) Free radical addition and electrophilic substitution

52. Dichloro difluoromethane CCl_2F_2 is widely used in aerosol propellants and as a refrigerant. Which statement helps to explain why dichloro difluoro methane is chemically inert ?

(a) The carbon-fluorine bond energy is large

(b) The carbon-fluorine bond has a low polarity

(c) Fluorine is highly electro negative

(d) Fluorine compounds are non-inflammable

53. Trichloroethene is widely used as a dry cleaning agent

With which of the following does trichloroethene react to give a chiral product?

(a) H_2 (b) Br_2 (c) HCl   (d) NaOH (aq)

54. Compound 'A' on treatment with NaOH followed by the addition of $AgNO_3$ gives white precipitate at room temperature which is soluble in NH_4OH. Compound A is ......

(a) Chlorobenzene   (b) Ethyl bromide

(c) Acetyl chloride   (d) Benzyl chloride

55. An optically active halide when allowed to react with KCN gives a racemic mixture, the halide is ......

(a) Primary halide   (b) Secondary halide   (c) Tertiary halide   (d) None of these

56. When sodium salt of ethanol is treated with ethyl bromide, in dry ether the product is ......

(a) Ethoxy ethanol   (b) Ethoxy ethane   (c) Ether   (d) Butanone

57. When tert-butyl bromide is treated with sodium ethoxide, the product is ......

(a) 2-methyl propene   (b) 2-ethyl-2-methyl propane

(c) tert butyl ethyl   (d) Hexanone

58. The following reaction is an example of

$$CH_3)_3C-Br \xrightarrow{alc.\ KOH} CH_2 = \underset{\underset{CH_3}{|}}{\overset{\overset{CH_3}{|}}{C}} + H_2O + KBr$$

(a) Electrophilic substitution   (b) Nucleophilic substitution

(c) Free radical substitution   (d) β-elimination

59. Which of the following ethyl halides is most reactive towards nucleophilic substitution ?

(a) C_2H_5I (b) C_2H_5Br (c) C_2H_5Cl (d) C_2H_5F

60. PVC has repeating units of

(a) 1,1-dichloroethene (b) Chloroprene   (c) Chloroethene   (d) 1,2-dichloroethene

61. $S_N 1$ reaction mechanism proceeds through the intermediate ....

(a) Carbonium ion   (b) Carbon ion   (c) Free radical   (d) Carbene

62. In $S_N 2$ reaction, the rate of reaction depends on the concentration of ....

(a) $(CH_3)_3C - Br$ (b) $CH_3 - Br$

(c) $(CH_3)_3C - Br$ and aq. KOH   (d) CH_3Br and aq. KOH

63. $S_N 2$ reaction proceeds to give ....

(a) 50% retention   (b) 50% inversion

(c) 100% inversion   (d) 50% retention and 50% inversion

64. $S_N 2$ mechanism proceeds through the intervention of ......

(a) Carbocation   (b) Transition state   (c) Free radical   (d) Carbanion

65. $S_N 1$ reaction of alkyl halides leads to ......

(a) Retention of configuration   (b) Racemisation

(c) Inversion of configuration   (d) None of these

66. The IUPAC name of the compound shown below is

(a) 2 - bromo - 6 - iodo cyclohex - 1 - ene   (b) 6 - bromo - 2 - iodo cyclohexene

(c) 3 - bromo - 1 - iodo cyclohexene   (d) 1 - bromo - 3 iodo cyclohexene

67. Which of the following is responsible for depletion of ozone layer in the copper strata of the atmosphere ?

(a) Ferrocene   (b) Fullerenes   (c) Freons   (d) Polyhalogens

68. Elimination of bromine from 2-bromobutane results in the formation of predominantly ....

(a) 2-butyne   (b) 1-butene

(c) 2-butene   (d) Mixture of 1 and 2-butene

69. Allyl bromide on dehydrobromination gives ......

(a) Propadiene   (b) Propylene   (c) Allyl alcohol   (d) Acetone

70. Chloropicrin is obtained by the reaction of ......

(a) Nitric acid on chlorobenzene   (b) Chlorine on picric acid

(c) Nitric acid on chloroform   (d) Steam on carbon tetrachloride

71. When primary amine reacts with chloroform in ethanolic KOH, then product is ....

(a) An isocyanide   (b) An aldehyde   (c) A cyanide   (d) An alcohol

72. Tertiary alkyl halides are practically inert to substitution by $S_N 2$ mechanism because of ....

(a) Steric hindrance   (b) Inductive effect   (c) Instability   (d) Insolubility

73. Which of the following is least reactive in a nucleophilic substitution reaction ?

(a) $CH_2 = CHCl$ (b) CH_3CH_2Cl

(c) $CH_2 = CH - CH_2Cl$ (d) $(CH_3)_3C - Cl$

74.

$$CH_3Li + CH_2-CH_2 \xrightarrow[\text{O}]{H_3O^+} A$$

$$CH_3MgBr + CH_2-CH_2 \xrightarrow[\text{O}]{H_3O^+} B$$

Which is incorrect statement ?

(a) Both are primary alcohols

(b) Both have same boiling points

(c) Isomer of both is symmetrical ether

(d) Both on oxidation give ablehydes

75. The order of reactivities of the following alkyl halides for S_N2 reaction is

(a) RF > RCl > RBr > RI

(b) RF > RBr > RCl > RI

(c) RCl > RBr > RF > RI

(d) RI > RBr > RCl > RF

76. The order of reactivity of alkyl halides towards elimination reaction is ......

(a) Tertiary > secondary > primary

(b) Secondary > primary > tertiary

(c) Tertiary > primary > secondary

(d) Primary > secondary > tertiary

77. Among the following the molecule with the highest dipole moment is ......

(a) CH_3Cl

(b) CH_2Cl_2

(c) $CHCl_3$

(d) CCl_4

78. Which of the following has highest nucleophilicity ?

(a) F^-

(b) OH^-

(c) CH_3^-

(d) NH_2^-

79. In the reaction of p-chlorotoluene with KNH_2 in liq. NH_3, the major product is ......

(a) o-toluidine

(b) m-toluidine

(c) p-toluidine

(d) p-chloro aniline

80. The intermediate during the addition of HCl to propene in the presence of peroxide is ....

(a) $CH_3CH_2CH_2Cl$

(b) $CH_3\overset{\oplus}{C}HCH_3$

(c) $CH_3CH_2\overset{\bullet}{C}H_2$

(d) $CH_3CH_2\overset{\oplus}{C}H_2$

81. Silver benzoate reacts with bromine to give ......

(a) C_6H_6

(b) C_6H_5COOBr

(c) $m-Br-C_6H_4-COOAg$

(d) C_6H_5Br

82. A set of compounds in which the reactivity of halogen atom in the ascending order is ....

(a) Chlorobenzene, vinyl chloride, chloroethane

(b) Chloroethane, chlorobenzene, vinyl chloride

(c) Vinyl chloride, chlorobenzene, chloroethane

(d) Vinyl chloride, chloroethane, chlorobenzene

83. In chlorination of benzene, the reactive species is

(a) Cl^+

(b) Cl^-

(c) Cl_2

(d) Cl_2^-

84. The correct order of S_N1 reactivity is ......

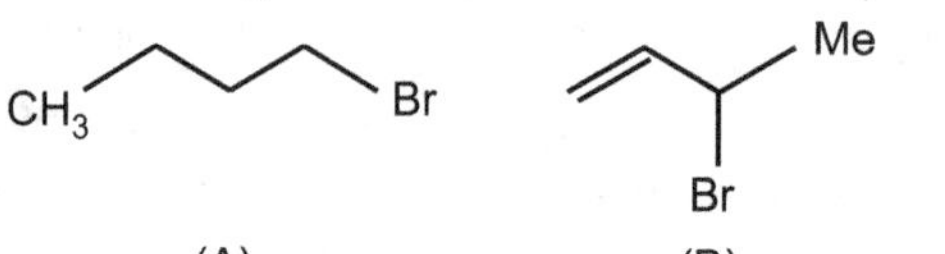

(a) A > B > C

(b) B > C > A

(c) B > A > C

(d) C > B > A

85. In Friedel-Craft's synthesis of toluene, reactants in addition to anhydrous $AlCl_3$ are ....
(a) $C_6H_6 + CH_4$ (b) $C_6H_6 + CH_3Cl$ (c) $C_6H_5Cl + CH_3Cl$ (d) $C_6H_5Cl + CH_4$

86. Which of the following reactions is most suitable for preparation of n-propyl benzene ?
(a) Friedel-Craft's reaction (b) Wurtz reaction
(c) Wurtz-Fittig reaction (d) Grignard reaction

87. Arrange the following compounds in order of increasing dipole moment : Toluene (I), m-dichlorobenzene (II), o-dichlorobenzene (III) and (IV) p-dichlorobenzene
(a) (I) < (IV) < (II) < (III) (b) (IV) < (I) < (II) < (III)
(c) (IV) < (I) < (III) < (II) (d) (IV) < (II) < (I) < (III)

88. Which among MeX, RCH_2X, R_2CHX, R_3CX is most reactive towards S_N2 reaction ?
(a) MeX (b) RCH_3X (c) R_2CHX (d) R_3CX

89. In the following groups :
(I) –OAc (II) –OMe (III) $–OSO_2Me$ (IV) $– OSO_2CF_3$
The order of ability of leaving group is ......
(a) (I) > (II) > (III) > (IV) (b) (IV) > (III) > (I) > (II)
(c) (III) > (II) > (I) > (IV) (d) (II) > (III) > (IV) > (I)

90. Among the following compounds, the decreasing order of reactivity towards electrophilic substitution is ......

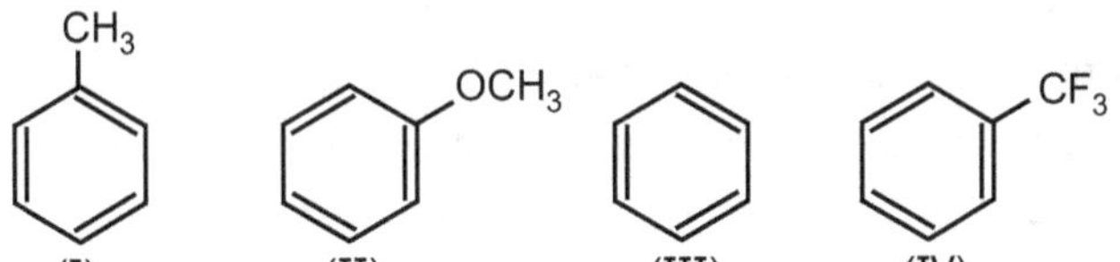

CH₃, OCH₃, CF₃

(I)   (II)   (III)   (IV)

(a) (III) > (I) > (II) > (IV) (b) (IV) > (I) > (II) > (III)
(c) (I) > (II) > (III) > (IV) (d) (II) > (I) > (III) > (IV)

91. An S_N2 reaction, at asymmetric carbon of a compound always gives ....
(a) an enantiomer of substrate (b) a product with opposite optical rotation
(c) a mixture of diastereomers (d) a single stereo isomer

92. Which of the following are arranged in decreasing order of dipole moment ?
(a) CH_3Cl, CH_3Br, CH_3F (b) CH_3Cl, CH_3F, CH_3Br
(c) CH_3Br, CH_3Cl, CH_3F (d) CH_3Br, CH_3F, CH_3Cl

93. The compound formed on heating chlorobenzene with chloral in the presence of concentrated sulphuric acid is ....
(a) Gammaxane (b) Hexachloromethane
(c) Freon (d) DDT

94. Fluorobenzene (C_6H_5F) can be synthesized in the laboratory ......
(a) By heating phenol with HF and KF
(b) From aniline by diazotization followed by heating with HBF_4
(c) By direct fluorination of benzene by F_2 gas
(d) By reacting bromobenzene with NaF solution

95. Which of the following undergoes nucleophilic substitution exclusively by S_N1 mechanism ?

(a) Ethyl chloride

(b) Isopropyl chloride

(c) Chlorobenzene

(d) Benzyl chloride

96. Among the following the most reactive towards alcoholic KOH is ......

(a) $CH_2 = CHCl$ (b) $CH_3COCH_2CH_2Cl$ (c) CH_3CH_2Cl (d) $CH_3CH_2CH_2Cl$

97. Aromatic nitriles (ArCN) are not prepared by the reaction :

(a) ArX + KCN   (b) ArN_2 + CuCN   (c) $ArCONH_2 + P_2O_5$ (d) $ArCONH_2 + SOCl_2$

98. For the following

(A) I^- (B) Cl^- (C) Br^-

the increasing order of nucleophilicity would be :

(a) $Br^- < Cl^- < I^-$ (b) $I^- < Br^- < Cl^-$ (c) $Cl^- < Br^- < I^-$ (d) $I^- < Cl^- < Br^-$

99. $CH_3Br + Nu^- \longrightarrow CH_3 - Nu + Br^-$

The decreasing order of the rate of above reaction with nucleophiles (Nu^-) A to D is ...

(Nu = (A) phe^- (B) OAc^- (C) OH^- (D) CH_3O^-

(a) D > C > A > B   (b) D > C > B > A   (c) A > B > C > D   (d) B > D > C > A

100. Which of the following is the correct order of decreasing S_N2 reactivity ?

(a) $R_3CX > R_2CHX > RCH_2X$

(b) $R_2CHX > R_3CX > RCH_2X$

(c) $RCH_2X > R_3CX > R_2CH_3X$

(d) $RCH_2X > R_2CHX > R_3CX$

101. The reaction of toluene with Cl_2 in the presence of $FeCl_3$ gives predominantly ......

(a) o and p-chlorotoluene

(b) m-chlorotoluene

(c) Benzyl chloride

(d) Benzoyl chloride

102. For conversion of $C_6H_5CH_2CH_3$ into $C_6H_5CH = CH_2$, following sequence of reagents can be used.

(a) $SOCl_2$; H_2O

(b) Cl_2/hv; alc. KOH

(c) Cl_2/hv; H_2O

(d) $SOCl_2$; alc. KOH

103. $CH_3-CH_2-CH = CH_2$ (A) $\xrightarrow[?]{HBr}$ (B) $\xrightarrow{aq.\ KOH}$ (C)

If compound C is butan-1-ol, then (A) undergoes ......

(a) Markownikoff's rule

(b) Peroxide rule

(c) Satyzeff's rule

(d) Dehydrohalogenation rule

104. 3-chloro-3-methyl heptane contains the following number of asymmetric carbon atoms ...

(a) Two   (b) Three   (c) One   (d) Zero

105. Isomers whose molecular structures are non-superimposable mirror images of each other are called ....

(a) Tautomers   (b) Diastereomers   (c) Mesomers   (d) Enantiomers

106. The reaction of an alkyl halide with alcoholic NH_3 is called as ....

(a) Hydrolysis   (b) Ammonolysis   (c) Pyrolysis   (d) Electrolysis

107. Chloroform cannot be prepared from the following compound ......

(a) Ethanol   (b) Ethanal   (c) Ethene   (d) Acetone

108. The number of asymmetric carbon atoms in lactic acid, $CH_3-CHOH-COOH$ is ....

    (a) 3   (b) 4   (c) 1   (d) 2

109. The disymmetry in the molecule is the essential condition for the existence of the following ......

    (a) Enantiomers   (b) Isomers   (c) Racemic mixture   (d) Epimers

110. A ray of light consisting of a single wavelength vibrating only in one direction is ......

    (a) Ordinary light   (b) Monochromatic light

    (c) Plane polarized light   (d) UV light

111. The product formed in the reaction of alcoholic silver nitrite with ethyl bromide is ......

    (a) Ethane   (b) Ethene   (c) Ethanol   (d) Nitroethane

112. The raw material of Raschig process is ......

    (a) Chlorobenzene   (b) Phenol   (c) Benzene   (d) Anisol

113. Auto-oxidation of chloroform in air and sunlight produces a poisonous gas called ......

    (a) Phosgene   (b) Mustard gas   (c) Benzophenone   (d) Acetophenone

114. Which of the following reagents will not convert ethyl alcohol into ethyl chloride?

    (a) $HCl\text{-}ZnCl_2$ (b) PCl_5 (c) $NaCl$ (d) $SOCl_2$

115. When an excess of ethyl chloride is heated with concentrated ammonia, the major product formed is?

    (a) Ethylamine   (b) Diethylamine

    (c) Ethylenediamine   (d) Tetraethylammonium chloride

116. The compound obtained by heating a mixture of an aliphatic primary amine and chloroform with alcoholic KOH is ......

    (a) Alkyl isocyanate   (b) Alkyl cyanate   (c) Alkyl cyanide   (d) Alkyl isocyanide

117. Which of the following processes does not occur during the formation of $CHCl_3$ from C_2H_5OH and bleaching powder?

    (a) Oxidation   (b) Chlorination   (c) Hydrolysis   (d) Reduction

118. Which of the following statements is not true about chloroform?

    (a) It is used as an anaesthetic   (b) It is a good organic solvent

    (c) It has an ideal sp^3 hybridized carbon   (d) It is carcinogenic

119. When CH_3CH_2Br reacts with sodium acetylide, the main product is ......

    (a) butane   (b) but-1-yne   (c) but-2-ene   (d) 2-butyne

120. The optically inactive compound is ......

    (a) Glucose   (b) Lactic acid   (c) 2-chlorobutane   (d) 2-chloropropane

121. Tetrabromoethane on treatment with alcoholic zinc gives ......

    (a) Ethylbromide   (b) Ethane   (c) Ethene   (d) Ethyne

122. Arrange the following halides in the decreasing order of S_N1 reactivity ......

    (i) $CH_3CH_2CH_2Cl$ (ii) $CH_2 = CHCH(Cl)CH_3$ (iii) $CH_3CH_2CH(Cl)CH_3$

    (a) (i) > (ii) > (iii)   (b) (ii) > (i) > (iii)   (c) (ii) > (iii) > (i)   (d) (iii) > (ii) > (i)

123. Which of the following halides will react most rapidly in a S_N2 reaction ?

    (a) CH_3F　　　　(b) CH_3Cl　　　　(c) CH_3Br　　　　(d) CH_3I

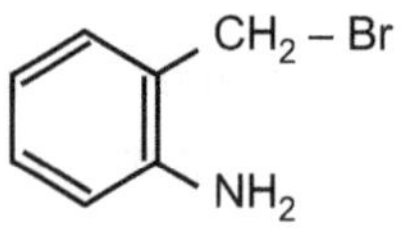

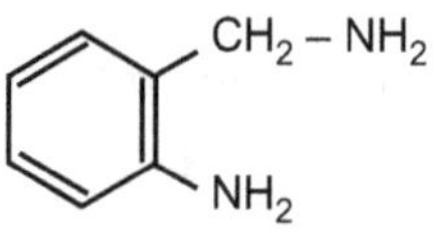

124.

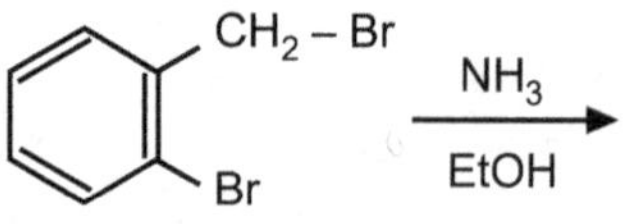

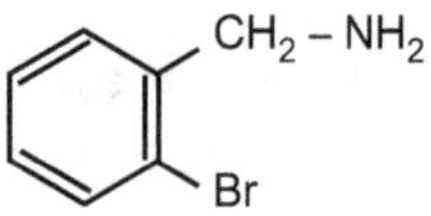

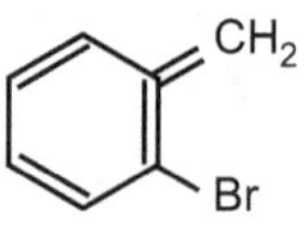

125. Predict the product

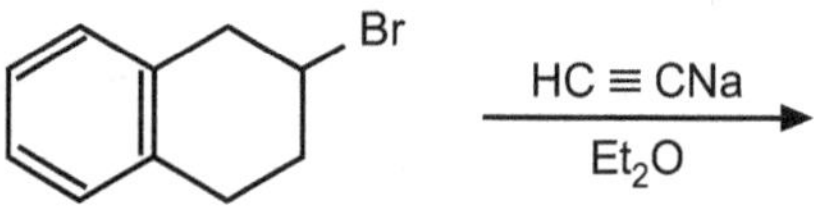

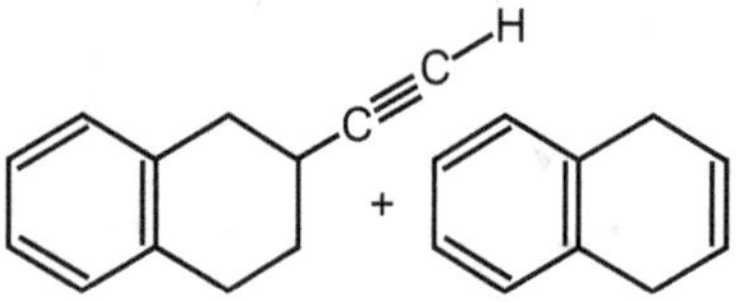

126. 50% inversion of configuration of molecules take place in a ......

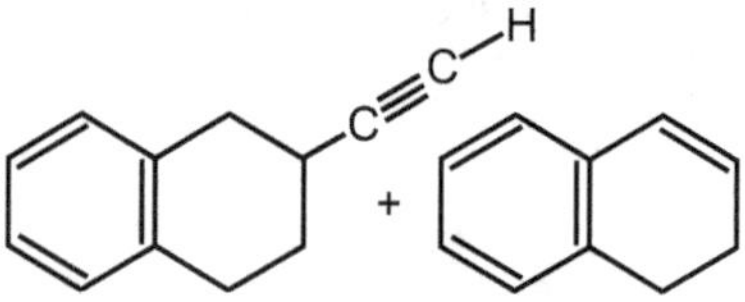

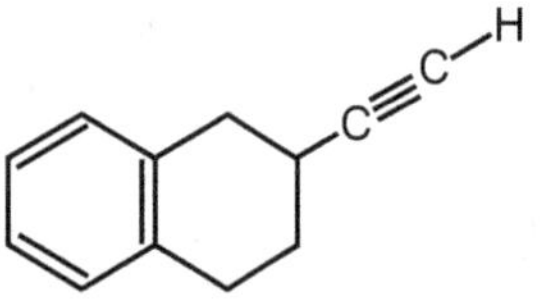

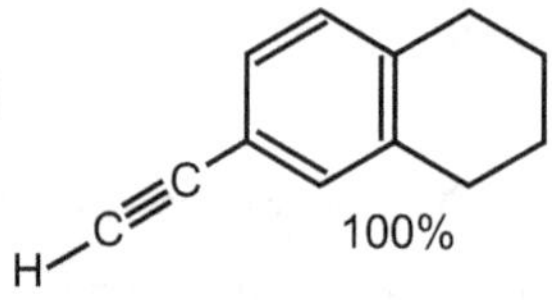

    (a) E1-reaction　　　(b) E2-reaction　　　(c) S_N1-reaction　　　(d) S_N2-reaction

127. Which set of reagents are used to carry out following reaction

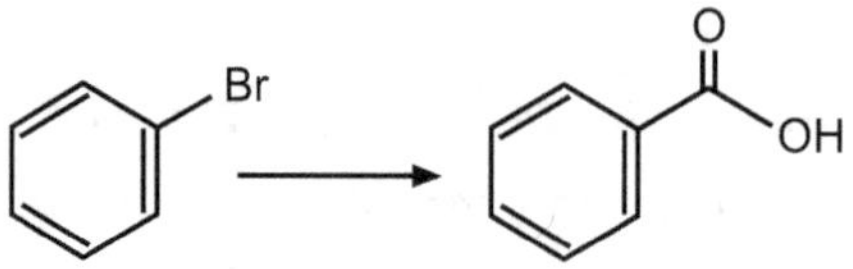

    (a) (1) Mg ether (2) CO_2 (3) H_3O^+　　　(b) (1) Mg (2) CO_2 (3) H_3O^+　　　(c) (1) Mg, ether (2) CH_4 (3) H_3O^+　　　(d) (1) Mg, ether (2) H_2CO (3) H_3O^+

128. Identify the product

$$\text{(o-toluidine)} \xrightarrow[\text{2) CuCl}]{\text{1) NaNO}_2,\ \text{HCl/H}_2\text{O}}$$

(a)   (b)   (c)   (d)

129. Which of the following shows correct order of reactivity towards nucleophilic substitution (aq. KOH) ?

(a), (b), (c), (d)

130.

$$\underset{\underset{C_3H_7}{|}}{\overset{\overset{C_2H_5}{|}}{CH_3 - C - Cl}} + OH^- \rightarrow \underset{\underset{C_3H_7}{|}}{\overset{\overset{C_2H_5}{|}}{CH_3 - C - OH}}$$

What is the stereochemistry of the above reaction?

(a) Complete racemisation

(b) Maximum racemisation along with partial inversion

(c) Complete inversion

(d) Maximum inversion with partial racemisation

131. $CCl_4 + H_2O \longrightarrow A + HCl$

'A' is also formed when another compound B is oxidised in air. What will be the product of the following reaction?

$$B + Ag \longrightarrow$$

(a) $COCl_2$ (b) $CH_3 - Cl$ (c) $CHCl_3$ (d) $HC \equiv CH$

132. What is the major product of the following reaction?

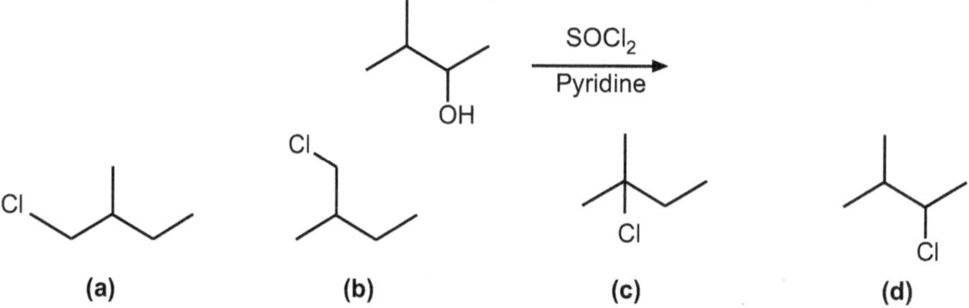

(a)   (b)   (c)   (d)

133. What is the major product of the following reaction?

(a)   (b)   (c)   (d)

134. Identify (A) and (B).

$$\text{Benzene} \xrightarrow[\text{2. Sn / HCl}]{\text{1. HNO}_3\text{ / H}_2\text{SO}_4} A \xrightarrow[\text{2. HBF}_4]{\text{1. HNO}_2} B$$

(a) Aniline and nitrobenzene

(b) Aniline and fluorobenzene

(c) BDC and fluorobenzene

(d) Benzene and fluorobenzene

135. When chlorine is passed through propene at 400°C, which of the following is formed?

(a) allyl chloride

(b) n-propyl chloride

(c) iso-propyl chloride

(d) sec-propyl chloride

136. Which of the following cannot be made by using Williamson's synthesis?

(a) anisole

(b) benzyl-p-nitrophenyl ether

(c) methyl-tert-butyl ether

(d) di-ter-butyl ether

137. DDT is prepared by reacting chlorobenzene with ......

(a) $CHCl_3$ (b) CCl_3CHO (c) CCl_4 (d) C_2H_6

PREVIOUS YEAR'S QUESTIONS

1. In the replacement reaction $\underset{|}{\overset{|}{C}}I + MF \rightarrow \underset{|}{\overset{|}{C}}F + MI$, the reaction will be most favourable if M happens to be ......   **[AIPMT 2012]**

(a) Na   (b) K   (c) Rb   (d) Li

2. In the following sequence of reactions,

$$CH_3Br \xrightarrow{\text{KCN}} A \xrightarrow{\text{H}_3\text{O}^+} B \xrightarrow{\text{LiAlH}_4} C \text{ the end product (C) is ......}$$ **[CBSE AIPMT 2012]**

(a) acetone   (b) methane   (c) acetaldehyde   (d) ethyl alcohol

3. Which products are formed when the following compared is treated with Br_2 in the presence of $FeBr_3$? **[AIPMT 2015]**

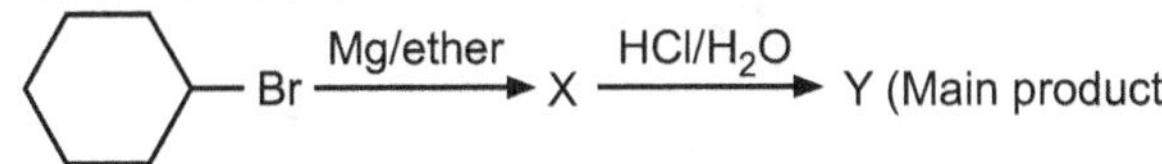

4. Which of the following compounds will undergo racemisation on hydrolysis ?

(i)

(ii) $CH_3CH_2CH_2Cl$

(iii) $(CH_3)_2CH–CH_2Cl$

(iv)

(a) (i)   (b) (ii)   (c) (iii)   (d) (iv)

5. Which of the following compounds will give a yellow precipitate with iodine and alkali? **[CBSE AIPMT 2012]**

(a) 3-Hydroxy pentane   (b) Methyl acetate   (c) Acetamide   (d) 2-Hydroxypropane

6. When alkyl halide is heated with dry Ag_2O, it produces ...... **[Manipal 2012]**

(a) ester   (b) ether   (c) ketone   (d) alcohol

7. In alkaline hydrolysis of a tertiary halide by aqueous solution of alkali if concentration of alkali is doubled, then the reaction ...... **[AIIMS 2012]**

(a) will be doubled   (b) will be halved

(c) will remain constant   (d) none of these

8. Given reaction, **[DUMET 2011]**

$$\text{Cyclohexyl–Br} \xrightarrow{\text{Mg/ether}} X \xrightarrow{\text{HCl/H}_2\text{O}} Y \text{ (Main product)}$$

'Y' in the reaction is ......

(a) hexane   (b) cyclohexane

(c) cyclohexyl cyclohexane   (d) cyclohexyl ether

9. Which one of the following is not true for the hydrolysis of butyl bromide with aqueous NaOH ? **[KCET 2011]**

(a) Reaction occurs through the S_N1 mechanism.

(b) The intermediate formed is a carbocation.

(c) Rate of the reaction doubles when the concentration of alkali is doubled.

(d) Rate of the reaction doubles when the concentration of butyl bromide is doubled.

10. Following is the substitution reaction in which –CN replaces –Cl.

$R - Cl + KCN \rightarrow R - CN + KCl$	**[KCET 2011]**

To obtain propanenitrile, $R - Cl$ should be ......

(a) chloroethane　　(b) 1-chloropropane　(c) chloromethane　(d) 2-chloropropane

11. An alkyl halide with molecular formula $C_6H_{13}Br$ on dehydrohalogenation gave two isomeric alkenes X and Y with molecular formula C_6H_{12}. On reductive ozonolysis, X and Y gave four compounds CH_3COCH_3, CH_3CH_2CHO and $(CH_3)_2CHCHO$. The alkyl halide is ......

(a) 2-bromohexane	**[Kerala CEE 2011]**

(b) 2,2-dimethyl-1-bromobutane　　　　(c) 4-bromo-2 methylpentane

(d) 2-bromo-2, 3-dimethylbutane　　　　(e) 3-bromo-2-methylpentane

12. The reaction of methyl bromide with aqueous sodium hydroxide involves ......

(a) racemisation　　　　　　　　　　(b) S_N^1 mechanism　　**[KCET 2010]**

(c) retention of configuration　　　　　(d) S_N^2 mechanism

13. Among the following, the correct statement is	**[AFMC 2009]**

(a) aniline is a weaker base than ammonia.

(b) in water, solubility order of alcohols is $CH_3OH > C_2H_5OH > C_6H_5OH$

(c) boiling point of alkyl halide is greater than its corresponding alkane.

(d) all of the given statements are correct.

14. The increasing order of hydrolysis of the following compounds is

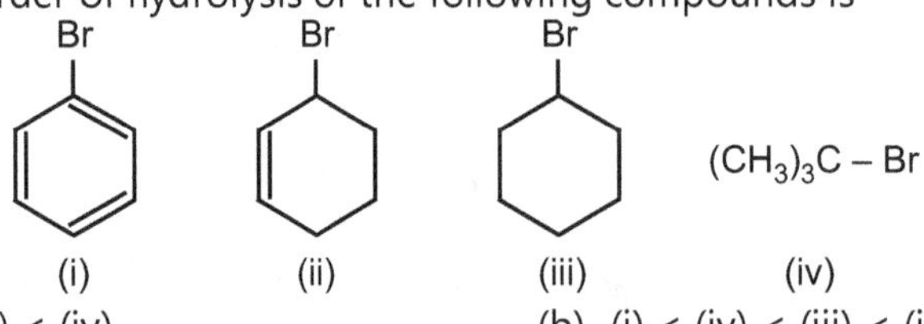

(a) (i) < (iii) < (ii) < (iv)　　　　　　　(b) (i) < (iv) < (iii) < (ii)

(c) (iv) < (ii) < (iii) < (i)　　　　　　　(d) (i) < (iii) < (iv) < (ii)

15. Which of the following compounds will not undergo Friedel Craft reaction ... **[AIPMT 2014]**

(a) cumene　　　　　(b) xylene　　　　　(c) nitrobenzene　(d) toluene

16. Identify A in the following sequence of reaction	**[NEET 2013)**

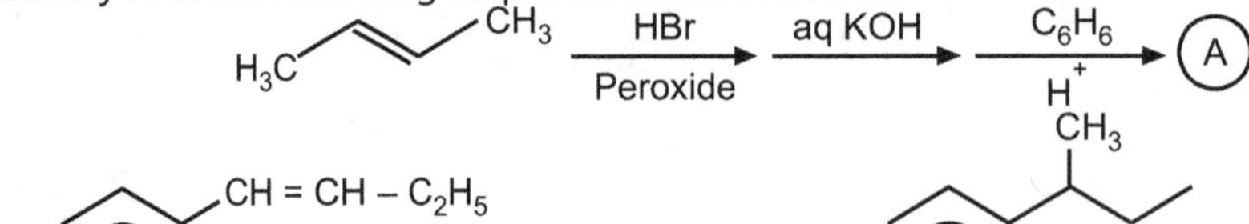

17. Which of the following reagents when heated with ethyl chloride, forms ethylene?

(a) aqueous KOH   (b) Zn/HCl   (c) Alcoholic KOH   (d) HI   **[AFMC 2008]**

18. The catalyst used in the preparation of an alkyl chloride by the action of dry HCl on an alcohol is ......   **[AFMC 2008]**

(a) anhyd. $AlCl_3$ (b) $FeCl_3$ (c) anhyd. $ZnCl_2$ (d) Cu

19. Which of the following can give a Grignard reagent when reacted with magnesium in dry ether?   **[CPMT 2008]**

(a) C_2H_6 (b) C_2H_5OH (c) C_2H_5Cl (d) C_2H_5CN

20. The alkyl halides that can be made by free radical halogenations of alkanes are ......

[Manipal 2008]

(a) RCl and RBr but not RF or RI   (b) RF, RCl and RBr but not RI

(c) RF, RCl, RBr, RI   (d) RF, RCl and RI but not RBr

21. Ethyl bromide is industrially prepared from ......   **[CPMT 2007]**

(a) ethyl alcohol + HBr   (b) ethanol + Br_2

(c) alcohol + HBr   (d) none of these

22. The major product formed in the following reaction   **[AIIMS 2006]**

$$CH_3CH(Cl)CH_2 - CH_2OH \xrightarrow{aq\ KOH} is\ ......$$

(a) $CH_3CH = CH - CH_2OH$ (b) $CH_2 = CH - CH_2 - CH_2OH$

(c) $CH_3 - \underset{\underset{\displaystyle O\!\!-\!\!-\!\!CH_2}{|\qquad|}}{CH - CH_2}$ (d) $H_3C - \underset{\underset{\displaystyle OH}{|}}{CH} - CH_2 - CH_2OH$

23. In the reaction $R - X \rightarrow A \rightarrow B$ the product is ......

(a) alkyl chloride   (b) aldehyde   (c) carboxylic acid   (d) ketone

24. The product obtained on reaction of C_2H_2Cl with hydrogen over palladium carbon is ......

[AFMC 2006]

(a) C_3H_8 (b) C_4H_{10} (c) C_2H_6 (d) C_2H_4

25. The major product formed in the following reaction is   **[AIIMS 2006]**

$$CH_3 - \underset{\underset{\displaystyle H}{|}}{\overset{\overset{\displaystyle CH_3}{|}}{C}} - CH_2Br \xrightarrow[CH_3OH]{CH_3O^-} ?$$

(a) $(CH_3)_2CHCH_2OCH_3$ (b) $CH_3 - \underset{\underset{\displaystyle OCH_3}{|}}{CH} - CH_2CH_3$

(c) $\underset{\displaystyle CH_3 - \overset{\overset{\displaystyle CH_3}{|}}{C} = CH_2}{}$ (d) $CH_3 - \underset{\underset{\displaystyle OCH_3}{|}}{\overset{\overset{\displaystyle CH_3}{|}}{C}} - CH_3$

26. The major product obtained on treatment of $CH_3CH_2CH(F)CH_3$ with CH_3O^-/CH_3OH is ......

 (a) $CH_3CH_2CH(OCH_3)CH_3$ (b) $CH_3CH = CHCH_3$

 (c) $CH_3CH_2CH = CH_2$ (d) $CH_3CH_2CH_2CH_2OCH_3$

27. C – Cl bond is stronger than C – I bond, because   **[MHT CET 2005]**

 (a) C – Cl bond is more ionic than C – I   (b) C – Cl bond is polar covalent bond

 (c) C – Cl bond is more covalent than C – Cl (d) C – Cl bond length is longer than C – I

28. Ethyl chloride is converted into diethyl ether by ......   **[Manipal 2004]**

 (a) Perkin reaction   (b) Grignard reagent

 (c) Wurtz reaction   (d) Williamson's synthesis

29. Which of the following statement is incorrect regarding benzyl chloride?

 (a) It gives white precipitate with alcoholic $AgNO_3$

 (b) It is an aromatic compound with substitution in the side chain.

 (c) It undergoes nucleophilic substitution reaction.

 (d) It is less reactive than vinyl chloride.

30. Hydrolysis of trichloromethane with aqueous KOH gives ......   **[AFMC 2010]**

 (a) methanol   (b) acetic acid   (c) ethanol   (d) formic acid

31. If 1, 3-dibromopropane reacts with zinc and NaI, the product obtained is **[AFMC 2010]**

 (a) propene   (b) propane   (c) cyclopropane   (d) hexane

32. The reaction of chloroform with KOH in the presence of a primary aromatic amine is called

 ......   **[Manipal 2010]**

 (a) carbylamine reaction   (b) reduction

 (c) hydrolysis   (d) Wurtz reaction

33. Ethylidene dibromide $\xrightarrow{A}$ $HC \equiv CH$. A is ......   **[CPMT 2009]**

 (a) $NaNH_2$ (b) alc. KOH   (c) conc. H_2SO_4 (d) all of these

34. A dihaloalkane 'X' having formula $C_3H_6Cl_2$, on hydrolysis gives a compound, that can reduce Tollen's reagent. The compound 'X' is ......   **[MHT 2009]**

 (a) 1,2-dichloropropane   (b) 1,1- dichloropropane

 (c) 1,3-dichloropropane   (d) 2,2- dichloropropane

35. Chloroform on reduction with zinc dust and water gives ......   **[MHT CET 2009]**

 (a) methyl chloride   (b) dichloromethane

 (c) chloromethane   (d) methane

36. Which one of the following does not undergo iodoform reaction ? **[J&K CET 2009]**

 (a) Secondary butyl alcohol   (b) Iso-propyl alcohol

 (c) Diethyl ketone   (d) Ethyl alcohol

37. Which of the following is added to chloroform to slow down its aerial oxidation in the presence of light?   **[AFMC 2008]**

 (a) Carbonyl chloride   (b) Ethyl alcohol

 (c) Sodium hydroxide   (d) Nitric acid

38. The chemical formula of 'tear gas' is ......   **[AIIMS 2008]**

(a) $COCl_2$ (b) CO_2 (c) $CH_3COCH_2NO_2$ (d) CCl_3NO_2

39. Iodoform gives a precipitate with $AgNO_3$ on heating but chloroform does not because ...

[CPMT 2008]

(a) $C - I$ bond in iodoform is weak and $C - Cl$ bond in chloroform is strong

(b) chloroform is covalent

(c) iodoform is ionic

(d) none of these

40. The reaction of toluene with Cl_2 in the presence of $FeCl_3$ gives X and reaction in the presence of light gives Y. Thus, X and Y are ......   **[CBSE AIPMT 2010]**

(a) X = benzyl chloride, Y = m-chlorotoluene

(b) X = benzal chloride, Y = o-chlorotoluene

(c) X = m-chlorotoluene, Y = p-chlorotoluene

(d) X = o-and p-chlorotoluene, Y = benzyl chloride

41. Which one is the most reactive towards S_N1 reaction?   **[CBSE AIPMT 2010]**

(a) $C_6H_5CH_2Br$ (b) $C_6H_5CH(C_6H_5)Br$

(c) $C_6H_5CH(CH_3)Br$ (d) $C_6H_5C(CH_3)(C_6H_5)Br$

42. In Dow's process, the starting raw material is ......   **[MHT CET 2009]**

(a) phenol   (b) chlorobenene   (c) aniline   (d) diazobenzene

43. Chlorobenzene react with Mg in dry ether to give a compound (1) which further reacts with ethanol to give ......   **[Manipal 2009]**

(a) phenol   (b) benzene   (c) ethyl benzene   (d) phenyl ether

44. Friedel-Craft's reaction of bromobenzene with methyl iodide gives ...   **[Manipal 2009]**

(a) o-bromotoluene   (b) p-bromotoluene

(c) o-and p-bromotoluene   (d) m-bromotoluene

45. Among the following which one has the weakest carbon-halogen bond?

(a) Benzyl bromide   (b) Bromobenzene

(c) Vinyl bromide   (d) Benzyl chloride   **[Manipal 2009]**

46. Match List I and List II and pick the correct matching from the codes given below.

List I (Halo enc)	List II (Applications)
A. Iodoform	1. CF_4
B. BHC	2. Antiseptic
C. Freon-14	3. Moth repellent
D. Halothanes	4. Inhalative anaesthetic
E. p-dichlorobenzene	5. Termite pesticide

	A	B	C	D	E
a	2	4	5	3	1
b	2	5	1	4	3
c	3	4	2	1	5
d	1	3	5	2	4
e	5	4	3	2	1

47. Which of the following statements about benzyl chloride is incorrect?

(a) It is less reactive than alkyl halides.   **[KCET 2004]**

(b) It can be oxidized to benzaldehyde by boiling with copper nitrate solution.

(c) It is a lachrymatory liquid and answers Beilstein's test.

(d) It gives a white precipitate with alcoholic silver nitrate.

48. Assertion : Benzyl bromide when kept in acetone water produces benzyl alcohol.

Reason : The reaction follows S_N2 mechanism.   **[AIIMS 2003]**

(a) Both Assertion and Reason are true and Reason is the correct explanation of Assertion.

(b) Both Assertion and Reason are true and Reason is not the correct explanation of Assertion.

(c) Assertion is true but Reason is false.

(d) Both Assertion and Reason are false.

49. Which of these can be used as moth repellant ?   **[CPMT 1987]**

(a) Benzene hexachloride   (b) Benzalchloride

(c) Hexachloroethane   (d) Tetrachloroethane

50. Freon (dichlorodifluoro methane) is used ...... **[CPMT 1986; DPMT 1983; CBSE PMT 2001]**

(a) As local anaesthetic

(b) For dissolving impurities in metallurgical process

(c) In refrigerator   (d) In printing industry

51. Which of the following is known as Freon which is used as a refrigerant ?

[CPMT 1979, 81, 89, AFMT 1995, Manipal MEE 1995, MPPET 1995, 2004]

(a) CCl_2F_2 (b) $CHCl_3$ (c) $CClF_3$ (d) CF_4

52. Which of the following is used in fire extinguishers ?   **[AFMC 1993]**

(a) $COCl_2$ (b) $CHCl_3$ (c) CH_2Cl_2 (d) CCl_4

53. Iodoform can be used as ......   **[NCERT 1981]**

(a) Anaesthetic   (b) Antiseptic   (c) Analgesic   (d) Antifebrin

54. In fire extinguisher, pyrene is ......   **[DPMT 1985]**

(a) CH_2Cl_2 (b) CCl_4 (c) CH_3CH_2Cl (d) $CHCl_3$

55. The number of double bonds in gammexane is ......   **[UPCPMT 2002]**

(a) 0   (b) 1   (c) 2   (d) 3

56. Ethyl bromide is industrially prepared from ......   **[UPCPMT 2007]**

(a) ethyl alcohol + HBr (b) ethanol + Br_2 (c) alcohol + HBr   (d) none of these

57. $AgNO_3$ does not give precipitate with $CHCl_3$ because ...... **[UPCPMT 2007]**
(a) $CHCl_3$ does not ionize in water
(b) $AgNO_3$ is chemically inert
(c) $CHCl_3$ is chemically inert
(d) none of these

58. Which of the following can give a Grignard reagent when reacted with magnesium in dry ether? **[UPCPMT 2008]**
(a) C_2H_6
(b) C_2H_5Cl
(c) C_2H_5OH
(d) C_2H_5CN

59. t-butyl chloride preferably undergo hydrolysis by ...... **[UPCPMT 2008]**
(a) S_N1 mechanism
(b) S_N2 mechanism
(c) any of (a) and (b)
(d) none of these

60. Identify A in the given sequence of reaction

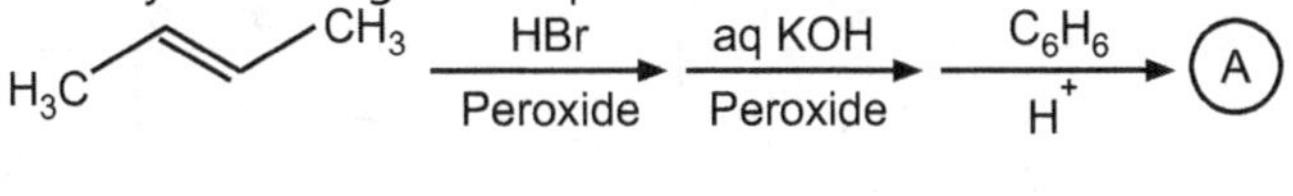

$$H_3C-CH=CH-CH_3 \xrightarrow[\text{Peroxide}]{HBr} \xrightarrow[\text{Peroxide}]{aq\ KOH} \xrightarrow[H^+]{C_6H_6} (A)$$

(a) 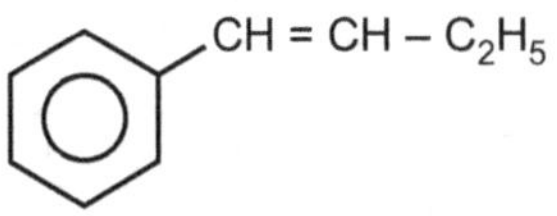 $C_6H_5-CH=CH-C_2H_5$

(b) $C_6H_5-CH(CH_3)-CH_2-CH_3$

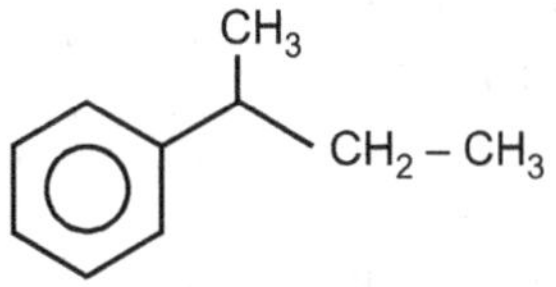

(c) $C_6H_5-CH(CH_3)-CH=CH_2$

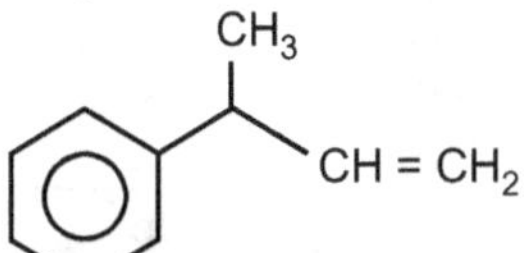

(d) 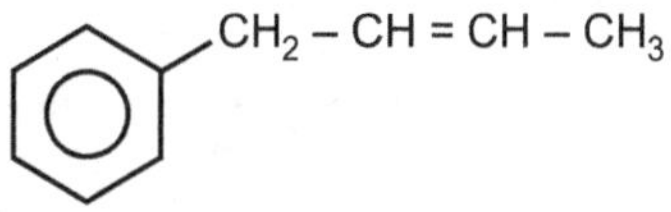 $C_6H_5-CH_2-CH=CH-CH_3$

61. How many monochlorobutanes will be possible on chlorination of n-butane ?
[Kerala C.E.E. 2000]
(a) 1
(b) 2
(c) 3
(d) 5

62. $C_7H_8 \xrightarrow{3Cl_2,\ Heat} A \xrightarrow{Fe/Br_2} B \xrightarrow{Zn/HCl} C$
Here the compound C is ...... **[D.C.E. 2000]**
(a) 3-bromo, 2, 4, 6-trichlorotoluene
(b) o-bromotoluene
(c) p-bromotoluene
(d) m-bromotoluene

63. The order of reactivity of alkyl halides towards elimination reaction is ...... **[Manipal 2002]**
(a) $3° > 2° > 1°$
(b) $2° > 1° > 3°$
(c) $3° > 1° > 2°$
(d) $1° > 2° > 3°$

64. When chloroform is boiled with NaOH, it gives ...... **[Orissa J.E.E. 2003]**
(a) Formic acid
(b) Trihydroxymethane
(c) Acetylene
(d) Sodium formate

65. S_N1 reaction is fastest in ...... **[Orissa J.E.E. 2004]**
(a) CH_3CH_2Cl
(b) 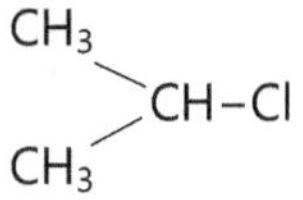 $(CH_3)_2CH-Cl$
(c) 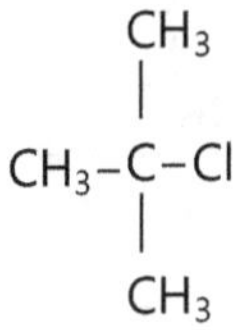 $CH_3-C(CH_3)_2-Cl$
(d) 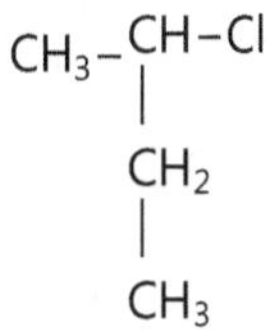 $CH_3-CH(Cl)-CH_2-CH_3$

66. Which represents nucleophilic aromatic substitution reaction ?   **[Orissa J.E.E. 2004]**

(a) Reaction of benzene with Cl_2 in sunlight.

(b) Benzyl bromide hydrolysis with water.

(c) Reaction of NaOH with dinitrofluoro benzene.

(d) Sulphonation of benzene.

67. On monochlorination of 2-methyl butane, the number of chiral compounds is ......

(a) 2   (b) 4   (c) 6   (d) 8

ANSWER KEY

1. (c)	2. (b)	3. (a)	4. (d)	5. (b)	6. (c)	7. (d)	8. (b)
9. (b)	10. (a)	11. (a)	12. (b)	13. (a)	14. (b)	15. (c)	16. (d)
17. (d)	18. (c)	19. (c)	20. (a)	21. (d)	22. (b)	23. (a)	24. (a)
25. (d)	26. (b)	27. (c)	28. (c)	29. (c)	30. (d)	31. (b)	32. (a)
33. (c)	34. (b)	35. (a)	36. (b)	37. (c)	38. (b)	39. (b)	40. (c)
41. (a)	42. (a)	43. (b)	44. (b)	45. (d)	46. (a)	47. (c)	48. (c)
49. (d)	50. (d)	51. (b)	52. (a)	53. (b)	54. (d)	55. (c)	56. (b)
57. (a)	58. (d)	59. (a)	60. (b)	61. (a)	62. (a)	63. (c)	64. (b)
65. (b)	66. (c)	67. (c)	68. (c)	69. (a)	70. (c)	71. (a)	72. (a)
73. (a)	74. (c)	75. (d)	76. (a)	77. (a)	78. (c)	79. (b)	80. (c)
81. (d)	82. (a)	83. (a)	84. (b)	85. (b)	86. (c)	87. (b)	88. (a)
89. (a)	90. (d)	91. (d)	92. (b)	93. (d)	94. (b)	95. (d)	96. (b)
97. (a)	98. (c)	99. (d)	100. (d)	101. (a)	102. (b)	103. (b)	104. (c)
105. (d)	106. (b)	107. (c)	108. (c)	109. (a)	110. (c)	111. (d)	112. (c)
113. (a)	114. (c)	115. (d)	116. (d)	117. (d)	118. (d)	119. (b)	120. (b)
121. (d)	122. (d)	123. (d)	124. (a)	125. (c)	126. (d)	127. (a)	128. (a)
129. (d)	130. (a)	131. (d)	132. (c)	133. (c)	134. (b)	135. (a)	136. (d)
137. (b)							

Previous Years Questions

1. (b)	2. (d)	3. (b)	4. (d)	5. (d)	6. (b)	7. (c)	8. (b)
9. (c)	10. (a)	11. (e)	12. (d)	13. (d)	14. (d)	15. (c)	16. (b)
17. (c)	18. (c)	19. (c)	20. (a)	21. (a)	22. (d)	23. (d)	24. (c)
25. (c)	26. (b)	27. (a)	28. (d)	29. (d)	30. (d)	31. (c)	32. (a)
33. (b)	34. (b)	35. (d)	36. (c)	37. (b)	38. (d)	39. (a)	40. (d)
41. (d)	42. (b)	43. (b)	44. (c)	45. (a)	46. (b)	47. (a)	48. (b)
49. (c)	50. (c)	51. (a)	52. (d)	53. (b)	54. (b)	55. (a)	56. (a)
57. (a)	58. (b)	59. (a)	60. (b)	61. (b)	62. (d)	63. (a)	64. (a)
65. (c)	66. (c)	67. (b)					

❏❏❏

ALCOHOLS, PHENOLS AND ETHERS

1. Identify the tertiary alcohol ......
   (a) $(CH_3)_2CHCH_2OH$
   (b) $CH_3CH_2CH_2CH_2OH$
   (c) $(CH_3)_3C–OH$
   (d) $CH_3CH–CH_2CH_3$
       |
       OH

2. Neo-pentyl alcohol is ......
   (a) 2, 2-dimethyl propan-1-ol
   (b) Dimethylbutyl propan-2-ol
   (c) 2, 2-dimethyl propan-2-ol
   (d) 2-Methylpentan-3-ol

3. 3–Ethyl–2–methylpentan–2–ol is ......
   (a) Primary alcohol
   (b) Secondary alcohol
   (c) Quaternary alcohol
   (d) Tertiary alcohol

4. Ethylene glycol is ......
   (a) Monohydric
   (b) Dihydric
   (c) Trihydric
   (d) Gem-dihydric

5. Aromatic alcohol is ......
   (a) Cresol
   (b) Mannitol
   (c) Pentanol
   (d) Neo-hexyl alcohol

6. Formula of benzyl alcohol is ......

(a) 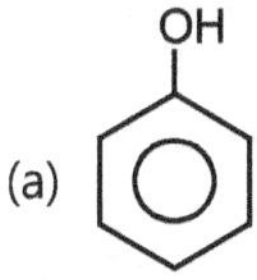
(b) 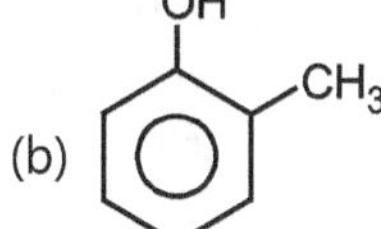
(c) 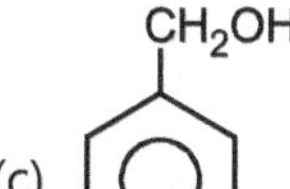
(d) $CH_2 – CH_2 – OH$ on benzene ring

7. IUPAC name of dichloromethyl carbinol is : Cl_2CHCH_2OH
   (a) 1, 2–dichloro methyl ethanol
   (b) 2, 2–dichloro ethanol
   (c) 1, 2–dichloro methanol
   (d) 2, 2–dichloro methanol

8. The number of primary, tertiary carbon atoms represented in the following alcohol is ......

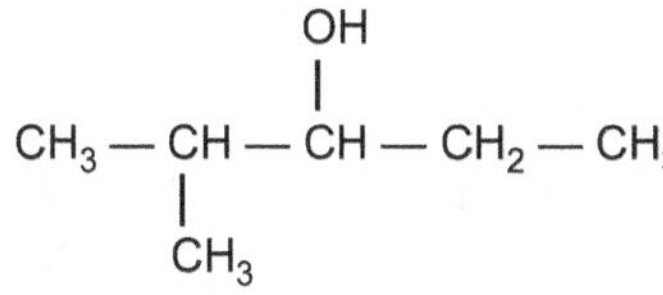

   (a) 2, 3
   (b) 1, 3
   (c) 3, 1
   (d) 3, 2

9. Hydroquinone is ......

(a) 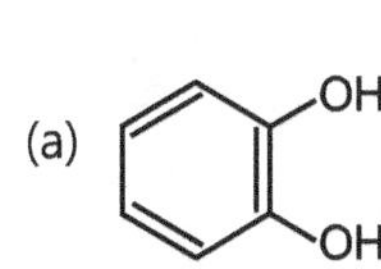
(b) 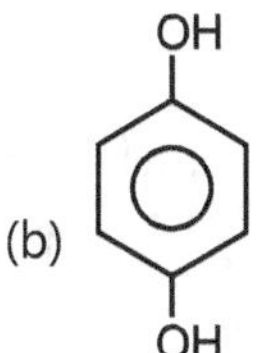
(c) 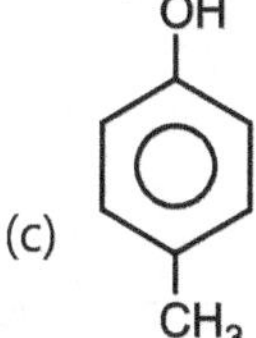
(d) 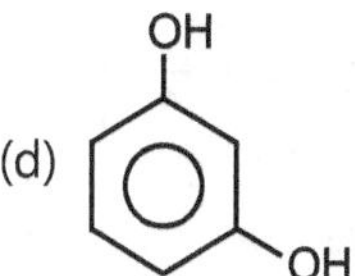

10. The name of following structure is ......

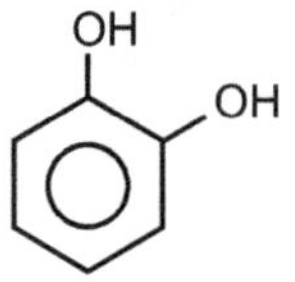

OH
OH

(a) Catechol   (b) Quinol   (c) Resorcinol   (d) Cresol

11. IUPAC name of tert-butyl alcohol is ......

(a) 3-butanol   (b) 2-methyl propan-2-ol
(c) 2-methyl propan-1-ol   (d) Dimethyl ethanol

12. What type of alcohol is 1–phenyl ethanol ?

(a) primary alcohol   (b) secondary alcohol
(c) tertiary alcohol   (d) quaternary alcohol

13. 2–methyl–2–phenyl propanol is a ......

(a) primary alcohol   (b) sec-alcohol   (c) tertiary alcohol (d) glycol

14. Glycerol is ......

(a) 1, 1, 2–propane triol   (b) Propane–1, 2, 3–triol
(c) Propane–1, 2–diol   (d) Propane–3–diol

15. Neo-pentyl alcohol is ......

(a) tertiary alcohol   (b) secondary alcohol
(c) primary alcohol   (d) aromatic alcohol

Preparation of alcohol

16. Tertiary butyl chloride reacts with aqueous KOH to give ......

(a) 2–methyl propan–2–ol   (b) 2–methyl propan–1–ol
(c) 2–Butanol   (d) Dimethyl ethanol

17. Product 'P' during the following reaction sequence is $CH_3CH_2Cl \xrightarrow{\text{moist } Ag_2O}$ 'P'

(a) CH_3CH_2-O- (b) CH_3CH_2OH (c) $AgCl$ (d) CH_3Cl

18. Propene on reaction with mercuric acetate in THF-water solution followed by reduction with $NaBH_4$ gives ......

(a) Propan–1–ol   (b) Propan–2–ol   (c) Propyl acetate (d) Mercuric propanate

19. Addition of water to an alkene in the presence of diborane is ......

(a) Wurtz reaction   (b) Benzilic rearrangement
(c) Hydroboration oxidation   (d) Meerwein Ponndorf reduction

20. Wood spirit is ......

(a) Ethanol   (b) Propanol   (c) Methanol   (d) Wood alcohol

21. Methylated spirit is ......

(a) Methanol   (b) Ethyl alcohol having 5–10% methanol
(c) Ethanol   (d) Absolute alcohol

22. Chromic acid dissolved in acetone used for the oxidation of alcohols is ......

(a) Fenton's reagent   (b) Benedict reagent
(c) Jones reagent   (d) Brady's reagent

23. The name of alcohol formed during the following reaction between CH_3–CH = CH–CHO and alcoholic $NaBH_4$ is ......

(a) Butan–1–ol   (b) Butan–2–ol   (c) But–2–en–1–ol   (d) Ethanol

24. Ethylene oxide with CH_3MgBr gives ......

(a) Tertiary alcohol   (b) Secondary alcohol

(c) Primary alcohol   (d) None of these

25. Cinnamaldehyde on reduction with $LiAlH_4$ gives ......

(a) 3–phenyl propan–1–ol   (b) 3–phenyl prop–2–en–1–ol

(c) Phenol   (d) Benzyl alcohol

26. Meerwein-Ponndorf reduction is the reaction between ......

(a) Ketone and primary alcohol in the presence of aluminium isopropoxide

(b) Ketone and secondary alcohol in the presence of aluminium isopropoxide

(c) Acetone reacts with secondary alcohol in the presence of aluminium isopropoxide

(d) Aldehyde and primary alcohol in the presence of aluminium isopropoxide

27. The name of the following reaction is ......

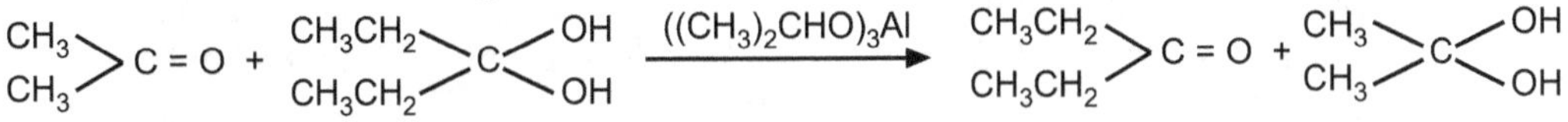

$$\underset{CH_3}{\overset{CH_3}{>}}C=O + \underset{CH_3CH_2}{\overset{CH_3CH_2}{>}}C\underset{OH}{\overset{OH}{<}} \xrightarrow{((CH_3)_2CHO)_3Al} \underset{CH_3CH_2}{\overset{CH_3CH_2}{>}}C=O + \underset{CH_3}{\overset{CH_3}{>}}C\underset{OH}{\overset{OH}{<}}$$

(a) Corey reaction   (b) Meerwein-Ponndorf

(c) Oppenauer oxidation   (d) Bouveault-Blanc reaction

28. Oxo process is the ......

(a) $CH_2 = CH_2 + O_2$ (b) $CH_2 = CH_2 + CO_2$

(c) $CH_2 = CH_2 + CO + H_2O$ (d) $C_2H_6 + CO + H_2O$

29. Which reagent is used to bring about the following reaction ?

(a) OsO_4 (b) $H_2O\,|\,H^+$ (c) $KMnO_4\,|\,H_2O$ (d) HNO_3

30. Acrolein can be converted to allyl alcohol by using reagent ......

(a) $NaBH_4$ (b) $LiAlH_4$ (c) $Ni\,|\,H_2$ (d) both (a) and (b)

31. Identify product 'P' in the following reaction sequence $CH_3CH_2CH_2NH_2 \xrightarrow{NaNO_2\,|\,HCl}$ 'P'

(a) $CH_3CH_2CH_2N_2^+Cl^-$ (b) $CH_3CH_2CH_2NO_2$ (c) $CH_3CH_2CH_2OH$ (d) $CH_3CH_2CH_2Cl$

32. Which of the following reagents is required for the following conversion ......

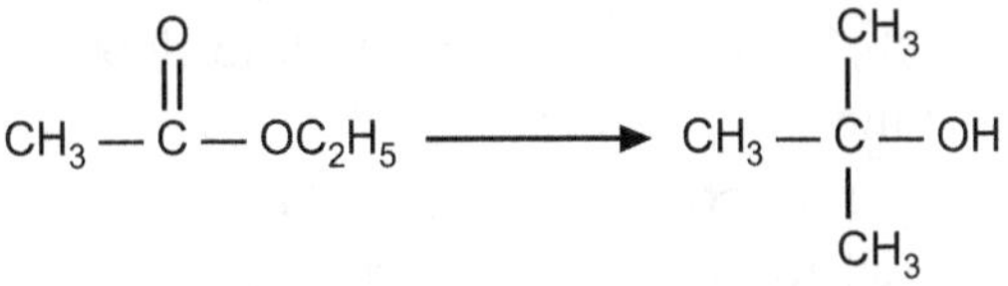

$$CH_3-\overset{\overset{O}{\|}}{C}-OC_2H_5 \longrightarrow CH_3-\underset{\underset{CH_3}{|}}{\overset{\overset{CH_3}{|}}{C}}-OH$$

(a) $H_2O\,|\,H^+$ (b) $2CH_3MgBr\,|\,H_2O\,|\,H^+$

(c) CH_3MgBr (d) $(CH_3)_3Br$

33. Enzymes used during fermentation of sucrose are ......

   (a) Maltase, Zymase
   (b) Zymase, Invertase
   (c) Invertase, Zymase
   (d) Sucrase, Invertase

34. Methanol is obtained from water gas, the reaction involved is ......

   (a) $CO + H_2O \rightarrow CH_3OH$

   (b) $CO + 2H_2 \xrightarrow[573\ °K]{ZnO-Cr_2O_3} CH_3OH$

   (c) $CO + 2H_2O \xrightarrow{ZnO-Cr_2O_3} CH_3OH$

   (d) $CO_2 + 2H_2 \xrightarrow[573\ °K]{ZnO-Cr_2O_3} CH_3OH$

35. Ethanol can be obtained by all methods except ......

   (a) $C_2H_5I + H_2O\,|\,OH^-$
   (b) $C_2H_5NH_2\,|\,NaNO_2\,|\,HCl$
   (c) $C_2H_5MgBr\,|\,H_2O$
   (d) $CH_3CHO\,|\,NaBH_4$

36. Grain alcohol is ......

   (a) Methanol
   (b) Ethanol
   (c) 2–Methyl propanol
   (d) Butan–1–ol

37. The compound 'R' in the following reaction sequence is ......

   $$R \xrightarrow[ether]{C_2H_5MgBr} I \xrightarrow{H_2O\,|\,H^+} \text{2-Methyl butan-2-ol}$$

   The compound 'R' in the sequence is ......

   (a) Butanone
   (b) Propanol
   (c) Propanone
   (d) Ethanol

38. Dow's process is ......

   (a) 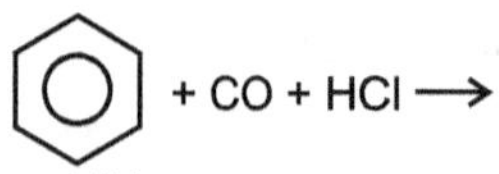 ⟨benzene⟩ $+ CO + HCl \rightarrow$

   (b) 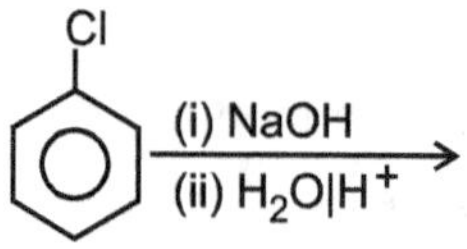 ⟨chlorobenzene⟩ $\xrightarrow[(ii)\ H_2O|H^+]{(i)\ NaOH}$

   (c)  ⟨aniline⟩ $\xrightarrow[\substack{HCl\\0-50}]{NaNO_2}$

   (d) 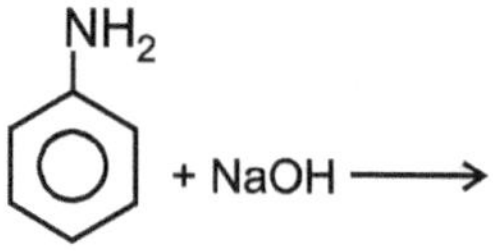 ⟨aniline⟩ $+ NaOH \longrightarrow$

39. Phenol on large scale is prepared from ......

   (a) Benzene
   (b) Cumene
   (c) Toluene
   (d) Xylene

40. Sodium salicylate on decarboxylation gives ......

   (a) Benzene
   (b) Salicylic acid
   (c) Phenol
   (d) Sodium benzoate

41. The product formed during the following reaction sequence is ......

   $$C_6H_5N_2^+Cl \xrightarrow[boil]{H_2O} \text{'P'}$$

   (a) Aniline
   (b) Benzene
   (c) Phenol
   (d) Chlorobenzene

42. Sodium salt of toluene sulphonic acid on alkali fusion gives ......

   (a) Catechol
   (b) p-cresol
   (c) Resorcinol
   (d) Phenol

43. Oxidation of benzene in the presence of V_2O_5 at 320°C gives ......

   (a) Phenol
   (b) Catechol
   (c) Cresol
   (d) Phloroglucinol

44. Propene can be converted to propan–1–ol by oxidation. Indicate which of the following reagents are used to carry out this reaction ?

   (a) $KMnO_4$ (alkaline)
   (b) $OsO_4CH_2Cl_2$
   (c) B_2H_6 and H_2O_2
   (d) OZn

45. Which one of the following reactions will yield propan–2–ol ?

(i)　$CH_3-CH = CH_2 + H_2O \xrightarrow{H^+}$

(ii)　$CH_3CHO \xrightarrow[\text{(ii) } H_2O]{\text{(i) } CH_3MgI}$

(iii)　$HCHO \xrightarrow[H_2O]{C_2H_5MgI}$

(iv)　$CH_3-CH = CH_2 \xrightarrow[KMnO_4]{\text{Neutral}}$

(a) (i) and (ii)　　(b) (ii) and (iii)　　(c) (iii) and (i)　　(d) (ii) and (iv)

46. The reaction by $\underset{\underset{O}{\diagdown \diagup}}{CH_2-CH_2}$ with RMgX leads to the formation of ......

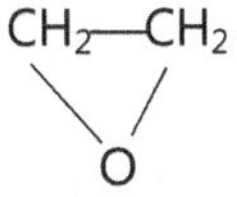

(a) RCHOH—R　　(b) RCHOH—CH_3　　(c) R_2CHCH_2OH　　(d) R—CH_2CH_2OH

47. A compound with molecular formula $C_4H_{10}O_3$ is converted by the action of acetyl chloride to a compound with molecular weight 190. The original compound has ......

(a) One OH group　　(b) 2 OH groups　　(c) 3 OH groups　　(d) No OH groups

48. $(CH_3)_3CMgBr$ on reaction with D_2O produces ......

(a) $(CH_3)_3CD$　　(b) $(CH_3)_3COD$　　(c) $(CD)_3CD$　　(d) $(CD)_3OD$

49. Acid catalysed hydration of alkenes except ethers leads to the formation of ......

(a) Primary alcohol

(b) Secondary or tertiary alcohol

(c) Mixture of primary and secondary alcohols

(d) Mixture of secondary and tertiary alcohols

50. The only alcohol that can be prepared by indirect hydration of alkene is ......

(a) Methyl alcohol　　(b) Ethyl alcohol　　(c) Propyl alcohol　　(d) Isobutyl alcohol

51. 3–Hydroxybutanal is formed when (X) reacts with (Y) in dilute (Z) solution. What are X, Y and Z ?

	(X)	(Y)	(Z)
(a)	CH_3CHO	$(CH_3CO)_2O$	NaOH
(b)	CH_3CHO	CH_3CHO	NaCl
(c)	$(CH_3CO)_2O$	$(CH_3CO)_2O$	HCl
(d)	CH_3CHO	CH_3CHO	NaOH

52. The product of the following reaction

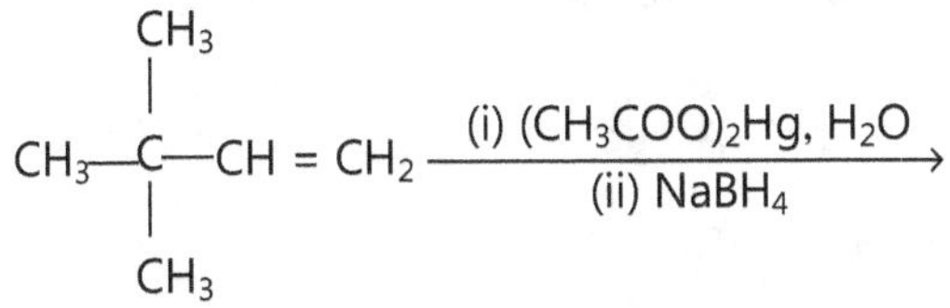

$$CH_3-\underset{\underset{CH_3}{|}}{\overset{\overset{CH_3}{|}}{C}}-CH = CH_2 \xrightarrow[\text{(ii) } NaBH_4]{\text{(i) } (CH_3COO)_2Hg,\ H_2O} \text{ is ......}$$

(a) $(CH_3)_3CH(OH)—CH_3$

(b) $(CH_3)_3C—CH_2—CH_2OH$

(c) 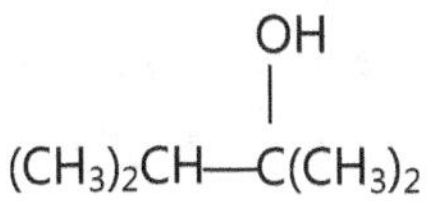 $(CH_3)_2CH—\underset{\underset{CH_3}{|}}{\overset{\overset{OH}{|}}{C}}(CH_3)_2$

(d) $CH_3CH_2—C(CH_3)_2—CH_2OH$

53. An alcohol produced during the manufacture of soap is ......

(a) Ethanol   (b) Ethylene glycol   (c) Glycerol   (d) Methanol

54. In the following reaction sequence

$$H_2C = CH_2 \xrightarrow{HOCl} 'A' \xrightarrow{'B'} \begin{array}{l} CH_2OH \\ | \\ CH_2OH \end{array}$$

'A', 'B' respectivly are ......

(a) $\begin{array}{l} CH_2 \\ | \quad \diagdown O \\ CH_2 \diagup \end{array}$ and heat

(b) CH_3CH_2Cl and NaOH

(c) CH_3CH_2OH and H_2SO_4

(d) $\begin{array}{l} CH_2Cl \\ | \\ CH_2OH \end{array}$ and $NaHCO_3$

55. The most soluble alcohol in water is ......

(a) Pentan-1-ol   (b) Butan-1-ol   (c) Propan-1-ol   (d) Ethanol

56. The most soluble isomer of C_4H_9OH in water is ......

(a) n-butyl alcohol   (b) Iso-butyl alcohol

(c) Sec-butyl alcohol   (d) Tert-butyl alcohol

57. Which statement is not correct about alcohol ?

(a) Alcohol is lighter than water

(b) Alcohol evaporates quickly

(c) Alcohol with lesser number of carbon atoms is less soluble in water than alcohol with higher number of carbon atoms

(d) All are correct

58. Which of the following is not true in case of reaction with heated copper at 300°C ?

(a) Phenol $\rightarrow$ Benzyl alcohol   (b) Primary alcohol $\rightarrow$ Aldehyde

(c) Secondary alcohol $\rightarrow$ Ketone   (d) Tertiary alcohol $\rightarrow$ Olefin

59. Which of the following will not give iodoform test ?

(a) Ethanol   (b) Ethanal

(c) Isopropyl alcohol   (d) Benzyl alcohol

60. When the vapours of ethyl alcohol are passed over red hot copper (300°C), then product formed is ......

(a) Ethylene   (b) Acetaldehyde   (c) Acetic acid   (d) None of these

61. 1-Propanol and 2-Propanol can be best distinguished by ......

(a) Reaction with Fehling's solution

(b) Oxidation with acidic dichromate followed by reaction with Fehling's solution

(c) Oxidation by heating with copper followed by reaction with Fehling's solution

(d) Oxidation with concentrated H_2SO_4 followed by reaction with Fehling's solution

62. n-propyl alcohol and isopropyl alcohol can be chemically distinguished by which reagent ...

(a) PCl_5

(b) Reduction

(c) Oxidation with potassium dichromate

(d) Ozonolysis

63. Propan-1-ol can be prepared from propene by ......

(a) H_2O/H_2SO_4

(b) $Hg(OAc)_2/H_2O$ followed by $NaBH_4$

(c) B_2H_6 followed by H_2O_2

(d) CH_3CO_2H/H_2SO_4

64. When alcohol reacts with concentrated H_2SO_4, the intermediate compound formed is ......

(a) Carbonium ion

(b) Alkoxy ion

(c) Alkyl hydrogen sulphate

(d) None of these

65. Arrange the following compounds in the order of increasing boiling point ......

(I) Hydroxy benzene

(II) Ortho dihydroxy benzene

(III) Meta dihydroxy benzene

(IV) Para dihydroxy benzene

(a) (IV) > (III) > (II) > (I)

(b) (III) > (IV) > (II) > (I)

(c) (II) > (III) > (I) > (IV)

(d) (I) > (II) > (III) > (IV)

66. Which one is primary alcohol ?

(a) Buten-2-ol

(b) Propan-2-ol

(c) Butan-1-ol

(d) 2,3-Dimethylhexane-4-ol

67. $C_6H_5OH \xrightarrow[\text{NaOH}_{(aq)}]{\text{ClCOCH}_3} C_6H_5OCOCH_3$

The above reaction is an example of ......

(a) Reimer-Tiemann reaction

(b) Schotten Baumann reaction

(c) Acetylation

(d) Benzoylation

68. Salol can be used as ......

(a) Antiseptic   (b) Antipyretic   (c) Both (a) & (b)   (d) None of these

69. Phenol is heated with CCl_4 and alkaline KOH when salicylic acid is produced. The reaction is known as ......

(a) Friedel-Craft reaction

(b) Riemer-Tiemann's reaction

(c) Rosenmund's reaction

(d) Sommelet reaction

70. Salicylaldehyde can be prepared from ......

(a) Phenol and chloroform

(b) Phenol, chloroform and sodium hydroxide

(c) Phenol, carbon tetrachloride and NaOH

(d) None of these

71. Ethanol containing some methanol is called ......

(a) Absolute spirit   (b) Rectified spirit   (c) Power alcohol   (d) Methylated spirit

72. Glycerol can be obtained from ......

(a) Fats   (b) Propylene   (c) Both of these   (d) None of these

73. Mild oxidation of glycerol with $H_2O_2/FeSO_4$ gives ......

(a) Glyceraldehyde

(b) Dihydroxy acetone

(c) Glycerose

(d) Glyceraldehyde and dihydroxy acetone

74. Hydrolytic conversion of sucrose into glucose and fructose is known as ......

(a) Induction　　(b) Inversion　　(c) Insertion　　(d) Inhibition

75. Alcohols of low molecular weight are ......

(a) Soluble in water

(b) Soluble in water on heating

(c) Insoluble in water

(d) Insoluble in all solvents

76. Alcohols react with Grignard reagent to form ......

(a) Alkanes　　(b) Alkenes　　(c) Alkynes　　(d) All of these

77. 23 g of Na will react with ethanol to give ......

(a) One mole of oxygen

(b) One mole of H_2

(c) 1/2 mole of H_2

(d) None of these

78. Epichlorohydrin is ......

(a) 3-Chloropropane

(b) 3-Chloropropan-1-ol

(c) 3-Chloro-1,2-epoxypropane

(d) None of these

79. The strongest acid among the following aromatic compound is ......

(a) Ortho-nitrophenol

(b) Para-chlorophenol

(c) Para-nitrophenol

(d) Meta-nitrophenol

80. Benzyl alcohol is obtained from benzaldehyde by ......

(a) Fittig's reaction

(b) Cannizzaro's reaction

(c) Kolbe's reaction

(d) Wurtz's reaction

81. Bayer's reagent is ......

(a) Alkaline $KMnO_4$

(b) Ammonical $AgNO_3$

(c) Ammonical $CuSO_4$

(d) $CaSO_4/Ca(OH)_2$

82. C_2H_5OH can be differentiated from CH_3OH by ......

(a) Reaction with HCl

(b) Reaction with NH_3

(c) Iodoform test

(d) Solubility in water

83. The reaction between alcohol and carboxylic acids is called ......

(a) Esterification　　(b) Hydrolysis　　(c) Saponification　　(d) Hydrogenation

84. Scientific study of fermentation was first made by ......

(a) Buchner　　(b) Liebig　　(c) Biot　　(d) Pasteur

85. Alcoholic beverages are made of ......

(a) Ethanol　　(b) Acetic acid　　(c) Formic acid　　(d) None of these

86. The conversion of ethyl alcohol into acetaldehyde is an example of ......

(a) Reduction

(b) Molecular rearrangement

(c) Hydrolysis

(d) Oxidation

87. To prepare 3-ethylpentan-3-ol, the reagents needed are ......

(a) $CH_3CH_2MgBr + CH_3COCH_2CH_3$

(b) $CH_3MgBr + CH_3CH_2CH_2COCH_2CH_3$

(c) $CH_3CH_2MgBr + CH_3CH_2COCH_2CH_3$

(d) $CH_3CH_2CH_2MgBr + CH_3COCH_2CH_3$

88. When wine is put in air, it becomes sour due to ......

(a) Bacteria

(b) Oxidation of C_2H_5OH into CH_3COOH

(c) Virus

(d) Formic acid formation

89. An organic compound (a) reacts with sodium metal and forms (b) on heating with conc. H_2SO_4 (a) gives diethyl ether. Then (a) and (b) respectively are ......

(a) C_2H_5OH and C_2H_5ONa

(b) C_3H_7OH and CH_3ONa

(c) CH_3OH and CH_3ONa

(d) C_4H_9OH and C_4H_9ONa

90. Benzyl amine reacts with nitrous acid to form ......

(a) Azobenzene　　　(b) Benzene　　　(c) Benzyl alcohol　　(d) Phenol

91. When 1° alkyl halide reacts with an alkoxide, the product is ......

(a) Hydrocarbon

(b) Ether

(c) Unsaturated hydrocarbon

(d) Alcohol

92. On boiling with concentrated HBr, phenyl ethyl ether will give ......

(a) Phenol and ethyl bromide

(b) Bromobenzene and ethanol

(c) Phenol and ethane

(d) Bromobenzene and ethane

93. Which of the following compounds is resistant to nucleophilic attack by OH^- ions ?

(a) Urea　　　(b) Acetonitrile　　　(c) Acetamide　　　(d) Diethyl ether

94. When diethyl ether is treated with excess of Cl_2 in the presence of sunlight, the product formed is ......

(a) $CH_3CHCl\text{-}O\text{-}CH_2CH_3$

(b) $CH_3CHCl\text{-}O\text{-}CHClCH_3$

(c) $CCl_3CCl_2\text{-}O\text{-}CCl_2CCl_3$

(d) $CH_3CCl_2\text{-}O\text{-}CHClCH_3$

95. In Williamson synthesis, ethoxy ethane is prepared by ......

(a) Passing ethanol over alumina

(b) Heating ethanol with dry Ag_2O

(c) Heating sodium ethoxide with ethyl bromide

(d) Treating ethyl alcohol with excess of H_2SO_4 at 443 K

96. Monochlorination of toluene in sunlight followed by hydrolysis with aq. NaOH yields ......

(a) o-cresol

(b) m-cresol

(c) 2, 4-Dihydroxytoluene

(d) Benzyl alcohol

97. How many alcohols with molecular formula $C_{14}H_{10}O$ are chiral in nature?

(a) 1　　　(b) 2　　　(c) 3　　　(d) 4

98. What is the correct order of reactivity of alcohols in the following reaction?

$$R - OH + HCl \xrightarrow{ZnCl_2} R - Cl + H_2O$$

(a) 1° > 2° > 3°　　　(b) 1° < 2° > 3°　　　(c) 3° > 2° > 1°　　　(d) 3° > 1° > 2°

99. CH_3CH_2OH can be converted into CH_3CHO by ......
(a) Catalytic hydrogenation (b) Treatment with $LiAlH_4$
(c) Treatment with pyridinium chlorochromate (d) Treatment with $KMnO_4$

100. The process of converting alkyl halides into alcohols involves ......
(a) Addition reaction (b) Substitution reaction
(c) Dehydrohalogenation reaction (d) Rearrangement reaction

101. The ether linkage is ......
(a) R—OO— (b) R—O—R' (c) —COO (d) —OO—R

102. Common name of following formula is
$$CH_3-\underset{\underset{CH_3}{|}}{\overset{\overset{CH_3}{|}}{C}}-OCH_2CH_3$$
(a) Ethyl neo butyl ether (b) Butyl ethyl ether
(c) Tert-butyl ethyl ether (d) Ethyl tert-butyl ether

103. IUPAC name of methyl iso-propyl ether is ......
(a) 2-methoxy propane (b) Propyl methane
(c) Isopropyl methane (d) Methoxy ethyl ethane

104. The structural formula of anisole is ......
(a) $C_6H_5OC_2H_5$ (b) $C_6H_5OC_6H_5$
(c) $C_6H_5-OCH_2C_6H_5$ (d) $C_6H_5OCH_3$

105. The isomerism shown by the following pairs of ether is $CH_3CH_2OCH_2CH_3$; $CH_3OCH_2CH_2CH_3$
(a) Cis-trans (b) Optical (c) Metamerism (d) Position isomerism

106. The common name of ether $CH_2 = CH-CH_2OCH_3$ is ......
(a) Vinyl methyl ether (b) Allyl methyl ether
(c) 1–methoxy propane (d) 3–methoxy propane

107. The IUPAC name of di-isopropyl ether is ......
(a) 2–propoxy propane (b) 2–(2–propoxy) propane
(c) 2–(1–propoxy) propane (d) Propoxy propane

108. Ethers are isomeric with ......
(a) Alcohols (b) Aldehydes (c) Ketones (d) Carboxyl compound

109. Hybridisation of oxygen atom is ......
(a) sp (b) sp^2 (c) sp^3 (d) sp^3d

110. The bond angle in ether is ...
(a) Same as water (b) Less than water
(c) More than water (d) None of these

111. Oxiranes are ...
(a) Open chain ethers (b) Cyclic ethers
(c) Three membered ring ethers (d) Four membered ring ethers

112. Following ether is ...

$$\begin{array}{ccc} O & - & CH_2 \\ | & & | \\ CH_2 & - & CH_2 \end{array}$$

(a) Oxirane   (b) Oxitane   (c) Propene oxide (d) Propane oxide

113. The IUPAC name of the following compound is ...

$$\triangleright\!-\!O\!-\!\underset{\underset{CH_3}{|}}{CH}\!-\!CH_2CH_3$$

(a) 3–cyclopropoxy butane   (b) 2–cyclopropyl butane

(c) 2–butoxy cyclopropane   (d) 3–butoxy cyclopropane

114. A Williamson's synthesis of ether is an example of ...

(a) Nucleophilic substitution   (b) Electrophilic substitution

(c) Nucleophilic addition   (d) Electrophilic addition

115. In Williamson's synthesis ...

(a) An alcohol is heated with conc. H_2SO_4 at 413 K

(b) An alkyl halide is treated with sodium alkoxide

(c) An alkyl halide is treated with an alcohol

(d) An alkaloid is treated with an alcohol

116. When ether reacts with air in the presence of silver catalyst, the product formed is ...

(a) Oxirane   (b) Oxitane   (c) Furan   (d) Pyran

117. The reaction of ethyl iodide with sodium methoxide is an example of ......

(a) Williamson's synthesis   (b) Elimination reaction

(c) Nucleophilic substitution   (d) Wurtz reaction

118. Tert-butyl ethyl ether can be prepared by treating ...

(a) Tert-butyl iodide with ethyl alcohol   (b) Sodium ethoxide with tert-butyl iodide

(c) Sodium tert-butoxide with ethyl chloride (d) Sodium butoxide with ethyl iodide

119. The product obtained when tert-butyl bromide is treated with sodium ethoxide is ......

(a) Isobutare   (b) Isobutylene

(c) Ether   (d) Tert-butyl ethyl ether

120. The reaction

$$R\!-\!X + R'ONa \xrightarrow{\text{dry ether}} R\!-\!O\!-\!R' + NaX \text{ is known as ......}$$

(a) Williamson's synthesis   (b) Wurtz reaction

(c) Wolff-Kishner   (d) Wurtz-Fettig

121. On heating sodium phenoxide with methyl iodide, the product is ......

(a) Phenetole   (b) Anisole   (c) Diphenyl ether (d) Dimethyl ether

122. The compounds having —O— group are ......

(a) Carboxylic acids   (b) Esters

(c) Ethers   (d) Carboxyl compounds

123. Identify the product ...

$$CH_3CH_2CH_2Br \xrightarrow{\text{NaOH (aq)}} A \xrightarrow{CH_3I} B$$

    (a) Butane   (b) Methyl n-propyl ether

    (c) Propyl iodide   (d) Propane

124. When ethanol is heated with conc. H_2SO_4 at $410 - 413\ °K$, the product is ......

    (a) Diethyl ether   (b) Ethane   (c) Ethene   (d) Butane

125. When ethyl hydrogen sulphate is heated with excess of ethanol at $137\,°C$, the product obtained is ......

    (a) Diethyl sulphate   (b) Ethylene   (c) Ethoxy ethane   (d) Ethane

126. When primary alkyl halide reacts with an alkoxide, the product is ......

    (a) A hydrocarbon   (b) Ether

    (c) Unsaturated hydrocarbon   (d) Alcohol

127. Which of the following cannot be prepared by using Williamson's synthesis ?

    (a) Methoxy benzene   (b) Benzyl-p-nitrophenyl ether

    (c) Methyl-tert-butyl ether   (d) Di-tert-butyl ether

128. How many isomeric ethers are represented by the molecular formula $C_4H_{10}O$?

    (a) 3   (b) 2   (c) 4   (d) 5

129. The number of metamers represented by molecular formula $C_4H_{10}O$ are ......

    (a) 4   (b) 3   (c) 2   (d) 1

130. The R—O—R' angle in ether is approximately ......

    (a) $105°$ (b) $110°$ (c) $109°$ (d) $180°$

131. The boiling point of ether is ......

    (a) Greater than alcohol

    (b) Lower than alcohol

    (c) Same as alcohol

    (d) Same as alkane of comparable molecular mass

132. Ethers have ......

    (a) Zero dipole moment   (b) 1.15 D to 1.30 D

    (c) 111.7 Debye   (d) 104.5 Debye

133. Ethers are ......

    (a) Basic   (b) Acidic   (c) Amphoteric   (d) Neutral

134. Diethyl ether is regarded as an anhydride of ......

    (a) Propanoic acid   (b) Ethanol   (c) Propanal   (d) Ethyl propanoate

135. The order of reactivity of halogen acids towards ether is ......

    (a) HI > HBr < HCl   (b) HCl < HBr < HI   (c) HCl > HBr > HI (d) HCl < HBr > HI

136. The products formed during the reaction of anisole with HI are ......

    (a) Phenol and methyl iodide   (b) Iodo benzene and methanol

    (c) Benzene and iodo methane   (d) Methane and iodo benzene

137. Identify product 'P' in the following reaction sequence

CH_3—O—$CH(CH_3)_2$ + HI → CH_3I + 'P'

(a) Propane   (b) Propan–2–ol   (c) Propan–1–ol   (d) Propyl iodide

138. Which of the following ethers is not cleaved by HI ?

(a) Tert butyl ethyl ether   (b) Methyl phenyl ether

(c) Dimethyl ether   (d) Diphenyl ether

139. Predict the main product 'P' in the following reaction

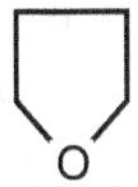

$$\text{THF} + 2HI \longrightarrow \text{'P'} + H_2O$$

(a) Iodobutane   (b) Butane

(c) 1, 4–Di iodobutane   (d) Butanol

140. Ether fire is extinguished by ......

(a) CO_2 only   (b) Pyrene only

(c) CO_2 and pyrene both   (d) Water

141. The mechanism for the reaction between conc. HI and tert-butyl methyl ether proceeds by ......

(a) SN_1 (b) SN_2

(c) SN_1 and SN_2 (d) Electrophilic substitution

142. The products formed during the following reaction

$$CH_3\text{—}\underset{\underset{CH_3}{|}}{\overset{\overset{CH_3}{|}}{C}}\text{—O—}CH_3 + HI_{conc} \longrightarrow \text{'A'} + \text{'B'}$$

A, B are ......

(a) Methyl alcohol and tert-butyl iodide   (b) Tert-butyl alcohol and methyl iodide

(c) 2–methyl propene and methyl iodide   (d) Isobutane and methyl iodide

143. During reaction of anisole with conc. HI at 375 K, which bond cleaves ......

(a) CH_3—O—   (b) C_6H_5—O—   (c) C—C   (d) Any one of these

144. Dimethyl ether with ice cold hydrochloric acid forms ......

(a) Dimethoxy methane   (b) Methyl chloride

(c) Methyl alcohol and methyl iodide   (d) Dimethyl oxonium chloride

145. Ethers are never distilled to dryness due to the formation of ......

(a) Explosive peroxide   (b) Ether oxide   (c) Alkane mixture   (d) Diethyl ether

146. Peroxide of ether with ferrous ammonium sulphate and potassium thiocyanate gives ......

(a) Blue colour   (b) Green colour   (c) Red colour   (d) Black colour

147. To remove peroxides from ethers, they are treated with an aqueous solution of ......

(a) KI   (b) KCNS   (c) $Na_2S_2O_3$ (d) Br_2

148. Ethers can be used as ......

(a) Refrigerants

(b) Anaesthetics

(c) Perfumery

(d) In all these mentioned

149. Ether reacts with carbon monoxide in the presence of BF_3 at 425 K to give ......

(a) Acid
(b) Ester
(c) Acid anhydride
(d) Ketones

150. The reaction $(CH_3)_3C—Br + C_2H_5ONa \rightarrow$ yields ......

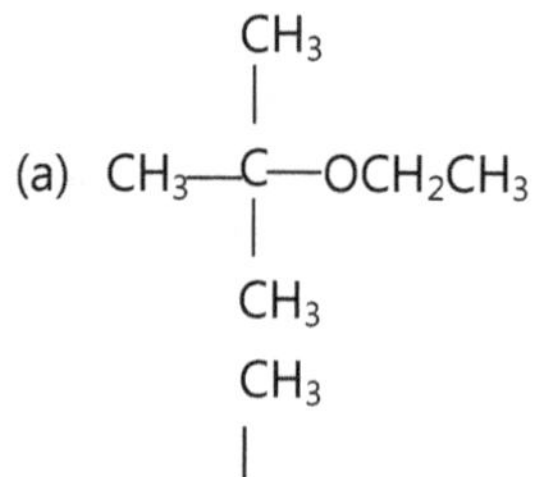

(a)
$$\underset{\underset{CH_3}{|}}{\overset{\overset{CH_3}{|}}{CH_3—C}}—OCH_2CH_3$$

(b)
$$\underset{\underset{CH_2CH_3}{|}}{\overset{\overset{CH_3}{|}}{CH_3—C}}—OCH_3$$

(c)
$$\overset{\overset{CH_3}{|}}{CH_3—C} = CH_2$$

(d) All of these

151. Which of the following compounds on boiling with alk. $KMnO_4$ and subsequent acidification will not give benzoic acid ?

(a) Benzyl alcohol
(b) Acetophenone
(c) Anisole
(d) Toluene

152. Which of the following is the correct route for the synthesis of phenyl n-propyl ether ?

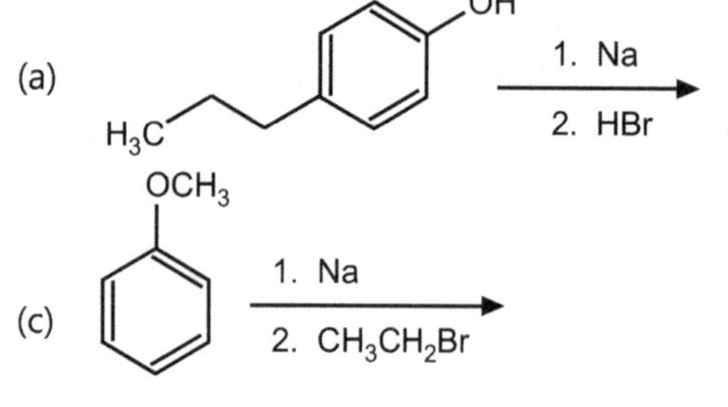

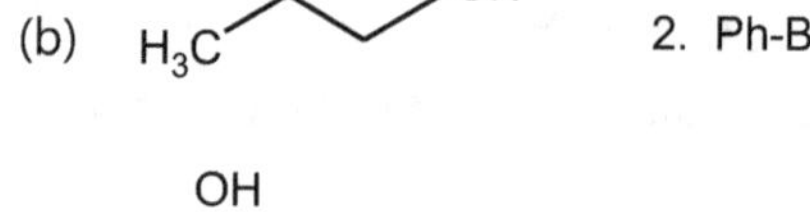

153. Among the following alkenes which one produces tertiary butyl alcohol on acid hydration ?

(a) $(CH_3)_2C = CH_2$

(b) $CH_3 – CH = CH – CH_3$

(c) $CH_3 – CH_2 – CH = CH_2$

(d) $CH_3 – CH = CH_2$

154. Among the following, which is least acidic?

(a) phenol
(b) o-cresol
(c) p-nitrophenol
(d) p-chlorophenol

155. An organic compound **A** containing C, H and O on boiling with concentrated H_2SO_4 produces a colourless gas which decolourises bromine water and alkaline $KMnO_4$. Organic compound **A** is ......

(a) $C_2H_5COOCH_3$
(b) C_2H_5OH
(c) C_2H_5Cl
(d) C_2H_6

156. Phenol can be converted to o-hydroxybenzaldehyde by ......

(a) Kolbe's reaction

(b) Reimer-Tiemann reaction

(c) Wurtz reaction

(d) Sandmeyer's reaction

157. Phenol can be distinguished from ethanol by the following reagents except ......

(a) sodium　　　　(b) $NaOH/I_2$　　　　(c) neutral $FeCl_3$　　(d) Br_2/H_2O

158. Phenol, when it first reacts with concentrated sulphuric acid and then with concentrated nitric acid, gives ......

(a) 2,4,6-trinitrobenzene　　　　　　　(b) o-nitrophenol

(c) p-nitrophenol　　　　　　　　　　(d) nitrobenzene

159. RCH_2CH_2OH can be converted to RCH_2CH_2COOH by the following sequence of steps ......

(a) KCN, H_3O^+　　　　　　　　　(b) $PBr_3, KCN, H_2/Pt$

(c) PBr_3, KCN, H_3O^+　　　　　　(d) HCN, PBr_3, H_3O^+

160. Which pair of products would result from the acid cleavage of phenyl propyl ether with excess concentrated HBr at an elevated temperature?

(a) Phenol and 1-propanol　　　　　　(b) Bromobenzene and 1-propanol

(c) Bromobenzene and 1-bromopropane　(d) Phenol and 1-bromopropane

161. What are the products when tert-butyl ethyl ether is cleaved with concentrated HI?

(a) iodoethane and tert-butyl alcohol

(b) iodoethane and 2-iodo-2-methylpropane

(c) ethanol and 2-iodo-2-methylpropane

(d) ethanol and tert-butyl alcohol

162. Which of the following is most acidic?

(a) m-Chlorophenol　　(b) Benzyl alcohol　　(c) Phenol　　　　(d) Cyclohexanol

163. The major products are ......

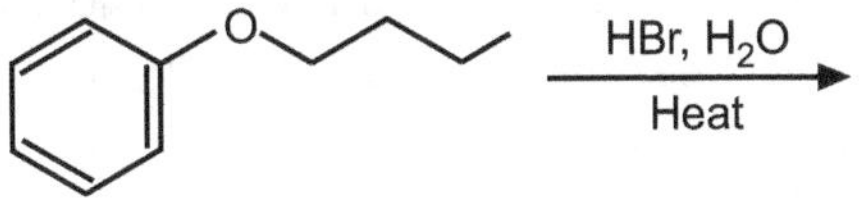

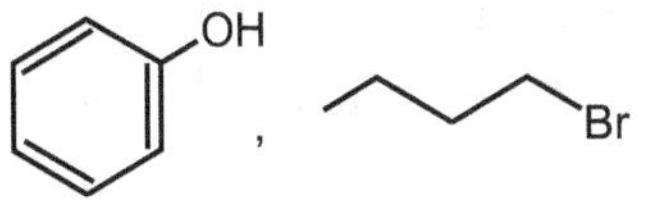

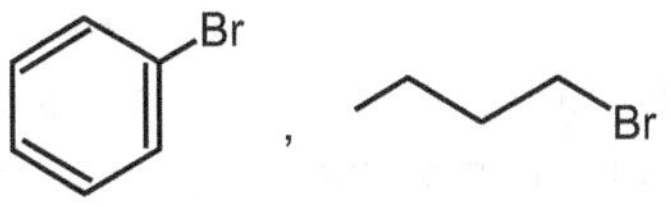

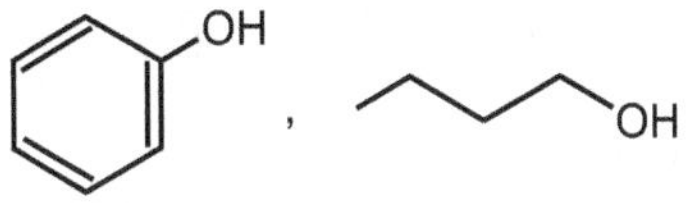

164. An ether is more volatile than an alcohol having the same molecular formula. This is due to ......

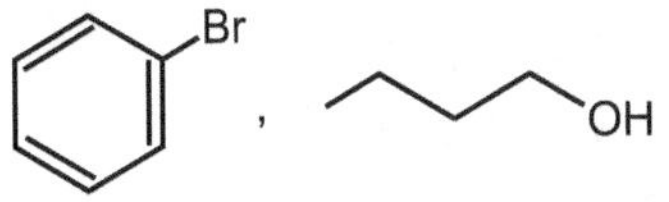

(a) Dipolar character of ethers

(b) Alcohols having resonance structure

(c) Intermolecular hydrogen bonding in ethers

(d) Intermolecular hydrogen bonding in alcohols

165. When methyl-t-butyl ether is formed ......

(a) $(C_2H_5)_3CONa + CH_3Cl$　　　　(b) $CH_3ONa + (CH_3)_3CCl$

(c) $(CH_3)_3CONa + C_2H_5Cl$　　　　(d) $(CH_3)_3CONa + CH_3Cl$

166. 2-Phenyl ethanol may be prepared by the reaction of phenyl magnesium bromide with ......

(a) HCHO

(b) CH_3CHO

(c) CH_3COCH_3

(d)

$$\overset{\displaystyle O}{\underset{\displaystyle CH_2-CH_2}{\triangle}}$$

167. During dehydration of alcohols to alkenes by heating with conc. H_2SO_4, the initial step is ...

(a) Formation of an ester

(b) Protonation of alcohol molecule

(c) Formation of carbocation

(d) Elimination of water

168. When ethyl hydrogen sulphate is heated with excess of alcohol at 410 K, the product obtained is ......

(a) Ethane

(b) Ethylene

(c) Diethyl ether

(d) Diethyl sulphate

169. Grignard reagent is not prepared in aqueous medium but it is prepared in ether medium, because ......

(a) The reagent forms complex with water

(b) The reagent becomes inactive in water

(c) It is insoluble in water

(d) The reagent is highly reactive in water

170. A liquid was mixed with ethanol and a drop of concentrated H_2SO_4 was added. A compound with a fruity smell was formed. The liquid was ......

(a) HCHO

(b) CH_3COCH_3

(c) CH_3COOH

(d) CH_3OH

171. Among the following sets of reactants, which one produces anisole?

(a) CH_3CHO; RMgX

(b) C_6H_5OH; NaOH; CH_3I

(c) C_6H_5OH; neutral $FeCl_3$

(d) $C_6H_5 - CH_3$; CH_3COCl; $AlCl_3$

172. Methyl alcohol when reacted with carbon monoxide using cobalt or rhodium as a catalyst, compound 'A' is formed. On heating 'A' with HI in the presence of red phosphorus as a catalyst, 'B' is formed. Identify 'B'.

(a) CH_3COOH

(b) CH_3CHO

(c) CH_3CH_2I

(d) CH_3CH_3

173. Which alcohol of molecular formula C_4H_9OH cannot be obtained by the reduction of carbonyl compound?

(a) 2-methylpropan-1-ol

(b) 2-methylpropan-2-ol

(c) butanol

(d) butan-2-ol

174. 1 mole alcohol react with Na to give what weight of hydrogen?

(a) 1 g

(b) 2 g

(c) 3 g

(d) 3.5 g

175. Which of the following species can act as the strongest base?

(a) ^-OH

(b) ^-OR

(c) $^-O\,C_6H_5$

(d) $^-O-C_6H_4-NO_2$

176. Which of the following alcohols cannot be prepared by reduction of carbonyl compounds?

(a) Pentan-1-ol

(b) Pentan-2-ol

(c) 2-methyl pentan-2-ol

(d) 3-methyl pentan-2-ol

177. Phenol is less acidic than ....
(a) Ethanol
(b) o-nitrophenol
(c) o-methyl phenol
(d) o-methoxy phenol

178. Which of the following compounds can be prepared from ethyl alcohol in a single step?
(a) Acetic acid
(b) Ethyl acetate
(c) Ethylene
(d) All of these

179. Which of the following conversions explain the acidic nature of alcohols?
(a) Ethanol $\xrightarrow{HBr}$ Bromoethane
(b) Ethanol $\xrightarrow{Na}$ Sodium ethoxide
(c) Ethanol $\xrightarrow{PCl_2}$ Chloroethane
(d) Ethanol $\xrightarrow{SOCl_2}$ Chloroethane

180. Ethers are considered as ......
(a) Monoalkyl derivatives of water
(b) Alkoxy derivatives of alkanes
(c) Alkyl derivatives of fatty acids
(d) Condensation products of acid and alcohol

PREVIOUS YEAR'S QUESTIONS

1. The reaction can be classified as ......   **(NEET-2016]**

$$\text{Cyclopentyl}-OH \xrightarrow{NaH} \text{Cyclopentyl}-O^{\ominus} Na^{\oplus} \xrightarrow{Me-I} \text{Cyclopentyl}-O^{Me}$$

(a) Dehydration reaction
(b) Williamson alcohol synthesis reaction
(c) Williamson ether synthesis reaction
(d) Alcohol formation reaction

2. Which of the following compounds has highest boiling point?   **[MHT-CET 2015]**
(a) Propan-1-ol
(b) n-Butane
(c) Chloroethane
(d) Propanal

3. Name the catalyst used in commercial method of preparation of phenol.   **[MHT-CET 2016]**
(a) Silica
(b) Calcium phosphate
(c) Anhydrous aluminium chloride
(d) Cobalt naphthenate

4. Which among the following phenolic compounds is most acidic in nature? **[MHT-CET 2016]**
(a) p-aminophenol
(b) phenol
(c) m-nitrophenol
(d) p-nitrophenol

5. The reaction which involves dichlorocarbene as an electrophile is ......

[KARNATAKA CET 2016]

(a) Reimer - Tiemann reaction
(b) Kolbe's reaction
(c) Friedel - Craft's acylation
(d) Fittig's reaction

6. The reaction is called ......   **[AIPMT 2015]**

$$\underset{\underset{CH_3}{|}}{\overset{\overset{CH_3}{|}}{CH_3-C}}-ONa + CH_3CH_2Cl \xrightarrow{-NaCl} \underset{\underset{CH_3}{|}}{\overset{\overset{CH_3}{|}}{CH_3-C}}-O-CH_2-CH_3$$

(a) Williamson synthesis
(b) Williamson continuous etherification process
(c) Etard reaction
(d) Gatterman - Koch reaction

7. Ethanol is converted into ethoxy ethane ...... **[KARNATAKA CET 2016]**
 (a) by heating excess of ethanol with conc. H_2SO_4 at 140°C
 (b) by heating ethanol with excess of conc. H_2SO_4 at 443 K
 (c) by treating with conc. H_2SO_4 at room temperature
 (d) by treating with conc. H_2SO_4 at 273 K

8. Isopropyl methyl ether when treated with cold hydrogen iodide gives ... **[MHT-CET 2016]**
 (a) isopropyl iodide and methyl iodide (b) isopropyl alcohol and methyl iodide
 (c) isopropyl alcohol and methyl alcohol (d) isopropyl iodide and methyl alcohol

9. The reaction of which among the following ethers with HI in cold leads to the formation of methyl alcohol ? **[MHT-CET 2015]**
 (a) ethyl methyl ether   (b) methyl propyl ether
 (c) isopropyl methyl ether   (d) tert-butyl methyl ether

10. Arrange the following compounds in the increasing order of their acidic strength :
                 [KARNATAKA CET 2015]

 (i) m-nitrophenol (ii) m-cresol (iii) phenol (iv) m-chlorophenol
 (a) iii < ii < iv < i (b) ii < iv < iii < i (c) ii < iii < iv < i (d) ii < iii < i < iv

11. Among the following sets of reactants which one produces anisole? **[AIPMT 2014]**
 (a) CH_3CHO; RMgX   (b) C_6H_5OH; NaOH; CH_3I
 (c) C_6H_5OH; neutral $FeCl_3$ (d) $C_6H_5 - CH_3$; CH_3COCl; $AlCl_3$

12. Select the ether among following that yields methanol as one of the products on reaction with cold hydroiodic acid. **[MHT-CET 2014]**
 (a) 1-Methoxybutane   (b) 1-Methoxy-2-methylpropane
 (c) 2-Methoxy-2-methylpropane   (d) Methoxybenzene

13. The most suitable reagent for the conversion of $R - CH_2 - OH \rightarrow R - CHO$ is ......
 (a) $K_2Cr_2O_7$ (b) CrO_3 **[JEE MAIN 2014]**
 (c) PCC (Pyridinium Chlorochromate) (d) $KMnO_4$

14. Which of the following will not be soluble in sodium hydrogen carbonate? **[AIPMT 2014]**
 (a) 2, 4, 6-trinitrophenol   (b) Benzoic acid
 (c) o-Nitrophenol   (d) Benzenesulphonic acid

15. Among the following ethers, which one will produce methyl alcohol on treatment with hot concentrated HI? **[NEET UG 2013]**
 (a) $CH_3–CH_2–CH_2–CH_2–O–CH_3$ (b) $CH_3CH_2–\underset{\underset{\displaystyle CH_3}{|}}{CH}–O–CH_3$

 (c) $CH_3–\underset{\underset{\displaystyle CH_3}{|}}{CH}–CH_2–O–CH_3$ (d) $CH_3 – \underset{\underset{\displaystyle CH_3}{|}}{\overset{\overset{\displaystyle CH_3}{|}}{C}}–O–CH_3$

16. Which of the following compounds can be used as antifreeze in automobile radiators?

[CBSE AIPMT 2012]

(a) Methyl alcohol   (b) Glycol   (c) Nitrophenol   (d) Ethyl alcohol

17. Which one of the following properties is exhibited by phenol?

(a) It is soluble in aq. NaOH and evolves CO_2 with aq. $NaHCO_3$

(b) It is soluble in aq. NaOH and does not evolve CO_2 with aq. $NaHCO_3$

(c) It is soluble in aq. NaOH but evolve CO_2 with aq. $NaHCO_3$

(d) It is insoluble in aq. NaOH and does not evolve CO_2 with aq. $NaHCO_3$

18. HCHO was treated with reagent X. The product formed upon hydrolysis in the presence of an acid gave C_2H_5OH. The reagent X is ......   **[KCET 2012]**

(a) alcoholic KOH   (b) alcoholic KCN   (c) CH_3MgI (d) aq. KOH

19. The most suitable reagent for the conversion of primary alcohol to an aldehyde is ......

[AFMC 2012]

(a) CrO_3 (b) $KMnO_4$ (c) PCC   (d) $K_2Cr_2O_7$

20. In the following reactions   **[CBSE AIPMT 2011]**

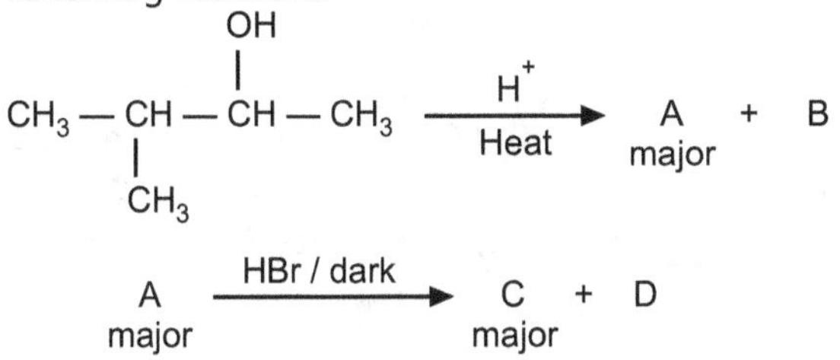

$$CH_3-\underset{\underset{CH_3}{|}}{\underset{|}{CH}}-\underset{\underset{}{\overset{\overset{OH}{|}}{}}}{CH}-CH_3 \xrightarrow[\text{Heat}]{H^+} \underset{\text{major}}{A} + B$$

$$\underset{\text{major}}{A} \xrightarrow{\text{HBr / dark}} \underset{\text{major}}{C} + D$$

The major products [A] and [C] are respectively ......

(a) $CH_2 = \underset{\overset{|}{CH_3}}{C} - CH_2 - CH_3 \ + \ CH_3 - \underset{\underset{Br}{|}}{\overset{\overset{CH_3}{|}}{C}} - CH_2 - CH_3$

(b) $CH_2 = \underset{\overset{|}{CH_3}}{C} - CH_2 - CH_3 \ + \ \underset{\underset{Br}{|}}{\overset{\overset{CH_3}{|}}{CH_2}} - CH - CH_2 - CH_3$

(c) $CH_3 - \underset{\overset{|}{CH_3}}{C} = CH - CH_3 \ + \ CH_3 - \underset{\underset{Br}{|}}{\overset{\overset{CH_3}{|}}{C}} - CH_2 - CH_3$

(d) $CH_3 - \underset{\overset{|}{CH_3}}{C} = CH - CH_3 \ + \ CH_3 - \underset{\underset{CH_3}{|}}{CH} - \overset{\overset{Br}{|}}{CH} - CH_3$

21. When vapours of isopropyl alcohol are passed over heated copper, the major product obtained is ...... **[Manipal 2010]**
    (a) propane　　　(b) propylene　　　(c) acetaldehyde　　(d) acetone

22. The correct order of dehydration of alcohols is ...... **[MHT GET 2010]**
    (a) $a° > 2° > 3°$　　(b) $3° > 2° > 1°$　　(c) $2° > 1° > 3°$　　(d) $1° > 3° > 2°$

23. The major product in the reaction Phenol $\xrightarrow[\text{KOH}]{K_2S_2O_8}$ is ...... **[Manipal 2010]**
    (a) p-benzoquinone　　　　　　　　(b) p-benzene diol
    (c) benzenesulphonic acid　　　　　(d) diphenyl ether

24. Phenol reacts with PCl_5 to give mainly ...... **[Manipal 2010]**
    (a) p-chlorophenol　　　　　　　　(b) chlorobenzene
    (c) o-and p-chlorophenols　　　　　(d) triphenylphosphate

25. Phenol is heated with phthalic anhydride in the presence of conc. H_2SO_4. The product gives pink colour with alkali. The product is ...... **[BVP 2010]**
    (a) phenolphthalein　　(b) Bakelite　　　(c) salicylic acid　　(d) fluorescein

26. The most suitable reagent for the conversion of $RCH_2OH \rightarrow RCHO$ is ......
    (a) $KMnO_4$　　　　　　　　　　　(b) $K_2Cr_2O_7$
    (c) CrO_3　　　　　　　　　　　　(d) PCC (pyridine chlorochromate)

27. Consider the following reaction, **[CBSE AIPMT 2009]**

    $$\text{Ethanol} \xrightarrow{PBr_3} X \xrightarrow{\text{alc. KOH}} Y \xrightarrow[\text{H}_2\text{O, heat}]{\text{conc. H}_2\text{SO}_4} Z$$

    The product Z is ......
    (a) $CH_2 = CH_2$　　　　　　　　　(b) $CH_3CH_2 - O - CH_2CH_3$
    (c) $CH_3CH_2 - O - SO_3H$　　　　　(d) CH_3CH_2OH

28. Dehydration of methyl alcohol with conc. H_2SO_4 yields...... **[CPMT 2009]**
    (a) methane　　　(b) ethane　　　(c) methyl ether　　(d) acetone

29. In the following reaction, Ethyl alcohol + $H^+ \rightarrow$ product, the product is ... **[MHT CET 2009]**
    (a) ethane　　　　　　　　　　　　(b) ethyl hydrogen sulphate
    (c) diethyl ether　　　　　　　　　(d) acetylene

30. Consider the following reaction: **[CBSE AIMPT 2009]**

    The product Z is ......
    (a) toluene　　　(b) Benzaldehyde　　　(c) Benzoic acid　　(d) Benzene

31. Phenol is heated with $CHCl_3$ and alcoholic KOH when salicylaldehyde is produced. The reaction is known as ...... **[Manipal 2009]**
    (a) Rosenmund's reaction　　　　　(b) Reimer-Tiemann reaction
    (c) Friedel-Craft's reaction　　　　(d) Sommelet reaction

32. Sulphonation of phenol with conc. H_2SO_4 at $288 - 298$ K gives ......
    (a) o-phenol sulphonic acid　　　　(b) sulphanilic acid
    (c) p-phenol sulphonic acid　　　　(d) sulphone　　**[Manipal 2009]**

33. Which of the following is most acidic?   **[Manipal 2009]**

(a) 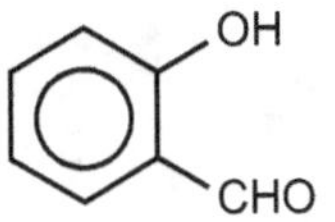 [benzene with OH and CHO groups (salicylaldehyde, ortho)]   (b) 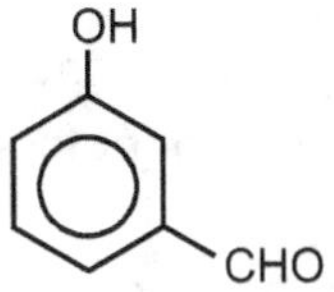 [benzene with OH and CHO groups (meta)]   (c)  [benzene with OH and CHO groups (para)]   (d) 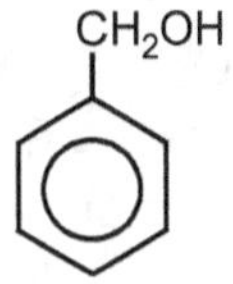 [benzene with CH_2OH group]

34. An organic compound 'X' is oxidized by using acidified $K_2Cr_2O_7$. The product obtained reacts with phenyl hydrazine but does not give silver mirror test. The possible structure of X is ......   **[KCET 2009]**

(a) CH_3COCH_3 (b) $(CH_3)_2CHOH$ (c) CH_3CHO (d) CH_3CH_2OH

35. Give IUPAC name of the compound given below :   **[A.M.U. 2009]**

$$CH_3-\underset{\underset{Cl}{|}}{CH}-CH_2-CH_2-\underset{\underset{OH}{|}}{CH}-CH_3$$

(a) 2-Chloro-5-hydroxyhexane   (b) 2-Hydroxy-5-chlorohexane
(c) 5-Chlorohexan-2-ol   (d) 2-Chlorohexan-5-ol

36. IUPAC name of m-cresol is ......   **[G.G.S.I.P.U. 2009]**
(a) 3-methylphenol   (b) 3-chlorophenol
(c) 3-methoxyphenol   (d) benzene-1,3-diol

37. **Assertion :** The ease of dehydration of following alcohols is ......   **[AIIMS 2008]**
Reason : Alcohols leading to conjugated alkene are dehydrated to a greater extent.
(a) Both Assertion and Reason are true and Reason is the correct explanation of Assertion.
(b) Both Assertion and Reason are true and Reason is not the correct explanation of Assertion.
(c) Assertion is true but Reason is false.
(d) Both Assertion and Reason are false

38. The correct order of boiling point for primary (1°), secondary (2°) and tertiary (3°) alcohols is ......   **[MHT-CET 2008]**
(a) 1° > 2° > 3°   (b) 3° > 2° > 1°   (c) 2° > 1° > 3°   (d) 2° > 3° > 1°

39. When o- or p-phenyl sulphonic acid is treated with bromine water, the product formed is ...   **[Manipal 2008]**

(a) 2-4-dibromophenol   (b) 2,4,6-tribromophenol
(c) 3-bromophenylbenzoic acid   (d) 3,5-dibromophenol

40. In the following reaction, 'A' is ......   **[AFMC 2007]**

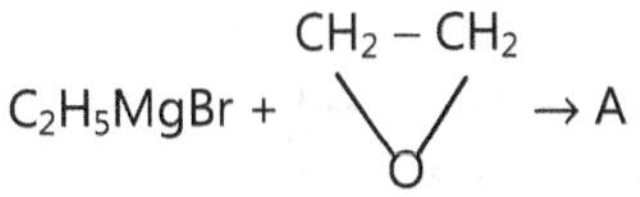

$$C_2H_5MgBr + \underset{O}{\overset{CH_2-CH_2}{\triangle}} \rightarrow A$$

(a) $C_2H_5CH_2CHO$ (b) $C_2H_5CH_2CH_2OH$ (c) $C_2H_5CH_2OH$ (d) C_2H_5CHO

41. The major product of the following reaction is ......   **[AIIMS 2007]**

$$CH_3-\underset{\underset{OH}{|}}{\overset{\overset{CH_3}{|}}{C}}-CH_2OH \xrightarrow[\Delta]{H_2SO_4}$$

(a) $(CH_3)_2C = CH_2$ (b) butan-2-one
(c) $(CH_3)_2C - CHO$ (d) iso-butyraldehyde

42. Methanol and ethanol are miscible in water due to ...... **[AFMC 2006]**
    (a) covalent character
    (b) hydrogen bonding character
    (c) oxygen bonding character
    (d) none of these

43. **Assertion :** Change in colour of acidic solution of potassium dichromate by breath is used to test drunk drivers. **[AIIMS 2006]**
    Reason : Change in colour is due to the complexation of alcohol with potassium dichromate.
    (a) Both Assertion and Reason are true and Reason is the correct explanation of Assertion.
    (b) Both Assertion and Reason are true and Reason is not the correct explanation of Assertion.
    (c) Assertion is true but Reason is false.
    (d) Both Assertion and Reason are false

44. When alcohol react with conc. H_2SO_4, intermediate compound formed is ......
    (a) carbonium ion
    (b) alkoxy ion **[AFMC 2005]**
    (c) alkyl hydrogen sulphate
    (d) none of these

45. The only alcohol that cannot be prepared by indirect hydration of alkene is ......
    (a) ethyl alcohol
    (b) propyl alcohol **[AFMC 2005]**
    (c) iso-butyl alcohol
    (d) methyl alcohol

46. A compound A has a molecular formula C_2Cl_3OH. It reduces Fehling's solution and on oxidation gives a monocarboxylic acid B. A can be obtained by the action of chlorine on ethyl alcohol. A is ...... **[KCET 2005]**
    (a) chloroform
    (b) chloral
    (c) methyl chloride
    (d) monochloroacetic acid

47. Identify B in the following scheme ...... **[Kerala CEE 2005]**

$$CH_3CH_2CH_2OH \xrightarrow{PCl_5} A \xrightarrow{alc.\ KOH} B$$

    (a) propyne　　(b) propene　　(c) propanol　　(d) propanone

48. Wood spirit is known as ...... **[AFMC 2004]**
    (a) methanol　　(b) ethanol　　(c) acetone　　(d) benzene

49. Wine (an alcoholic beverage) contains ...... **[A.I.I.M.S. 2004]**
    (a) CH_3OH　　(b) C_2H_5OH　　(c) CH_3COOH　　(d) C_6H_5OH

50. **Assertion :** Alcohols are dehydrated to hydrocarbons in the presence of acidic zeolites
    Reason : Zeolites are porous catalysts. **[AIIMS 2004]**
    (a) Both Assertion and Reason are true and Reason is the correct explanation of Assertion.
    (b) Both Assertion and Reason are true and Reason is not the correct explanation of Assertion.
    (c) Assertion is true but Reason is false.
    (d) Both Assertion and Reason are false

51. Propan-1-ol can be prepared from propene by ...... **[AIIMS 2004]**
    (a) H_2O/H_2SO_4
    (b) $Hg(OAc)_2/H_2O$ followed by $NaBH_4$
    (c) B_2H_6 followed by H_2O_2
    (d) CH_3CO_2H/H_2SO_4

52. Iso-propylbenzene on air oxidation in the presence of dilute acid gives ......

(a) C_6H_5COOH　　(b) $C_6H_5COCH_3$　　(c) C_6H_5CHO　　(d) C_6H_5OH

53. Which of the following compounds would not evolve CO_2 when treated with $NaHCO_3$ solution? **[KCET 2006]**

(a) Salicylic acid　　　　　　　　(b) Phenol

(c) Benzoic acid　　　　　　　　(d) 4-nitrobenzoic acid

54. Which one of the following compounds is most acidic? **[CBSE AIPMT 2005]**

(a) $Cl - CH_2 - CH_2OH$

(b) 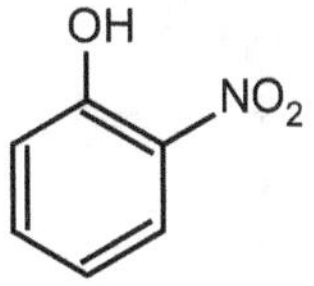 2-nitrophenol

(c) 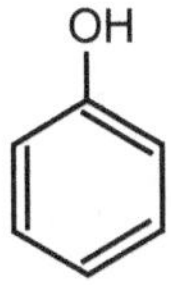 phenol

(d) 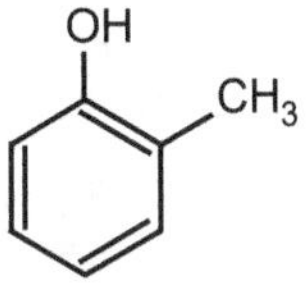 2-methylphenol

55. X is identified as ...... **[AFMC 2003]**

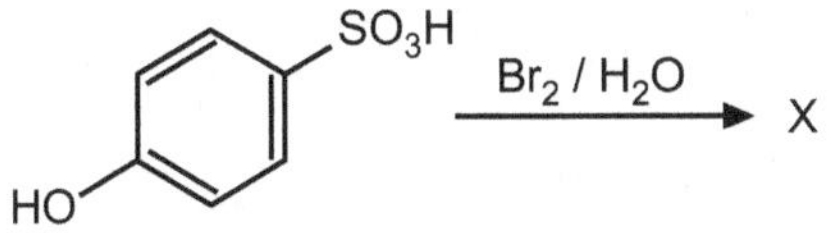

4-hydroxybenzene sulphonic acid $\xrightarrow{Br_2 / H_2O}$ X

(a) 2, 4, 6-tribromophenol

(b) 2-bromo-4-hydroxyl benzene sulphonic acid

(c) 3, 5-dibromo-4 hydroxy benzene sulphonic acid

(d) 2-bromophenol

56. When alkyl aryl ether is heated with HX, it gives ...... **[CPMT 2009]**

(a) alcohol and phenol　　　　　(b) alcohol and aryl halide

(c) phenol and alkyl halide　　　(d) alkyl halide and aryl halide

57. In which of the following reactions, the product obtained is tert-butyl methyl ether? **[AIIMS 2008]**

(a) $CH_3OH + HO - CH_2 - CH_3 \rightarrow$

(b) $CH_3 - \underset{\underset{CH_3}{|}}{\overset{\overset{CH_3}{|}}{C}} - Br + CH_3OH \rightarrow$

(c) $CH_3Br + Na^+O^- - \underset{\underset{CH_3}{|}}{\overset{\overset{CH_3}{|}}{C}} - CH_3$

(d) $CH_3 - O^-Na^+ + CH_3 - CH_2 - Br \rightarrow$

58. Tert-butyl methyl ether on heating with anhydrous HI in ether gives ......

(a) $CH_3OH + (CH_3)_3CCl$　　　　(b) $CH_3I + (CH_3)_3COH$

(c) $CH_3I + (CH_3)_3CCl$　　　　　(d) None of these

59. An organic compound, C_3H_6O does not give a precipitate with 2,4-dinitrophenyl hydrazine reagent and does not react with metallic sodium. It could be ...... **[Manipal 2008]**

(a) $CH_3 - CH_2 - CHO$

(b) $CH_2 = CH - CH_2OH$

(c) $CH_3 - CO - CH_3$

(d) $CH_2 = CH - O - CH_3$

60. In the reaction, $2A$ + dry silver oxide $\rightarrow$ ether + $2AgX$ **[MHT-CET 2008]**

A is a/an ......

(a) primary alcohol (b) acid (c) alkyl halide (d) alcohol

61. The reaction : $CH_3 - \underset{\underset{CH_3}{|}}{CH} - CH_2 - O - CH_2 - CH_3 \xrightarrow{\ HI\ }$ **[CBSE AIPMT 2007]**

Which of the following compounds will be formed?

(a) $CH_3 - \underset{\underset{CH_3}{|}}{CH} - CH_2 - I + CH_3 - CH_2 - OH$

(b) $CH_3 - \underset{\underset{CH_3}{|}}{CH} - CH_2 - OH + CH_3 - CH_2 - I$

(c) $CH_3 - \underset{\underset{CH_3}{|}}{CH} - CH_2 - OH + CH_3 - CH_3$

(d) $CH_3 - \underset{\underset{CH_3}{|}}{CH} - CH_3 + CH_3 - CH_2 - OH$

62. Assertion : Alcohols have higher boiling points than ethers of comparable molecular masses. **[AIIMS 2007]**

Reason : Alcohols and ethers are isomeric in nature.

(a) Both Assertion and Reason are true and Reason is the correct explanation of Assertion.

(b) Both Assertion and Reason are true and Reason is not the correct explanation of Assertion.

(c) Assertion is true but Reason is false.

(d) Both Assertion and Reason are false

63. In Williamson's synthesis, ethoxyethane is prepared by ...... **[Manipal 2007]**

(a) passing ethanol over heated alumina

(b) heating sodium ethoxide with ethyl bromide

(c) treating ethyl alcohol with excess of H_2SO_4 at $430 - 440$ K

(d) heating ethanol with dry Ag_2O

64. Assertion : t-butyl methyl ether is not prepared by the reaction of t-butyl bromide with sodium methoxide. **[AIIMS 2005]**

Reason : Sodium methoxide is a strong nucleophile.

(a) Both Assertion and Reason are true and Reason is the correct explanation of Assertion.

(b) Both Assertion and Reason are true and Reason is not the correct explanation of Assertion.

(c) Assertion is true but Reason is false.

(d) Both Assertion and Reason are false.

65. **Assertion :** The major products formed by heating $C_6H_5CH_2OCH_3$ with HI are $C_6H_5CH_2I$ and CH_3OH.

Reason : Benzyl cation is more stable than methyl cation.   **[AIIMS 2004]**

(a) Both Assertion and Reason are true and Reason is the correct explanation of Assertion.

(b) Both Assertion and Reason are true and Reason is not the correct explanation of Assertion.

(c) Assertion is true but Reason is false.

(d) Both Assertion and Reason are false.

66. Which one of the following can be oxidised to the corresponding carbonyl compound ?

[CBSE AIPMT 2004]

(a) o-Nitrophenol   (b) Phenol

(c) 2-methyl-2-hydroxy propane   (d) 2-hydroxy propane

67. Which of the following will not form a yellow precipitate on heating with an alkaline solution of iodine ?   **[CBSE AIPMT 2004]**

(a) $CH_3CH_2CH(OH)CH_3$ (b) CH_3OH

(c) CH_3CH_2OH (d) $CH_3CH(OH)CH_3$

68. Which of the following combination can be used to synthesize isopropyl alcohol ?

[Karnataka C.E.T. 2004]

(a) CH_3MgI and CH_3COCH_3 (b) CH_3MgI and C_2H_5OH

(c) CH_3MgI and $CH_3COOC_2H_5$ (d) CH_3MgI and $HCOOC_2H_5$

69. Salicylic acid is prepared from phenol by ......   **[A.F.M.C. 2005]**

(a) Reimer-Tiemann reaction   (b) Kolbe's reaction

(c) Kolbe electrolysis reaction   (d) None of these

70. What is formed when glycerol reacts with HI ?   **[K.C.E.T. 2000]**

<table>
<tr><td>(a)</td><td>$\begin{array}{c} CH_2OH \\ | \\ CHI \\ | \\ CH_2OH \end{array}$</td><td>(b)</td><td>$\begin{array}{c} CH_2 \\ \| \\ C \\ | \\ CH_2I \end{array}$</td><td>(c)</td><td>$\begin{array}{c} CH_3 \\ | \\ CH_2 \\ | \\ CH_3 \end{array}$</td><td>(d)</td><td>$\begin{array}{c} CH_2OH \\ | \\ C=O \\ | \\ CH_3 \end{array}$</td></tr>
</table>

71. The order of susceptibility of nucleophilic attack on aldehydes follows the order ......

[A.F.M.C. 2003]

(a) $1^o > 3^o > 2^o$ (b) $1^o > 2^o > 3^o$ (c) $3^o > 2^o > 1^o$ (d) $2^o > 3^o > 1^o$

72. During dehydration of alcohols to alkenes by heating with conc. H_2SO_4 the initiation step is ......   **[AIEEE 2003]**

(a) formation of carbocation   (b) elimination of water

(c) formation of an ester   (d) protonation of alcohol molecule

73. When ethylene glycol is heated with acidified potassium permanganate, the main organic compound obtained is ......   **[Kerala C.E.T. 2001]**

(a) Oxalic acid   (b) Glyoxal   (c) Formic acid   (d) Acetaldehyde

74. Which of the following is correct ?   **[C.B.S.E. P.M.T. 2001]**

    (a) Reduction of any aldehyde gives secondary alcohol

    (b) Reaction of vegetable oil with H_2SO_4 gives glycerine

    (c) Alcoholic iodine with NaOH gives iodoform

    (d) Sucrose on reaction with NaCl gives invert sugar

75. Vinyl carbinol is ......   **[U.P.S.E.A.T. 2001]**

    (a) $HO - CH_2CH = CH_2$ (b) $CH_3C(OH) = CH_2$

    (c) $CH_3 - CH = CH - OH$ (d) $CH_3C(CH_2OH) = CH_2$

76. Absolute alcohol (100% alcohol) is prepared by distilling rectified spirit over ......

                                                      [E.A.M.C.E.T. 2001]

    (a) Na   (b) $CaCl_2$ (c) Mg   (d) $Mg(OC_2H_5)_2$

77. An organic compound A react with methyl magnesium iodide to form an addition product which on hydrolysis forms the compound B. Compound B gives blue colour salt in Victor Meyer's test. The compounds A and B are respectively ......   **[Tamil Nadu 2002]**

    (a) Acetaldehyde, tertiary butyl alcohol   (b) Acetaldehyde, ethyl alcohol

    (c) Acetaldehyde, isopropyl alcohol   (d) Acetone, isopropyl alcohol

78. Which of the following is most acidic?   **[CBSE-AIPMT-2005]**

    (a) Benzyl alcohol   (b) Cyclohexanol   (c) Phenol   (d) m-Chlorophenol

79. Mark the correct order of decreasing acid strength of the following compounds......

                                                        [K.C.E.T. 2005]

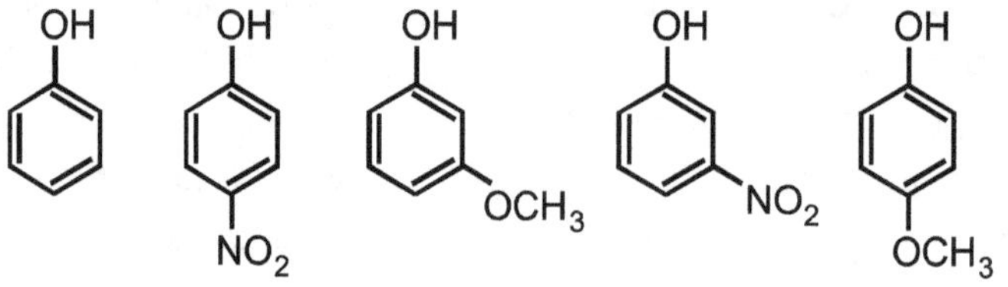

        (A)   (B)   (C)   (D)   (E)

    (a) $E > D > B > A > C$ (b) $B > D > A > C > E$

    (c) $D > E > C > B > A$ (d) $E > D > C > B > A$

80. Mark the correct increasing order of reactivity of the following compounds with HBr/HCl.

                                                   [Haryana P.M.T. 2005]

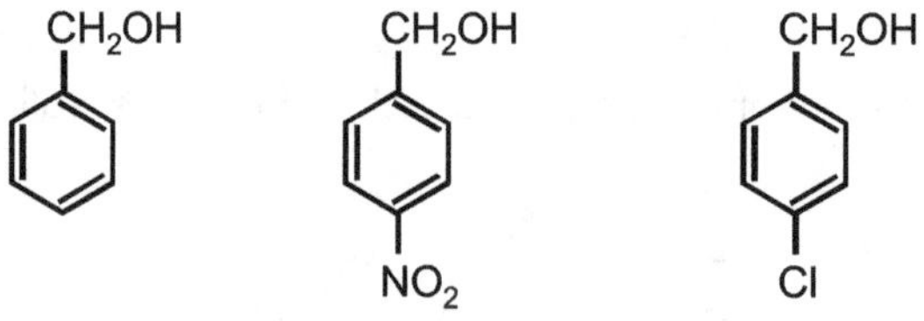

        (A)   (B)   (C)

    (a) $A < B < C$ (b) $B < A < C$ (c) $B < C < A$ (d) $C < B < A$

81. Arrange the following compounds in increasing order of boiling point : Propan-1-ol, butan-1-ol, butan-2-ol, pentan-1-ol   **[Wardha 2005]**

    (a) Propan-1-ol, butan-2-ol, butan-1-ol, pentan-1-ol

    (b) Propan-1-ol, butan-1-ol, butan-2-ol, pentan-1-ol

    (c) Pentan-1-ol, butan-2-ol, butan-1-ol, propan-1-ol

    (d) Pentan-1-ol, butan-1-ol, butan-2-ol, propan-1-ol

82. Which of the following is a Lucas reagent? **[C.M.C. Ludhiana 2006]**
    (a) Conc. HCl and anhydrous $ZnCl_2$
    (b) Dilute HCl and $ZnCl_2$
    (c) Conc. H_2SO_4 and anhydrous $ZnCl_2$
    (d) Conc. HCl and zinc

83. Glycerol reacts with phosphorus triiodide to form ...... **[J.I.P.M.E.R. 2008]**
    (a) Allyl alcohol
    (b) Allyl iodide
    (c) Acrolein
    (d) 1, 2, 3-triiodopropane

84. Which among the following enzymes convert both glucose and fructose into ethanol?
    [Manipal 2004]
    (a) Diastase   (b) Invertase   (c) Zymase   (d) Maltase

85. Rectified spirit contains approximately ...... **[A.I.I.M.S. 2002]**
    (a) 45% w/w ethanol
    (b) 85% w/w ethanol
    (c) 99.5% w/w ethanol
    (d) 95% w/w ethanol

86. Ethanol reacts with chlorine water to give ...... **[C.B.S.E.-A.I.P.M.T. 2003]**
    (a) Ethyl chloride   (b) Chloroform   (c) Acetaldehyde   (d) Chloral

87. The order of esterification of alcohols is ...... **[Rajasthan P.M.T. 2002]**
    (a) t > s > p   (b) s > t > p   (c) p > s > t   (d) None of these

88. The compound 'A' when treated with methyl alcohol and few drops of H_2SO_4 gave smell of wintergreen. The compound 'A' is ...... **[M.P. C.E.T. 2002]**
    (a) Succinic acid   (b) Salicylic acid   (c) Tartaric acid   (d) Oxalic acid

89. n-propyl alcohol and isopropyl alcohol can be chemically distinguished by which reagent ?
    [C.B.S.E. P.M.T. 2002]
    (a) PCl_5
    (b) Reduction
    (c) Oxidation with potassium dichromate
    (d) Ozonolysis

90. The wrong statement about glycerol is ...... **[Kerala P.M.T. 2001]**
    (a) It is a trihydric alcohol
    (b) It is generally obtained by hydrolysis of oils/fats
    (c) Acidified $KMnO_4$ converts it to oxalic acid   (d) It is a tertiary alcohol

91. Phenol is treated with bromine water and shaken well to get white precipitate. The white precipitate is ...... **[Kerala C.E.T. 2001]**
    (a) 1-Bromophenol
    (b) 2, 4, 6-Tribromophenol
    (c) 2, 4-Dibromophenol
    (d) Mixture of o, p-bromophenol

92. Ethylene may be obtained by the treatment of concentrated H_2SO_4 and X at 160-170°C. X is ...... **[M.P. P.E.T. 2001]**
    (a) C_2H_5OH (b) CH_3OH (c) C_3H_7OH (d) $(CH_3)_2CHCH_2OH$

93. Which of the following alcohols is prepared by acid catalyzed hydration of alkenes?
    [CBSE-AIPMT 2000]
    (a) Butan-1-ol   (b) Propan-1-ol   (c) Ethanol   (d) Methanol

94. Which of the following compounds is obtained as a major product on reaction of ethoxybenzene with nitrating mixture? **[J.I.P.M.E.R. 2010]**
    (a) 2-nitro ethoxy benzene
    (b) 3-nitro ethoxy benzene
    (c) 4-nitro ethoxy benzene
    (d) Nitrobenzene

95. Which one of the following will most readily be dehydrated in acidic condition ?
    [A.I.I.M.S. 2000]

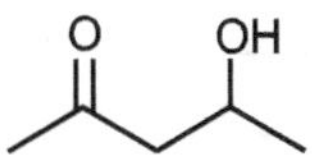

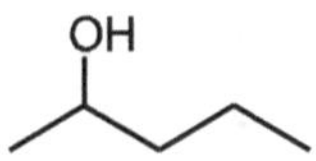

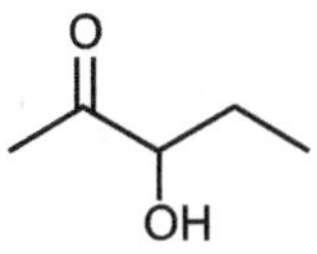

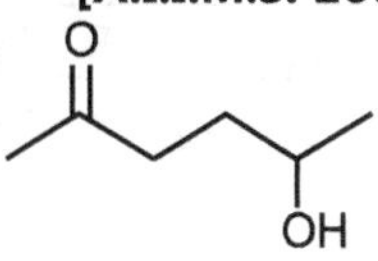

96. 1-hydroxypropane can be obtained from propene by treating with...... **[C.B.S.E. 2000]**

(a) B_2H_6 + NaOH

(b) B_2H_6 + H_2O_2/OH^-

(c) $LiAlH_4$ + H_2O/H^+

(d) HCl + H_2O/H^+

ANSWER KEY

1. (c)	2. (c)	3. (d)	4. (b)	5. (a)	6. (c)	7. (b)	8. (c)
9. (b)	10. (a)	11. (b)	12. (b)	13. (c)	14. (b)	15. (c)	16. (a)
17. (b)	18. (b)	19. (c)	20. (c)	21. (b)	22. (c)	23. (c)	24. (c)
25. (a)	26. (b)	27. (c)	28. (c)	29. (b)	30. (b)	31. (c)	32. (b)
33. (c)	34. (b)	35. (c)	36. (b)	37. (c)	38. (b)	39. (b)	40. (c)
41. (c)	42. (b)	43. (a)	44. (c)	45. (a)	46. (d)	47. (b)	48. (a)
49. (b)	50. (b)	51. (d)	52. (a)	53. (c)	54. (d)	55. (d)	56. (d)
57. (c)	58. (a)	59. (d)	60. (b)	61. (c)	62. (c)	63. (c)	64. (c)
65. (a)	66. (c)	67. (b)	68. (a)	69. (b)	70. (b)	71. (d)	72. (c)
73. (d)	74. (b)	75. (a)	76. (a)	77. (c)	78. (c)	79. (c)	80. (b)
81. (a)	82. (c)	83. (a)	84. (a)	85. (a)	86. (d)	87. (c)	88. (b)
89. (a)	90. (c)	91. (b)	92. (a)	93. (d)	94. (c)	95. (c)	96. (d)
97. (a)	98. (c)	99. (c)	100. (b)	101. (b)	102. (a)	103. (a)	104. (d)
105. (c)	106. (b)	107. (b)	108. (a)	109. (c)	110. (c)	111. (b)	112. (b)
113. (b)	114. (a)	115. (b)	116. (a)	117. (b)	118. (c)	119. (b)	120. (a)
121. (b)	122. (c)	123. (b)	124. (a)	125. (c)	126. (b)	127. (a)	128. (a)
129. (b)	130. (b)	131. (b)	132. (b)	133. (a)	134. (b)	135. (a)	136. (a)
137. (b)	138. (d)	139. (c)	140. (c)	141. (a)	142. (a)	143. (a)	144. (d)
145. (a)	146. (c)	147. (a)	148. (d)	149. (b)	150. (c)	151. (c)	152. (d)
153. (a)	154. (b)	155. (b)	156. (b)	157. (c)	158. (a)	159. (c)	160. (d)
161. (c)	162. (a)	163. (d)	164. (a)	165. (d)	166. (d)	167. (b)	168. (c)
169. (d)	170. (c)	171. (b)	172. (d)	173. (b)	174. (a)	175. (b)	176. (c)
177. (b)	178. (b)	179. (b)	180. (b)				

Previous Year's Questions

1. (c)	2. (a)	3. (c)	4. (d)	5. (a)	6. (a)	7. (a)	8. (b)
9. (d)	10. (c)	11. (b)	12. (c)	13. (c)	14. (c)	15. (d)	16. (b)
17. (b)	18. (c)	19. (c)	20. (c)	21. (d)	22. (b)	23. (a)	24. (d)
25. (a)	26. (d)	27. (d)	28. (c)	29. (c)	30. (c)	31. (b)	32. (a)
33. (c)	34. (b)	35. (c)	36. (a)	37. (a)	38. (a)	39. (b)	40. (b)
41. (d)	42. (b)	43. (c)	44. (a)	45. (d)	46. (b)	47. (b)	48. (a)
49. (b)	50. (b)	51. (c)	52. (d)	53. (b)	54. (b)	55. (a)	56. (c)
57. (c)	58. (a)	59. (d)	60. (c)	61. (b)	62. (b)	63. (b)	64. (a)
65. (a)	66. (d)	67. (b)	68. (d)	69. (b)	70. (b)	71. (b)	72. (d)
73. (a)	74. (c)	75. (a)	76. (d)	77. (c)	78. (d)	79. (b)	80. (c)
81. (a)	82. (a)	83. (b)	84. (c)	85. (d)	86. (b)	87. (c)	88. (b)
89. (c)	90. (d)	91. (b)	92. (a)	93. (c)	94. (c)	95. (a)	96. (b)

❑ ❑ ❑

ALDEHYDES, KETONES AND CARBOXYLIC ACIDS

1. What is the IUPAC name of the compound shown ?

$$CH_3 - CH_2 - CH_2 - \overset{\displaystyle O}{\overset{\|}{C}} - \overset{\displaystyle CH_3}{\overset{|}{CH}} - CH_3$$

(a) 4-heptanone
(b) 2-methyl-3-hexanone
(c) isopropyl n-propyl ketone
(d) 4-methyl-5-hexanone

2. What is the IUPAC name of the compound shown?

$$H - \overset{\displaystyle O}{\overset{\|}{C}} - CH_2 - \overset{\displaystyle CH_3}{\overset{|}{CH}} - CH_3$$

(a) isopentanal
(b) 2-methyl-4-butanone
(c) 3-methylbutanal
(d) 2-methylbutanal

3. Give IUPAC name of mesityl oxide $(CH_3)_2C = CHCOCH_3$

(a) iso-propylhexanone
(b) 2-Methylpent-2-en-3-one
(c) 4-Methylpent-3-en-2-one
(d) 2, 2-Dimethyl butanone

4. Write IUPAC name of the following compound.

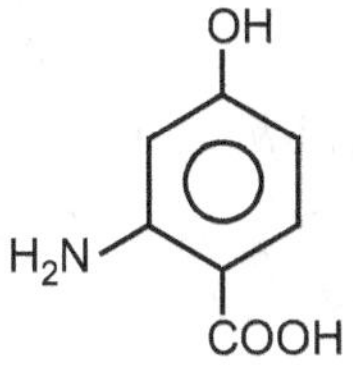

(a) 2-Amino-4-hydroxybenzoic acid
(b) 6-Amino-4-hydroxybenzoic acid
(c) 3-Amino-4-carboxyphenol
(d) 2-Carboxy-5-hydroxyaniline

5. Which of the following reaction sequences would be the best synthesis of 2-pentanone ?

$$CH_3 - \overset{\displaystyle O}{\overset{\|}{C}} - CH_2 - CH_2 - CH_3$$

(a) $CH_3 - CH_2 - CH_2 - \overset{\displaystyle O}{\overset{\|}{C}} - H \xrightarrow[\text{Et}_2\text{O}]{CH_3MgI \quad H_3O^{\oplus}}$

(b) $CH_3 - CH - O \xrightarrow[\text{Et}_2\text{O}]{CH_3MgI \quad H_3O^{\oplus}}$ (with $CH_2 - CH_2$ ring)

(c) $CH_3 - CH_2 - CH_2 - C \equiv N \xrightarrow[\text{Et}_2\text{O}]{CH_3MgI \quad H_3O^{\oplus}}$

(d) $CH_3 - CH_2 - CH_2 - \overset{\displaystyle O}{\overset{\|}{C}} - H \xrightarrow[\text{Et}_2\text{O}]{CH_3MgI \quad H_3O^{\oplus}} \xrightarrow[H^{\oplus}]{KMnO_4}$

6. Which of the functional groups on the following molecule are susceptible to nucleophilic attack ?

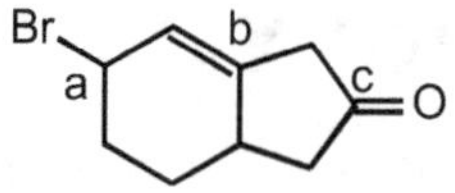

(a) a, b   (b) a, c   (c) c, b   (d) a, b, c

7. Which of the following reaction sequences would be the best synthesis of t-butyl alcohol ?

(a) $CH_3CH_2MgBr +$ (ethylene oxide) $\xrightarrow[]{Et_2O,\ H_3O^{\oplus}}$

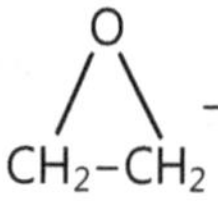

(b) $CH_3CH_2CH_2MgBr \xrightarrow[Et_2O]{CO_2,\ H_3O^{\oplus}}$

(c) $CH_3MgBr + CH_3-\overset{\overset{\displaystyle O}{\|}}{C}-CH_3 \xrightarrow[]{Et_2O,\ H_3O^{\oplus}}$

(d) $CH_3CH_2MgBr + CH_3-\overset{\overset{\displaystyle O}{\|}}{C}-H \xrightarrow[]{Et_2O,\ H_3O^{\oplus}}$

8. Which of these reagents could accomplish the following reduction ?

$$N \equiv C - CH_2 - \overset{\overset{\displaystyle O}{\|}}{C} - CH_2 - CH = CH_2 \longrightarrow N \equiv C - CH_2 - \overset{\overset{\displaystyle OH}{|}}{\underset{\underset{\displaystyle H}{|}}{C}} - CH_2 - CH = CH_2$$

(a) $NaBH_4$ (b) $LiAlH_4$

(c) 1 mole H_2 poisoned catalyst, low pressure   (d) H_3O^+

9. What is the major product of the following reaction ?

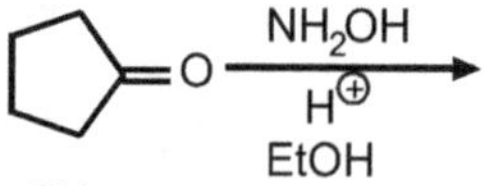

(cyclopentanone) $=O \xrightarrow[\substack{H^{\oplus} \\ EtOH}]{NH_2OH}$

(a) 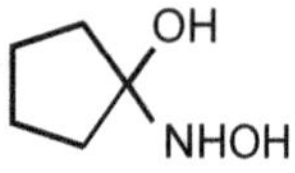 (structure with OH and NHOH)

(b) 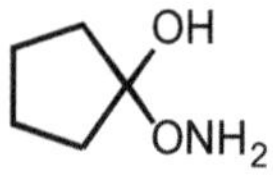 (structure with OH and ONH_2)

(c) 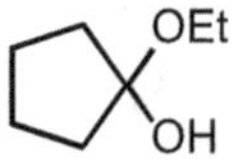 (structure with OEt and OH)

(d) 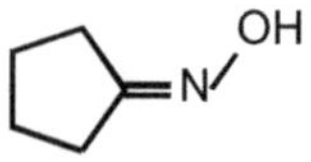 (structure with $=N-OH$)

10. Which of the following reactions is a good method for preparing an aldehyde?

(a) Jones' reagent and 1°-alcohol   (b) Jones' reagent and 2°-alcohol

(c) PCC and 1°-alcohol   (d) H_2SO_4, 1°-alcohol and heat

11. Which of the following statements is not generally true?

(a) C=O is stronger than an equivalent C=C

(b) C=O has a larger bond dipole than C=C

(c) Aldehydes and ketones have higher boiling points than similarly sized alkenes

(d) Alkenes add nucleophiles more rapidly than aldehydes or ketones of similar structure

12. The reaction of $C_6H_5CHBr_2$ with NaOH in aqueous THF is likely to produce which product?

(a) $C_6H_5CHBrOH$ (b) $C_6H_5CH(OH)_2$ (c) C_6H_5CHO (d) $C_6H_5CO_2H$

13. Which of the following carbonyl compounds reacts most rapidly with nucleophilic reagents?

(a) Benzaldehyde

(b) 3,3-dimethylbutanal

(c) Acetophenone

(d) 2,2-dimethylcyclohexanone

14. Which reaction or sequence of reactions would best accomplish the following synthesis?

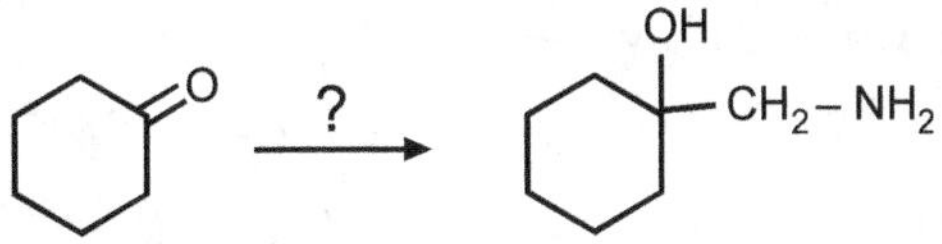

(a) CH_3NH_2, acid catalyst and heat

(b) $CH_2=NH$, acid catalyst and heat

(c) (i) NH_3 acid catalyst and heat; (ii) CH_2I_2 and Zn(Cu)

(d) (i) HCN and NaCN; (ii) $LiAlH_4$ in ether

15. Heating cyclopentanone with either: **I** ethyl amine, or **II** diethylamine, together with an acid catalyst leads to different results. Which of the following best describes this difference?

(a) **I** gives an imine and **II** fails to react

(b) **I** gives an enamine and **II** fails to react

(c) **I** gives an imine and **II** gives an enamine

(d) **I** gives an enamine and **II** gives an imine

16. Which of the following reaction sequences would be best for converting cyclohexanol to methylene-cyclohexane ?

(a) (i) H_3PO_4 and heat; (ii) CH_2I_2 + Zn(Cu)

(b) (i) PCC in CH_2Cl_2; (ii) CH_3MgBr; (iii) H_3PO_4 and heat

(c) (i) PCC in CH_2Cl_2; (ii) $(C_6H_5)_3P=CH_2$

(d) CH_2N_2 and heat

17. Which of the following reactions would not be a useful way of preparing 1-phenyl-2-butanol?

(a) Phenylacetaldehyde + ethyl magnesium bromide

(b) Butanal + phenyl magnesium bromide

(c) Propanal + benzyl magnesium bromide

(d) 1-phenyl-2-butanone + $NaBH_4$

18. Which of the following is a semicarbazone derivative of an aldehyde (RCHO)?

(a) $RCH = N-NHCONH_2$

(b) $RCH = N-OH$

(c) $RCH = N-NH_2$

(d) $RCH = N-C(CH_3)_3$

19. What is the product of the following reaction?

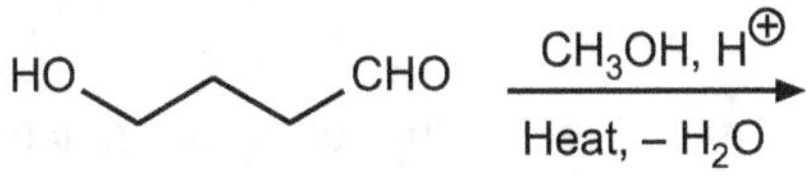

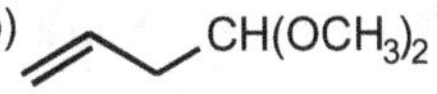

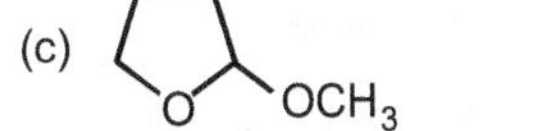 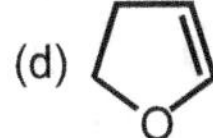

20. Which of the following aldehydes, used alone, will undergo an aldol reaction?

(a) formaldehyde, CH_2O

(b) butanal, $CH_3(CH_2)_2CHO$

(c) benzaldehyde, C_6H_5CHO

(d) 2-propenal, $CH_2 = CHCHO$

21. A $C_7H_{12}O_2$ compound gives a positive Tollens' silver mirror test and a positive iodoform test. Which of the following would satisfy these facts?

(a) 2-hydroxy-3,3-dimethylcyclopentanone

(b) 2,5-heptanedione

(c) 2,2-dimethyl-3-oxopentanal

(d) 2,2-dimethyl-4-oxopentanal

22. An aldol condensation is used to prepare 1,3-diphenyl-2-propenone, $C_6H_5CH=CHCOC_6H_5$. Which combination of reactants will lead to this product?

(a) Enolate donor = acetaldehyde; carbonyl acceptor = benzaldehyde

(b) Enolate donor= phenylacetaldehyde; carbonyl acceptor = phenylacetaldehyde

(c) Enolate donor= acetophenone; carbonyl acceptor = benzaldehyde

(d) Enolate donor=propiophenone; carbonyl acceptor = benzaldehyde

23. Addition of water to alkynes occurs in acidic medium and in the presence of Hg^{2+} ions as a catalyst. Which of the following products will be formed on addition of water to but-1-yne under these conditions?

(a) $CH_3-CH_2-CH_2-\overset{\displaystyle O}{\overset{\|}{C}}-H$

(b) $CH_3-CH_2-\overset{\displaystyle O}{\overset{\|}{C}}-CH_3$

(c) $CH_3-CH_3-\overset{\displaystyle O}{\overset{\|}{C}}-OH + CO_2$

(d) $CH_3-\overset{\displaystyle O}{\overset{\|}{C}}-OH + H-\overset{\displaystyle O}{\overset{\|}{C}}-H$

24. Which of the following compounds is most reactive towards nucleophilic addition reactions?

(a) $CH_3-\overset{\displaystyle O}{\overset{\|}{C}}-H$

(b) $CH_3-\overset{\displaystyle O}{\overset{\|}{C}}-CH_3$

(c) $C_6H_5-\overset{\displaystyle O}{\overset{\|}{C}}-H$

(d) $C_6H_5-\overset{\displaystyle O}{\overset{\|}{C}}-CH_3$

25. The reagent which does not react with both, acetone and benzaldehyde is ......

(a) Fehling's reagent

(b) Phenyl hydrazine

(c) Grignard reagent

(d) Sodium hydrogen sulphite

26. Structure of 'A' and type of isomerism in the following reaction are respectively ......

$$CH_3-C\equiv CH \xrightarrow[1\% \ H_2SO_4]{40\% \ H_2SO_4} A \xrightarrow{\text{Isomerisation}} CH_3-\underset{\underset{O}{\|}}{C}-CH_3$$

(a) Prop–1–en–2–ol, metamerism

(b) Prop-1-en-1-ol, tautomerism

(c) Prop-2-en-2-ol, geometrical isomerism

(d) Prop-1-en-2-ol, tautomerism

27. Compounds A and C in the following reaction are

$$CH_3CHO \xrightarrow[\text{(ii) } H_2O]{\text{(i) } CH_3 MgBr} (A) \xrightarrow{H_2SO_4, \Delta} (B) \xrightarrow{\substack{\text{Hydroboration} \\ \text{oxidation}}} (C)$$

 (a) Identical   (b) Positional isomers

 (c) Functional isomers   (d) Optical isomers

28. Which is the most suitable reagent for the following conversion?

$$CH_3-CH=CH-CH_2-\overset{\overset{\displaystyle O}{\|}}{C}-CH_3 \longrightarrow CH_3-CH=CH-CH_2-\overset{\overset{\displaystyle O}{\|}}{C}-OH$$

 (a) Tollen's reagent   (b) Benzoyl peroxide

 (c) I_2 and NaOH solution   (d) Sn and NaOH solution

29. In Clemmensen reduction, carbonyl compound is treated with ......

 (a) Zinc amalgam + HCl   (b) Sodium amalgam + HCl

 (c) Zinc amalgam + nitric acid   (d) Sodium amalgam + HNO_3

30. Aldehydes and ketones do not give addition reaction with ......

 (a) HCN   (b) $NaHSO_3$ (c) Both (a) and (b) (d) $HCl_{(aq)}$

31. Propan-2-ol on treatment with copper at 300°C forms ......

 (a) Acetone   (b) Acetaldehyde   (c) Ethane   (d) Both (a) and (b)

32. On heating calcium acetate and calcium formate, the major product formed is ......

 (a) CH_3COCH_3 (b) CH_3CHO

 (c) $HCHO + CaCO_3$ (d) $CH_3CHO + CaCO_3$

33. Tollen's reagent is ......

 (a) Ammonical cuprous chloride   (b) Ammonical cuprous chloride

 (c) Ammonical silver bromide   (d) Ammonical silver nitrate

34. Silver mirror is a test for ......

 (a) Aldehydes   (b) Thioalcohols   (c) Acids   (d) Ethers

35. Propyne on hydrolysis in the presence of H_2SO_4 and $HgSO_4$ gives ......

 (a) Acetaldehyde   (b) Acetone   (c) Formaldehyde (d) None of these

36. Which of the following does not turn Schiff's reagent to pink ?

 (a) Formaldehyde   (b) Benzaldehyde   (c) Acetone   (d) Acetal dilhyde

37. Which does not react with Fehling solution ?

 (a) Acetaldehyde   (b) Propanone   (c) Glucose   (d) Formic acid

38. The compound obtained by the reduction of propionaldehyde by amalgamated zinc and concentrated HCl is ......

 (a) Propanol   (b) Propane   (c) Propene   (d) All of these

39. Benzyl alcohol is obtained from benzaldehyde by ......

 (a) Fittig's reaction   (b) Clemmensen's reduction

 (c) Kolbe's reaction   (d) Reduction with $LiAlH_4$

40. During reduction of carbonyl compounds by H_2NNH_2 and KOH, the first intermediate is ...

    (a) $RC = N$ (b) $RCONH_2$ (c) $RCH = NH$ (d) $RCH = NNH_2$

41. Which of the following is hypnotic ?

    (a) Acetaldehyde   (b) Metaldehyde   (c) Paraldehyde   (d) None of these

42. Acetone is prepared by ......

    (a) Oxidation of n-propyl alcohol   (b) Oxidation of acetaldeyhde

    (c) Pyrolysis of calcium acetate

    (d) Pyrolysis of calcium acetate as well as acetic acid

43. A compound possessing α-hydrogen atom, in the presence of dilute alkali forms β-hydroxy aldehyde. This product on heating with dilute acid forms unsaturated crotonaldehyde. The compound is ......

    (a) CH_3CHO (b) CH_3CH_2CHO

    (c) $CH_2 = CH - CHO$ (d) $H_2C = CH - CHO$

44. Reduction of aldehydes with HI and P give ......

    (a) Primary alcohols   (b) Secondary alcohols

    (c) Alkanes   (d) Tertiary alcohols

45. Which reaction yields Bakelite ?

    (a) Urea with HCHO

    (b) Tetramethyl glycol with hexamethylene diisocyanate

    (c) Phenol and HCHO

    (d) Ethylene glycol and dimethylterephthalate

46. Formalin is an aqueous solution of ......

    (a) Furfural   (b) Fluorescein   (c) Formaldehyde   (d) Formic acid

47. Cyanohydrin of which of the following forms lactic acid ?

    (a) HCHO   (b) CH_3COCH_3 (c) CH_3CHO (d) CH_3CH_2CHO

48. Which of the following compounds does not react with $NaHSO_3$?

    (a) C_6H_5CHO (b) Acetophenone   (c) Acetone   (d) Acetaldehyde

49. Acetal is produced by reacting alcohol in the presence of dry HCl with ......

    (a) Acetaldehyde   (b) Ketone   (c) Ether   (d) Carboxylic acid

50. Aldol condensation will not occur in ......

    (a) HCHO   (b) CH_3CH_2CHO (c) CH_3COCH_3 (d) CH_3CHO

51. Reductive ozonolysis of benzene produces ......

    (a) Acetone   (b) Maleic anhydride

    (c) Phthalic acid   (d) Glyoxal

52. The reduction of benzoyl chloride with H_2/Pd-BaSO$_4$ produces ......

    (a) Benzyl alcohol   (b) Benzaldehyde   (c) Benzoic acid   (d) Benzoyl cyanide

53. $C_6H_5CHO + HCN \rightarrow C_6H_5CH(CN)OH$.

    The product would be ......

    (a) Racemate   (b) Optically active

    (c) A meso compound   (d) Mixture of diastereomers

54. Formaldehyde when reacted with methyl magnesium bromide gives ......

(a) C_2H_5OH　　(b) CH_3COOH　　(c) HCHO　　(d) CH_3CHO

55. If acetyl chloride is reduced in the presence of $BaSO_4/H_2$ and Pd, then ......

(a) CH_3CHO is formed　　　　(b) CH_3CH_2OH is formed

(c) CH_3COOH is formed　　　　(d) CH_3COCH_3 is formed

56. Which one of the following undergoes reaction with 50% sodium hydroxide solution to give the corresponding alcohol and acid ?

(a) Phenol　　(b) Benzoic acid　　(c) Butanal　　(d) Benzaldehyde

57. $CH_3CHO + HCHO \xrightarrow[\text{Heat}]{\text{dil. NaOH}} A \xrightarrow[H_3O^+]{\text{HCN}} B$. The structure of compound B is ......

(a) $CH_2 = CH - \underset{\underset{\displaystyle OH}{|}}{CH} - COOH$

(b) $CH_2 = \underset{\underset{\displaystyle CN}{|}}{C} - CH_2 - OH$

(c) $CH_3 - CH_2 - \underset{\underset{\displaystyle OH}{|}}{CH} - COOH$

(d) $CH_2 = \underset{\underset{\displaystyle OH}{|}}{C} - COOH$

(e) $CH_3 - \underset{\underset{\displaystyle OH}{|}}{\overset{\overset{\displaystyle CN}{|}}{C}} - COOH$

58. Self condensation of acetaldehyde in the presence of dilute alkalies gives ......

(a) An acetal　　(b) An aldol　　(c) Mesitylene　　(d) Propionaldehyde

59. The reaction of cyclohexanone with dimethylamine in the presence of catalytic amount of an acid forms a compound. If water during the reaction is continuously removed, the compound formed is generally known as ......

(a) A Schiff's base　　(b) An enamine　　(c) An imine　　(d) An amine

60. Calcium acetate when dry distilled gives ......

(a) Formaldehyde　　(b) Acetaldehyde　　(c) Acetone　　(d) Acetic anhydride

61. On heating calcium acetate and calcium formate, the major product formed is ......

(a) CH_3COCH_3　　(b) CH_3CHO　　(c) $HCHO + CaCO_3$　　(d) $CH_3CHO + CaCO_3$

62. Which of the following alcohols cannot be produced by treatment of aldehydes or ketones with $NaBH_4$ or $LiAlH_4$?

(a) 1-Propanol　　　　(b) 2-Propanol

(c) 2-Methyl-2-propanol　　　　(d) Ethanol

63. Oxidation of Butan-2-one to propionic acid can be achieved by ......

(a) Tollen's reagent　　　　(b) $NaOH + I_2$

(c) Br_2 water　　　　(d) Atmospheric oxidation

64. In public urinals, we observe some nascent smell. This smell is due to ......

(a) Hydrolysis of urea by urease of atmosphere into NH_3 and CO_2

(b) Formation of sulphamic acid by urea of urine

(c) Reaction of CO_2 of atmosphere with urea mononitrate in urine

(d) Hydrogen present in air reacts with nitrogen forming NH_3

65. Heating a mixture of sodium benzoate and soda lime gives ......

(a) Methane   (b) Benzene

(c) Sodium benzoate   (d) Calcium benzoate

66. Which of the following compound will give brisk effervescences of CO_2 on treatment with $NaHCO_3$?

(a) Phenol   (b) Acetic acid   (c) Both of these   (d) None of these

67. Given below are some statements concerning formic acid, which of them is true ?

(a) It is weaker acid than acetic acid

(b) It is a reducing agent

(c) It is heated with calcium salts, it forms a ketone

(d) It is an oxidising agent

68. Which of the following undergoes hydrolysis ?

(a) CH_3COONa (b) $C_6H_5CH_3$ (c) CH_3CONH_2 (d) Both (a) and (c)

69. Acetic acid is obtained when ......

(a) Methyl alcohol is oxidised with potassium permanganate

(b) Calcium acetate is distilled in the presence of calcium formate

(c) Acetaldehyde is oxidised with potassium dichromate and sulphuric acid

(d) Glycerol is heated with sulphuric acid

70. Among the following compounds, the one which will produce ethyl methyl ketone on oxidation is ......

(a) isobutyl alcohol   (b) s-butyl alcohol

(c) t-butyl alcohol   (d) isopropyl alcohol

71. Propyne is treated with aqueous H_2SO_4 in the presence of $HgSO_4$. The product formed is ...

(a) Propan-1-ol   (b) Propan-2-ol   (c) Propanol   (d) Propanone

72. A mixture of calcium ethanoate and calcium methanoate is heated strongly. The expected product is ......

(a) Acetaldehyde   (b) Ethyl methyl ketone

(c) Diethyl ketone   (d) Dimethyl ketone

73. Calcium succinate on strong heating produces ......

(a) diethyl ketone   (b) dimethyl ketone   (c) acetaldehyde   (d) cyclopropane

74. The reaction $CH_2 = CH_2 \xrightarrow[PdCl_2;\ CuCl_2,\ H_2O]{O_2}$ is employed for the industrial preparation of ......

(a) CH_3CH_2OH (b) CH_3COOH (c) CH_3CHO (d) CH_3OCH_3

75. Acetaldehyde does not respond positively to ......

(a) Iodoform test   (b) Benedict's test   (c) Tollen's test   (d) Lucas test

76. 2-pentanone can be distinguished from 3-pentanone by the reagent ......

(a) 2, 4-dinitrophenyl hydrazine   (b) Tollen's reagent

(c) I_2 and dilute $NaOH$ (d) $NaHSO_3$

77. Which one of the following is a stable compound?

(a) $CH_2 = CHOH$ (b) $CH_3CH(OH)_2$ (c) $CH(OH)_3$ (d) $CCl_3CH(OH)_2$

78. Acetaldehyde usually reacts with ......

(a) Electrophiles

(b) Free radicals

(c) Nucleophiles

(d) Both electrophiles and nucleophiles

79. Which of the following will react with water?

(a) $CHCl_3$ (b) CCl_4 (c) CH_2ClCH_2Cl (d) Cl_3CCHO

80. Among the following carboxylic acids, the one which exhibits stereoisomerism is ......

(a) 2-methyl propanoic acid

(b) 2-2 dimethyl propanoic acid

(c) 2-methyl butanoic acid

(d) 3-methyl butanoic acid

81. Which of the following carboxylic acids has the smallest ionization constant?

(a) CH_3CHFCO_2H (b) $BrCH_2CH_2CO_2H$ (c) $FCH_2CH_2CO_2H$ (d) $CH_3CHBrCO_2H$

82. Out of the four pK_a values 3.75, 9.89, 15.54 and 19.30, the highest pK_a value corresponds to ......

(a) Methanol (b) Acetone (c) Phenol (d) Formic acid

83. Among the following reagents, which one is able to reduce a carboxylic acid into a primary alcohol?

(a) $NaBH_4$

(b) $LiAlH_4$

(c) Na, C_2H_5OH

(d) $(Me_2CHO)_3Al/Me_2CHOH$

84. Which one of the following products is formed when adipic acid is heated?

(a)   (b)

(c)   (d)

85. Which one among the following is the strongest reducing agent?

(a) Ethanoic acid (b) Methanoic acid (c) Benzoic acid (d) Carbolic acid

86. Which of the following acids can decolourise the purple colour of $KMnO_4$ solution acidified with H_2SO_4?

(a) HCOOH (b) HOOC – COOH (c) both (a) and (b) (d) none of these

87. Formic acid can be distinguished from formaldehyde by using ______

(a) Tollen's reagent

(b) Fehling's solution

(c) $HgCl_2$ solution

(d) Na_2CO_3 solution

88. When acetic acid is heated with P_4O_{10}, it is converted into ......

(a) $CH_2 = C = O$ (b)   (c) $(CH_3CO)_2O$ (d) CH_3COCH_2COOH

89. Dry distillation of a mixture of calcium formate and calcium acetate gives ______

(a) Formaldehyde (b) Acetaldehyde (c) Acetone (d) Acetophenone

90. Acetonitrile on acidic hydrolysis gives ......

(a) $HCOOH$ (b) CH_3NC (c) CH_3COONa (d) CH_3COOH

91. α-halogenation of carboxylic acid is called _____

(a) Gattermann reaction (b) Reimer-Tiemann reaction
(c) Sandmeyer's reaction (d) HVZ reaction

92. Schiff's reagent gives pink colour with ......

(a) Acetone (b) Acetic acid (c) Acetaldehyde (d) Methyl acetate

93. The acid which does not undergo HVZ reaction is ......

(a) Acetic acid (b) Formic acid
(c) Propanoic acid (d) 2-methyl propanoic acid

94. $CO + NaOH \rightarrow$ Product

(a) $HCOONa$ (b) $C_2H_2O_4$ (c) $HCOOH$ (d) CH_3COOH

95. Rosenmund's reduction is useful in the formation of aldehydes using ......

(a) Ester (b) Alcohol (c) Acid (d) Acid halide

96. $(CH_3)_2C = O \xrightarrow[\text{(HCl)}]{NaCN} A \xrightarrow[\Delta]{H_3O^+} B$

In the above sequence of reactions, A and B are ......

(a) $CH_3 - \underset{\underset{CH_3}{|}}{\overset{\overset{OH}{|}}{C}} - CN$ and $CH_3 - \underset{\underset{CH_3}{|}}{\overset{\overset{OH}{|}}{C}} - COOH$

(b) $CH_3 - \underset{\underset{CH_3}{|}}{\overset{\overset{OH}{|}}{C}} - CN$ and $CH_3 - \underset{\underset{CH_3}{|}}{\overset{\overset{H}{|}}{C}} - COOH$

(c) $CH_3 - \underset{\underset{CH_3}{|}}{\overset{\overset{OH}{|}}{C}} - Cl$ and $CH_3 - \underset{\underset{CH_3}{|}}{\overset{\overset{OH}{|}}{C}} - OH$

(d) $CH_3 - \underset{\underset{CH_3}{|}}{\overset{\overset{OH}{|}}{C}} - Cl$ and $CH_3 - \underset{\underset{CH_3}{|}}{C} = O$

97. In the following reaction, product P is ......

$$R - \underset{\underset{O}{\|}}{C} - Cl \xrightarrow[Pd - BaSO_4]{H_2} P$$

(a) RCH_2OH (b) $RCOOH$ (c) $RCHO$ (d) RCH_3

98. Picric acid and benzoic acid can be distinguished by ......

(a) aq. $NaHCO_3$ (b) aq. $FeCl_3$ (c) aq. Na_2CO_3 (d) aq. $NaOH$

99. The most suitable reagent for the conversion of $RCH_2OH \rightarrow RCHO$ is ......

(a) $KMnO_4$ (b) $K_2Cr_2O_7$
(c) CrO_3 (d) PCC (Pyridine chloro chromate)

100. Carboxylic acids are functional isomers of ......

(a) Alcohols (b) Esters
(c) Both alcohols and esters (d) Acid anhydride

101. A carbonyl compound reacts with hydrogen cyanide to form cyanohydrin which on hydrolysis forms a racemic mixture of α-hydroxy acid. The carbonyl compound is ......

(a) Acetone (b) Diethyl ketone (c) Formaldehyde (d) Acetaldehyde

102. In a set of reactions, propionic acid yielded a compound D.

$$CH_3CH_2COOH \xrightarrow{SOCl_3} B \xrightarrow{NH_3} C \xrightarrow[Br_2]{KOH} D$$

The structure of D would be ......

(a) $CH_3CH_2CONH_2$ (b) $CH_3CH_2NHCH_3$ (c) $CH_3CH_2NH_2$ (d) $CH_3CH_2CH_2NH_2$

103. The increasing order of rate of HCN addition to compounds I to IV is ......

(I) HCHO   (II) CH_3COCH_3 (III) $PhCOCH_3$ (IV) PhCOPh

(a) III < IV < II < I   (b) I < II < III < IV   (c) IV < II < III < I   (d) IV < III < II < I

104. The compound formed as a result of oxidation of ethyl benzene by $KMnO_4$ is ......

(a) Benzyl alcohol   (b) Benzophenone   (c) Acetophenone   (d) Benzoic acid

105. $CH_3CH_2CN \xrightarrow{X} CH_3CH_2CHO$. The compound X is ......

(a) $SnCl_2/HCl/H_2O$, boil   (b) $H_2/Pd–BaSO_4$

(c) $LiAlH_4/ether$ (d) $NaBH_4/ether/H_3O^+$

106. The end product of the following reaction sequence is

$$CH_3CH_2COOH \xrightarrow{Cl_2} X \xrightarrow[KOH]{Alcoholic} Y$$

(a) $CH_3\underset{\underset{OH}{|}}{CH}COOH$ (b) $CH_3\underset{\underset{OH}{|}}{CH}COOH$ (c) $CH_2 = CHCOOH$ (d) $CH_2\underset{\underset{Cl}{|}}{\overset{}{C}}\underset{\underset{OH}{|}}{\overset{}{H}}COOH$

107. Following conversion can be carried out by using ......

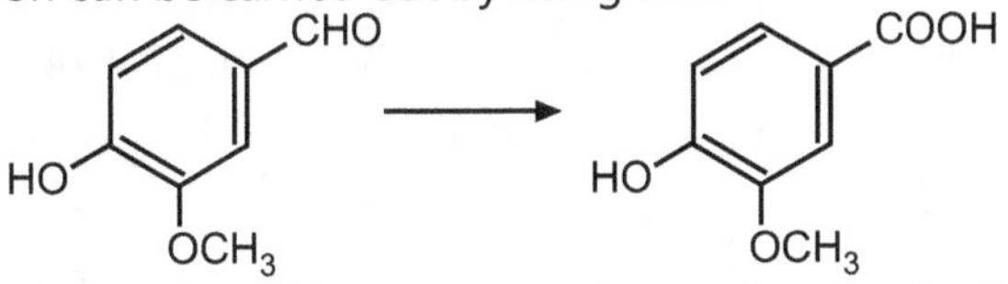

(a) $KMnO_4$ in alcohol   (b) $NaClO_4$ in a buffer

(c) $Ag_2O/NaOH$, HCl   (d) $FeCl_3$ in a buffer

108. Propionic acid with Br_2/P yields a dibromo product. Its structure would be ......

(a) $CH_3\overset{\overset{\displaystyle Br}{|}}{\underset{\underset{\displaystyle Br}{|}}{C}}COOH$ (b) $CH_2Br – CH_2Br – COOH$

(c) $H\overset{\overset{\displaystyle Br}{|}}{\underset{\underset{\displaystyle Br}{|}}{C}}CH_2COOH$ (d) $CH_2Br–CH_2–COBr$

109. Which of the following on heating with aqueous KOH, produces acetaldehyde ?

(a) CH_3COCl (b) CH_3CH_2Cl (c) CH_2ClCH_2Cl (d) CH_3CHCl_2

110. In which of the following reactions, the product obtained is chiral ?

(a) $CH_3COCH_3 \xrightarrow{NaBH_4}$ (b) $CH_3COCl \xrightarrow{Rosenmund\ reduction}$

(c) $CH_3CH_2COCH_2CH_3 \xrightarrow{Sn,\ HCl}$ (d) $CH_3CH_2COCH_3 \xrightarrow{LiAlH_4}$

111. In the following reaction sequence

$$CH_3CHO \xrightarrow[NaOH]{Cl_2} X \xrightarrow[Alc.\ KOH]{C_6H_5NH_2} Y, \quad Y \text{ is } \ldots\ldots$$

(a) $CH_3CH = NHC_6H_5$　　(b) $C_6H_5NHCH_3$　　　(c) C_6H_5NC　　　　(d) C_6H_5NCO

112. α-Hydroxypropionic acid has .... asymmetric carbon atoms.

(a) 4　　　　　　　(b) 3　　　　　　　(c) 2　　　　　　　(d) 1

113. Aldehydes and ketones are ......

(a) Chain isomers　　　　　　　　(b) Functional isomers

(c) Position isomers　　　　　　　(d) Optical isomers

114. But-2-enal is the IUPAC name of ......

(a) Mesityl oxide　　　　　　　　(b) Aspirin

(c) Crotonaldehyde　　　　　　　(d) Benzaldehyde

115. Ethanol on condensation with acetone (in dil. NaOH) forms ......

(a) 4-hydroxy pentan-2-one　　　　(b) 4-hydroxy hexanone

(c) 4-hydroxy hexanal　　　　　　(d) 4-hydroxy-2-pentanone

116. Ethyl methyl ketone is formed, when the following alcohols are oxidized.

(a) n-butyl alcohol　　　　　　　(b) sec-butyl alcohol

(c) Tertiary butyl alcohol　　　　(d) iso-butyl alcohol

117. When a Grignard's reagent is treated with CO_2, followed by hydrolysis ......

(a) Aldehyde is formed　　　　　　(b) Ketone is formed

(c) Alcohol is formed　　　　　　(d) Acid is formed

118. When propanone is boiled with ammonia, the following compound is formed.

(a) Propane oxime　　　　　　　(b) Diacetone ammonia

(c) Diacetonamine　　　　　　　(d) Acetoxime

119. When ethanaldehyde is reduced in presence of Na–Hg and water, it forms ......

(a) Acetone　　　　(b) Ethanol　　　　(c) Propanol　　　　(d) Ethane

120. Ketones cannot be prepared by dry distillation of ......

(a) Calcium acetate　　　　　　　(b) Calcium formate

(c) Calcium propionate　　　　　(d) Calcium butyrate

121. The following salt is known as Rochelle salt ......

(a) Sodium potassium tartarate　　(b) Sodium tartarate

(c) Potassium tartarate　　　　　(d) Sodium ammonia sulphate

122. Aldehydes and ketones form a crystalline compound with ......

(a) NH_3　　　　　(b) HCN　　　　　(c) NH_2OH　　　　(d) $NaHSO_3$

123. The compound obtained when acetaldehyde reacts with dilute aqueous sodium hydroxide exhibits ......

(a) geometrical isomerism　　　　　　(b) optical isomerism

(c) neither optical nor geometrical isomerism　(d) both optical and geometrical isomerism

124. Oxalic acid on heating with conc. H_2SO_4 gives ......

  (a) CO only   (b) CO_2 only   (c) CO, CO_2; H_2O (d) $CO + CO_2$

125. Identify the intermediate during the mechanism of the acid catalyzed formation of an ester?

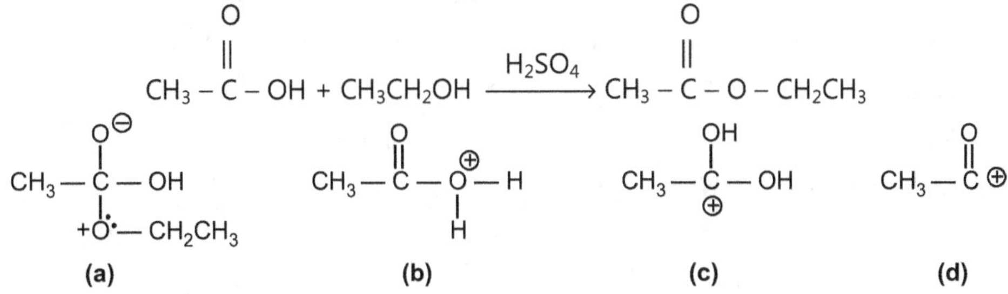

               (a)   (b)   (c)   (d)

126. Which one of the following reactions is called Rosenmund reaction?

  (a) Aldehydes are reduced to alcohols   (b) Acids are converted to acid chlorides

  (c) Aldehydes are reduced to hydrocarbons   (d) Acid chlorides are reduced to aldehydes

127. Ethyl acetate is obtained when methyl magnesium bromide reacts with ......

  (a) ethyl formate   (b) ethyl chloroformate

  (c) acetyl chloride   (d) carbon dioxide

128. If heavy water is taken as a solvent instead of normal water while performing Cannizzaro reaction, the products of the reaction are ......

  (a) $RCOO^- + RCH_2OH$ (b) $RCOO^- + RCH_2OD$

  (c) $RCOOD + RCD_2OD$ (d) $CROO^- + RCD_2OD$

129. 3-hydroxylbutanal is formed when (X) reacts with (Y) in dilute (Z) solution. What are X, Y and Z ?

  (a) CH_3CHO, $(CH_3)_2CO$, NaOH   (b) CH_3CHO, CH_3CHO, NaCl

  (c) $(CH_3)_2CO$, $(CH_3)_2CO$, HCl   (d) CH_3CHO, CH_3CHO, NaOH

130. In a set of reactions, propionic acid yielded a compound D.

$$CH_3CH_2COOH \xrightarrow{NH_3} B \xrightarrow{\Delta} C \xrightarrow[KOH]{Br_2} D$$

  The structure of D would be ......

  (a) $CH_3CH_2CH_2NH_2$ (b) $CH_3CH_2CONH_2$ (c) $CH_3CH_2NHCH_3$ (d) $CH_3CH_2NH_2$

131. $C_6H_5CHO + C_6H_5NH_2 \rightarrow C_6H_5N = HCC_6H_5 + H_2O$, the compound $C_6H_5N = CHC_6H_5$ is known as ......

  (a) Aldol   (b) Schiff's reagent   (c) Schiff's base   (d) Benedict reagent

132. For making distinction between 2-pentanone and 3-pentanone, the reagent to be employed is ......

  (a) $K_2Cr_2O_7/H_2SO_4$ (b) Zn-Hg/HCl   (c) SeO_2 (d) Iodine/NaOH

133. The compound $C_6H_5\text{-}COOC_6H_5$ can be prepared by the reaction of ....

  (a) Phenol and benzoic acid in the presence of NaOH

  (b) Phenol and benzoyl chloride in the presence of pyridine

  (c) Phenol and benzoyl chloride in the presence of $ZnCl_2$

  (d) Phenol and benzaldehyde in the presence of palladium

134. The reagent which does not react with both acetone and benzaldehyde is ......

(a) Sodium hydrogen sulphite

(b) Phenyl hydrazine

(c) Fehling's solution

(d) Grignard reagent

135. In which of the following reactions, new carbon-carbon bond is not formed ?

(a) Cannizzaro reaction

(b) Wurtz reaction

(c) Aldol condensation

(d) Friedel-Craft's reaction

136. The appropriate reagent for the transformation is ......

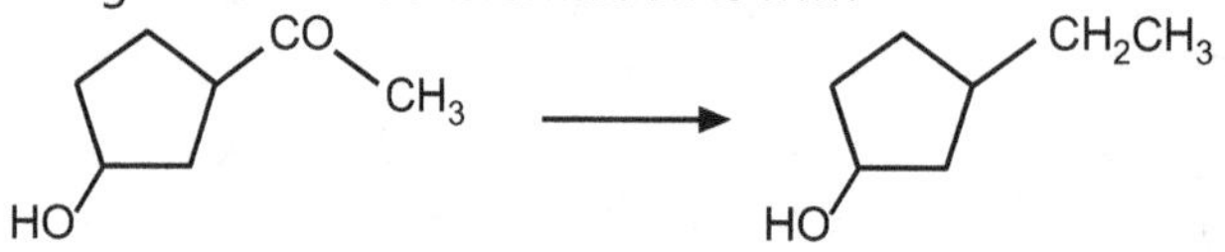

(a) Zn(Hg), HCl   (b) NH_2NH_2, OH^- (c) H_2, Ni   (d) $NaBH_4$

137. m-chlorobenzaldehyde on reaction with conc. KOH at room temperature gives ......

(a) potassium m-chlorobenzoate and m-chlorobenzyl alcohol

(b) m-hydroxy benzaldehyde and m-chlorobenzyl alcohol

(c) m-chlorobenzyl alcohol and m-hydroxy benzyl alcohol

(d) potassium m-chlorobenzoate and m-hydroxy benzaldehyde

138. In the Cannizzaro's reaction given below, the slowest step is

$$2C_6H_5CHO \xrightarrow{KOH} C_6H_5CH_2OH + C_6H_5COO^-$$

(a) The attack of – OH at the carbonyl group

(b) The transfer of hydride to the carbonyl group

(c) The abstraction of proton from the carboxylic acid

(d) The deprotonation of $Ph - CH_2OH$

139. In Cannizzaro's reaction, the intermediate which is the best hydride donor is ......

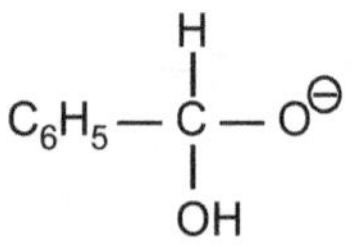

(a) 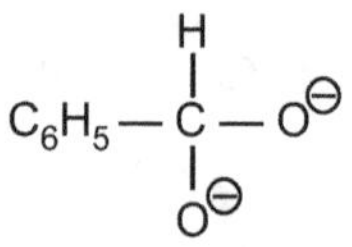   (b) 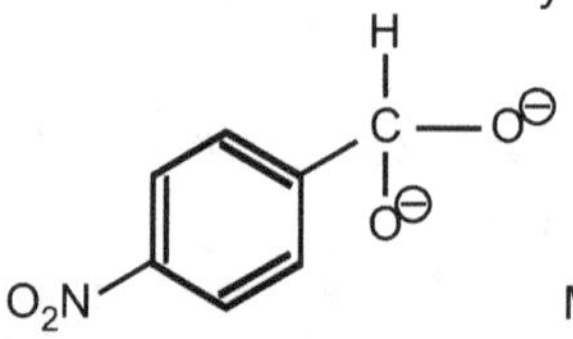   (c) 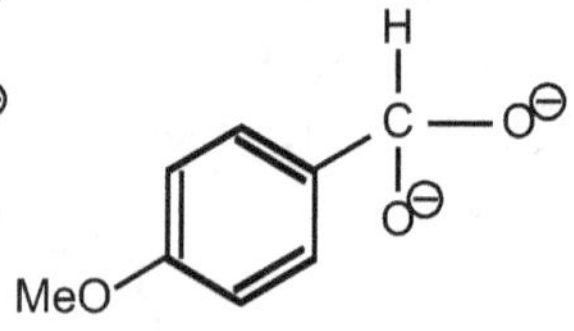   (d)

140. Identify A in the following reaction $PhC \equiv CMe \xrightarrow{H_3O^+, Hg^{2+}} A$

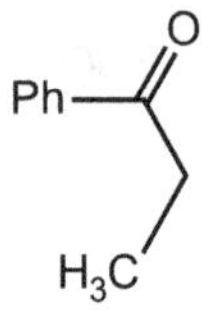

(a) 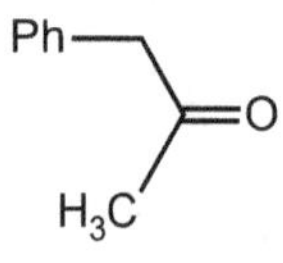   (b) 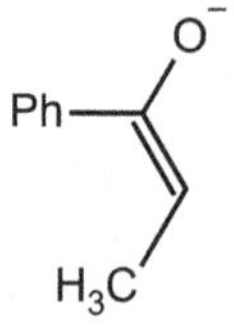   (c) 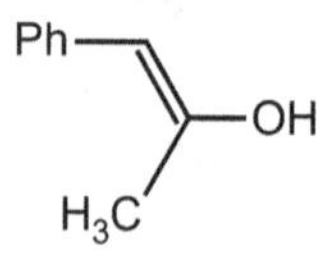   (d)

141. 4-methyl benzene sulphonic acid reacts with sodium acetate to give ......

(a) 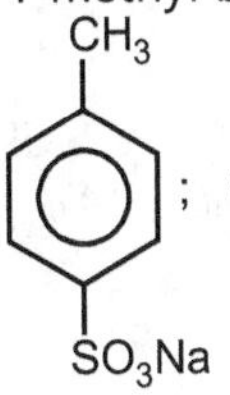 [structure: benzene with CH_3 top and SO_3Na bottom] ; CH_3CO_2H
(b) 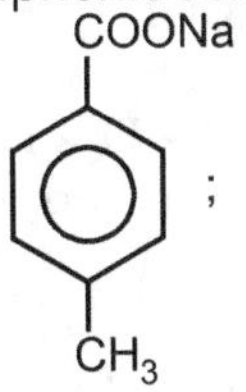 [structure: benzene with COONa top and CH_3 bottom] ; SO_3
(c) 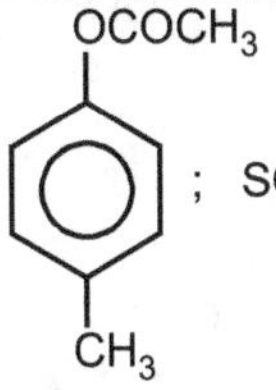 [structure: benzene with $OCOCH_3$ top and CH_3 bottom] ; SO_3
(d) 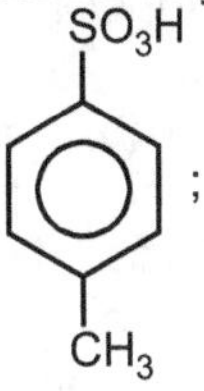 [structure: benzene with SO_3H top and CH_3 bottom] ; NaOH

142. Which of the following reactants on reaction with conc. NaOH followed by acidification give following lactone as the main product?

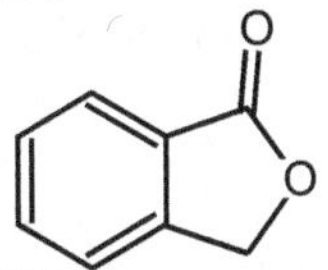

[lactone structure]

(a) 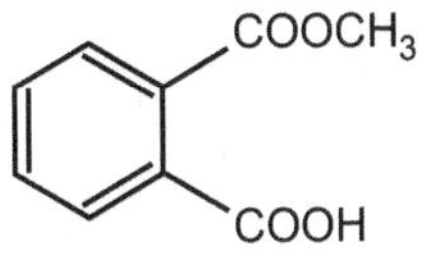 [benzene with $COOCH_3$ and COOH ortho]
(b) 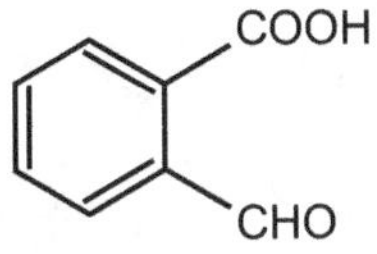 [benzene with COOH and CHO ortho]
(c) 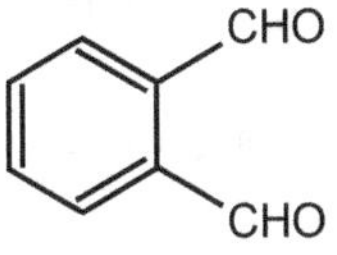 [benzene with CHO and CHO ortho]
(d) 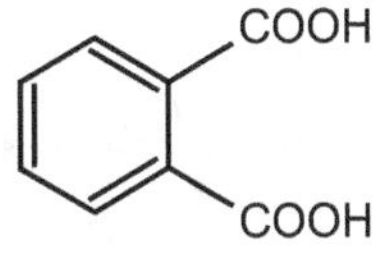 [benzene with COOH and COOH ortho]

143. Cannizzaro's reaction is not given by ____________.

(a) 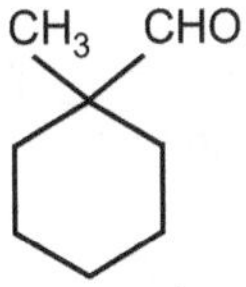 [cyclohexane with CH_3 and CHO]
(b) 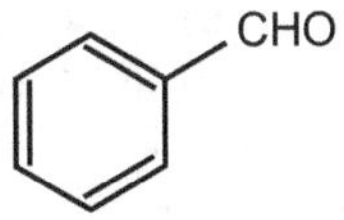 [benzene with CHO]
(c) HCHO
(d) CH_3CHO

144. Which product is formed when benzaldehyde is treated with concentrated aqueous KOH solution?

(a) 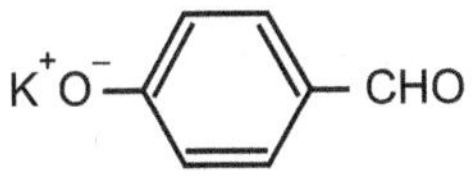 K^+O^-—[benzene]—CHO

(b) 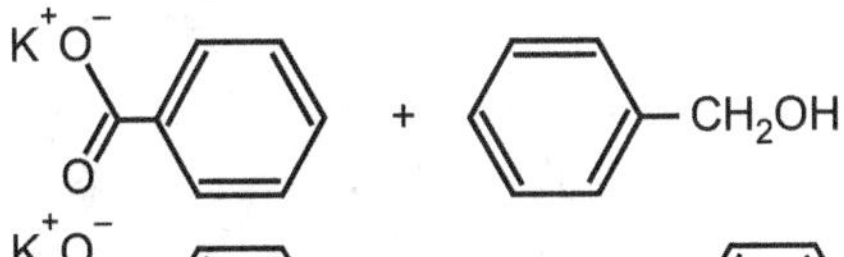 K^+O^-[benzene ring with C=O] + [benzene]—CH_2OH

(c) K^+O^-[benzene ring with C=O]—O^-K^+ + K^+O^-—[benzene]—O^-K^+

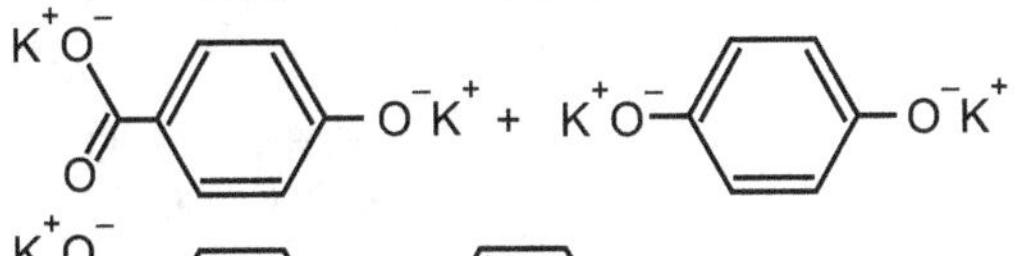

(d) 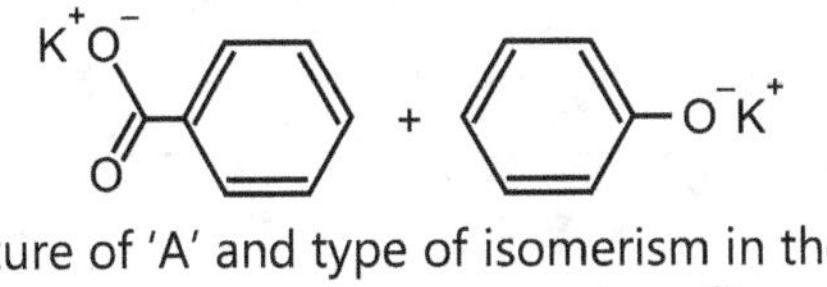 K^+O^-[benzene ring with C=O] + [benzene]—O^-K^+

145. Structure of 'A' and type of isomerism in the above reaction are respectively ......

$$CH_3 - C \equiv CH \xrightarrow{H_3O^+, \ Hg^{2+}} A \xrightarrow{\text{tautomerism}} CH_3 - \underset{\underset{O}{\|}}{C} - CH_3$$

(a) Prop–1–en–2–ol, metamerism
(b) Prop-1-en-1-ol, tautomerism
(c) Prop-2-en-2-ol, geometrical isomerism
(d) Prop-1-en-2-ol, tautomerism

146. The correct order of decreasing acidic strength of the following compounds is ......

FCH_2COOH	$ClCH_2COOH$	$BrCH_2COOH$	ICH_2COOH
I	II	III	IV

(a) I < II < III < IV   (b) I > II > III > IV   (c) II > I > III > IV   (d) II > I > IV > III

147. The correct order of increasing acidic strength of p-methoxy benzoic acid (A), p-nitro benzoic acid (B), benzoic acid (C) is :

(a) B > C > A   (b) B > A > C   (c) A > B > C   (d) B > C > A

148. Arrange following acids in decreasing order of acidic strength :

$p\text{-}CH_3C_6H_4COOH$ (pK$_a$ 4.37); $pCH_3OC_6H_4COOH$ (pK$_a$ 4.47); $p\text{-}ClC_6H_4COOH$ (pK$_a$ 3.99)

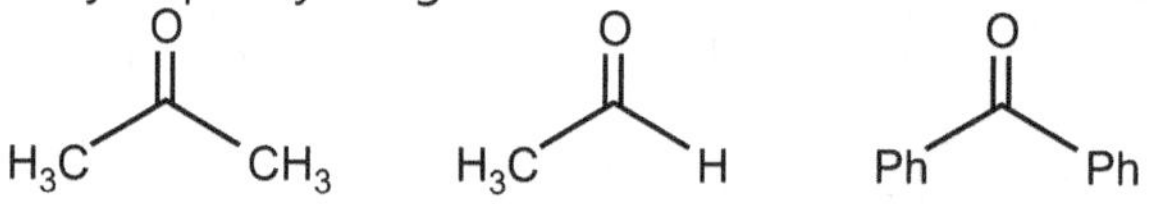

       I   II   III

(a) I > II > III   (b) I < II < III   (c) III > I > II   (d) III > I > II

149. In the scheme given below, the total number of intramolecular aldol condensation products formed from 'Y' is ......

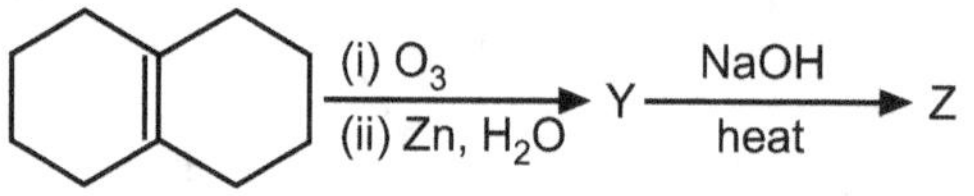

(i) O$_3$ / (ii) Zn, H$_2$O   Y   NaOH / heat   Z

(a) 1   (b) 2   (c) 3   (d) 4

150. The order or reactivity of phenyl magnesium bromide with the following compound is ......

H$_3$C—CO—CH$_3$ (I)   H$_3$C—CO—H (II)   Ph—CO—Ph (III)

(a) (II) > (III) > (I)   (b) (I) > (III) > (II)

(c) (II) > (I) > (III)   (d) All react with the same rate

151. What is the major product ?

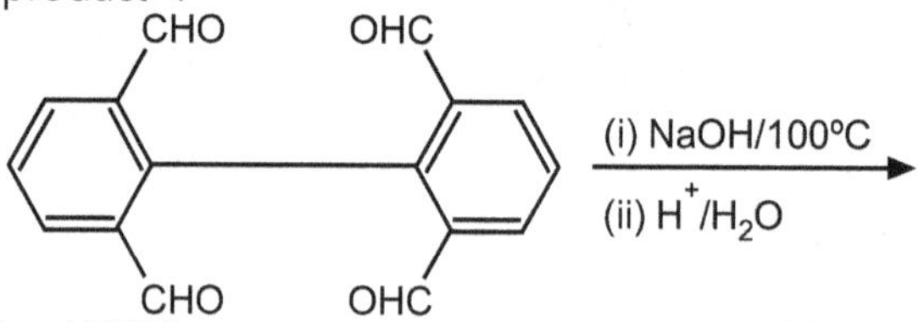

CHO / OHC   CHO / OHC   (i) NaOH/100°C   (ii) H$^+$/H$_2$O

(a) 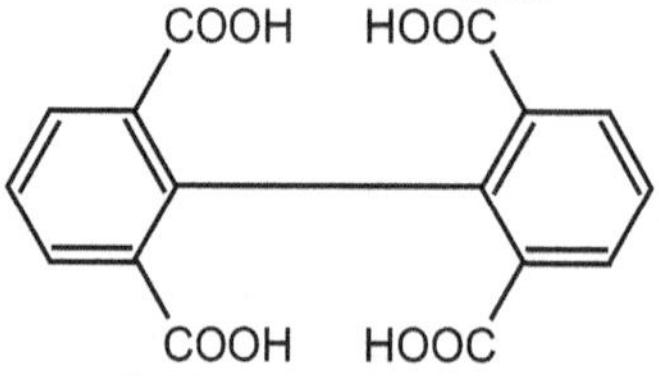 COOH / HOOC   COOH / HOOC

(b) 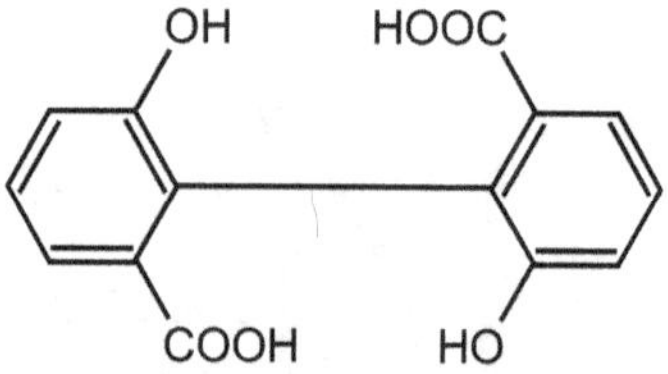 OH / HOOC   COOH / HO

(c) (dilactone structure)

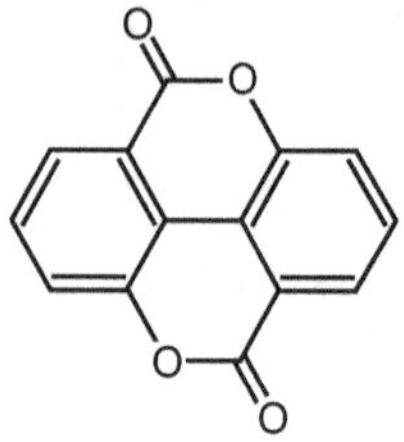

(d) 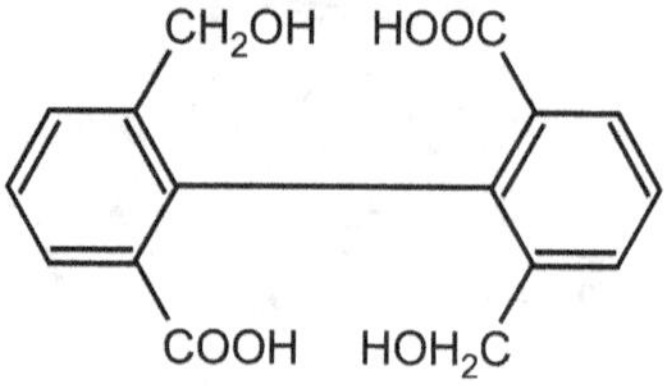 CH$_2$OH / HOOC   COOH / HOH$_2$C

152. Predict the correct order of decreasing acidic strength

C_6H_5COOH; $o\text{-}HOC_6H_4COOH$; $m\text{-}HOC_6H_4COOH$; $p\text{-}HOC_6H_4COOH$

        I   II   III   IV

(a) II > III > I > IV   (b) II < III < IV < I   (c) IV > II > III > I   (d) II > IV > I > III

153. A hypnotic drug is formed when ......

(a) chloroform reacts with HNO_3

(b) acetone reacts with chloroform

(c) chloroform reacts with acetaldehyde

(d) chloroform reacts with acetic acid

154. An organic compound gives silver mirror test and decomposes sodium bicarbonate but does not give iodoform test. Identify the compound.

(a) Formaldehyde   (b) Formic acid   (c) Benzoic acid   (d) Acrylic acid

155. One mole of symmetrical alkene on ozonolysis gives two moles of an aldehyde having molecular mass of 44u. The alkene is ......

(a) Ethene   (b) Propene   (c) 1-butene   (d) 2-butene

156. A mixture of benzaldehyde and formaldehyde on heating with aqueous NaOH solution gives ......

(a) benzyl alcohol and sodium formate

(b) sodium benzoate and methyl alcohol

(c) sodium benzoate and sodium formate

(d) benzyl alcohol and methyl alcohol

157. Which of the following has most acidic hydrogen?

(a) 3-Hexanone

(b) 2, 4-Hexanedione

(c) 2, 5-Hexanedione

(d) 2, 3-Hexanedione

158. Addition of water to alkynes occurs in acidic medium and in the presence of Hg^{2+} ions as a catalyst. Which of the following products will be formed on addition of water to but-1-yne under these conditions ?

(a) $CH_3CH_2CH_2CHO$

(b) $CH_3CH_2COCH_3$

(c) $CH_3CH_2COOH + CO_2$

(d) $CH_3COOH + HCOOH$

159. Suggest the best route for the synthesis of 2-methylpropanoic acid

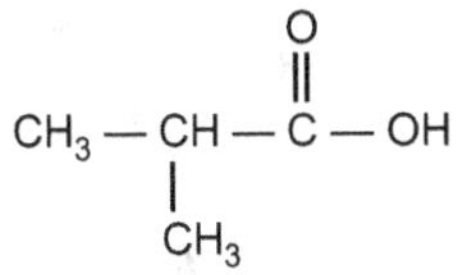

$$CH_3-CH(CH_3)-\overset{\overset{\displaystyle O}{\|}}{C}-OH$$

(a) $CH_3-CH(CH_3)-Br \xrightarrow{KCN} \xrightarrow[\text{heat}]{NaOH \; H_2O}$

(b) $CH_3-C(CH_3)=CH_2 \xrightarrow[H^{\oplus} \, cold]{KMnO_4}$

(c) $CH_3-CH(CH_3)-Br \xrightarrow{Mg \; Et_2O} \xrightarrow{H_2C=O} \xrightarrow{H_3O^{\oplus}} \xrightarrow[H^{\oplus} \, cold]{KMnO_4}$

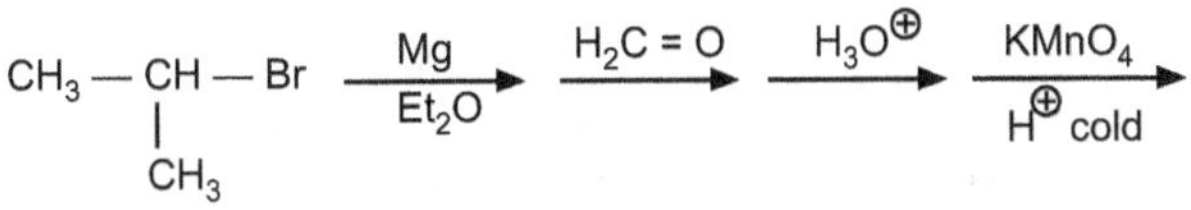

(d) 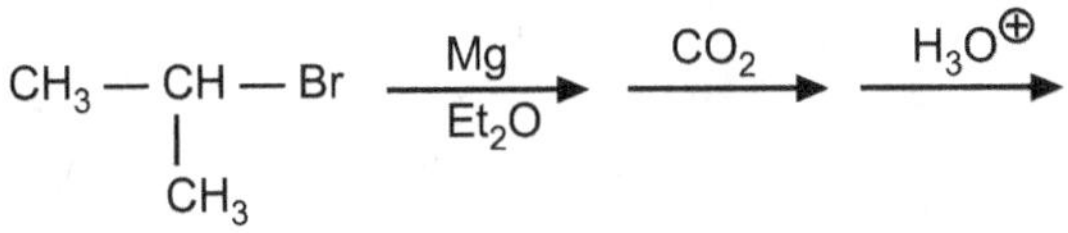 $CH_3-CH(CH_3)-Br \xrightarrow{Mg \; Et_2O} \xrightarrow{CO_2} \xrightarrow{H_3O^{\oplus}}$

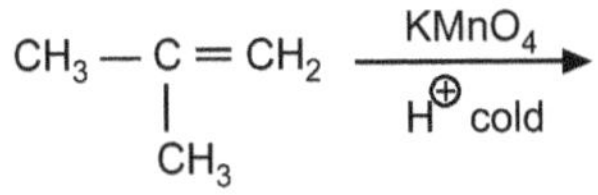

160. Which of the following compounds is most reactive towards nucleophilic addition reactions?

(a) CH_3CHO (b) CH_3COCH_3 (c) C_6H_5CHO (d) $C_6H_5COCH_3$

161. The correct order of increasing acidic strength is ………. .
(a) Phenol < Ethanol < Chloroacetic acid < Acetic acid
(b) Ethanol < Phenol < Chloroacetic acid < Acetic acid
(c) Ethanol < Phenol < Acetic acid < Chloroacetic acid
(d) Chloroacetic acid < Acetic acid < Phenol < Ethanol

162. Compounds A and C in the following reaction are …………

$$CH_3CHO \xrightarrow[H_2O]{CH_3MgBr} A \xrightarrow[Heat]{H_2SO_4} B \xrightarrow[Oxidation]{Hydroboration} C$$

(a) identical   (b) positional isomers
(c) functional isomers   (d) optical isomers

163. The acidity of carboxylic acids increases in the order

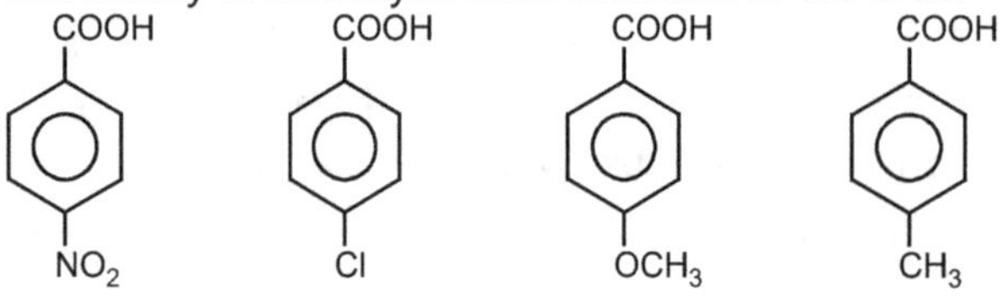

I (COOH, NO_2)   II (COOH, Cl)   III (COOH, OCH_3)   IV (COOH, CH_3)

(a) III < IV < II < I   (b) III > IV > II > I   (c) III < II < IV < I   (d) IV < III < I < II

164. Identify the major product in the following reaction?

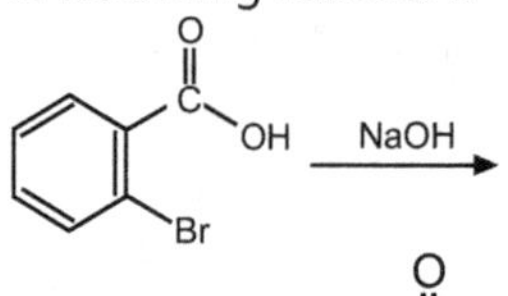

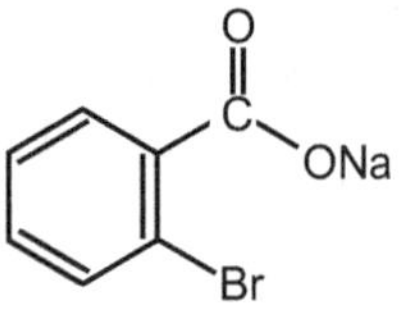

(a) 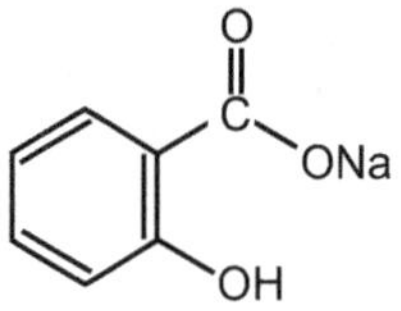   (b) 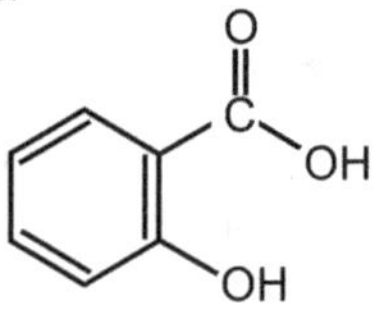   (c) 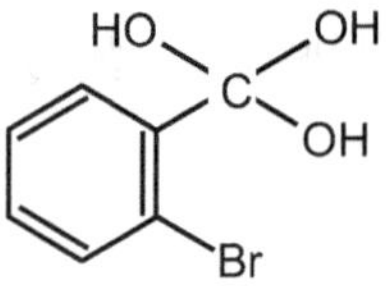   (d)

165. Identify the product in the following reaction

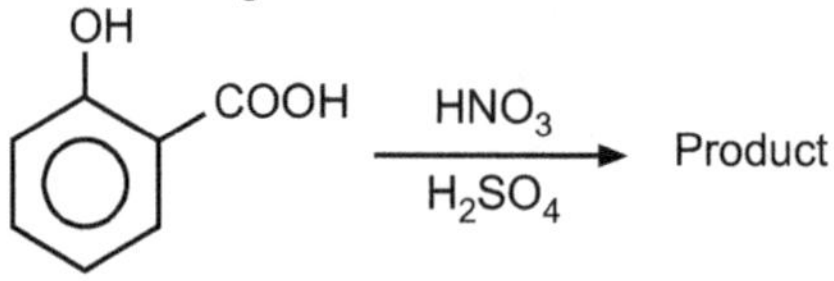

(a) 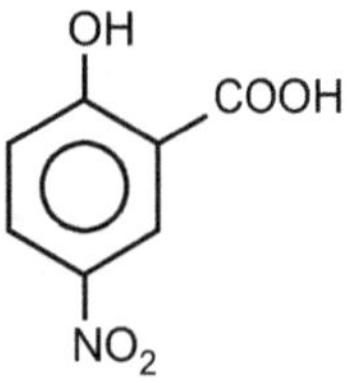   (b) 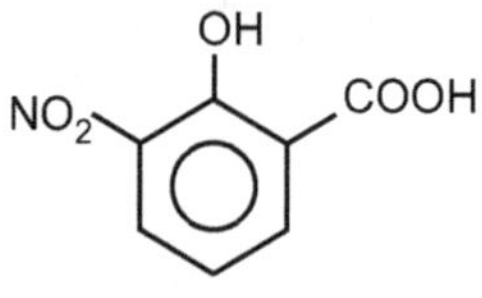   (c) 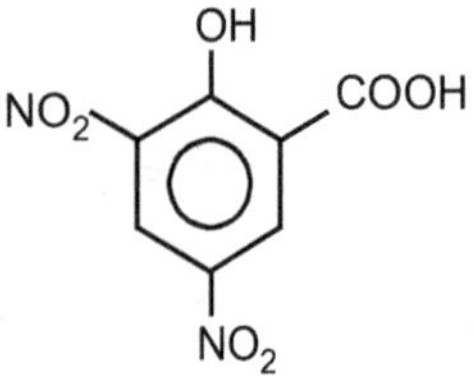   (d)

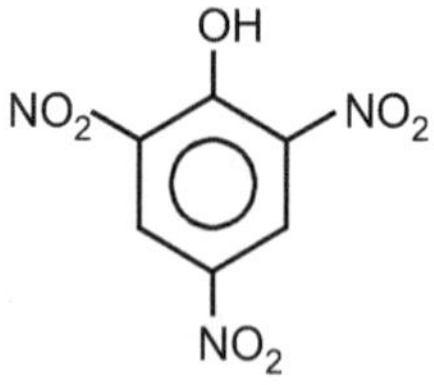

166. Toluene with chromyl chloride/CS_2 followed by hydrolysis gives

(a) Benzaldehyde   (b) Benzoyl chloride   (c) Benzyl chloride   (d) Phenyl chloride

167. Which of the following compounds is the strongest Bronsted acid ?

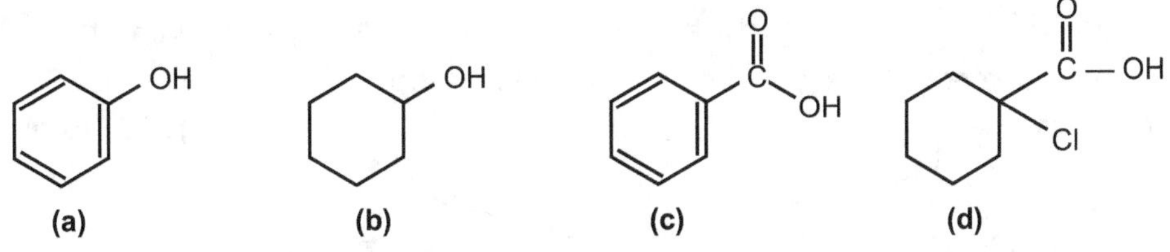

    (a)   **(b)**   **(c)**   **(d)**

PREVIOUS YEAR'S QUESTIONS

1. An organic compound 'X' having molecular formula $C_5H_{10}O$ yields phenyl hydrazone and gives negative response to the Iodoform test and Tollen's test. It produces n-pentane on reduction. 'X' could be ...... **[AIPMT 2015]**

(a) 2-pentanone   (b) 3-pentanone   (c) n-amyl alcohol   (d) pentanal

2. Treatment of cyclopentanone with methyl lithium gives which of the following species? **[AIPMT 2015]**

(a) Cyclopentanoyl cation   (b) Cyclopentanoyl radical

(c) Cyclopentanoyl biradical   (d) Cyclopentanoyl anion

3. Which one is most reactive towards nucleophilic addition reaction? **[CBSE AIPMT 2014]**

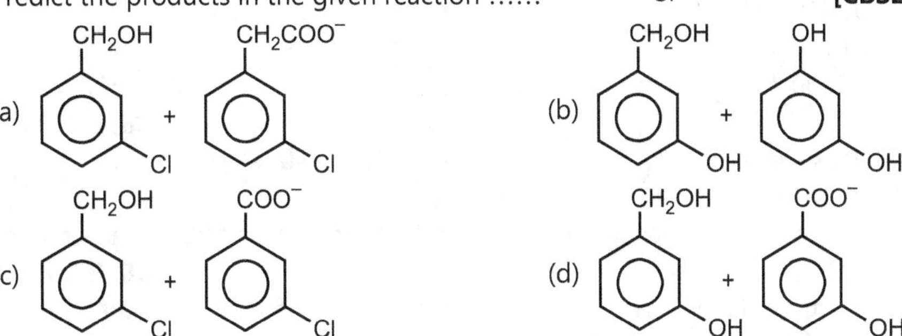

4. Predict the products in the given reaction ...... **[CBSE AIPMT 2012]**

5. Consider the following reaction :

$$C_6H_5COCl \xrightarrow[\text{Pd-BaSO}_4]{H_2} A$$

[CBSE AIPMT, AMU 2012]

The product 'A' is ......

(a) C_6H_5CHO (b) C_6H_5OH (c) $C_6H_5COCH_3$ (d) C_6H_5Cl

6. Acetone is treated with excess of ethanol in the presence of hydrochloric acid. The product obtained is : **[CBSE AIPMT 2012]**

(a)
$$(CH_3)_2C\begin{array}{l} {}^{\nearrow OH} \\ {}_{\searrow OC_2H_5} \end{array}$$

(b)
$$(CH_3)_2C\begin{array}{l} {}^{\nearrow OC_2H_5} \\ {}_{\searrow OC_2H_5} \end{array}$$

(c) $CH_3CH_2CH_2 - \overset{\overset{\displaystyle O}{\|}}{C} - CH_3$

(d) $CH_3CH_2CH_2 - \overset{\overset{\displaystyle O}{\|}}{C} - CH_2CH_2CH_3$

7. Which of the following compounds undergoes both Cannizzaro reaction and aldol condensation? **[AFMC 2012]**

(a) $(CH_3)_2CH \cdot CHO$ (b) $HCHO$ (c) C_6H_5CHO (d) CH_3CHO

8. The product formed when acetone reacts with nitromethane in the presence of a base is ...

[AFMC 2012]

(a)
$$H_3C - \overset{\overset{\displaystyle CH_3}{|}}{\underset{\underset{\displaystyle OH}{|}}{C}} - CH_2NO_2$$

(b)
$$H_3C - \overset{\overset{\displaystyle CH_3}{|}}{\underset{\underset{\displaystyle OH}{|}}{C}} - \underset{\underset{\displaystyle OH}{|}}{CH} - NO_2$$

(c)
$$H_3C - \underset{\underset{\displaystyle CH_3}{|}}{C} = CHNO_2$$

(d) $CH_3COCH = CHNO_2$

9. The reagent used in Clemmensen's reduction is ...... **[Manibal 2012]**

(a) conc. H_2SO_4 (b) Zn-Hg/conc. HCl

(c) aq. KOH   (d) alc. KOH

10. $CH_3COOH \xrightarrow{LiAlH_4} A + CH_3COOH \xrightarrow{H_3O^+} B + H_2O$ **[UP CPMT 2012]**

In the above reaction, 'A' and 'B' respectively are ......

(a) $CH_3COOC_2H_5$, C_2H_5OH (b) CH_3CHO, C_2H_5OH

(c) C_2H_5OH, CH_3CHO (d) CH_3COOH

11. Clemmensen reduction of a ketone is carried out in the presence of which of the following?

[CBSE AIPMT 2011]

(a) H_2 and Pt as a catalyst   (b) Glycol with KOH

(c) Zn - Hg with CHI_3 (d) $LiAlH_4$

12. Which of the following reations will not result in the formation of carbon-carbon bonds?

[CBSE AIPMT 2010]

(a) Friedel-Crafts' acylation   (b) Reimer-Tiemann reaction

(c) Cannizzaro reaction   (d) Wurtz reaction

13. Clemmensen reduction of a ketone is carried out in the presence of which of the following?

[CBSE AIPMT 2011]

(a) H_2 and Pt as catalyst   (b) Glycol with KOH

(c) Zn-Hg with HCl   (d) $LiAlH_4$

14. Which is not true about acetophenone ?   **[Manipal 2002]**

(a) Reacts to form 2, 4-dinitrophenyl hydrazine

(b) Reacts with Tollen's reagent to form silver mirror

(c) Reacts with I_2/NaOH to form iodoform

(d) On oxidation with alkaline $KMnO_4$ followed by hydrolysis gives benzoic acid

15. Which of the following statements is not correct?   **[DELHI PMT 2010]**

(a) Aldehydes and ketones undergo nucleophilic addition

(b) Aldehydes and ketones undergo electrophilic substitution

(c) Aldehydes and ketones contain polar carbonyl group

(d) Lower members of aldehydes and ketones are soluble in water due to hydrogen bonding

16. Compound 'A' undergoes formation of cyanohydrins which on hydrolysis give lactic acid ($CH_3CHOHCOOH$). Therefore, compound 'A' is ......   **[DELHI PMT 2010]**

(a) formaldehyde   (b) acetaldehyde   (c) acetone   (d) benzaldehyde

17. Trichloroacetaldehyde, CCl_3CHO reacts with chlorobenzene in the presence of sulphuric acid and produces ......   **[CBSE AIPMT 2009]**

(a) 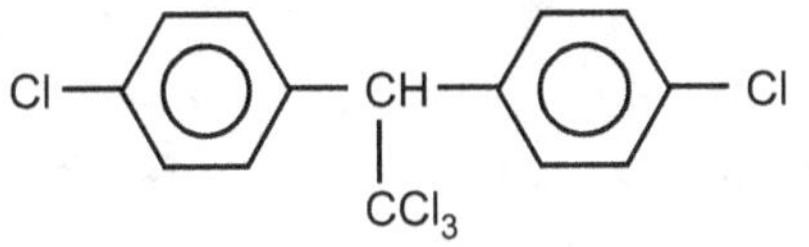 $Cl-C_6H_4-CH(CCl_3)-C_6H_4-Cl$

(b) $Cl-C_6H_4-C(Cl)(CH_2Cl)-C_6H_4-Cl$

(c) $Cl-C_6H_4-C(H)(C_6H_4Cl)-C_6H_4-Cl$ with a Cl-phenyl group on central carbon

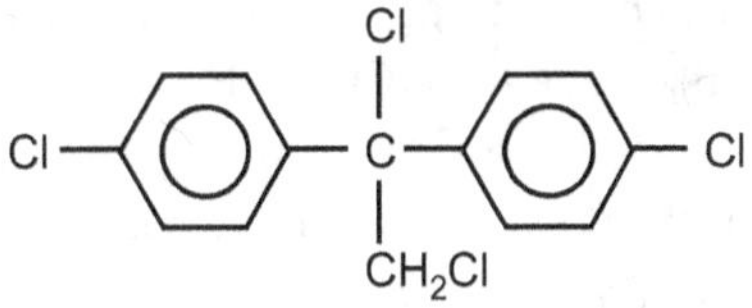

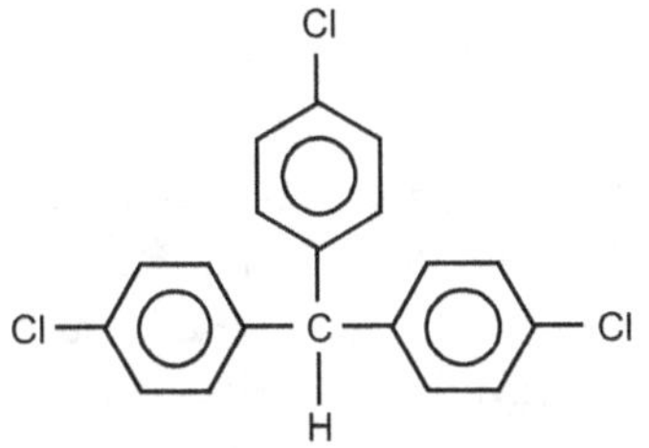

(d) 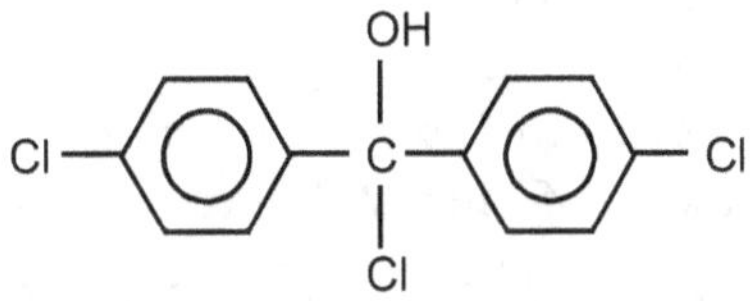 $Cl-C_6H_4-C(OH)(Cl)-C_6H_4-Cl$

18. The compound which forms acetaldehyde when heated with dilute NaOH is ......

[Karnataka CET 2009]

(a) 1-chloro ethane   (b) 1, 1-dichloro ethane

(c) 1, 2-dichloro ethane   (d) 1, 1, 1-trichloro ethane

19. An organic compound X is oxidized by using acidified $K_2Cr_2O_7$. The product obtained reacts with phenyl hydrazine but does not answer silver mirror test. The possible structure of X is ......   **[Karnataka CET 2009]**

(a) $(CH_3)_2CHOH$ (b) CH_3CHO (c) CH_3CH_2OH (d) CH_3COCH_3

20. A strong base can abstract an α-hydrogen from ......   **[CBSE AIPMT 2008]**

(a) Amine   (b) Alkane   (c) Alkene   (d) Ketone

21. Ketones react with Mg-Hg over water to give ...... **[A.F.M.C. 2005]**
    (a) pinacolone   (b) pinacols   (c) alcohols   (d) none of these

22. The product formed in aldol condensation is ...... **[CBSE AIPMT 2007]**
    (a) a beta-hydroxy aldehyde or a beta-hydroxy ketone.
    (b) an alpha-hydroxy aldehyde or ketone.
    (c) an alpha, beta unsaturated ester
    (d) a beta-hydroxy acid

23. The incorrect IUPAC name is ...... **[CBSE AIPMT 2001]**

(a) $CH_3 \underset{\underset{O}{\|}}{C} - \underset{\underset{CH_3}{|}}{CH} - CH_3$ (b) $CH_3 \underset{\underset{CH_2}{|}}{CH} - \underset{\underset{CH_2 - CH_3}{|}}{CH} - CH_3$

    2-methyl-3-butanone   2, 3-dimethyl pentane

(c) $CH_3 - C \equiv COH(CH_3)_2$ (d) $CH_3 - \underset{\underset{Cl}{|}}{CH} - \underset{\underset{Br}{|}}{CH} - CH_3$

    4-methyl-3-butanone   2-bromo-3-chloro butane

24. Which of the following acids does not exhibit optical isomerism? **[CBSE AIPMT 2012]**
    (a) Lactic acid   (b) Tartaric acid   (c) Maleic acid   (d) α-amino acids

25. CH_3CHO and $C_6H_5CH_2CHO$ can be distinguished chemically by ...... **[CBSE AIPMT 2012]**
    (a) Tollen's reagent test   (b) Fehling solution test
    (c) Benedict test   (d) Iodoform test

26. The correct order of decreasing acid strength of trichloroacetic acid (A), trifluoroacetic acid (B), acetic acid (C) and formic acid (D) is ...... **[CBSE AIPMT 2012]**
    (a) A > B > C > D   (b) A > C > B > D   (c) B > A > D > C   (d) B > D > C > A

27. Which of the following does not undergo Cannizzaro's reaction ? **[Kerala Engg. 2005]**
    (a) Benzaldehyde   (b) 2-Methylpropanal
    (c) p-Methoxybenzaldehyde   (d) 2, 2-Dimethyl propanal
    (e) Formaldehyde

28. One mole of an organic compound 'A' with the formula C_3H_8O reacts completely with two moles of HI to form X and Y. When 'Y' is boiled with aqueous alkali, it forms Z. Z answers the iodoform test. The compound 'A' is .... **[Karnataka CET 2010]**
    (a) Propan-1-ol   (b) Propan-2-ol   (c) ethoxyethane   (d) methoxyethane

29. The IUPAC name of   [structure: CHO group and Br on a branched carbon chain]   is _____. **[Karnataka CET 2010]**
    (a) 2-methyl-3-bromohexanal   (b) 2-methyl-3-bromobutanal
    (c) 3-bromo-2-methylbutanal   (d) 3-bromo-2-methylpentanal

30. The correct sequence of steps involved in the mechanism of Cannizzaro's reaction is _____. **[Karnataka CET 2010]**
    (a) nucleophilic attack, transfer of H^- and transfer of H^+
    (b) electrophilic attack by OH^-, transfer of H^+ and transfer of H^-
    (c) transfer of H^-, transfer of H^+ and nucleophilic attack
    (d) transfer of H^+, nucleophilic attack and transfer of H^-

31. The compound obtained when acetaldehyde reacts with dilute aqueous sodium hydroxide exhibits ...... **[Karnataka CET 2010]**

(a) geometrical isomerism
(b) optical isomerism
(c) both optical and geometrical isomerism
(d) neither optical nor geometrical isomerism

32. Aldehydes and acetone can be best distinguished by using ...... **[Karnataka CET 2010]**

(a) hydrazine
(b) Tollen's reagent
(c) sodium hydroxide solution
(d) 2, 4-DNP

33. Which of the following is correct? **[CBSE AIPMT 2001]**

(a) Any aldehyde gives secondary alcohol on reduction
(b) Reaction of vegetable oil with H_2SO_4 gives glycerine
(c) C_2H_5OH, iodine with NaOH gives iodoform
(d) Sucrose on reaction with NaCl gives invert sugar

34. Aldehydes and ketones are differentiated by using ...... **[CPMT 2010]**

(a) $NaOH/I_2$
(b) $NaHSO_3$
(c) $AgNO_3/NH_4OH$
(d) $NH_2 - NH_2$

35. In the following reaction sequence, **[MHT CET 2010]**

$$CH_3CHO \xrightarrow[Ca(OH)_2]{Cl_2} X \xrightarrow[alc\ KOH]{C_6H_5\ NH_2} Y$$ Y is ......

(a) $CH_3CH = NHC_6H_5$
(b) $C_6H_5NHCH_3$
(c) C_6H_5NC
(d) C_6H_5NCO

36. Ethyl methyl ketone is obtained by heating calcium salts of ...... **[MHT CET 2010]**

(a) formic acid + propionic acid
(b) acetic acid + propionic acid
(c) acetic acid only
(d) acetic acid + methanoic acid

37. Benzaldehyde and acetone can be best distinguished by using ...... **[KCET 2010]**

(a) Fehling's solution
(b) Sodium hydroxide solution
(c) 2, 4-DNP
(d) Tollen's reagent

38. Aldol condensation would not occur in ...... **[Manipal 2010]**

(a) CH_3COCH_3
(b) CH_3CH_2CHO
(c) HCHO
(d) CH_3CHO

39. Oxidation of acetaldehyde with selenium dioxide produces ...... **[BVP 2010]**

(a) ethanoic acid
(b) methanoic acid
(c) glyoxal
(d) oxalic acid

40. Benzophenone can be converted into benzene by using ...... **[BVP 2010]**

(a) fused alkali
(b) anhydrous $AlCl_3$
(c) sodium amalgam in water
(d) acidified dichromate

41. The compound with which ethanal does not react, is ...... **[AFMC 2009]**

(a) HCl
(b) Cl_2
(c) PCl_5
(d) aq. $NaHSO_3$

42. The reaction by which benzaldehyde is converted into benzyl alcohol, is

(a) Fittig reaction
(b) Cannizzaro reaction
(c) Wurtz reaction
(d) Aldol condensation

43. **Assertion :** 2-butenal lacks enolisable H-atom, carbonyl group, still it has sufficient acidic character.

Reason : The conjugate base of 2-butenal is stabilized by resonance.

(a) Both Assertion and Reason are true and Reason is the correct explanation of Assertion.

(b) Both Assertion and Reason are true and Reason is not the correct explanation of Assertion.

(c) Assertion is true but Reason is false.

(d) Both Assertion and Reason are false

44. Cannizzaro's reaction is not given by ...... **[MHT CET 2009]**

(a) CCl_3CHO (b) CH_3CHO (c) $HCHO$ (d) C_6H_5CHO

45. Pentan-3-one is not obtained from ...... **[MHT CET 2009]**

(a) 2, 2-dichloro pentane   (b) 3, 3-dichloro pentane

(c) pentan-3-ol   (d) pent-2-yne

46. Which of the following will respond to Cannizzaro's reaction? **[Manipal 09]**

(a) 2, 2-dimethyl propanal   (b) Acetaldehyde

(c) Propionaldehyde   (d) Cinnamaldehyde

47. Calcium formate on dry heating yields ...... **[Manipal 2009]**

(a) acetone   (b) formaldehyde   (c) acetic acid   (d) acetaldehyde

48. Acetophenone when reacted with a base, C_2H_5ONa yields a stable compound which has the structure ...... **[CBSE AIPMT 2008]**

(a)

(b)

(c)

(d)

49. The reagent used for the separation of acetaldehyde from acetophenone is... **[A.I.I.M.S. 2004]**

(a) $NaHSO_3$ (b) $C_6H_5NHNH_2$ (c) NH_2OH (d) $NaOH - I_2$

50. 3-hydroxy butanal is formed when X reacts with Y in dilute Z solution. What are X, Y and Z? **[AIIMS 2008]**

	X	Y	Z
(a)	CH_3CHO	$(CH_3)_2CO$	NaOH
(b)	CH_3CHO	CH_3CHO	NaCl
(c)	$(CH_3)_2CO$	$(CH_3)_2CO$	HCl
(d)	CH_3CHO	CH_3CHO	NaOH

51. An organic compound X on treatment with pyridinium chloro chromate in dichloromethane gives compound Y. Compound Y reacts with iodine and alkali to form triiodomethane. The compound 'X' is ...... **[AIIMS 2008]**

(a) C_2H_5OH (b) CH_3CHO (c) CH_3COCH_3 (d) CH_3COOH

52. The product formed when hydroxylamine condenses with carbonyl compound is called ...

[KCET 2007]

(a) hydrazide   (b) oxime   (c) hydrazine   (d) hydrazone

53. The aldol condensation of CH_3CHO results in the formation of ......   **[MHT CET 2007]**

(a) $CH_3 - COCH(OH)CH_3$ (b) $CH_3 - CH(OH)CH_2 - CHO$

(c) $CH_3 - CH_2 - CH(OH)CHO$ (d) $CH_3CH_2OH + CH_3OH$

54. Formalin is the commercial name of ......   **[MHT CET 2007]**

(a) formic acid   (b) fluoroform

(c) 40% aqueous solution of methanol   (d) para formaldehyde

55. A carbonyl compound reacts with hydrogen cyanide to form cyanohydrins which on hydrolysis forms a racemic mixture of α-hydroxy acid. The carbonyl compound is ......

[CBSE AIPMT 2006]

(a) acetaldehyde   (b) acetone   (c) diethyl ketone   (d) formaldehyde

56. Which does not react with Fehling's solution?   **[CPMT 2006]**

(a) CH_3CHO (b) C_6H_5CHO (c) CH_3COCH_3 (d) Glucose

57. Ketones react with Mg - Hg over water to give ......   **[AFMC 2005]**

(a) pinacolone   (b) pinacols   (c) alcohols   (d) none of these

58. From two calcium salts of carboxylic acids, we are preparing 2-butanone. Find the correct pair of the following ......   **[MHT CET 2005]**

(a) calcium formate + calcium propanoate   (b) calcium acetate + calcium propanoate

(c) calcium acetate + calcium acetate   (d) calcium formate + calcium acetate

59. Which one of the following can be oxidized to the corresponding carbonyl compound?

[CBSE AIPMT 2004]

(a) 2-hydroxy propane   (b) ortho-nitrophenol

(c) Phenol   (d) 2-methyl-2-hydroxy-propane

60. Acetone is mixed with bleaching powder to give ......   **[AFMC 2004]**

(a) chloroform   (b) acetaldehyde   (c) ethanol   (d) phosgene

61. The reagent used for the separation of acetaldehyde from acetophenone is ...**[AIIMS 2004]**

(a) $NaHSO_3$ (b) $C_6H_5NHNH_2$ (c) NH_2OH (d) $NaOH - I_2$

62. **Assertion :** Isobutanal does not give iodoform test.   **[AIIMS 2004]**

Reason : It does not have α-hydrogen.

(a) Both Assertion and Reason are true and Reason is the correct explanation of Assertion.

(b) Both Assertion and Reason are true and Reason is not the correct explanation of Assertion.

(c) Assertion is true but Reason is false.

(d) Both Assertion and Reason are false

63. Propionic acid with Br_2/P yields a dibromo product. Its structure would be ......

[CBSE AIPMT 2009]

(a) $CH_2Br - CHBr - COOH$ (b) $CH_2Br - CH_2 -$

(c) $CH_2Br - CH_2 - COBr$ (d) $CH_3 - CBr_2 - COOH$

$$X \xrightarrow{\text{Fehling solution}} Cu_2O$$

$$X \xrightarrow[\text{Pyridine}]{SOCl_2} RCOCO^-$$

64. The compound X can be

(a) acetic acid   (b) formaldehyde   (c) formic acid   (d) propionic acid

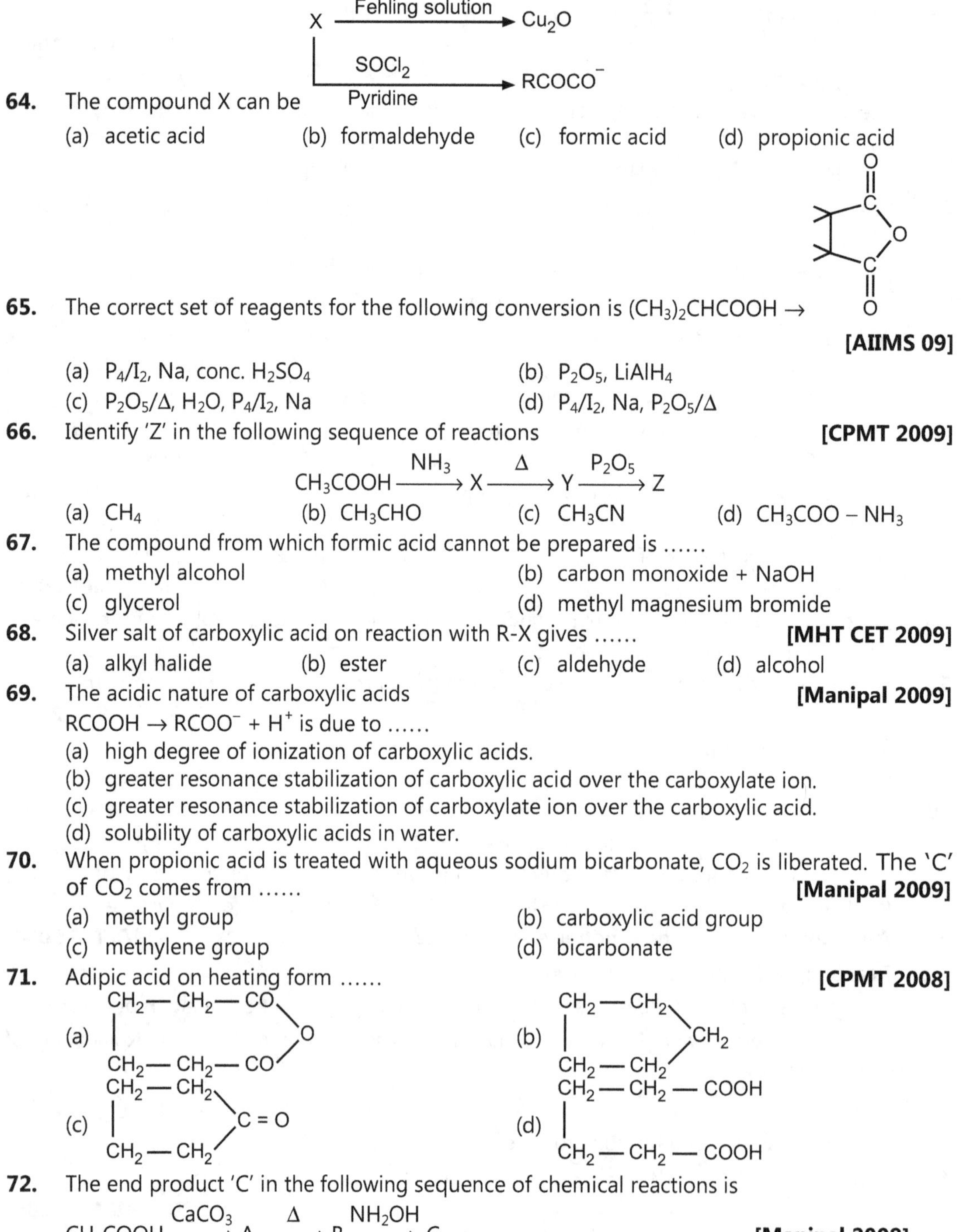

65. The correct set of reagents for the following conversion is $(CH_3)_2CHCOOH \rightarrow$

[AIIMS 09]

(a) P_4/I_2, Na, conc. H_2SO_4 (b) P_2O_5, $LiAlH_4$

(c) P_2O_5/Δ, H_2O, P_4/I_2, Na   (d) P_4/I_2, Na, P_2O_5/Δ

66. Identify 'Z' in the following sequence of reactions   **[CPMT 2009]**

$$CH_3COOH \xrightarrow{NH_3} X \xrightarrow{\Delta} Y \xrightarrow{P_2O_5} Z$$

(a) CH_4 (b) CH_3CHO (c) CH_3CN (d) $CH_3COO - NH_3$

67. The compound from which formic acid cannot be prepared is ......

(a) methyl alcohol   (b) carbon monoxide + NaOH

(c) glycerol   (d) methyl magnesium bromide

68. Silver salt of carboxylic acid on reaction with R-X gives ......   **[MHT CET 2009]**

(a) alkyl halide   (b) ester   (c) aldehyde   (d) alcohol

69. The acidic nature of carboxylic acids   **[Manipal 2009]**

$RCOOH \rightarrow RCOO^- + H^+$ is due to ......

(a) high degree of ionization of carboxylic acids.

(b) greater resonance stabilization of carboxylic acid over the carboxylate ion.

(c) greater resonance stabilization of carboxylate ion over the carboxylic acid.

(d) solubility of carboxylic acids in water.

70. When propionic acid is treated with aqueous sodium bicarbonate, CO_2 is liberated. The 'C' of CO_2 comes from ......   **[Manipal 2009]**

(a) methyl group   (b) carboxylic acid group

(c) methylene group   (d) bicarbonate

71. Adipic acid on heating form ......   **[CPMT 2008]**

72. The end product 'C' in the following sequence of chemical reactions is

$$CH_3COOH \xrightarrow{CaCO_3} A \xrightarrow{\Delta} B \xrightarrow{NH_2OH} C$$

[Manipal 2008]

(a) acetaldehyde oxime   (b) formaldehyde oxime

(c) methyl nitrate   (d) acetoxime

73. Carboxylic acids readily dissolve in aqueous sodium bicarbonate, liberating carbon dioxide. Which one of the following is correct?   **[Manipal 2008]**

(a) The free carboxylic acid and its conjugate base are of comparable stability

(b) The free carboxylic acid is more stable than its conjugate base.

(c) The conjugate base of the carboxylic acid is more stable than the free carboxylic acid.

(d) The conjugate acid of the carboxylic acid is more stable than the free carboxylic acid.

74. Corrosive sublimate, $HgCl_2$ can be used to distinguish between ......   **[MHT CET 2007]**

(a) formic acid and acetic acid   (b) acetaldehyde and butanone

(c) formaldehyde and propanone   (d) All of these

75. ...... is the percentage of acetic acid present in vinegar?   **[AFMC 2004]**

(a) 6-10%   (b) 70-80%   (c) 7-8%   (d) 90-100%

76. Among the following, the strongest acid is ......   **[AIIMS 2003]**

(a) CH_3COOH (b) C_6H_5COOH

(c) $m - CH_3OC_6H_4COOH$ (d) $p - CH_3OC_6H_4COOH$

77. In the following reaction : $C_6H_5COOCH_3 \xrightarrow[H_2O/H^+]{LiAlH_4} A + B$ **[CPMT 2010]**

A and B are respectively ......

(a) $C_6H_5CH_2OH + HCOOH$ (b) $C_6H_5CH_2OH + CH_3OH$

(c) $C_6H_5OH + CH_3COOH$ (d) $C_6H_5COOH + CH_3OH$

78. CH_3COOH when react with C_2H_5OH it gives a product. The same product is obtained by which reaction?   **[MHT CET 2010]**

(a) Acetic acid + methanol   (b) Acetic anhydride + water

(c) Acetic anhydride + ethanol   (d) Acetamide + methanol

79. Methyl acetate will be obtained by reacting CH_3OH with ......   **[Manipal 2010]**

(a) CH_3COOH (b) CH_3COCl (c) $(CH_3CO)_2O$ (d) All of these

80. Rosenmund reduction is used for the preparation of ......   **[Manipal 2010]**

(a) aldehydes   (b) ketones   (c) ethers   (d) fatty acids

81. In the following reaction, ethanol acts as   **[AFMC 2009]**

$$C_2H_5OH + CH_3COOH \rightarrow CH_3COOC_2H_5$$

(a) electrophile   (b) nucleophile

(c) dehydrating agent   (d) all of these

82. Ethyl butyrate has the flavour of which fruit?   **[MHT CET 2009]**

(a) Apple   (b) Pineapple   (c) Orange   (d) Banana

83. The relative reactivities of acyl compounds towards nucleophilic substitution are in the order of ......   **[CBSE AIPMT 2008]**

(a) acyl chloride > acid anhydride > ester > amide

(b) ester > acyl chloride > amide > acid anhydride

(c) acid anhydride > amide > ester > acyl chloride

(d) acyl chloride > ester > acid anhydride > amide

84. Which of the following compounds when heated with CO at 150°C and 500 atm pressure in the presence of BF_3 forms ethyl propionate?

    (a) C_2H_5OH (b) CH_3OCH_3 (c) $C_2H_5OC_2H_5$ (d) $CH_3OC_2H_5$

85. Acid hydrolysis of which of the following compounds yields two different organic compounds? **[AIIMS 2009]**

    (a) CH_3COOH (b) CH_3CONH_2 (c) $CH_3COOC_2H_5$ (d) $(CH_3CO)_2O$

86. The reagent which does not give acid chloride on treating with a carboxylic acid is **[AFMC 2007]**

    (a) PCl_5 (b) Cl_2 (c) $SOCl_2$ (d) PCl_3

87. Methyl acetate and ethyl acetate can be distinguished by ...... **[AIIMS 2007]**

    (a) hot alkaline $KMnO_4$ (b) neutral $FeCl_3$

    (c) iodoform test   (d) none of these

88. Hydrogenation of benzoyl chloride in the presence of Pd on $BaSO_4$ gives ...... **[J & K Med. 2004]**

    (a) Benzyl alcohol   (b) Benzaldehyde   (c) Benzoic acid   (d) Phenol

89. Two moles of ethyl acetate in the presence of sodium ethoxide yields ......

    (a) ethyl butyrate   (b) acetoacetic ester

    (c) ethyl acetoacetate   (d) ethyl propionate

90. Sodium formate on heating gives ...... **[AFMC 2006]**

    (a) oxalic acid and H_2 (b) sodium oxalate and H_2

    (c) sodium oxalate   (d) CO_2 and caustic soda

91. The following sequence of reactions of A gives **[AIIMS 2006]**

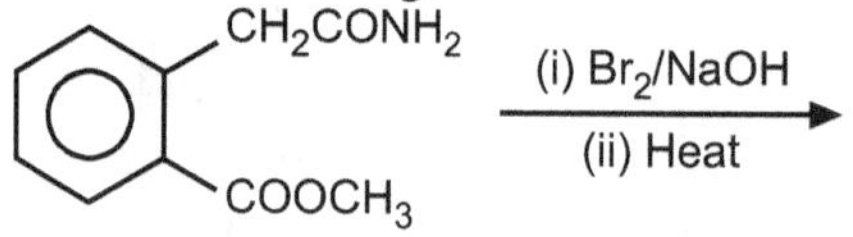

(A 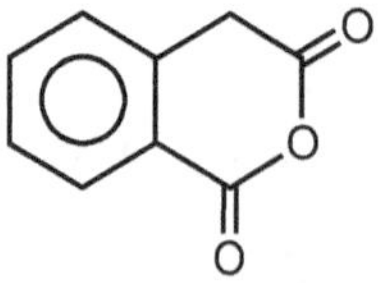 is an ortho-disubstituted benzene bearing CH_2CONH_2 and $COOCH_3$ groups)

$\xrightarrow{\text{(i) } Br_2/NaOH,\ \text{(ii) Heat}}$

(a) isochroman-1,3-dione (benzene ring fused to a six-membered ring with two C=O and one ring O)

(b) 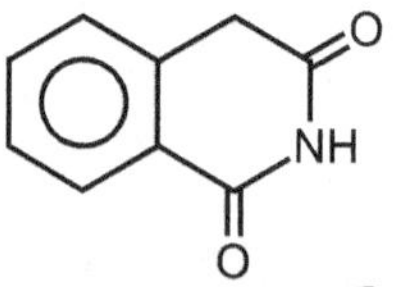 2,3-dihydroisoquinoline-1,3(2H)-dione type structure (benzene ring fused ring with NH and two C=O)

(c) isoindoline-1-one (benzene ring fused to five-membered ring with NH and C=O)

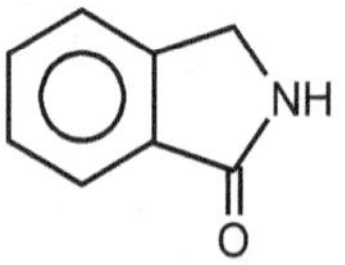

(d) 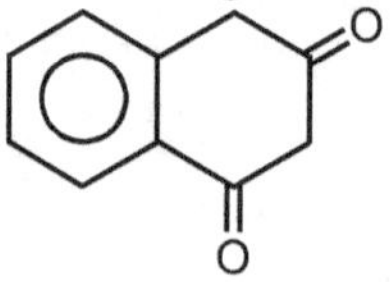 1,3-dioxo-tetralin type structure (benzene ring fused to six-membered ring with two C=O)

92. Among the following which one does not act as an intermediate in Hoffmann rearrangement? **[AIIMS 2005]**

    (a) RNCO   (b) RCON   (c) RCONHBr   (d) RNC

93. $CH_3CO_2C_2H_5$ on reaction with sodium ethoxide in ethanol gives A, which on heating in the presence of acid gives B. Compound B is ...... **[AIIMS 2005]**

    (a) CH_3COCH_2COOH (b) CH_3COCH_3

    (c) $HO = \langle\ \rangle = O$ (cyclic structure with O)   (d) $H_2C = C \begin{cases} OC_2H_5 \\ OC_2H_5 \end{cases}$

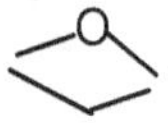

94. $CH_3COOC_2H_5$ with excess of C_2H_5MgBr on hydrolysis gives ......   **[MHT CET 2004]**

(a) $CH_3COC_2H_5$

(b) $CH_3 - \underset{\underset{\displaystyle C_2H_5}{|}}{\overset{\overset{\displaystyle C_2H_5}{|}}{C}} - OH$

(c) CH_3COCH_3

(d) $CH_3 - \underset{\underset{\displaystyle CH_3}{|}}{\overset{\overset{\displaystyle C_2H_5}{|}}{C}} - OH$

95. Reaction of $R - CO - NH_2$ with a mixture of Br_2 and KOH produce RNH_2. During the reaction which of the intermediate product is formed?   **[AFMC 2003]**

(a) $R - NH - Br$ (b) $H - CO - NBr_2$ (c) $R - N = C = O$ (d) All of these

96. In the following reaction, product P is $R - \overset{\overset{\displaystyle O}{||}}{C} - Cl \xrightarrow[\text{Pd-BaSO}_4]{H_2} P$ **[C.B.S.E. P.M.T. 2002]**

(a) RCH_2OH (b) $RCOOH$ (c) $RCHO$ (d) RCH_3

97. The compound that yields only ketonic compound/s on ozonolysis is ...... **[MHT-CET 2014]**
(a) But-2-ene   (b) Pent-2-ene
(c) 2, 3-Dimethylbut-2-ene   (d) 2-Methylbut-2-ene

98. Benzene can be conveniently converted into n-propyl benzene by ......   **[MHT-CET 2014]**
(a) Friedel – Craft alkylation with n-propyl chloride
(b) Friedel – Craft acylation with propionyl chloride followed by Wolff – Kishner reduction
(c) Friedel – Craft acylation with propionyl chloride followed by catalytic hydrogenation
(d) Friedel – Craft acylation with propionyl chloride followed by reduction with $LiAlH_4$

99. When sodium oxalate is treated with dilute H_2SO_4, the product is/are ......   **[Manipal 2006]**
(a) CO   (b) CO_2
(c) both CO and CO_2 (d) both CO_2 and SO_2

100. Which of the following gives aldol condensation reaction?   **[C.B.S.E. 2004]**

(a) $C_6H_5 - OH$ (b) $C_6H_5 - \overset{\overset{\displaystyle O}{||}}{C} - C_6H_5$ (c) $CH_3CH_2 - \overset{\overset{\displaystyle O}{||}}{C} - CH_3$ (d) $(CH_3)_2C - \overset{\overset{\displaystyle O}{||}}{C} - C_6H_5$

101. On vigorous oxidation by hot acidified permanganate solution, $(CH_3)_2C = CH-CH_2-CHO$ gives ......

(a) $CH_3 - \underset{\underset{\displaystyle CH_3}{|}}{\overset{\overset{\displaystyle OH \ OH}{| \ \ |}}{C} - CH} - CH_2CH_3$ **[C.P.M.T. 2000]**

(b) $\underset{CH_3}{\overset{CH_3}{>}}COOH + CH_3CH_2COOH$

(c) $\underset{CH_3}{\overset{CH_3}{>}}CH - OH + CH_3CH_2CH_2OH$

(d) $\underset{CH_3}{\overset{CH_3}{>}}C = O + \underset{\underset{\displaystyle COOH}{|}}{\overset{\overset{\displaystyle COOH}{|}}{CH_2}}$

102. Which one of the following order of acid strength is correct ?   **[Uttranchal PMT 2007]**

(a) $RCOOH > HC \equiv CH > HOH > ROH$

(b) $RCOOH > ROH > HOH > HC \equiv CH$

(c) $RCOOH > HOH > ROH > HC \equiv CH$

(d) $RCOOH > HOH > HC \equiv CH > ROH$

103. Which of these does not contain – COOH group?   **[A.F.M.C. 2008]**

(a) Aspirin   (b) Benzoic acid   (c) Picric acid   (d) Salicylic acid

104. The reactivity towards nucleophilic addition reaction of

I.   HCHO   II. CH_3CHO III. CH_3COCH_3 is   **[Orissa J.E.T. 2004]**

(a) II > III > I   (b) III > II > I   (c) I > II > III   (d) I > II < III

105. On mixing ethyl acetate with aqueous sodium chloride, the composition of the resultant solution is ......   **[D.P.M.T. 2001]**

(a) $CH_3COOC_2H_5 + NaCl$

(b) $CH_3Cl + C_2H_5COONa$

(c) $CH_3COCl + C_2H_5OH + NaOH$

(d) $CH_3OONa + C_2H_5OH$

106. Which one of the following undergoes reaction with 50% sodium hydroxide solution to give the corresponding alcohol and acid ?   **[AIIMS 2003]**

(a) Phenol   (b) Benzoic acid   (c) Butanal   (d) Benzaldehyde

107. Ozonolysis of which of the following will give HCHO ?   **[MPPMT 2001]**

(a) C_2H_2

(b) C_2H_4

(c) C_6H_6

(d) $CH_3CH = CHCH = CHCH_3$

108. Aniline reacts with which of these to form Schiff base ?   **[A.F.M.C. 2004]**

(a) Acetic acid   (b) Benzaldehyde   (c) Ethanol   (d) NH_3

109. Reduction of aldehydes and ketones into hydrocarbons using hydrazine and sodium ethoxide is called ......   **[GGSIPU 2009]**

(a) Clemmensen reduction

(b) Cope reduction

(c) Dow reduction

(d) Wolff-Kishner reduction

110. Which of the following reagent is used to distinguish acetone and acetophenone ?

[Rajasthan P.M.T. 2002]

(a) $NaHSO_3$

(b) Grignard's reagent

(c) Na_2SO_4

(d) NH_4Cl

111. The fatty acid which shows reducing property is ......   **[Kerala C.E.T. 2000]**

(a) Acetic acid   (b) Ethanoic acid   (c) Oxalic acid   (d) Formic acid

112. Clemmensen's reduction of ketones is carried out in ......   **[B.H.U. 2000]**

(a) H_2 with Pd catalyst

(b) Glycol with KOH

(c) $LiAlH_4$ in water

(d) Zn-Hg with conc. HCl

113. Identify the product Y in the sequence

$$CH_3CHO + CH_3MgI \xrightarrow{\text{Ether}} X \xrightarrow{H_2O/H^+} Y$$

[Kerala P.M.T. 2001]

(a) CH_3OH (b) CH_3CH_2OH (c) $(CH_3)_2CHOH$ (d) $(CH_3)_3COH$

(e) CH_3CH_2CHO

114. Which of the following organic compounds exhibits positive Fehling test as well as Iodoform test ?   **[Karnataka C.E.T. 2001]**

(a) Methanal   (b) Ethanol   (c) Propanone   (d) Ethanal

115. Chromyl chloride and toluene react to produce ......   **[A.F.M.C. 2001]**

(a) p-chlorotoluene   (b) Benzaldehyde   (c) Benzyl chloride (d) Benzoic acid

116. The addition of HCN to carbonyl compounds is an example of ...   **[Haryana C.E.E.T. 2000]**

(a) Nucleophilic substitution   (b) Electrophilic addition

(c) Nucleophilic addition   (d) Electrophilic substitution

117. $(CH_3)_2CO \xrightarrow[(HCl)]{NaCN} A \xrightarrow{H_3O^+} B$ **[C.P.M.T. 2000]**

In the above sequence of reactions, A and B are ......

(a) $(CH_3)_2C(OH)CN, (CH_3)_2C(OH)COOH$ (b) $(CH_3)_2C(OH)CN, (CH_3)_2C(OH)_2$

(c) $(CH_3)_2C(OH)CN, (CH_3)_2CHCOOH$ (d) $(CH_3)_2C(OH)CN, (CH_3)_2C = O$

118. From which of the following tertiary butyl alcohol is obtained by the action of methyl magnesium iodide ?   **[M.P.C.E.T. 2000]**

(a) $HCHO$ (b) CH_3CHO (c) CH_3COCH_3 (d) CO_2

119. Acetone reacts with Grignard reagent to form ......   **[A.F.M.C. 2004]**

(a) 3° alcohol   (b) 2° alcohol   (c) Ether   (d) No reaction

120. Which of the following statements regarding chemical properties of acetophenone are wrong ?   **[Tamil Nadu C.E.T. 2001]**

I.   It is reduced to methylphenyl carbinol by sodium and ethanol

II. It is oxidized to benzoic acid with acidified $KMnO_4$

III. It does not undergo electrophilic substitution like nitration at meta position

IV. It does not undergo iodoform reaction with iodine and alkali.

(a) I and II   (b) II and IV   (c) III and IV   (d) I and III

121. Predict the product 'B' in the sequence of reactions

$HC \equiv CH \xrightarrow[HgSO_4]{30\% \ H_2SO_4} A \xrightarrow{NaOH} B$ **[C.B.S.E. P.M.T. 2001]**

(a) CH_3COONa (b) CH_3COOH (c) CH_3CHO (d) $CH_3-\underset{\underset{OH}{|}}{CH}-CH_2CHO$

122. Which of the following is incorrect ?   **[C.B.S.E. P.M.T. 2001]**

(a) $FeCl_3$ is used in the detection of phenols

(b) Fehling solution is used in the detection of glucose

(c) Tollen's reagent is used in the detection of unsaturation

(d) $NaHSO_3$ is used in the detection of carbonyl compounds

123. Which alkene is formed from the following ylide carbonyl pair ?   **[Manipal 2001]**

$CH_3CH_2CH_2CH = PPh_3$ + 2-Butanone

(a) 3-Methyl-3-heptene

(b) 4-Methyl-3-heptene

(c) 5-Methyl-3-heptene

(d) 1-Methyl-5-methane

124. Consider the following statements. Acetophenone can be prepared by ...... **[Manipal 2001]**

I.   Oxidation of 1-phenylethanol

II.   Reaction of benzaldehyde with methyl magnesium bromide

III. Friedel Craft's reaction of benzene with acetyl chloride

IV.   Distillation of calcium benzoate

Which of the above statements are correct ?

(a) I and II

(b) I and IV

(c) I and III

(d) III and IV

125. Which one of the following pairs is not correctly matched ?   **[S.C.R.A.E. 2001]**

(a) $> C = O \xrightarrow{\text{Clemmensen's reduction}} > CH_2$

(b) $>C = O \xrightarrow[\text{reduction}]{\text{Wolff-Kishner}} > CHOH$

(c) $- COCl \xrightarrow{\text{Rosenmund's reduction}} CHO$

(d) $- C \equiv N \xrightarrow{\text{Stephen reduction}} CHO$

126. The IUPAC name of $CH_3COCH(CH_3)_2$ is ......   **[A.I.E.E.E. 2003]**

(a) 4-Methylisopropyl ketone

(b) 3-Methyl-2-butanone

(c) Isopropylmethyl ketone

(d) 2-Methyl-3-butanone

127. The product formed by the reaction of chlorine with benzaldehyde in the absence of a catalyst is ......   **[Tamil Nadu C.E.T. 2002]**

(a) Chlorobenzene

(b) Benzyl chloride

(c) Benzoyl chloride

(d) o-Chlorobenzaldehyde

128. An organic compound 'A' has the molecular formula C_3H_6O, it undergoes iodoform test. When saturated with HCl it gives 'B' of molecular formula $C_9H_{14}O$. A and B respectively are ......   **[Tamil Nadu 2002]**

(a) Propanal and mesitylene

(b) Propanone and mesityl oxide

(c) Propanone and 2, 6-dimethyl-2, 5-heptadien-4-one

(d) Propanone and mesitylene oxide

129. In this reaction   **[C.B.S.E. Med. 2003]**

$CH_3CHO + HCN \longrightarrow CH_3CH(OH)CN \xrightarrow{H_2O/H^+} CH_3CH(OH)COOH$

an asymmetric centre is generated. The acid obtained would be ......

(a) 20% d + 80% *l*-isomer

(b) d-isomer

(c) *l*-isomer

(d) 50% d + 50% *l*-isomer

ANSWER KEY

1. (b)	2. (c)	3. (c)	4. (a)	5. (c)	6. (b)	7. (c)	8. (a)
9. (d)	10. (c)	11. (b)	12. (c)	13. (b)	14. (d)	15. (c)	16. (c)
17. (b)	18. (a)	19. (c)	20. (b)	21. (d)	22. (c)	23. (b)	24. (a)
25. (a)	26. (d)	27. (b)	28. (c)	29. (a)	30. (d)	31. (a)	32. (d)
33. (d)	34. (a)	35. (b)	36. (c)	37. (b)	38. (b)	39. (d)	40. (d)
41. (c)	42. (d)	43. (a)	44. (c)	45. (c)	46. (c)	47. (c)	48. (b)
49. (a)	50. (a)	51. (d)	52. (b)	53. (a)	54. (a)	55. (a)	56. (d)
57. (a)	58. (b)	59. (d)	60. (c)	61. (b)	62. (a)	63. (b)	64. (a)
65. (b)	66. (b)	67. (b)	68. (d)	69. (c)	70. (b)	71. (d)	72. (a)
73. (d)	74. (c)	75. (d)	76. (c)	77. (a)	78. (c)	79. (d)	80. (c)
81. (b)	82. (b)	83. (b)	84. (c)	85. (b)	86. (c)	87. (d)	88. (c)
89. (b)	90. (d)	91. (d)	92. (c)	93. (b)	94. (a)	95. (d)	96. (a)
97. (c)	98. (b)	99. (d)	100. (b)	101. (d)	102. (c)	103. (d)	104. (d)
105. (a)	106. (c)	107. (a)	108. (a)	109. (d)	110. (d)	111. (c)	112. (d)
113. (b)	114. (c)	115. (a)	116. (b)	117. (d)	118. (c)	119. (b)	120. (b)
121. (a)	122. (d)	123. (a)	124. (c)	125. (a)	126. (d)	127. (b)	128. (b)
129. (d)	130. (d)	131. (c)	132. (d)	133. (b)	134. (c)	135. (a)	136. (b)
137. (a)	138. (b)	139. (c)	140. (a)	141. (a)	142. (c)	143. (d)	144. (b)
145. (d)	146. (b)	147. (d)	148. (c)	149. (a)	150. (c)	151. (d)	152. (a)
153. (b)	154. (b)	155. (d)	156. (a)	157. (b)	158. (b)	159. (d)	160. (a)
161. (c)	162. (b)	163. (a)	164. (a)	165. (d)	166. (a)	167. (d)	

Previous Year's Questions

1. (b)	2. (d)	3. (b)	4. (c)	5. (a)	6. (b)	7. (a)	8. (c)
9. (b)	10. (c)	11. (c)	12. (c)	13. (c)	14. (b)	15. (b)	16. (b)
17. (a)	18. (b)	19. (a)	20. (d)	21. (b)	22. (b)	23. (a)	24. (c)
25. (d)	26. (c)	27. (b)	28. (b)	29. (d)	30. (a)	31. (b)	32. (b)
33. (c)	34. (c)	35. (c)	36. (b)	37. (d)	38. (c)	39. (c)	40. (a)
41. (a)	42. (b)	43. (a)	44. (b)	45. (b)	46. (a)	47. (b)	48. (a)
49. (a)	50. (d)	51. (a)	52. (b)	53. (b)	54. (c)	55. (a)	56. (b)
57. (b)	58. (b)	59. (a)	60. (a)	61. (d)	62. (a)	63. (d)	64. (c)
65. (d)	66. (c)	67. (d)	68. (b)	69. (c)	70. (d)	71. (a)	72. (d)
73. (c)	74. (a)	75. (c)	76. (b)	77. (b)	78. (c)	79. (a)	80. (a)
81. (b)	82. (b)	83. (a)	84. (c)	85. (c)	86. (b)	87. (c)	88. (b)
89. (b)	90. (b)	91. (c)	92. (d)	93. (a)	94. (b)	95. (c)	96. (c)
97. (c)	98. (a)	99. (c)	100. (c)	101. (d)	102. (c)	103. (c)	104. (c)
105. (d)	106. (d)	107. (b)	108. (b)	109. (d)	110. (a)	111. (d)	112. (d)
113. (c)	114. (d)	115. (b)	116. (c)	117. (a)	118. (c)	119. (a)	120. (c)
121. (d)	122. (c)	123. (a)	124. (c)	125. (b)	126. (b)	127. (c)	128. (c)
129. (d)							

AMINES

1. The IUPAC name of CH_3CN is ......
   (a) Methyl cyanide (b) Methyl nitrile (c) Ethane nitrile (d) Methane nitrile

2. Which one of the following is a secondary amine?
   (a) 2-butanamine (b) N-methyl propanamine
   (c) 3-methyl pentanamine (d) p-amino aniline

3. The name of 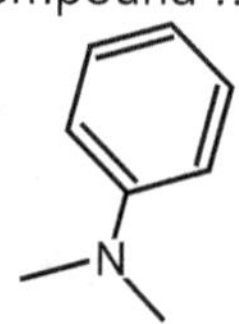 is ......
   (a) N, N, N-tri-isopropylamine (b) N-ethylpropylamine
   (c) N-isopropyl N, N-dipropylamine (d) diethylisopropylamine

4. The name of $CH_3-CH_2-CH_2-CH_2-CH_2-NH-CH_2-CH_3$ is ......
   (a) N,N-ethylpentanamine (b) N,N-isopropylpentanamine
   (c) N-ethylpentanamine (d) N-isopropylpentanamine

5. Give IUPAC name of the following compound ......

   (a) dimethylbenzylamine (b) N,N-dimethyltoluene
   (c) N,N-dimethylaniline (d) dimethylphenolamine

6. The formula of acrylonitrile is ......
   (a) $CH_2 = CHCN$ (b) CH_3CH_2CN (c) CH_3CN (d) $CH_3-CH = CH_2CN$

7. Which of the following is not an ambident nucleophile?
   (a) SCN^- (b) CN^- (c) NO_2^- (d) OF^-

8. The IUPAC name of CH_3CH_2CN is ......
   (a) Ethyl isocyanide (b) Propane nitrile (c) Ethyl nitrile (d) Ethane nitrile

9. The name of the following reaction is ......

$$CH_3CN \xrightarrow{Na/C_2H_5OH} CH_3CH_2NH_2$$

   (a) Stephen's reduction (b) Clemmensen's reduction
   (c) Mendius reduction (d) Wolff-Kishner reduction

10. Name the product N.

$$CH_3C \equiv N \xrightarrow[\text{(2) } H_2O/H^+]{\text{(1) } Sn/HCl} N$$

   (a) Ethanamine (b) Ethanol (c) Ethanal (d) Ethanoic acid

11. Identify the reagent for the following sequence of reaction.

$CH_3CH_2CN \xrightarrow{\text{'A'}} CH_3CH_2COOH$. 'A' is ......

(a) aq. NaOH　　　(b) aq. HCl　　　(c) H_2O　　　(d) H_3O^+

12. Give the IUPAC name of the product 'P' formed during the reaction sequence.

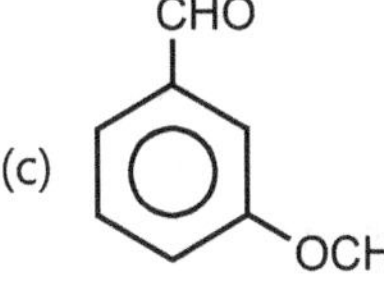

(a) Propanone　　　(b) Propanal　　　(c) Butanone　　　(d) Methyl ethyl ketone

13. Benzaldoxime on heating in the presence of P_2O_5 gives ......

(a) Phenyl isocyanide　(b) Benzaldehyde　(c) Benzamide　(d) Benzonitrile

14. Grignard reagent on treatment with cyanogen chloride gives ......

(a) Cyanides　　　(b) Chlorides　　　(c) Isocyanates　　　(d) Isocyanides

15. Cyanides and isocyanides are ...... isomers.

(a) Functional　　　(b) Positional　　　(c) Optical　　　(d) Geometrical

16.

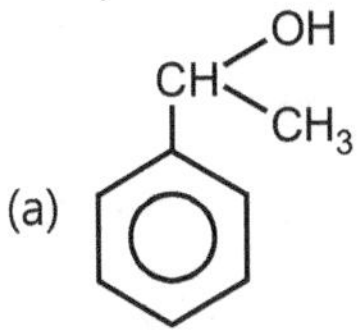

The product 'P' in the above reaction is ......

(a) 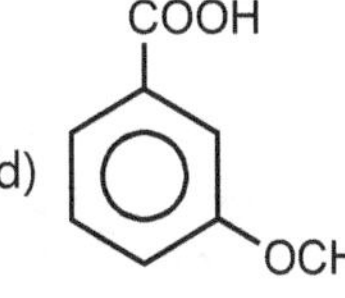

(b)

(c)

(d)

17. Aniline with chloroform and alcoholic potash gives a bad smelling compound which is ......

(a) Cyanide　　　(b) Isocyanide　　　(c) Amine　　　(d) Amide

18. Aromatic nitriles are not prepared by ......

(a) ArX + KCN

(b) $ArN_2^+ + CuCN$

(c) $ArCONH_2 + P_2O_5$

(d) $ArCONH_2 + SOCl_2$

19. Aniline reacts with which of the following to form Schiff's base ?

(a) Acetic acid　　　(b) Benzaldehyde　　　(c) Acetone　　　(d) NH_3

20. Identify the product in the following reaction

$CH_3CH_2Cl + AgCN \xrightarrow[\text{Heat}]{C_2H_5OH} ?$

(a) Propane nitrile

(b) Ethyl carbylamine

(c) Propanyl carbylamine

(d) Ethane nitrile

21. The name of the poisonous gas which caused Bhopal gas tragedy in 1964 is ......

   (a) Methyl isocyanide   (b) Methyl isocyanate

   (c) Ethyl isocyanide   (d) Methyl carbylamine

22. The formula of the poisonous gas in Bhopal gas tragedy is ......

   (a) CH_3CN (b) CH_3CNO_2 (c) $CH_3-N=C=O$ (d) CH_3CNO

23. The product of the reaction of ethyl bromide and alcoholic silver nitrite is ......

   (a) Ethane   (b) Ethyl nitrite   (c) Nitroethane   (d) Ethanol

24. A primary nitro alkane on reaction with nitrous acid gives ......

   (a) Pseudonitrol   (b) Nitrolic acid   (c) Primary amine   (d) Primary alcohol

25. The ease of nitration of the type of alkanes is maximum for ......

   (a) 1°   (b) 2°   (c) 3°   (d) 4°

26. Which of the following compounds does not show tautomerisation ?

   (a) Nitromethane   (b) 2-nitropropane   (c) Nitroethane   (d) Nitrobenzene

27. The major product 70% to 80% of the reaction between m-dinitrobenzene with NH_4HS is ...

   (a) 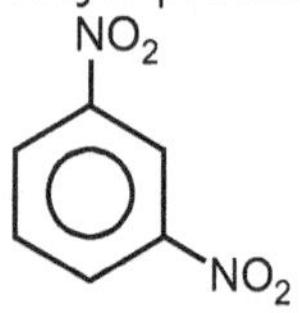   (b) 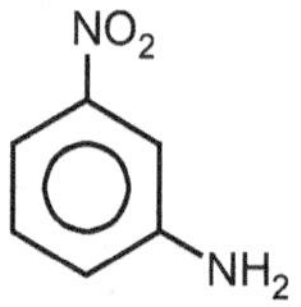   (c) 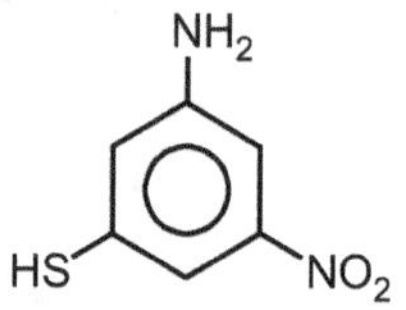   (d)

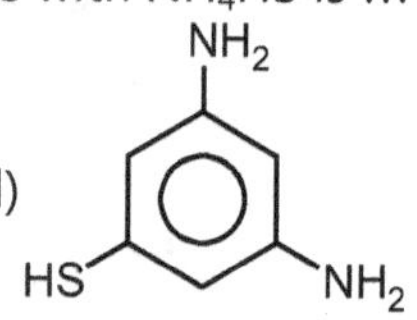

28. A group which deactivates the benzene ring towards electrophilic substitution but which directs the incoming group principally to the o- and p- portion is ......

   (a) $-NH_2$ (b) $-Cl$ (c) $-NO_2$ (d) $-C_6H_5$

29. Which species represents the electrophile in aromatic nitration?

   (a) NO_2^- (b) NO_2^+ (c) NO_2 (d) NO_3^-

30. What is the sequence of reagents that will accomplish the synthesis of the following aromatic amine from benzene?

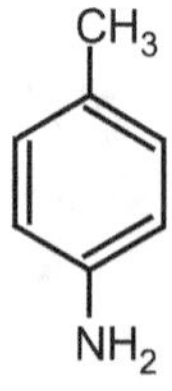

   (a) CH_3Cl, $AlCl_3$; HNO_3, H_2SO_4; H_2

   (b) CH_3Cl, $AlCl_3$; HNO_3, H_2SO_4; Fe, HCl; NaOH

   (c) HNO_3, H_2SO_4; Fe, HCl; NaOH; CH_3Cl, $AlCl_3$

   (d) HNO_3, H_2SO_4; CH_3Cl, $AlCl_3$; Fe, HCl; NaOH

31. Which of the following will give red colour with NaOH?

   (a) $R-\overset{\overset{\textstyle O}{\|}}{C}-NO_2$ (b) $R-\overset{\overset{\textstyle R}{|}}{\underset{\underset{\textstyle NO_2}{|}}{C}}-NO$ (c) R_3C-NO_2 (d) R_3CONO

32. Hydrazobenzene is formed when nitrobenzene is reduced with ......

(a) Zn/HCl

(b) $Zn/NaOH/CH_3OH$

(c) Zn/NaOH

(d) Zn/NH_4Cl

33. $Na_3AsO_4/NaOH$ reagent reduces nitrobenzene to ......

(a) Azobenzene   (b) Aniline   (c) Hydrobenzene (d) Azoxybenzene

34. Identify A, B in the following reaction $CH_3NO_2 \xrightarrow{\text{Zn + HCl}} A \xrightarrow[\text{reaction}]{\text{Carbylamine}} B$

(a) CH_3NH_2, CH_3NC (b) $(CH_3)_2NH$, HCN (c) CH_3OH, CH_4 (d) CH_3NH_2, CH_3CN

35. The major product of the reaction between ethyl bromide with potassium nitrite solution is ......

(a) Nitroethane   (b) Ethyl nitrite   (c) Ethene   (d) Ethyl amine

36. Treatment of cyclohydryl methanamine with HNO_2 does not give ......

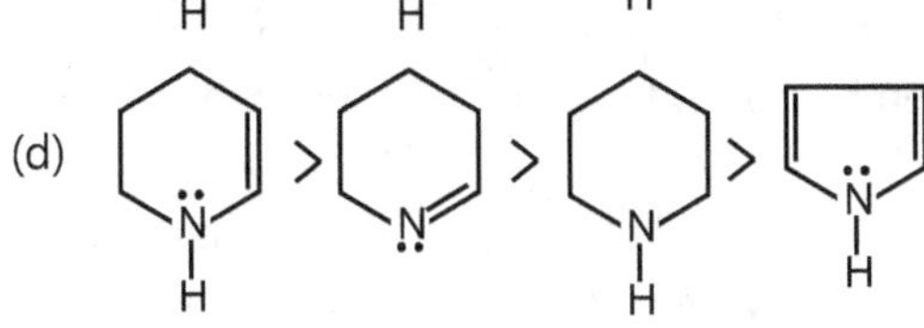

37. Which one of the following amines cannot be prepared by Gabriel's synthesis?

(a) Butylamine

(b) Isobutylamine

(c) Aniline

(d) N-methyl benzylamine

38. The weakest base among the following is ......

(a) Dimethyl amine (b) Aniline   (c) Methyl amine (d) Ethyl amine

39. If n-Butylamine (I), diethylamine (II) and N, N-dimethyl ethyl amine (III) have the same molar mass then the increasing order of their boiling point is ......

(a) III < II < I   (b) I < II < III   (c) II < I < III   (d) III < I < II

40. Correct decreasing order of basic strength is ......

41. Hisenberg's reagent is ......

    (a) $C_6H_5SO_2Cl$ (b) $C_6H_5SO_2NH_2$ (c) $C_6H_5SO_3H$ (d) $C_6H_5N_2Cl$

42. Which one of the following reagents could be used to separate a mixture of phenylamine and methyl benzene ......

    (a) Ethane   (b) Dilute HCl   (c) Propanone   (d) Dilute H_2SO_4

43. When aqueous bromine is added in the solution of phenylamine, the colour of the bromine disappears. Which one of the following statements explain this observation?

    (a) Bromine replaces hydrogen in the benzene ring

    (b) Phenyl amine oxidizes bromine to Br

    (c) Bromine adds to the double bond of benzene

    (d) Bromine forms a colourless complex with phenyl amine

44. Which one of the following reagents can be used in school laboratory to convert ......

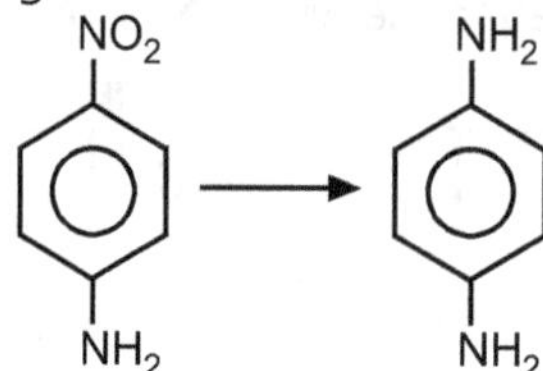

    (a) conc. aq. NH_3 (b) Sn/HCl   (c) SO_2 (d) Fe/HNO_3

45. Compound **K** extracted from naturally occurring substance is found to have molecular formulae $C_9H_9O_3N$ which has a chiral centre. Identify **K**.

(a) HOOC—⬡—NH_2 with —CH_2OH

(b) HO—⬡—CH(—NH_2)(—COOH)

(c) HOOC—⬡—CH_2NH_2 with —OH

(d) NH_2—⬡—CH(—COOH)(—OH)

46. Which one of the following statements explain why $C_6H_5NH_2$ is a weaker base than CH_3NH_2?

    (a) CH_3 group is more polar than C_6H_5 group

    (b) The lone pair of electron present on the nitrogen is delocalised

    (c) Benzene ring is proton releasing

    (d) It is not soluble in water

47. Which of the following does not produce amine?

    (a) Mendius   (b) Gabriel

    (c) Hoffmann's mustard oil reaction   (d) Carbylamine

48. Toluene is nitrated and the resulting product is reduced with tin and hydrochloric acid. The product so obtained is diazotised and then heated with cuprous bromide HBr. The reaction mixture so formed contains ......

    (a) Mixture of o– and m-bromotoluene   (b) Mixture of o– and p-bromotoluene

    (c) Mixture of o– and p-dibromobenzene   (d) Mixture of o– and p-bromo aniline

49. m-bromo aniline can be prepared by ......

(a) $C_6H_6 \xrightarrow[\text{H}_2\text{SO}_4]{\text{HNO}_3} \xrightarrow[\text{NaOH/H}_2\text{O}]{\text{Sn/HCl}} \xrightarrow[\text{H}_2\text{O}]{\text{Br}_2}$

(b) $C_6H_6 \xrightarrow[\text{FeBr}_3]{\text{Br}_2} \xrightarrow[\text{H}_2\text{SO}_4]{\text{HNO}_3} \xrightarrow{\text{H}_2/\text{Pt}}$

(c) m-BrC$_6$H$_4$COOH $\xrightarrow{\text{SOCl}_2} \xrightarrow{\text{NH}_3} \xrightarrow[\text{H}]{\text{Br}_2/\text{NaOH}}$

(d) $C_6H_5NH_2 \xrightarrow[\text{Cu}_2\text{Br}_2]{\text{NaNO}_2/\text{HCl}} \xrightarrow{\text{NaNH}_2}$

50. Predict X, Y in the following reaction ......

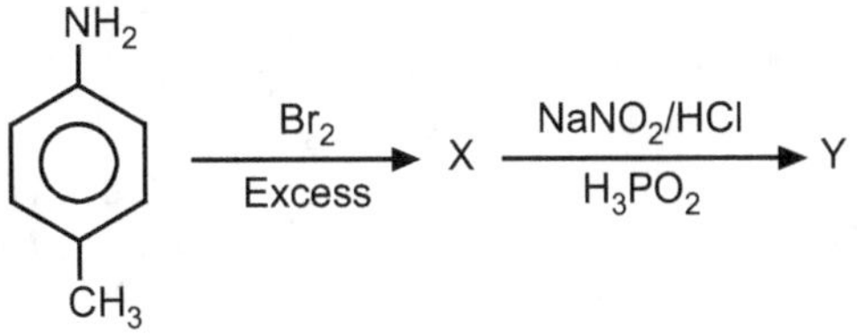

$$\text{(structure: p-toluidine)} \xrightarrow[\text{Excess}]{\text{Br}_2} \text{X} \xrightarrow[\text{H}_3\text{PO}_2]{\text{NaNO}_2/\text{HCl}} \text{Y}$$

(a) 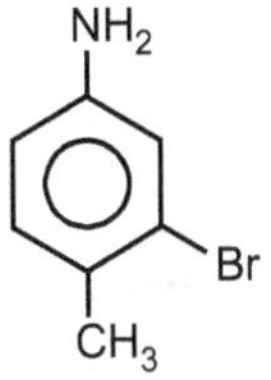 [structure: 3-bromo-4-methylaniline] and [structure: 2-bromotoluene]

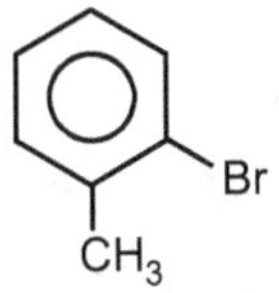

(b) 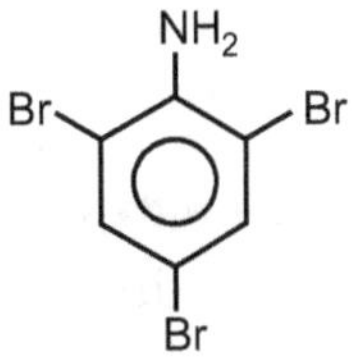 [structure: 2,6-dibromoaniline with para Br] and [structure: 1,3,5-tribromobenzene]

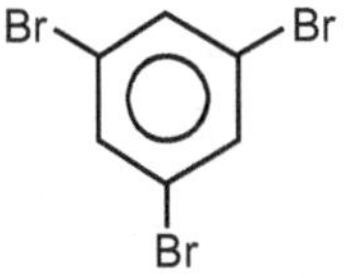

(c) 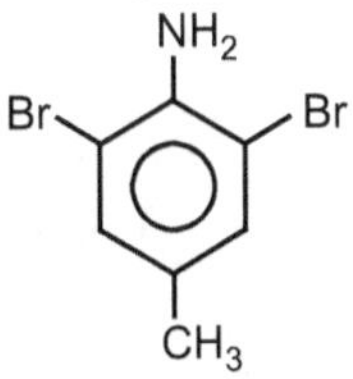 [structure: 2,6-dibromo-4-methylaniline] and [structure: 3,5-dibromotoluene]

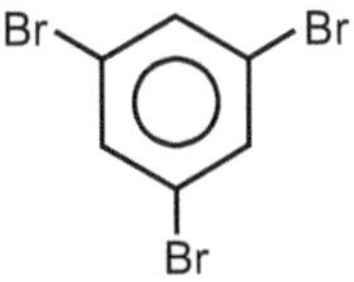

(d) 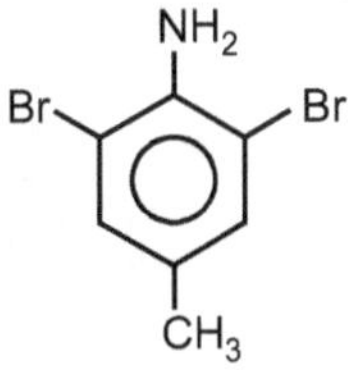 [structure: 2,6-dibromo-4-methylaniline] and [structure: 3,5-dibromotoluene]

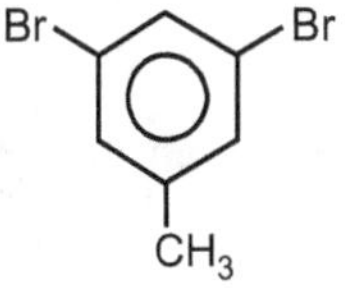

51. The correct sequence of the reagents used to convert an alcohol to primary amine having one carbon more is ...... e.g.

$CH_3CH_2OH \longrightarrow CH_3CH_2CH_2NH_2$

(a) KCN, H$_3$O$^+$, H$_2$/Pt   (b) PBr$_3$, KCN, H$_2$/Pt   (c) PBr$_3$, KCN, H$_3$O$^+$ (d) NH$_3$, H$_3$O$^+$, KCN

52. Which is the most likely product of the reaction between aniline and benzoyl chloride?

(a) 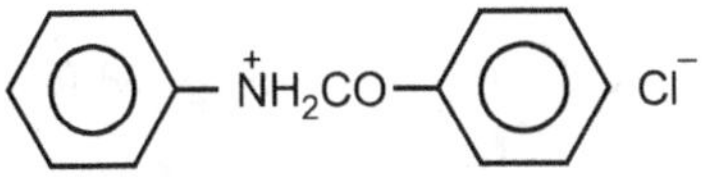 [structure: C$_6$H$_5$–$\overset{+}{N}$H$_2$CO–C$_6$H$_5$ Cl$^-$]

(b) [structure: C$_6$H$_5$–NHCO–C$_6$H$_5$]

(c) [structure: C$_6$H$_5$–CO–C$_6$H$_4$–NH$_2$]

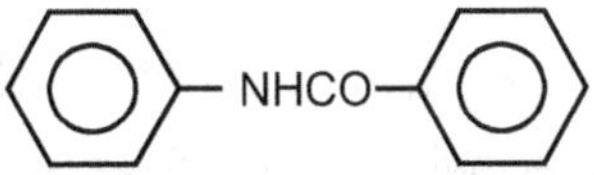

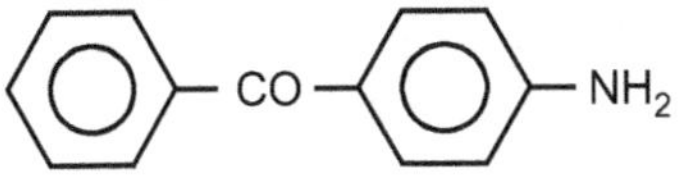

(d) 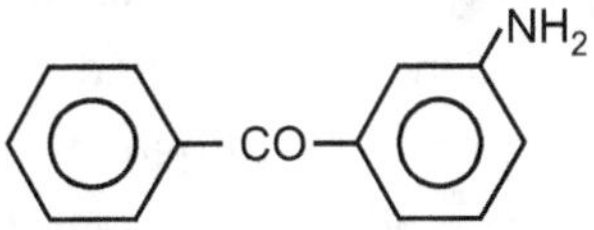 [structure: C$_6$H$_5$–CO–C$_6$H$_4$ with NH$_2$]

53. The pain killer which can be made from compound 4-ethoxy aniline is ......

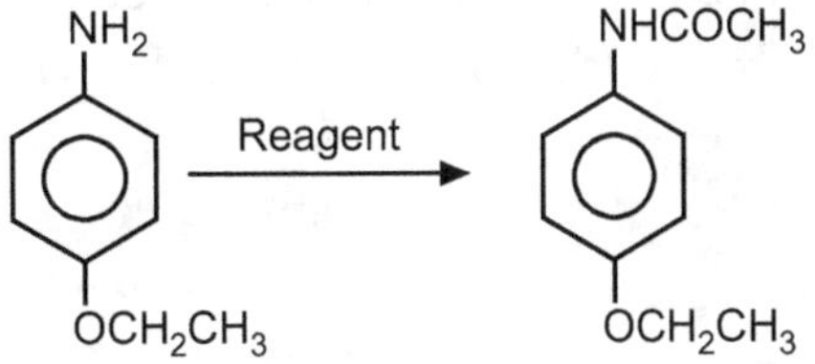

$$\text{(structure: 4-ethoxyaniline, NH}_2\text{/OCH}_2\text{CH}_3) \xrightarrow{\text{Reagent}} \text{(structure: NHCOCH}_3\text{/OCH}_2\text{CH}_3)$$

Which could be the reagent?

(a) CH$_3$COCH$_3$ (b) CH$_3$COCl   (c) CH$_3$CONH$_2$ (d) CH$_3$COOCH$_2$CH$_3$

54. Following compound reacts with ethanoyl chloride.

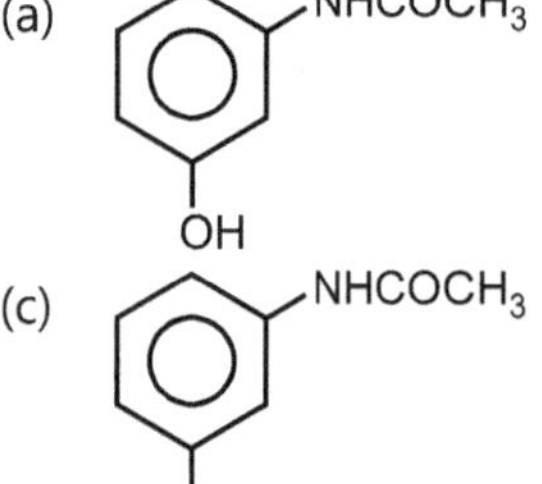

What is the formula of the product when ethanoyl chloride is in excess?

(a) 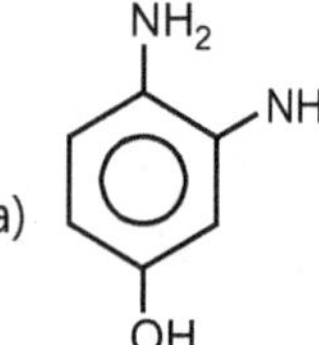

(b)

(c)

(d)

55. The reaction of aniline with benzaldehyde is ......

(a) Substitution　　(b) Condensation　　(c) Addition　　(d) Polymerization

56. Which of the following could form an aqueous solution with highest pH?

(a)

(b) $C_2H_5NH_2$　　(c) C_2H_5OH　　(d) CH_3COOH

57. The reagent that react with nitromethane to form methyl hydroxylamine is ......

(a) Zn/HCl　　(b) Zn/NH_4Cl　　(c) $Zn/NaOH$　　(d) Sn/HCl

58. Aniline on oxidation with $K_2Cr_2O_7/H_2SO_4$ produces ......

(a) p-Benzoquinone　　(b) Nitrobenzene　　(c) Benzonitrile　　(d) Benzamide

59. Schiff's base is ......

(a) $RCH = NR$　　(b) RCH_2NH_2　　(c) $RCH_2NH_3^+OH^-$　　(d) RNH_2OH

60. During acetylation of amines, what is replaced by acetyl group?

(a) Hydrogen atom attached to nitrogen

(b) One or more hydrogen attached to carbon

(c) One or more hydrogen attached to nitrogen

(d) Hydrogen atom attached to carbon and nitrogen both

61. When primary amine reacts with chloroform in the presence of alcoholic KOH, the reaction is ......

(a) Hofmann

(b) Curtius

(c) Carbylamine reaction

(d) Reimer-Tiemann

62. Which of the following can react with $CHCl_3/CCl_4$ and KOH to produce carbylamine?

(a) R_3N　　(b) R_2NH　　(c) RNH_2　　(d) All three amines

63.

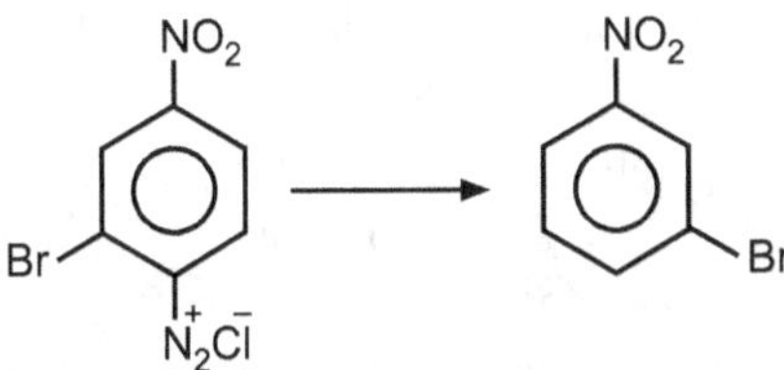

$$CH_3-\underset{CH_3}{\overset{CH_3}{C}} = O \xrightarrow{NH_2OH} A \xrightarrow{LiAlH_4} B$$

The name of B is ......

(a) N-methyl ethanamine

(b) N, N-dimethyl amine

(c) Propan-2-amine

(d) 1-propanamine

64. Ethyl amine on oxidation in the presence of $KMnO_4$ gives ......

(a) An aldehyde   (b) An acid   (c) An alcohol   (d) An N-oxide

65. In the following reaction, compound 'A' is ......

$C_2H_5NH_2 + CH_3MgBr \longrightarrow$ 'A'

(a) Ethane   (b) Methane   (c) Ammonia   (d) Propane

66. Hydrolysis of benzonitrile gives ......

(a) Benzylamine   (b) Aniline   (c) Benzoic acid   (d) Benzene

67. In the reaction

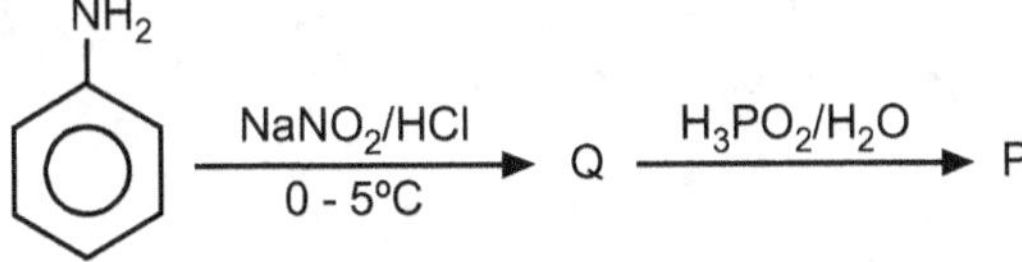

(a) H_3PO_2 (b) Cu_2Cl_2 (c) $HgSO_4/H_2SO_4$ (d) H_2O

68. A colourless, odourless and non-corrosive gas is formed when ethylamine reacts with ......

(a) H_2SO_4 (b) NaOH   (c) CH_3COCl (d) $NaNO_2/HCl$

69. Primary and secondary amines can be distinguished by ......

(a) Br_2/KOH (b) HClO   (c) HNO_2 (d) NH_3

70. The name of the product during following reaction sequence is ......

$$CH_3CH_2NH_2 \xrightarrow[H_2SO_4]{KMnO_4} (A) \xrightarrow[Water]{Hydrolysis}$$

(a) Ethanoic acid   (b) Ethanal   (c) Neo ethane   (d) Ethane nitrile

71. Among o-nitroaniline (I), p-nitroaniline (II), m-nitroaniline (III), the order of basic strength is ....

(a) I < III < II   (b) I < II < III   (c) I > II > III   (d) III > I > II

72. Which of the following does not undergo Friedel Craft reaction ?

(a) Aniline   (b) Phenone   (c) Nitrobenzene   (d) Chlorobenzene

73. Identify 'P' in the following reaction sequence,

$$\underset{0-5^\circ C}{\overset{NH_2}{\bigcirc}} \xrightarrow[0-5^\circ C]{NaNO_2/HCl} Q \xrightarrow{H_3PO_2/H_2O} P$$

(a) Phenol

(b) Benzene

(c) Benzene phosphate

(d) BDC

74. The compounds A, B are ......

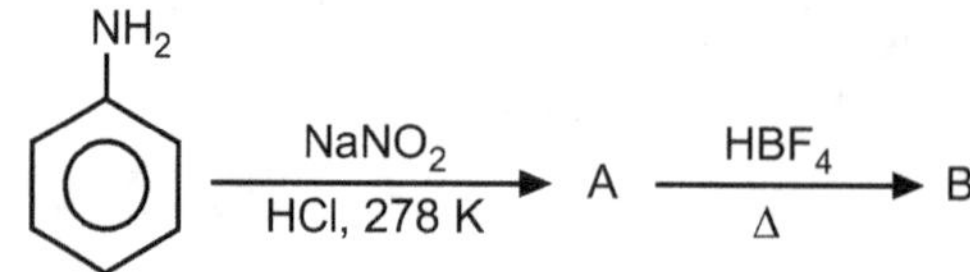

(a) nitrobenzene, chlorobenzene
(b) nitrobenzene, fluorobenzene
(c) phenol and benzene
(d) benzene diazonium chloride and fluorobenzene

75. Which of the following is the correct increasing order of variety of amines in gaseous phase?
(a) $(CH_3)_2NH > CH_3NH_2 > (CH_3)_3N > NH_3$
(b) $(CH_3)_3N > (CH_3)_2NH > CH_3NH_2 > NH_3$
(c) $(CH_3)_2NH > (CH_3)_3N > CH_3NH_2 > NH_3$
(d) $(CH_3)_3N > CH_3NH_2 > (CH_3)_2NH > NH_3$

76. Which of the following reagents can be used to convert acetamide into methanamine ?
(a) P_2O_5 (b) NaOBr   (c) $LiAlH_4 | H_2O$ (d) $Na(Hg) | C_2H_5OH$

77. Aniline reacts with phosgene to give ......
(a) Chlorobenzene   (b) Phenyl isocyanide (c) Phenyl cyanide (d) Phenyl isocyanide

78. Which of the following is the least basic amine ?
(a) Ethyl amine   (b) Diethylamine   (c) Aniline   (d) Benzylamine

79. Amine that cannot be prepared by Gabriel phthalimide synthesis is ......
(a) Aniline   (b) Benzylamine   (c) Methyl amine   (d) Isobutylamine

80. Which of the follownig amines give yellow oily liquid with HNO_2 ?
(a) Dimethyl amine   (b) Aniline
(c) 3-methyl benzylamine   (d) Methyl amine

81. In the following reaction sequence, $CH_3CHO \xrightarrow[Ca(OH)_2]{Cl_2} X \xrightarrow[Alc\ KOH]{C_6H_5NH_2} Y$

Y is ......
(a) $CH_3CH = NHC_6H_5$ (b) $C_6H_5NHCH_3$ (c) C_6H_5NC (d) C_6H_5NCO

82. Mark the correct statement ......
(a) Methylamine is slightly acidic   (b) Methylamine is less basic than ammonia
(c) Methylamine is stronger base than NH_3 (d) Methylamine forms salt with alkalies

83. The compound obtained by heating a mixture of a primary amine and chloroform with ethanolic potassium hydroxide (KOH) is ......
(a) An alkyl isocyanide   (b) An alkyl halide
(c) An amide   (d) An amide and nitro compound

84. On reaction with HNO_2, $C_2H_5NH_2$ produces ......
(a) C_2H_5OH (b) $C_2H_5 - NO_2$ (c) CH_3CHO (d) CH_3COOH

85. Which is carbylamine reaction ?
(a) $C_2H_5NH_2 + 3KOH + CHCl_3 \longrightarrow C_2H_5NC + 3KCl + 3H_2O$

(b) $C_6H_6 + CH_3Cl \xrightarrow[Anhydrous]{AlCl_3} C_6H_5CH_3 + HCl$

(c) $2HCHO + NaOH \rightarrow CH_3OH + HCOONa$

(d) $2CH_3Cl + 2Na \rightarrow CH_3 - CH_3 + 2NaCl$

86. The correct order of increasing basic nature for bases NH_3, CH_3NH_2 and $(CH_3)_2NH$ is ...

(a) $CH_3NH_2 < NH_3 < (CH_3)_2NH$　　　　(b) $(CH_3)_2NH < NH_3 < CH_3NH_2$

(c) $NH_3 < CH_3NH_2 < (CH_3)_2NH$　　　　(d) $CH_3NH_2 < (CH_3)_2NH < NH_3$

87. Ethyl isocyanide on hydrolysis in acidic medium generates ......

(a) Ethylamine salt and methanoic acid　　　(b) Propanoic acid and ammonium salt

(c) Ethanoic acid and ammonium salt　　　　(d) Methylamine salt and ethanoic acid

88. Among the following the weakest base is ......

(a) $C_6H_5CH_2NH_2$　　　(b) $C_6H_5CH_2NHCH_3$　　　(c) $O_2NCH_2NH_2$　　　(d) CH_3NHCHO

89. An organic compound having molecular mass 60 is found to contain C = 20%, H = 6.67% and N = 46.67% while rest is oxygen. On heating it gives NH_3 alongwith a solid residue. The solid residue gives violet colour with alkaline copper sulphate solution. The compound is ...

(a) CH_3NCO　　　(b) CH_3CONH_2　　　(c) $(NH_2)_2CO$　　　(d) $CH_3CH_2CONH_2$

90. Which of the following is more basic than aniline ?

(a) Triphenylamine　　　(b) p-Nitroaniline　　　(c) Benzylamine　　　(d) Diphenylamine

91. The following sequence of reactions on X gives,

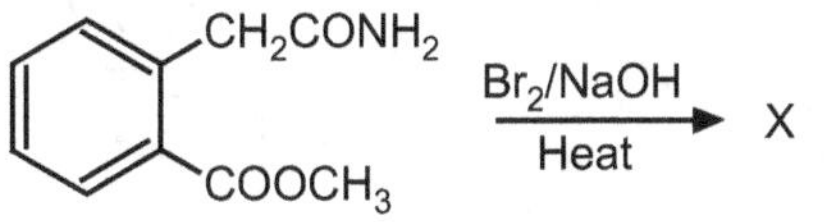

(a) 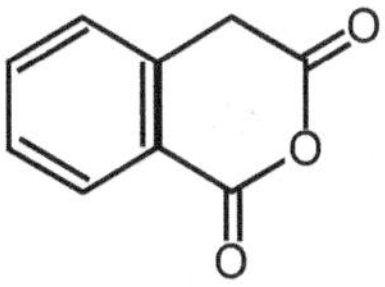　(b) 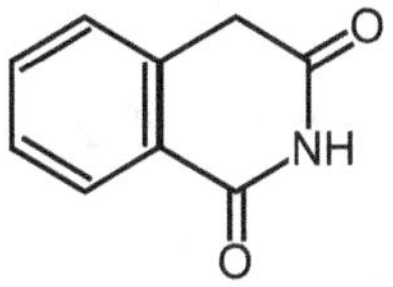　(c) 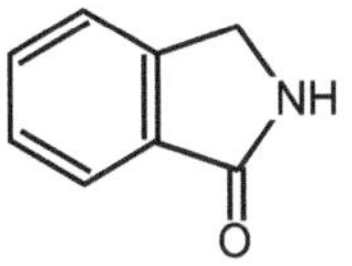　(d)

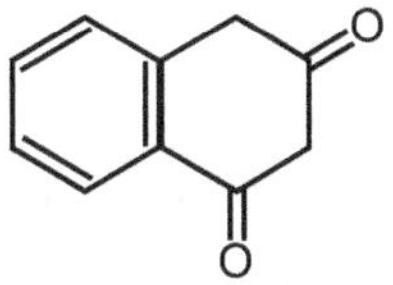

92. Aniline in a set of following reactions yielded a coloured product 'Y'. Y is ......

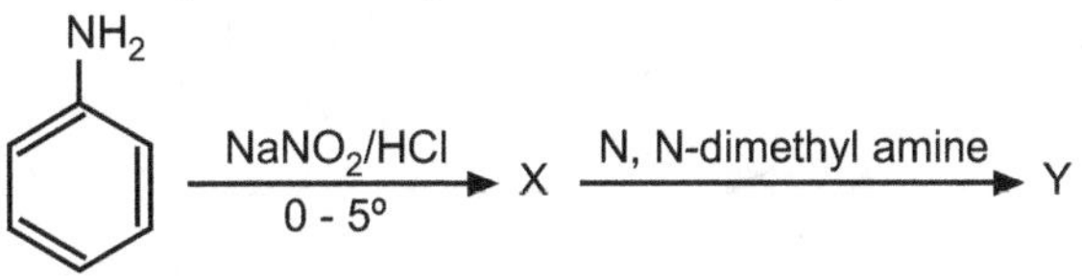

(a) 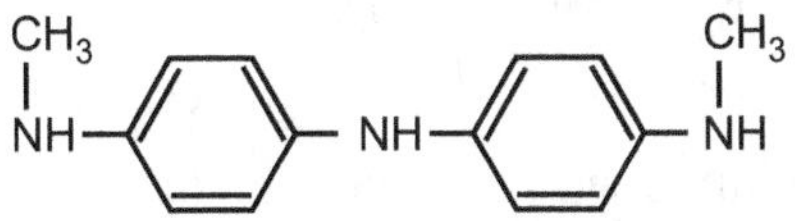　(b) 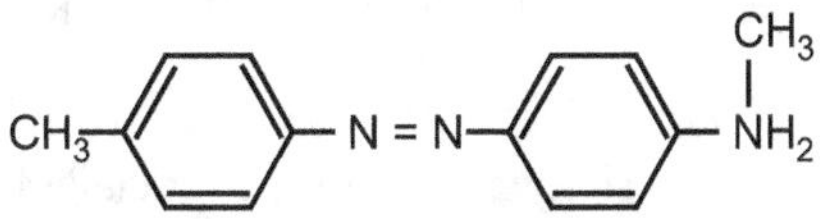　(c) 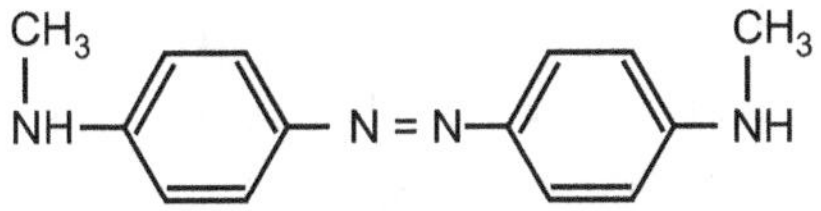　(d)

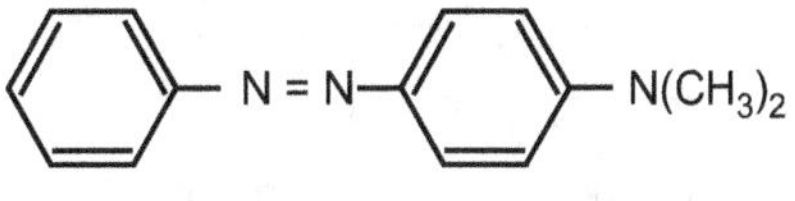

93. Identify compound B ......

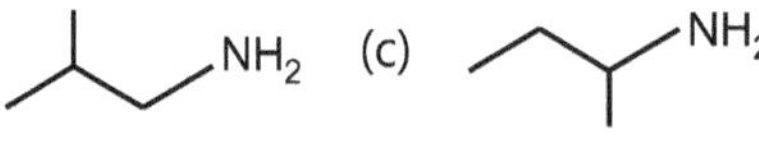

$$HO-\overset{\overset{O}{\|}}{C}-\overset{\overset{CH_3}{|}}{\underset{\underset{CH_3}{|}}{C}}-C\equiv N \xrightarrow{200°C} A \xrightarrow[H_2O]{LiAlH_4} B;$$

(a) 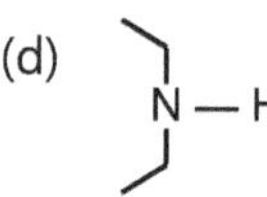

(b)

(c) $HO-H_2C-\overset{\overset{CH_3}{|}}{\underset{\underset{CH_3}{|}}{C}}-CH_2-NH_2$

(d) $\underset{CH_3}{\overset{CH_3}{\diagdown}}CH-CH_2-NH_2$

94. An organic compound (A) on reduction gives compound (B) which on reaction with $CHCl_3$ and NaOH form (C). The compound (C) on catalytic reduction gives N-methylaniline. The compound (A) is ......

(a) $C_6H_5-NO_2$

(b) $C_6H_5-C\equiv N$

(c) $C_6H_5-\overset{\overset{O}{\|}}{C}-NH_2$

(d) $C_6H_5-\overset{..}{N}H_2$

95. Which one among the following is expected to form a secondary alcohol on treatment with HNO_2?

(a)  (b) (c) (d)

96. The major product (X) of the reaction is ......

$$\text{(cyclopentane with OH and NH}_2) \xrightarrow[dil.\ HCl]{NaNO_2} X$$

(a) (b) (c) (d)

97. Which of the following compounds cannot be identified by carbylamine test ?

(a) $C_6H_5NHC_6H_5$ (b) $CH_3CH_2NH_2$ (c) $CHCl_3$ (d) $C_6H_5NH_2$

98. The basicity of anilines, especially when substituted with electron-withdrawing groups such as nitro group ....

(a) increase; ortho or para

(b) increase; meta

(c) decrease; ortho or para

(d) decrease ; meta

99. Predict the product of the following reaction $C_6H_5N_2^+Cl^- + CuCN \rightarrow$

    (a) $(C_6H_5)_2CuCl$ (b) C_6H_5-CN (c) $(C_6H_5)_2CuLi$ (d) $C_6H_5-N=N-CN$

100. Which reaction sequence will carry out the following transformation?

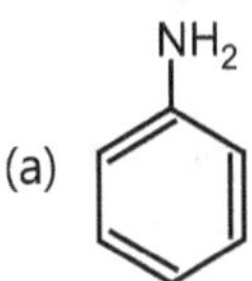

    (a) $Sn/HCl, NaNO_2/HCl$ 0-5°C $(CH_3)_2NC_6H_4NH_2$

    (b) $LiAlH_4$ (excess), $NaNO_2/HCl$ 0-5°C $(CH_3)_2NC_6H_4NH_2$

    (c) $(CH_3)_2NC_6H_4NH_2$, $NaNO_2/HCl$ 0-5°C

    (d) Sn/HCl, $(CH_3)_2NC_6H_4N_2^+Cl^-$

101. The reason that $CH_3\ddot{N}H_2$ is a stronger base than $CH_3\ddot{O}H$ is due to the fact that ......

    (a) hyperconjugation resonance of the product, $CH_3NH_3^+$, is better than for $CH_3OH_2^+$.

    (b) resonance of the product, $CH_3NH_3^+$, is better than for $CH_3OH_2^+$.

    (c) the electronegativity of nitrogen is less than oxygen, thus making the electron pair more available.

    (d) the oxygen atom has two non-bonded pairs of electrons making it twice as basic.

102. Which of the following compounds is the strongest Bronsted acid?

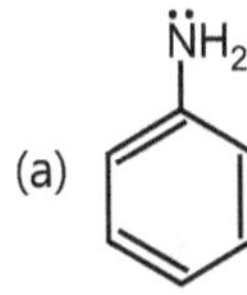

103. Which of the following compounds is the strongest Bronsted base?

PREVIOUS YEAR'S QUESTIONS

1. Choose the correct statement regarding the basicity of arylamine from the following :

[NEET-2016]

    (a) Arylamines are less basic than alkyl amines due to the delocalization of lone pair of nitrogen with the π electron of benzene nucleus.

    (b) Arylamines are more basic than alkyl amines due to the delocalization of lone pair of nitrogen with the π electron of benzene nucleus.

    (c) Arylamines are more basic than alkyl amines because of aryl group.

    (d) Arylamines are more basic than alkyl amines because the nitrogen atom is attached to sp^2 hybridized carbon.

2. A given aromatic compound A reacts with tin and HCl followed by nitrous acid to give a unstable compound which reacts with phenol and gives beautiful coloured compound of molecular formula $C_{12}H_{10}N_2O$. Identify compound A.   **[NEET-2016]**

(a) [benzene ring with NH_2]   (b) [benzene ring with $CONH_2$]   (c) [benzene ring with NO_2]   (d) [benzene ring with CN]

3. The electrolytic reduction of nitrobenzene in strongly acidic medium produces ......
(a) aniline   (b) azobenzene   (c) p-aminophenol (d) azoxybenzene

4. Which of the following will be most stable diazonium salt $RN_2^+X^-$?   **[AIPMT 2014]**
(a) $CH_3CH_2N_2^+X^-$ (b) $C_6H_5CH_2N_2^+X^-$ (c) $CH_3N_2^+X^-$ (d) $C_6H_5N_2^+X^-$

5. Nitrobenzene on reaction with conc. HNO_3/H_2SO_4 at 80° - 100°C forms which one of the following products?   **(AIPMT 2013)**
(a) 1, 2, 4-Trinitrobenzene   (b) 1, 2-Dinitrobenzene
(c) 1, 3-Dinitrobenzene   (d) 1, 4-Dinitrobenzene

6. The reaction of aniline with acetyl chloride in the presence of NaOH gives ...**[Manipal 2012]**
(a) acetanilide   (b) p-chloroaniline   (c) a red dye   (d) aniline hydrochloride

7. Isocyanide can be prepared by alkyl halide on treatment with ......   **[VMMC 2010]**
(a) AgCN   (b) AgNC   (c) KNC   (d) None of these

8. $CH_3 - CH_2C \equiv N \xrightarrow{X} CH_3CH_2CHO$

The compound $\overset{.}{X}$ is ......   **[AIIMS 2008]**
(a) $SnCl_2/HCl/H_2O$, boil   (b) $H_2/Pd - BaSO_4$
(c) $LiAlH_4/ether$ (d) $NaBH_4/ether/H_3O^+$

9. Hydrolysis of phenyl isocyanide forms ......   **[AFMC 2006]**
(a) benzoic acid   (b) formic acid   (c) acetic acid   (d) none of these

10. The nitration of aniline is achieved by ......   **[Kerala Med. 2005]**
(a) Direct treatment with nitrating mixture under reflux
(b) Using fuming HNO_3
(c) Acetylation followed by nitration and subsequent hydrolysis
(d) Using dil. HNO_3 in ice

11. Which of the following chemicals are used to manufacture methyl isocyanate that caused "Bhopal Tragedy" ?   **[A.I.I.M.S. 2005]**
(i) Methylamine   (ii) Phosgene   (iii) Phosphine   (iv) Dimethylamine
(a) (i) and (iii)   (b) (iii) and (iv)   (c) (i) and (ii)   (d) (ii) and (iv)

12. **Assertion :** Alkyl isocyanides in acidified water give alkyl formamides.   **[AIIMS 2005]**
Reason : In isocyanides, carbon first acts as a nucleophile and then as an electrophile.
(a) Both Assertion and Reason are true and Reason is the correct explanation of Assertion.
(b) Both Assertion and Reason are true and Reason is not the correct explanation of Assertion.
(c) Assertion is true but Reason is false.
(d) Both Assertion and Reason are false.

13. The strongest base in aqueous solution among the following amines is ......

(a) N, N-diethylethanamine

(b) N-ethylethanamine

(c) N-methylmethanamine

(d) ethanamine

(e) phenylmethanamine

14. Which of the following statements about primary amines is 'False'?

(a) Alkyl amines are stronger bases than ammonia　　　　**[CBSE AIPMT 2010]**

(b) Alkyl amines are stronger bases than amines

(c) Alkyl amines react with nitrous acid to produce alcohols.

(d) Aryl amines react with nitrous acid to produce phenols.

15. N_2 gas will not be evolved upon reaction of HNO_2 with which of the following amines?

(a) 1°　　　　　(b) 2°　　　　　(c) 3°　　　　　(d) Both (b) and (c)

16. Among the amines (a) $C_6H_5NH_2$ (b) CH_3NH_2 (c) $(CH_3)_2NH$ (d) $(CH_3)_3N$, the order of basicity is

......　　　　　　　　　　　　　　　　　　　**[Kerala Engg. 2005]**

(a) a < b < d < c　　　(b) d < c < b < a　　　(c) a > b > c > d　　　(d) b < c < d < a

(e) d < c < b < a

17. Which of the following amines gives yellow oily liquid with HNO_2 ?

(a) Ethyl methyl amine

(b) Aniline　　　　**[MHT-CET 2010]**

(c) 3-methyl benzylamine

(d) Methyl amine

18. N-ethyl-N-methylpropan-1 amine is ......　　　　　　　**[MHT 2010]**

(a) 1° amine　　　(b) 2° amine　　　(c) 3° amine　　　(d) 4° amine

19. The strongest base among the following is ......　　　　　**[Manipal 2010]**

(a) $C_6H_5NH_2$　　　(b) $(C_6H_5)_2NH$　　　(c) NH_3　　　(d) $(C_2H_5)_2NH$

20. Acetamide and ethylamine can be distinguished by reacting with ......　　**[Manipal 2010]**

(a) aqueous HCl and heat

(b) aqueous NaOH and heat

(c) acidified $KMnO_4$

(d) bromine water

21. Amines are basic in character because they have ......　　　　　**[BVP 2010]**

(a) a lone pair of electrons on the nitrogen atom.

(b) a hydroxyl group in the molecule.

(c) replaceable hydrogen atom.

(d) tetrahedral structure.

22. **Assertion :** Basicity of $CH_3CH_2NH_2(I)$, $NH_3(II)$ and $C_6H_5NH_2(III)$ is in order I>II>III

[VMMC 2010]

Reason : Electron donating groups (such as alkyl group) increase the basicity of amines, and electron withdrawing groups (such as aryl group) decrease the basicity of amines.

(a) Both Assertion and Reason are true and Reason is the correct explanation of Assertion.

(b) Both Assertion and Reason are true and Reason is not the correct explanation of Assertion.

(c) Assertion is true but Reason is false.

(d) Both Assertion and Reason are false.

23. Predict the product,　　　　　　　　**[CBSE AIPMT 2009]**

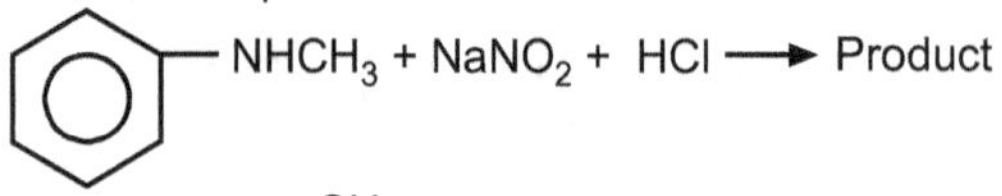

$$\text{(Ph)}-NHCH_3 + NaNO_2 + HCl \longrightarrow \text{Product}$$

(a) 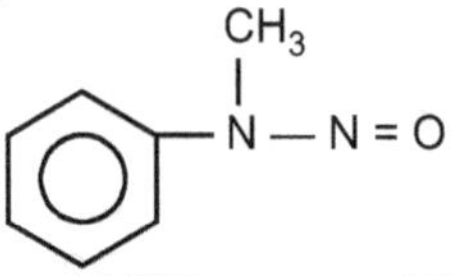 Ph–N(CH$_3$)–N=O

(b) 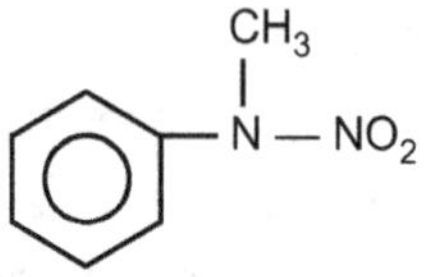 Ph–N(CH$_3$)–NO$_2$

(c) 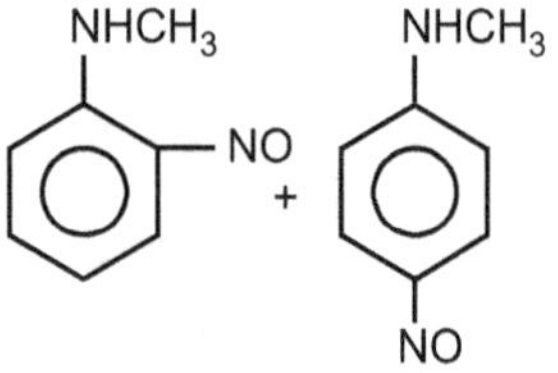 o-NHCH$_3$–C$_6$H$_4$–NO + p-NHCH$_3$–C$_6$H$_4$–NO

(d) 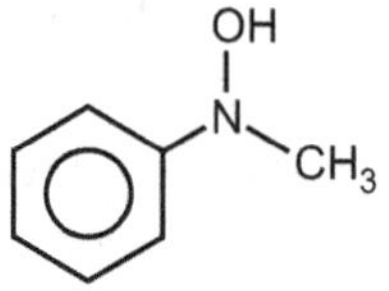 Ph–N(OH)–CH$_3$

24. Aromatic nitriles (ArCN) are not prepared by reaction ......　　**[A.I.I.M.S. 2004]**

(a) ArX + KCN

(b) ArN_2^+ + CuCN

(c) ArCONH$_2$ + P$_2$O$_5$

(d) ArCONH$_2$ + SOCl$_2$

25. Identify the product in the following sequence

$$3, 4, 5\text{-Tribromoaniline} \xrightarrow[\text{(2) } H_3PO_2]{\text{(1) Diazotisation}} ?$$

　　　　　　　　[Kerala Engg. 2005]

(a) 3, 4, 5-Tribromobenzene

(b) 1, 2, 3-Tribromobenzene

(c) 2, 4, 6-Tribromobenzene

(d) 3, 4, 5-Tribromonitrobenzene

(e) 3, 4, 5-Tribromophenol

26. Isopropyl amine is ......　　　　　　　　**[MHT-CET 2009]**

(a) primary amine　　(b) secondary amine　(c) tertiary amine　(d) quaternary amine

27. The reaction of nitrous acid with aliphatic primary amine in cold gives ...... **[Manipal 2009]**

(a) a diazonium salt　　(b) an alcohol　　　(c) a nitrite　　　(d) aldehyde

28. The reaction of primary amine with chloroform and ethanolic solution KOH is called ......

　　　　　　　　[AFMC 2008]

(a) Hofmann's reaction

(b) Reimer-Tiemann's reaction

(c) Carbylamine reaction

(d) Kolbe's reaction

29. During acetylation of amines, what is replaced by acetyl group?　　**[CPMT 2008]**

(a) Hydrogen atom attached to nitrogen atom.

(b) One or more hydrogen atoms attached to carbon atom.

(c) One or more hydrogen atoms attached to nitrogen atom.

(d) Hydrogen atoms attached to either carbon atom or nitrogen atom.

30. Which one of the following on reduction with lithium aluminium hydride yields a secondary amine?　　　　　　　　**[CBSE AIPMT 2007]**

(a) Nitroethane

(b) Methylisocyanide

(c) Acetamide

(d) Methyl cyanide

31. Aniline react with acetaldehyde to form ......　　　　　　　　**[AFMC 2007]**

(a) Schiff's base　　(b) Carbylamine　　(c) Immine　　(d) None of these

32. An aliphatic amine on treatment with alcoholic carbon disulphide and mercuric chloride forms ethyl isothiocyanate, the reaction is known as ...... **[AIIMS 2007]**

(a) Hofmann's reaction

(b) Hofmann's rearrangement

(c) Hofmann's mustard oil reaction

(d) Hofmann's bromamide degradation reaction

33. **Assertion :** Amines are more basic than esters and ethers.

Reason : Nitrogen is less electronegative than oxygen. It is in better position to accommodate the positive charge on the proton. **[AIIMS 2007]**

(a) Both Assertion and Reason are true and Reason is the correct explanation of Assertion.

(b) Both Assertion and Reason are true and Reason is not the correct explanation of Assertion.

(c) Assertion is true but Reason is false.

(d) Both Assertion and Reason are false

34. A nitrogen containing organic compound gave an oily liquid on heating with bromine and potassium hydroxide solution. On shaking the product with acetic anhydride, an antipyretic drug was obtained. The reaction indicate that the starting compound is ......

[Karnataka, 2004]

(a) Aniline   (b) Benzamide   (c) Acetamide   (d) Nitrobenzene

35. Isopropyl amine with excess of acetyl chloride will give ...... **[MHT-CET 2007]**

(a) $(CH_3CO)_2N - CH - (CH_3)_2$

(b) $(CH_3)_2CH - \overset{\overset{\displaystyle H}{\displaystyle |}}{N} - COCH_2$

(c) $(CH_3)_2CHN(COCH_3)_2$

(d) $CH_3CH_2CH_2 - \underset{\underset{\displaystyle H}{\displaystyle |}}{N} - COCH_3$

36. Which of the following is more basic than aniline? **[CBSE AIPMT 2006]**

(a) Diphenylamine   (b) Triphenylamine   (c) p-nitroaniline   (d) Benzylamine

37. **Assertion :** Anilinium chloride is more acidic than ammonium chloride. **[AIIMS 2006]**

Reason : Anilinium ion is resonance stabilised.

(a) Both Assertion and Reason are true and Reason is the correct explanation of Assertion.

(b) Both Assertion and Reason are true and Reason is not the correct explanation of Assertion.

(c) Assertion is true but Reason is false.

(d) Both Assertion and Reason are false

38. The basicity of aniline is less than that of cyclohexylamine. This is due to ...... **[KCET 2006]**

(a) +R effect of $-NH_2$ group   (b) $-I$ effect of $-NH_2$ group

(c) $-R$ effect of $-NH_2$ group   (d) hyperconjugation effect

39. Pyridine is less basic than triethylamine because ...... **[AIIMS 2005]**

(a) pyridine has aromatic character   (b) nitrogen in pyridine is sp^2 hybridised

(c) pyridine is a cyclic system

(d) in pyridine lone pair of nitrogen is delocalized.

40. Methyl amine reacts with methyl iodide. For completion of reaction, how many moles of methyl iodide are required?   **[MHT-CET 2005]**
(a) 1   (b) 2   (c) 3   (d) 4

41. Melting points are normally highest for ......   **[AIIMS 2004]**
(a) tertiary amides   (b) secondary amides
(c) primary amides   (d) amines

42. Ethyl isocyanide on hydrolysis in acidic medium generates ......   **[A.I.E.E. 2003]**
(a) Ethylamine salt and methanoic acid   (b) Propanoic acid and ammonium salt
(c) Ethanoic acid and ammonium salt   (d) Methylamine salt and ethanoic acid

43. Which of the following compounds does not undergo Schotten-Baumann reaction?
(a) Phenol   (b) Primary amine   **[Manipal 2004]**
(c) Secondary amine   (d) Tertiary amine

44. Complete the following reaction $RNH_2 + H_2SO_4 \rightarrow$

(a) $[RNH_3]^+HSO_4^-$ (b) $[RNH_3]_2^+SO_4^{2-}$ (c) $RNH_2H_2SO_4$ (d) No reaction

45. The final product C obtained in this reaction is ......

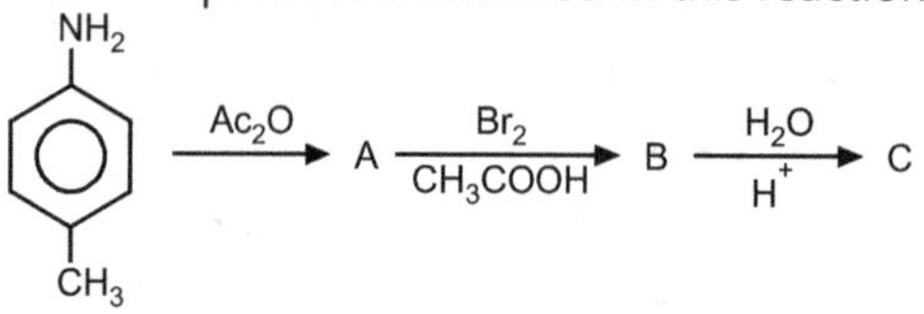

$$\text{(p-toluidine)} \xrightarrow[CH_3COOH]{Ac_2O} A \xrightarrow{Br_2} B \xrightarrow[H^+]{H_2O} C$$

[CBSE AIPMT 2003]

(a) [structure: 2-amino-5-bromo-toluene, NH_2, Br, CH_3]

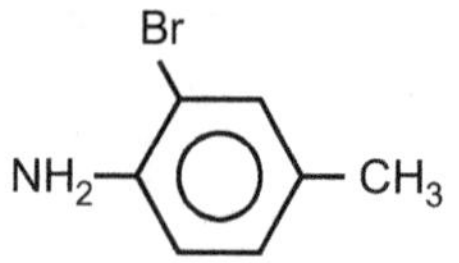

(b) [structure: $NHCOCH_3$, Br, CH_3]

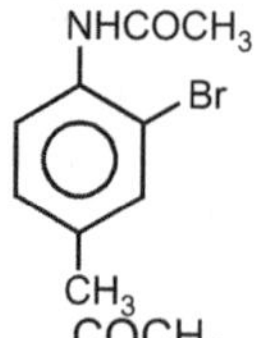

(c) [structure: NH_2, CH_3, $COCH_3$]

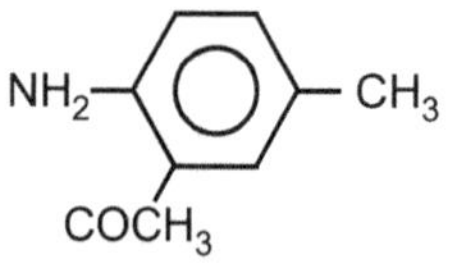

(d) [structure: $COCH_3$, Br, CH_3]

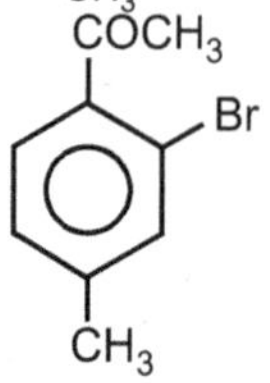

46. Among the following, the weakest base is ......   **[AIIMS 2004]**
(a) $C_6H_5CH_2NH_2$ (b) $C_6H_5CH_2NCH_3$ (c) $O_2NCH_2NH_2$ (d) CH_3NHCHO

47. What is the product obtained in the following reaction?   **[CBSE AIPMT 2011]**

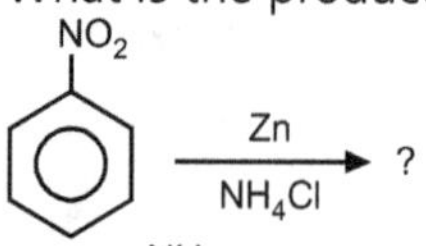

$$\text{(nitrobenzene)} \xrightarrow[NH_4Cl]{Zn} \text{?}$$

(a) [structure: benzene ring with NH_4]

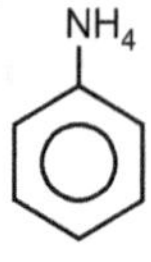

(b) [structure: benzene ring with $NHOH$]

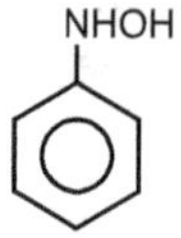

(c) [structure: azobenzene, $N=N$ diphenyl]

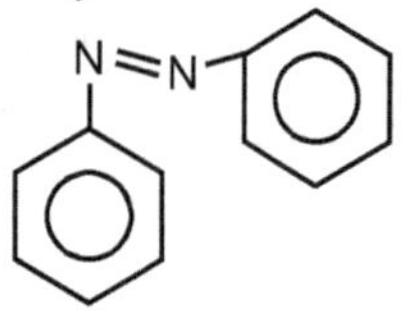

(d) [structure: azoxybenzene, $N=N^+$ with O^-]

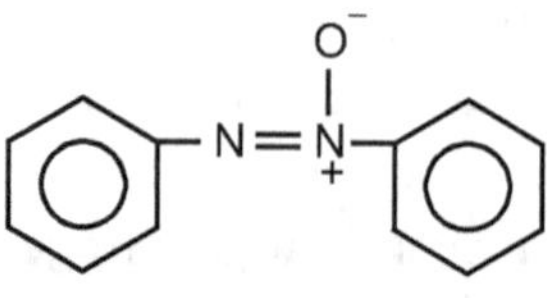

48. The product 'Y' in the following reaction sequence is ......　　　　　　**[AIIMS 2009]**

$$\text{Benzene} \xrightarrow[\text{H}_2\text{SO}_4]{\text{HNO}_3} X \xrightarrow{\text{LiAlH}_4} Y$$

(a) (structure: benzene ring with NH_2)

(b) (structure: benzene ring with $NHOH$)

(c) (structure: $C_6H_5-N=N-C_6H_5$)

(d) (structure: $C_6H_5-NH-NH-C_6H_5$)

49. Which of the following reaction can produce aniline as a main product ?
(a) $C_6H_5NO_2 + Zn/KOH$
(b) $C_6H_5NO_2 + Zn/NH_4Cl$
(c) $C_6H_5NO_2 + LiAlH_4$
(d) $C_6H_5NO_2 + Zn/HCl$

50. Assertion : Nitrobenzene is used as a solvent in Friedel-Craft's reaction.
Reason : Fusion of nitrobenzene with solid KOH gives a low yield of a mixture of o- and p-nitrophenols.
(a) Both Assertion and Reason are true and Reason is the correct explanation of Assertion.
(b) Both Assertion and Reason are true and Reason is not the correct explanation of Assertion.
(c) Assertion is true but Reason is false.
(d) Both Assertion and Reason are false

51. Assertion : $p - O_2N - C_6H_5COCH_3$ is prepared by Friedel-Craft's acylation of nitrobenzene.
Reason : Nitrobenzene easily undergoes electrophilic substitution reaction.
(a) Both Assertion and Reason are true and Reason is the correct explanation of Assertion.
(b) Both Assertion and Reason are true and Reason is not the correct explanation of Assertion.
(c) Assertion is true but Reason is false.
(d) Both Assertion and Reason are false

52. Nitrobenzene gives N-phenylhydroxylamine by ......　　　　　　**[A.I.I.M.S. 2003]**
(a) Sn/HCl　　　　(b) $H_2/Pd-C$　　　　(c) $Zn/NaOH$　　　　(d) Zn/NH_4Cl

53. Benzene diazonium chloride on treatment with hypo phosphorus acid and water in presence of Cu^+ catalyst produce ......　　　　　　**[MHT-CET 2006]**
(a) benzene　　　　(b) toluene　　　　(c) aniline　　　　(d) chlorobenzene

54. Aniline on treatment with sodium nitrite and HCl at 0°C to produce which of the following compound?　　　　　　**[AFMC 2003]**
(a) Diazonium salt
(b) Phenol and N_2
(c) Hydrozo compound
(d) Nitroaniline

55. In the reaction $CH_3CH_2COONH_4 \xrightarrow{P_2O_5} A \xrightarrow{H^+/H_2O} B$　　　　　　**[C.B.S.E. 2000]**
A and B are ......
(a) $CH_3CH_2CONH_2$; CH_3CH_2COOH
(b) CH_3CH_2COONH; CH_3CH_2COOH
(c) CH_3CH_2CN; CH_3CH_2COOH
(d) CH_3CH_2CN; CH_3CH_2COOH

56. Nitrobenzene undergoes reduction with Zn/Alcoholic KOH to form a compound A. The number of sigma and pi bonds in A respectively are ...... **[D.P.M.T. 2001]**
    (a) 17, 6   (b) 27, 6   (c) 27, 8   (d) 17, 8

57. Which of the following will not give primary amine? **[M.P.P.M.T. 2001]**

    (a) $CH_3CONH_2 \xrightarrow{Br_2/KOH}$ (b) $CH_3CN \xrightarrow{LiAlH_4}$

    (c) $CH_2NC \xrightarrow{LiAlH_4}$ (d) $CH_2CONH_2 \xrightarrow{LiAlH_4}$

58. m-Bromoaniline can be prepared by ...... **[G.G.S.I.P.U. 2009]**

    (a) $C_6H_6 \xrightarrow[H_2SO_4]{HNO_3} A \xrightarrow[FeBr_3]{Br_2} B \xrightarrow{SnHCl} C$ (b) $C_6H_6 \xrightarrow[FeBr_3]{Br_2} A \xrightarrow[H_2SO_4]{HNO_3} B \xrightarrow{Pt/H_2} C$

    (c) $C_6H_5NH_2 \xrightarrow{SOCl_2} A \xrightarrow{NH_3} B \xrightarrow[NaOH]{Br_3} C$ (d) $C_6H_5NH_2 \xrightarrow[Cu_2Br_2]{NaNO_2, HCl} A \xrightarrow{NaNH_2} C$

59. Primary, secondary and tertiary amines can be distinguished by ...... **[Manipal 2001]**
    (a) Schiff's test   (b) Fehling's test   (c) Tollen's test   (d) Hinsberg test

60. C_3H_9N cannot represent ...... **[B.H.U. 2000]**
    (a) 1° amine   (b) 2° amine   (c) 3° amine   (d) quaternary salt

61. Compound A on reduction gives B which on further reaction with $CHCl_3$ and alcoholic KOH gives compound C which on further hydrolysis gives aniline. The compound A is ...... **[C.B.S.E. 2000]**
    (a) Nitrobenzene   (b) Methylamine   (c) Nitromethane   (d) Nitrosobenzene

62. Which among the following compounds will give offensive smell when heated with chloroform and alcoholic potash ? **[Kerala C.E.T. 2001]**
    (a) $C_2H_5NH_2$ (b) $(C_2H_5)_2NH$ (c) $(CH_3)_3N$ (d) CH_3CN
    (e) $C_6H_5CONH_2$

63. In the reaction $CH_3CN + 2H \xrightarrow[ether]{Sn, Cl} X \xrightarrow[\Delta]{H_2O} Y$. Y is ......
    (a) Dimethylamine   (b) Ethanamine   (c) Acetaldehyde   (d) Acetone

64. Nitrobenzene gives azoxybenzene and hydrazo-benzene when reduced ......
    (a) In acidic medium   (b) In neutral medium
    (c) Electrolytically   (d) In alkaline medium

65. An organic compound (X) having molecular formula C_2H_3N on reduction gave another compound Y. Upon treatment with nitrous acid Y gave ethyl alcohol KOH, it formed an offensive smelling compound (Z). The compound Z is ......
    (a) $CH_3CH_2NH_2$ (b) CH_3CH_2NC (c) $CH_3N \equiv N$ (d) CH_3CH_2OH

66. $CH_3CH_2Cl \xrightarrow{NaCN} X \xrightarrow{Ni/H_2} Y \xrightarrow[anhydride]{Acetic} Z$. Z in the above reaction sequence is ......
    (a) $CH_3CH_2CH_2NHCOCH_3$ (b) $CH_3CH_2CH_2NH_2$ **[C.B.S.E. P.M.T. 2002]**
    (c) $CH_3CH_2CH_2CONHCH_3$ (d) $CH_3CH_2CH_2CONHCOCH_3$

67. The reaction of aniline with benzaldehyde is ...... **[Karnataka C.E.T. 2002]**
    (a) Substitution   (b) Addition   (c) Condensation   (d) Polymerisation

68. On heating benzylamine with chloroform and ethanolic KOH, product obtained is ...... **[A.I.E.E.E. 2002]**
    (a) Benzyl alcohol   (b) Benzaldehyde   (c) Benzonitrile   (d) Benzyl isocyanide

ANSWER KEY

1. (c)	2. (b)	3. (c)	4. (c)	5. (c)	6. (a)	7. (d)	8. (b)
9. (c)	10. (c)	11. (d)	12. (c)	13. (d)	14. (a)	15. (a)	16. (b)
17. (b)	18. (a)	19. (b)	20. (b)	21. (b)	22. (c)	23. (c)	24. (b)
25. (c)	26. (d)	27. (b)	28. (b)	29. (b)	30. (b)	31. (a)	32. (c)
33. (d)	34. (a)	35. (b)	36. (c)	37. (c)	38. (b)	39. (a)	40. (a)
41. (a)	42. (b)	43. (a)	44. (b)	45. (b)	46. (b)	47. (d)	48. (b)
49. (c)	50. (d)	51. (b)	52. (b)	53. (b)	54. (c)	55. (b)	56. (b)
57. (c)	58. (a)	59. (a)	60. (a)	61. (c)	62. (c)	63. (a)	64. (d)
65. (b)	66. (c)	67. (a)	68. (d)	69. (c)	70. (b)	71. (c)	72. (a)
73. (b)	74. (d)	75. (b)	76. (b)	77. (b)	78. (c)	79. (a)	80. (a)
81. (c)	82. (c)	83. (a)	84. (a)	85. (a)	86. (c)	87. (a)	88. (d)
89. (c)	90. (c)	91. (c)	92. (d)	93. (d)	94. (b)	95. (c)	96. (d)
97. (a)	98. (c)	99. (b)	100. (d)	101. (c)	102. (d)	103. (d)	

Previous Year's Questions

1. (a)	2. (c)	3. (c)	4. (d)	5. (c)	6. (a)	7. (a)	8. (a)
9. (b)	10. (c)	11. (a)	12. (a)	13. (b)	14. (d)	15. (d)	16. (a)
17. (a)	18. (c)	19. (d)	20. (b)	21. (a)	22. (a)	23. (a)	24. (a)
25. (b)	26. (a)	27. (b)	28. (c)	29. (c)	30. (b)	31. (a)	32. (c)
33. (a)	34. (b)	35. (c)	36. (d)	37. (c)	38. (a)	39. (d)	40. (c)
41. (d)	42. (a)	43. (d)	44. (a)	45. (a)	46. (c)	47. (b)	48. (c)
49. (d)	50. (b)	51. (d)	52. (c)	53. (a)	54. (a)	55. (a)	56. (b)
57. (c)	58. (a)	59. (d)	60. (d)	61. (a)	62. (a)	63. (c)	64. (d)
65. (b)	66. (a)	67. (c)	68. (d)				

❑❑❑

BIOMOLECULES

1. Fructose is an example of ......

   (a) Ribose   (b) Aldose   (c) Ketose   (d) Disaccharide

2. Glycosidic linkage is ......

   (a) Ester linkage   (b) Ether linkage   (c) Amido linkage   (d) Peptide linkage

3. Carbohydrate present in fruits is in the form of ......

   (a) Glucose   (b) Ribose   (c) Maltose   (d) Fructose

4. Which of the following is not a monosaccharide?

   (a) Sucrose   (b) Glucose   (c) Fructose   (d) Ribose

5. Which of the following is a non-reducing sugar?

   (a) Glucose   (b) Sucrose   (c) Maltose   (d) Fructose

6. A monosaccharide is given D configuration if ......

   (a) – OH group attached to carbon next to – CH_2OH group is on right side

   (b) – OH group attached to carbon next to – CH_2OH group is on left side

   (c) – OH group attached to any carbon is on right side

   (d) – OH group attached to any carbon is on left side

7. Anomers are ......

   (a) Enantiomers   (b) Diastereomers   (c) Epimers   (d) Stereoisomers

8. Anomers are those which have ......

   (a) Same configuration at C–1   (b) Different configuration at C–1

   (c) Same configuration at C–2   (d) Different configuration at C–2

9. Epimers are those which have ......

   (a) Different configuration at C–1   (b) Different configuration at C–2

   (c) Same configuration at C–1   (d) Same configuraton at C–2

10. The sweetest sugar is ......

    (a) Sucrose   (b) Glucose   (c) Fructose   (d) Lactose

11. The change in specific rotation of either form of glucose in aqueous solution is ......

    (a) Optical rotation   (b) Mutarotation

    (c) Dextrorotation   (d) Laevorotation

12. Straight chain structure of glucose cannot give ......

    (a) Schiff's test   (b) Tollen's test

    (c) Fehling's test   (d) Benedict's test

13. Ring structure of the glucose is an example of ......

    (a) Dehydration   (b) Acetal formation

    (c) Hemiacetal formation   (d) Dehydrogenation

14. Cyclic structure of glucose resembles heterocyclic compound ......

(a) Furan　　　　　(b) Pyran　　　　　(c) Pyrrole　　(d) Pyridine

15. The optical rotation of equilibrium mixture when any of the α or β anomer is dissolved in water is ......

(a) 110°　　　　　(b) 52.5°　　　　　(c) 19.2°　　(d) 25.2°

16. Fructose has which functional group ......

(a) Ketone　　　　　(b) Aldehyde　　　　　(c) Carboxylic　　(d) Ester

17. Fructose has ketonic group but it still reduces Tollen's and Fehling solution when dissolved in water. What is the reason for this ?

(a) Tautomerism　　　　　　　　　(b) Bruyn-van Ekenstein

(c) Resonance　　　　　　　　　(d) Isomerisation

18. Fructose has cyclic amidine which resembles heterocyclic compound ......

(a) Pyran　　　　　(b) Pyrrole　　　　　(c) Furan　　(d) Pyrene

19. Hemiacetal ring in glucose resembles ......

(a) Lactone　　　　(b) Lactam　　　　(c) Glycerides　　(d) Ether

20. Lactose on hydrolysis gives ......

(a) Glucose and fructose　　　　　(b) Glucose and galactose

(c) Glucose only　　　　　　　　(d) Fructose only

21. Sucrose is ......

(a) α, β - glycosidic linkage　　　　(b) α-glycosidic linkage

(c) β-glycosidic linkage　　　　　　(d) None of these

22. Maltose on hydrolysis gives 2 moles of glucose which are joined through ......

(a) α, β-glycosidic linkage　　　　(b) β-glycosidic linkage

(c) α-glycosidic linkage　　　　　(d) α-α-glycosidic linkage

23. In lactose, glucose and galactose are linked through ......

(a) β-glycosidic　　　　　　　(b) β, β-glycosidic linkage

(c) α, β-glycosidic　　　　　(d) α-glycosidic linkage

24. Invert sugar is ......

(a) Sucrose　　　　　　　　　　(b) Glucose

(c) Fructose

(d) Equimolar mixture of glucose and fructose

25. Starch is a polymer of ......

(a) Glucose　　　　(b) α-glucose　　　　(c) β-glucose　　(d) α and β glucose

26. Amylose is a constituent of ....

(a) Starch　　　　(b) Cellulose　　　　(c) Pectin　　(d) Glycogen

27. Amylose is a ......

(a) Branched polymer of α-glucose　　　　(b) Branched polymer of β-glucose

(c) Linear polymer of α-glucose　　　　(d) Linear polymer of β-glucose

28. Amylopectin is a ......
    (a) Linear polymer of α-glucose
    (b) Branched polymer of α-glucose
    (c) Linear polymer of β-glucose
    (d) Branched polymer of β-glucose

29. Cellulose is a ......
    (a) Linear polymer of α-glucose
    (b) Linear polymer of β-glucose
    (c) Branched polymer of α-glucose
    (d) Branched polymer of β-glucose

30. Animal starch is ......
    (a) Glycogen
    (b) Starch
    (c) Amylopectin
    (d) Amylose

31. Cellulose acetate is used as ......
    (a) Explosive
    (b) Plastics and wrapping films
    (c) Cosmetics
    (d) Plastic coats and films

32. Rayon is a ......
    (a) Processed cellulose
    (b) Cellulose
    (c) Natural polymer
    (d) None of these

33. Grazing animals can digest cellulose because they have ......
    (a) Enzyme
    (b) Bacteria
    (c) Enzyme and bacteria
    (d) HCl acid in stomach

34. Disaccharides are formed by the condensation of two monosaccharides linked to each other by a ......
    (a) Peptide bond
    (b) Ester linkage
    (c) Glycosidic linkage
    (d) Hydrogen bond

35. Sucrose is converted into glucose and fructose by the enzyme ......
    (a) Zymase
    (b) Invertase
    (c) Diastase
    (d) Maltose

36. Starch is hydrolysed to maltose by an enzyme ......
    (a) Diastase
    (b) Lipase
    (c) Zymase
    (d) Invertase

37. The polysaccharides that are present in fruit components are ......
    (a) Cellulose
    (b) Gums
    (c) Ribose
    (d) Pectin

38. The general molecular formula of polysaccharides is ......
    (a) $C_6H_{10}O_5$
    (b) $(C_6H_{10}O_5)_n$
    (c) $(C_6H_{12}O_6)_n$
    (d) $C_{16}H_{44}O_{22}$

39. Proteins are polymers of ......
    (a) Amines
    (b) Carboxylic acid
    (c) Amino acid
    (d) None of these

40. Simplest amino acid is ......
    (a) Alanine
    (b) Glycine
    (c) Valine
    (d) Serine

41. Amino acids required for protein synthesis are ......
    (a) 20
    (b) 10
    (c) 26
    (d) 30

42. The amino acids which are synthesized by the body are ......
    (a) Essential amino acids
    (b) Non-essential amino acids
    (c) Both (a) and (b)
    (d) None of these

43. Protein is a ......
    (a) Addition polymer
    (b) Condensation polymer
    (c) Both addition and condensation polymer
    (d) Resin

44. Protein is better known as ......
    (a) Polypeptide
    (b) Polyamide
    (c) Polyamino acid
    (d) Poly amines

45. Myoglobin protein's function is ......
    (a) Involved in muscle movement
    (b) Stores oxygen in muscles until it is needed for energy production
    (c) Catalyses biochemical reaction
    (d) Blood transport

46. The difference in the chemical and biological properties of various proteins are due to difference in their ......
    (a) Secondary structure
    (b) Tertiary structure
    (c) Primary structure
    (d) Quaternary structure

47. Haemoglobin, the molecule in blood that carries oxygen consists of .... amino acids.
    (a) 574   (b) 570   (c) 475   (d) 754

48. The change in one specific amino acid sequence in a defective haemoglobin causes ......
    (a) Diabetes
    (b) Sickle-cell anaemia
    (c) Pernicious anaemia
    (d) Anaemia

49. Insulin has .... arranged in ....
    (a) 51 amino acids, 2 polypeptide chains
    (b) 21 amino acids, 1 polypeptide chain
    (c) 30 amino acids, 1 polypeptide chain
    (d) 51 amino acids, 1 polypeptide chain

50. Secondary structures are ......
    (a) Fibrous
    (b) Globular
    (c) β-pleated
    (d) α-helical and β-pleated

51. Which one of the following is not a protein ?
    (a) Wool   (b) Nail   (c) Hair   (d) DNA

52. The main structural feature of proteins is ......
    (a) Peptide linkage
    (b) Ether linkage
    (c) Ester linkage
    (d) Glycosidic linkage

53. Antibodies are ......
    (a) Carbohydrates   (b) Proteins   (c) Lipids   (d) Enzymes

54. Enzymes are ......
    (a) Fatty acids   (b) Vitamins   (c) Proteins   (d) None of these

55. Insulin, a hormone, chemically is ......
    (a) A fat   (b) A steroid   (c) A protein   (d) A carbohydrate

56. Disruption of the native nature of a protein is called ......

(a) Hydrolysis   (b) Emulsification   (c) Denaturation (d) Condensation

57. The non-amino acid group of proteins is called ......

(a) Prosthetic group   (b) Co-factor

(c) Non-prosthetic group   (d) None of these

58. The amino acids which must be present in our food are called ......

(a) Non-essential amino acids   (b) Essential amino acids

(c) Proteins   (d) None of these

59. The proteins which are associated with lipids are ......

(a) Fat   (b) Oil   (c) Lipoprotein   (d) Oil protein

60. The pH value at which an amino acid does not migrate in the presence of electric field is ...

(a) Acidic   (b) Neutral   (c) Basic   (d) Isoelectric point

61. Amino acid which contains sulphur is known as ......

(a) Alanine   (b) Cystine   (c) Valine   (d) Leucine

62. The protein present in nails is ......

(a) Tryptophan   (b) Myoglobin   (c) Lipoprotein   (d) Collagen

63. Scientist who suggested α-helical or β-pleated structure of protein was ......

(a) Linus Pauling   (b) Fisher   (c) Haworth   (d) Newmann

64. The stretching property of hair is due to ......

(a) β-pleated   (b) α-Keratin   (c) β-Keratin   (d) Globular

65. Different polypeptide chains in α-pleated structure are held by ......

(a) Van der Waal's force   (b) Dipole-dipole forces of attraction

(c) Intermolecular hydrogen bonding   (d) Electrostatic forces of attraction

66. Globular protein is an example of ......

(a) Primary protein   (b) Secondary structure

(c) Tertiary structure   (d) Quaternary structure

67. The loss of biological activity of a protein is due to the disruption of ......

(a) Tertiary structure   (b) Secondary structure

(c) Primary structure   (d) Quaternary structure

68. Nucleoproteins are responsible for ......

(a) Regulation of hormone   (b) Genetic information

(c) Synthesis of hormone thyroxine   (d) None of these

69. Enzymes are examples of ......

(a) Carbohydrates   (b) Nucleic acids   (c) Proteins   (d) Lipids

70. The protein present in milk is ......

(a) Casein   (b) Fibrinogen   (c) Albumin   (d) Lactogen

71. Enzymes are produced by ......
 (a) Non-living cells   (b) Living cells
 (c) Tissues   (d) Both living and non-living cells

72. Enzymes are examples of ......
 (a) Globular protein   (b) Fibrous protein
 (c) Globular and fibrous both   (d) β-pleated protein

73. The non-protein part associated with some of the enzymes is called prosthetic group. If prosthetic group is a metal then it is called ......
 (a) Co-enzyme   (b) Co-factor
 (c) Metallic factor   (d) Non-metallic factor

74. Co-enzyme when prosthetic group is ......
 (a) A metal   (b) A non-metal
 (c) Small organic molecule   (d) Amphoteric molecule

75. The enzyme which maintains the carbon dioxide levels in the body fluids and tissues is ......
 (a) Carbonic acid   (b) Carbonic anhydrase
 (c) Sulphonic anhydrase   (d) Anhydride

76. Some mentally challenged children suffer from phenyl ketonurea disease, which is due to the deficiency of the enzyme ......
 (a) Phenyl ketone urea   (b) Phenylalanine hydroxylase
 (c) Phenyl hydroxylase   (d) Alanine hydroxylase

77. If the temperature is increased above 37°C, the enzyme activity ......
 (a) Decreases   (b) Increases
 (c) Remains unchanged   (d) None of these

78. Nucleic acids are ......
 (a) Polynucleotides   (b) Polynucleosides   (c) Nucleotides   (d) Nucleosides

79. Nuclecotide is a combination of ......
 (a) Sugar-base-phosphate   (b) Sugar-base
 (c) Base-sugar-phosphate   (d) Sugar-phosphate

80. Adenine and guanine ......
 (a) Both are pyrimidine bases
 (b) Both are purines
 (c) Adenine is purine and guanine is pyrimidine
 (d) Adenine is pyrimidine and guanine is purine

81. Uracil, thymine, cytosine are ......
 (a) Pyrimidine bases
 (b) Purine bases
 (c) Uracil in pyrimidine and thymine, cytosine at purine
 (d) Thymine and cytosine are pyrimidine bases and uracil purine

82. Sugar present in RNA is ......

    (a) Arabinose   (b) Ribose   (c) Dextrose   (d) Glucose

83. Base is attached to sugar at ...... carbon.

    (a) C–5   (b) C–4   (c) C–3   (d) C–1

84. The linkage present in nucleic acid is ......

    (a) Ester linkage   (b) Ether linkage

    (c) Phosphodiester linkage   (d) Diester linkage

85. In deoxyribose sugar, oxygen is missing at ......

    (a) C–1   (b) C–2   (c) C–3   (d) C–4

86. In DNA, the base absent is ......

    (a) Thymine   (b) Uracil   (c) Cytosine   (d) Adenine

87. Which one of the following is not present in RNA ?

    (a) Uracil   (b) Thymine   (c) Ribose   (d) Phosphate

88. Which is responsible for hereditary character ?

    (a) DNA   (b) RNA   (c) Protein   (d) Hormones

89. Mutation in DNA occurs due to changes in the sequence of ......

    (a) Ribose units   (b) Nitrogenous base   (c) Phosphates   (d) None of these

90. In nucleotide of nucleic acids, the sequence is ......

    (a) Phosphate-base-sugar   (b) Sugar-base-phosphate

    (c) Base-sugar-phosphate   (d) Base-phosphate-sugar

91. The RNA which take part in the synthesis of proteins is/are

    (a) m-RNA   (b) r-RNA   (c) t-RNA   (d) All these RNAs

92. If the sequence of bases in one strand of DNA is TAGCCGAT, then the sequence of bases in its complimentary strand is ......

    (a) ATCGGCTA   (b) UACGGCTA   (c) ATCGGCAU   (d) AACGGCUA

93. If the sequence of bases in templates of DNA is GACGAAT, the sequence of bases on m-RNA during transcription is ......

    (a) CTGCTTA   (b) CUGCUUA   (c) UUACGUC   (d) CTGCUUA

94. Which one of the following is vitamin ?

    (a) Glucose   (b) Ribose   (c) Cholesterol   (d) Riboflavin

95. Which of the following is not a vitamin ?

    (a) Ergocalciferol   (b) Thiamine   (c) Riboflavin   (d) Vasopressin

96. Which vitamin deficiency causes haemorrhage ?

    (a) E   (b) D   (c) K   (d) C

97. Which of the following vitamins is not water soluble ?

    (a) B complex   (b) A   (c) K   (d) D

98. Vitamin B-6 deficiency causes ......

    (a) Pernicious anaemia   (b) Beriberi   (c) Pellagra   (d) Scurvy

99. The vitamins soluble in oil and fat are ......

(a) A, B complex   (b) A, D   (c) E, C   (d) K, B complex

100. Ascorbic acid is a chemical name of ......

(a) Vitamin B-12   (b) Vitamin E   (c) Vitamin C   (d) Vitamin A

101. Deficiency of vitamin D causes ......

(a) Night blindness   (b) Rickets   (c) Xerosis   (d) Loss of appetite

102. The minimum number of carbon atoms that should be present in a carbohydrate is ____

(a) 2   (b) 3   (c) 4   (d) 6

103. Which of the following carbohydrates is a monosaccharide?

(a) Sucrose   (b) Galactose   (c) Maltose   (d) Lactose

104. The number of chiral centres in the open-chair structure of fructose is ____

(a) 2   (b) 3   (c) 4   (d) 5

105. The most commonly encountered disaccharide has the molecular formula ____

(a) $C_{10}H_{18}O_9$ (b) $C_{11}H_{20}O_{10}$ (c) $C_{14}H_{26}O_{13}$ (d) $C_{12}H_{22}O_{11}$

106. Starch is a polymer of ____

(a) Fructose   (b) Glucose   (c) Lactose   (d) Ribose

107. Transporting oxygen is an important function of blood. Partial pressure of oxygen is highest and lowest, respectively in ____

(a) Muscles and heart   (b) Lungs and muscles

(c) Heart and lungs   (d) Muscles and lungs

108. The portions of proteins having the highest mobility are ____

(a) α-helical   (b) β-pleated sheets

(c) Peptide bonds   (d) Side chains outward

109. Proteins can be detected by ____

(a) Beilstein's test   (b) Benedict's test   (c) Biuret test   (d) Molisch test

110. The metal ion which forms a violet-coloured complex with a protein in the presence of an alkali is ____

(a) Cu^{2+} (b) Zn^{2+} (c) Co^{3+} (d) Fe^{3+}

111. The functional unit that is repeated in a protein molecule is ____

(a) An ester linkage   (b) An ether linkage

(c) A peptide linkage   (d) A secondary amine linkage

112. The monomeric unit, composed of a nitrogenous base, a sugar and a phosphate, that is present in nucleic acid is called a ____

(a) Nucleoside   (b) Phosphatide

(c) Base phosphate   (d) Nucleotide

113. Which of the following is not a pyrimidine base?

(a) Uracil   (b) Thymine   (c) Cytosine   (d) Guanine

114. Which of the following bases is present in RNA but usually not in DNA?

(a) Thymine   (b) Guanine   (c) Adenine   (d) Uracil

115. Which of the following units is not present in an RNA molecule?

(a) D-ribose   (b) Phosphate   (c) Thymine   (d) Uracil

116. Which of the following is not present in nucleotides?

(a) Guanine   (b) Cytosine   (c) Adenine   (d) Thyroxine

117. To which class of compounds do enzymes usually belong?

(a) Carbohydrate   (b) Protein   (c) Lipid   (d) Nucleic acid

118. The enzyme that hydrolyses fats into fatty acids and glycerol is ____

(a) Amylase   (b) Maltase   (c) Lipase   (d) Pepsin

119. The vitamin which is fat-soluble and is an antioxidant is ____

(a) Vitamin E   (b) Vitamin C   (c) Vitamin D   (d) Vitamin A

120. Deficiency of vitamin E causes ____

(a) Sterility   (b) Rickets   (c) Beriberi   (d) Scurvy

121. Vitamin B1 is also known as ____

(a) Ascorbic acid   (b) Riboflavin   (c) Pyridoxine   (d) Thiamine

122. Insulin is a ......

(a) Hormone   (b) Antibiotic   (c) Antiseptic   (d) Vitamin

123. A biological catalyst is essentially ____

(a) An amino acid   (b) An enzyme

(c) A nitrogen molecule   (d) A carbohydrate

124. Complete hydrolysis of cellulose gives ......

(a) D-ribose   (b) D-glucose   (c) L-glucose   (d) D-fructose

125. Milk sugar is ____

(a) Sucrose   (b) Lactose   (c) Maltose   (d) Glucose

126. Which of the following contains the element, cobalt?

(a) Vitamin C   (b) Vitamin B_{12} (c) Chlorophyll   (d) Haemoglobin

127. The reagent which forms crystalline osazone derivative when treated with glucose is ......

(a) Fehling solution   (b) Phenyl hydrazine

(c) Benedict solution   (d) Hydroxyl amine

128. Which of the following compounds is responsible for the transmission of heredity characters ?

(a) RNA   (b) DNA   (c) Glucose   (d) Haemoglobin

129. Calorific value is in order ......

(a) Fats >> carbohydrates >> proteins   (b) Carbohydrates >> fats >> proteins

(c) Proteins >> carbohydrates >> fats   (d) Fats >> proteins >> carbohydrates

130. Nucleic acids are polymers of ......

(a) Nucleosides   (b) Bases   (c) Sugars   (d) Nucleotides

131. Saliva contains ......

(a) Amylases or ptyalins

(b) Trypsin

(c) Bile fluid

(d) Vitamins

132. Which has maximum protein content ?

(a) Ground nut　　　(b) Cow milk　　　(c) Egg　　　(d) Wheat

133. The bond that determines the secondary structure of a protein is ......

(a) Co-ordinate bond

(b) Covalent bond

(c) Hydrogen bond

(d) Ionic bond

134. Which of the following is a molecular disease ?

(a) Allergy

(b) Cancer

(c) German measles

(d) Sickel cell anemia

135. Which of the following vitamins is present in cod liver oil ?

(a) A　　　(b) B_{12}　　　(c) B_1　　　(d) C

136. Enzymes are ......

(a) Proteins　　　(b) Minerals　　　(c) Oils　　　(d) Fatty acids

137. Glucose gives silver mirror test with Tollen's reagent, it shows the presence of ......

(a) An acidic group

(b) An alcoholic group

(c) A ketonic group

(d) An aldehydic group

138. The change in optical rotation at the time of freshly prepared solution of sugar (with enzymes) is known as ......

(a) Specific rotation

(b) Inversion

(c) Rotatory motion

(d) Mutarotation

139. On heating glucose with Fehling's solution, we get a precipitate whose colour is ......

(a) Yellow　　　(b) Red　　　(c) Black　　　(d) White

140. Which of the following statements about ribose is incorrect ?

(a) It is polyhydroxy compound

(b) It is an aldehyde sugar

(c) It has six carbon atoms

(d) It exhibits optical activity

141. Which of the following food stuffs contains nitrogen ?

(a) Carbohydrates

(b) Fats

(c) Proteins

(d) None of these

142. The monomeric units of starch is/are ......

(a) glucose

(b) fructose

(c) glucose and fructose

(d) mannose

143. In nucleic acids, the sequence is ......

(a) Phosphate-Base-Sugar

(b) Sugar-Base-Phosphate

(c) Base-Sugar-Phosphate

(d) Base-Phosphate-Sugar

144. The pH of the blood does not appreciably change by small addition of an acid or a base because blood ......
(a) contains serum protein which acts as a buffer
(b) contains iron as a part of the molecule
(c) can be easily coagulated
(d) is a body fluid

145. The enzyme which convert glucose into ethyl alcohol is
(a) Diastase   (b) Invertase   (c) Maltase   (d) Zymase

146. Protein is a polymer of
(a) Glucose   (b) Terephthalic acid   (c) Amino acid   (d) Glycol.

147. Which amino acid has no asymmetric carbon atom ?
(a) Histidine   (b) Glycine   (c) α-Alanine   (d) Threonine

148. Molish's test is answered by ......
(a) All carbohydrates   (b) Sucrose   (c) Fructose   (d) Glucose

149. In DNA the complementary bases are
(a) adenine and thymine; guanine and cytosine
(b) uracil and adenine; cytosine and guanine
(c) adenine and guanine ; thymine and cytosine
(d) adenine and thymine; guanine and uracil

150. Which carbohydrate is an essential constituent of plant cells ?
(a) Starch   (b) Cellulose   (c) Sucrose   (d) Vitamins

151. The enzyme pepsin hydrolyses ......
(a) proteins to amino acids   (b) fats to fatty acids
(c) glucose to ethyl alcohol   (d) polysaccharides to monosaccharides

152. On heating with conc. HNO_3, proteins give yellow colour. This test is called ......
(a) Oxidizing test   (b) Xanthoproteic test
(c) Hoppe's test   (d) Acid base test

153. Which of the following compounds can be detected by Molisch's test ?
(a) Nitro compounds   (b) Sugars
(c) Amines   (d) Primary alcohols

154. Which of the following is correct about hydrogen bonding in DNA?
(a) A – T, G – C   (b) A – G, T – C   (c) G – T, A – C   (d) A – A, T – T

155. Which of the following amino acids is basic in nature?
(a) Valine   (b) Tyrosine   (c) Arginine   (d) Leucine

156. Glycogen is ......
(a) a polymer of β-D-glucose units
(b) a structural polysaccharide
(c) structurally very much similar to amylopectin
(d) structurally similar to amylopectin but extensively branched

157. Glucose on oxidation with bromine water yields gluconic acid. This reaction confirms the presence of ......

(a) six carbon atoms linked in straight chain (b) secondary alcoholic group in glucose

(c) aldehyde group in glucose (d) primary alcoholic group in glucose

158. The presence or absence of hydroxyl group on which carbon atom of sugar differentiates RNA and DNA?

(a) 1st (b) 2nd (c) 3rd (d) 4th

159. An example of a sulphur containing amino acid is ...... **[KARNATAKA CET 2005]**

(a) Lysine (b) Serine (c) Cysteine (d) Tyrosine

160. A nucleoside on hydrolysis gives ......

(a) an aldopentose and a heterocyclic base.

(b) an aldopentose and orthophosphoric acid.

(c) a heterocyclic base and orthophosphoric acid.

(d) an aldopentose, a heterocyclic base and orthophosphoric acid.

161. Which of the following polymer is stored in the liver of animals as animal starch?

(a) Amylose (b) Cellulose (c) Amylopectin (d) Glycogen

162. The number of amino acids and number of peptide bonds in a linear tetrapeptide (made of different amino acids) are respectively ......

(a) 4 and 4 (b) 5 and 5 (c) 5 and 4 (d) 4 and 3

163. The statement that is NOT correct is ......

(a) Aldose or ketose sugars in alkaline medium do not isomerise.

(b) Carbohydrates are optically active.

(c) Penta acetate of glucose does not react with hydroxylamine.

(d) Lactose has glycosidic linkage between C_4 of glucose and C_1 of galactose unit.

164. Which of the following gives positive Fehling's solution test?

(a) Surcose (b) Glucose (c) Fats (d) Protein

165. Thiol group is present in ...... **[JEE MAIN 2016]**

(a) Cystine (b) Cysteine (c) Methionine (d) Cytosine

166. Biuret test is not given by ...... **[AIEEE 2010]**

(a) proteins (b) carbohydrates (c) polypeptides (d) urea

167. Which one of the following is an essential amino acid ? **[KARNATAKA CET 2015]**

(a) Tyrosine (b) Cysteine (c) Isoleucine (d) Serine

168. Cheilosis and digestive disorders are due to the deficiency of ... **[KARNATAKA CET 2015]**

(a) Thiamine (b) Ascorbic acid (c) Riboflavin (d) Pyridoxine

169. Adenosine is an example of ...... **[KARNATAKA CET 2015]**

(a) Nucleotide (b) Purine base

(c) Pyrimidine base (d) Nucleoside

170. Which of the following carbohydrates are branched polymers of glucose?

    (i) Amylose   (ii) Amylopectin   (iii) Cellulose   (iv) Glycogen

    (a) (ii) and (iv)   (b) (i) and (ii)   (c) (iii) and (iv)   (d) (ii) and (iv)

171. Which of the vitamins given below is water soluble?	**[JEE MAIN 2015]**

    (a) Vitamin K   (b) Vitamin C   (c) Vitamin D   (d) Vitamin E

172. Which one of the following bases is not present in DNA?

    (a) Adenine   (b) Cytosine   (c) Thymine   (d) Quinoline

173. Which of the following proteins is globular?

    (a) Collagen   (b) Albumin   (c) Myosin   (d) Fibroin

174. The reason for double helical structure of DNA is the operation of ......

    (a) dipole-dipole interaction   (b) hydrogen bonding

    (c) electrostatic attraction   (d) van der Waals' forces

175. Which one of the following acids is a vitamin?

    (a) Ascorbic acid   (b) Aspartic acid   (c) Adipic acid   (d) Saccharic acid

176. During conversion of glucose into glucose cyanohydrin, what functional group/atom of glucose is replaced?

    (a) hydrogen   (b) aldehydic group

    (c) primary alcoholic group   (d) secondary alcoholic group

177. Insulin production and its action on human body are responsible for the level of diabetes. This compound belongs to which of the following categories?

    (a) A co-enzyme   (b) A hormone   (c) An enzyme   (d) An antibiotic

178. In DNA, the consecutive deoxynucleotides are connected via

    (a) phosphodiester linkage   (b) phospho monoester linkage

    (c) phosphotriester linkage   (d) amide linkage

179. Which of the following is not present in a nucleotide?

    (a) cytosine   (b) guanine   (c) adenine   (d) tyrosine

PREVIOUS YEAR'S QUESTIONS

1. Which one given below is a non-reducing sugar?	**[NEET 2016]**

    (a) Lactose   (b) Glucose   (c) Sucrose   (d) Maltose

2. In a protein molecule, various amino acids are linked together by	**[NEET 2016]**

    (a) Peptide bond   (b) Dative bond

    (c) α-glycosidic bond   (d) β-glycosidic bond

3. Which one of the following compounds shows the presence of intramolecular hydrogen bond?	**[NEET 2016]**

    (a) H_2O_2 (b) HCN

    (c) Cellulose   (d) Concentrated acetic acid

4. The central dogma of molecular genetics states that the genetic information flows from ...	**[NEET 2016]**

    (a) Amino acids $\rightarrow$ Proteins $\rightarrow$ DNA   (b) DNA $\rightarrow$ Carbohydrates $\rightarrow$ Proteins

    (c) DNA $\rightarrow$ RNA $\rightarrow$ Proteins   (d) DNA $\rightarrow$ RNA $\rightarrow$ Carbohydrates

5. The correct statement regarding RNA and DNA respectively is ......   **[NEET 2016]**

(a) The sugar component in RNA is ribose and the sugar component in DNA is 2-deoxyribose

(b) The sugar component in RNA is arabinose and the sugar component in DNA is ribose

(c) The sugar component in RNA is 2'-deoxyribose and the sugar component in DNA is arabinose

(d) The sugar component in RNA is arabinose and the sugar component in DNA is 2'-deoxyribose

6. The function of "Sodium pump" is biological process operating in each and every cell of all animals. Which of the following biologically important ions is also a constituent of this pump?   **[AIPMT 2015]**

(a) Mg^{2+} (b) K^+ (c) Fe^{2+} (d) Ca^{2+}

7. D(+) glucose reacts with hydroxyl amine and yields an oxime. The structure of the oxime would be ......   **[AIPMT 2014]**

(a) $CH_2OH(CHOH)_4CH=NOH$ (b) $CH_2OH(CHOH)_4CHONOH$

(c) $CH_2NOH(CHOH)_4CHO$ (d) $CH_2OH(CHOH)_4CH_2NOH$

8. Which of the following hormones is produced under the condition of stress which stimulates glycogenolysis in the liver of human beings?   **[NEET 2013]**

(a) Adrenaline   (b) Estradiol   (c) Thyroxin   (d) Insulin

9. Which one of the following statements is incorrect about enzyme catalysis?

[CBSE AIPMT 2012]

(a) Enzymes are mostly proteinous in nature

(b) Enzyme action is specific

(c) Enzymes are denaturated by ultraviolet rays and at high temperature

(d) Enzymes are least reactive at optimum temperature

10. Iodine value is related to ......   **[AFMC 2012]**

(a) fats and oils   (b) alcohols   (c) ethers   (d) esters

11. The conversion of maltose to glucose is possible by the enzyme ......

[M.G.I.M.S. Wardha 2010]

(a) zymase   (b) lactase   (c) maltase   (d) diastase

12. A codon has a sequence of A and specifies particulars that are to be incorporated into C. What are A, B, C?   **[Manipal 2012]**

	A	B	C
(a)	3 bases	amino acid	carbohydrate
(b)	3 acids	carbohydrate	protein
(c)	3 bases	protein	amino acid
(d)	3 bases	amino acid	protein

13. Which one of the following statements is not true regarding (+) Lactose?

    (a) (+) lactose, $C_{12}H_{22}O_{11}$ contains 8 OH groups.   **[CBSE AIPMT 2011]**

    (b) On hydrolysis (+) lactose gives equal amount of D(+) glucose and a molecule of D(+) galactose.

    (c) (+) lactose is a β-glycoside formed by the union of molecule of D(+) glucose and a molecule of D(+) galactose.

    (d) (+) lactose is reducing sugar and does not exhibit mutarotation.

14. α-maltose consists of ......   **[KCET 2011]**

    (a) one α-D-glucopyranose unit and one β-D-glucopyranose unit with 1-2 glycosidic linkage.

    (b) two α-D-glucopyranose units with 1-2 glycosidic linkage.

    (c) two β-D-glucopyranose units with 1-4 glycosidic linkage.

    (d) two α-D-glucopyranose units with 1-4 glycosidic linkage.

15. How can you say that glucose is cyclic compound?   **[Guj. CET 2011]**

    (a) Glucose undergoes Tollen's reaction

    (b) Glucose reacts with phenyl hydrazine

    (c) Glucose fails to react with sodium hydrogen sulphite

    (d) Glucose reacts with nitric acid

16. Which of the following does not exhibit phenomenon of mutarotation?

    (a) (–) fructose   (b) sucrose   **[CBSE AIPMT 2010]**

    (c) (+) lactose   (d) (+) maltose

17. Glucose on reaction with Fehling solution gives ......   **[MHT CET 2010]**

    (a) cupric oxide   (b) cuprous oxide   (c) saccharic acid   (d) both (a) and (b)

18. The change in optical rotation of freshly prepared solution of cane sugar with time is known as ......   **[Manipal 2010]**

    (a) mutarotation   (b) inversion   (c) specific rotation   (d) rotator motion

19. Glucose + Tollen's reagent → Silver mirror.

    The above process shows ......   **[VMMC 2010]**

    (a) presence of –COOH group   (b) presence of keto group

    (c) presence of –CHO group   (d) presence of $-CONH_2$ group

20. Stachyose is a ......   **[MHT CET 2010]**

    (a) monosaccharide   (b) disaccharide   (c) trisaccharide   (d) tetrasaccharide

21. When sucrose is heated with conc. HNO_3, the product formed is ......   **[Manipal 2010]**

    (a) sucrose nitrate   (b) adipic acid   (c) oxalic acid   (d) citric acid

22. Glucose forms many derivatives. The derivative which will help to prove the furanose structure is ......   **[Manipal 2010]**

    (a) osazone   (b) benzoyl   (c) acetyl   (d) isopropylidene

23. The beta and alpha glucose have different specific rotations. When either is dissolved in water, their rotation changes until the same fixed value results. This is called   **[AIIMS 2008]**
(a) epimerization　　(b) racemisation　　(c) anomerisation　(d) mutarotation

24. The reagent which forms crystalline osazone derivative when reacted with glucose is ......
(a) Fehling solution　　　　　　　(b) phenyl hydrazine　　**[AFMC 2007]**
(c) Benedict solution　　　　　　(d) hydroxyl amine

25. The number of chiral carbon atoms in $\beta - D(+)-$ glucose is ......　　**[Manipal 2007]**
(a) five　　　　(b) six　　　　(c) three　　　(d) four

26. Glucose gives silver mirror with ammoanical silver nitrate because it has ......
(a) aldehyde　　　　　　　　　(b) ester　　　　**[MHT CET 2007]**
(c) ketone　　　　　　　　　(d) alcoholic silver nitrate

27. Methyl -α-D- glucoside and methyl-β-D- glucoside are ......　　**[AIIMS 2006]**
(a) epimers　　　　　　　　(b) anomers
(c) enantiomers　　　　　　(d) conformational diastereomers

28. Glucose reacts with excess of phenyl hydrazine and forms ......　　**[CPMT 2006]**
(a) glucosazone　　　　　　(b) glucose phenyl hydrazine
(c) glucose-oxime　　　　　(d) sorbitol

29. **Assertion :** Maltose is a reducing sugar which gives two moles of D-glucose on hydrolysis.
Reason : Maltose has a 1, 4 - β-glycosidic linkage
(a) Both Assertion and Reason are true and Reason is the correct explanation of Assertion.
(b) Both Assertion and Reason are true but Reason is not the correct explanation of Assertion.
(c) Assertion is true but Reason is false.
(d) Both Assertion and Reason are false.

30. **Assertion :** Sucrose is a non-reducing sugar.　　　　　　**[AIIMS 2004]**
Reason : It has glycosidic linkage.
(a) Both Assertion and Reason are true and Reason is the correct explanation of Assertion.
(b) Both Assertion and Reason are true but Reason is not the correct explanation of Assertion.
(c) Assertion is true but Reason is false.
(d) Both Assertion and Reason are false.

31. Glucose on oxidation gives the acid containing 3C – chiral atoms equal to......
(a) 2　　　　　　(b) 3　　　　　　(c) 4　　　　　(d) 5　　**[MHT CET 2004]**

32. Glycolysis is ......　　　　　　　　　　　　　**[CBSE AIPMT 2003]**
(a) oxidation of glucose to pyruvate　　(b) conversion of glucose to haem
(c) oxidation of glucose to glutamate　(d) conversion of pyruvate to citrate

33. **Assertion :** Glycosides are hydrolysed in acidic conditions.　　　**[AIIMS 2003]**
Reason : Glycosides are acetals.
(a) Both Assertion and Reason are true and Reason is the correct explanation of Assertion.
(b) Both Assertion and Reason are true but Reason is not the correct explanation of Assertion.
(c) Assertion is true but Reason is false.
(d) Both Assertion and Reason are false.

34. Glucose is readily hydrolysed by zymase into ......   **[Manipal 2003]**
   (a) amino acids   (b) alcohol
   (c) aromatic acids   (d) dicarboxylic acid

35. Assertion : Disruption of the natural structure of a protein is called denaturation.

   [AIIMS 2008]

   Reason : The change in colour and appearance of egg during cooking is due to denaturation.
   (a) Both Assertion and Reason are true and Reason is the correct explanation of Assertion.
   (b) Both Assertion and Reason are true but Reason is not the correct explanation of Assertion.
   (c) Assertion is true but Reason is false.
   (d) Both Assertion and Reason are false.

36. The compound which gives a positive ninhydrin test and a negative Benedict's solution test is ....   **[MHT CET 2008]**
   (a) a monosaccharide   (b) a disaccharide
   (c) a lipid   (d) a protein

37. Protein can be denatured by ......   **[AIIMS 2007]**
   (a) carbon dioxide   (b) carbon monoxide
   (c) heat   (d) oxygen

38. The linkage present in proteins and peptides is ......   **[CPMT 2007]**
   (a) ester   (b) amide   (c) phosphodiester   (d) glycosidic

39. The helical structure of protein is stabilised by ......   **[Manipal 2007]**
   (a) dipeptide bonds   (b) hydrogen bonds
   (c) ether bonds   (d) peptide bonds

40. During the process of digestion, the proteins present in food materials are hydrolysed to amino acids. The two enzymes A and B, involved in the process. Proteins → Polypeptides → Amino acids are respectively ......   **[AIPMT 2006]**
   (a) amylase and maltase   (b) diastase and lipase
   (c) pepsin and trypsin   (d) invertase and zymase

41. Thiamine is......   **[AIIMS 2006]**
   (a) 5-methyluracil   (b) 4-methyluracil
   (c) 3-methyluracil   (d) 1-methyluracil

42. Lysine is least soluble in water in the pH range ......   **[AIIMS 2006]**
   (a) 3-4   (b) 5-6   (c) 6-7   (d) 8-9

43. On treatment with ninhydrin, which of the following give blue colour?   **[CPMT 2006]**
   (a) Proteins   (b) Peptides   (c) α-amino acids   (d) All of these

44. The reaction of enzymes in living system is to ......   **[Manipal 2006]**
   (a) supply energy to tissues   (b) create immunity
   (c) circulate oxygen
   (d) enhance the rate of biochemical reaction.

45. The enzyme which hydrolyses triglycerides to acids and glycerol is called ......

(a) maltase   (b) lipase   **[CBSE AIPMT 2004]**

(c) zymase   (d) pepsin

46. **Assertion :** Carboxypeptidase is an exopeptidase.   **[AIIMS 2004]**

Reason : It cleaves the N-terminal bond.

(a) Both Assertion and Reason are true and Reason is the correct explanation of Assertion.

(b) Both Assertion and Reason are true and Reason is not the correct explanation of Assertion.

(c) Assertion is true but Reason is false.

(d) Both Assertion and Reason are false.

47. Among the following the achiral amino acid is ......   **[AIIMS 2003]**

(a) 2-ethylalanine   (b) 2-methylglycine

(c) 2-hydroxymethyl serine   (d) tryptophan

48. **Assertion :** Activity of an enzyme is pH dependent.   **[AIIMS 2003]**

Reason : Change in pH affects the solubility of enzyme in water.

(a) Both Assertion and Reason are true and Reason is the correct explanation of Assertion.

(b) Both Assertion and Reason are true and Reason is not the correct explanation of Assertion.

(c) Assertion is true but Reason is false.

(d) Both Assertion and Reason are false.

49. The segment of DNA which acts as the instrument - manual for the synthesis of proteins is

......   **[CBSE AIPMT 2009]**

(a) nucleotides   (b) ribose   (c) gene   (d) nucleoside

50. The base found only in the nucleotides of RNA is ......   **[AFMC 2009]**

(a) adenine   (b) uracil   (c) guanine   (d) cytosine

51. In DNA, the complementary bases are ......   **[CBSE AIPMT 2008]**

(a) adenine and thymine; guanine and cytosine.

(b) adenine and thymine; guanine and uracil.

(c) adenine and guanine, thymine and cytosine.

(d) uracil and adenine; cytosine and guanine.

52. A sequence of how many nucleotides in messenger RNA makes a codon for amino acid?

[Manipal 2007]

(a) Three   (b) Four   (c) One   (d) Two

53. Which one of the following is not present in RNA?   **[Manipal 2006]**

(a) Uracil   (b) Thymine   (c) Ribose   (d) Phosphate

54. The cell membranes are mainly composed for ......   **[CBSE AIPMT 2005]**

(a) carbohydrates   (b) proteins   (c) phospholipids   (d) fats

55. Which one of the following statement is true for protein synthesis (translation)?

[AIIMS 2005]

(a) Amino acids are directly recognized by m-RNA.

(b) The third base of the codon is less specific

(c) Only one codon codes for an amino acid.

(d) Every t-RNA molecule has more than one amino acid attachment.

56. The nucleic acid base having two possible binding sites is ...... **[AIIMS 2004]**

(a) thymine　　(b) cytosine　　(c) guanine　　(d) adenine

57. Which of the following has magnesium ? **[C.B.S.E.P.M.T. 2000]**

(a) Carbonic anhydrase (b) Haemocyanin　　(c) Chlorophyll　(d) Vitamin B_{12}

58. In polysaccharides, the linkage connecting monosaccharide is called ... **[M.P.P.M.T. 2000]**

(a) glycoside linkage　　　　　　　　(b) nucleoside linkage

(c) glycogen linkage　　　　　　　　(d) peptide linkage

59. The structural feature which distinguishes proline from other natural α-amino acids is ......

[Kerala P.M.T. 2000]

(a) It is optically inactive　　　　　　(b) It contains two amino groups

(c) It is a dicarboxylic acid　　　　　(d) It is a secondary amine

60. An organic compound with the formula $C_6H_{12}O_6$ forms a yellow crystalline solid with phenylhydrazine and gives a mixture of sorbitol and mannitol when reduced with sodium. Which among the following could be the compound ? **[J.I.P.M.E.R. 2001]**

(a) Fructose　　(b) Glucose　　(c) Mannose　　(d) Sucrose

61. Which substance chars when heated with conc. H_2SO_4 ? **[A.I.I.M.S. 2001]**

(a) Carbohydrate　　(b) Hydrocarbon　　(c) Fat　　(d) Protein

62. A nucleotide consists of ...... **[Manipal P.M.T. 2001]**

(a) Carbon sugar　　　　　　　　(b) Nitrogen containing base

(c) Phosphoric acid　　　　　　　(d) All of these

63. What is correct statement ? **[C.B.S.E.P.M.T. 2001]**

(a) Starch is a polymer of α-glucose

(b) Amylose is a component of cellulose

(c) Proteins are compounds of only one type of amino acid

(d) In cyclic structure of fructose, there are four carbons and one oxygen atom

64. Vitamin B_{12} contains ...... **[C.B.S.E Med. 2003]**

(a) Fe (II)　　(b) Co (II)　　(c) Zn (II)　　(d) Ca (II)

65. When glucose is heated with Fehling's solution then a red precipitate is obtained. This red precipitate is .... **[A.M.U. 2010]**

(a) Fe_2O_3　　(b) Sb_2O_3　　(c) Cu_2O　　(d) CuO

66. Which is a peptide linkage ? **[M.H.T.-C.E.T. 2012]**

(a) $-CO-NH$　　(b) $-\overset{\displaystyle |}{\underset{\displaystyle |}{C}}-N=O$　　(c) $-CO-NH_2$　　(d) $-CO-O-NH_4$

67. The one which is not present in DNA is ...... **[C.M.C. Vellore 2011]**

(a) uracil　　(b) thiamine　　(c) adenine　　(d) guanine

68. Identify the correct statement regarding enzymes ...... **[A.I.I.M.S. 2008]**

(a) Enzymes are specific biological catalysts that normally function at very high temperatures (T = 100 K)

(b) Enzymes are specific biological catalysts that possess well-defined active sites

(c) Enzymes are specific biological catalysts that cannot be poisoned

(d) Enzymes are normally heterogeneous catalysts that are very specific in their action

ANSWER KEY

1. (c)	2. (b)	3. (a)	4. (a)	5. (b)	6. (a)	7. (b)	8. (b)
9. (b)	10. (c)	11. (b)	12. (a)	13. (c)	14. (b)	15. (b)	16. (a)
17. (b)	18. (c)	19. (a)	20. (b)	21. (a)	22. (c)	23. (a)	24. (d)
25. (b)	26. (a)	27. (c)	28. (b)	29. (b)	30. (a)	31. (b)	32. (a)
33. (c)	34. (c)	35. (b)	36. (a)	37. (d)	38. (b)	39. (c)	40. (b)
41. (a)	42. (b)	43. (b)	44. (a)	45. (b)	46. (c)	47. (a)	48. (b)
49. (a)	50. (d)	51. (d)	52. (a)	53. (b)	54. (c)	55. (b)	56. (c)
57. (a)	58. (b)	59. (c)	60. (d)	61. (b)	62. (c)	63. (a)	64. (b)
65. (c)	66. (c)	67. (d)	68. (b)	69. (c)	70. (a)	71. (c)	72. (a)
73. (b)	74. (c)	75. (b)	76. (b)	77. (b)	78. (a)	79. (c)	80. (b)
81. (a)	82. (b)	83. (d)	84. (c)	85. (b)	86. (b)	87. (b)	88. (a)
89. (b)	90. (c)	91. (d)	92. (a)	93. (b)	94. (d)	95. (d)	96. (c)
97. (d)	98. (a)	99. (b)	100. (c)	101. (b)	102. (b)	103. (b)	104. (b)
105. (d)	106. (b)	107. (b)	108. (d)	109. (c)	110. (a)	111. (c)	112. (d)
113. (d)	114. (d)	115. (c)	116. (d)	117. (b)	118. (c)	119. (a)	120. (a)
121. (d)	122. (a)	123. (b)	124. (b)	125. (b)	126. (b)	127. (b)	128. (b)
129. (a)	130. (d)	131. (a)	132. (a)	133. (c)	134. (d)	135. (a)	136. (a)
137. (d)	138. (d)	139. (b)	140. (c)	141. (c)	142. (a)	143. (c)	144. (a)
145. (d)	146. (c)	147. (b)	148. (a)	149. (a)	150. (b)	151. (a)	152. (b)
153. (b)	154. (a)	155. (c)	156. (d)	157. (c)	158. (b)	159. (c)	160. (a)
161. (d)	162. (c)	163. (a)	164. (b)	165. (b)	166. (b)	167. (c)	168. (c)
169. (d)	170. (a)	171. (b)	172. (d)	173. (b)	174. (b)	175. (a)	176. (b)
177. (b)	178. (a)	179. (d)					

Previous Year's Questions

1. (c)	2. (a)	3. (c)	4. (c)	5. (a)	6. (b)	7. (a)	8. (a)
9. (d)	10. (a)	11. (c)	12. (d)	13. (d)	14. (d)	15. (c)	16. (b)
17. (b)	18. (a)	19. (c)	20. (d)	21. (c)	22. (d)	23. (d)	24. (b)
25. (a)	26. (a)	27. (b)	28. (a)	29. (a)	30. (a)	31. (b)	32. (a)
33. (d)	34. (b)	35. (b)	36. (d)	37. (c)	38. (b)	39. (b)	40. (c)
41. (a)	42. (c)	43. (d)	44. (d)	45. (b)	46. (c)	47. (c)	48. (b)
49. (c)	50. (b)	51. (a)	52. (a)	53. (b)	54. (c)	55. (b)	56. (d)
57. (c)	58. (a)	59. (b)	60. (a)	61. (a)	62. (d)	63. (a)	64. (a)
65. (c)	66. (a)	67. (a)	68. (b)				

POLYMERS

1. Which one of the following is a co-polymer?
   (a) PMMA   (b) PAN   (c) SBR   (d) Nylon-6
2. Addition polymerisation proceeds by ......
   (a) Free radical   (b) Anionic
   (c) Cationic   (d) Anionic and cationic both
3. Dacron is an example of ......
   (a) Addition polymer   (b) Homopolymer
   (c) Polyester   (d) Polyamide polymer
4. Monomers used for the synthesis of Dacron are ......
   (a) Adipic acid and hexamethylene diamine   (b) Phthalic acid and ethylene glycol
   (c) Terephthalic acid and ethylene glycol   (d) Terephthalic acid and ethanol
5. Nylon-66 means ......
   (a) Monomers having 66 carbon
   (b) Both monomers having 6 carbon atoms each
   (c) Molecular weight of Nylon is 66
   (d) Polymer made by 6 monomers of each type
6. Terylene is a polymer of ......
   (a) Phenol and fomaldehyde   (b) Adipic acid and hexamethylene diamine.
   (c) Terephthalic acid and ethylene glycol   (d) Acrylonitrile
7. Buna-S is obtained by addition polymerisation of Butadiene and ......
   (a) Adipic acid   (b) Styrene   (c) Polythene   (d) Acrylonitrile
8. Caprolactum is obtained from ......
   (a) Benzene   (b) Caproic acid   (c) Cyclohexane   (d) Aniline
9. Melamine is a ...... polymer.
   (a) Elastomer   (b) Thermoplastic   (c) Fibre   (d) Thermosetting
10. The monomer of PVC is ......

   (a) $CH_2 = CH - CH_3$ (b) $-(- CH_2 -CH-)_n$ with Cl on the CH
   (c) $CH_2 = CH$ with Cl   (d) $CH_3CH_2CH_2Cl$

11. Teflon is ......
    (a) Tetrafluoro ethene   (b) Polytetrafluoro ethylene
    (c) Chlorotrifluoro ethene   (d) Poly chloro trifluoro ethene
12. Nylon-6 is a polymer of ......
    (a) Caproic acid   (b) Caprolactum
    (c) Adipic acid   (d) Hexamethylene diamine

13. Bakelite is a condensation copolymer of ......
(a) Phenol and formaldehyde
(b) Formaldehyde and ethylene glycol
(c) Formaldehyde and melamine
(d) Phenol and acetaldehyde

14. Novolac is linear polymer of ......
(a) formaldehyde and caprolactum
(b) caproic acid and glycol
(c) phenol and formaldehyde
(d) phenol and nitroalkane

15. Which one of the following is a natural polymer?
(a) Nylon-6
(b) Nylon-66
(c) Polythene
(d) Cellulose

16. Which one of the following is a synthetic polymer?
(a) Neoprene
(b) Silk
(c) Starch
(d) Wool

17. The monomer of neoprene is ......
(a) Neopentane
(b) Chloroprene
(c) Isoprene
(d) Nitroprin

18. Which one of the following is a homopolymer?
(a) Bakelite
(b) Novolac
(c) Glyptal
(d) PAN

19. Natural rubber is ......
(a) Isoprene
(b) Polyisoprene
(c) Polychloroprene
(d) Polynitroprin

20. Vulcanization is the heating of ......
(a) Thermoplastic with sulphur
(b) Thermoacting with sulphur
(c) Natural rubber with sulphur
(d) Nylon fibre with sulphur

21. The monomer of PMMA is ......
(a) Methyl acrylate
(b) Methyl methacrylate
(c) Met methylacrylate
(d) Acrylic acid

22. Plexi glass is a commercial name of ......
(a) Poly ethyl acrylate
(b) Poly methyl acrylate
(c) Poly methyl methacrylate
(d) Polyacrylonitrile

23. Which one of the following is an elastomer ?
(a) Natural rubber
(b) Silk
(c) Teflon
(d) Bakelite

24. Some of the common plasticizers are ......
(a) n-butyl phthalate
(b) Cresyl phthalate
(c) Dialkyl phthalate
(d) All of these

25. Which one of the following is a thermosetting polymer?
(a) Bakelite
(b) Polythene
(c) Teflon
(d) Rubber

26. Which one of the following is a polyamide ?
(a) Dacron
(b) Nylon-66
(c) Orlon
(d) Teflon

27. Nylon 6, 10 is obtained by polymerisation of hexamethylene diamine and ......
(a) Adipic acid
(b) Sebacic acid
(c) Succinic acid
(d) None of these

28. Ziegler-Natta catalyst used in polymerisation of ethylene is ......
(a) Trialkyl aluminium and $TiCl_4$
(b) PhRhCl
(c) Triethyl aluminium and $TiCl_4$
(d) None of these

29. Rayon is a ......
(a) Natural polymer
(b) Synthetic polymer
(c) Semi-synthetic
(d) Bipolymer

30. PHBV is a ......
(a) Biodegradable polymer
(b) Natural polymer
(c) Mammal polymer
(d) Semi-synthetic polymer

31. The S in Buna-S refers to ......
(a) Sulphur
(b) Styrene
(c) Sodium
(d) None of these

32. The N in Buna-N refers to ......
(a) Nitrile
(b) Sodium
(c) Nitrogen
(d) Natural

33. Among following which one has weakest forces of attraction?
(a) Fibre
(b) Thermoplastic
(c) Elastomer
(d) Thermosetting

34. Alkyl resin is ......
(a) Glyptal
(b) Melamine formaldehyde resin
(c) Phenol formaldehyde resin
(d) Melmac

35. Which one of the following has an ester linkage ?
(a) Nylon-66
(b) Nylon-6
(c) Nylon-6, 10
(d) Dacron

36. For natural polymer, the polydispersity index is ......
(a) 0
(b) 1
(c) 100
(d) 1000

37. Number average molecular mass is ......

(a) $\bar{M}_n = \dfrac{\Sigma N_x M_x}{\Sigma N x^2}$
(b) $\bar{M}_n = \dfrac{\Sigma N_x M_x^2}{\Sigma N x^2}$
(c) $\bar{M}_n = \dfrac{\Sigma N_x M_x}{\Sigma N_x}$
(d) $\bar{M}_n = \dfrac{\Sigma N_x}{\Sigma N_x \cdot M_x}$

38. Weight average molecular mass is ......

(a) $\bar{M}_w = \dfrac{\Sigma N_x M_x^2}{\Sigma N_x M_x}$
(b) $\bar{M}_w = \dfrac{\Sigma N_x M_x}{\Sigma N_x M_x^2}$
(c) $\bar{M}_w = \dfrac{\Sigma N_x M_x^2}{M_x^2}$
(d) $\bar{M}_w = \dfrac{\Sigma N_x M_x^2}{N_x^2}$

39. PDI for synthetic polymer is ......
(a) -1
(b) 0
(c) > 1
(d) < 1

40. Repeat unit in PVC is ......
(a) $CH_2 = CH - Cl$

(b) $(- CH_2 - CH-)_n$
$\quad\quad\quad\quad\ |$
$\quad\quad\quad\quad Cl$

(c) $CH_2 - CH-$
$\quad\quad\ |$
$\quad\quad Cl$

(d) $CH_2 = CH - Cl -$

41. Hair wigs are made from a copolymer of vinyl chloride and acrylonitrile and is called ......
(a) PVC
(b) Dynel
(c) Polyacrylonitrile
(d) Glyptal

42. Which one of the following is the correct representation of initial reaction in the preparation of Bakelite ?
(a) Aromatic electrophilic substitution
(b) Aromatic nucleophilic substitution
(c) Free radical reaction
(d) Aldol reaction

43. Among the following polymers, strong hydrogen bonds are formed in ......
(a) Elastomers
(b) Fibres
(c) Thermoplastic
(d) Thermosetting

44. Which one of the following is used to make non-stick cookware ?
(a) PVC
(b) Polyalyrene
(c) Polythylene
(d) Polytetrafluoro ethene

45. Teflon, Stayroform and Neoprene are all ......
(a) Co-polymers (b) Condensation (c) Homopolymers (d) Monomers

46. Interparticle forces present in Nylon-66 are ......
(a) Vander Waals (b) Hydrogen bonding
(c) Dipole-dipole interaction (d) Dipole-induced dipole

47. Soft drink bottles and baby feeders are generally made of ......
(a) Polyester (b) Polystyrene (c) Polyurethane (d) Polyamides

48. Polymer used in optical lenses is ......
(a) PMMA (b) Lexane (c) Nomex (d) Kevlar

49. Polythene is an example of ......
(a) Step growth polymer (b) Chain growth polymer
(c) Both step and chain growth (d) None of these

50. Light weight bullet proof vests are made from polymer ......
(a) PMMA (b) PAN (c) PTFE (d) Kevlar

51. Bullet proof windows are made up of polymer ......
(a) Lexan (b) Dynel (c) Polyurethane (d) Plexi glass

52. Ebonite is ......
(a) Natural rubber (b) Highly vulcanized rubber
(c) Neoprene (d) Isoprene

53. Dynel polymer used for making hair-like fibres is obtained by polymerisation of ......
(a) Acrylonitrile (b) Acrylonitrile and vinyl chloride
(c) Vinyl chloride (d) Acrylonitrile and allyl chloride

54. Artificial silk is ......
(a) Cellulose (b) PAN (c) Nylon-6 (d) Rayon

55. Natural rubber is ......
(a) Poly isoprene (b) Poly cis-isoprene
(c) Poly trans isoprene (d) None of these

56. Identify X^+ in the following reaction

$$\underset{\text{(cyclohexanone)}}{\bigcirc\!=\!O} \xrightarrow{NH_2OH} \underset{\text{(caprolactam)}}{\bigcirc\!-\!NH} \xrightarrow[\text{Polymerisation}]{H_2O\,/\,H^+} X$$

(a) Nylon-66 (b) Nylon-6 (c) Polyester (d) Nylon-6, 10

57. Which of the following is obtained by condensation polymerisation ?
(a) Polyethene (b) Teflon
(c) Phenol formaldehyde resin (d) Nitrile rubber

58. Natural rubber is a polymer of ......
(a) Ethylene (b) Vinyl chloride (c) Phenol (d) Isoprene

59. Synthetic polymer prepared from caprolactum is known as ......
(a) Nylon 66 (b) Teflon (c) Terylene (d) Nylon-6

60. Orlon is a polymer of ......
(a) Tetrafluoroethylene (b) Acrylonitrile (c) Ethanoic acid (d) Benzene

61. Which one of the following fibres are made of polyamides ?

(a) Dacron　　(b) Orlon　　(c) Nylon　　(d) Rayon

62. The raw material to form nylon is ......

(a) Adipic acid　　(b) Butadiene　　(c) Isoprene　　(d) Ethylene

63. Which one of the following pairs is not correctly matched ?

(a) Terylene-condensation polymer of terephthalic acid and ethylene glycol

(b) Teflon-thermally stable cross-linked polymer of phenol and formaldehyde

(c) Perspex – A homopolymer of methyl methacrylate

(d) Synthetic rubber – A copolymer of butadiene and styrene

64. The product of addition polymerization reaction is ......

(a) PVC　　(b) Nylon　　(c) Terylene　　(d) Polyamide

65. Tetrafluoroethene is the monomer of ......

(a) Polyethene　　(b) PVC　　(c) Teflon　　(d) Nylon-66

66. Bakelite is prepared by the reaction between ......

(a) Urea and formaldehyde

(b) Tetramethylene glycol and hexamethylene isocyanate

(c) Phenol and formaldehyde

(d) Ethylene glycol and dimethyl terephthalate

67. Among the following polymers, the strongest molecular forces are present in ......

(a) elastomers　　　　　　(b) fibres

(c) thermoplastics　　　　(d) thermosetting polymers

68. Glyptal polymer is obtained from glycol on reacting with ......

(a) Malonic acid　　(b) Phthalic acid　　(c) Maleic acid　　(d) Acetic acid

69. Which of the following is not an example of addition polymer ?

(a) Polyethene　　(b) Polystyrene　　(c) Neoprene　　(d) Terylene

70. On the basis of mode of their formation, the polymers can be classified ......

(a) As addition polymers only

(b) As condensation polymers only

(c) As copolymers

(d) Both as addition and condensation polymers

71. Terylene is a condensation polymer of ethylene glycol and ......

(a) Benzoic acid　　(b) Phthalic acid　　(c) Salicylic acid　　(d) Terephthalic acid

72. Ziegler-Natta catalyst is ......

(a) $K[PtCl_3(C_2H_4)]$　　　　　(b) $(Ph_3P)_3RhCl$

(c) $Al_2(C_2H_5)_6 + TiCl_4$　　　　(d) $Fe(C_2H_5)_6$

73. The process involving heating of rubber with sulphur is called ......

(a) Galvanisation　　　　(b) Vulcanization

(c) Bessemerisation　　　(d) Sulphonation

74. Bakelite is .....

(a) Addition polymer　　(b) Elastomer　　(c) Thermoplastic　　(d) Thermosetting

75. Buna-S is .....

(a) Natural polymer　　　　(b) Synthetic polymer

(c) Sulphur polymer　　　　(d) None of these

76. The 'S' in Buna-S refers to .....
 (a) Sodium (b) Sulphur (c) Styrene (d) Trade name

77. The repeating units in PTFE are ......
 (a) Cl_2CH-CH_3 (b) $F_2C = CF_2$ (c) $-F_2C - CF_2 -$ (d) $FClC = CF_2$

78. The interparticle forces between linear chains in nylon 66 are .....
 (a) H-bonds   (b) Covalent bonds
 (c) Ionic bonds   (d) Unpredictable

79. Nylon - 66 is a polyamide of .....
 (a) Vinyl chloride and formaldehyde (b) Adipic acid and methyl amine
 (c) Adipic acid and hexamethylene diamine (d) Formaldehyde and melamine

80. Which of the following is not a condensation polymer?
 (a) Glyptal (b) Nylon - 66 (c) Dacron (d) PTFE

81. Which of the following is a condensation polymer ?
 (a) Polystyrene   (b) Neoprene
 (c) PAN   (d) Poly (ethylene glycol phthalate)

82. The monomer of PVC is ....
 (a) Ethylene   (b) Tetra fluoro ethylene
 (c) Chloroethene   (d) None of these

83. Which of the following polymers is a copolymer ?
 (a) Polypropylene (b) Nylon - 66 (c) PVC (d) Teflon

84. Which of the following polymer is a homopolymer ?
 (a) Bakelite (b) Nylon - 66 (c) Terylene (d) Neoprene

85. Which of the following types of polymers has the strongest interparticle forces ?
 (a) Elastomers   (b) Thermoplastics
 (c) Fibres   (d) Thermosetting polymers

86. Caprolactum is a starting material for ....
 (a) Nylon - 6 (b) Terylene (c) Nylon - 6, 10 (d) Nylon - 66

87. Natural rubber is a polymer of .....
 (a) Styrene   (b) Styrene and 1, 3-butadiene
 (c) Tetrafluoroethylene (d) 2-methyl-1, 3-butadiene

88. Synthetic polymer prepared by using ethylene glycol and terephthalic acid is known as .....
 (a) Teflon (b) Terylene (c) Nylon (d) PVC

89. Bakelite is obtained from phenol by reacting with ......
 (a) Ethanal (b) Methanal (c) Vinyl chloride (d) Ethylene glycol

90. Which of the following is a copolymer ?
 (a) Buna - S (b) PVC (c) Orlon (d) Neoprene

91. Which of the following is a natural fibre ?
 (a) Starch (b) Cellulose (c) Rubber (d) Nylon - 6

92. Polymer used in bullet proof glass is .....
 (a) PMMA (b) Lexan (c) Nomex (d) Kevlar

93. Nylon - 6 is made from ......
 (a) 1, 3-butadiene (b) Chloroprene (c) Adipic acid (d) Caprolactum

94. Which of the following is used for the formation of nylon - 66 ?
(a) Sulphur hexafluoride   (b) Adipic acid
(c) Sulphurous acid   (d) Phthalic acid

95. $F_2C = FC_2$ is a monomer of .....
(a) Teflon   (b) Glyptal   (c) Nylon - 6   (d) Buna - S

96. Soft drinks and baby feeding bottles are generally made up of ......
(a) Polyester   (b) Polyurethane   (c) Polyurea   (d) Polyamide
(e) Polystyrene

97. Perlon is .....
(a) Rubber   (b) Nylon   (c) Terylene   (d) Orlon

98. Nylon threads are made of ......
(a) Polyvinyl polymer   (b) Polyester polymer
(c) Polyamide polymer   (d) Polyethylene polymer

99. Which one of the following monomers give the polymer neoprene on polymerization ?
(a) $CH_2 = CH - Cl$ (b) $CCl_2 = CCl_2$
(c) $CH_2 = C - CH = CH_2$ (d) $CF_2 = CF_2$
      $|$
      Cl

100. $-(NH(CH_2)_6 - NHCO(CH_2)_4CO)_n$ is a ......
(a) Homopolymer   (b) Copolymer
(c) Addition polymer   (d) Thermosetting polymer

101. Which is not a polymer ?
(a) Sucrose   (b) Enzyme   (c) Starch   (d) Teflon

102. Which one of the following polymers is prepared by condensation polymersiation ?
(a) Styrene   (b) Nylon - 66   (c) Teflon   (d) Rubber screen

103. Nylon - 6 is .....
(a) Polyester fibre   (b) Protein fibre
(c) Polyamide fibre   (d) Polycaprolactum fibre

104. Which one of the following polymer contains nitrogen?
(a) Nylon   (b) Terylene   (c) Dacron   (d) Both (b) and (c)

105. Car - tyre - cords are made up of .....
(a) Nylon - 6   (b) Nylon - 66   (c) Terylene   (d) Rayon

106. The monomer used in the preparation of terylene is known as ......
(a) Dihydroxy diethyl terephthalate   (b) Dimethyl terephthalate
(c) Ethylene glycol   (d) DMT and ethylene glycol

107. An example of protein fibre is .....
(a) Acetate rayon   (b) Cotton   (c) Terylene   (d) Wool

108. A powerful dipole-dipole attraction in polar carbonyl groups occurs in .....
(a) Nylon - 6   (b) Nylon - 66   (c) Terylene   (d) Ethanamine

109. The terylene polymer is cast into a film, which is known as .....
(a) Monomer   (b) Mylor   (c) Flex   (d) Sisal

110. The naturally occurring polymer in animals is ......

(a) Fats　　　　(b) Glucose　　　　(c) Protein　　　　(d) Fructose

111. The process involved in the preparation of Dacron is

(a) Elimination　　(b) Condensation　　(c) Polymerisation　(d) Substitution

112. The molar mass of terylene is ......

(a) Low

(b) High

(c) Always fixed

(d) Very high and variable

113. The natural polyamide polymer is .....

(a) Cotton　　　　(b) Rubber　　　　(c) Protein　　　　(d) Teflon

114. The true statement regarding terylene polymer is ......

(a) It is heat resistant

(b) It can be blended with cotton and silk

(c) It absorbs water easily

(d) It is soluble in organic solvents

115. Chemically pure cotton is named as .....

(a) Viscose rayon　　(b) Acetate rayon　　(c) Cellulose　　(d) Polyester

116. Hairs are natural fibres obtained from the source .....

(a) Carbohydrates　　(b) Proteins　　(c) Cellulose　　(d) Starch

117. Cellulose acetate is a ......

(a) Natural polymer

(b) Semi-synthetic polymer

(c) Synthetic polymer

(d) Plasticizer

118. Which of the following is fully fluorinated polymer?

(a) Neoprene　　　　(b) Teflon　　　　(c) Thiokol　　　　(d) PVC

119. Give the monomers of Nylon-66.

(a) Butadiene and acrylonitrile

(b) Ethylene glycol and terephthalic acid

(c) Hexamethylenediamine and adipic acid

(d) Melamine and formaldehyde

120. The average number molecular mass and mass average molecular mass of a polymer are respectively 30,000 and 40,000. The polydispersity index of the polymer is ......

(a) < 1　　　　(b) > 1　　　　(c) 1　　　　(d) 0

121. Which one of the following catalyst is used in the polymerisation of $HC \equiv CH$ to C_6H_6 ?

(a) $AlCl_3$　　　　(b) H_2SO_4　　　　(c) $NbCl_5$　　　　(d) HCl

122. Which of the following is a constituent of nylon ?

(a) Adipic acid　　(b) Styrene　　(c) Teflon　　(d) None of these

123. Nylon threads are made up of ......

(a) Polyamide polymers

(b) Polyethylene polymers

(c) Polyvinyl polymers

(d) Polyester polymers

PREVIOUS YEAR'S QUESTIONS

1. Which of the following organic compounds polymerize to form the polyester Dacron?

[AIPMT 2014]

(a) Terephthalic acid and ethylene glycol

(b) Benzoic acid and para $HO - (C_6H_4) - OH$

(c) Propylene and para $HO - (C_6H_4) - OH$

(d) Benzoic acid and ethanol

2. Which of the following is an example of a thermosetting polymer?　　**[AIPMT 2014]**

(a) Dacron　　　　(b) Orlon　　　　(c) Teflon　　　　(d) Novolac

3. Nylon is an example of ......   **[NEET 2013]**

(a) Polythene   (b) Polyester   (c) Polysaccharide   (d) Polyamide

4. Which is the monomer of Neoprene in the following?   **[NEET 2013]**

(a) $CH_2 = CH - C \equiv CH$

(b) $CH_2 = CH - CH = CH_2$

(c) $CH_2 = \underset{\underset{Cl}{|}}{C} - CH = CH_2$

(d) $CH_2 = \underset{\underset{CH_3}{|}}{C} - CH = CH_2$

5. Which one of the following is not a condensation polymer?   **[CBSE AIPMT 2012]**

(a) Melamine   (b) Glyptal   (c) Dacron   (d) Neoprene

6. Which one of the following sets form the biodegradable polymer?   **[CBSE AIPMT 2012]**

(a) $CH_2 = CH - CN$ and $CH_2 = CH - CH = CH_2$

(b) $H_2N - CH_2 - COOH$ and $H_2N - (CH_2)_5 - COOH$

(c) $HO - CH_2CH_2 - OH$ and $HOOC - COOH$

(d) $C_6H_5 - CH - CH_2$ and $H_2C = CH - CH = CH_2$

7. Which of the following is a polymer?   **[AFMC 2012]**

(a) Carnuaba wax   (b) Carbowax   (c) Bees wax   (d) Paraffin wax

8. A condensation polymer among the following polymers is ......   **[UP CPMT 2012]**

(a) Teflon   (b) Polystyrene   (c) PVC   (d) Dacron

9. Which of the following is a biodegradable polymer?   **[Manipal 2012]**

(a) Polythene   (b) Bakelite   (c) PHBV   (d) PVC

10. Out of the following, which one is classified as polyester polymer?

(a) Nylon-66   (b) Terylene   (c) Bakelite   (d) Melamine

11. Which of the following structures represents neoprene polymer?   **[CBSE AIPMT 2010]**

(a) $\left(CH - CH_2 \right)_n$ with C_6H_5 substituent

(b) $\left(CH_2 - \underset{\underset{Cl}{|}}{C} = CH - CH_2 \right)_n$

(c) $\left(CH_2 - \underset{\underset{CN}{|}}{CH} \right)_n$

(d) $\left(CH_2 - \underset{\underset{Cl}{|}}{CH} \right)_n$

12. Neoprene is ......   **[CPMT 2010]**

(a) a monomer of rubber   (b) synthetic rubber

(c) natural rubber   (d) vulcanized rubber

13. Which polymer is used for coating cookware to make them non-sticky? **[CPMT 2010]**

(a) PET   (b) PAN   (c) Teflon   (d) Perlon

14. For the formation of terylene, the number of moles of ethylene glycol required per mole of terephthalic acid is ......   **[MHT CET 2010]**

(a) 1   (b) 2   (c) 3   (d) 4

15. Structures of some common polymers are given. Which one is not correctly represented?

[CBSE AIPMT 2009]

(a) Teflon $\left(CF_2 - CF_2 \right)_n$

(b) Neoprene $\left(CH_2 - \underset{\underset{Cl}{|}}{C} = CH - CH_2 - CH_2 \right)_n$

(c) $\left(OC - \underset{}{C_6H_4} - COOCH_2 - CH_2O \right)_n$

(d) $\left(CH_2 \right)_4 CONH \left(CH_2 \right)_6 NH - CO \right)_n$

16. Which is an example of thermosetting polymer? **[AFMC 2009]**

(a) Polythene (b) PVC (c) Neoprene (d) Bakelite

17. The rubber used for manufacturing tyres, is vulcanized with ...... **[AIIMS 2009]**

(a) 3% S (b) 7% S (c) 1% S

(d) All of the above can be used

18. A petrol pump hose pipe for delivery of petrol is made up of ...... **[CPMT 2009]**

(a) natural rubber   (b) vulcanized rubber

(c) neoprene   (d) butadiene rubber

19. Adipic acid is used in the preparation of ...... **[MHT CET 2009]**

(a) Nylon-6 (b) Dacron (c) Nylon-66 (d) Novolac

20. Which of the following statements is not true? **[CBSE AIPMT 2008]**

(a) In vulcanization, the formation of sulphur bridges between different chains make rubber harder and stronger.

(b) Natural rubber has the trans -configuration at every double bond.

(c) Buna-S is a copolymer of butadiene and styrene.

(d) Natural rubber is a 1,4-polymer of isoprene.

21. Which of the following alkenes is most reactive towards cationic polymerization?

    [Manipal 2008]

(a) $CH_2 = CHCH_3$ (b) $H_2C = CHCl$ (c) $H_2C = CHC_6H_5$ (d) $H_2C = CHCO_2CH_3$

22. Which one of the following polymers is prepared by condensation polymerization?

    [CBSE AIPMT 2007]

(a) Nylon-66 (b) Teflon (c) Rubber (d) Styrene

23. Three dimensional molecules with cross links are formed in the case of a ...... **[AFMC 2007]**

(a) Thermoplastic   (b) Thermosetting plastic

(c) Both (a) and (b)   (d) None of these

24. Plexi glass is a commercial name of ...... **[AIIMS 2007]**

(a) glyptal   (b) chloroprene

(c) polymethyl methacrylate   (d) polyethyl acrylate

25. Assertion – 1,3 - butadiene is the monomer for natural rubber. **[AIIMS 2006]**

Reason – Natural rubber is formed through anionic addition polymerization.

(a) Both Assertion and Reason are true and Reason is the correct explanation of Assertion.

(b) Both Assertion and Reason are true and Reason is not the correct explanation of Assertion.

(c) Assertion is true but Reason is false.

(d) Both Assertion and Reason are false.

26. The monomer of the polymer, $CH_3 - \overset{\overset{\displaystyle CH_3}{|}}{\underset{\underset{\displaystyle CH_3}{|}}{C}} - CH_2 - \overset{+}{C} \overset{CH_3}{\underset{CH_3}{\diagup}}$ is ...... **[CBSE AIPMT 2005]**

(a) $CH_2 = C \overset{CH_3}{\underset{CH_3}{\diagup}}$ (b) $C(CH_3)_2 = C(CH_3)_2$

(c) $CH_3CH = CH - CH_3$ (d) $CH_3 - CH = CH_2$

27. Which one of the following is a chain growth polymer?   **[CBSE AIPMT 2004]**

    (a) Starch   (b) Nucleic acid   (c) Polystyrene   (d) Protein

28. Which of the following is used in vulcanization of rubber?   **[MHT CET 2004]**

    (a) SF_6 (b) CF_4 (c) Cl_2F_2 (d) C_2F_2

29. Biodegradable polymer which can be produced from glycine and aminocaproic acid is ......

                                                                  [AIPMT 2015]

    (a) PHBV   (b) Buna – N   (c) Nylon 6, 6   (d) Nylon 2 - Nylon 6

30. Orlon is a polymer of ......   **[J.I.P.M.E.R. 2002]**

    (a) PVC   (b) Bakelite   (c) Acrylonitrile   (d) Nylon

31. Acrilan is a hard, horny and a high melting material. Which of the following represents the structure ?   **[J.I.P.M.E.R. 2002]**

(a) $\left(-CH_2-\underset{\underset{Cl}{|}}{CH}-\right)_n$

(b) $\left(-CH_2-\underset{\underset{CN}{|}}{CH}-\right)_n$

(c) $\left(-CH-\underset{\underset{COOCH_3}{|}}{\overset{\overset{CH_3}{|}}{C}}-\right)_n$

(d) $\left(-CH_2-\underset{\underset{COOCH_3}{|}}{CH}-\right)_n$

32. Which one of the following is a biodegradable polymer?   **[D.P.M.T. 2005]**

    (a) Cellulose   (b) Polythene

    (c) Polyvinyl chloride   (d) Nylon-6

33. Which one of the following is a polyamide ?   **[D.P.M.T. 2007]**

    (a) Teflon   (b) Nylon-66   (c) Terylene   (d) Bakelite

34. Structures of some common polymers are given. Which one is not correctly represented ?   **[J.I.P.M.E.R. 2000]**

    (a) Nylon 66 $[NH(CH_2)_6NHCO(CH_2)_4-CO-]_2$ (b) Teflon $(CF_2 - CF_2-)_n$

    (c) Neoprene $\left(-CH_2C = C - CH_2 - CH_2 - \atop \quad\quad|\quad\;\; |\atop \quad\quad H\quad Cl\right)$

    (d) Terylene $-(OC -\!\!\langle O \rangle\!\!- COOCH_2 - CH_2 - O -)_n$

35. $F_2C = CF_2$ is a monomer of ......   **[C.B.S.E. P.M.T. 2000]**

    (a) Teflon   (b) Glyptal   (c) Nylon-6   (d) Buna-S

36. Soft drinks and baby feeding bottles are generally made up of ......   **[Kerala P.M.T. 2000]**

    (a) Polyester   (b) Polyurethane   (c) Polyurea   (d) Polyamide

37. Caprolactum polymerises to give ......   **[J.I.P.M.E.R. 2001]**

    (a) Terylene   (b) Teflon   (c) Glyptal   (d) Nylon-6

38. Which of the following is a polyamide molecule ?   **[U.P. S.E.A.T. 2002]**

    (a) Terylene   (b) Rayon   (c) Nylon-6   (d) Polystyrene

39. Which of the following is not correctly matched ?   **[C.B.S.E. P.M.T. 2002]**

(a) $-[CH_2 - C = CH - CH_2 -]$ Neoprene
$\quad\quad\quad\quad |$
$\quad\quad\quad\quad Cl$

(b) $-[NH-(CH_2)_6 - NHCO - (CH_2)_4 - CO]_n$ Nylon-66

(c) $[- CH_2 - \overset{\overset{\textstyle COOCH_3}{|}}{\underset{\underset{\textstyle CH_3}{|}}{C}} -]_n$ PMMA

(d) $[-\overset{\overset{\textstyle O}{||}}{C}-\langle\bigcirc\rangle-\overset{\overset{\textstyle O}{||}}{C}-O - CH_2 - CH_2 - OH -]$
$\quad\quad\quad\quad\quad\quad\quad\quad\quad\quad\quad\quad$ Polyester

40. Monomer of $\left[-\overset{\overset{\textstyle CH_3}{|}}{\underset{\underset{\textstyle CH_3}{|}}{C}} - CH_2 - \right]_n$ is ......   **[C.B.S.E. P.M.T. 2002]**

(a) 2-Methylpropene   (b) Styrene   (c) Polystyrene   (d) Teflon

41. The catalyst used for the polymerisation of olefins is ......   **[Kerala C.E.T. 2002]**

(a) Ziegler-Natta catalyst   (b) Wilkinson's catalyst

(c) Pd-catalyst   (d) Zeise's salt complex   (e) Zeolite

42. Polymer formation for monomers starts by ......   **[A.I.E.E.E. 2002]**

(a) Condensation reaction between monomers

(b) Coordination reaction between monomers

(c) Conversion of monomer to monomer ions by protons

(d) Hydrolysis of monomers

43. Teflon is a polymer of ......   **[A.I.I.M.S. 2002]**

(a) Tetrafluoroethylene   (b) Tetraiodoethylene

(c) Tetrabromoethylene   (d) Tetrachloroethylene

44. The components of nylon-66 are ......   **[D.C.E. 2002]**

(a) Hexamethylene diamine and adipic acid   (b) Hexamethylene diamine and sebacic acid

(c) Hexamethylene only   (d) None of these

45. Natural rubber is which type of polymer ?   **[D.C.E. 2002]**

(a) Condensation polymer   (b) Addition polymer

(c) Co-ordination polymer   (d) None of these

46. Which is a protein ?   **[Pb. C.E.T. 2002]**

(a) Nylon   (b) Rayon   (c) Natural silk   (d) Terylene

47. Natural rubber is a polymer of ......   **[Pb. C.E.T. 2002]**

(a) Isoprene   (b) Styrene   (c) Ethylene   (d) Butadiene

48. Which of the following has ester linkage ?   **[Kerala P.M.T. 2002]**

    (a) Nylon   (b) Bakelite   (c) Terylene   (d) PVC

    (e) Rubber

49. Acrilan is a hard, horny and a high melting material. Which of the following represents its structure ......   **[C.B.S.E. Med. 2003]**

(a) $\left(- CH_2 - \underset{\underset{CN}{|}}{CH} - \right)_n$ (b) $\left(- CH_2 - \underset{\underset{COOCH_3}{|}}{\overset{\overset{CH_3}{|}}{C}} - \right)_n$

(c) $\left(- CH_2 - \underset{\underset{COOC_2H_5}{|}}{CH_2} - \right)_n$ (d) $\left(- CH_2 - \underset{\underset{Cl}{|}}{CH} - \right)_n$

50. Which of the following is a biodegradable polymer ?   **[A.I.I.M.S. 2004]**

    (a) Cellulose   (b) Polythene

    (c) Polyvinyl chloride   (d) Nylon-6

51. Which of the following is a chain growth polymer ?   **[C.B.S.E. Med. 2004]**

    (a) Starch   (b) Nucleic acid   (c) Polystyrene   (d) Protein

52. Orlon has a unit ......   **[A.F.M.C. 2004]**

    (a) Vinyl cyanide   (b) Acrolein   (c) Glycol   (d) Isoprene

53. The substance used to harden the rubber for tyre manufacture is ......   **[H.P.M.T. 2005]**

    (a) Wax   (b) 1, 3-Butadiene   (c) CaC_2 (d) Carbon black

ANSWER KEY

1. (c)	2. (a)	3. (c)	4. (c)	5. (b)	6. (c)	7. (b)	8. (c)
9. (d)	10. (c)	11. (b)	12. (b)	13. (a)	14. (c)	15. (d)	16. (a)
17. (b)	18. (d)	19. (b)	20. (c)	21. (b)	22. (c)	23. (a)	24. (d)
25. (a)	26. (b)	27. (b)	28. (c)	29. (c)	30. (a)	31. (b)	32. (a)
33. (c)	34. (a)	35. (d)	36. (b)	37. (c)	38. (a)	39. (c)	40. (c)
41. (b)	42. (a)	43. (b)	44. (d)	45. (c)	46. (b)	47. (c)	48. (a)
49. (b)	50. (d)	51. (a)	52. (b)	53. (b)	54. (d)	55. (b)	56. (b)
57. (c)	58. (d)	59. (d)	60. (b)	61. (c)	62. (a)	63. (b)	64. (a)
65. (c)	66. (c)	67. (d)	68. (b)	69. (d)	70. (d)	71. (d)	72. (c)
73. (b)	74. (d)	75. (b)	76. (c)	77. (c)	78. (a)	79. (c)	80. (d)
81. (d)	82. (c)	83. (b)	84. (d)	85. (d)	86. (a)	87. (d)	88. (b)
89. (d)	90. (a)	91. (b)	92. (b)	93. (d)	94. (b)	95. (a)	96. (b)
97. (b)	98. (c)	99. (c)	100. (b)	101. (b)	102. (b)	103. (c)	104. (a)
105. (a)	106. (c)	107. (d)	108. (c)	109. (b)	110. (c)	111. (c)	112. (d)
113. (c)	114. (b)	115. (c)	116. (c)	117. (b)	118. (b)	119. (c)	120. (b)
121. (a)	122. (a)	123. (a)					

Previous Year's Questions

1. (a)	2. (d)	3. (d)	4. (c)	5. (d)	6. (b)	7. (b)	8. (d)
9. (c)	10. (b)	11. (b)	12. (b)	13. (c)	14. (a)	15. (b)	16. (d)
17. (b)	18. (d)	19. (c)	20. (b)	21. (c)	22. (a)	23. (b)	24. (c)
25. (d)	26. (a)	27. (c)	28. (a)	29. (d)	30. (c)	31. (b)	32. (a)
33. (b)	34. (c)	35. (a)	36. (b)	37. (d)	38. (c)	39. (b)	40. (a)
41. (a)	42. (a)	43. (a)	44. (a)	45. (b)	46. (c)	47. (a)	48. (c)
49. (a)	50. (a)	51. (c)	52. (a)	53. (d)			

❑❑❑

CHEMISTRY IN EVERYDAY LIFE

1. The most useful classification of drugs for medicinal chemists is ________.
   - (a) on the basis of chemical structure
   - (b) on the basis of drug action
   - (c) on the basis of molecular targets
   - (d) on the basis of pharmacological effect

2. Antipyretics are given to patients suffering from ......
   - (a) Pain
   - (b) Fever
   - (c) Cut infection
   - (d) Drastic problems

3. Analgesics are ......
   - (a) Pain killers
   - (b) Tetracycline
   - (c) Enzymes
   - (d) Antibiotics

4. Which of the following is used for lowering down of fever?
   - (a) Penicillin
   - (b) Aspirin
   - (c) Chloroquine
   - (d) Streptomycin

5. Phenacetin is used as an ......
   - (a) Antibiotic
   - (b) Analgesic
   - (c) Antipyretic
   - (d) Antihistamine

6. Which one is a broad spectrum antibiotic ?
   - (a) Streptomycin
   - (b) Penicillin
   - (c) Chloroquine
   - (d) Omeprazole

7. Amoxicillin is an example of ......
   - (a) Broad spectrum antibiotic
   - (b) Narrow spectrum antibiotic
   - (c) Antimalarial drug
   - (d) Tranquillizer

8. Chloramphenicol, a broad spectrum antibiotic is used for the treatment of ......
   - (a) Malaria
   - (b) Meningitis
   - (c) Tuberculosis
   - (d) Allergy

9. Which of the following can be used as antiseptic as well as disinfectant ?
   - (a) Phenol
   - (b) Chlorine
   - (c) Iodine
   - (d) Sulphur dioxide

10. Dettol is a mixture of ......
    - (a) Phenol and terpeneol
    - (b) Chloroxylenol and terpeneol
    - (c) Chloroxylenol and phenol
    - (d) Terpeneol and solid

11. Luminal and seconal are used as ......
    - (a) Tranquillizers
    - (b) Antiseptics
    - (c) Analgesics
    - (d) Antiallergic

12. Antihistamines are used for ......
    - (a) Fever
    - (b) Pain
    - (c) Allergy
    - (d) Dysentry

13. Heroin, a powerful analgesic is ......
    - (a) Narcotic
    - (b) Non-narcotic
    - (c) Antibiotic
    - (d) Antibacterial

14. Omeprazole and Lansoprazole are used for the treatment of ......
    - (a) Malaria
    - (b) Acidity
    - (c) Pneumonia
    - (d) Allergy

15. Which one of the following is employed as a tranquilizer drug ?
    - (a) Valium
    - (b) Naproxen
    - (c) Mifepristone
    - (d) None of these

16. Aspirin, an antipyretic drug is chemically ......
    - (a) Methyl salicylate
    - (b) Ethyl salicylate
    - (c) Acetyl salicylic acid
    - (d) o-hydroxy benzoic acid

17. Which of the following is not an analgesic ?
    - (a) Ibuprofen
    - (b) Naproxen
    - (c) Valium
    - (d) Aspirin

18. The antibiotic streptomycin is specific against ......
    (a) Tuberculosis   (b) Typhoid   (c) Malaria   (d) AIDS

19. Chloroquine is used to control ......
    (a) Pneumonia   (b) Malaria   (c) Pain   (d) Fever

20. Arsenic drugs are mainly used in the treatment of ......
    (a) Jaundice   (b) Typhoid   (c) Syphilis   (d) Cholera

21. Saccharin is an artificial sweetener which is _____ times sweeter than sugar.
    (a) 10   (b) 600   (c) 400   (d) 40

22. Sodium metabisulphite is used as ......
    (a) Food colour   (b) Food preservative
    (c) Food sweetener   (d) Antioxidants

23. Sulphur dioxide is used in juices as ......
    (a) Bleaching agent   (b) Food preservative
    (c) Food sweetener   (d) Antioxidant

24. Antioxidants are added to food to prevent ......
    (a) Spillage of food   (b) Oxidation of fats
    (c) Oxidation of carbohydrates   (d) Oxidation of proteins

25. BHA and BHT are examples of ......
    (a) Antioxidants   (b) Food preservatives
    (c) Food sweeteners   (d) None of these

26. Sweetener used in cold drinks is ......
    (a) Alitame   (b) Sucralose   (c) Aspartame   (d) Dextrose

27. Out of the following sweeteners, which is unstable to heat and has high potency of sweeteners ?
    (a) Sucralose   (b) Alitame   (c) Aspartame   (d) Saccharin

28. The artificial sweetener having chlorine that has the appearance and taste of sugar and is stable at cooking temperature is ......
    (a) Sucrallone   (b) Aspartame   (c) Sucralose   (d) Alitame

29. Which of the following can be possibly used for analysis without causing addiction and mood modification ?
    (a) Morphine   (b) Diazepam
    (c) Tetrahydrocortisone   (d) N-acetyl-p-amino-phenol

30. Sodium dodecyl benzene sulphonate is used as a ......
    (a) Insecticide   (b) Detergent   (c) Soap   (d) Sweetener

31. Cetyl trimethyl ammonium bromide is a popular ......
    (a) Anionic detergent   (b) Cationic detergent
    (c) Nonionic detergent   (d) Antioxidant

32. Cetyl trimethyl ammonium chloride is an example of ......
    (a) Soap   (b) Non-ionic detergent
    (c) Anionic detergent   (d) Cationic detergent

33. Salt which can keep detergent dry is ......
    (a) Sodium silicate   (b) Sodium chloride
    (c) Sodium nitrate   (d) Sodium bromide

34. Sodium lauryl sulphate is an example of ......
    (a) Soap   (b) Detergent   (c) Fat   (d) Oil

35. Which of the following enhances lathering property of soap?
    (a) Sodium carbonate   (b) Sodium rosinate
    (c) Sodium stearate   (d) Trisodium phosphate

36. CMC is added to detergent to ......
    (a) Dry   (b) Kill bacteria
    (c) Keep the dirt particles suspended in water   (d) Give whiteness to clothes

37. Which chemical is added to detergent to give whiteness to clothes ?
    (a) Sodium perborate   (b) CMC
    (c) Sodium silicate   (d) Bleaching powder

38. Soaps are ......
    (a) Biodegradable   (b) Non-biodegradable
    (c) Both of these   (d) None of these

39. Detergents are ......
    (a) Biodegradable   (b) Non-biodegradable
    (c) Both of these   (d) None of these

40. Polyethylene glycol stearate is ......
    (a) Cationic detergent   (b) Anionic detergent
    (c) Nonionic detergent   (d) Cationic and anionic both

41. Which of the following are very harmful for aquatic life ?
    (a) Soaps   (b) Detergents
    (c) Both (a) and (b)   (d) None of these

42. Which of the salts, present in detergents cause rapid growth of algae in water which leads to deoxygenation of water ?
    (a) Carbonate salts   (b) Sulphate salts
    (c) Phosphate salts   (d) Chloride salts

43. Non-biodegradable nature of detergent is due to the presence of ......
    (a) Branching   (b) Straight chain
    (c) Cyclic structure   (d) Aromatic structure

44. Aspirin is used as ______
    (a) An antibiotic   (b) An analgesic
    (c) A sedative   (d) A psychedelic drug

45. The chemical name of aspirin is ______
    (a) Methyl salicylate   (b) Ethyl salicylate
    (c) 2-hydroxy benzoic acid   (d) 2-acetoxy benzoic acid

46. Which statement about aspirin is not true ......
    (a) Aspirin belongs to narcotic analgesics.   (b) It is effective in relieving pain.
    (c) It has antiblood clotting action.   (d) It is a neurologically active drug.

47. A narrow spectrum antibiotic is active against ......
    (a) gram positive or gram negative bacteria.
    (b) gram negative bacteria only.
    (c) single organism or one disease.
    (d) both gram positive and gram negative bacteria.

48. Chloramphenicol is used as an ......

(a) Analgesic   (b) Antibiotic   (c) Anaesthetic   (d) Antiseptic

49. Which of the following is a potent hallucinogen?

(a) DNA   (b) LSD   (c) DDT   (d) TNT

50. Phenol is commonly used as ......

(a) An insecticide   (b) An antiseptic   (c) A disinfectant (d) An anaesthetic

51. Paracetamol is used as _______

(a) An analgesic   (b) An antipyretic

(c) Both analgesic and antipyretic   (d) An antimalarial

52. The commonly used analgesic that does not lead to addiction is _______

(a) Morphine   (b) Pethidine

(c) Diazepam   (d) N-acetyl-p-aminophenol

53. Which of the following is an antipyretic?

(a) Quinine   (b) Luminal   (c) Paracetamol   (d) Piperazine

54. 2-acetoxy benzoic acid is known as _______

(a) Coumarin   (b) Oil of wintergreen

(c) Aspirin   (d) Salol

55. Which of the following is useful as a refrigerant?

(a) Carbon tetrachloride   (b) Carbon tetrafluoride

(c) Dichlorodifluoromethane   (d) Acetone

56. The hormone that is used in the treatment of diabetes is ......

(a) Insulin   (b) Oxytocin   (c) Esterone   (d) Cortisone

57. For the efficient distribution of pesticides, which of the following compounds is used as a propellant in the aerosol spray cans?

(a) Freon 11   (b) Freon 12   (c) Freon C318   (d) All of these

58. Iodex contains ......

(a) Methyl acetate   (b) Ethyl propionate

(c) Methyl salicylate   (d) Methyl benzoate

59. Cetyl trimethyl ammonium chloride is an example of ......

(a) Anionic detergent   (b) Cationic detergent

(c) Analgesic   (d) Tranquilizer

60. Glycerol is added to soap. It functions ......

(a) as a filler   (b) to increase leathering

(c) to prevent rapid drying   (d) to make soap granules

61. Food preservative in tomato ketchup is ......

(a) Sodium acetate   (b) Sodium benzoate

(c) Sodium salicylate   (d) Sodium propionate

62. Valium is used as a ......

(a) Tranquilizer   (b) Analgesic   (c) Antipyretic   (d) Antibiotic

63. Which of the following is a bactericidal antibiotic?

(a) Erythromycin   (b) Ofloxacin   (c) Tetracycline   (d) Chloramphenicol

64. Which of the following is an analgesic ?

(a) Chloramphenicol   (b) Penicillin   (c) Paracetamol (d) Streptomycin

65. Which of the following is used for the treatment of tuberculosis ?

(a) Penicillin   (b) Aspirin

(c) Chloramphenicol   (d) Streptomycin

66. Antipyretics are medicinal compounds which ......

(a) Lower body temperature   (b) Relieve pain

(c) Control malaria   (d) Can kill other micro-organisms

67. Aspirin is an ....

(a) Analgesic   (b) Antipyretic

(c) Antimalarial   (d) Both analgesic and antipyretic

68. The drug used for the treatment of typhoid is ....

(a) Novalgin   (b) Quinine

(c) Chloromycetin   (d) Paracetamol

69. Chloroquine is a drug which is used to control ......

(a) Pneumonia   (b) Malaria   (c) Pain   (d) Ordinary fever

70. Streptomycin is a specific drug against ....

(a) Typhoid   (b) Tuberculosis   (c) Maleria   (d) Whooping cough

71. Veronal, a barbituric drug is used as ......

(a) Hypnotic   (b) Sedative   (c) Antiseptic   (d) None of these

72. The compound which acts on the central nervous system belongs to ......

(a) analgesics   (b) tranquilizers

(c) narcotic analgesics   (d) antihistamines

73. Which of the following is a hypnotic drug ?

(a) Luminal   (b) Salol   (c) Catechol   (d) Phenol

74. Which of the following is insecticide ?

(a) DDT   (b) TNT   (c) TNB   (d) Aspirin

75. Which of the following antibiotic contains NO_2 group attached to aromatic nucleus in its structure ?

(a) Penicillin   (b) Streptomycin

(c) Chloramphenicol   (d) All of these

76. The correct structure of drug paracetamol is ....

(a) OH — $CONH_2$ (b) OH — $NHCOCH_3$ (c) Cl — $NHCOCH_3$ (d) Cl — $CONH_2$

77. Amoxillin is semisynthetic modification of ....

(a) Tetracycline   (b) Penicillin   (c) Streptomycin (d) Chloramphenicol

78. The compound [structure: benzene ring with $OCOCH_3$ and $COOH$ substituents] is used as ....
    (a) Antiseptic   (b) Antibiotic   (c) Analgesic   (d) Pesticide

79. The following structure given below is known as ......

    [structure: benzene ring $-CH_2-C(=O)-NH-$ ... penicillin ring with S, CH_3, CH_3, $COOH$, N, O]

    (a) Penicillin F   (b) Penicillin G   (c) Penicillin K   (d) Ampicillin
    (e) Sulfadiazine

80. Barbituric acid is used as ......
    (a) An antipyretic   (b) A tranquilizer   (c) An analgesic   (d) An antibiotic

81. Which of the following statements is correct?
    (a) Some tranquilizers function by inhibiting the enzymes which catalyse the degradation of noradrenaline.
    (b) Tranquilizers are narcotic drugs.
    (c) Tranquilizers are chemical compounds that do not affect the message transfer from nerve to receptor.
    (d) Tranquilizers are chemical compounds that can relieve pain and fever.

82. A non-antibiotic is ....
    (a) Bithional   (b) Tetracycline   (c) Penicillin   (d) Barbiturate

83. Tranquilizers are used in ....
    (a) Reducing pain   (b) Reducing fever   (c) Demensia   (d) Nausea

84. A non-antipyretic compound is ....
    (a) Aspirin   (b) Phenacetin   (c) Paracetamol   (d) Ampicillin

85. The iodine compound used as an antiseptic is ......
    (a) CH_3I (b) CHI_3 (c) CH_2I_2 (d) None of these

86. The antacid which releases CO_2 and causes bleaching is ....
    (a) $MgCO_3$ (b) Na_2CO_3 (c) K_2CO_3 (d) $CaCO_3$

87. (Terpinol + Chloroxylenol) in ethanol gives rise to ...
    (a) o-phenylphenol   (b) Equanil   (c) Chloroform   (d) Dettol

88. Bithional is added to which of the following substances to impart antiseptic properties :
    (a) Drinking water   (b) Soaps   (c) Fertilizers   (d) Perfumes

89. The drug used for H-influenza is ......
    (a) Chloramphenicol   (b) Tetracycline   (c) Streptomycin   (d) Ofloxacin

90. The drug used for the treatment of rickettsia and acne vulgaris is ......
    (a) Erythromycin   (b) Streptomycin   (c) Tetracycline   (d) Penicillin

91. The drug which is used in serious infection caused by pseudomonas is ....
    (a) Piperacillin   (b) Cloxacillin   (c) Carbenicillin   (d) Ampicillin

92. Benzyl penicillin is also known as .....
    (a) Penicillin - B   (b) Penicillin - V   (c) Penicillin - G (d) Penicillin - P
93. BHT prevents development of flavour in ....
    (a) Glucose   (b) Saccharides   (c) Edible oils   (d) Proteins
94. For dehydration of alcohol and antiseptic, the acid used is ....
    (a) H_3BO_3 (b) H_3PO_3 (c) H_3PO_4 (d) H_2SO_4
95. The chemical substance, used to kill the microorganisms, but they cannot be applied on living tissues is ....
    (a) Disinfectant   (b) Antiseptic   (c) Antioxidant   (d) Analgesic
96. The narrow spectrum antibiotic is ....
    (a) Penicillin   (b) Bacitracin   (c) Ofloxacin   (d) Both (a) and (b)
97. The given structure represents ......

$$\underset{OCH_3}{\overset{OH}{\bigcirc}}\!\!-C(CH_3)_3$$

...

    (a) BHA   (b) Butylated parahydroxy anisole
    (c) Butylated parahydroxy phenol   (d) Both (a) and (b)
98. The antacid magnesium trisilicate is used in the treatment of ....
    (a) Hyper acidity   (b) Reflux oesophagitis
    (c) Flatulent dyspepsia   (d) All of these
99. For violent and mentally agitated person, the tranquilizers suggested are ....
    (a) Sedatives   (b) Antidepressants
    (c) Both (a) and (b)   (d) None of these
100. Chloroxylenol of terpineol are present in ....
    (a) Dettol   (b) Phenol
    (c) Absolute spirit   (d) Chloroform
101. Which of the following statements is not correct ?
    (a) Some antiseptics can be added to soaps.
    (b) Dilute solutions of some disinfectants can be used as antiseptic.
    (c) Disinfectants are antimicrobial drugs.
    (d) Antiseptic medicines can harm living tissues
102. When chemicals are used for the treatment of various diseases, the therapy is called as ....
    (a) physiotherapy   (b) cobalt-therapy
    (c) chemical therapy   (d) chemotherapy
103. A powerful disinfectant is ....
    (a) Iodine   (b) Thymol   (c) Bithional   (d) Dettol
104. The compound which is not used as an antipyretic is ....
    (a) Chloramphenicol   (b) Aspirin   (c) Phenacetin   (d) Paracetamol
105. The compound which is not used as a tranquilizer is .....
    (a) Seconal   (b) Luminal   (c) Phenacetin   (d) Barbituric acid

106. Antiseptics and disinfectants are ....
 (a) Same
 (b) Different
 (c) Harmful to living tissues
 (d) Not harmful to living tissues

107. One of the uses of barbiturates is given as follows :
 (a) Antiblood clotting agents
 (b) Hypnotics
 (c) Antioxidant
 (d) Both (a) and (b)

108. In case of epilepsy, the drug used is ....
 (a) Diacetyl amine
 (b) Diphenyl amine
 (c) Dial
 (d) Dettol

109. The antacid, sodium bicarbonate, have the following side effect
 (a) Abdominal pain
 (b) Weakness
 (c) Belching
 (d) All of these

110. Aspirin is toxic to ....
 (a) Lungs
 (b) Brain
 (c) Liver
 (d) Kidney

111. Which is the correct statement about birth control pills?
 (a) Contain estrogen only.
 (b) Contain progesterone only.
 (c) Contain a mixture of estrogen and progesterone derivatives.
 (d) Progesterone enhances ovulation.

112. The preservative which is used in sauces and ketchups is ....
 (a) Acetic acid
 (b) Analgesic
 (c) Disinfectant
 (d) Cleaning agent

113. Pathogens, from food are removed by ....
 (a) Heating
 (b) Pasteurisation
 (c) Salting
 (d) Addition of acid

114. Ampicillin can be given in case of ....
 (a) Urinary tract infection
 (b) Respiratory tract infection
 (c) Gastro intestinal infection
 (d) All of these

115. An antioxidant, which is mostly used in the food preservation is ....
 (a) Aspirin
 (b) Methylated hydroxyanisole
 (c) Saccharin
 (d) Phenol

116. The odd man out from the following compounds is ......
 (a) Penicillin
 (b) Streptomycin
 (c) Amoxycillin
 (d) Saccharine

117. The side effects, vomiting, nausea, abdominal pain, diarrhoea are caused by the drug ....
 (a) Anacin
 (b) Erythromycin
 (c) Quanoline
 (d) Crocin

118. Cephalosporin is given in case of ......
 (a) Headache
 (b) High fever
 (c) Respiratory tract infection
 (d) Stomach pain

119. Gentamycin can be used for ......
 (a) Infected burn wounds
 (b) Any kind of wounds
 (c) Swelling and inflammation
 (d) Cuts

120. The rate of biochemical reaction is reduced by .....
 (a) Heating
 (b) Moderate cooling
 (c) Refrigeration
 (d) Maintaining constant temperature

121. Tetracyclines are effective in case of ....
 (a) Whooping cough
 (b) Chronic bronchitis
 (c) Tetanus
 (d) All of these

122. Streptomycin is an organic compound, which is used as ....
    (a) Antibiotic   (b) Antiseptic   (c) Antipyretic   (d) Tranquilizer

123. The following substance is used as an antiseptic ......
    (a) Boric acid   (b) Hydrogen peroxide
    (c) Dettol   (d) All of these

124. BHA and BHT are most familiar examples of .....
    (a) Antioxidants   (b) Hypnotics
    (c) Food preservatives   (d) Antipyretics

125. The chemical substances, which neutralize the acid in gastric juice are called ......
    (a) Analgesics   (b) Antacids   (c) Antiallergic   (d) Antibiotics

126. Which one of the following is used as an antioxidant?
    (a) Naproxen   (b) Butylated hydroxy toluene
    (c) Equanil   (d) Ofloxacin

127. Salvarsan is arsenic containing drug which was first used for the treatment of ......
    (a) syphilis   (b) typhoid   (c) meningitis   (d) dysentry

128. Equanil is ......
    (a) artificial sweetener (b) tranquilizer   (c) antihistamine (d) antifertility drug

129. Which of the following is an example of liquid dishwashing detergent?
    (a) $CH_3(CH_2)_{10}—CH_2OSO_3^-Na^+$ (b) $CH_3(CH_2)_{16}COO(CH_2CH_2O)_nCH_2CH_2OH$
    (c) $[CH_3(CH_2)_{15}N^+(CH_3)_3]^-$ (d) $CH_3(CH_2)_{11}–C_6H_4–SO_3^-Na^+$

130. Polyethylene glycols are used in the preparation of which type of detergents?
    (a) Cationic detergents   (b) Anionic detergents
    (c) Non-ionic detergents   (d) Soaps

131. Which of the following is not a target molecule for drug function in body?
    (a) Carbohydrates   (b) Lipids   (c) Vitamins   (d) Proteins

132. Which of the following chemicals can be added for sweetening of food items at cooking temperature and does not provide calories?
    (a) Sucrose   (b) Glucose   (c) Aspartame   (d) Sucrolose

133. Which of the following statements is not true about enzyme inhibitors?
    (a) Inhibit the catalytic activity of the enzyme.
    (b) Prevent the binding of substrate.
    (c) Generally a strong covalent bond is formed between an inhibitor and an enzyme.
    (d) Inhibitors can be competitive or non-competitive.

134. Which of the following is not used as a food preservative ?
    (a) Table salt   (b) Sodium hydrogen carbonate
    (c) Sodium benzoate   (d) Cane sugar

135. The compound with antiseptic properties is ......
    (a) $CHCl_3$ (b) CHI_3
    (c) 2% solution of phenol   (d) 0.3 ppm aqueous solution of Cl_2

136. Which of the following statements is correct about barbiturates?
    (a) Hypnotics or sleep producing agents.   (b) Used to control depression
    (c) Non-narcotic analgesics.
    (d) Pain reducing without disturbing the nervous system.

137. Which of the following are sulpha drugs?
(a) Arsenaphenamine   (b) Prontosil   (c) Salvarsan   (d) Dysidazarine

138. Which of the following is antidepressant ?
(a) Iproniazid   (b) Phenelzine   (c) Equanil   (d) Salvarsan

139. Which of the following statements is incorrect about penicillin?
(a) An antibacterial fungus.
(b) Ampicillin is its synthetic modification.
(c) It has bacteriostatic effect.
(d) It is a narrow spectrum antibiotic.

140. Which of the following compounds are administered as antacids?
(a) Sodium carbonate
(b) Sodium hydrogen carbonate
(c) Aluminium carbonate
(d) Magnesium phosphate

141. The chemical name of anisole is ......
(a) Ethanoic acid   (b) Methoxybenzene   (c) Propanone   (d) Acetone

142. Amongst the following antihistamines, which are antacids?
(a) Ranitidine   (b) Brompheniramine   (c) Terfenadine   (d) Cimetidine

143. Veronal and luminal are derivatives of barbituric acid which are ......
(a) Tranquilizers.
(b) Non-narcotic analgesics
(c) Antiallergic drugs.
(d) Neurologically non-active drugs.

144. Which of the following are anionic detergents?
(a) Sodium salts of sulphonated long chain alcohol, Ester of stearic acid and polyethylene glycol
(b) Ester of stearic acid and polyethylene glycol, Quaternary ammonium salt of amine with acetate ion
(c) Quaternary ammonium salt of amine with acetate ion, Sodium salts of sulphonated long chain alcohol.
(d) Sodium salts of sulphonated long chain hydrocarbons, Sodium salts of sulphonated long chain alcohol

145. Which of the following statements is incorrect?
(a) Cationic detergents have germicidal properties
(b) Bacteria can degrade the detergents containing highly branched chains.
(c) Anionic detergents are polyethylene glycol and stearic acid
(d) Synthetic detergents are not soaps.

146. Which one of the following statements about aspirin is not true?
(a) It belongs to narcotic analgesics.
(b) It is effective in relieving pain.
(c) It has anti-blood clotting action.
(d) It is a neurologically active drug.

147. Which one of the following drugs prevents the interaction of histamine with its receptor?
(a) Antihistamines   (b) Analgesics   (c) Antibiotics   (d) Disinfectants

148. Which one of the following compounds is added to soap to impart antiseptic properties ?
(a) sodium lauryl sulphate
(b) sodium dodecyl benzene sulfonate
(c) rosin
(d) bithional

149. Which one of the following is not a correct match?
(a) Analgesics - Pain killing effect
(b) Antacids - Treatment of acidity
(c) Disinfectants - Applied to non-living objects
(d) Tranquilizers - Applied to diseased skin surfaces

150. The substances which affect the central nervous system and induce sleep are called ......
(a) Tranquilizers   (b) Antipyretics   (c) Analgesics   (d) None of these

PREVIOUS YEAR'S QUESTIONS

1. Which of the following is an analgesic?   **[NEET 2016]**
    (a) Penicillin   (b) Streptomycin
    (c) Chloromycetin   (d) Novalgin

2. Which of the following is an anionic detergent?   **[JEE MAIN 2016]**
    (a) Sodium lauryl sulphate   (b) Cetyl trimethyl ammonium bromide
    (c) Glyceryl oleate   (d) Sodium stearate

3. Which of the following is an analgesic?   **[MHT CET 2016]**
    (a) Ofloxacin   (b) Penicillin   (c) Aminoglycosides   (d) Paracetamol

4. Butylated hydroxy anisole is ......   **[MHT-CET 2016]**
    (a) an antioxidant   (b) cleansing agent   (c) disinfectant   (d) an antihistamine

5. Which of the following is employed as tranquilizer?   **[KARNATAKA CET 2016]**
    (a) Tetracycline   (b) Equanil   (c) Dettol   (d) Naproxen

6. What is the combining ratio of glycerol and fatty acids when they are combined to form triglyceride?   **[MHT-CET 2016]**
    (a) 3 : 4   (b) 3 : 2   (c) 1 : 3   (d) 1 : 2

7. Which among the following detergents is non-ionic in character?   **[MHT CET 2015]**
    (a) Sodium lauryl sulphate   (b) Pentaerythrityl stearate
    (c) Cetyl trimethyl ammonium chloride   (d) Sodium n-dodecyl benzene sulphonate

8. Which of the following compounds is not an antacid?   **[JEE MAIN 2015]**
    (a) Aluminium hydroxide   (b) Cimetidine
    (c) Phenelzine   (d) Ranitidine

9. Which among the following is a tranquilizer?   **[MHT CET 2015]**
    (a) Aspirin   (b) Valium   (c) Penicillin   (d) Sulphanilamide

10. Butylated hydroxy toluene is used in ......   **[MH-CET 2014]**
    (a) preventing oxidative rancidity of fats   (b) preserving food grains
    (c) killing bacteria in living tissues   (d) reducing stress and anxiety

11. Bithional is generally added to soaps as an additive to function as a/an ......
                    [CBSE AIPMT 2015]
    (a) Softener   (b) Dryer   (c) Buffering agent   (d) Antiseptic

12. Butylated hydroxyl toluene as a food additive acts as ......   **[KARNATAKA CET 2014]**
    (a) antioxidant   (b) flavouring agent
    (c) colouring agent   (d) emulsifier

13. Artificial sweetener which is stable under cold conditions only is ......   **[AIPMT 2014]**
    (a) Aspartame   (b) Alitame   (c) Saccharine   (d) Sucralose

14. Antiseptics and disinfectants either kill or prevent growth of microorganism. Identify which of the following statements is not true ?   **[NEET 2013]**
    (a) Disinfectants harm the living tissues
    (b) A 0.2% solution of phenol is an antiseptic while 1% solution acts as a disinfectant
    (c) Chlorine and iodine are used as strong disinfectants
    (d) Dilute solutions of boric acid and hydrogen peroxide are strong antiseptics

15. Chloramphenicol is an ......   **[CBSE AIPMT 2012]**
   (a) antifertility drug
   (b) antihistamin
   (c) antiseptic drug
   (d) antibiotic broad spectrum

16. The enzymes which have control site in addition to active site are called...... **[AFMC 2012]**
   (a) holozymes
   (b) coenzymes
   (c) apoenzymes
   (d) allosteric enzymes

17. The antiseptic present in dettol is ......   **[AIIMS 2012]**
   (a) quadine
   (b) chloroxylenol
   (c) bithional
   (d) none of these

18. 2-Acetoxy benzoic acid is used as ......   **[Karnataka CET 2004]**
   (a) Antiseptic
   (b) Antidepressant
   (c) Antimalarial
   (d) Antipyretic

19. Potassium metabisulphite is a (an) ......   **[MHTCET 2010]**
   (a) preservative
   (b) antioxidant
   (c) artificial sweetener
   (d) both of these

20. Arsenic drugs are mainly used in the treatment of ......   **[BVP 2010]**
   (a) jaundice
   (b) typhoid
   (c) syphilis
   (d) cholera

21. Which one of the following is employed as a tranquilizer?   **[CBSE AIPMT 2009]**
   (a) Equanil
   (b) Naproxan
   (c) Tetracycline
   (d) Chlopheniramine

22. The sweetest artificial sugar among the following is ......   **[AIIMS 2009]**
   (a) aspartame
   (b) sucralose
   (c) alitame
   (d) sucrose

23. Antipyretics are used to ......   **[MHT CET 2009]**
   (a) relieve pain
   (b) bring down body temperature
   (c) kill micro-organisms
   (d) relieve from anxiety

24. Tranquilizers are also known as ......   **[MHT CET 2008]**
   (a) psychosomatic drugs
   (b) psychotherapeutic drugs
   (c) psychosystolic drugs
   (d) none of these

25. Chloramine-T is a ......   **[AFMC 2007]**
   (a) disinfectant
   (b) antiseptic
   (c) analgesic
   (d) antipyretic

26. Tincture of iodine is ......   **[AIIMS 2006]**
   (a) alcoholic solution of I_2
   (b) solution of I_2 in aqueous KI
   (c) aqueous solution of I_2
   (d) aqueous solution of KI

27. The pair whose both species are used in antiacid medicinal preparations are ...**[AIIMS 2006]**
   (a) $NaHCO_3$ and $Mg(OH)_2$
   (b) Na_2CO_3 and $Ca(HCO_3)_2$
   (c) $Ca(HCO_3)_2$ and $Mg(OH)_2$
   (d) $Ca(OH)_2$ and $NaHCO_3$

28. Amphetamine is used as ......   **[Punjab PMET 2006]**
   (a) anaesthetic
   (b) antidepressant
   (c) antimalarial
   (d) analgesic

29. Which of the following compounds is used as a broad spectrum antibiotic ?
   (a) Ampicillin
   (b) Penicillin G   **[Punjab PMET 2006]**
   (c) Penicillin K
   (d) Tetracycline

30. Which one of the following is employed as antihistamine?   **[CBSE AIPMT 2011]**
   (a) Omeprazole
   (b) Chloramphenicol
   (c) Diphenhydramine
   (d) Norethindrone

31. Which one of the following is employed as a tranquilizer drug?   **[AIPMT 2010]**
   (a) Promethazine
   (b) Valium
   (c) Naproxen
   (d) Mifepristone

32. Arsenic containing medicine used for the treatment of syphilis, is ...... **[Kerala PMT 2010]**

(a) Tetracycline　　(b) Ofloxacin　　(c) Erythromycin　(d) Salvarsan

33. The artificial sweetener containing chlorine that has the appearance and taste as that of sugar and is stable at cooking temperature is ...... **[Kerala PMT 2010]**

(a) Aspartame　　(b) Saccharin　　(c) Sucralose　　(d) Alitame

34. The class of drugs used for the treatment of stress is ...... **[JK CET 2010]**

(a) Analgesic　　(b) Antiseptic　　(c) Antihistamine　(d) Tranquilizer

35. Aspirin is ...... **[West Bengal JEE 2010]**

(a) Acetyl salicylic acid

(b) Benzoyl salicylic acid

(c) Chlorobenzoic acid

(d) Anthranilic acid

36. The role of phosphate in detergent powder is to ...... **[Delhi PMT 2009]**

(a) Control pH level of the detergent water mixture

(b) Remove Ca^{2+} and Mg^{2+} ions from the water that causes the hardness of water

(c) Provide whiteness to the fabrics

(d) Form solid detergent as phosphateless detergents are liquid in nature

37. The oxidant which is used as an antiseptic is ...... **[West Bengal JEE 2009]**

(a) $KBrO_3$　　(b) $KMnO_4$　　(c) CrO_3　　(d) KNO_3

38. Bithional is generally added to soaps as an additive to function as a/an ......

[Kerala PMT 2009]

(a) Softener　　(b) Dryer　　(c) Buffering agent　(d) Antiseptic

39. Which among the following is not an antibiotic? **[Kerala PMT 2008]**

(a) Erythromycin　　(b) Oxytocin　　(c) Penicillin　　(d) Tetracycline

40. Which of the following is used as a "morning after pill"? **[Kerala PMT 2007]**

(a) Mifepristone　　(b) Ethynylestradiol　(c) Norethindrone　　(d) Promethazine

ANSWER KEY

1. (d)	2. (b)	3. (a)	4. (b)	5. (b)	6. (a)	7. (b)	8. (b)
9. (a)	10. (b)	11. (a)	12. (c)	13. (a)	14. (b)	15. (a)	16. (c)
17. (c)	18. (a)	19. (b)	20. (c)	21. (b)	22. (b)	23. (b)	24. (b)
25. (a)	26. (c)	27. (b)	28. (c)	29. (d)	30. (b)	31. (b)	32. (d)
33. (a)	34. (a)	35. (b)	36. (c)	37. (a)	38. (a)	39. (b)	40. (c)
41. (b)	42. (c)	43. (a)	44. (b)	45. (d)	46. (a)	47. (a)	48. (b)
49. (b)	50. (c)	51. (c)	52. (d)	53. (c)	54. (c)	55. (c)	56. (a)
57. (d)	58. (c)	59. (b)	60. (c)	61. (b)	62. (a)	63. (b)	64. (c)
65. (d)	66. (a)	67. (d)	68. (c)	69. (b)	70. (b)	71. (a)	72. (b)
73. (a)	74. (a)	75. (c)	76. (b)	77. (b)	78. (a)	79. (b)	80. (b)
81. (a)	82. (a)	83. (c)	84. (d)	85. (b)	86. (a)	87. (d)	88. (b)
89. (a)	90. (c)	91. (c)	92. (c)	93. (c)	94. (a)	95. (a)	96. (a)
97. (d)	98. (d)	99. (a)	100. (a)	101. (d)	102. (d)	103. (b)	104. (a)
105. (c)	106. (b)	107. (b)	108. (c)	109. (d)	110. (c)	111. (c)	112. (a)

113. (b)	114. (d)	115. (b)	116. (d)	117. (b)	118. (c)	119. (a)	120. (d)
121. (d)	122. (a)	123. (d)	124. (a)	125. (b)	126. (b)	127. (a)	128. (b)
129. (b)	130. (c)	131. (c)	132. (d)	133. (a)	134. (b)	135. (b)	136. (a)
137. (b)	138. (c)	139. (c)	140. (b)	141. (b)	142. (d)	143. (a)	144. (d)
145. (c)	146. (d)	147. (a)	148. (d)	149. (d)	150. (a)		

Previous Year's Questions

1. (d)	2. (a)	3. (d)	4. (a)	5. (b)	6. (c)	7. (b)	8. (c)
9. (b)	10. (a)	11. (d)	12. (a)	13. (a)	14. (d)	15. (d)	16. (d)
17. (b)	18. (d)	19. (a)	20. (c)	21. (a)	22. (b)	23. (b)	24. (b)
25. (b)	26. (a)	27. (a)	28. (b)	29. (b)	30. (c)	31. (b)	32. (d)
33. (c)	34. (d)	35. (a)	36. (b)	37. (b)	38. (d)	39. (b)	40. (a)

❑❑❑

PRACTICE QUESTION PAPERS
Practice Paper - I

1. Identify the correct statement for change of Gibbs energy for a system (ΔG_{system}) at constant temperature and pressure ......
   (a) If $\Delta G_{system} > 0$, the process is spontaneous
   (b) If $\Delta G_{system} = 0$, the system has attained equilibrium
   (c) If $\Delta G_{system} = 0$, the system is still moving in a particular direction
   (d) If $\Delta G_{system} < 0$, the process is not spontaneous

2. A solution containing 10 g per dm^3 of urea (molecular mass = 60 g mol^{-1}) is isotonic with a 5% solution of a non-volatile solute. The molecular mass of this non-volatile solution is ......
   (a) 250 g mol^{-1} (b) 300 g mol^{-1} (c) 350 g mol^{-1} (d) 200 g mol^{-1}

3. A plot of log x/m versus log p for the adsorption of a gas on a solid gives a straight line with slope equal to ......
   (a) $-\log K$ (b) n   (c) 1/n   (d) log K

4. Assume each reaction is carried out in an open container. For which reaction will $\Delta H = \Delta E$?
   (a) $H_{2(g)} + Br_{2(g)} \rightarrow 2HBr_{(g)}$ (b) $C_{(s)} + 2H_2O_{(g)} \rightarrow 2H_{2(g)} + CO_{2(g)}$
   (c) $PCl_{5(g)} \rightarrow PCl_{3(g)} + Cl_{2(g)}$ (d) $2CO_{(g)} + O_{2(g)} \rightarrow 2CO_{2(g)}$

5. In a set of reactions, propionic acid yielded a compound D.

$$CH_3CH_2COOH \xrightarrow{SOCl_2} B \xrightarrow{NH_3} C \xrightarrow[Br_2]{KOH} D$$

   (a) $CH_3CH_2CH_2NH_2$ (b) $CH_3CH_2CONH_2$ (c) $CH_2CH_2NHCH_3$ (d) $CH_3CH_2NH_2$

6. During the process of digestion, the proteins present in food materials are hydrolysed to amino acids. The two enzymes involved in the process are ......

$$\text{Proteins} \xrightarrow{\text{Enzyme (A)}} \text{Polypeptides} \xrightarrow{\text{Enzyme (B)}} \text{Amino acids}$$

   (a) Amylase and Maltase   (b) Diastase and Lipase
   (c) Pepsin and Trypsin   (d) Invertase and Zymase

7. The human body does not produce ......
   (a) DNA   (b) Vitamins   (c) Hormones   (d) Enzymes

8. CsBr crystallizes in a body centred cubic lattice. The unit cell length is 436.6 pm. Given that the atomic mass of Cs = 133 and that of Br = 80 amu and Avogadro number being 6.02×10^{23} mol^{-1}, the density of CsBr is ......
   (a) 42.5 g/cm^3 (b) 0.425 g/cm^3 (c) 8.25 g/cm^3 (d) 4.25 g/cm^3

9. More number of oxidation states are exhibited by actinoids than by lanthanoids. The main reason for this is ......
   (a) More energy difference between 5f and 6d orbitals than that between 4f and 5d orbitals
   (b) Lesser energy difference between 5f and 6d orbitals than that between 4f and 5d orbitals
   (c) Greater metallic character of lanthanoids than that of corresponding actinoids
   (d) More active nature of actinoids

P.1

10. Given: The mass of electron is 9.11×10^{-31} kg, Planck constant is 6.626×10^{-34} Js, the uncertainty involved in the measurement of velocity within a distance of 0.1 Å is ......
(a) $5.79 \times 10^6 \, ms^{-1}$　　　(b) $5.79 \times 10^7 \, ms^{-1}$　　　(c) $5.79 \times 10^8 \, ms^{-1}$　(d) $5.79 \times 10^5 \, ms^{-1}$

11. Copper sulphate dissolved in excess of KCN to give ......
(a) CuCN　　　　(b) $[Cu(CN)_4]^{3-}$　　　(c) $[Cu(CN)_4]^{2-}$　　　(d) $Cu(CN)_2$

12. In which of the following pairs are both the ions coloured in aqueous solution ......
(a) Ni^{2+}, Ti^{3+}　　　　(b) Sc^{3+}, Ti^{3+}　　　　(c) Sc^{3+}, Co^{2+}
(d) Ni^{2+}, Cu^+ [At. No. of Sc = 21, Ti = 22, Ni = 28, Cu = 29, Co = 27]

13. The enthalpy and entropy change for the reaction: $Br_2(l) + Cl_2(g) \rightarrow 2BrCl(g)$ are 30 kJ mol^{-1} and 105 J $K^{-1}mol^{-1}$ respectively. The temperature at which the reaction will be in equilibrium is ......
(a) 285.7 K　　　　(b) 273 K　　　　(c) 450 K　　　　(d) 300 K

14. The appearance of colour in solid alkali metal halides is generally due to ......
(a) F-centres　　　　　　　　　　(b) Schottky defect
(c) Frenkel defect　　　　　　　　(d) Interstitial positions

15. If $E^o_{Fe/Fe^{2+}} = -0.441$ V and $E^o_{Fe^{2+}/Fe^{3+}} = 0.771$ V, the standard EMF of the reaction $Fe + 2Fe^{3+} \rightarrow 3Fe^{2+}$ will be ......
(a) 0.330 V　　　　(b) 1.653 V　　　　(c) 1.212 V　　　　(d) 0.111 V

16. For the reaction : $2A + B \rightarrow 3C + D$, which of the following does not express the reaction rate ?
(a) $-\dfrac{d[C]}{3dt}$　　　　(b) $-\dfrac{d[B]}{dt}$　　　　(c) $\dfrac{d[D]}{dt}$　　　　(d) $-\dfrac{d[A]}{2dt}$

17. For the reaction $CH_{4(g)} + 2O_{2(g)} \rightleftharpoons CO_{2(g)} + 2H_2O_{(l)}$, $\Delta H_r = -170.8$ kJ mol^{-1}, which of the following statements is not true ?
(a) At equilibrium, the concentrations of $CO_{2(g)}$ and $H_2O_{(l)}$ are not equal
(b) The equilibrium constant for the reaction is given by $K_p = \dfrac{[CO_2]}{[CH_4]\,[O_2]}$
(c) Addition of $CH_{4(g)}$ or $O_{2(g)}$ at equilibrium will cause a shift to the right
(d) The reaction is exothermic

18. $[NH(CH_2)NHCO(CH_2)_4CO]_n$ is a ......
(a) Copolymer　　　　　　　　　(b) Addition polymer
(c) Thermosetting polymer　　　　(d) Homopolymer

19. A carbonyl compound reacts with hydrogen cyanide to form cyanohydrin which on hydrolysis forms a racemic mixture of α-hydroxy acid. The carbonyl compound is ......
(a) Acetaldehyde　　　(b) Acetone　　　(c) Diethyl ketone　(d) Formaldehyde

20. Which one of the following is a peptide hormone ?
(a) Glucagon　　　(b) Testosterone　　　(c) Thyroxin　　　(d) Adrenaline

21. The major organic product in the reaction $CH_3-O-CH(CH_3)_2 + HI \rightarrow$ Product is ......
(a) $CH_3OH + (CH_3)_2CHI$　　　　　　(b) $ICH_2OCH(CH_3)_2$
(c) $CH_3OC(CH_3)_2I$　　　　　　　　(d) $CH_3I + (CH_3)_2CHOH$

22. Nucleophilic addition reaction will be most favoured in ......
(a) $CH_3-CH_2-CH_2CO-CH_3$　　　　　(b) $(CH_3)_2C = O$
(c) CH_3CH_2CHO　　　　　　　　　　(d) CH_3CHO

23. The enthalpy of hydrogenation of cyclohexene is -119.5 kJ mol^{-1}. If resonance energy of benzene is -150.4 kJ mol^{-1}, its enthalpy of hydrogenation would be ......
(a) -508.9 kJ mol^{-1}　　　(b) -208.1 kJ mol^{-1}　　　(c) -269.9 kJ mol^{-1} (d) -358.5 kJ mol^{-1}

24. Self condensation of two moles of ethyl acetate in the presence of sodium ethoxide yields ......
(a) Ethyl butyrate
(b) Acetoacetic ester
(c) Methyl acetoacetate
(d) Ethyl propionate

25. $N_{2(g)} + 3H_{2(g)} \rightarrow 2NH_{3(g)}$. The equality relationship between $\dfrac{d[NH_3]}{dt}$ and $-\dfrac{d[H_2]}{dt}$ is ......
(a) $\dfrac{d[NH_3]}{dt} = -\dfrac{1}{3}\dfrac{d[H_2]}{dt}$
(b) $+\dfrac{d[NH_3]}{dt} = -\dfrac{2}{3}\dfrac{d[H_2]}{dt}$
(c) $+\dfrac{d[NH_3]}{dt} = -\dfrac{3}{2}\dfrac{d[H_2]}{dt}$
(d) $\dfrac{d[NH_3]}{dt} = -\dfrac{d[H_2]}{dt}$

26. Which of the following is not chiral ?
(a) 2-Butanol
(b) 2, 3-Dibromopentane
(c) 3-Bromopentane
(d) 2-Hydroxypropanoic acid

27. $[Co(NH_3)_4(NO_2)_2]Cl$ exhibits ......
(a) Linkage isomerism, ionization isomerism and optical isomerism
(b) Linkage isomerism, ionization isomerism and geometrical isomerism
(c) Ionization isomerism, geometrical isomerism and optical isomerism
(d) Linkage isomerism, geometrical isomerism and optical isomerism

28. $[Cr(H_2O)_6]Cl_3$ (At. No. of Cr = 24) has a magnetic moment of 3.83 B.M. The correct distribution of 3d electrons in the Chromium of the complex is ......
(a) $(3d_{x^2-y^2})^1, 3d_z^2, 3d_{xz}^1$
(b) $3d_{xz}^1, (3d_{x^2-y^2})^1, 3d_{yz}^1$
(c) $3d_{xy}^1, 3d_{yz}^1, 3d_{xz}^1$
(d) $3d_{xy}^1, 3d_{yz}^1, 3d_z^2$

29. 1.0 g of a non-electrolyte solute (molar mass 250 g mol^{-1}) was dissolved in 51.2 g of benzene. If the freezing point depression constant K_f of benzene is 5.12 K kg mol^{-1}, the freezing point of benzene will be lowered by ......
(a) 0.4 K　　　(b) 0.3 K　　　(c) 0.5 K　　　(d) 0.2 K

30. Which of the following pairs constitutes a buffer ......
(a) HNO_2 and $NaNO_2$
(b) $NaOH$ and $NaCl$
(c) HNO_3 and NH_4NO_3
(d) HCl and KCl

31. The hydrogen ion concentration of a 10^{-8} M HCl aqueous solution at 298 K ($K_W = 10^{-14}$) is ......
(a) 1.0×10^{-6} M　　　(b) 1.0525×10^{-7} M　　　(c) 9.525×10^{-8} M　　　(d) 1.0×10^{-8} M

32. A solution of acetone in ethanol ......
(a) shows a negative deviation from Raoult's law
(b) shows a positive deviation from Raoult's law
(c) behaves like a near ideal solution
(d) obeys Raoult's law

33. A hypothetical electrochemical cell is shown below : $\overset{\ominus}{A} \mid A^+ \text{ (xM)} \parallel B^+ \text{ (yM)} \mid \overset{\oplus}{B}$
The emf measured is $+0.20$ V. The cell reaction is ......
(a) $A^+ + B \rightarrow A + B^+$
(b) $A^+ + e^- \rightarrow A; B^+ + e^- \rightarrow B$
(c) The cell reaction cannot be predicted
(d) $A + B^+ \rightarrow A^+ + B$

34. Ethylene oxide when treated with Grignard reagent yields ......
    (a) Secondary alcohol   (b) Tertiary alcohol
    (c) Cyclopropyl alcohol   (d) Primary alcohol

35. During osmosis, flow of water through a semipermeable membrane is ......
    (a) From solution having higher concentration only
    (b) From both sides of semipermeable membrane with equal flow rates
    (c) From both sides of semipermeable membrane with unequal flow rates
    (d) From solution having lower concentration only

36. Which of the following is more basic than aniline ?
    (a) Diphenylamine   (b) Triphenylamine   (c) p-Nitroaniline   (d) Benzylamine

37. In which of the following molecules, all the bonds are not equal ?
    (a) ClF_3 (b) BF_3 (c) AlF_3 (d) NF_3

38. The electronegativity difference between N and F is greater than that between N and H yet the dipole moment of NH_3 (1.5 D) is larger than that of NF_3 (0.2 D). This is because ......
    (a) In NH_3 as well as in NF_3 the atomic dipole and bond dipole are in the same direction
    (b) In NH_3 the atomic dipole and bond dipole are in the same direction whereas in NF_3 these are in opposite directions
    (c) In NH_3 as well as NF_3 the atomic dipole and bond dipole are in opposite directions
    (d) In NH_3 the atomic dipole and bond dipole are in opposite directions whereas in NF_3 these are in the same direction

39. The correct order of the mobility of alkali metal ions in aqueous solution is ......
    (a) $Li^+ > Na^+ > K^+ > Rb^+$ (b) $Na^+ > K^+ > Rb^+ > Li^+$
    (c) $K^+ > Rb^+ > Na^+ > Li^+$ (d) $Rb^+ > K^+ > Na^+ > Li^+$

40. The correct order regarding the electronegativity of hybrid orbitals of carbon is ......
    (a) $sp > sp^2 < sp^3$ (b) $sp > sp^2 > sp^3$ (c) $sp < sp^2 > sp3$ (d) $sp < sp^2 < sp^3$

41. Which of the following species has a linear shape ?
    (a) NO_2^- (b) SO_2 (c) NO_2^+ (d) O_3

41. The orientation of an atomic orbital is governed by ......
    (a) Azimuthal quantum number   (b) Spin quantum number
    (c) Magnetic quantum number   (d) Principal quantum number

42. Which of the following is not a correct statement ?
    (a) The electron-deficient molecules can act as Lewis acids
    (b) The canonical structures have no real existence
    (c) Every AB_5 molecule does infact have square pyramid structure
    (d) Multiple bonds are always shorter than corresponding single bonds

43. The number of unpaired electrons in a paramagnetic diatomic molecule of an element with atomic number 16 is ......
    (a) 2   (b) 3   (c) 4   (d) 1

44. Which one of the following orders is not in accordance with the property stated against it ?
    (a) $F_2 > Cl_2 > Br_2 > I_2$; Oxidising power
    (b) $HI > HBr > HCl > HF$; Acidic property in water
    (c) $F_2 > Cl_2 > Br_2 > I_2$; Electronegativity
    (d) $F_2 > Cl_2 > Br_2 > I_2$; Bond dissociation energy

45. The IUPAC name of [structure: CH₃CH₂–CH(CH₃)–CH(CH₃)–C(=O)Cl] is ......

   (a) 3, 4-dimethylpentanoyl chloride   (b) 1-chloro-1-oxo-2,3-dimethylpentane

   (c) 2-ethyl-3-methylbutanoyl chloride   (d) 2, 3-dimethylpentanoyl chloride

ANSWER KEY

1. (b)	2. (b)	3. (c)	4. (a)	5. (d)	6. (c)	7. (b)	8. (d)
9. (b)	10. (a)	11. (b)	12. (a)	13. (a)	14. (a)	15. (c)	16. (d)
17. (b)	18. (a)	19. (a)	20. (a)	21. (d)	22. (d)	23. (b)	24. (b)
25. (b)	26. (d)	27. (d)	28. (c)	29. (a)	30. (c)	31. (b)	32. (a)
33. (d)	34. (d)	35. (d)	36. (d)	37. (a)	38. (b)	39. (b)	40. (b)
41. (c)	42. (c)	43. (a)	44. (d)	45. (d)			

Practice Paper - II

1. Which one of the following on reduction with lithium aluminium hydride yields a secondary amine?

   (a) Methyl isocyanide   (b) Acetamide   (c) Methyl cyanide   (d) Nitroethane

2. RNA and DNA are chiral molecules, their chirality is due to ......

   (a) chiral bases   (b) chiral phosphate ester units

   (c) D-sugar component   (d) L-sugar component

3. A weak acid, HA, has a K_a of 1.00×10^{-5}. If 0.100 mole of this acid dissolved in one litre of water, the percentage of acid dissociated at equilibrium is closest to ......

   (a) 1.00%   (b) 99.9%   (c) 0.100%   (d) 99.0%

4. The efficiency of a fuel cell is given by ......

   (a) $\dfrac{\Delta G}{\Delta S}$ (b) $\dfrac{\Delta G}{\Delta H}$ (c) $\dfrac{\Delta S}{\Delta G}$ (d) $\dfrac{\Delta H}{\Delta G}$

5. The correct order of increasing thermal stability of K_2CO_3, $MgCO_3$, $CaCO_3$ and $BeCO_3$ is ......

   (a) $BeCO_3 < MgCO_3 < CaCO_3 < K_2CO_3$ (b) $MgCO_3 < BeCO_3 < CaCO_3 < K_2CO_3$

   (c) $K_2CO_3 < MgCO_3 < CaCO_3 < BeCO_3$ (d) $BeCO_3 < MgCO_3 < K_2CO_3 < CaCO_3$

6. In a first-order reaction A ⇌ B, if k is a rate constant and initial concentration of the reactant A is 0.5 M, then the half-life is ......

   (a) $\dfrac{\log 2}{k}$ (b) $\dfrac{\log 2}{k\sqrt{0.5}}$ (c) $\dfrac{\ln 2}{k}$ (d) $\dfrac{0.693}{0.5k}$

7. Consider the following compounds :

   (i) C_6H_5COCl (ii) O_2N–C₆H₄–COCl

   (iii) H_3C–C₆H₄–COCl   (iv) OHC–C₆H₄–COCl

The correct decreasing order of their reactivity towards hydrolysis is ......

   (a) (i) > (ii) > (iii) > (iv)   (b) (iv) > (ii) > (i) > (iii)

   (c) (ii) > (iv) > (i) > (iii)   (d) (ii) > (iv) > (iii) > (i)

8. Predict the product C obtained in the following reaction of butyne-1.

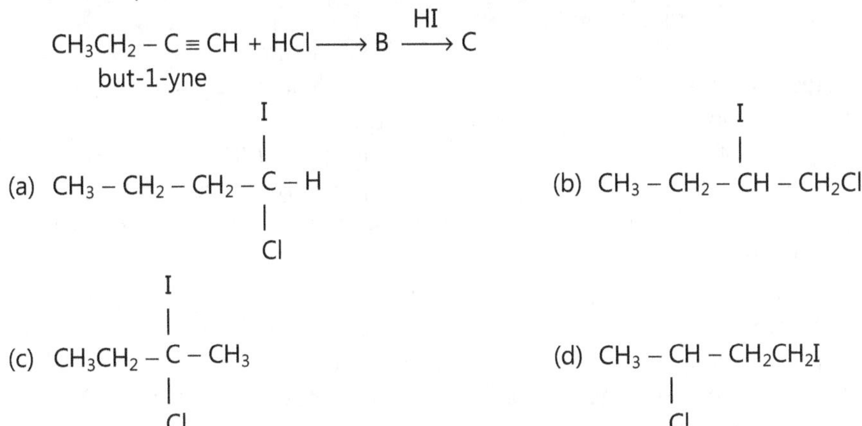

9. Concentrated aqueous sulphuric acid is 98% H_2SO_4 by mass and has a density of 1.80 gm/litre^{-1}. Volume of acid required to make one litre of 0.1 M H_2SO_4 solution is ......

(a) 16.65 ml   (b) 22.20 ml   (c) 5.55 ml   (d) 11.10 ml

10. Reduction of aldehydes and ketones into hydrocarbons using zinc amalgam and conc. HCl is called as ......

(a) Cope reduction   (b) Dow reduction

(c) Wolf-Kishner reduction   (d) Clemmensen reduction

11. Given that bond energies of H – H and Cl – Cl are 430 kJ mol^{-1} and 240 kJ mol^{-1} respectively and ΔH_f for HCl is – 90 kJ mol^{-1}, bond enthalpy of HCl is ......

(a) 380 kJ mol^{-1} (b) 425 kJ mol^{-1} (c) 245 kJ mol^{-1} (d) 290 kJ mol^{-1}

12. Which of the following represents the correct order of the acidity in the given compounds?

(a) $FCH_2COOH > CH_3COOH > BrCH_2COOH > ClCH_2COOH$

(b) $BrCH_2COOH > ClCH_2COOH > FCH_2COOH > CH_3COOH$

(c) $FCH_2COOH > ClCH_2COOH > BrCH_2COOH > CH_3COOH$

(d) $CH_3COOH > BrCH_2COOH > ClCH_2COOH > FCH_2COOH$

13. If there is no rotation of plane polarised light by a compound in a specific solvent, though to be chiral, it may mean that ......

(a) the compound is certainly meso   (b) there is no compound in the solvent

(c) the compound may be a racemic mixture   (d) the compound is certainly achiral

14. Which of the following is water soluble?

(a) Vitamin E   (b) Vitamin K   (c) Vitamin A   (d) Vitamin B

15. Identify the correct order of the size of the following:

(a) $Ca^{2+} < K^+ < Ar < Cl^- < S^{2-}$ (b) $Ar < Ca^{2+} < K^+ < Cl^- < S^{2-}$

(c) $Ca^{2+} < Ar < K^+ < Cl^- < S^{2-}$ (d) $Ca^{2+} < K^+ < Ar < S^{2-} < Cl^-$

16. 0.5 molal aqueous solution of a weak acid (HX) is 20% ionised. If K_f for water is 1.86 K kg mol^{-1}, the lowering in freezing point of the solution is ......

(a) 0.56 K   (b) 1.12 K   (c) –0.56 K   (d) –1.12 K

17. Sulphide ores of metals are usually concentrated by froth floatation process. Which one of the following sulphide ores offer an exception and is concentrated by chemical leaching?

(a) Galena   (b) Copper pyrite   (c) Sphalerite   (d) Argentite

18. If 60% of a first order reaction was completed in 60 minutes, 50% of the same reaction would be completed in approximately ......

(a) 45 minutes
(b) 60 minutes
(c) 40 minutes
(d) 50 minutes (log 4 = 0.60, log 5 = 0.69)

19. Which of the following will give a pair of enantiomorphs?

(a) $[Cr(NH_3)_6][Co(CN)_6]$
(b) $[Co(en)_2Cl_2]Cl$
(c) $[Pt(NH_3)_4][PtCl_6]$
(d) $[Co(NH_3)_3Cl_3]NO_2$

20. If NaCl is doped with 10^{-4} mol % of $SrCl_2$, the concentration of cation vacancies will be ... ($Na = 6.02 \times 10^{23}$ mol^{-1})

(a) $6.02 \times 10^{16}\ mol^{-1}$
(b) $6.02 \times 10^{17}\ mol^{-1}$
(c) $6.02 \times 10^{14}\ mol^{-1}$
(d) $6.02 \times 10^{15}\ mol^{-1}$

21. The d electron configurations of Cr^{2+}, Mn^{2+}, Fe^{2+} and Ni^{2+} are $3d^4$, $3d^5$, $3d^6$ and $3d^8$ respectively. Which one of the following aqua complexes will exhibit the minimum paramagnetic behaviour?
(At. No. of Cr = 24, Mn = 25, Fe = 26, Ni = 28)

(a) $[Fe(H_2O)_6]^{2+}$
(b) $[Ni(H_2O)_6]^{2+}$
(c) $[Cr(H_2O)_6]^{2+}$
(d) $[Mn(H_2O)_6]^{2+}$

22. In which of the following the hydration energy is higher than the lattice energy?

(a) $MgSO_4$
(b) $RaSO_4$
(c) $SrSO_4$
(d) $BaSO_4$

23. Which of the compounds with molecular formula C_5H_{10} yields acetone on ozonolysis?

(a) 3-methyl-1-butene
(b) cyclopentane
(c) 2-methyl-1-butene
(d) 2-methyl-2-butene

24. With which of the following electronic configurations, an atom has the lowest ionization enthalpy?

(a) $1s^2\ 2s^2\ sp^3$
(b) $1s^2\ 2s^2\ 2p^5\ 3s^1$
(c) $1s^2\ 2s^2\ 2p^6$
(d) $1s^2\ 2s^2\ 2p^5$

25. Which one of the following ionic species has the greatest proton affinity to form stable compound?

(a) NH_2^-
(b) F^-
(c) I^-
(d) HS^-

26. The following equilibrium constants are given :

$$N_2 + 3H_2 \rightleftharpoons 2NH_3;\ K_1 \qquad N_2 + O_2 \rightleftharpoons 2NO;\ K_2 \qquad H_2 + \frac{1}{2}O_2 \rightleftharpoons H_2O;\ K_3$$

The equilibrium constant for the oxidation of NH_3 by oxygen to give NO is ......

(a) $\dfrac{K_2\ K_3^2}{K_1}$
(b) $\dfrac{K_2^2\ K_3}{K_1}$
(c) $\dfrac{K_1\ K_2}{K_3}$
(d) $\dfrac{K_2\ K_3^3}{K_1}$

27. Which one of the following ions is the most stable in aqueous solution?

(a) V^{3+}
(b) Ti^{3+}
(c) Mn^{3+}
(d) Cr^{3+}

(At. No. of Ti = 22, V = 23, Cr = 24, Mn = 25)

28. Which one of the following orders correctly represent the increasing acid strengths of the given acids?

(a) $HOClO < HOCl < HOClO_3 < HOClO_2$
(b) $HOClO_2 < HOClO_3 < HOClO < HOCl$
(c) $HOClO_3 < HOClO_2 < HOClO < HOCl$
(d) $HOCl < HOClO < HOClO_2 < HOClO_3$

29. Which one of the following on treatment with 50% aqueous sodium hydroxide yield the corresponding alcohol and acid?

(a) C_6H_5CHO
(b) $CH_3CH_2CH_2CHO$
(c) CH_3COCH_3
(d) $C_6H_5CH_2CHO$

30. For (i) I^-, (ii) Cl^-, (iii) Br^-, the increasing order of nucleophilicity would be ......

    (a) $Cl^- < Br^- < I^-$ (b) $I^- < Cl^- < Br^-$ (c) $Br^- < Cl^- < I^-$ (d) $I^- < Br^- < Cl^-$

31. Calculate the pOH of a solution at 25°C that contains 1×10^{-10} M of hydronium ions, i.e. H_3O^+.

    (a) 4.000   (b) 9.0000   (c) 1.000   (d) 7.000

32. Consider the following sets of quantum numbers :

	n	l	m	s
(i)	3	0	0	+1/2
(ii)	2	2	1	+1/2
(iii)	4	3	−2	−1/2
(iv)	1	0	−1	−1/2
(v)	3	2	3	+1/2

Which of the following sets of quantum numbers is not possible?

    (a) (i), (ii), (iii) and (iv)   (b) (ii), (iv) and (v)   (c) (i) and (iii)   (d) (ii), (iii) and (iv)

33. The equilibrium constant of the reaction :

$$Cu(s) + 2Ag^+ \rightleftharpoons Cu^{2+} + 2Ag(s); \quad E° = 0.46 \text{ V at } 298 \text{ K is}$$

    (a) 2.0×10^{10} (b) 4.0×10^{10} (c) 4.0×10^{15} (d) 2.4×10^{10}

34. Which one of the following polymers is prepared by condensation polymerisation?

    (a) Teflon   (b) Natural rubber   (c) Styrene   (d) Nylon-66

35. The order of decreasing reactivity towards an electrophilic reagent, for the following would be ......

(i) benzene (ii) toluene (iii) chlorobenzene (iv) phenol

    (a) (ii) > (iv) > (i) > (iii)   (b) (iv) > (iii) > (ii) > (i)

    (c) (iv) > (ii) > (i) > (iii)   (d) (i) > (ii) > (iii) > (iv)

36. An element X has the following isotopic compositions: 200X : 90%, 199X : 8.0%, 202X : 2.0%. The weighted average atomic mass of the naturally occurring element X is closest to ......

    (a) 201 amu   (b) 202 amu   (c) 199 amu   (d) 200 amu

37. The fraction of total volume occupied by atoms present in a simple cube is ......

    (a) $\dfrac{\pi}{3\sqrt{2}}$ (b) $\dfrac{\pi}{4\sqrt{2}}$ (c) $\dfrac{\pi}{4}$ (d) $\dfrac{\pi}{6}$

38. In the reaction $CH_3 - \overset{\overset{\displaystyle CH_3}{|}}{CH} - CH_2 - O - CH_2 - CH_3 + HI \xrightarrow{\text{Heated}} ?$

which of the following compounds will be formed?

    (a) $CH_3 - \overset{\overset{\displaystyle CH_3}{|}}{CH} - CH_3 + CH_3CH_2OH$ (b) $CH_3 - \overset{\overset{\displaystyle CH_3}{|}}{CH} - CH_2OH + CH_3CH_3$

    (c) $CH_3 - \overset{\overset{\displaystyle CH_3}{|}}{CH} - CH_2OH + CH_3 - CH_2 - I$ (d) $CH_3 - \overset{\overset{\displaystyle CH_3}{|}}{CH} - CH_2 - I + CH_3CH_2OH$

39. The product formed in aldol condensation is ......
   (a) a beta-hydroxy aldehyde or a beta-hydroxy ketone
   (b) an alpha-hydroxy aldehyde or ketone
   (c) an alpha, beta unsaturated ester
   (d) a beta-hydroxy acid

40. The number of moles of $KMnO_4$ that will be needed to react with one mole of sulphite ion in acidic solution is ......
   (a) 4/5   (b) 2/5   (c) 1   (d) 3/5

41. Identify the incorrect statement among the following :
   (a) Lanthanoid contraction is the accumulation of successive shrinkages.
   (b) As a result of lanthanoid contraction, the properties of 4d series of the transition elements have no similarities with the 5d series of elements.
   (c) Shielding power of 4f electrons is quite weak.
   (d) There is decrease in radii of atoms or ions as one proceeds from La to Lu.

42. Which of the following compounds will give a yellow precipitate with iodine and alkali ?
   (a) 3-Hydroxy pentane   (b) Acetophenone
   (c) Methyl acetate   (d) Acetamide

43. Chloramphenicol is an ......
   (a) Antibiotic–broad spectrum   (b) Antifertility drug
   (c) Antiseptic and disinfectant   (d) Antibiotic–narrow spectrum

44. The correct order of C – O bond length among CO, CO_3^{2-}, CO_2 is ......
   (a) $CO < CO_3^{2-} < CO_2$ (b) $CO_3^{2-} < CO_2 < CO$
   (c) $CO < CO_2 < CO_3^{2-}$ (d) $CO_2 < CO_3^{2-} < CO$

45. Consider the following reactions :
   (i) $H^+(aq) + OH^-(aq) \rightarrow H_2O(l), \ \Delta H = - X_1 \text{ kJ mol}^{-1}$

   (ii) $H_2(g) + \frac{1}{2} O_2(g) \rightarrow H_2O \ (l), \Delta H = - X_2 \text{ kJ mol}^{-1}$

   (iii) $CO_2(g) + H_2(g) \rightarrow CO(g) + H_2O, \ \Delta H = - X_3 \text{ kJ mol}^{-1}$

   (iv) $5C_2H_2 + \frac{5}{2} O_2 \rightarrow 2CO_2(g) + H_2O(l), \ \Delta H = - X_4 \text{ kJ mol}^{-1}$

   Enthalpy of formation of H_2O (l) is
   (a) $+ X_3 \text{ kJ mol}^{-1}$ (b) $- X_4 \text{ kJ mol}^{-1}$ (c) $+ X_1 \text{ kJ mol}^{-1}$ (d) $- X_2 \text{ kJ mol}^{-1}$

ANSWER KEY							
1. (a)	2. (c)	3. (a)	4. (b)	5. (a)	6. (c)	7. (c)	8. (c)
9. (c)	10. (d)	11. (b)	12. (c)	13. (a)	14. (d)	15. (a)	16. (b)
17. (d)	18. (a)	19. (b)	20. (b)	21. (b)	22. (a)	23. (d)	24. (b)
25. (a)	26. (d)	27. (d)	28. (d)	29. (a)	30. (a)	31. (a)	32. (b)
33. (c)	34. (d)	35. (c)	36. (c)	37. (d)	38. (c)	39. (a)	40. (b)
41. (d)	42. (b)	43. (a)	44. (c)	45. (d)			

❑❑❑

1. A hydrogen gas electrode is made by dipping platinum wire in a solution of HCl of pH = 10 and by passing hydrogen gas around the platinum wire at one atmosphere pressure. The oxidation potential of the electrode would be ......

   (a) 0.059 V
   (b) 0.59 V
   (c) 0.118 V
   (d) 1.18 V

2. A reaction having equal energies of activation for forward and reverse reactions has ......

   (a) $\Delta S = 0$
   (b) $\Delta G = 0$
   (c) $\Delta H = 0$
   (d) $\Delta H = \Delta G = \Delta S = 0$

3. At 25°C molar conductance of 0.1 molar aqueous solution of ammonium hydroxide is $9.54 \ ohm^{-1} \ cm^2 \ mol^{-1}$ and at infinite dilution its molar conductance is $238 \ ohm^{-1} \ cm^2 \ mol^{-1}$. The degree of ionisation of ammonium hydroxide at the same concentration and temperature is ......

   (a) 2.080%
   (b) 20.800%
   (c) 4.008%
   (d) 40.800%

4. Based on equation $E = -2.178 \times 10^{-18} \ J \left(\dfrac{Z^2}{n^2}\right)$, certain conclusions are written. Which of them is not correct ?

   (a) The negative sign in equation simply means that the energy of electron bound to the nucleus is lower than it would be if the electrons were at the infinite distance from the nucleus

   (b) Larger the value of n, the larger is the orbit radius

   (c) Equation can be used to calculate the change in energy when the electron changes its orbit

   (d) For n = 1, the electron has a more negative energy than it does for n = 6 which means that the electron is more loosely bound in the smallest allowed orbit.

5. A button cell used in watches functions as following :

   $$Zn(s) + Ag_2O(s) + H_2O(l) \rightleftharpoons 2Ag(s) + Zn^{2+} (aq) + 2OH^- (aq)$$

   If half cell potentials are $Zn^{2+} (aq) + 2e^- \rightarrow Zn(s); \ E° = -0.76 \ V$

   $Ag_2O(s) + H_2O(l) + 2e^- \rightarrow 2Ag(s) + 2OH^- (aq), \ E° = 0.34 \ V$

   The cell potential will be ......

   (a) 1.10 V
   (b) 0.42 V
   (c) 0.84 V
   (d) 1.34 V

6. How many grams of concentrated nitric acid solution should be used to prepare 250 ml of 2.0 M HNO_3 ? The concentrated acid is 70% HNO_3.

   (a) 45.0 g conc. HNO_3
   (b) 90.0 g conc. HNO_3
   (c) 70.0 g conc. HNO_3
   (d) 54.0 g conc. HNO_3

7. The number of carbon atoms per unit cell of diamond unit cell is ......

   (a) 4
   (b) 8
   (c) 6
   (d) 1

8. Maximum deviation from ideal gas is expected from ......

   (a) $H_2(g)$
   (b) $N_2(g)$
   (c) $CH_4(g)$
   (d) $NH_3(g)$

9. A metal has a fcc lattice. The edge length of the unit cell is 404 pm. The density of the metal is 2.72 g cm^{-3}. The molar mass of the metal is ......
(N_A = Avogadro's constant = 6.02×10^{23} mol^{-1})
(a) 40 g mol^{-1} (b) 30 g mol^{-1} (c) 27 g mol^{-1} (d) 20 g mol^{-1}

10. Dipole-induced dipole interactions are present in which of the following pairs ?
(a) H_2O and alcohol   (b) Cl_2 and CCl_4
(c) HCl and He atoms   (d) SiF_4 and He atoms

11. A magnetic moment of 1.73 BM will be shown by one among the following ......
(a) $[Cu(NH_3)_4]^{2+}$ (b) $[Ni(CN)_4]^{2-}$ (c) $TiCl_4$ (d) $[CoCl_6]^{4-}$

12. Roasting of sulphides gives the gas X as a by-product. This is a colourless gas with choking smell of burnt sulphur and causes great damage to respiratory organs as a result of acid rain. Its aqueous solution is acidic and acts as a reducing agent and its acid has never been isolated. The gas X is ......
(a) H_2S (b) SO_2 (c) CO_2 (d) SO_3

13. Which is the strongest acid in the following ?
(a) H_2SO_4 (b) $HClO_3$ (c) $HClO_4$ (d) H_2SO_3

14. Which of the following is paramagnetic ?
(a) CO   (b) O_2^- (c) CN^- (d) NO^+

15. Which of the following structure is similar to graphite ?
(a) BN   (b) B   (c) B_4C (d) B_2H_6

16. The basic structural unit of silicates is ......
(a) SiO^- (b) SiO_4^{4-} (c) SiO_3^{2-} (d) SiO_4^{2-}

17. The reaction by which benzaldehyde cannot be prepared is ......
(a) (toluene, $C_6H_5CH_3$) + CrO_2Cl_2 in CS_2 followed by H_3O^+
(b) (benzoyl chloride, C_6H_5COCl) + H_2 in the presence of Pd-BaSO$_4$
(c) (benzene, C_6H_6) + CO + HCl in the presence of anhydrous $AlCl_3$
(d) (benzoic acid, C_6H_5COOH) + Zn/Hg and conc. HCl

18. Which of the following does not give oxygen on heating ?
(a) $KClO_3$ (b) $Zn(ClO_3)_2$ (c) $K_2Cr_2O_7$ (d) $(NH_4)_2Cr_2O_7$

19. Which of the following lanthanoid ions is diamagnetic ?
(At. No. of Ce = 58, Sm = 62, Eu = 63, Yb = 70)
(a) Ce^{2+} (b) Sm^{2+} (c) Eu^{2+} (d) Yb^{2+}

20. Identify the correct order of solubility in aqueous medium
(a) CuS > ZnS > Na_2S (b) ZnS > Na_2S > CuS
(c) Na_2S > CuS > ZnS   (d) Na_2S > ZnS > CuS

21. XeF_2 is isostructural with ......

    (a) TeF_2　　　　(b) ICl_2^-　　　　(c) $SbCl_3$　　　　(d) $BaCl_2$

22. An excess of $AgNO_3$ is added to 100 ml of a 0.01 M solution of dichlorotraaquachromium(III) chloride. The number of moles of AgCl precipitated would be ......

    (a) 0.001　　　　(b) 0.002　　　　(c) 0.003　　　　(d) 0.01

23. Which of these is least likely to act as a Lewis base ?

    (a) CO　　　　(b) F^-　　　　(c) BF_3　　　　(d) PF_3

24. $KMnO_4$ can be prepared from K_2MnO_4 as per the reaction :

$$3MnO_4^{2-} + 2H_2O \rightleftharpoons 2MnO_4^- + MnO_2 + 4OH^-$$

The reaction can go to completion by removing OH^- ions by adding ......

    (a) HCl　　　　(b) KOH　　　　(c) CO_2　　　　(d) SO_2

25. Which of the following is electron deficient ?

    (a) $(CH_3)_2$　　　　(b) $(SiH_3)_2$　　　　(c) $(BH_3)_2$　　　　(d) PH_3

26. Structure of the compound whose IUPAC name is 3-ethyl-2-hydroxy-4-methylhex-3-en-5-ynoic acid is ......

(a) structure with OH, COOH, ethynyl and methyl substituents
(b) structure with OH, COOH, vinyl and methyl substituents
(c) structure with OH, COOH, vinyl and methyl substituents
(d) structure with COOH and OH substituents

27. Which of these is not a monomer for high molecular mass silicone polymer ?

    (a) $MeSiCl_3$　　　　(b) Me_2SiCl_2　　　　(c) Me_3SiCl　　　　(d) $PhSiCl_3$

28. Which of the following statements about the interstitial compounds is incorrect ?

    (a) They retain metallic conductivity

    (b) They are chemically reactive

    (c) They are much harder than the pure metal

    (d) They have higher melting points than the pure metal

29. Which one of the following molecules contain no π bond ?

    (a) CO_2　　　　(b) H_2O　　　　(c) SO_2　　　　(d) NO_2

30. Antiseptics and disinfectants either kill or prevent growth of microorganisms. Identify which of the following statements is not true ?

    (a) A 0.2% solution of phenol is an antiseptic while 1% solution acts as a disinfectant

    (b) Chlorine and iodine are used as strong disinfectants

    (c) Dilute solutions of boric acid and hydrogen peroxide are strong antiseptics

    (d) Disinfectants harm the living tissues

31. Among the following ethers, which one will produce methyl alcohol on treatment with hot concentrated HI ?

(a) $CH_3 - CH_2 - CH_2 - CH_2 - O - CH_3$

(b) $CH_3 - CH_2 - \underset{\underset{CH_3}{|}}{CH} - O - CH_3$

(c) $CH_3 - \underset{\underset{CH_3}{|}}{\overset{\overset{CH_3}{|}}{C}} - O - CH_3$

(d) $CH_3 - \underset{\underset{CH_3}{|}}{CH} - CH_2 - O - CH_3$

32. Nylon is an example of ......

(a) Polyester   (b) Polysaccharide   (c) Polyamide   (d) Polythene

33. The structure of isobutyl group in an organic compound is

(a) $\underset{CH_3}{\overset{CH_3}{>}} CH - CH_2 -$

(b) $CH_3 - \underset{\underset{CH_3}{|}}{CH} - CH_2 - CH_3$

(c) $CH_3 - CH_2 - CH_2 - CH_2 -$

(d) $CH_3 - \underset{\underset{CH_3}{|}}{\overset{\overset{CH_3}{|}}{C}} -$

34. Nitrobenzene on reaction with conc. HNO_3/H_2SO_4 at 80-100°C forms which one of the following products ?

(a) 1, 2-Dinitrobenzene

(b) 1, 3-Dinitrobenzene

(c) 1, 4-Dinitrobenzene

(d) 1, 2, 4-Trinitrobenzene

35. Some meta-directing substituents in aromatic substitution are given. Which one is most deactivating ?

(a) $- C \equiv N$ (b) $- SO_3H$ (c) $- COOH$ (d) $- NO_2$

36. 6.02×10^{20} molecules of urea are present in 100 mL of its solution. The concentration of solution is ......

(a) 0.02 M   (b) 0.01 M   (c) 0.001 M   (d) 0.1 M

37. Which of the following is a polar molecule ?

(a) BF_3 (b) SF_4 (c) SiF_4 (d) XeF_4

38. Which is the monomer of Neoprene in the following ?

(a) $CH_2 = CH - C \equiv CH$

(b) $CH_2 = \underset{\underset{CH_3}{|}}{C} - CH = CH_2$

(c) $CH_2 = \underset{\underset{Cl}{|}}{C} - CH = CH_2$

(d) $CH_2 = CH - CH = CH_2$

39. In the reaction (a 4-nitro-2-bromo benzenediazonium chloride) $\xrightarrow{A}$ (3-bromonitrobenzene) , A is

(a) $HgSO_4/H_2SO_4$ 　　(b) Cu_2Cl_2 　　(c) H_3PO_2 and H_2O 　(d) H^+/H_2O

40. The radical (phenyl)$-CH_2\cdot$ is aromatic because it has

......

(a) 6 p-orbitals and 6 unpaired electrons 　　(b) 7 p-orbitals and 6 unpaired electrons

(c) 7 p-orbitals and 7 unpaired electrons 　　(d) 6 p-orbitals and 7 unpaired electrons

41. The order of stability of the following tautomeric compounds is

$$CH_2 = \underset{\underset{I}{OH}}{C} - CH_2 - \overset{O}{C} - CH_3 \rightleftharpoons CH_3 - \overset{O}{\underset{II}{C}} - CH_2 - \overset{O}{C} - CH_3 \rightleftharpoons CH_3 - \underset{\underset{III}{OH}}{C} = CH - \overset{O}{C} - CH_3$$

(a) $I > II > III$ 　　(b) $III > II > I$ 　　(c) $II > I > III$ 　　(d) $II > III > I$

42. Which of the following compounds will not undergo Friedel-Craft's reaction easily ?

(a) Cumene 　　(b) Xylene 　　(c) Nitrobenzene 　(d) Toluene

43. The value of Planck's constant is 6.63×10^{-34} Js. The speed of light is 3×10^{17} nm s^{-1}. Which value is closest to the wavelength in nanometer of a quantum of light with frequency of 6×10^{13} s^{-1} ?

(a) 10 　　(b) 25 　　(c) 50 　　(d) 75

44. What is the maximum number of electrons that can be associated with the following set of quantum numbers ? $n = 3$, $l = 1$ and $m = -1$

(a) 10 　　(b) 6 　　(c) 4 　　(d) 2

45. What is the activation energy for a reaction if its rate doubles when the temperature is raised from 20°C to 35°C ? (R = 8.314 J mol^{-1} K^{-1})

(a) 342 kJ mol^{-1} 　　(b) 269 kJ mol^{-1} 　　(c) 34.7 kJ mol^{-1} 　(d) 15.1 kJ mol^{-1}

ANSWER KEY

1. (b)	2. (c)	3. (c)	4. (d)	5. (a)	6. (a)	7. (b)	8. (d)
9. (c)	10. (c)	11. (a)	12. (b)	13. (c)	14. (b)	15. (a)	16. (b)
17. (d)	18. (d)	19. (d)	20. (d)	21. (b)	22. (a)	23. (c)	24. (c)
25. (c)	26. (b)	27. (c)	28. (b)	29. (b)	30. (c)	31. (c)	32. (c)
33. (a)	34. (b)	35. (d)	36. (b)	37. (b)	38. (c)	39. (c)	40. (a)
41. (b)	42. (c)	43. (c)	44. (d)	45. (c)			

❑❑❑

July 2014

1. Which of the following compounds will undergo racemisation when solution of KOH hydrolyses ?

(i) [benzyl chloride: C_6H_5–CH_2Cl]

(ii) $CH_3CH_2CH_2Cl$

(iii) $H_3C-CH-CH_2Cl$ (with CH_3 substituent on the CH)

(iv) a carbon bonded to CH_3, H, C_2H_5 and Cl

(a) (ii) and (iv)   (b) (iii) and (iv)   (c) (i) and (iv)   (d) (i) and (ii)

2. The reaction of aqueous $KMnO_4$ with H_2O_2 in acidic conditions gives ......

(a) Mn^{2+} and O_2 (b) Mn^{2+} and O_3 (c) Mn^{4+} and MnO_2 (d) Mn^{4+} and O_2

3. Which one of the following is not a common component of photochemical smog ?

(a) Acrolein

(b) Peroxyacetyl nitrate

(c) Chlorofluorocarbons

(d) Ozone

4. Which of the following will be most stable diazonium salt $RN_2^+X^-$?

(a) $C_6H_5 \overset{+}{N_2} X^-$ (b) $CH_3CH_2 \overset{+}{N_2} X^-$ (c) $C_6H_5CH_2 \overset{+}{N_2} X^-$ (d) $CH_3 \overset{+}{N_2} X^-$

5. Which of the following hormones is produced under the condition of stress which stimulates glycogenolysis in the liver of human beings ?

(a) Insulin   (b) Adrenaline   (c) Estradiol   (d) Thyroxin

6. 1.0 g of magnesium is burnt with 0.56 g O_2 in a closed vessel. Which reactant is left in excess and how much ? (At. wt. of Mg = 24, O = 16)

(a) O_2, 0.16 g   (b) Mg, 0.44 g   (c) O_2, 0.28 g   (d) Mg, 0.16 g

7. What products are formed when the following compound is treated with Br_2 in the presence of $FeBr_3$?

8. Which of the following organic compounds polymerizes to form the polyester Dacron ?

    (a) Benzoic acid and ethanol   (b) Terephthalic acid and ethylene glycol

    (c) Benzoic acid and para $HO - (C_6H_4) - OH$ (d) Propylene and para $HO - (C_6H_4) - OH$

9. In acidic medium, H_2O_2 changes $Cr_2O_7^{-2}$ to CrO_5 which has two ($- O- O-$) bonds. Oxidation state of Cr in CrO_5 is ......

    (a) +3   (b) +6   (c) −10   (d) +5

10. Which of the following orders of ionic radii is correctly represented ?

    (a) $Na^+ > F^- > O^{2-}$ (b) $F^- > O^{2-} > Na^+$

    (c) $Al^{3+} > Mg^{2+} > N^{3-}$ (d) $H^- > H^+ > H$

11. Which of the following salts will give highest pH in water ?

    (a) NaCl   (b) Na_2CO_3 (c) $CuSO_4$ (d) KCl

12. Which of the following will not be soluble in sodium hydrogen carbonate ?

    (a) Benzoic acid   (b) o-Nitrophenol

    (c) Benzenesulphonic acid   (d) 2, 4, 6-trinitrophenol

13. For the reaction $X_2O_4(l) \longrightarrow 2XO_2(g)$

    ΔU = 2.1 kcal, ΔS = 20 cal K^{-1} at 300 K. Hence, ΔG is ......

    (a) −2.7 kcal   (b) 9.3 kcal   (c) −9.3 kcal   (d) 2.7 kcal

14. In the following reaction, the product (A) is :

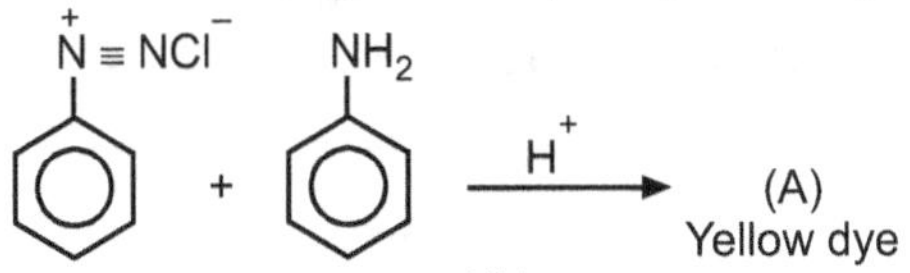

$\overset{+}{N} \equiv NCl^- \quad NH_2$ (benzene diazonium chloride + aniline) $\xrightarrow{\overset{+}{H}}$ (A) 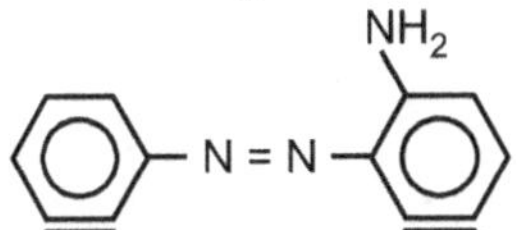 Yellow dye

    (a) ⟨C₆H₅⟩$- N = N -$⟨C₆H₃(NH_2)⟩   (b) 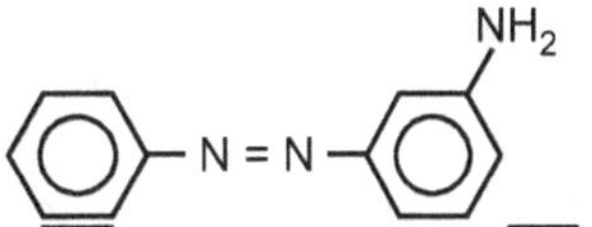 ⟨C₆H₅⟩$- N = N -$⟨C₆H₄(NH_2)⟩

    (c) 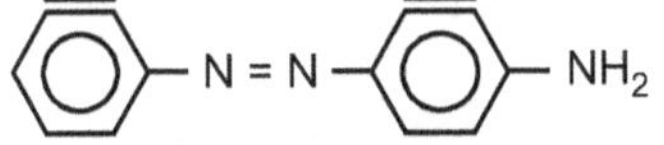 ⟨C₆H₅⟩$- N = N -$⟨C₆H₃⟩$- NH_2$ (d) 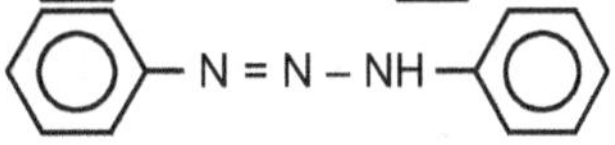 ⟨C₆H₅⟩$- N = N - NH -$⟨C₆H₅⟩

15. Using the Gibbs energy change, $\Delta G° = +63.3$ kJ, for the following reaction,

    $Ag_2CO_3(s) \rightleftharpoons 2Ag^+ (aq) + CO_3^{2-} (aq)$, the K_{sp} of $Ag_2CO_3(s)$ in water at 25°C is ......

    $(R = 8.314\ JK^{-1}\ mol^{-1})$

    (a) 8.0×10^{-12} (b) 2.9×10^{-3} (c) 7.9×10^{-2} (d) 3.2×10^{-26}

16. Identify Z in the squence of reactions :

$$CH_3CH_2CH = CH_2 \xrightarrow{HBr/H_2O_2} Y \xrightarrow{C_2H_5ONa} Z$$

    (a) $(CH_3)_2CH_2 - O - CH_2CH_3$ (b) $CH_3(CH_2)_4 - O - CH_3$

    (c) $CH_3CH_2 - CH(CH_3) - O - CH_2CH_3$ (d) $CH_3 - (CH_2)_3 - O - CH_2CH_3$

17. In the Kjeldahl's method for estimation of nitrogen present in an soil sample, ammonia evolved from 0.75 g of sample neutralized 10 ml of 1 M H_2SO_4. The percentage of nitrogen in the soil is ......

    (a) 45.33   (b) 35.33   (c) 43.33   (d) 37.33

18. Which property of colloids is not dependent on the charge of colloidal particles ?

(a) Electrophoresis   (b) Electro-osmosis   (c) Tyndall effect   (d) Coagulation

19. For a given exothermic reaction, K_p and K_p' are the equilibrium constants at temperatures T_1 and T_2, respectively. Assuming that heat of reaction is constant in the temperature range between T_1 and T_2, it is readily observed that ......

(a) $K_p < K_p'$ (b) $K_p = K_p'$ (c) $K_p = \dfrac{1}{K_p'}$ (d) $K_p > K_p'$

20. When 22.4 litres of H_2 (g) is mixed with 11.2 litres of Cl_2(g), each at S.T.P., the moles of HCl(g) formed is equal to ......

(a) 2 mol of HCl (g)   (b) 0.5 mol of HCl (g)

(c) 1.5 mol of HCl (g)   (d) 1 mol of HCl (g)

21. Which one of the following is an example of a thermosetting polymer ?

(a) $\left[CH_2 - \underset{\underset{Cl}{|}}{CH} \right]_n$

(b) $\left[\underset{\underset{H}{|}}{N} - (CH_2)_6 - \underset{\underset{H}{|}}{N} - \overset{\overset{O}{||}}{C} - (CH_2)_4 - \overset{\overset{O}{||}}{C} \right]_n$

(c) 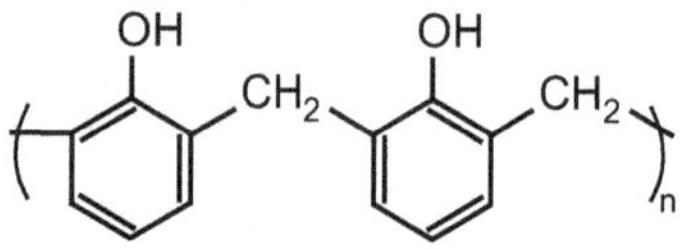 A phenol-formaldehyde type structure with two benzene rings each bearing OH and connected by CH_2 groups.

(d) $\left[CH_2 - \underset{\underset{Cl}{|}}{C} = CH - CH_2 \right]_n$

22. Which one is the most reactive towards nucleophilic addition reaction ?

(a) 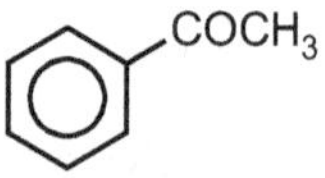 Benzene ring with $COCH_3$ substituent

(b) 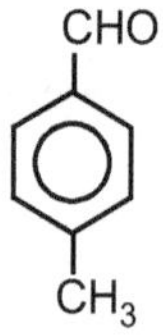 Benzene ring with CHO (top) and CH_3 (bottom)

(c) 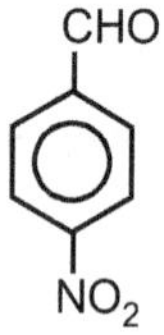 Benzene ring with CHO (top) and NO_2 (bottom)

(d) 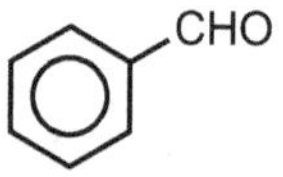 Benzene ring with CHO substituent

23. Calculate the energy in joule corresponding to light of wavelength 45 nm : (Planck's constant $h = 6.63 \times 10^{-34}$ Js; Speed of light $c = 3 \times 10^8$ ms^{-1}).

(a) 6.67×10^{11} (b) 4.42×10^{-15} (c) 4.42×10^{-18} (d) 6.67×10^{15}

24. Which of the following organic compounds has same hybridization as its combustion product (CO_2) ?

(a) Ethyne   (b) Ethene   (c) Ethanol   (d) Ethane

25. Be^{2+} is isoelectronic with which of the following ions ?

(a) Li^+ (b) Na^+ (c) Mg^{2+} (d) H^+

26. Magnetic moment 2.83 BM is given by which of the following ions ?

(At. No. of Ti = 22, Cr = 24, Mn = 25, Ni = 28)

(a) Ni^{2+} (b) Cr^{3+} (c) Mn^{2+} (d) Ti^{3+}

27. The weight of silver (At. Wt. = 108) displaced by a quantity of electricity which displaces 5600 ml of O_2 at STP will be ......

(a) 10.8 g   (b) 54.0 g   (c) 108.0 g   (d) 5.4 g

28. For the reversible reaction $N_2(g) + 3H_2(g) \rightleftharpoons 2NH_3(g) + \text{heat}$

    the equilibrium shifts in the forward direction ......

    (a) by decreasing the pressure

    (b) by decreasing the concentrations of $N_2(g)$ and $H_2(g)$

    (c) by increasing pressure and decreasing temperature

    (d) by increasing the concentration of $NH_3(g)$

29. The pair of compounds that can exist together is ......

    (a) $HgCl_2$, $SnCl_2$ (b) $FeCl_2$, $SnCl_2$ (c) $FeCl_3$, KI   (d) $FeCl_3$, $SnCl_2$

30. Which of the following complexes is used to be as an anticancer agent ?

    (a) $cis - [PtCl_2(NH_3)_2]$ (b) $cis - K_2[PtCl_2Br_2]$

    (c) Na_2CoCl_4 (d) $mer - [Co(NH_3)_3Cl_3]$

31. Among the following complexes the one which shows zero crystal field stabilization energy (CFSE) is ......

    (a) $[Fe(H_2O)_6]^{3+}$ (b) $[Co(H_2O)_6]^{2+}$ (c) $[Co(H_2O)_6]^{3+}$ (d) $[Mn(H_2O)_6]^{3+}$

32. If a is the length of the side of a cube, the distance between the body centered atom and one corner atom in the cube will be ......

    (a) $\dfrac{4}{\sqrt{3}} a$ (b) $\dfrac{\sqrt{3}}{4} a$ (c) $\dfrac{\sqrt{3}}{2} a$ (d) $\dfrac{2}{\sqrt{3}} a$

33. Which of the following species has plane triangular shape ?

    (a) NO_3^- (b) NO_2^- (c) CO_2 (d) N_3

34. Which of the following molecules has the maximum dipole moment ?

    (a) CH_4 (b) NH_3 (c) NF_3 (d) CO_2

35. Acidity of diprotic acids in aqueous solutions increases in the order ......

    (a) $H_2Se < H_2S < H_2Te$ (b) $H_2Te < H_2S < H_2Se$

    (c) $H_2Se < H_2Te < H_2S$ (d) $H_2S < H_2Se < H_2Te$

36. The reason of lanthanoid contraction is ......

    (a) Increasing nuclear charge   (b) Decreasing nuclear charge

    (c) Decreasing screening effect   (d) Negligible screening effect of 'f' orbitals

37. Which of the following statements is correct for the spontaneous adsorption of gas ?

    (a) ΔS is negative and therefore, ΔH should be highly negative

    (b) ΔS is positive and therefore, ΔH should be negative

    (c) ΔS is positive and therefore, ΔH should also be highly positive

    (d) ΔS is negative and therefore, ΔH should be highly positive

38. Artificial sweetner which is stable under cold conditions only is ......

    (a) Sucralose   (b) Aspartame   (c) Alitame   (d) Saccharine

39. Equal masses of H_2, O_2 and methane have been taken in a container of volume V at temperature 27°C in identical conditions. The ratio of the volumes of gases $H_2 : O_2 :$ methane would be ......

(a) $16 : 8 : 1$ (b) $16 : 1 : 2$ (c) $8 : 1 : 2$ (d) $8 : 16 : 1$

40. (i) $H_2O_2 + O_3 \rightarrow H_2O + 2O_2$, (ii) $H_2O_2 + Ag_2O \rightarrow 2Ag + H_2O + O_2$

The role of hydrogen peroxide in the above reactions is respectively ......

(a) reducing in (i) and oxidizing in (ii)   (b) reducing in (i) and (ii)

(c) oxidizing in (i) and (ii)   (d) oxidizing in (i) and reducing in (ii)

41. Among the following sets of reactants, which one produces anisole ?

(a) C_6H_5OH; NaOH; CH_3I (b) C_6H_5OH; neutral $FeCl_3$

(c) $C_6H_5 - CH_3$; CH_3COCl; $AlCl_3$ (d) CH_3CHO; RMgX

42. When 0.1 mol MnO_4^{2-} is oxidised, the quantity of electricity required to completely oxidise MnO_4^{2-} to MnO_4^{-} is ......

(a) 2×96500 C   (b) 9650 C   (c) 96.50 C   (d) 96500 C

43. Of the following 0.10 m aqueous solutions, which one will exhibit the largest freezing point depression ?

(a) $C_6H_{12}O_6$ (b) $Al_2(SO_4)_3$ (c) K_2SO_4 (d) KCl

44. What is the maximum number of orbitals that can be identified with the following quantum numbers $n = 3, l = 1, m_l = 0$?

(a) 2   (b) 3   (c) 4   (d) 1

45. D(+) glucose reacts with hydroxyl amine and yields an oxime. The structure of the oxime would be ...

(a)
```
       CH = NOH
        |
 HO – C – H
        |
 HO – C – H
        |
  H – C – OH
        |
  H – C – OH
        |
       CH₂OH
```

(b)
```
       CH = NOH
        |
 HO – C – H
        |
  H – C – OH
        |
 HO – C – H
        |
  H – C – OH
        |
       CH₂OH
```

(c)
```
       CH = NOH
        |
  H – C – OH
        |
 HO – C – H
        |
  H – C – OH
        |
  H – C – OH
        |
       CH₂OH
```

(d)
```
       CH = NOH
        |
  H – C – OH
        |
 HO – C – H
        |
 HO – C – H
        |
  H – C – OH
        |
       CH₂OH
```

ANSWER KEY

1. (c)	2. (d)	3. (b)	4. (c)	5. (b)	6. (a)	7. (d)	8. (a)
9. (d)	10. (d)	11. (b)	12. (c)	13. (c)	14. (b)	15. (b)	16. (d)
17. (c)	18. (a)	19. (b)	20. (a)	21. (b)	22. (d)	23. (c)	24. (b)
25. (a)	26. (c)	27. (a)	28. (c)	29. (d)	30. (d)	31. (c)	32. (b)
33. (b)	34. (b)	35. (a)	36. (a)	37. (b)	38. (c)	39. (c)	40.
41.	42.	43.	44. (b)	45. (c)			

□□□

July 2015

1. 2, 3-Dimethyl-2-butene can be prepared by heating which of the following compounds with a strong acid ?
   (a) $(CH_3)_2C = CH - CH_2 - CH_3$
   (b) $(CH_3)_2CH - CH_2 - CH = CH_2$
   (c) $(CH_3)_2CH - \underset{\underset{CH_3}{|}}{CH} - CH = CH_2$
   (d) $(CH_3)_3C - CH = CH_2$

2. Gadolinium belongs to 4f series. Its atomic number is 64. Which of the following is the correct electronic configuration of Gadolinium ?
   (a) $[Xe]\ 4f^7 5d^1 6s^2$
   (b) $[Xe]\ 4f^6 5d^2 6s^2$
   (c) $[Xe]\ 4f^8 6d^2$
   (d) $[Xe]\ 4f^9 5s^1$

3. The formation of the oxide ion, $O^{2-}(g)$, from oxygen atom requires first an exothermic and then an endothermic step as shown below.

   $O(g) + e^- \rightarrow O^-(g);\ \Delta_f H^\ominus = -141\ kJ\ mol^{-1}$

   $O^-(g) + e^- \rightarrow O^{2-}(g);\ \Delta_f H^\ominus = +780\ kJ\ mol^{-1}$

   Thus process of formation of O^{2-} in gas phase is unfavourable even though O^{2-} is isoelectronic with neon. It is due to the fact that ......
   (a) oxygen is more electronegative
   (b) addition of electron in oxygen results in larger size of the ion
   (c) electron repulsion outweighs the stability gained by achieving noble gas configuration
   (d) O^- ion has comparatively smaller size than oxygen atom

4. The number of structural isomers possible from the molecular formula C_3H_9N is ......
   (a) 2
   (b) 3
   (c) 4
   (d) 5

5. If the equilibrium constant for $N_2(g) + O_2(g) \rightleftharpoons 2NO(g)$ is K, the equilibrium constant for $\frac{1}{2} N_2(g) + \frac{1}{2} O_2(g) \rightleftharpoons NO(g)$ will be ......
   (a) K
   (b) K^2
   (c) $K^{1/2}$
   (d) $\frac{1}{2} K$

6. Which one of the following pairs of solution is not an acidic buffer ?
   (a) H_2CO_3 and Na_2CO_3
   (b) H_3PO_4 and Na_3PO_4
   (c) $HClO_4$ and $NaClO_4$
   (d) CH_3COOH and CH_3COONa

7. Aqueous solution of which of the following compounds is the best conductor of electric current ?
   (a) Ammonia, NH_3
   (b) Fructose, $C_6H_{12}O_6$
   (c) Acetic acid, $C_2H_4O_2$
   (d) Hydrochloric acid, HCl

8. Caprolactam is used for the manufacture of ......
   (a) Terylene
   (b) Nylon - 6, 6
   (c) Nylon - 6
   (d) Teflon

9. On heating which of the following releases CO_2 most easily ?
   (a) $MgCO_3$
   (b) $CaCO_3$
   (c) K_2CO_3
   (d) Na_2CO_3

10. Strong reducing behaviour of H_3PO_2 is due to ......

(a) High oxidation state of phosphorus

(b) Presence of two – OH groups and one P – H bond

(c) Presence of one – OH group and two P – H bonds

(d) High electron gain enthalpy of phosphorus

11. Decreasing order of stability of O_2, O_2^-, O_2^+ and O_2^{2-} is ......

(a) $O_2 > O_2^+ > O_2^{2-} > O_2^-$

(b) $O_2^- > O_2^{2-} > O_2^+ > O_2$

(c) $O_2^+ > O_2 > O_2^- > O_2^{2-}$

(d) $O_2^{2-} > O_2^- > O_2 > O_2^+$

12. The number of water molecules is maximum in ......

(a) 18 grams of water

(b) 18 moles of water

(c) 18 molecules of water

(d) 1.8 grams of water

13. In which of the following pairs, both the species are not isostructural ?

(a) NH_3, PH_3

(b) XeF_4, XeO_4

(c) $SiCl_4$, PCl_4^+

(d) diamond, silicon carbide

14. In the reaction with HCl, an alkene reacts in accordance with the Markovnikov's rule, to give a product 1-chloro-1-methylcyclohexane. The possible alkene is ......

(a) (A)   (b) (B)   (c) (A) and (B)   (d)

15. Assuming complete ionization, same moles of which of the following compounds will require the least amount of acidified $KMnO_4$ for complete oxidation ?

(a) FeC_2O_4

(b) $Fe(NO_2)_2$

(c) $FeSO_4$

(d) $FeSO_3$

16. The reaction of phenol with chloroform in the presence of dilute sodium hydroxide finally introduces which one of the following functional group ?

(a) $-CHCl_2$

(b) $-CHO$

(c) $-CH_2Cl$

(d) $-COOH$

17. The vacant space in bcc lattice unit cell is ......

(a) 23%

(b) 32%

(c) 26%

(d) 48%

18. Which of the statements given below is incorrect ?

(a) ONF is isoelectronic with O_2N^-

(b) OF_2 is an oxide of fluorine

(c) Cl_2O_7 is an anhydride of perchloric acid

(d) O_3 molecule is bent

19. The name of complex ion, $[Fe(CN)_6]^{3-}$ is ......

(a) Tricyanoferrate(III) ion

(b) Hexacyanidoferrate(III) ion

(c) Hexacyanoiron(III) ion

(d) Hexacyanatoferrate(III) ion

20. If Avogadro number N_A is changed from 6.022×10^{23} mol^{-1} to 6.022×10^{20} mol^{-1}, this would change ......

    (a) the ratio of chemical species to each other in a balanced equation

    (b) the ratio of elements to each other in a compound

    (c) the definition of mass in units of grams

    (d) the mass of one mole of carbon

21. Which of the following statements is not correct for a nucleophile ?

    (a) Nucleophiles attack low electron density sites

    (b) Nucleophiles are not electron seeking

    (c) Nucleophile is a Lewis acid

    (d) Ammonia is a nucleophile

22. A gas such as carbon monoxide would be most likely to obey the ideal gas law at ......

    (a) high temperatures and high pressures   (b) low temperatures and low pressures

    (c) high temperatures and low pressures   (d) low temperatures and high pressures

23. The hybridization involved in complex $[Ni(CN)_4]^{2-}$ is ...... (At. No. of Ni = 28)

    (a) d^2sp^2 (b) d^2sp^3 (c) dsp^2 (d) sp^3

24. The heat of combustion of carbon to CO_2 is -393.5 kJ/mol. The heat released upon formation of 35.2 g of CO_2 from carbon and oxygen gas is ......

    (a) -630 kJ   (b) -3.15 kJ   (c) -315 kJ   (d) $+315$ kJ

25. 20.0 g of a magnesium carbonate sample decomposes on heating to give carbon dioxide and 8.0 g magnesium oxide. What will be the percentage purity of magnesium carbonate in the sample ? (At. Wt. of Mg = 24)

    (a) 60   (b) 84   (c) 75   (d) 96

26. What is the mole fraction of the solute in 1.00 M aqueous solution ?

    (a) 0.0354   (b) 0.0177   (c) 0.177   (d) 1.770

27. The correct statement regarding defects in stalline solids is ......

    (a) Frenkel defect is a dislocation defect

    (b) Frenkel defect is found in halides of alkaline metals

    (c) Schottky defects have no effect on the density of crystalline solids

    (d) Frenkel defects decrease the density of crystalline solids

28. The stability of +1 oxidation state among Al, Ga, In and Ti increases in the sequence ......

    (a) Tl < In < Ga < Al   (b) In < Tl < Ga < Al   (c) Ga < In < Al < Tl   (d) Al < Ga < In < Tl

29. Two possible stereo structures of $CH_3CHOHCOOH$, which are optically active are called as ...

    (a) Enantiomers   (b) Mesomers   (c) Diastereomers   (d) Atropisomers

30. The following reaction [structure: aniline NH_2 + benzoyl chloride Cl—CO—] $\xrightarrow{NaOH}$ [benzanilide structure] is known by the name ...

    (a) Acetylation reaction
    (b) Schotten-Baumen reaction
    (c) Friedel-Craft's reaction
    (d) Perkin's reaction

31. The sum of coordination number and oxidation number of the metal M in the complex $[M(en)_2(C_2O_4)]Cl$ (where en is ethylenediamine) is ......

    (a) 7   (b) 8   (c) 9   (d) 6

32. The reaction of a carbonyl compound with one of the following reagents involves nucleophilic addition followed by elimination of water. The reagent is ......

    (a) hydrocyanic acid
    (b) sodium hydrogen sulphite
    (c) a Grignard reagent
    (d) hydrazine in the presence of feebly acidic solution

33. Which one of the following esters get hydrolysed most easily under alkaline conditions ?

    (a) [phenyl-$OCOCH_3$]
    (b) [4-Cl-phenyl-$OCOCH_3$]
    (c) [4-O_2N-phenyl-$OCOCH_3$]
    (d) [4-H_3CO-phenyl-$OCOCH_3$]

34. In an S_{N^1} reaction on chiral centres, there is ......

    (a) 100% retention   (b) 100% inversion   (c) 100% racemization
    (d) inversion more than retention leading to partial racemization

35. The rate constant of the reaction A → B is 0.6×10^{-3} mole per second. If the concentration of A is 5 M then concentration of B after 20 minutes is ......

    (a) 0.36 M   (b) 0.72 M   (c) 1.08 M   (d) 3.60 M

36. What is the pH of the resulting solution when equal volumes of 0.1 M NaOH and 0.01 M HCl are mixed ?

    (a) 7.0   (b) 1.04   (c) 12.65   (d) 2.0

37. The number of possible isomers for the complex $[Co(en)_2Cl_2]Cl$ will be ......
    (en = ethylenediamine)

    (a) 3   (b) 4   (c) 2   (d) 1

38. The variation of boiling points of hydrogen halides is in the order HF > HI > HBr > HCl. What explains the higher boiling point of hydrogen fluoride ?

    (a) The bond energy of HF molecules is greater than in other hydrogen halides.
    (b) The effect of nuclear shielding is much reduced in fluorine which polarises the HF molecule.
    (c) The electronegativity of fluorine is much higher than for other elements in the group.
    (d) There is strong hydrogen bonding between HF molecules

39. What is the mass of the precipitate formed when 50 ml of 16.9% solution of $AgNO_3$ is mixed with 50 ml of 5.8% NaCl solution ? (Ag = 107.8, N = 14, O = 16, Na = 23, Cl = 35.5)

    (a) 7 g　　　　　(b) 14 g　　　　　(c) 28 g　　　　　(d) 3.5 g

40. The oxidation of benzene by V_2O_5 in the presence of air produces ......

    (a) benzoic acid　　　　　(b) benzaldehyde　　　　　(c) benzoic anhydride

    (d) maleic anhydride

41. Which of the following is not the product of dehydration of 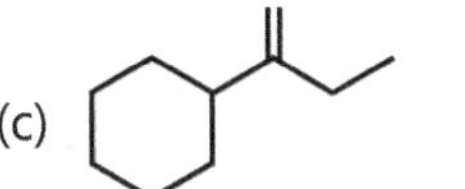 ?

    (a) 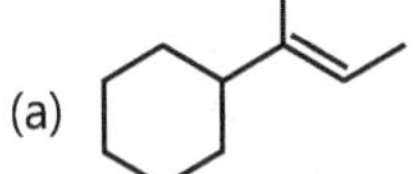　　　　　(b) 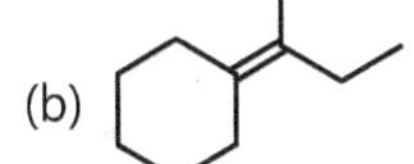　　　　　(c)　　　　　(d) 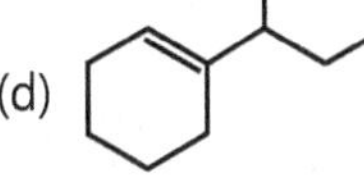

42. The method by which aniline cannot be prepared is ......

    (a) reduction of nitrobenzene with H_2/Pd in ethanol

    (b) potassium salt of phthalimide treated with chlorobenzene followed by hydrolysis with aqueous NaOH solution

    (c) hydrolysis of phenylisocyanide with acidic solution

    (d) degradation of benzamide with bromine in alkaline solution

43. Which of the following reaction(s) can be used for the preparation of alkyl halides ?

    (i) CH_3CH_2OH + HCl $\xrightarrow{\text{anh. ZnCl}_2}$　　　　　(ii) CH_3CH_2OH + HCl $\longrightarrow$

    (iii) $(CH_3)_3COH$ + HCl $\longrightarrow$　　　　　(iv) $(CH_3)_2CHOH$ + HCl $\xrightarrow{\text{anh. ZnCl}_2}$

    (a) (iv) only　　　　　(b) (iii) and (iv) only　　　　　(c) (i), (iii) and (iv) only

    (d) (i) and (ii) only

44. Which is the correct order of increasing energy of the listed orbitals in the atom of titanium ? (At. No. Z = 22)

    (a) 3s 3p 3d 4s　　　　　(b) 3s 3p 4s 3d　　　　　(c) 3s 4s 3p 3d　　　　　(d) 4s 3s 3p 3d

45. In the extraction of copper from its sulphide ore, the metal is finally obtained by the reduction of cuprous oxide with ......

    (a) copper(I) sulphide　　　(b) sulphur dioxide　　　(c) iron(II) sulphide　　(d) carbon monoxide

ANSWER KEY

1.	2. (a)	3. (c)	4. (d)	5. (c)	6. (b)	7. (a)	8. (c)
9. (b)	10. (c)	11. (c)	12. (b)	13. (b)	14. (a)	15.	16. (b)
17. (b)	18. (b)	19. (d)	20. (a)	21. (c)	22. (c)	23. (c)	24. (c)
25.	26. (b)	27. (d)	28. (d)	29. (a)	30. (a)	31. (a)	32. (b)
33. (c)	34. (c)	35. (a)	36.	37. (c)	38. (d)	39.	40. (a)
41. (b)	42. (d)	43. (c)	44. (b)	45. (b)			

July 2016

1. A given nitrogen containing aromatic compound A react with Sn/HCl, followed by HNO_2 to give an unstable compound B. B on treatment with phenol, forms a beautiful coloured compound C with the molecular formula $C_{12}H_{10}N_2O$. The structure of compound A is ......

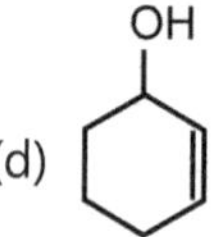

(a) [benzene ring with $CONH_2$] (b) [benzene ring with $CONH_2$] (c) [benzene ring with NO_2] (d) [benzene ring with CN]

2. Consider the reaction : Image showing the reaction (1) Water, (2) Ethanol, (3) Methanol, (4) N, N'-dimethyl formamide (DMF)

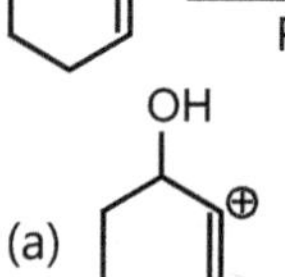

(a) [cyclohexene with OH and ⊕] (b) [cyclohexadiene with OH] (c) [cyclohexanone, O] (d) [cyclohexene with OH]

3. The correct structure of the product A formed in the reaction is ......

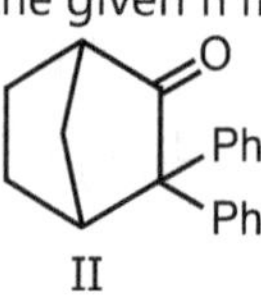

$$\xrightarrow[\text{Pd/carbon, ethanol}]{H_2 \text{ (gas, 1 atmosphere)}} A$$

(a) [cyclohexene with OH and ⊕] (b) [cyclohexadiene with OH] (c) [cyclohexanone, O] (d) [cyclohexene with OH]

4. Which among the given n molecules can exhibit tautomerism ?

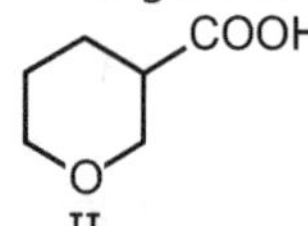

I II III

(a) Both (II) and (III) (b) (III) only (c) Both (I) and (III) (d) Both (I) and (II)

5. The correct order of strengths of the carboxylic acids is

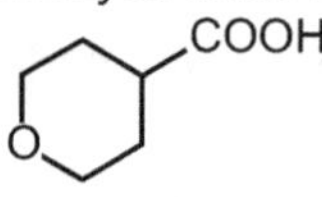

I II III

(a) (II) > (I) > (III) (b) (I) > (II) > (III) (c) (II) > (III) > (I) (d) (III) > (II) > (I)

6. The compound that will react most readily with gaseous bromine has the formula ......

(a) C_2H_4 (b) C_3H_6 (c) C_2H_2 (d) C_4H_{10}

7. Which one of the following compounds show the presence of intramolecular hydrogen bond ?

(a) Concentrated acetic acid (b) H_2O_2

(c) HCN (d) Cellulose

8. The molar conductivity of 0.5 mol/dm^3 solution of $AgNO_3$ with electrolytic conductivity of 5.76×10^{-3} S cm^{-1} at 298 K is ......

(a) 28.8 S cm^2/mol (b) 2.88 S cm^2/mol (c) 11.52 S cm^2/mol (d) 0.086 S cm^2/mol

9. The decomposition of phosphine (PH_3) on tungsten at low pressure is a first-order reaction. It is because ......
   (a) Rate of decomposition is very slow
   (b) Rate is proportional to the surface coverage
   (c) Rate is inversely proportional to the surface coverage
   (d) Rate is independent of the surface coverage

10. The coagulation values in millimoles per litre of electrolytes used for the coagulation of As_2S_3 are given below : I. (NaCl) = 52, II. ($BaCl_2$) = 0.69, III. ($MgSO_4$) = 0.22. The correct order of their coagulating power is ......
   (a) III > I > II　　　(b) I > II > III　　　(c) II > I > III　　　(d) III > II > I

11. During the electrolysis of molten sodium chloride, the time required to produce 0.10 mol of chlorine gas using a current of 3 amperes is ......
   (a) 330 minutes　　　(b) 55 minutes　　　(c) 110 minutes　　　(d) 220 minutes

12. How many electrons can fit in the orbital for which n = 3 and l = 1 ?
   (a) 14　　　(b) 2　　　(c) 6　　　(d) 10

13. For a sample of perfect gas when its pressure is changed isothermally from p_i to p_r the entropy change is given by ......
   (a) $\Delta S = RT \ln \dfrac{p_i}{p_r}$　　　(b) $\Delta S = RT \ln \dfrac{p_r}{p_i}$　　　(c) $\Delta S = nRT \ln \dfrac{p_i}{p_r}$　　　(d) $\Delta S = nRT \ln \dfrac{p_r}{p_i}$

14. The van't Hoff factor (i) for a dilute aqueous solution of strong electrolyte barium hydroxide is ......
   (a) 3　　　(b) 0　　　(c) 1　　　(d) 2

15. The percentage of pyridine (C_5H_5N) that forms pyridinium ion (C_5H_5NH) in a 0.10 M pyridine solution (K_b for $C_5H_5N = 1.7 \times 10^{-9}$) is ......
   (a) 1.6%　　　(b) 0.0060%　　　(c) 0.013%　　　(d) 0.77%

16. In calcium fluoride, having the fluorite structure, the coordination number for calcium ion (Ca^{2+}) and fluoride ion (F^-) are ......
   (a) 4 and 8　　　(b) 4 and 2　　　(c) 6 and 6　　　(d) 8 and 4

17. If the E^{o}_{cell} for a given reaction has a negative value, which of the following give the correct relationship for the value of $\Delta G°$ and K_{eq} ?
   (a) $\Delta G° < 0; K_{eq} < 1$　　　(b) $\Delta G° > 0; K_{eq} < 1$　　　(c) $\Delta G° > 0; K_{eq} > 1$　　　(d) $\Delta G° < 0; K_{eq} > 1$

18. Which one of the following is incorrect for ideal solution ?
   (a) $\Delta G_{mix} = 0$　　　(b) $\Delta H_{mix} = 0$　　　(c) $\Delta U_{mix} = 0$
   (d) $\Delta P_{mix} = P_{\text{Calculated by Raoult's law}} = 0$

19. The solubility of AgCl (S) with solubility product 1.6×10^{-10} in 0.1 M NaCl solution would be ......
   (a) zero　　　(b) 1.26×10^{-5} M　　　(c) 1.6×10^{-9} M　　　(d) 1.6×10^{-11} M

20. Suppose the elements X and Y combine to form two compounds XY_2 and X_3Y_2. When 0.1 mole of XY_2 weighs 10 g and 0.05 mole of X_3Y_2 weighs 9 g, the atomic weights of X and Y are ......
   (a) 30, 20　　　(b) 40, 30　　　(c) 60, 40　　　(d) 20, 30

21. The number of electrons delivered at the cathode during the electrolysis by a current of 1 ampere in 60 seconds is (charge on electron = 1.60×10^{-19} C) ......
    (a) 7.48×10^{23} (b) 6×10^{23} (c) 6×10^{20} (d) 3.75×10^{20}

22. Boric acid is an acid because its molecule ......
    (a) Combines with proton from water molecule   (b) Contains replaceable H^+ ion
    (c) Gives up a proton
    (d) Accepts OH^- from water releasing proton

23. AlF_3 is soluble in HF only in the presence of KF. It is due to the formation of ......
    (a) $K[AlF_3H]$ (b) $K_3[AlF_3H_3]$ (c) $K_3[AlF_6]$ (d) AlH_3

24. Zinc can be coated on iron to produce galvanized iron but the reverse is not possible. It is because ......
    (a) Zinc has higher negative electrode potential than iron
    (b) Zinc is lighter than iron
    (c) Zinc has lower melting point than iron
    (d) Zinc has lower negative electrode potential than iron

25. The suspension of slaked lime in water is known as ......
    (a) Aqueous solution of slaked lime   (b) Lime water
    (c) Quick lime   (d) Milk of lime

26. The hybridizations of atomic orbitals of nitrogen in NO_2, NO_3^- and NH_4^+ respectively are ......
    (a) sp^2, sp and sp^3 (b) sp, sp^3 and sp^2 (c) sp^2, sp^3 and sp   (d) sp, sp^2 and sp^3

27. Which of the following fluoro compounds is most likely to behave as a Lewis base ?
    (a) SiF_4 (b) BF_3 (c) PF_3 (d) CF_4

28. Which one of the following pairs of ions is isoelectronic and isostructural ?
    (a) ClO_3^-, SO_3^{2-} (b) CO_3^{2-}, NO_3^- (c) ClO_3^-, CO_3^{2-} (d) SO_3^{2-}, CO_3^{2-}

29. In context with beryllium, which one of the following statements is incorrect ?
    (a) Its hydride is electron-deficient and polymeric
    (b) It is rendered passive by nitric acid
    (c) It forms Be_2C
    (d) Its salt rarely hydrolyze

30. Hot concentrated sulphuric acid is a moderately strong oxidizing agent. Which of the following reaction does not show oxidizing behaviour ?
    (a) $CaF_2 + H_2SO_4 \rightarrow CaSO_4 + 2HF$ (b) $Cu + 2H_2SO_4 \rightarrow CuSO_4 + SO_2 + 2H_2O$
    (c) $2S + 2H_2SO_4 \rightarrow 2SO_2 + 2H_2O$ (d) $C + 2H_2SO_4 \rightarrow CO_2 + 2SO_2 + 2H_2O$

31. Which of the following pairs of d-orbitals will have electron density along the axes ?
    (a) d_{xy}, $d_{x^2-y^2}$ (b) d_{z^2}, d_{xz} (c) d_{xz}, d_{yz} (d) d_{z^2}, $d_{x^2-y^2}$

32. The correct geometry and hybridization for XeF_4 are ......
    (a) square planar, sp^3d^2 (b) octahydral, sp^3d^2
    (c) trigonal bipyramidal, sp^3d (d) planar triangle, sp^3d^3

33. Among the following, which one is a wrong statement ?
    (a) I^{3+} has bent geometry   (b) PH_5 and $BiCl_5$ do not exist
    (c) $p\pi$–$d\pi$ bonds are present in SO_2 (d) SeF_4 and CH_4 have same shape

34. The correct increasing order of trans-effect of the following species is ......

(a) $CN^- > Br^- > C_6H_5^- > NH_3$

(b) $NH_3 > CN^- > Br^- > C_6H_5^-$

(c) $CN^- > C_6H_5^- > Br^- > NH_3$

(d) $Br^- > CN^- > NH_3 > C_6H_5^-$

35. Which one of the following statement related to lanthanons is incorrect ?

(a) Ce^{4+} solutions are widely used as oxidizing agent in volumetric analysis

(b) Europium shows +4 oxidation state

(c) The basicity decreases as the ionic radius decreases from Pr to Lu

(d) All the lanthanons are much more reactive than aluminium

36. Jahn-Teller effect is not observed in high spin complexes of ......

(a) d_9
(b) d_7
(c) d_8
(d) d_4

37. Which of the following can be used as the halide component for Friedel-Craft's reaction ?

(a) Isopropyl chloride
(b) Chlorobenzene
(c) Bromobenzene
(d) Chloroethene

38. In which of the following molecules, all atoms are coplanar ?

(a) 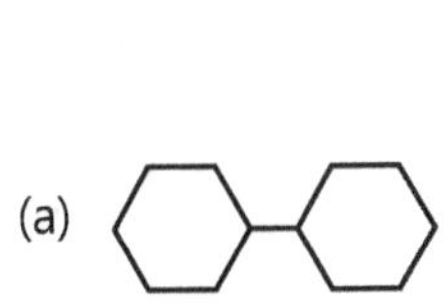
(b) 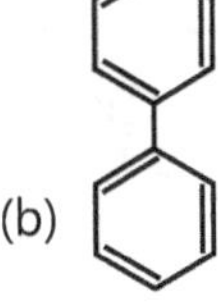
(c)
(d)

39. Which one of the following structure represent Nylon-6, 6 polymer ?

(a)
(b)
(c)
(d)

40. In pyrrole

the electron density is maximum on ......

(a) 2 and 5
(b) 2 and 3
(c) 3 and 4
(d) 2 and 4

41. Which of the following compounds shall not produce propene by reaction with HBr followed by elimination or direct only elimination reaction ?

(a) $H_3C - CH_2 - CH_2Br$
(b)
(c) $H_3C - CH_2 - CH_2OH$
(d) $H_2C = C = O$

42. Which one of the following nitro compounds does not react with nitrous acid ?

(a) 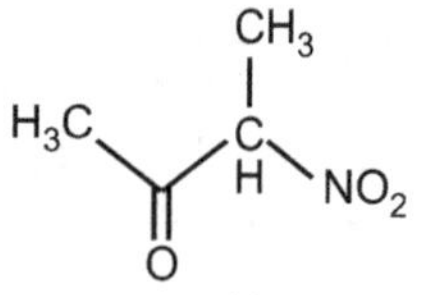 (structure: H_3C–C(=O)–CH(CH_3)–H–NO_2)

(b) (structure: H_3C–CH_2–CH_2–NO_2)

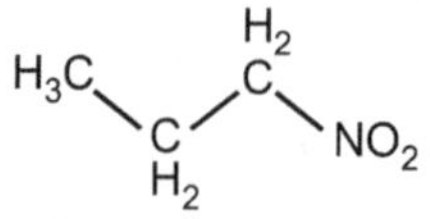

(c) (structure: $(H_3C)_2CH$–CH_2–NO_2)

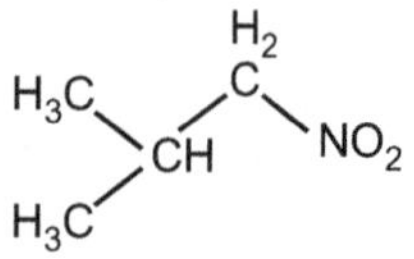

(d) 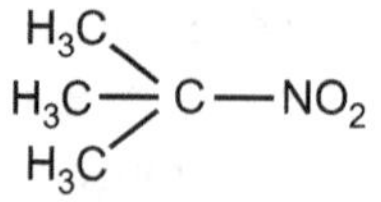 $(H_3C)_3C$—NO_2

43. The central dogma of molecular genetics states that the genetic information flows from ...
(a) DNA → RNA → Carbohydrates
(b) Amino acids → Proteins → DNA
(c) DNA → Carbohydrates → Proteins
(d) DNA → RNA → Proteins A

44. The correct corresponding order of names of four aldoses with configuration are given below. Image showing the names of four aldoses with configuration

(Fischer projections:)

1) CHO / H—OH / H—OH / CH₂OH
2) CHO / HO—H / H—OH / CH₂OH
3) CHO / HO—H / HO—H / CH₂OH
4) CHO / H—OH / HO—H / CH₂OH

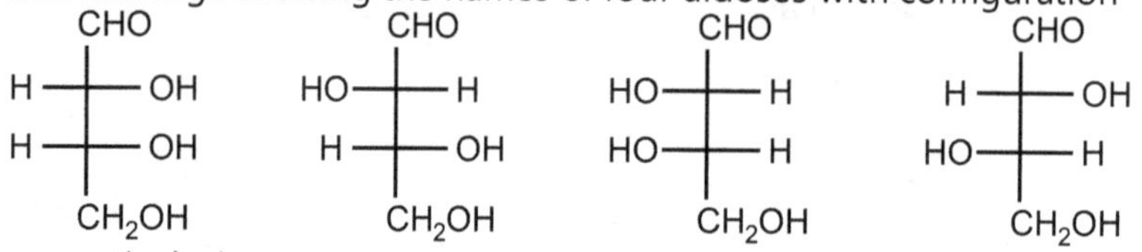

respectively, is ......
(a) D-erythrose, D-threose, L-erythrose, L-threose
(b) L-erythrose, L-threose, L-erythrose, D-threose
(c) D-threose, D-erythrose, L-threose, L-erythrose
(d) L-erythrose, L-threose, D-erythrose, D-threose

45. In the given reaction

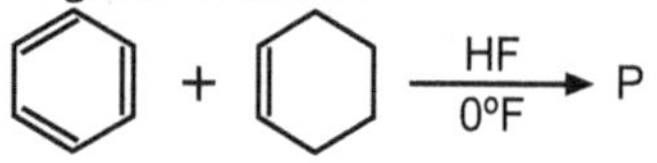

(benzene) + (cyclohexene) $\xrightarrow[0°F]{HF}$ P

The product P is ......

(a) 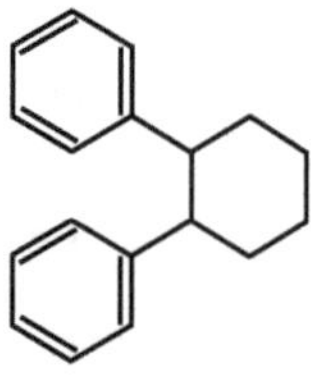 (diphenyl-cyclohexane structure)

(b) 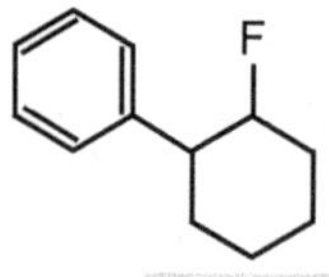 (phenyl-fluorocyclohexane structure)

(c) 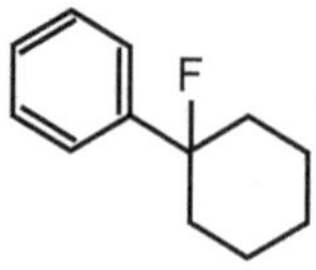 (methyl... fluorocyclohexane structure)

(d) 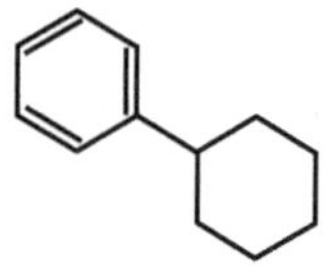 (phenylcyclohexane structure)

ANSWER KEY

1. (c)	2. (d)	3. (c)	4. (b)	5. (c)	6. (b)	7. (d)	8. (c)
9. (b)	10. (d)	11. (c)	12. (b)	13. (c)	14. (a)	15. (c)	16. (d)
17. (b)	18. (a)	19. (c)	20. (b)	21. (d)	22. (d)	23. (c)	24. (a)
25. (d)	26. (d)	27. (c)	28. (b)	29. (d)	30. (a)	31. (d)	32. (b)
33. (d)	34. (c)	35. (b)	36. (c)	37. (a)	38. (b)	39. (a)	40. (a)
41. (d)	42. (d)	43. (d)	44. (a)	45. (d)			

❑❑❑